God's World Science Series

God's World Science Series

God's
Inspiring World

Grade 4

with special reference
to the
Book of Job

Rod and Staff Publishers, Inc.
P.O. Box 3, Hwy. 172, Crockett, Kentucky 41413
Telephone: (606) 522-4348

ISBN 978-07399-0611-8
Catalog no. 14401

7   8   9   10   11   12   —   24   23   22   21   20   19   18   17   16   15

In Appreciation

For the greatness of God and His inspiring world, we give thanks and praise. From the biggest star to the smallest seed, we see the power and wisdom of God. To inspire our children with these wonders, that they might love and fear God, is a sacred privilege and responsibility. We are thankful for the freedom, ability, and resources to have Christian schools. We are thankful for the vision to publish textbooks that exalt God and are based on the truth of His Word. We are thankful for the church to whom God has given gifts to produce this science textbook, *God's Inspiring World.*

We are grateful to God for enabling Sister Naomi Eicher Lapp to do most of the original writing. Brother Jonathan Showalter wrote the electricity unit. Many were involved in reviewing, classroom testing, and revising. Brother Lester Showalter served as editor. Brother Lester Miller and Sister Barbara Schlabach drew the illustrations. As each did his part in response to the Lord of the church, there was a blending of efforts, for which we are thankful.

The publishing of this text does not yet meet its objective. These pages have not served their purpose until they become a tool for increasing knowledge about God's created world and, with that knowledge, inspiring the rising generation to worship and serve their Creator. As God has blessed the efforts to produce this textbook, may He further bless the teachers and students who use it.

—The Publishers

Contents

Photo Acknowledgments

Lester Showalter supplied all the photos except those listed below.

Bentley, Wilson: 33

Davidson, Josiah: front cover

©Comstock.com Images: 97

©Eric Martin/Iconotec.com: 16

Hoover, Samuel: 14

Miller, Elaine: 52

Shank, Kevin: 49 (top left and bottom), 223 (right)

Showalter, Mervin: 172, 219

Showalter, Joseph: 13 (left)

Introduction

"Hearken unto this, O Job: stand still, and consider the wondrous works of God" (Job 37:14).

All of the wonderful things that you see and use are the works of God; He made them. Sometimes we are so busy and in such a hurry that we do not see how wonderful the works of God really are.

There may be some beautiful clouds in the sky, but you do not see them, because you are going for the mail and are watching that you do not trip over something. Mother calls out, "Look at the interesting shapes of the clouds." You stop and look up. Yes, they are wonderful! You watch them drifting across the sky, slowly changing their shapes. You try to think what kind of clouds they are. You wonder what kind of weather they foretell. You remember that rain comes out of the clouds. You think about how the water in the clouds was once in the ocean. You consider that the clouds are an important part of the way God waters the earth. You are doing what Job was asked to do: "Stand still, and consider the wondrous works of God."

Considering the wondrous works of God is called science. This year you will be studying science with the help of this science textbook. In the first unit, you will be studying about clouds and the weather. Later you will study about animals, stars, light, and electricity. God made all of these things. It is good for you to stand still and consider these wondrous works of God.

Your science textbook is called *God's Inspiring World*. When something stirs up good thoughts and feelings, it is inspiring. Many things about God's world stir up good thoughts and feelings. God's world is very inspiring.

Many times in this book, you will find Bible verses from the Book of Job. God used the wonderful things in creation to inspire Job with how great and wonderful God is. He wanted Job to trust Him completely and not to worry about being sick. God wants you to trust Him too. Considering God's wondrous works can inspire you to trust in God, as it did Job.

Unit One

God Gives Us Weather

"Canst thou lift up thy voice to the clouds?" (Job 38:34).

Weather is a gift from God. We cannot make rain and sunshine. We must wait until God gives us these different kinds of weather.

In the Book of Job, we read: "Fair weather cometh out of the north: with God is terrible majesty" (Job 37:22). "Majesty" means that God is great and wonderful. "Terrible majesty" means that God is so great and wonderful that we are afraid of His power. Only God has the power to make a storm that can uproot trees and blow down buildings. Only God can cause the wind to change and bring beautiful fair weather. We trust in God's wisdom to give us weather.

Remember the story of Job? He lost his great riches, his children, and his good health. Job felt sad. He wanted God to explain why He let this happen.

God did not tell Job why. Instead, God asked Job questions about His creation. "Canst thou lift up thy voice to the clouds, that abundance of waters may cover thee?" (Job 38:34). In dry weather, farmers wish for rain. It would be foolish for them to call to the clouds, but they can call to God who controls the weather.

God wanted Job to trust Him. The weather teaches us to trust God. We can learn from Job's lesson. The beautiful, orderly earth God made reminds us of His greatness. God knows so much more than we do. He does not explain everything to us. God is good even when He lets sad things happen to us.

Lesson 1

Different Climates

New Words

arid climate (ar′·id), the yearly weather pattern that has very little rain in a year.

atmosphere (at′·mə·sfir′), the layer of air around the earth.

climate, the kind of weather a place has from year to year.

polar climate, the yearly weather pattern that does not get warm enough in the summertime to raise crops.

temperate climate, the yearly weather pattern that has a warm summer and a cold winter.

tropical climate (trop′·i·kəl), the yearly weather pattern that has warm weather all the time.

weather, the condition of the atmosphere from day to day, such as sunny or stormy.

Men live on almost all of the earth. God made the earth as a place for men to live. Over most of the earth, men can find enough to eat. They have enough water to drink. They can keep warm enough and do not get too warm. The earth is a very good place for us to live.

Only a few places on the earth do not make a good home for men. Some of the desert areas are too hot and dry to be good places to live. In the Far North and at the South Pole, it is too cold to be a good place to live. Some of the mountains are so high that the air is too thin and cold to be a good place to live. But in most places, people find what they need. The earth was created by God as a home for you and all living creatures.

Weather happens in the atmosphere. The earth is covered with a thick layer of air called the *atmosphere.* You breathe the air of the atmosphere. Birds and airplanes use the air against their wings to fly. Another very important use of the atmosphere is to give us our weather.

How many parts of weather can you see on this picture?

We put thermometers into the air to find the temperature. Weather-vanes tell us the direction the wind is blowing. We look up into the atmosphere to see the clouds. Rain gauges measure the amount of rain that comes out of the atmosphere. Temperature, wind, clouds, and rain are all part of the *weather.*

You know that the weather changes very often. Some days are bright and sunny. Others are cloudy and rainy. One day of spring may be warm and pleasant. The next day may be cold and windy. These changes of weather are God's way of giving us different things that we need.

Climate remains the same. Even if the weather changes from day to day, you know that you get about the same weather from year to year. If you live at one place for several years, you learn what kind of weather to expect at each season of the year. If you live in Pennsylvania, you can expect to get some snow each winter. If you live in the Philippines, you would not expect to get snow all year around. In the Philippines you would expect the rainy season to begin in June. Pennsylvania and the Philippines have two different kinds of *climate.*

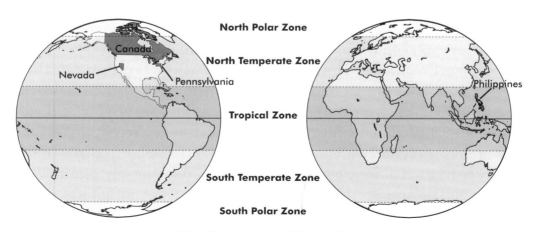

The climate zones of the earth

Pennsylvania has a ***temperate climate.*** This means that the weather is about half way between hot and cold. People who have a temperate climate have a warm summer season when they can grow crops. Then they have a cold winter season when the trees and fields are bare. There are two main areas of temperate climate. Pennsylvania is in the North Temperate Zone. The North Temperate Zone is

A soybean field of Paraguay in February

a belt around the earth about half way between the equator and the North Pole. There is a South Temperate Zone about half way between the equator and the South Pole. The people of Paraguay live in a temperate climate of the South Temperate Zone.

The Philippines has a ***tropical climate.*** The tropical climate is found in a wide belt around the

Plants grow well in the tropical climate of the Philippines.

center of the earth with the equator running through the center. It is warm all year around in a tropical climate. They do not have a winter with snow in a tropical climate. There is often a wet and a dry season. Crops and trees grow all year around. Bananas and mangoes grow well in this climate. Tropical countries with a lot of rain often have thick jungles containing many interesting animals, such as parrots and monkeys.

People in upper Canada live in the ***polar climate.*** This land is so far north that the ground beneath the surface stays frozen all year long. The winters are very long. The summers are so short and cool that only some very hardy plants will grow. High mountains can also have a polar climate even if they are far from the North or South Pole.

Deserts are caused by a climate that has very little rainfall. Such places have an ***arid climate.*** Most of Nevada has an arid climate, which means that the climate is

Sand dunes in a Nevada desert

dry. There is often less than eight inches of rainfall each year in Nevada. Grass grows so poorly that people sometimes cover their yards with crushed stones. In such desert and partly desert lands, much of the ground is bare sand. Because the sky is often clear in an arid climate, the temperature can get very high during the daytime and very low during the night.

People live in all of these different climates. Different people like different climates. Someone raised in a tropical climate may not like the cold winters of a temperate climate. A person raised to like the refreshing snow of winter may be very uncomfortable in a tropical climate. God gave us many kinds of climate. Each climate has its own special yearly weather pattern.

———————— **Test Your Reading (Group A)** ————————

For each sentence, write the missing word from your lesson.
1. God wisely gave us all we need to live on the ———.
2. One day the ——— may be sunny, and the next day it may be raining.
3. The yearly weather pattern at the same place is called ———.
4. If you have a cold winter and a long-enough summer to grow crops, then you have a ——— climate.
5. People who live in a ——— climate have no winter.
6. People who live in a ——— climate have no summer that will grow crops.
7. An ——— climate has hot days, cool nights, and very little rainfall.

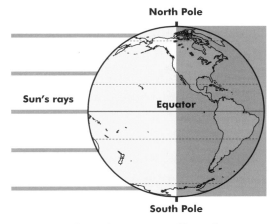

Distance from the equator affects climate.

What causes different climates? The kind of climate you have depends on four important things.

First, the distance from the equator makes a big difference in the climate. If you look at the map above, you see that the equator circles the middle of the earth. There the sun is shining straight down. This makes warm temperatures. The warmest climates are those near the equator. The coldest climates are those near the North Pole and the South Pole. There the sun is shining at a slant, and the ground does not warm up very much.

Second, the distance from the ocean makes a difference in the climate. If you live near the ocean, your climate is probably neither very hot nor very cold. The water of the ocean stores the heat of summer and gives off heat in the winter. If you live far from the ocean, you probably have hotter summers and colder winters. For example, the gardens in Delaware produce food earlier than in Pennsylvania. Delaware has water on both sides of it.

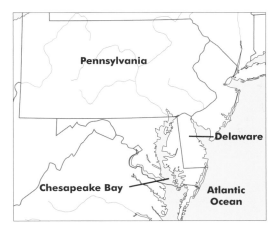

Distance from the ocean affects climate.

Third, the height above sea level makes a difference in the climate. The higher you go up a mountain, the colder the climate is. Some high mountaintops have snow on them all year even though they are close to the equator. In the highlands of Guatemala, the climate is springlike all year around. The lands near sea level have a hot, tropical climate.

Height above sea level affects climate.

Fourth, the land around you makes a difference in the climate. Mountains, deserts, and cities all help cause differences. The tall mountain range in California causes rain to fall on its west side. East of the mountains, it is very dry. That is why Nevada has an arid climate. Deserts and cities are likely warmer than grasslands and forests.

God made the sun, wind, mountains, oceans, and deserts all work together to give us the climates of the earth. It is interesting to learn about weather and climate. God gave us the ability to understand some things about climate and weather. But we shall never understand everything. Only God understands everything!

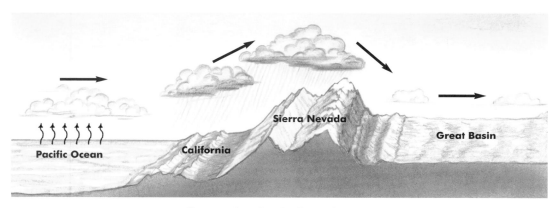

Surrounding land affects climate.

Test Your Reading (Group B)

Choose the best answer.

8. A tropical climate will be
   a. near the equator.
   b. far from the equator.
   c. half way between the equator and a pole.

9. Living near the ocean will make your climate
    a. colder all the year.
    b. cooler in the summer and warmer in the winter.
    c. warmer in the summer and colder in the winter.
10. There could be a cool climate near the equator if
    a. the land was very near the ocean.
    b. the land was close to a mountain.
    c. the land was very high.
11. If you live close to a very big mountain range, your climate could be
    a. cool in the summertime.
    b. very different from those on the other side of the mountain.
    c. more like those who live close to the ocean.

Answer the following question.

12. What four things help to make the climates different from one place to another?

Extra Activities

1. Read about your state or country in an encyclopedia. Be sure to read the sections about your climate. Find out whether you live close to or far from the equator and ocean, how high you are above sea level, and what kind of land is around you. Find information about the climates of the world. What other places of the world have the same climate that you have?
2. Write a description of your climate that would be interesting to someone in a different climate. Be sure to include what seasons you have and what the weather is like in each season. Tell the highest and lowest temperatures you can expect to have in the year. Do you have frost and snow? Do you expect any storms? Do you have much rainfall?

    Send your description to a school in a country that has a very different climate from yours. Ask them to write back and tell you about their climate. Perhaps you can send to some Christian school in a country where your church has missionaries.

Lesson 2

Wind and Weather

New Words

cyclone (sī′·klōn), a large circle of moist, warm air that is slowly turning.

hurricane (hėr′·i·kān′), a storm with wind moving in a large circle.

prevailing westerlies (pri·vā′·ling wes′·tər·lēz), wide belts of winds that blow from the west.

thunderstorm (thun′·dər·stôrm′), a storm with wind, thunder, and lightning caused by rapidly rising warm air.

tornado (tôr·nā′·dō), a storm with wind circling at high speed in a small area.

trade winds, wide belts of winds that always blow from the east next to each side of the equator.

If there were no wind, the weather would be almost the same day after day. There would be no rain over the land because the moist ocean air would stay over the ocean. Part of God's wise plan for the weather was the wind.

A weathervane telling a west wind

What is the wind? Wind is simply air moving across the earth. Sometimes it is so soft you hardly feel it. At other times it is strong enough to uproot trees and smash houses.

Jesus said that the wind goes where it will and you can hear the sound of it, but you cannot tell where it is coming from or where it is going (John 3:8). We cannot see the wind. We know that wind is blowing by the rustling sound as it passes through the trees. We see how it moves a weathervane to tell which direction the wind is blowing.

What makes the wind blow?

It is the sun! Although the same sun shines over the earth, the earth heats up unevenly. Places near the North and South Poles stay cold because the sun stays low in the sky like our evening sun. Places near the equator stay warm because the sun shines straight down. So the air near the equator stays warm, and the air near the Poles stays cold.

You know that warm air rises and cold air sinks. In a room that is heated with a stove, the air rises above the stove and cold air moves toward the bottom of the stove. This makes a big circle of air in the room so that the entire room can be heated. This is called convection.

The same thing happens in a much bigger way in the atmosphere.

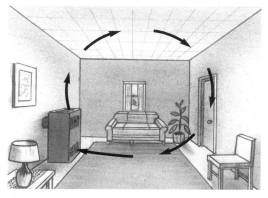

Convection that moves the air in a room causes the wind to blow on the earth.

The light, warm air rises. The heavy, cold air sinks and pushes the warm air. This pushing or moving air is the wind blowing. The air circles around and around through the atmosphere, heating and cooling again and again. Year after year, the winds follow the same paths, all because of the sun!

Thousands of years ago, King Solomon clearly described these wind patterns or cycles. "The wind goeth toward the south, and turneth about unto the north; it whirleth about continually, and the wind returneth again according to his circuits" (Ecclesiastes 1:6). How did Solomon know so much about the wind? He got his wisdom from our wise God who rules the wind.

Which way do the winds blow? If the cold air blows toward the equator from the North and South Poles, most winds come from the north and south, right? Wrong. They might if the earth were holding still. But since the earth spins on its axis, the winds curve and blow mainly east and west.

The winds that blow from the west are called ***prevailing westerlies.*** The prevailing westerlies blow around the earth in two great belts.

Can you find them on the map? Much of North America, Europe, and Asia lies in the path of these west winds.

The two wide wind belts next to each side of the equator that blow from the east are called *trade winds.* They blow across South America, Australia, and southern Africa. The two wide belts of trade winds are on both sides of the equator.

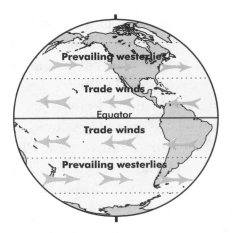

Wind belts of the earth

─────── **Test Your Reading (Group A)** ───────

Choose the best ending for each sentence. Write the letter on your paper.

1. The sun
2. The air at the Poles
3. Warm air
4. Moving air
5. A trade wind
6. Earth's spinning on its axis
7. A prevailing westerly

a. blows over most of the United States.
b. gives wind an east or west direction.
c. causes the wind to blow.
d. blows from the east year after year.
e. is light and rises.
f. receives little heat from the sun.
g. is called wind.

Match each number on this map of the earth with one of the words at the right. Some words get used more than once.

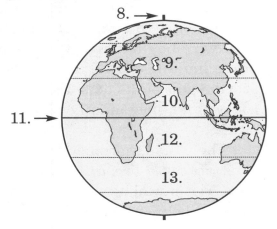

equator

pole

trade winds

prevailing westerlies

Cyclones bring us rain. Within these wind belts are some smaller patterns of wind called *cyclones.* A cyclone is a large circle of moist air that is warmer than the air around it. It is often a few hundred miles across. A cyclone is like a huge "top" of warm, moist air slowly spinning.

A cyclone often begins circling over an ocean or a gulf. Much water evaporates from the ocean and makes the air humid. Then, full of warm, moist air, it moves over the land. As the cyclone moves along, it drops its water, bringing us the rain we need. This is how God planned for the water of the ocean to supply us with the precious rain we need.

We can tell when a cyclone is coming because the direction of the wind changes. If you live in the prevailing westerlies, the wind usually blows from the west. But when a cyclone is coming, you begin to have a south or east wind. When that happens, you know that you may have rain in a day or so.

Men knew about this weather sign for a long time. They knew that the direction of the wind could be used to predict the weather.

One of Job's friends described the direction of the wind and the weather: "Out of the south cometh the whirlwind: and cold out of the north. . . . Fair weather cometh out of the north" (Job 37:9, 22).

Strong winds are storms. Most of the time the wind blows gently. But sometimes the wind begins moving very fast. These stormy winds can uproot trees, blow roofs off houses, or even destroy whole houses.

Often the winds of a storm move in a circle. If the circle is very big so that it covers an entire state, it is called a *hurricane.* If the spinning air is only as wide as your schoolyard, we call it a *tornado.* A tornado is much smaller than a hurricane, but the wind is going faster in a tornado.

A tornado

A common kind of storm is called a ***thunderstorm.*** The air in a thunderstorm is very warm and moist. It rises rapidly and makes the wind blow fast. The wind of a thunderstorm does not blow as fast as a tornado, but it can be fast enough to blow a big tree down. Thunderstorms get their name from the loud thunder we hear after the lightning during these storms.

When we see that a storm is coming, we close the windows and doors. We go inside a building and maybe even to the basement. We know that a storm has great power. During a storm we think about the greatness of God. God made the sun that gives the storms their power. God controls the storms, and He has good reasons for allowing storms.

Job knew what a storm could do. One day while his children were eating in a house, a storm blew the house down and killed all of Job's children. God allowed this storm as a test for Job's faith. When we are in a storm, it is a test of our faith to see if we trust in God.

———————— Test Your Reading (Group B) ————————

Answer the following questions.

14. How do the winds move in a cyclone?
15. Where do cyclones often begin?
16. What do cyclones bring to us?
17. How can we tell that a cyclone is coming?
18. How are a hurricane and a tornado the same?
19. In what two ways is a tornado different from a hurricane?
20. What causes the strong wind in a thunderstorm?
21. What do storms teach us about God?
22. What should we do when we are afraid in a storm?

Reviewing What You Have Learned

1. Climate is the weather patterns we have
   a. from day to day.
   b. for one year.
   c. from year to year.
2. Places with a cold winter and a warm summer have a ——— climate.

3. True or false? People in a tropical climate live close to the equator.
4. The higher a land is above sea level, the ——— will be the climate.
5. The distance from the equator, the height above sea level, and the land around you help to make your climate what it is. What is the fourth thing that makes a difference in your climate?

Extra Activities

1. Start keeping a weather record by making a chart like the one below. For this lesson, do only the *Date* and *Wind Name and Speed* sections. You will do the other sections in later lessons.

    To find the name and speed of the wind today, look at the *Wind Description* on page 24. Which sentence most nearly describes the wind today? Choose one, then find the *Wind Name and Speed* across from it. Write it on your own chart, just like the chart below shows. Keep doing this every day about the same time each day.

My Weather Record

Date	Wind Name and Speed	Clouds	Precipitation
Sept. 10	gentle breeze, 8–12 mph		

Wind Description	Wind Name and Speed
Smoke rises straight up	Calm, less than 1 mph (2 kmph)
Smoke drifts with the air	Light air, 1–3 mph (2–5 kmph)
Leaves rustle; wind can be felt	Light breeze, 4–7 mph (6–11 kmph)
Leaves and small twigs move	Gentle breeze, 8–12 mph (12–20 kmph)
Small branches sway; dust blows	Moderate breeze, 13–18 mph (21–29 kmph)
Small trees sway	Fresh breeze, 19–24 mph (30–39 kmph)
Large branches sway	Strong breeze, 25–31 mph (40–50 kmph)
Whole trees sway; walking is difficult	Moderate gale, 32–38 mph (51–61 kmph)
Twigs are broken from trees	Fresh gale, 39–46 mph (62–74 kmph)
Loose shingles and siding, etc. are blown from buildings	Strong gale, 47–54 mph (75–87 kmph)
Trees are uprooted	Whole gale, 55–63 mph (88–101 kmph)
Much widespread damage	Storm, 64–73 mph (102–117 kmph)
Severe destruction	Hurricane, 74 mph (118 kmph) and above

2. Read about hurricanes. What is a hurricane-like storm called that comes from the Pacific Ocean? How are hurricanes named? What do people do to their houses if they know a hurricane is coming? What direction do hurricanes move? Which parts of the United States have hurricanes? Tell or write about what you learned.

3. Read about tornadoes. What do tornadoes look like? How do they move? What should a person do if there is danger of a tornado? What parts of the United States have the most tornadoes? What is a tornado called if it is over water? Tell or write about what you learned.

Lesson 3

Clouds and Rain

New Words

cirrus clouds (sir′·əs), feathery clouds high in the sky.
cumulus clouds (kyüm′·yə·ləs), fluffy, heaped-up clouds.
fog, a thick mist or cloud just above the ground.
front, the line where warm air meets cold air.
humid (hyü′·mid), damp or moist.
stratus clouds (strā′·təs), thick, gray, low-hanging clouds.

If the sky was clear and there were no clouds, would you expect it to rain? Of course not. You know that rain comes from clouds. You also know that clouds do not always give rain. You are glad for the shade that clouds give you when you are working hard in the garden. Clouds are beautiful. Their fluffy shapes against a blue sky add to the beauty of the outdoors. A sunset is made more beautiful as the bars of clouds glow with red and orange. Clouds are part of the wonderful world God made for us to live in.

Questions about clouds. "Who can number the clouds in wisdom? or who can stay the bottles of heaven?" (Job 38:37). These are questions God asked Job. Who indeed can count the clouds and hold water in the "bottles" of the clouds? Only God can do that! He does it with wise laws He made for weather. These laws explain how clouds are formed.

What makes clouds? The atmosphere is made of air, and the air holds some water. Water goes into the air by evaporation from plants, rivers, lakes, and oceans. When the air contains much water, we say it is *humid.*

Because of one of God's laws, when humid air is cooled, some of the water comes out of the air. The moisture comes out of the air as tiny drops of water. A large body of tiny water droplets is a cloud. A cloud is formed when humid air has been cooled to form tiny water droplets. If the cloud is cooled more,

more moisture must come out of the air. The droplets get bigger and fall out of the cloud. This is the way God's laws work to make it rain.

What makes the air get cooler? As you learned in Lesson 1, the higher you go above sea level, the colder it gets. When air is pushed upward, it gets cooler. This cooling is what makes clouds form.

One way air is pushed up to get cooler is by mountains. As the wind pushes air up the side of a mountain, the air gets cooler. If the air is humid, clouds are formed and it rains. That is why California gets plenty of rain. After the air has gotten to the top of the mountains, it has lost much of its water. That is

why the land on the other side of the mountain has an arid climate.

Another way air is pushed up is by cold air. When warm air meets cold air, the cold air slides under the warm air and the warm air rises over the cold air. This meeting of the air makes a long line called a *front.* Fronts often happen in cyclones. This is the way the warm, humid air of a cyclone makes rain. At a front, warm, humid air meets cold air. The warm air rises over the cold air. As it rises, the warm air cools. Cooling humid air causes clouds to form. If the air is cooled enough, the clouds will give rain. In this way, God's laws are at work to bring us needed rain.

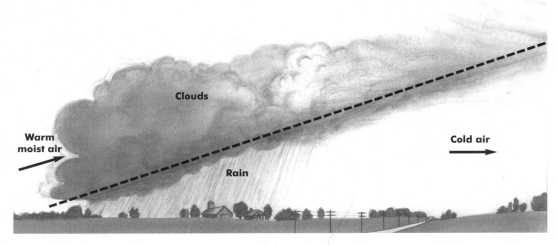

A front

Now we can give a step-by-step process of how the ocean water becomes rain.

1. Heat from the sun causes the ocean water to evaporate into the air.
2. Winds carry the humid air over the land.
3. A mountain or front causes the humid air to rise.
4. As the air rises, it becomes cool.
5. Cooling causes some of the moisture to come out of the humid air to form a cloud.
6. If the humid air is cooled more, enough water comes out to make rain.

We thank God for making the laws to give us rain. Rain is a precious gift from God. We pray to God to send us rain. We thank Him when He sends rain.

——————— **Test Your Reading (Group A)** ———————

Read each sentence below. Write *true* if the statement is true. Write *false* if the statement is false.

1. God made the laws of rain and weather.
2. All rain comes from clouds.
3. All clouds give us rain.
4. When humid air becomes warmer, it causes clouds and rain.
5. As air is raised, it becomes cooler.
6. Mountains can cause rain to fall.
7. When warm air meets cold air, the cold air rises over the warm air.
8. A front is the line between areas that have much rain and areas that have little rain.

Complete these statements to give the steps of how ocean water becomes rain.

9. The ocean water ——— because of the heat of the ———.
10. The ——— blows the ——— air over the land.
11. The air is ——— by a ——— or a mountain.
12. The air gets ——— as it is forced to ———.
13. Some of the moisture comes ——— of the air in tiny water droplets to form a ———.
14. It will ——— if the humid air is ——— enough.

Kinds of clouds. As you know, not all clouds bring us rain. Sometimes a cloud is so low that it touches the ground. We call this thick mist a *fog.* You know that raindrops do not come out of fog. If you have ever wondered what it would be like to be inside a cloud, now you know. A fog is a cloud that touches the ground.

When you see fluffy clouds like piles of whipped cream against a blue sky, you know that the weather will be fair and sunny. These puffy clouds are called *cumulus clouds.* We sometimes call them fair-weather clouds.

Cumulus clouds do not usually bring us rain, but sometimes they do. A thunderstorm develops when cold air pushes the warm air straight upward to form a big, dark cumulus cloud called a thunderhead. Lightning flashes, thunder rumbles, and soon heavy rain showers spill out.

The rain clouds that bring us a slow, steady rain are thick, low-hanging *stratus clouds.* They look like a gray blanket or layer above us. *Stratus* means "layer." Stratus clouds are a layer of clouds.

Stratus clouds

Cumulus clouds

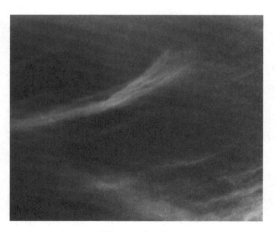

Cirrus clouds

High, thin clouds are *cirrus clouds.* They are so high and cold that they are made of fine pieces of ice instead of droplets of water. They look like long, sweeping feathers. They are so thin that you can see the sun through them. Rain or snow does not fall from cirrus clouds, but they give us a clue that rain may be coming.

Weather signs. You can use cirrus clouds to predict the weather. When you see cirrus clouds, you can say, "We'll probably have rain in a few days." Often when we see cirrus clouds, the wind changes from its usual direction. A cyclone is on the way. Now you know two weather signs for rain. The direction of the wind

A ring around the moon predicts rain or snow.

changes, and you can see cirrus clouds.

When the moon shines through cirrus clouds, a big ring of light forms around the moon. When the sun shines through cirrus clouds, it can also make a big ring. Sometimes it makes two bright spots in the clouds, one on each side of the sun. We call them sundogs. A ring around the moon, a ring around the sun, and sundogs are more signs that rain may be on the way. The laws of God for the weather are so orderly that they make it possible for us to predict the weather.

Jesus described how we can predict the weather. He said, "When it is evening, ye say, It will be fair weather: for the sky is red. And in the morning, It will be foul weather to day: for the sky is red and lowring" (Matthew 16:2, 3). You have probably heard this poem to help you predict the weather from the evening and morning skies.

> Evening red, morning gray,
> Sends the traveler on his way.
> Evening gray, morning red,
> Sends the rain upon his head.

——————— Test Your Reading (Group B) ———————

Choose the correct ending for each sentence. Write the letter on your paper.

15. You know that it is not beautiful inside a cloud because
    a. it is like a rainy day.
    b. fog makes things whitish and hard to see.
    c. it has cooled enough to make droplets of water.

16. If you saw many cumulus clouds in the sky, you could predict
    a. there will be nice weather for the rest of the day.
    b. there will be a thunderstorm before the end of the day.
    c. there is a cyclone coming.

17. On a cloudy day, we cannot see the sun because of
    a. cumulus clouds.
    b. stratus clouds.
    c. cirrus clouds.

18. If you saw a ring around the moon, you would know there were
    a. cumulus clouds.
    b. stratus clouds.
    c. cirrus clouds.

19. We can predict weather because
    a. God has told us what causes the weather.
    b. men have learned to control the weather.
    c. the weather works by the laws of God.

Identify each of the following clouds.

20.

21.

22.

23.

24.

Reviewing What You Have Learned

1. The weather is the condition of the atmosphere from
   a. day to day. b. year to year. c. country to country.
2. The wind blows because ——— air rises.
3. True or false? The trade winds blow from the east next to each side of the equator.
4. Most of our rains come from
   a. prevailing westerlies.
   b. cyclones.
   c. thunderstorms.
5. The ——— climate has no winter season.

Extra Activity

Keep working on the weather record you started in the last lesson. Start working on the *Clouds* section. Look at the sky, and decide which kind of clouds you see. Your teacher may also help you decide. Write *cumulus, cirrus, stratus, thunderheads,* or *fog.* If no clouds are in the sky, write *clear* in the space.

Lesson 4

Kinds of Precipitation

New Words

dew, waterdrops that form on grass, etc. at night when humid air cools.

frost, ice crystals that form on grass, etc. at night when humid air cools below freezing.

hail, balls of ice that fall during a thunderstorm.

precipitation (pri·sip′·i·tā′·shən), rain, snow, dew, and other forms of water that come out of the air.

sleet, raindrops that freeze as they fall.

Kinds of precipitation. Rain is not the only way God waters the earth. If the rain freezes on the way down from the cloud, then we have *sleet.* Sleet is really frozen rain.

Rain and sleet are two kinds of precipitation. *Precipitation* is the name for the forms of water that come out of the air. In this lesson you will be learning about four more kinds of precipitation.

God asked Job questions about some of the kinds of precipitation. He asked Job where rain comes from when He said, "Hath the rain a father?" (Job 38:28). When we have one inch of rain over miles of farmland, that is more water than man can pump with his best irrigation system. Rain is worth thousands of dollars to the farmers, but they do not pay a penny for it. God sends the rain free.

If the clouds are freezing cold, the water comes out of the air as six-sided ice crystals. You know the name of this kind of precipitation. It is snow!

The snowflakes grow from tiny bits of ice into beautiful art patterns. The pattern for each snowflake is a result of the changes in the temperature of the air. Since no two flakes grow in the same temperature changes, no two flakes are alike. We marvel how anything so beautiful can be made high up in

Photographs of snowflakes: artwork of God

the air even in the dark of night. God is the artist. He loves beauty and can make beauty that is better than what man can make.

God asked Job about snow: "Hast thou entered into the treasures of the snow?" (Job 38:22). Did you ever see snowflakes against your dark coat sleeve? Did you ever look at the flakes with a magnifying glass? If you do this, you are "entering into the treasures of the snow." But even if you examine snowflakes very closely, you will still not understand the way God makes water to freeze into such beautiful patterns.

Hail. God also asked Job a question about hail: "Hast thou seen the treasures of the hail?" (Job 38:22). ***Hail*** is a very unusual form of precipitation because it is balls of ice that drop in the warm summertime. A hailstone starts as an ice crystal or frozen raindrop high in a thunderhead where it is cold. As it falls, it touches cold raindrops, which quickly freeze onto it. The upward wind sweeps the ball of ice high up into the thunderhead again and again. Each time it falls, it meets more raindrops, adding more icy layers and getting bigger. Finally it becomes so heavy that it falls all the way to the ground.

Hailstones are often the size of peas, but sometimes they are as big as potatoes. The larger they are, the more damage they do to crops and buildings.

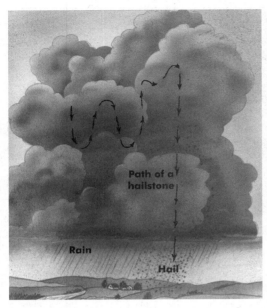

Hail is formed by traveling up and down in a thunderhead.

must be humid, and the ground must be cold.

At night the ground loses heat and becomes cold. If it becomes cold enough and the air is humid enough, water will come out of the air and make beads of water on the grass. You have seen water come out of the air onto the side of a cold glass of water on a humid day.

If the ground is below freezing, the water comes out of the air as frost. The frost gives the outdoors a fuzzy coat of ice crystals. It paints feathery swirls and lacy designs on our windows.

Nighttime precipitation. God asked Job about two more kinds of precipitation: "Who hath begotten the drops of dew? . . . and the hoary frost of heaven, who hath gendered it?" (Job 38:28, 29). Both *dew* and *frost* are kinds of precipitation that happen at night. Both happen on the ground. Two things must be true to have dew or frost. The air

We need precipitation. Again and again these kinds of precipitation bring water to thirsty plants, animals, and people. We need the water for drinking and cleaning. How glad we should be for God's wise plan for the earth! By His wisdom He keeps the water moving from sea to land and then back again for our good.

──────── Test Your Reading ────────

For each sentence, write *rain, sleet, snow, hail, dew,* or *frost.* The number after each sentence will show you how many answers are needed.

1. It comes from clouds that are cold but not freezing. (1)
2. It is made of ice balls or crystals. (4)
3. It is made of beautiful, six-sided crystals. (1)
4. It is rain that freezes as it falls. (1)

5. It falls during thunderstorms. (2)
6. It is made of several layers of ice. (1)
7. It only forms during a cool night from humid air. (2)
8. It forms on ground that is freezing. (1)
9. It is a form of precipitation that waters the earth. (6)

Answer the following questions.

10. How are snowflakes formed?
11. How are hailstones formed?

Reviewing What You Have Learned

1. A place may have a polar climate because it is high above sea level or because it is far from ———.
2. Which of the following is true?
   a. Trade winds blow from the west.
   b. Cyclone winds blow from the north.
   c. Hurricane winds blow in a circle.
3. The ——— causes the wind to blow.
4. Clouds are formed when
   a. humid air is forced to rise.
   b. evaporation from the ocean makes the air humid.
   c. a front causes the humid air to mix with cold air.
5. True or false? When you see cumulus clouds, you know that it may rain before long.

Extra Activity

Keep working on the weather record. Start filling in the *Precipitation* section. If there is any precipitation, write *rain, sleet, snow, hail, dew,* or *frost.* You will need to check for dew or frost early in the morning. If it rains or snows, give the amount.

Lesson 5

Do You Remember?

Match each letter to the correct number.

1. A cloud on ground level
2. A layer of clouds
3. Wide, slowly rotating warm air that may bring rain
4. A climate without winter
5. The air around us
6. Frozen rain
7. Wide belts of wind
8. Strong winds in a wide circle
9. Water in the air

a. atmosphere
b. cyclone
c. fog
d. humid
e. hurricane
f. prevailing westerlies
g. sleet
h. stratus
i. tropical

From the word box, find and write the correct word for each blank.

arid	front	precipitation	thunderstorm
climate	frost	snowflakes	tornado
dew	hail	sundogs	weather
equator	mountain		

10. The ——— can be rainy, sunny, or windy.
11. Your ——— is the kind of weather you usually have each year.
12. A ——— can cause some land to have very little rain.
13. When there are cirrus clouds, you may see ———.
14. A ——— can do great damage in a narrow path.
15. Warm air meets cold air along a ———.
16. The tropical climate is close to the ———.
17. A desert would be found at a place where the climate is ———.
18. The dark cumulus clouds of a ——— are caused when warm air is pushed up.
19. The different patterns of ——— are made by differences of temperature.

20. On cool nights in the summer, —— may form on the grass.
21. —— will not form unless the ground is freezing.
22. During thunderstorms, sometimes icy —— falls to the ground.
23. Rain, sleet, and frost are forms of ——.

Choose the best answer to finish each sentence.

24. Weather can be predicted because
    a. we have the same weather year after year.
    b. the weather is controlled by the laws of God.
    c. the Bible gives us weather signs.
25. The wind blows because
    a. the sun heats the air more at some places than at others.
    b. the air is more humid over the land than over the ocean.
    c. the air is cooled as it rises.
26. Winds that blow from the east next to each side of the equator are
    a. trade winds.
    b. prevailing westerlies.
    c. cyclones.
27. When warm air meets cold air,
    a. the warm air goes under the cold air.
    b. the warm air goes above the cold air.
    c. the cold air goes around the warm air.
28. Clouds form and rain falls when
    a. a cold air mass becomes warmer.
    b. ocean water evaporates.
    c. humid air is raised and cooled.
29. Cumulus clouds look like
    a. piles of whipped cream.
    b. long, sweeping feathers.
    c. layers of blankets.
30. A steady rain comes from
    a. cumulus clouds.
    b. stratus clouds.
    c. cirrus clouds.

31. We can tell that a cyclone is coming when
    a. the air cools off.
    b. the wind's direction changes from the usual.
    c. there is a fog in the early morning.
32. Cirrus clouds are a good
    a. source of snow.
    b. beginning for a thunderhead.
    c. sign that rain may be coming in a few days.

Write *true* if the sentence is true; write *false* if it is not true.

33. God asked Moses many questions about the weather.
34. God uses storms to show us His greatness and to test our faith.
35. Because the earth rotates on its axis, the winds blow mainly north and south.
36. The winds follow the same paths around the earth year after year.
37. We receive precipitation according to God's laws for weather.
38. When warm air is pushed up, dark cumulus clouds may be formed.
39. Stratus clouds cause a ring around the moon.
40. Snow is made when raindrops fall through freezing air.

Label the pictures with these words: *cumulus clouds, thunderhead, cirrus clouds, fog,* or *stratus clouds.*

41.

42.

43.

44.

45.

Answer these questions.

46–49. What four things make the kind of climate a land has?

50. What wind belt blows over the United States most of the time?

Unit Two

God Created the Animals

"The LORD God formed every beast of the field, and every fowl of the air" (Genesis 2:19).

Are you glad God made butterflies, puppies, robins, and deer? Many people like these animals. They look pretty or are friendly. These animals are good and important animals.

Are you glad God made flies, spiders, snails, and worms? Some people do not like such animals because of how they look or crawl or feel. Yet these are also good and important animals.

All the animals are important. Each fits into God's wise plan. How are animals important to us? Animals eat plants or other animals. Later, they become food for other animals or people. Their dead bodies help make the soil richer. The rich soil feeds the plants that feed the animals and people.

Can you see the beauty of God's plan? The animals and plants work together on the earth. Each one does what God planned for it. But people do not always use animals and plants wisely. How does God want us to treat animals? God wants us to be kind to them. We may eat their meat and use their hides for shoes. We may kill insects that ruin our garden plants and bother us inside our houses. But we should not kill animals just for fun.

God cares about the animals. When an animal dies, God notices it. Jesus, the Son of God, said, "Are not two sparrows sold for a farthing? and one of them shall not fall on the ground without your Father" (Matthew 10:29).

Lesson 1

Animals With Skeletons

New Words

backbone, the main bone of the back in animals and humans.

characteristic (kar′·ək·tə·ris′·tik), a special way a living thing is made or acts that is different from other living things.

exoskeleton (ek′·sō·skel′·i·tən), the tough shell or covering of insects and other animals.

skeleton (skel′·i·tən), the hard parts of an animal's body that protect and support the body.

vertebra (vėr′·tə·brə), one of the small bones that make up the backbone.

Animals in the Book of Job. God talked to Job about a very large animal. He said, "Behold now behemoth, which I made with thee. . . . His bones are as strong pieces of brass; his bones are like bars of iron" (Job 40:15, 18). God created large animals with strong bones to hold up their big bodies.

Many different animals are mentioned in the Book of Job. Sheep, camels, lions, peacocks, grasshoppers, and hawks are just a few of them. All of these have something in common except the grasshopper. Do you know how the grasshopper is different from the other animals?

Animals with skeletons. Animals have soft body parts such as the brain, heart, and stomach. Many animals also have hard body parts made of hard materials. All the hard body parts together make up the animal's *skeleton.* The hard skeleton protects the soft body parts from bumps and cuts. The skeleton also supports the body. The hard parts that support and protect many animals are bones. You have bones in your body that hold you up and protect your brain, heart, and other soft parts.

The skeletons of some animals are on the outside. The grasshopper does not have bones

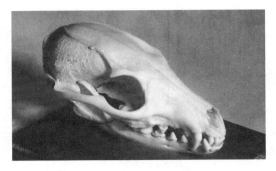

A cicada skeleton. Some insects shed their old exoskeletons and grow new ones. You may have found these empty skeletons clinging to tree trunks.

The skull of a fox. How is this part of a skeleton like the cicada shell? How is it different?

inside its body. Its skeleton is a hard shell on the outside. Such a skeleton is called an *exoskeleton.* The prefix *ex-* means "out" as in *exit.* Animals with exoskeletons do not have bones on the inside, but stiff, horny material on the outside. Now you know how the grasshopper is different from many other animals mentioned in the Book of Job. The grasshopper has an exoskeleton.

You often see animals with exoskeletons. They are in your back yard and even in your house. Flies, ants, butterflies, grasshoppers, and all other insects have exoskeletons. So do spiders, centipedes, and millipedes (sometimes called "hundred leggers" or "thousand leggers"). Some animals with exoskeletons, such as shrimp, crabs, and lobsters, live in the ocean. Their exoskeletons are thicker and tougher than those of insects and spiders.

Many common animals have skeletons inside their bodies. The inside skeletons allow these animals to be larger in size than animals with exoskeletons. An elephant can be almost 12 feet (4 meters) tall and weigh over 6 tons! Giant bones inside its body hold up this weight and allow the elephant to walk.

A very important part of an inside skeleton is the *backbone.* The backbone passes down the back of the animal's body. Like other bones, it helps to support the animal's body.

The backbone is not just one bone. It is made up of many little bones. Each one of these bones is a *vertebra.* The vertebrae give the back many joints that allow it to bend and turn. You use these joints when you stoop over and when you turn to see something behind you.

Look at the picture of the vertebra. Do you see the vertebra shaped like a triangle? Do you see the hole in it? All vertebrae have holes in the center. The holes are in a line down the back. The animal's main cord of nerves, called the spinal cord, passes through the hole of each vertebra. God made the strong backbone to protect the soft spinal cord. God made the backbone strong to hold up the body. If a vertebra of the backbone is broken, it is very serious. The spinal cord may be cut, and the animal may not be able to move parts of the body below the break. The animal may die.

Skeletons are God's wise plan to support and protect the bodies of animals. For some animals, an exoskeleton is best. For other animals, it is best to have an inside skeleton with a backbone.

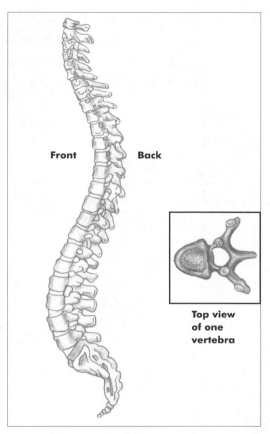

Front **Back**

Top view of one vertebra

The human backbone is made up of 33 vertebrae that allow you to bend your body forward and turn it from side to side.

Test Your Reading (Group A)

Write the missing words.
1. An animal's skeleton is important for ——— and ———.
2. Flies, spiders, and crabs have ———, which means that their skeletons are on the outside of their bodies.
3. The skeletons on the inside of animals' bodies are made of hard parts called ———.
4. A backbone is made of many bones called ———.
5. The backbone is important to ——— the body and to ——— the spinal cord.

Answer the following questions.
6. What do the many vertebrae of the backbone allow you to do?
7. How are the vertebrae made to protect the spinal cord?
8. Why is a broken back very serious?

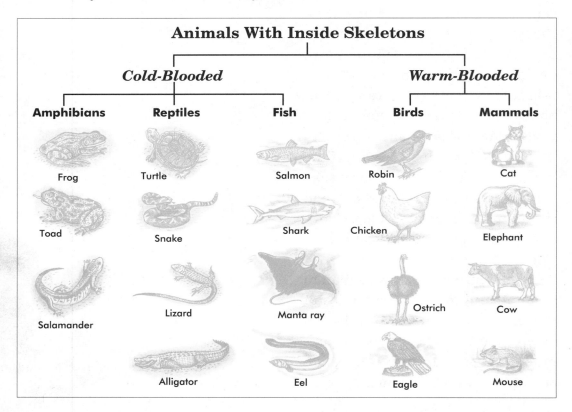

Animals With Inside Skeletons

Cold-Blooded — **Warm-Blooded**

| Amphibians | Reptiles | Fish | Birds | Mammals |

Frog · Turtle · Salmon · Robin · Cat
Toad · Snake · Shark · Chicken · Elephant
Salamander · Lizard · Manta ray · Ostrich · Cow
Alligator · Eel · Eagle · Mouse

Animal groups. The animal group with inside skeletons is divided into several smaller groups: mammals, birds, reptiles, amphibians, and fish.

Last year you studied about amphibians, reptiles, and mammals. Can you still name some animals in each group? Could you put snakes, chipmunks, frogs, cows, and turtles in the right group? In this unit you will have a special study about birds and fish. But before we study those lessons, we shall review each of the other three groups of backbone animals. We divide the animals into groups by their special characteristics. A *characteristic* is the special way a living thing is made or acts that is different from other living things.

Amphibians. Frogs, toads, and

salamanders have the characteristics that put them in the animal group called amphibians. An amphibian lives part of its life in water and part of its life on land. In the tadpole part of a frog's life, it lives in the water. Then it loses its tail and grows legs and can live on land. All amphibians are cold-blooded. So when the water or air gets cold, the body of a frog gets cold too.

Reptiles. Reptiles are also cold-blooded. Their bodies are covered with plates or scales. Turtles are covered with horny plates. The bodies of snakes, lizards, and alligators are covered with scales. Scales and plates are characteristics of the reptile group of animals.

Mammals. All mammals drink their mothers' milk when they are babies. That is a characteristic of mammals. They have hair and are warm-blooded. *Warm-blooded* means that their body temperature is warm and will stay warm even if the surrounding air or water is cold. Mammals include dogs, cats, elephants, deer, bears, cows, monkeys, and mice.

All of these animals have skeletons inside their bodies. All of them have a backbone with a spinal cord going through it.

Man. God created man a special living thing in a group of his own. None of the animals were given a living soul. You are not an animal, but you do have an inside skeleton with a backbone. Your bones support and protect your body in the same way as those of backbone animals. Yet an animal does not know that God made it. It cannot choose to praise God. But you can!

--------- **Test Your Reading (Group B)** ---------

Use each animal on this list twice to match with the groups and characteristics.

| cat | frog | grasshopper | snake |

9. A reptile
10. An insect
11. A mammal
12. An amphibian
13. Feeds its babies milk

14. Lives some of its life in water and some on land
15. Covered with scales
16. Has an exoskeleton

Answer the following questions.

17. What does being warm-blooded mean?
18. What characteristic do you have that makes you different from an animal?

Extra Activities

1. You can see for yourself why an animal's skeleton is important. You need an animal puppet that is large enough for you to put your hand inside. You also need a large balloon and some water.

   Fill the balloon about half full of water. Knot the opening so that the balloon is watertight. (You may need an adult to help you.) Then put the balloon inside the puppet. Try to make the animal sit or stand up. What happens? Now put your hand inside the animal puppet. Make it nod its head and move its legs. How is this different from having the balloon inside?

   Materials needed:
   - animal puppet
   - large balloon
   - water

2. Try to find a bone to study. Perhaps someone in the class can bring a chicken leg bone. Try to break it. Cut it with a saw. Examine it with a magnifying glass. Cut near the end of the bone and look for the spongy bone that protects the end of the bone. In what ways is the bone made to do its job of supporting the animal?

3. If you can find a grasshopper, examine its exoskeleton. Notice how the body and legs are covered with a hard layer. How is the exoskeleton made at the joints that allows it to bend?

Lesson 2

God Created Birds

New Words

beak, the bill of a bird.

down, soft, fluffy feathers that help birds stay warm.

gizzard (giz′·ərd), a part of the stomach that has strong muscles to crush food.

instinct (in′·stingkt′), a ready-made ability to do a difficult task without learning.

markings, colored patterns, such as stripes or patches, on birds.

perching, sitting on a high place such as a branch.

preen, to arrange or smooth the feathers with the beak.

quill, the long, stiff center tube of a feather.

streamlined, having a long, smooth shape that can move easily through air or water.

God made birds to fly. We admire birds because they can do something we cannot do. They can fly! "Doth the hawk fly by thy wisdom, and stretch her wings toward the south?" (Job 39:26). The flight of birds is a wonder of God's creation.

Why did God make birds to fly? God gave flight to birds in order to protect them from their enemies. Most birds are too small to fight with enemies, such as cats or foxes. They cannot run fast enough to get away, but they can fly away.

Most birds use flying to get their food. Hawks have very good eyesight and can drop out of the air very fast to catch mice or rabbits.

How can a bird fly? God designed a bird's body to be streamlined so that it can move easily through air. A *streamlined* shape is long, smooth, and somewhat pointed at each end. As a bird flies, the air flows easily over the streamlined shape without much resistance. Most birds also have lightweight bodies with many hollow bones. This

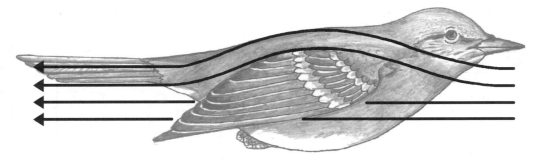

The streamlined shape of the bird's body helps it to move easily through the air.

makes their skeletons light and yet strong enough to support and protect them.

God gave birds strong wings and long feathers. Each feather is made stiff by a strong, hollow center tube called a *quill.* The branches coming out from the quill have barbs that hook the branches together to form a flat surface. With a microscope, you can examine this marvelous design. No bird could fly without long feathers with smooth surfaces and stiff quills.

In order to get off the ground, a

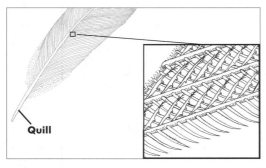

Quill

The design of a feather shows the wisdom of God.

bird must beat its wings rapidly. A small bird keeps beating its wings as it flies, but some larger birds, such as eagles, fly without much beating of the wings. They do this by riding on strong, steady winds high in the sky.

Men have copied the birds to make airplanes. Highly educated men spend hours designing a new airplane. Many experiments are done to test out new ideas. Millions of dollars are needed to design and make airplanes. In many ways, an airplane is like a bird. Both have wings. Both have streamlined bodies. Both can take off from the ground and land. But compared to a bird, an airplane is clumsy and wastes fuel. An airplane cannot change direction as quickly as a bird. An airplane cannot take off and land as easily. An airplane is dead; a bird is alive. Men design airplanes, but God designed birds.

Who designed each? Which has the best design?

Birds hatch from eggs. Have you ever watched a baby chick or duck hatching from an egg? First, you see a few cracks in the shell. You hear a soft tapping from inside the shell. The cracks grow larger as the baby bird keeps pecking away. Finally the egg splits apart, and the baby chick or duck struggles out into its bright new world.

All baby birds hatch from eggs.

A robin's nest

Usually the eggs are laid in a nest. God made each kind of bird to build its own special nest just the right size and shape. The ability to do a difficult task without learning is called an ***instinct.*** God gives animals various instincts. A robin has an instinct to make a good robin nest the first time it tries. It does not need to see a robin nest to make one. How God makes instincts to work is still His secret. It is a miracle to us. God reminded Job of these facts when He asked, "Doth the eagle mount up at thy command, and make her nest on high?" (Job 39:27).

How do birds grow and live? When they are hatched, chicks, ducks, and many other baby birds have soft, fluffy feathers called ***down*** over their bodies. The down helps them stay warm. As they grow older, they grow quill feathers so they can fly. But they still have down close to their bodies to keep them warm. Birds are warm-blooded. In fact, birds have a higher body temperature than you do. The human body temperature is 98.6°F (37°C); birds have a body temperature from 101° to 112°F (38° to 44°C). You would be sick if your temperature was that high.

Birds use their **beaks** to gather their food. Woodpeckers have pointed beaks for drilling holes in trees to find insects. Sparrows have short, strong beaks for cracking seeds. Ducks have broad beaks called bills for gathering plants and insects for food from water. Birds do not have teeth to chew their food as we do. So God gave them special stomachs called **gizzards.** The birds swallow small stones for the strong muscles in their gizzards to use to grind their food. Birds that eat seeds have gizzards strong enough to crush seeds. God gave the birds everything they need.

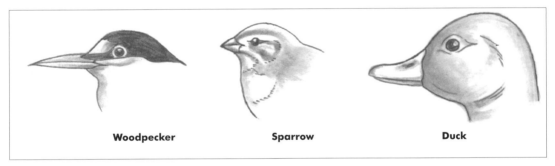

Woodpecker   Sparrow   Duck

Why do these beaks have different shapes?

Test Your Reading (Group A)

Find the correct ending that completes each sentence.

1. God gave birds wings and feathers
2. God gave birds hollow bones
3. God gave birds streamlined bodies
4. God gave birds the instinct
5. God gave birds down
6. God gave birds quills
7. God gave birds gizzards
8. God gave the birds beaks

a. to grind their food.
b. to keep warm.
c. to gather their food.
d. to fly.
e. to have stiff, light feathers.
f. to glide through the air.
g. to be lightweight.
h. to build nests for their eggs.

Write the correct answers.
9. What makes the flat, smooth surface of the feather?
10. What is an instinct?
11. How does a baby bird hatch, or come out of its egg?
12. Give an example of how God gave a bird a special beak for a special use.

Feet are for sleeping and swimming. Of course, birds walk on their feet. But just as God gave special beaks to the birds, so He also gave them special feet. For example, God gave the chicken special feet for *perching.* Its feet have three toes in front and one behind. These feet can lock around a branch. The chicken can even go to sleep up in a tree away from danger while its toes are locked around a branch. Many other common birds, such as robins, cardinals, and blackbirds, are also perching birds.

Woodpeckers cling onto the sides of trees while they peck the bark for insects. God gave them feet with two toes in front and two behind. Each toe has a sharp claw for fastening into the tree. Owls also have sharp claws. They use their claws for holding mice and other small animals that they catch.

God designed the duck's feet for water. He made them with webs between the toes for swimming. They are like small paddles that help the duck swim across streams and ponds.

Feathers for floating. Birds use their beaks for smoothing their feathers. This is called *preening.* Ducks not only preen their feathers, but they also add oil. The oil is produced by an oil gland near the tail. A duck smoothes the oil over its feathers with its beak. Water will not stick to oil, so it keeps the duck dry and allows it to float for hours

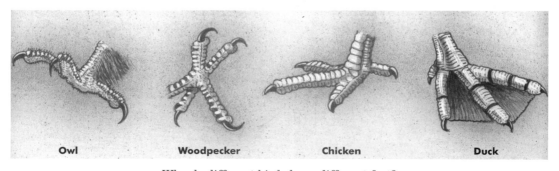

Owl   Woodpecker   Chicken   Duck

Why do different birds have different feet?

without water soaking the feathers. A duck must keep adding oil to its shiny raincoat to keep it watertight.

Birds are interesting creatures. They lay eggs, fly, swim, perch, preen, and sing. They are beautifully designed and colored. No wonder many people have a hobby of bird watching.

Bird watching. Do you like to hear birds singing? Can you tell the kind of bird by its songs? Can you identify a bird by its *markings,* or patterns of color? Do you notice the shape of the tail and beak? Do you know which birds swoop as they fly and which soar high overhead? If so, you make a good bird watcher. Who does not look up to see the V-shaped pattern of a flock of geese, honking as they fly north or south?

One good way to watch birds is to feed them. They need food especially in the wintertime when plants are

Birds eating sunflower seeds

not growing. You can put sunflower seeds and bread crumbs in a bird feeder. Hang the feeder on a bush or tree that is near your house. That way you can watch birds close up.

Birds tend to be very excitable. A little noise or movement will send them flying away. A bird watcher needs patience. Often he uses a binocular to be able to get a good look at the markings of a bird that is at a distance.

A bird book is helpful to the bird watcher. Whenever you see a bird that is new to you, notice the bird's markings. Try to remember the shape of its head, body, and tail. Then find the same bird in a bird book to learn its name.

The farmer's friend. Sometimes when birds are eating our peas or cherries, we wish they would go away. But on the whole, birds help the farmer and gardener. They eat harmful insects and weed seeds. One bird might eat dozens of insects or thousands of weed seeds in a single day.

We have many reasons to thank God for the birds. We like birds because they sing. They are colorful and interesting to watch. They are helpful to gardens and farms. They call our attention to the wise God who made them.

———————— **Test Your Reading (Group B)** ————————

Copy and complete the following chart about birds' feet. The first one is done for you.

	Description of Feet	**Special Use for Feet**
Robin	*three toes in front, one behind*	*perching*
13. Woodpecker	a. ———	b. ———
14. Owl	a. ———	b. ———
15. Duck	a. ———	b. ———

Choose the best answer.

16. A duck can float on water because
    a. it can paddle with its feet to get it up.
    b. oil on the feathers keeps out the water.
    c. the bottom of the duck's body is very light.

17. If you saw a duck preening, you would see it
    a. rubbing its feathers with its beak.
    b. moving its feet over its feathers.
    c. fluffing its feathers by flapping its wings.

18. A good way to attract birds to your house is to
    a. plant pretty flowers around the house.
    b. keep bird feed in a bird feeder.
    c. wait patiently under a tree.

19. If you want to identify a strange bird you saw,
    a. you need a binocular.
    b. you need some bird food.
    c. you need a bird book.

20. A farmer can be glad if blackbirds are in his field as he disks it because
    a. then they can get close enough for him to shoot them.
    b. he knows that he will have less problem with insects.
    c. they give him something interesting to watch while he works.

Reviewing What You Have Learned

1. The backbone is part of the
   a. skeleton.   b. exoskeleton.   c. spinal cord.
2. Skeletons ———— the soft parts of animals.
3. The small bones that protect an animal's spinal cord are called ————.
4. Which group of animals all have external skeletons?
   a. amphibians, reptiles, birds
   b. crabs, centipedes, insects
   c. mammals, millipedes, spiders
5. Which group of animals all have backbones?
   a. amphibians, reptiles, birds
   b. crabs, centipedes, insects
   c. mammals, millipedes, spiders

Extra Activities

1. Use a bird book or an encyclopedia to study the different kinds of bird feet and bills. Find out how each bird is designed for getting a certain kind of food.
2. Keep a class record of the birds you see this year. Write a list of birds commonly seen in your area down the left side of a paper with lines. Leave room below the list for additional birds. You and your classmates can sign your initials the first time you see that kind of bird.
3. Try writing with a quill as people did long ago before there were pencils and ballpoint pens. You need a bottle of ink and a stiff feather. Ask an adult to sharpen the feather to a point with a knife. Now dip the tip of the quill into the ink and try to finish a lesson assignment.

   ### *Materials needed:*
   - bottle of ink   - stiff feather   - knife

4. Look at feathers with a microscope. Pull some of the branches apart so that you can see the barbs that hold the branches together to form a clothlike covering. Notice the order and beauty God has used in making feathers.

Lesson 3

God Created Fish

New Words

air bladder, a small sack of air inside a fish's body.

fins, the fanlike body parts of a fish, which it uses to swim.

gills, the body part with which a fish breathes underwater.

scales, the many small, tough plates covering the body of a fish.

Fish live all their lives in water. They do not have legs to walk on the land. They do not have wings to fly in the air. God did not make them to live on land or in the air. In many ways, we can see how they are designed to live in water.

Fish swim. Did you ever see a fish swish its tail? Perhaps you watched a goldfish in an aquarium. The fish wags its tail in order to swim. Strong muscles in the sides of the fish move the tail back and forth. The wagging tail pushes the fish forward through the water. Fish can move quickly through the water. A goldfish can go 4 miles (6 kilometers) per hour. That is fast for such a small animal. Some fish can go 30 miles (50 kilometers) per hour.

A fish swims fast for two reasons. First, it must catch its own food. It might be after a worm or a smaller fish. Second, a fish swims fast to escape its enemies. Big water birds, bigger fish, or fishermen may be looking for some good fish for food.

Do you wonder why fish have so many enemies? Both people and animals like to eat fish. God planned that we may eat fish to get some of the materials our bodies need for good health. Some of Jesus' disciples were fishermen. Fishing is still an important occupation for many people who supply us with this healthful food.

Fish can swim fast because God designed their bodies to move easily through the water. Most fish are covered with many thin, hard *scales.* The scales provide a smooth body surface just right for swimming. They are tough enough to protect the fish from cuts and scrapes.

A slippery liquid comes out between the fish's scales. It forms a coating all over the fish's body. This slippery coating allows a fish to glide smoothly through the water. The fish's enemies must work hard to hold such a slippery body.

Streamlined fish. Another important part of God's design for a fish is its streamlined shape. The pointed head, sleek body, and thin tail help the fish glide through the water. The water easily flows around the fish. Fish are streamlined to swim easily through the water just as birds are streamlined to fly easily through the air. Today man copies God's art of streamlining in making boats and ships. Airplanes and cars are streamlined for fast travel through the air. Without their streamlined shape, these vehicles would use more fuel because they would have to push harder. You know how hard it is to ride against the wind on a bicycle. If you lower your head to make yourself more streamlined, it is easier to ride against the wind.

Fish have *fins* to help them swim. Most fins have a fanlike shape with skin stretched over thin bones. The fin on the end of the tail helps give the fish speed. This tail fin is also used in steering. Fins on the top and bottom help the fish to keep balanced so that it stays right side up. A pair of fins on the side are used to steer and stop.

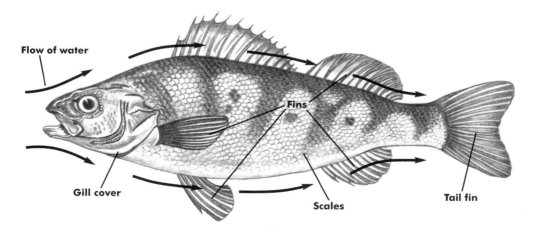

Flow of water

Fins

Gill cover

Scales

Tail fin

The body of a fish, the handiwork of God

———————— **Test Your Reading (Group A)** ————————

Write the missing words.

1. The fish pushes itself forward with its ———.
2. Fish have many enemies because they are good ———.
3. It is good that fish can swim fast so that they can get their ———.
4. The hard cover of ——— makes the outside of the fish smooth and protects the skin of the fish.
5. The outside of the fish is made ——— by a material that comes out between the fish's scales.
6. The ——— shape of the fish helps it glide easily through the water.
7. Most fins have ——— stretched over thin ———.
8. The fins on the top and bottom of the fish help the fish keep its ———.
9. If a fish wants to stop, it can put out its side ———.

More ways God made fish to live in the water. In water, objects usually sink to the bottom or float to the surface. A swimming fish does not want to do either of these things. To be able to stay in the middle of the water, its weight and size must be just right. God gave most fish an *air bladder,* a sack of air inside its body. The air bladder is used to adjust the size of the body so that it does not sink or float.

As the fish goes deeper, the pressure of the water increases. More air must be added to the air bladder to keep up the size of the fish. This air is added by the blood. If the pressure would not increase in the air bladder, the

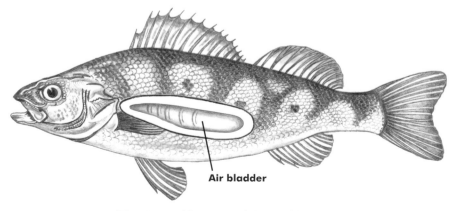

Air bladder

The size and location of the air bladder

water pressure would squeeze the body of the fish and make it sink to the bottom. God made the body of the fish to make changes in the air bladder without thinking, just as you do not need to think to make your heart beat. Everywhere we look in the natural world, we see the wisdom of God. One of those wonders is the air bladder of a fish.

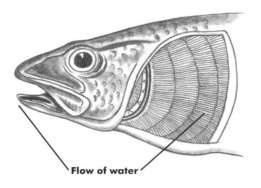

Flow of water

Fish breathe with gills.

How does a fish "breathe"? Man and animals need oxygen to live. You get oxygen from the air when you breathe. Your lungs take oxygen from the air and put it in the blood. But a fish does not rise to the water surface for air. If a fish is taken out of the water, it will soon die.

Instead of breathing air, fish get their oxygen from the water. That is why air is bubbled into fish aquariums. The oxygen of the air goes into the water so that the fish can breathe. A fish breathes by opening and closing its mouth. It takes in water through its mouth and forces it through its *gills.* The water then goes out through the gill openings found on each side of its head.

The gills are made of several layers of threadlike fingers. Each tiny finger has blood flowing through it. This gives much surface

for the oxygen in the water to get into the blood. This oxygen then circles throughout the fish's body where it is needed. The gills continually take oxygen from the water, just as your lungs take oxygen from the air. Gill-breathing is just as normal to a fish as lung-breathing is to you.

Because fish use up the oxygen in the water, oxygen must be replaced in the water of an aquarium, or the water must be changed often. One way of replacing the oxygen is to bubble air into the water from an air pump. Another way is to have many green water plants growing in the aquarium. As green plants grow in light, they give off oxygen. The oxygen from the green plants is just what the fish need to breathe.

Fish are cold-blooded animals. The body temperature of a fish becomes the same as the water it lives in. That way it does not need a layer of insulating fur or down to keep it warm. A layer of insulation would make its body fat and harder to move through the water. The thin, streamlined body of the fish is just right for swimming in water. If fish were warm-blooded, they would need to eat more food to make the extra heat.

God was able to make warm-blooded sea animals. The whale is warm-blooded, but then it is very large. It has a thick layer of fat that is insulation for its body. A whale is not a fish. It is a mammal that breathes air. That is why a whale must come to the surface of the water to breathe. It has a hole on the top of its body so that it does not need to come out of the water very far to breathe. The whale has everything it needs to stay alive. A fish has everything it needs to stay alive. Both were made by God.

The more we study fish, the more we see that they were designed by Someone much wiser than man. Job must have known this because he said, "The fishes of the sea shall declare unto thee. Who knoweth not in all these that the hand of the LORD hath wrought [made] this?" (Job 12:8, 9).

———— Test Your Reading (Group B) ————

Read each sentence below. Write *true* if the statement is true. Write *false* if the statement is false.

10. A fish stores oxygen for breathing in its air bladder.
11. The pressure in the air bladder changes because of changes in the depth of the fish.
12. Air is bubbled into an aquarium to supply air for the fish's air bladder.
13. The gills do the same thing for a fish that lungs do for you.
14. The gills are made of many flat, platelike fins.
15. Putting green plants in an aquarium helps the fish get oxygen.
16. Being cold-blooded allows the fish to have a thin body.
17. The whale is a very large, warm-blooded fish.

Reviewing What You Have Learned

1. True or false? A skeleton gives an animal its support.
2. A bird ——— its feathers when it smoothes them with its beak.
3. God designed birds to fly by giving them
   a. fluffy down.
   b. feet that can perch.
   c. hollow bones and quills.
4. A ——— takes the place of teeth in a bird.
5. A good bird watcher
   a. carefully looks for a bird's markings.
   b. carefully counts the insects a bird eats.
   c. carefully watches a bird preening its feathers.

Extra Activities

1. Find "Fish" in an encyclopedia or get a library book about fishes. Try to find as many pictures of different kinds of fish as you can. Then compare the pictures. In what ways are all fishes alike? In what ways are they different?

   Now read your encyclopedia article or library book. What are some new things you learned? Tell or write about them.

2. A fish aquarium is an interesting way to learn about fish. Perhaps you could borrow an aquarium and some tropical fish for your classroom. Learn how to feed them. Do not overfeed the fish. You will need an air pump to supply oxygen for the water. Why? If you do not supply oxygen with an air pump, you will need to change the water every few days. Putting green water plants in the aquarium will help to supply the needed oxygen. You will need to keep the water clean for the fish.

   Read in an encyclopedia or pet book how to best care for tropical fish.

Lesson 4

God Created Mollusks

New Words

clam, a water mollusk with a two-part shell and a hatchet-shaped foot.

mollusks (mol′·əsks), a group of animals with soft bodies, many of which are protected by shells.

octopus (ok′·tə·pəs), a sea mollusk having eight arms with sucking pads.

oyster (oi′·stər), a mollusk that makes pearls and has a rough, two-part shell.

slug, a common garden mollusk without a shell.

snail, a land or water mollusk with a spiral shell and a wide foot.

Animals with no skeletons. In Lesson 1 of this unit, you learned that some animals have skeletons inside their bodies and some have exoskeletons. You have already studied birds and fish, which have skeletons and backbones. Now we shall study animals that have no skeletons at all. The *mollusks* are a group of such animals.

Do you remember seeing a snail with its round shell, moving slowly across the ground and leaving a slippery trail? A *snail* is an example of a mollusk.

The mollusks have soft, moist bodies. Most of them live in the water. How does God protect them from hungry enemies? A few kinds of mollusks can swim fast like a fish, and a few can sting their enemies

One-part shells were beautifully designed by God.

with poison. But most of the mollusks cannot do these things.

Shells. God gave many of the mollusks hard, strong shells around their soft bodies. A mollusk's shell is so hard and strong that most animals cannot break or open it. The round, hard covering on the back of a snail is its shell. The seashells that you can find on the seashore are the shells of mollusks that lived in the ocean.

Mollusk shells are also beautiful and neatly made. Each shell has its own shape and color design. Some are spirals, and some have butterfly shapes when open. Some look as if they were painted with reds, oranges, and yellows. Mollusk shells show us that God likes beauty and order.

Mollusks with one-part shells. The largest group of mollusks has shells all in one piece. We call such a shell a one-part shell. Snails have one-part shells. A one-part shell has a spiral pattern that winds toward the center.

A mollusk with a one-part shell has a kind of foot at the opening of the shell. The mollusk uses its wide foot in a wavelike motion to slowly push its body forward. You know how slow it is if you have ever

watched a snail creeping. But no wonder it is so slow. It makes its own slippery road!

The snail's road, or trail, is sticky, slippery slime, made inside the snail's body. The slime allows the snail to slide forward easily. It protects the snail's soft body from rough twigs and stones. In fact, the snail could crawl right across the sharp edge of a knife without being cut.

Snails are sometimes put into aquariums to keep the glass clean. They crawl over the glass, eating the green algae as they go. One kind of snail does not have a shell at all. It is called a *slug*. You may have seen slugs on lettuce and other garden vegetables. They move slowly over slippery trails like other snails.

A snail makes its own trail.

———————— Test Your Reading (Group A) ————————

Find the correct ending for each sentence, and write the letter on your paper.

1. Mollusks are a group of animals that have
   a. smooth, tough skin.
   b. soft, moist bodies.
   c. hard inside skeletons.
2. God protected many mollusks with
   a. hard shells.
   b. streamlined bodies.
   c. strong fins.
3. All mollusk shells
   a. have no exact shape.
   b. are thick and leathery.
   c. show that God is orderly.
4. The mollusk group containing snails has shells
   a. in three pieces.
   b. in two pieces.
   c. in one piece.
5. You could see where a snail has walked by
   a. a rounded groove.
   b. a slimy path.
   c. a line of rough ground.
6. A snail uses slippery slime
   a. to trap other mollusks.
   b. to protect its body from sharp objects.
   c. to keep its shell watertight.
7. A slug is a snail without
   a. a shell.   b. a foot.   c. a slippery trail.

Answer the following questions.

8. In what way does a seashell show that God likes beauty and order?
9. How does a snail move?
10. What mollusk with a one-part shell may you see in a garden?

Two-part shells were beautifully designed by God.

Mollusks with two-part shells. Many mollusks have two matching shells, or a two-part shell. *Clams* and *oysters* are in this group. The two shells are connected by hinges. They are usually kept slightly open. But when the clam becomes frightened, it snaps the shells shut with a strong muscle. This is the way God made it to protect itself.

The mollusks with two-part shells all live in water. They creep along with a foot shaped like a hatchet. They eat small plants or animals as the other mollusks do. Both oysters and clams are used for food. Clams can be dug from mud along the seashore.

Many oysters are harvested from underwater "farms" for food. The oyster farmer spreads old shells or clay tiles over the sea bottom. He then "plants" baby oysters. The oysters fasten themselves on the sea bottom and grow. In about three years, the farmer can harvest his crop of oysters and sell them for food.

The outside of oyster shells is rough, but oysters can make shiny, round pearls on the inside. An oyster does not know that pearls look pretty. It makes a pearl because something inside is hurting. Perhaps a grain of sand gets stuck inside the oyster's body. Of course, the oyster has no hands to get it back out. So the oyster coats the grain of sand with layers and more layers of shiny material, thus forming a pearl. The smooth, round pearl does not bother the oyster as the grain of sand did.

Another kind of mollusk is a strange sea animal called the ***octopus.*** *Octo-* means "eight." An octopus has 8 long arms. These arms are lined with many sucking pads to catch food. The arms wrap

An octopus has 8 arms.

around the captured animal and pull it to the mouth. Strong jaws tear and crush it. An octopus is usually about the size of a softball, but big ones can have arms over 12 feet (4 meters) long.

Like other mollusks, the octopus has a soft body. But it does not have a shell. It has two other ways to protect itself. It can shoot water forward so that it moves backward like a jet airplane. The octopus can also shoot a black inklike liquid into the water to make a dark cloud. This hides the octopus until it can escape from its enemy.

What interesting creatures God made! The soft-bodied mollusks are only one group of the many animals God created. Some have one shell, some have two shells, and some have no shells at all. But all are given what they need to live and grow.

--------- **Test Your Reading (Group B)** ---------

Match each word with the best description.

11. The shape of the foot of a clam
12. Raised on "farms" for food
13. Grown around a grain of sand
14. Dug from mud on seashore
15. Mollusk with long arms and strong jaws
16. Eight
17. Used to move quickly
18. Used to hide from enemy

a. jet
b. octopus
c. hatchet
d. pearl
e. *octo-*
f. black liquid
g. oyster
h. clam

Answer the following questions.

19. What pulls the parts of a two-part shell together?
20. What two things does an oyster farmer do to grow oysters?

Reviewing What You Have Learned

1. When a bird sits or sleeps while grasping a branch, we say it is
   a. preening.
   b. perching.
   c. streamlining.
2. Baby birds are covered with —— to keep them warm.
3. Fish get oxygen from the water with their
   a. scales.   b. fins.   c. gills.
4. True or false? An air bladder helps a fish stay in the middle of the water.
5. A fish moves through the water by wagging its —— from side to side.

Extra Activities

1. Often homes have some shells that were found along a seashore. Some may even have large souvenir whelk shells. Bring various shells to school and make a labeled display of them. Use reference books to identify them.
2. Hunt for shells and start a collection! If you live close to a seashore, you will have a good source for shells. For the sake of safety, always take someone else along with you to the seashore. If you do not live along a sea, you can look for shells in streams and ditches.

   Label each shell neatly with its name and the date and place you found it. You may want to display your shells on a shelf or table. Another good method is to lay them on a bed of cotton in a large, shallow wooden frame, and lay a glass cover on top. (If sharp glass edges are exposed, be sure to tape them.)

Lesson 5

Animals With Strange Bodies

New Words

earthworm, a brown, segmented worm that lives in the soil.

jellyfish, a swimming sea animal with stinging tentacles.

planaria (plə·nar′·ē·ə), a harmless flatworm that lives in ponds and streams.

regeneration (ri·jen′·ə·rā′·shən), the ability to grow missing body parts.

sponge, a plantlike sea animal having a rubbery or soft skeleton.

starfish, a star-shaped, spiny-skinned sea animal, having five or more arms.

tentacles (ten′·tə·kəlz), stringlike body parts that contain stinging cells.

God has made so many different animals that you could study them all year and still not learn about all of them. In the last lesson, you learned about the octopus, which has a strange body. In this lesson you will be learning about five more strange animals.

The earthworm. If you dig in a garden, you will find brown *earthworms.* The long body of an earthworm is divided into more than 75 pieces or segments. The earthworm is an example of a segmented worm. Except for the first and the last, each segment has eight short bristles on the sides and bottom.

The earthworm has muscles that squeeze it out long and others that pull it up short. The earthworm pushes forward and holds its

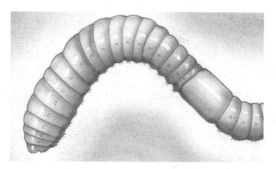

How does the earthworm use its bristles to move?

head end with front bristles. Then it pulls its tail end up and holds its tail with back bristles. Then it is ready to push its head forward again. As it tunnels through the soil, it eats the soil. It digests dead plant material and passes the rest out of its body.

As earthworms tunnel through the soil and digest it, they make the soil better. If you have many earthworms in your garden, you know that you have good soil and that it is being made better. The tunnels help to make the soil loose. The digestion helps to fertilize the soil. Earthworms are very helpful to us.

Planaria. *Planaria* are harmless flatworms that live in freshwater streams and ponds. They are about ¼–1½ inches (6–38 millimeters) long, with a triangular head at one end and a rounded tail at the other. In the head are two eyespots that let them see light or darkness.

If you lift a dead leaf or a stick from a stream, you may find some of these tiny black, white, or brown animals. You will enjoy seeing them glide over a surface if you put them in a dish with a little water. They do this gliding motion with many small hairs on their undersides.

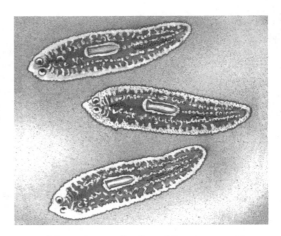

Planaria can be found in streams.

Planaria are just one of the many kinds of small moving creatures that live in the mud and along the banks of streams. They help to eat the dead plants and animals that fall into the water. They make the streams an interesting place to study.

Sponges. Have you ever scrubbed a car or bathtub with a sponge? You probably used a man-made sponge. But if you used a real sponge, you were scrubbing with the skeleton of an animal! The sponge skeleton is soft and rubberlike. It has many small holes that can hold a large amount of water. That is why it is useful for cleaning and scrubbing things.

A live *sponge* is like slippery, raw liver. It is plantlike and does not move, for it is fastened to the ocean bottom. Without a head or gills, how can it eat or breathe? Thousands of tiny, threadlike whips inside the sponge keep sweeping seawater throughout its body. The ocean water contains oxygen and bits of food, which the sponge uses to keep it alive. The sponge has a strange body, and yet men have found use for its skeleton.

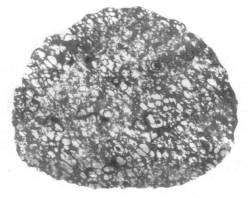

A sponge sweeps seawater through the many holes in its body.

―――――― **Test Your Reading (Group A)** ――――――

From the word box, find and write a word for each blank.

bristles	fertilize	segments
dead	flatworm	skeleton
earthworm	glide	sponge
eyespots	planaria	

1. The rubbery ――― of a sponge is useful for washing and scrubbing.
2. The planaria is a ―――.
3. The earthworm is an example of a worm with ―――.
4. The earthworm uses ――― to hold itself when making a tunnel.
5. You can see a planaria ――― over a surface with the many small hairs on its underside.
6. The earthworm helps to ――― the soil.
7. Both the planaria and earthworm help to use up ――― plants.
8. The planaria have two ――― in its head to see light.
9. The ――― stays fastened at one place on the ocean floor.
10. You can find an ――― by digging in the garden.
11. You may find ――― by looking on the undersides of dead leaves in freshwater streams.

What use does the jellyfish make of its long tentacles?

The starfish is a spiny-skinned animal.

Jellyfish. The *jellyfish* looks like an umbrella floating in the water with frilly streamers and long, stringlike *tentacles.* Though the body of the jellyfish is jellylike and has no skeleton, it is not weak. Its tentacles contain stinging cells, which are dangerous. If you ever see a blob of jelly along a seashore, do not touch it. It could give you very hurtful stings.

As the jellyfish swims in the water, its tentacles may brush against a small fish. They sting the fish so that it cannot swim away. Then the jellyfish can eat the fish.

Some jellyfish are so small you can hardly see them. Others are over 6 feet (2 meters) across with tentacles spreading out more than 20 feet (6 meters).

Starfish. The *starfish* are in a group of strange animals called spiny-skinned animals because of their hard, rough skins.

The starfish gets its name from its star shape. Most starfish have five arms. Each arm has many tiny, tubelike feet with sucking pads on them that work somewhat like those on an octopus. These arms are all fastened to the center like spokes on a wheel.

How does a starfish get food? The starfish slowly pulls its body along the ocean bottom until it finds a clam or an oyster. With the sucking pads, it holds each side of the shell and begins to pull. The clam or oyster is much stronger than the starfish and clamps its shell shut. The starfish keeps pulling and pulling until the mollusk becomes tired. The shell opens just a crack. The starfish pushes its baglike stomach into that small crack and eats the mollusk inside its own shell. What a strange animal! Starfish are a problem to oyster farmers.

If a starfish loses an arm, it can grow a new one. The ability to grow missing body parts is called *regeneration.* Even one arm with some of the center can regenerate the missing parts and become a new starfish. Animals such as planaria, sponges, and octopuses have this ability of regeneration too. Your body cannot regenerate missing parts. If you should lose your arm, no new arm will grow in its place.

Each kind of animal is made to show God's glory in its own way. The strange and interesting animals you studied in this lesson are the work of God. They fit into God's wise plan. They teach us about the wisdom of God.

———— Test Your Reading (Group B) ————

Answer the following questions.
  12. Where do jellyfish get their name?
  13. Why should you not pick up a jellylike mass along a seashore?
  14. How do jellyfish use their tentacles to get food?
  15. Where do starfish get their name?
  16. What kind of covering do starfish have to protect their bodies?
  17. What does a starfish have on its arms that can hold to something?
  18. How does a weaker starfish open the shell of a stronger oyster?
  19. What does it mean that starfish have the power of regeneration?
  20. Why would it be unwise for oyster fishermen to cut up starfish they catch and throw them back into the water?

Reviewing What You Have Learned
  1. Which group has streamlined bodies?
     a. birds, fish
     b. amphibians, reptiles
     c. snails, slugs
  2. The parts of a two-part mollusk shell are held together by a ———.

3. True or false? An oyster makes a pearl when a grain of sand bothers it.
4. Fish get oxygen from the water with their ———.
5. An octopus can move rapidly by
   a. running on its eight arms.
   b. swimming with special fins.
   c. shooting water.

Extra Activities

1. Read more about the strange animals in your lesson in an encyclopedia or library book. You might look for the titles "Earthworm," "Planaria (Planarian)," "Sponge," "Jellyfish," and "Starfish." Share with the class interesting facts about these animals that are not given in your textbook.
2. Dig in a garden to find some earthworms. Pull an earthworm gently over your finger to feel the bristles. Watch an earthworm crawl. Notice how it squeezes its body and makes it thin when it makes itself long. Be sure to give the earthworms moist leaves and soil to live in. Earthworms breathe through their moist skin. You should return them to the soil so that they can continue to help build up the soil.
3. Try to find some live planaria in a pond or stream. They are often on the undersides of dead tree leaves. Put some with a few dead leaves in a dish. Watch how they glide over the surface of a leaf. Examine them with a magnifying glass or a microscope. Notice their eyespots.

   Planaria have the power of regeneration. With a sharp razorblade, cut a planaria in two. Check it each day. Notice how the head end will grow a tail and the tail end will grow a new head.

Lesson 6

Do You Remember?

Match each letter to the correct number.

a. clam   d. mollusks   g. slug
b. earthworm   e. oyster   h. snail
c. jellyfish   f. planaria   i. sponge

1. A sea animal that makes pearls
2. A slippery-path maker with a one-part shell
3. A group with soft bodies usually protected by shells
4. A floating sea animal that is like an umbrella
5. An animal that digs tunnels through soil
6. A flatworm that lives in ponds and streams
7. A mollusk with a hatchet-shaped foot found in mud
8. A common land mollusk that has no shell
9. An animal with a rubbery skeleton used for washing

From the word box, find and write a word for each blank.

air bladder	gills	regeneration
backbone	gizzard	scales
beak	markings	streamlined
down	perch	tentacles
exoskeletons	preen	vertebrae
fins	quills	

10. Insects, spiders, and lobsters have stiff ———— to support their bodies.
11. The spinal cord of a horse is protected by a strong ————.
12. Many small ———— connected together form the backbone.
13. A bird needs stiff ———— in its feathers in order to fly.
14. The small, soft feathers that keep a bird warm are called ————.

15. Birds, fish, cars, and ships need to be ——— for easy travel through air or water.
16. A woodpecker uses its ——— to find its food.
17. A chicken will ——— on its roost and sleep without falling off.
18. We can learn to tell birds apart by studying their ———.
19. Ducks and geese ——— their feathers by smoothing them.
20. A robin's ——— grinds up the hard food in its stomach.
21. A goldfish uses its ——— to turn, slow down, and stop.
22. A salmon or any other fish needs its ——— in order to get oxygen from the water.
23. A tough covering of ——— protects the outside of a fish's body.
24. When a fish wants to swim at a higher or lower level, it uses its ——— to rise or sink.
25. Octopuses and starfish have the power of ——— to grow missing body parts.
26. Jellyfish use their stinging ——— to get food.

Choose the best answer to finish each sentence.
27. The animal groups with inside skeletons and backbones include
    a. mammals, reptiles, and insects.
    b. fish, birds, and amphibians.
    c. reptiles, worms, and mammals.
28. In order to fly, a bird must have
    a. hollow bones and perching feet.
    b. strong wings and stiff feathers.
    c. oily feathers and hollow quills.
29. A fish moves forward by
    a. wagging its tail.
    b. squeezing its air bladder.
    c. opening its gills.
30. A clam has
    a. an inside shell.
    b. a one-part shell.
    c. a two-part shell.

31. An oyster's enemy is the
    a. starfish.
    b. jellyfish.
    c. sea anemone.

Write *true* if the sentence is true; write *false* if it is not true.
32. God designed the bodies of most birds especially for flying.
33. Baby birds hatch from eggs laid in a nest.
34. The meat of fish is a healthful food.
35. Many earthworms in a garden are a sign that the soil is poor.
36. Jellyfish float around the sea, but sponges and starfish fasten themselves to rocks.
37. The octopus has five arms with sucking pads on them.

Copy and finish each sentence correctly.
38–39. Two reasons why many animals need skeletons are ———.
40. God made a bird's bones to be hollow because ———.
41. Geese, ducks, and swans need oiled feathers in order to ———.
42–43. We like birds for these two reasons: ———.
44. The way the bodies of animals are made reminds us of ———.
45. The starfish's arms can hold tightly with feet that have ———.

Unit Three

The Stars Inspire Wonder

Have you ever wondered how big the stars really are? Do you ever think about how far away they are from the earth? Do you think about the One who keeps each star in its place?

God wants us to ask such questions about the stars. While we learn to know the stars, we can also learn about God. The great number and size of the stars teach us of God's power. The vast distances between the stars teach us of God's greatness. The position and movement of the stars teach us of God's order.

"Canst thou . . . loose the bands of Orion?" (Job 38:31).

Even though Job lived thousands of years ago, he saw the very same stars that we see today! God asked Job some questions about the stars to teach Job of God's greatness and Job's weakness.

When God talked to Job about the stars, He said their names. Notice the names in the following verses: "Canst thou bind the sweet influences of *Pleiades,* or loose the bands of *Orion?* Canst thou bring forth *Mazzaroth* in his season? or canst thou guide *Arcturus* with his sons?" (Job 38:31, 32). In this unit you will study most of these star names.

In these questions God was asking Job, "Can you change any of the stars? Can you keep them in their proper places?" Of course, Job knew that he could never take care of the stars. Only God could do that.

God wanted to remind Job that only God was great enough to take care of the stars. Only God was great and wise enough to take care of Job. God wanted Job to trust and obey Him, just as He wants us to trust and obey Him today.

Lesson 1

Star Pictures

New Words

Big Dipper, a group of stars forming a picture of a large dipper.

constellation (kon′·stə·lā′·shən), a group of stars that forms a picture.

Little Dipper, a group of stars shaped like a small dipper.

Orion (ō·rī′·ən), a large constellation shaped like a hunter.

Pleiades (plē′·ə·dēz′), a cluster of six bright stars said to be sisters.

God made the stars. Can you tell how the stars got into the sky? Of course—God put them there! The Bible says that God made the stars on the fourth day of the Creation week. "And God made two great lights [the sun and moon]; . . . he made the stars also" (Genesis 1:16).

Job knew that God created the stars. Job said, "By his spirit he hath garnished [or decorated] the heavens" (Job 26:13).

Job also knew that God set each star in its position. The order of the stars is very exact. Tonight you can see the same star pictures that Job did.

Star study is very old. Ever since God made the stars, people have studied them. They wanted to learn the positions of the stars. But it was hard to learn the many, many stars one by one. It was easier to learn groups of stars.

So the bright stars were put into groups called ***constellations.*** Each constellation was named for the picture it seemed to form, such as a man, a fish, or a rabbit. In this way, people divided the sky into star pictures called constellations. Then they learned the name of each constellation and its neighbor constellations. When they talked about a certain star, they named the constellation to which it belonged. That made it easier to tell in which part of the sky the star was.

Can you see the relation of the stars in Orion to an imagined picture of a hunter?

Today we still use this same method to learn the star positions. We still imagine that we can see pictures in the constellations. We still use some of the same star and constellation names that Job and other men did long ago.

Two familiar constellations. One of the brightest star groups is the *Big Dipper.* Can you guess what picture it forms? Yes, if you draw lines from one star to the next, it looks like a large dipper with a bent handle.

The *Little Dipper* is smaller than the Big Dipper. Most of the stars in the Little Dipper are dim.

But three of the stars of the Little Dipper are bright—the end of the handle and the side of the dipper.

You can use the Big Dipper to find the Little Dipper. Look at the picture below. Do you see the two "pointer stars" at the side of the Big Dipper? Imagine that they form a straight line. Then follow that line until you reach a bright star. This bright star is the end of the Little Dipper's handle. The handle of the Little Dipper curves backward. The Big and Little Dippers can be seen on a clear night any time of the year. They are always in the northern part of the sky.

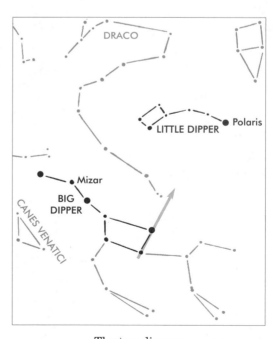

The two dippers

——————— Test Your Reading (Group A) ———————

Choose the best answer.

1. Job said that he knew that God
    a. made the night sky beautiful with stars.
    b. created the stars on the fourth day with the sun and moon.
    c. gave the constellations their names.

2. When you find a constellation, you will see
    a. many stars to form a milky patch of light.
    b. several stars in a row to form lines.
    c. bright stars that look like a picture.

3. The names we use for stars and constellations
    a. are sometimes the same as the names used in the Bible.
    b. were given by God at Creation.
    c. were made by modern scientists.

4. The Big and Little Dippers can be seen
    a. best at midnight.
    b. all year around.
    c. in the southern sky.

5. Two stars of the Big Dipper are called "pointer stars" because
    a. they form the handle of the dipper.
    b. they can be used to find a bright star in another constellation.
    c. they are easy to point to in the sky.

Give the name for each of these constellations.

6.

7.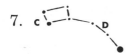

8. Which letter is beside two stars that are dim?
9. Which letter is beside two stars that are "pointer stars"?

An easy constellation to find. When you first try to find constellations, you will see that some of them are small and some are made of dim stars. But the constellation *Orion* is big and made of bright stars. That makes it easy to find. Orion is a marvelous and inspiring constellation. Be sure to find it in the sky.

Look at the map of Orion. What shape or picture do the stars form

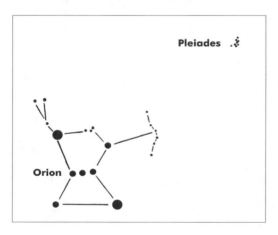

in your mind? People long ago thought these stars looked like a hunter with a belt of three stars and a bow or shield. This beautiful constellation is called Orion, the hunter. As you learned, the Big and Little Dippers can be seen in the northern sky all year around. But many constellations can be seen in the evening sky during

only part of the year. Orion is such a constellation. It can be seen best during the winter months.

A star cluster. Not far from Orion is a patch of stars called *Pleiades,* the seven sisters. Perhaps the star watchers long ago could see seven bright stars, but today we see only six. If you have sharp eyes, you can see all six stars in the sky on a clear night. To you, they might look like a fuzzy patch of light. Like Orion, Pleiades is seen during winter evenings.

Look for the constellations. Both the Big Dipper and Orion are made of very bright stars. This makes these star groups two of the easiest ones to find. Try it for yourself on a clear night. Look for the Big Dipper toward the north. If it is a winter evening, look in the southeast sky for the three bright stars in a row that form Orion's belt. Then find the rest of the constellation. Next, try to find Pleiades almost overhead.

God is pleased when we study His stars and praise Him for His great works. It is not hard to learn some stars and constellations. All you need is some time to look at the night sky and some patience to keep trying. It is helpful to have someone with you who can show you where to find some constellations.

Job knew about Orion and Pleiades. Twice in the Book of Job, these star names are mentioned. Job said that it is God who "maketh . . . Orion, and Pleiades, and the chambers of the south" (Job 9:9). God asked Job, "Canst thou bind the sweet influences of Pleiades, or loose the bands of Orion?" (Job 38:31). How exciting it is to look in the sky and see groups of stars that Job could see! How wonderful it is to look at the constellations and know that our great God put them there!

─────── Test Your Reading (Group B) ───────

Write the missing words.

10. The bright constellation named ─── looks like a hunter.
11. Three stars in a row form the ─── of Orion.
12. Orion can be seen in the evening sky during the ─── months.
13. One cluster of stars is called ───, the seven sisters.
14. God asked Job if he could "loose the bands of ───."
15. To learn the constellations, you need to spend ─── watching the night sky.
16. As you learn the constellations, be sure to ─── God for His marvelous works.

Extra Activities

1. Is the sky clear? Is the moon dim? If so, tonight is a good night for star watching. You may ask someone who knows the stars to go with you. Take a strong flashlight along to help you find your way in the dark and to use as a pointer in the sky.

   Follow the instructions in this lesson to find the Dippers toward the north and Orion toward the south and southeast. In the fall months, Orion will not be in the east until 1 A.M. (2 A.M., D.S.T.) in September, 11 P.M. (12 midnight, D.S.T.) in October, and 9 P.M. in November.

2. Start a star-watching chart such as the one below. Fill it in each time you go star watching. In the middle column, mark all the stars or star groups you could pick out in the sky. In the right-hand column, write the names of the ones you saw for the first time.

My Star-Watching Chart

Date	Time	Stars or Star Groups I Saw	New Stars or Groups
12-9-98	8:30	Big and Little Dippers	Pleiades
12-9-98	8:30	Orion	

Lesson 2

The Stars Move

New Words

Arcturus (ärk·tür′·əs), the brightest star of the constellation Boötes.

Boötes (bō·ō′·tēz), a constellation whose name means "herdsman."

Polaris (pə·lar′·is), the North Star, and the brightest star of the Little Dipper.

Ursa Major (ėr′·sə), the constellation meaning "big bear," which includes the Big Dipper.

Ursa Minor (ėr′·sə), the constellation meaning "little bear," which includes the Little Dipper.

The stars move. You know that the sun rises in the east and sets in the west. You have seen this happen all your life. Do you know what causes this movement? It is not the sun at all, but the earth. The earth is turning on its axis all the time—one turn every day. The turning earth makes it look as if the sun were moving across the sky.

Does the earth stop spinning at night? No, of course not. It keeps rotating just the same, day or night. So, like the sun, the stars rise in the east and set in the west. You can see this for yourself by choosing a bright star to watch some evening. Look at it early in the evening, then again an hour later, and once more another hour later. You will see that it moves from east to west just like the sun.

One star is still. *Polaris* is a special star that hardly moves at all. It is found at the end of the Little Dipper's handle and is the brightest star of the Little Dipper.

Other stars circle around Polaris at night. You can see this in the picture on page 84. This is how far the stars move in one hour. Can you find the stars of the Little Dipper in the picture?

Stars that are closest to Polaris make little circles every night. Stars farther away make bigger circles. Most stars make such

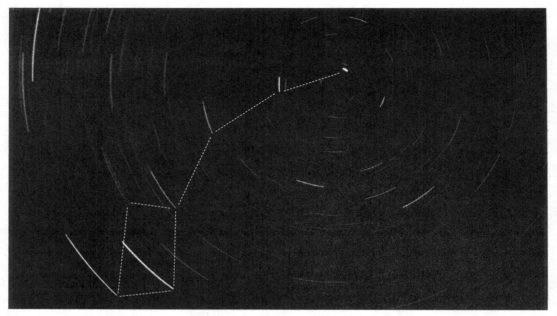

The movement of the stars around Polaris for about one hour. The dashed lines show the Little Dipper.

large circles that we only see part of the circles. That is why we see most stars rise in the east, move across the sky, and set in the west like the sun.

Why does Polaris stay in one spot all the time? Polaris is located in the sky right above the North Pole of the earth. The star Polaris is often called the North Star because it is north, above the North Pole. Just as the earth rotates around the North Pole, so the sky seems to rotate around Polaris, the North Star.

For many years Polaris has been helpful to travelers at night. When they were not sure of their directions, they looked for the North Star. They knew that Polaris was always toward the north. When they discovered which way north was, they could quickly figure out where south, east, or west was.

The stars change through the year. While the earth rotates on its axis, it also revolves around the sun. It makes one big circle, or revolution, around the sun every year. Each day the earth moves a little farther in its circle around the sun.

This daily progress of the earth's revolution causes each star to rise about 4 minutes earlier

The two motions of the earth

The same stars are not in the evening sky in the summer as in the winter.

Every day some stars disappear into the west before it gets dark, and every day some "new" stars become visible in the eastern night sky. By the end of six months, most of the night sky has completely changed. So most of the stars you see in the summer evening sky will be different from the stars you see in the winter evening sky.

each night than the night before. With all these minutes added up day after day, the stars change in the evening sky through the year.

─────── Test Your Reading (Group A) ───────

Decide which of the three choices is best. Write the letter of the best choice on your paper.

1. The stars move
   a. from east to west.
   b. toward the north.
   c. away from Polaris.
2. The stars move during the night because
   a. the stars revolve around the earth.
   b. the sun rises in the east and sets in the west.
   c. the earth rotates on its axis.
3. Polaris hardly moves at all because
   a. it is at the end of the handle of the Little Dipper.
   b. it is above the North Pole of the earth.
   c. the other stars make circles around it.
4. Polaris may be useful to you sometime if
   a. you need to know what time it is.
   b. you need to locate Orion in the sky.
   c. you need to know which direction is west.

5. Every night the stars rise 4 minutes earlier in the east because
   a. the earth rotates on its axis.
   b. the stars revolve around the earth.
   c. the earth revolves around the sun.

6. If you can see a constellation high overhead this evening, in six months
   a. it will not be visible in the evening sky.
   b. it will be farther west in the evening sky.
   c. it will be farther south in the evening sky.

Answer the following questions.

7. How does the earth move in its rotation?
8. How does the earth move in its revolution?
9. Which of these motions makes the stars move during the night?

Telling time by the stars. The people who lived in Job's time long ago knew how the stars change. They could tell time by looking at the sun and stars. During the day they looked at the sun. They noticed where it was in the sky. The sun told them the time of day.

At night the stars told these people the time of year. They knew the constellations very well. They knew which stars could be seen on spring evenings, on summer evenings, on autumn evenings, and on winter evenings. When they began to see Orion and Pleiades, they knew that winter was there to stay. When they saw *Arcturus* in the east, they knew that spring had come.

Arcturus is a very bright star. In the summertime after the sun sets, Arcturus is one of the first stars you can see. Arcturus is the brightest star in the constellation *Boötes,* which means "herdsman."

Dippers or bears? God talked to Job about Arcturus. He

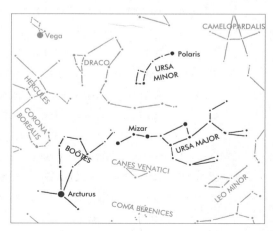

What other names do you know for two constellations on this map?

said, "Canst thou guide Arcturus with his sons?" (Job 38:32). The name *Arcturus* means "bear keeper." The "sons" of Arcturus may have been the bears, Ursa Major and Ursa Minor. In the language used long ago, *ursa* meant "bear." *Major* means "big," and *minor* means "little." So **Ursa Major** and **Ursa Minor** are the constellation names for the big bear and the little bear.

Ursa Major is actually the Big Dipper with some extra stars. Likewise, Ursa Minor includes the Little Dipper. The handles of the Dippers were supposed to be the tails of the two bears even though bears do not have long tails. Since the star patterns look more like dippers than bears, many people call them by their dipper names. Scientists and star watchers still use the proper constellation names: Ursa Major and Ursa Minor.

When God made the sun, moon, and stars, He planned that they would be used to measure time. God said, "Let there be lights in the firmament of the heaven to divide the day from the night; and let them be for signs, and for seasons, and for days, and years" (Genesis 1:14). Today God's plan for timekeeping still works. The rotation of the earth makes our day. The revolution of the earth makes our year. These two movements help men to use the sun, moon, and stars to measure time just as God said they would.

─────── Test Your Reading (Group B) ───────

Choose the best ending for each sentence.

10. Stars can be used
11. Arcturus can be used
12. Boötes is the constellation
13. *Ursa* is an old name
14. *Ursa Minor* is the proper name
15. *Major* is a word
16. *Ursa Major* is the proper name
17. The revolution of the earth makes
18. God gave the sun and stars

a. where you find Arcturus.
b. one year.
c. for the Big Dipper.
d. for days and years.
e. for a calendar.
f. meaning "big."
g. meaning "bear."
h. for the Little Dipper.
i. to tell when spring has come.

Reviewing What You Have Learned

1. Two stars of the Big Dipper will help you find
   a. Orion. b. Pleiades. c. the Little Dipper.
2. Orion is a ——— that looks like a hunter.
3. True or false? The Bible uses names for the stars that we use today.
4. One small group of stars is called ———, the seven sisters.
5. The best way to learn the constellations is
   a. to use patience and time hunting constellations.
   b. to read books about the stars.
   c. to listen to your teacher talk about constellations.

Extra Activities

1. Would you like to see Arcturus? Though you cannot see Arcturus on a winter evening, you can see it in the early morning sky. Be sure to get up while it is still very dark. First find the Big Dipper. Follow the curving arc of the Big Dipper's handle on out to the first bright star. The bright star at the end of the arc is Arcturus.

   Now look for Boötes (bō·ō′·tēz), the constellation to which Arcturus belongs. Arcturus is brighter than the rest of the stars in Boötes. Notice on the map on page 86 that the end of Boötes's arm is near the Big Dipper.

   If you started keeping a star-watching chart, fill it in after doing this activity or the next one.

2. For a bigger challenge, find Serpens, probably the "crooked serpent" mentioned in Job 26:13. Use Arcturus and the next brightest star beside it to form an imaginary line pointing east. Follow that line to the first clump of stars, which is the head of Serpens.

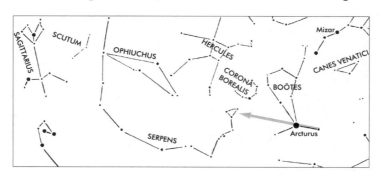

Lesson 3

Learning the Constellations

New Words

Cassiopeia (kas′·ē·ə·pē′·ə), a W-shaped constellation that was named after a queen.

Cygnus (sig′·nəs), a cross-shaped constellation whose name means "swan."

Gemini (jem′·ə·nī′), a bright winter constellation whose name means "twins."

Hercules (hėr′·kyə·lēz′), a summer constellation named after a giant.

horizon (hə·rī′·zən), the line where the sky seems to meet the earth.

Leo (lē′·ō), a spring constellation whose name means "lion."

Pegasus (peg′·ə·səs), a boxlike constellation named after a winged horse.

zenith (zē′·nith), the point that is directly overhead in the sky.

The star calendar. When we want to know what time of the year it is, we look at a calendar hanging on the wall. God gave us a much greater calendar. Would you like to use this calendar? God's calendar is the stars!

Whenever you see Orion high in the evening sky, you know it is wintertime. Since the earth revolves around the sun, Orion rises 4 minutes earlier each evening. In the summertime Orion is not in the evening sky at all. But by December, you can see it in the east a few hours after the sun goes down.

Other constellations are in the sky in different seasons. Each season has its special constellations in the evening sky. If you want to see all the constellations you can possibly see from where you live, you should study them during all four seasons. In this lesson you will learn about two constellations for each of the four seasons.

Winter constellations. To learn the star calendar, you will need to learn which constellations can be seen during the evenings of each season. You

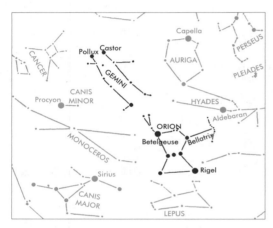

Winter constellations

already know that Orion is a winter constellation.

Another bright winter constellation is **Gemini,** which means "twins." The twins are standing side by side near Orion. In fact, Orion's upraised arm points to the feet of Gemini.

Spring constellations. What constellations can you see during spring evenings? Orion and Gemini

have moved toward the west. But Boötes, the herdsman, has risen in the east. Remember that the bright star Arcturus is at Boötes's feet. Boötes seems to be reaching for the handle of the Big Dipper, which is the tail of Ursa Major, the big bear.

Watch out, Boötes! A lion is nearby. **Leo,** the lion, is south of the

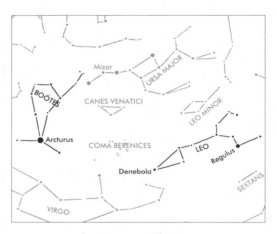

Spring constellations

Big Dipper and directly west of Arcturus. In the springtime Leo is almost overhead.

Summer constellations. During summer evenings, Boötes and Leo have moved west. Then **Hercules,** the giant, is overhead, just east of Boötes.

Boötes, the herdsman, is like David in the Bible. On one side are a lion and a bear. On the other side is a giant. Maybe David gazed at these constellations and was reminded to say, "Thank You, God, for helping me fight a bear, a lion, and a giant."

Directly east of Hercules is another summer constellation called *Cygnus.* Cygnus is often called the Northern Cross because

autumn is here? The boxlike shape of *Pegasus* overhead is a good clue. Pegasus was the name of a winged horse. Even though there is really no such animal, the people long ago imagined they saw a horse with wings in the stars of Pegasus.

Also overhead is *Cassiopeia,*

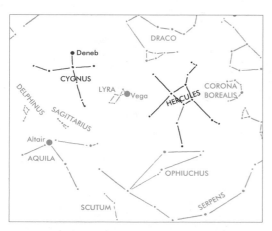

Summer constellations

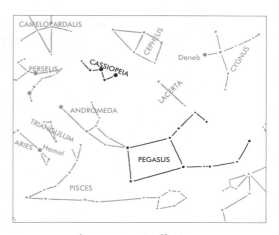

Autumn constellations

its five brightest stars form a cross. But the name *Cygnus* really means "swan." Think of it as flying, with the lower part of the cross its long neck and head. The upper stars of the cross are the swan's tail and outstretched wings.

Autumn constellations. What constellation tells you that

the queen. Cassiopeia looks like a W. Cassiopeia is found half way between Pegasus and Polaris, the North Star. In fact, Cassiopeia is close enough to Polaris that it can be seen in the sky at any time of the year. But it is best seen in the evening when it is high in the sky during the autumn months.

———————— **Test Your Reading (Group A)** ————————

Label each constellation with its name. After each constellation, write the common name, and then write *spring, summer, autumn,* or *winter* to tell which season it is seen best in the evening. The first one is done for you.

4.

Orion, hunter, winter

1.

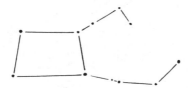

5.

2.

6.

3.

7.

Finding your way in the sky. Four times already in this lesson, the word *overhead* is used. The spot directly overhead is called the **zenith.** *Zenith* means "the highest point." To see zenith stars, you must look straight upward to the highest point in the sky. Zenith is easy to find, and so it is easy to find stars at the zenith.

The stars are brighter at the zenith than at the **horizon,** where the sky seems to meet the earth. A star near the horizon is harder to see. Its light travels through much more air and looks blurred and dim.

The star guide. If you want to learn the constellations, it is helpful to use a **star guide,** or star map. The stars seem to be moving, slowly circling Polaris. At one time Boötes is at the zenith, and at another time it is near the horizon. This might seem confusing without a star guide. The star guide shows you where and when you can see any star or constellation. The star guide is made so that you can set it to show the sky for any time of the night and any day of the year. A mask covers the stars that are not in the sky. The oval shape inside the mask shows the stars you can see.

With a star guide, you can find which stars are at the zenith. On a star map, the zenith is the center of the oval shape left by the mask. First, you find what constellation is at the zenith on the map and then you find that constellation in the sky by looking straight overhead. This is a good way to begin learning where to find the constellations.

Another good method is to look for a bright star group you already know. Next, find one of its neighbors on the map and look for the same star shape in the sky.

Often constellations are remembered by a special figure made by the stars. Here is a list of the special figures in some of the constellations you have learned.

Orion—Three stars form a **belt** (called "bands" in God's question to Job).
Leo—Six stars on the right form the shape of a **sickle.**
Boötes—The body forms the shape of a **kite.**
Hercules—The body has a **keystone** shape.

Cygnus—Four stars one way and three the other way form a **cross.**

Pegasus—The main part is in the shape of a big **square.**

Cassiopeia—The constellation forms a big **W.**

When you find the constellations, you are, like Job, looking at the handiwork of God. God asked Job questions about Orion, Pleiades, and Arcturus. By now, you should know what stars these name.

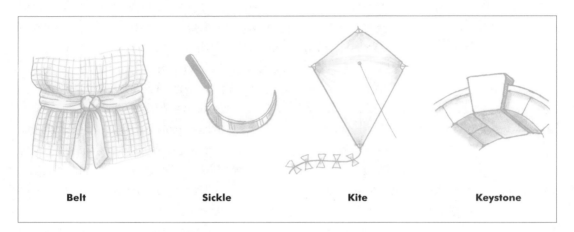

Belt   **Sickle**   **Kite**   **Keystone**

Test Your Reading (Group B)

Answer the following questions.

8. Where is the zenith in the sky?

9. Why are stars easier to see at the zenith than at the horizon?

10. What does the mask of a star guide do?

11. Where are the zenith stars on a star guide?

12. If you can find Orion easily, how can you learn the constellations around Orion?

13. What constellation is in the form of a cross and is sometimes called the Northern Cross?

14. Arcturus, a star of Boötes, is at the bottom of what shape of stars?

15. If you were not sure if you had found Leo, you could look to see if it had what shape?

16. What shape would you look for to find Pegasus?

17. What letter is formed by Cassiopeia?
18. God asked Job if he could loosen what special group of stars in Orion?
19. If you saw a keystone of stars high in the summer sky, what constellation would you see?

Reviewing What You Have Learned

1. The stars appear to travel around the earth once a day because
   a. the earth revolves around the sun.
   b. the earth rotates on its axis.
   c. the stars revolve around the earth.
2. Orion, Ursa Major, and Boötes are names of ———.
3. If you were lost, you could find which direction was north by finding the star named ———.
4. Which of the following names is wrong?
   a. Arcturus, the bear keeper
   b. Pleiades, the twin sisters
   c. Orion, the hunter
5. True or false? Each night the stars rise ten minutes later than the night before.

Extra Activities

1. If the sky is clear tonight, find the constellations for this season. You may also see the next season's constellations if you get up early in the morning before sunrise. You could ask another star watcher to help you find the constellations and use the star guide. Do not forget to record your sightings on your star-watching chart.
2. Compare the stars overhead with the stars near the horizon. Can you see which ones appear clearer and brighter? Stay outside long enough for your eyes to become adjusted to the darkness.
3. Find out what baby swans are called. Compare this word with the name for the swan constellation.

Lesson 4

Stars Are Useful

New Words

observatory (əb·zėr′·və·tôr′·ē), a place with telescopes for studying the stars.

sextant (sek′·stənt), a tool for measuring the angle between the earth and a star.

Sirius (sir′·ē·əs), a very bright star near the constellation Orion.

telescope (tel′·i·skōp′), a tool for seeing faint stars and other distant objects.

The star calendar. Long ago the farmers of Egypt watched for the star Sirius. *Sirius* is a very bright star that rises in the east about an hour after Orion. The Egyptian farmers knew that after they saw Sirius, the Nile River would begin to flood and they could soon plant their fields and gardens. Without much rain to water the land, how glad the farmers were for the Nile River! How glad they were for Sirius to show them every year when the Nile would water the land! The stars were a calendar to them to tell them what time of the year it was.

Today some farmers still use the star calendar. In South America, some farmers use the stars to tell them the right time to plant their yams, a vegetable much like a sweet potato. They watch for the night when Pleiades sets just after the sun. Pleiades tells the farmers the right time to plant their yams.

Our calendars are set by the stars. Today most farmers use printed calendars. But even these calendars need the stars. Men need the stars to measure the exact time it takes the earth to revolve around the sun. That tells them exactly how long a year is.

Men have special places to study the stars. Such a place to *observe* stars is an *observatory.* Observatories have *telescopes* to

Palomar Observatory in California

A telescope shows faint objects more clearly.

see faint stars and other distant objects in the night sky. Some special observatories have special telescopes to measure time by the stars. The stars are used to find out exactly how long the year is. The sun, moon, and stars set the dates on our calendars.

Many calendars tell the first day of each season. The first day of winter is close to December 21. The first day of spring is close to March 21. These days are set by the position of the sun compared with the position of the stars. Many calendars also give the days for the changes of the moon. They tell on which day the moon will be a quarter moon or a full moon. Our calendars are set by what is happening in the sky.

September

Sun	Mon	Tue	Wed	Thu	Fri	Sat
	1 New Moon	2	3	4	5	6
7	8	9 First Quarter	10	11	12	13
14	15	16 Full Moon	17	18	19	20
21	22 Beginning of Autumn	23 Last Quarter	24	25	26	27
28	29	30				

A calendar page showing phases of the moon and the first day of a season

—————— Test Your Reading (Group A) ——————

Write the missing words.

1. Egyptians used to know when the Nile River would overflow by the star ———, which rises about one hour after ———.

2. Some farmers of South America use the setting of ——— to help them know when to plant their yams.

3. Men use the stars so that they have the right number of days in their ———.

4. At a special place called an ———, men study stars and can use the stars to determine the exact time.

5. A ——— helps men see faint stars and other distant objects.

6. Besides showing the days, weeks, and months, many calendars tell the first day of each ——— and the days for the changes in the shape of the ———.

Sailors use the stars. On the ocean, sailors have no roads or signs to follow. They can use the stars to find out where they are and what direction they are going.

To find his location, the sailor can use a special tool called a *sextant.* With a sextant, he measures the angle between the earth and a star, or how far the star is above the horizon. He repeats the process with two other stars. He then uses a book of star tables and the exact time he measured the stars to find out where his ship is on the ocean. God made the position and movement of the stars so exact that sailors can use them to find the position of a ship.

Stars show us God's glory. When we look at the stars and praise God for His wonderful creation, we are using the stars for a good purpose. God is glorified when we study His stars and give Him the credit for their greatness and exactness. The constellations show how God has kept the stars

A sailor using a sextant

in their positions for thousands of years. The motion of the earth that makes the stars appear to move is part of God's wisdom and power. Even our clocks and calendars are set by the stars God created.

Psalm 19 tells us that "the heavens declare the glory of God." As you study about the stars, you can learn about the glory of God that the stars show us. The stars inspire us to worship God.

Star study is a very inspiring hobby. Some people collect butterflies. Many people are bird watchers. Still others enjoy seeing and naming the stars. Like butterflies and birds, stars are the handiwork of God. Stars are beautiful. Stars are so far away that even though they are very big, they look like tiny points of light. With our eyes alone, we can see the greatness and beauty of the stars. With a telescope, we can see even more of the wonders of God's created world. The stars show us the glory of God.

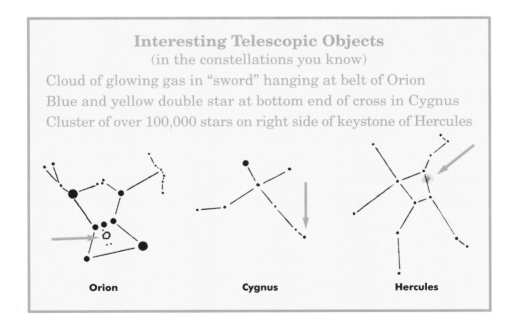

Interesting Telescopic Objects
(in the constellations you know)
Cloud of glowing gas in "sword" hanging at belt of Orion
Blue and yellow double star at bottom end of cross in Cygnus
Cluster of over 100,000 stars on right side of keystone of Hercules

Orion   **Cygnus**   **Hercules**

Wrong use of the stars. Thus far, you have learned some good uses for the stars. But not all star study is good. Some people use the stars to try to foretell the future. They trust in the stars more than they trust God and His Word. In this way they actually worship the stars instead of God.

Job knew that God is Lord over the stars. He knew that it is wrong to worship anything except God, for he said, "If I beheld the sun when it shined, or the moon walking in brightness; and my heart hath been secretly enticed . . . : this also were an iniquity . . . : for I should have denied the God that is above" (Job 31:26–28). We are to worship God who made the stars. It is wrong to worship the stars.

—————— Test Your Reading (Group B) ——————

Answer *true* if the statement is true. Answer *false* if the statement is not true.

7. Sailors can use the stars to find out where they are on the ocean.
8. The sextant tells how far a star is from the zenith.
9. To find where he is, a sailor would need to have a star guide.
10. The motion of the stars shows us God's exactness.
11. Stars look like points of light because the stars are so small.
12. Stars are different colors.
13. Star study is an inspiring hobby.
14. With a telescope, you can see clouds of glowing gases among the stars.
15. The stars show us the glory of God.
16. God gave us the stars to help us foretell the future.
17. Since God created the stars, we should worship them.

Reviewing What You Have Learned

1. The brightest star of the constellation Boötes is
   a. Arcturus.   b. Sirius.   c. Polaris.
2. The stars look brightest at the ——— of the sky.
3. Which of the sentences about constellations and seasons is wrong?
   a. Orion is a winter constellation.
   b. Cygnus is a summer constellation.
   c. Pegasus is a spring constellation.

4. The stars appear to travel around Polaris because the earth is ——— .

5. True or false? Two stars of the Little Dipper point to a bright star in the Big Dipper.

Extra Activities

1. Use a calendar that has special days of the seasons and the moon marked on it. Make a list of the first days of the seasons for this year. Make a list of the days of the new moon, first quarter, full moon, and last quarter for this year. How far is it from one new moon to the next? Check to see if the calendar dates for the moon agree with the actual moon. From new moon to full moon, the moon can be seen in the evening. From full moon to new moon, the moon can be seen in the morning. Do you expect the calendar to agree with the moon? Why? How do the calendar makers know when to put these special days on their calendars?

2. Use an encyclopedia to find out about leap year. Why can we not have the same number of days in each calendar year? What would happen if we did not have leap year?

3. Find out what "sun time" is at your school. Make a simple sundial by driving a metal stake or rod into the ground. Choose a place where the noon sun will shine on it. Make the stake very straight. Your teacher can come to school some evening after dark to find true north by sighting toward Polaris. Have your teacher lay a second rod or stake on the ground, placing one end against the upright stake and pointing the other end toward Polaris. When the shadow of the stake crosses the true north line, that is twelve o'clock noon. Set a clock to run on "sun time." Depending where you live in your time zone, "sun time" will either be ahead or behind standard time. Only if you live in the exact center of your time zone will the two times be the same.

4. What is the closest observatory to you? Some colleges have observatories. See if you can find some information about the United States Naval Observatory in Washington, D.C. Perhaps you can visit an observatory.

Lesson 5

Do You Remember?

From the word box, find and write a word for each blank.

constellation	sextant	telescope
horizon	star guide	zenith
observatory		

1. The stars look dim and blurred near the ———.
2. Learning the ———s helps us remember the arrangement of the stars.
3. A constellation that is directly overhead is at the ———.
4. A ——— measures the angle between a star and the horizon.
5. A ——— is used to see faint objects in the sky.
6. A ——— would help you find the stars that are visible tonight.
7. Men study the stars with a telescope at an ———.

Give the scientific name for these constellations, and then tell what that name means.

8.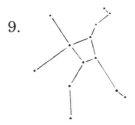

10.

9.

11.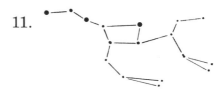

12.

15.

13.

16.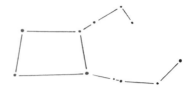

14.

17.

Name these stars.

18. The North Star

19. The bright star that comes up about one hour after Orion

20. The star God mentioned to Job that is in Boötes

21. The "seven sisters"

Choose the best answer to finish each sentence.

22. The Northern Cross is the name that is sometimes used for
    a. Cygnus.   b. Boötes.   c. Hercules.

23. Each day the stars circle around
    a. Sirius.
    b. Arcturus.
    c. Polaris.

24. The stars can be used as a calendar because
    a. a constellation rises at the same time year around.
    b. a star sets 4 minutes later each night than the night before.
    c. each different season has its own set of constellations.
25. One of the constellations best seen in spring is
    a. Orion.
    b. Gemini.
    c. Leo.
26. Pegasus can be found by looking for
    a. a big square.
    b. a kite shape.
    c. a keystone shape.
27. Both Ursa Major and Ursa Minor can be seen
    a. in the south.
    b. in the autumn.
    c. all year around.
28. The Bible talks about the bands of
    a. Hercules.
    b. Orion.
    c. Boötes.

Write *true* if the sentence is true, and write *false* if it is not true.
29. You can learn many constellations by taking time to study the stars with a helper and a star guide.
30. The reason most constellations can be seen only part of the year is mostly because of the earth's rotation.
31. God wants us to worship Him rather than the stars.
32. Some observatories use the stars to keep exact time.
33. God wants us to use the stars to tell the future.

Answer these questions.
34. How were the stars helpful to farmers long ago?
35. How could you use the stars if you were lost?
36. Why do the stars appear to be moving around the earth?
37. How can you use the Big Dipper to find Polaris?

Unit Four

God Heals Our Diseases

No one likes to be sick. Neither did Job. All over his body were painful sores called boils. Job felt very tired, yet he could not sleep well. He tossed about during the night and wished for night to end. He said, "My flesh is clothed with worms and clods of dust; my skin is broken, and become loathsome" (Job 7:5). Job was miserable. With a bit of broken pottery, he scraped his hot, crusted body. Perhaps this gave him some relief from itching.

"And he took him a potsherd to scrape himself withal; and he sat down among the ashes" (Job 2:8).

The Bible does not tell us that he had pills or doctors to help him. Job had help that is better than doctors and medicine. God was watching over Job and saw how miserable Job was. He had allowed Satan to make Job sick. Satan had thought that Job's sickness would make him hate God. But God knew that it would help Job know God better and trust Him more.

That is just what happened. Job knew God better after his sickness than he had before. He said to God, "I have heard of thee by the hearing of the ear: but now mine eye seeth thee" (Job 42:5). God healed Job's sickness and made him well again.

Job was thankful that God healed him. This is the same God who heals us. Doctors can help us when we are sick. Medicine can help us. But God heals us.

In this unit you can learn how God heals us when we get sick. You can learn how He has designed your body to stay healthy. You can discover how He has given your body many little "soldiers" to fight disease. You can trust God to help you when you get sick.

Lesson 1

Causes of Sickness

New Words

diet (dī′·it), the kinds and amounts of food you eat from day to day.

fever (fē′·vər), overheating of the body during sickness.

germs, tiny plants or animals that can cause disease and are seen only with a microscope.

minerals (min′·ər·əlz), iron, calcium, and other materials needed for good health.

symptom (sim′·təm), coughing, sore throat, or another sign of illness.

vitamins (vī′·tə·minz), a group of materials which are needed by the body for good health and are named by letters, such as vitamin A or vitamin C.

A poor diet can make us sick. Long ago many British sailors became sick at sea. But they were not just seasick. Their sickness was called scurvy. This sickness could make sailors very weak and tired. Their joints and mouths felt sore, and their gums bled easily. Cuts and scratches healed very slowly. Some sailors even died of scurvy.

Then some sailors discovered a secret. They found out that if they drank lime juice from time to time, they would not get scurvy. Limes are green fruit shaped about like lemons. Soon the good news spread, and sailors took limes along on their trips. They drank so much lime juice that people started calling the sailors "limeys."

The sailors did not know why lime juice kept them from getting scurvy. They were just glad it did. Neither did they know why they were more likely to get scurvy at sea than at home on land. But today we know these answers.

When the sailors were at home, they ate more vegetables and fruit than when they were out on the ocean. At sea, they had only dried beef and hard biscuits to eat for months at a time. Beef and biscuits did not supply their bodies with all the vitamins they needed. The sailors got scurvy because their bodies lacked one vitamin called vitamin C. But the lime juice they drank had plenty of vitamin C in it, so it kept them from getting scurvy.

A lime would be good medicine for these sailors sick with scurvy.

Your body needs several *vitamins* to stay healthy. They are vitamins A, B, C, and D. Your body also needs some *minerals* like iron and calcium. The mineral iron is needed to make blood, and calcium is needed to make bones. You need only a little of

each kind of vitamin and mineral. If you get too much of some of them at once, they make you sick. God has put just the right amount of them in vegetables, grains, meat, and milk products. If you eat a wide variety of these good foods, you are likely to get the right amount of vitamins and minerals.

What about foods such as candy, cake, and potato chips? These foods do not contain many vitamins or minerals. If you want to be strong and healthy, you should not eat much of these foods. Instead, you should eat more whole-grain bread, milk, cheese or meat, and plenty of fruits and vegetables.

If you have a wide variety of good food in your diet, you are likely to stay healthy. Your *diet* is the kinds and amounts of food you eat from day to day. Your parents care for you by providing many kinds of food for your diet. That is why they have you eat plenty of vegetables and fruit. They do not want you to get sick because of a poor diet that lacks the vitamins and minerals your body needs.

Fats, oils, & sweets Use sparingly		**Key** • Fat ▼ Added sugars These symbols show fats and added sugars in foods.
Milk, yogurt, & cheese group 2–3 servings		**Meat, dry beans, eggs, & nuts group** 2–3 servings
Vegetable group 3–5 servings		**Fruit group;** 2–4 servings
		Bread, cereal, rice, & pasta group 6–11 servings

A Food Guide: Eat a variety of foods every day.

Test Your Reading (Group A)

Write the missing words.

1. Sailors used to get a disease called ———, which made their mouths and gums get very sore.

2. The sailors got the disease because they did not get enough vitamin ——— in their diet.

3. When they drank ——— juice, they did not get the disease, because it had the vitamin their bodies needed to stay healthy.

4. Your body needs small amounts of ——— A, B, C, and D.

5. Your body needs some of the ——— iron to make blood.

6. Your body needs some ——— to grow strong bones.

7. ——— put the right amount of vitamins and minerals into the foods we eat.

8. Be sure to eat enough ——— like beans, carrots, and lettuce so that you get the vitamins and minerals your body needs.

9. Your parents provide you with different foods in your ———.

Write *yes* if the food is a good source of vitamins and minerals. Write *no* if the food is not a good source of vitamins and minerals.

10. a. meat
     b. candy
     c. fruit
     d. whole-wheat bread
     e. potato chips
     f. cake
     g. vegetables
     h. milk

Germs can make us sick. You may not know of anyone who is sick because of a lack of vitamins and minerals. That is because we eat healthful foods that God has made for us. But maybe you know people who are sick because of germs. *Germs* are very tiny plants or animals that can grow in our bodies and make us sick. These living things are so small that a microscope is needed to see them. But they can make even a big man feel very sick.

Germs feed, grow, and multiply,

How can something as small as germs make a man sick?

feed, grow, and multiply; and in a single day, one germ can become hundreds of germs! The many germs harm and even kill cells of the body. They make poisons that hurt the body. The more cells they destroy and the more poisons they make, the more sick a person becomes.

Germs cause diseases such as leprosy, strep throat, whooping cough, and scarlet fever. Germs also cause more common diseases such as colds, flu, mumps, measles, and chicken pox.

What are some symptoms of sickness? Whenever germs are multiplying or making poisons inside a person's body, they cause certain signs, or *symptoms.* Cold germs may cause the symptoms of coughing, sneezing, a runny nose, and a sore throat. Chicken pox germs cause the symptoms of a rash, sore muscles, a headache, and a fever. The symptoms do not cause the disease; they are signs that a person has a disease. Doctors use these symptoms to decide what kind of disease the person has.

You have likely had a fever already. It is a common symptom of many diseases. A *fever* is the overheating of your body because of sickness. It is not the same as feeling hot on a sticky summer day. If you have a fever, you feel hot and sick all over. You may be sweating one minute and shivering the next. This is called "chills and fever."

A fever can be measured by taking a person's temperature with a fever thermometer. If you have only a slight fever, your mother might tell you to rest and drink plenty of liquids. But if you have a high fever, she probably would take you to a doctor. If a high fever is not treated quickly, it can damage the brain.

Job knew what it was like to have a germ disease. Satan "smote Job with sore boils from the sole of his foot unto his crown" (Job 2:7).

What symptom will the thermometer show?

Boils are one kind of germ disease. It seems that Job had the symptom of fever with his sickness. He said, "My bones are burned with heat" (Job 30:30).

Job was glad when God healed him, just as you are glad when God heals you from a sickness. In the next lessons, you will study some ways God made your body to fight germs. You will learn how you can do your part to get well and stay well.

—————— Test Your Reading (Group B) ——————

Answer the following questions.

11. What are the tiny living things that can make a person sick?
12. How can only a few germs make a person sick in three or four days?
13. What are two ways that germs make the body sick?
14. How do doctors know what disease a person has?
15. What are three symptoms of a cold?

16. When you tell your mother, "I have a fever," is the fever a disease or a symptom?
17. How will you feel if you have a fever?
18. How can you know for sure if you have a fever?
19. When someone has a boil, is it because he lacks a vitamin or because he has germs?

Extra Activities

1. Find the names for as many vitamins and minerals as you can from food package labels.
2. Learn more about germs. Look up the names *bacteria* and *virus* in a dictionary or encyclopedia. Draw pictures of the different kinds of germs. Label each picture with its name and the disease it causes.
3. Learn more about vitamins and about diseases caused by a poor diet. You could read the articles under "Nutrition," "Vitamin," and "Disease" in an encyclopedia. Tell or write what you have learned.
4. Ask your teacher or mother to help you take your temperature with a fever thermometer. You could take your temperature twice: first after you have been reading or resting quietly for a while, and next after you have been running or working hard. Are both temperatures alike? Can you guess why or why not?

Lesson 2

Fighting Germs

New Words

antibodies (an′·ti·bod′·ēz), materials made by the body to fight germs.

immune (i·myün′), protected from getting a certain disease.

vaccine (vak·sēn′), a mixture of weak or dead disease germs that causes the body to protect itself from the disease.

white blood cells, tiny living parts of the blood that destroy disease germs.

Germs make us sick. One morning you wake up with a sore, scratchy throat. Your eyes hurt. Your bones ache, and you feel hot all over. "I don't feel good at all," you say. "I feel sick!"

A flu germ may be making you sick. There are many other kinds of germs that can make your body sick. If you could see all the germs around you, you would say, "I'm surprised that I'm not sick all the time!"

When God made us, He knew about all these germs. He knows all about keeping us healthy. So He gave us a body that fights hard to stay well.

How does your body protect itself from germs? First of all, God

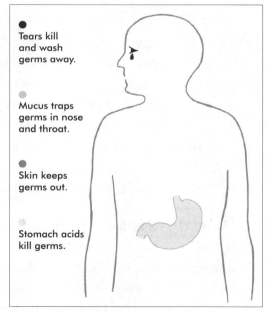

Tears kill and wash germs away.

Mucus traps germs in nose and throat.

Skin keeps germs out.

Stomach acids kill germs.

God made it hard for germs to enter the body.

protected your body with a tough wrapping of skin. Germs cannot get inside unless they enter through openings in the skin: either through your eyes, nose, and mouth, or through a cut in your skin.

For the germs that do enter in these ways, God made three more protections within your body. He made tears to wash away the germs in your eyes. He made a sticky mucus to trap any germs in your nose and throat. He made stomach liquids to kill germs that you swallow with your food. With your skin on the outside and these three on the inside, most germs around you do not make you sick.

But why do you ever get sick? If you breathe in enough cold or flu germs, some may stay inside your nose or throat and start multiplying. Or if you cut your skin, germs start getting inside right away. Some may find their way into your bloodstream.

Your blood is like a river with many streams that flow to every part of your body. Germs that get into your blood can spread everywhere unless they are stopped.

Test Your Reading (Group A)

Write *true* if the statement is true. Write *false* if the statement is not true.

1. Germs can give you a sore throat.
2. Sometimes you come in contact with germs without getting sick.
3. The skin lets germs get into your body.
4. The tears of the eyes help the germs make you sick.
5. The body has a way to trap or kill germs that enter your nose and throat.
6. Germs enter your stomach through a cut in your skin.

How do white blood cells destroy germs? God put many millions of special cells called *white blood cells* in your blood. White blood cells are like tiny soldiers, always ready to fight enemy germs. When your throat or any other body part is hurt by germs, it somehow sends a HELP call to the white blood cells. They rush to the rescue,

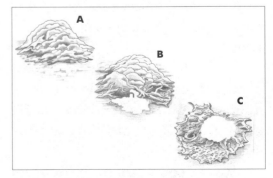

A white blood cell surrounds the germs and then kills them.

swarm over the disease germs, and eat them up. If necessary, your body quickly makes millions more of these white blood cells to help fight germs.

Some of the white blood cells eat so many germs that they die. You see them in the yellowish pus of a sore. The pus is a mixture of dead white blood cells, dead germs, and body liquids. Wherever you see it, you can be sure that your white blood cells were working hard to get rid of germs.

Sometimes enemy germs sneak inside your body without your body knowing it. Usually the sneakiest germs are those that your body has never fought before. For example, if your body has never fought measles or chicken pox germs before, they sneak right in and make you sick.

How do antibodies fight germs? God created your body to make special materials called ***antibodies.*** When many chicken pox germs attack your body, it starts making chicken pox antibodies. These antibodies find chicken pox germs and either make their poison harmless, kill them, or make it easier for the white blood cells to eat them. Each time your body fights a new kind of germ, it makes antibodies to fight only that kind of germ or germ family.

When you have had measles or chicken pox once, some of the antibodies that your body made stay in the blood. Never again will they let those kinds of germs multiply and make you sick. You have become ***immune*** to them.

But why does not your body become immune to colds and the flu? These germs are tricky. There are many different kinds of germs that cause a cold, and the antibodies for these germs do not last very long. So just having a cold does not make you immune to all cold germs. They can slip inside your body and make you sick again and again.

———————— Test Your Reading (Group B) ————————

Write the missing words.
7. When germs get into the body, the ——— blood cells can kill them.
8. The ——— in a sore shows that germs are being killed.
9. Different diseases are caused by different ———.
10. Your body can best fight the germs of a disease if it has the right ——— against that disease.

11. When a new germ gets into the body, the body ——— the needed antibody.

12. If you had a certain disease, you may be ——— to it and never get that disease again.

13. The antibodies made for ——— germs do not last very long.

How does a vaccine protect you from germs? For many diseases, there is another way of becoming immune besides having the disease. You can get a vaccine as a shot in your arm or as a liquid to drink. A *vaccine* causes your body to make antibodies for a certain disease *before* the live germs get inside.

When you were a baby, you may have gotten some shots of different vaccines. One such vaccine had dead mumps germs in it. Your body could not tell that the mumps germs were harmless. It "thought" that you were actually getting sick with mumps. So it got busy making lots of mumps antibodies. Now, if you get normal mumps germs

inside you today, your body is all ready to destroy them. The vaccine has caused you to become immune to mumps.

Why does your body feel weak? Germ fighting does not last long in a small cut on your finger. You hardly notice that there is any battle at all. But sometimes your body must fight longer to get rid of disease germs—maybe a few days, weeks, or even months. During this time, your body is rather weak. And you are more likely to get other diseases. This is why you should take extra good care of your body while you are sick.

In the next lessons, you can learn about taking care of your body to get well and stay healthy.

——————— Test Your Reading (Group C) ———————

Choose the best answer.

14. When you get a vaccine,
    a. your body is given antibodies for a disease.
    b. your body makes antibodies for a disease.
    c. your body gets sick from a disease.
    d. your body gets better from a disease.

15. Babies are sometimes given a vaccine for a disease because
    a. they have brothers and sisters who have the disease.
    b. the doctor thinks they have the disease.
    c. this gives the doctor work to do.
    d. they can become immune to the disease without having the disease.
16. After getting better from a disease, you should still take care because
    a. a weak body can more easily get another disease.
    b. the body needs time to make antibodies.
    c. the germs may not all be dead.
    d. you may give the germs to another person.

Reviewing What You Have Learned

1. To be healthy, our bodies need
    a. scurvy and symptoms.
    b. vitamins and minerals.
    c. diet and vaccines.
2. We must use a microscope to see the ———— that cause disease.
3. A poor diet could cause you to get
    a. fever.
    b. chicken pox.
    c. scurvy.
4. True or false? Germs can harm body cells with poisons.
5. When Job said, "My bones are burned with heat," he probably had a ————.

Extra Activities

1. Ask your parents to tell you which vaccinations you have received, and ask to see your health records if you have them at home.
2. Learn more about how your body fights germs by reading articles in an encyclopedia under these titles: "Blood," "Immunity," "Immunization," and "Lymphatic System." Tell or write what you learned.

Lesson 3

Getting Well

New Words

diagnosis (dī´·əg·nō´·sis), the careful study of symptoms to determine which disease one has.

medicine (med´·i·sin), something used to prevent or treat a disease.

prescription (pri·skrip´·shən), written directions used for getting and taking medicine.

God heals our diseases. You know that God is better than any doctor. He did not need pills to heal Job's sickness. At the right time, God simply made Job well.

God and His Son Jesus have made many people well in this way. Think of Moses' sister, Miriam, and of Naaman, whom God healed of leprosy. Think of all the blind, deaf, and lame that Jesus healed. Think of the people that God still heals today.

So whom should you expect to heal you when you are sick? It is God! God sometimes heals right away. Sometimes He heals after a time of waiting. At other times, God does not heal until His children go to heaven. But God always heals His children of their diseases.

Doctors do not heal our bodies. They only give us advice and help to make healing come more quickly and easily. It is God who does the actual healing.

We can help our bodies get well. Although God does the work of healing, He still wants you to do your part when you are sick. First of all, God wants you to trust Him. He wants you to be as cheerful as you can be, even though you are sick. The Bible says, "A merry heart doeth good like a medicine" (Proverbs 17:22). A cheerful, peaceful person is likely to get well faster than one who is worried and grouchy.

God also wants you to take good care of your body while you are sick. During this time you should not work hard. Instead, you need plenty of rest and sleep to get well.

Cleaning a wound and bandaging it are important for healing, but what makes the wound heal?

The ability of the body to heal is a wonderful gift from God. When you cut yourself, the skin will grow back together. When you clean a wound and keep it clean with a bandage, you are helping to keep germs out that would slow down the healing that God made for you.

In some sicknesses we need to give our stomachs and digestion a rest. Then it is best to eat soups, toast, fruit, and custard. We should not eat foods that have much fat in them, such as meat and nuts. During a time of sickness, it is important to drink plenty of liquids. Parts of the body that remove poisons can work better if they have plenty of water.

God does the healing, but we want to be careful that we do not work against that healing by eating a poor diet or by not being clean.

Others can help us get well.

When Job was sick, three of his friends visited him. They felt so sorry for Job that they tore their clothes and cried. They did not talk to him for seven days because they saw how sad he was.

But then Job's friends said some unkind things. They said he must be sick because he had done bad things. They said God must be punishing him for his sins. This only made Job feel worse. He said, "Miserable comforters are ye all" (Job 16:2).

Now when you visit a sick person, think of the story of Job. Do not add to their discomfort with unkind or unpleasant talk. Try to bring comfort and cheer to the sick one. Doctors know that if their patient is cheerful, healing can happen faster. Friends can do much to help a sick person be cheerful with cards, gifts, and visits. These help a sick person feel better.

Friends can help a sick person get better, but who does the healing?

——————— Test Your Reading (Group A) ———————

Choose the best ending for each sentence.

1. God
2. Worry and grumbling
3. A sick person
4. A cut finger
5. Soup and toast
6. Plenty of liquids and rest
7. A get-well card
8. A visitor to a sick person

a. help the body remove poisons and become well.
b. can cheer a faraway sick friend.
c. and not the doctor does the healing.
d. may keep us from getting well soon.
e. should trust God for healing.
f. should talk to bring comfort and cheer.
g. will heal slowly if it is not kept clean.
h. give the digestion a needed rest.

Medicine can help us get well. It is often helpful for a sick person to take *medicine.* A vaccine is one kind of medicine. Other medicines fight germs. They are poisons to the germs and need to be used only as a doctor directs. Some medicines help weakened body parts work properly. You may know someone who takes stomach or heart medicine. Many medicines simply reduce pain or discomfort. When you have a cold, the medicine you take does not cure the cold, but it helps to lessen the symptoms so you feel better. Some medicines come from materials in plants, animals, and minerals, but some medicines are manmade.

God made all these materials that help the body, but man has to work hard to find them and has to learn how to use them wisely. Each year medical workers learn new ways to fight disease. Each year new medicines are made that seem to work better than the ones used before.

Doctors can help us get well. In most cases a doctor must tell you which medicine to use. First he checks your symptoms, such as a fever, a cough, or swelling. Then he makes his diagnosis. A *diagnosis* means that he decides which disease you probably have. The doctor can do this because he has studied many medicines and the symptoms of many diseases. He knows which medicine is likely the best for your illness.

In order to make a proper diagnosis, your doctor may have your blood tested. He wants to know whether your body has made more white blood cells than normal. A high white-cell count tells him that your body is indeed fighting some disease.

When the doctor has made a diagnosis of your disease, he often writes out a *prescription.* The prescription tells the name of the proper medicine, how much of it to take, and how often to take it. If the medicine is for a common illness such as a cold or the flu, the doctor might give the medicine to you at his office. Otherwise, he tells you to take the prescription to a druggist, who then gives you the right medicine.

It is important to follow directions when taking any kind of medicine. All medicines can be harmful if used improperly.

You have learned that doctors, medicines, cards and visits, good body care, and a cheerful attitude can all be helpful when you are sick. But do not forget that God's work of healing is the most important. Remember to thank God and others who have helped you to get well again.

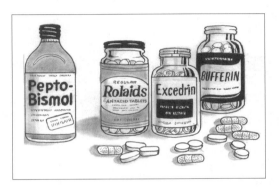

Medicines can do much to help a sick person get better, but what heals the person?

─────────── Test Your Reading (Group B) ───────────

Write the missing words.

9. God has created many plants and minerals that can be used to make ——— that will help you get well.

10. Some medicines, like penicillin, help you get well by fighting the ——— that cause disease.

11. If you have a weak stomach, you might take a medicine to help your stomach ——— properly.

12. Sometimes if you have the flu, you may take aspirin to reduce ———, even though the aspirin does not fight the disease.

13. The doctor looks at the ——— of your disease to help him make the right ——— of your disease.

14. If the doctor does not have the right medicine at his office, he will send you to the drugstore with a ———.

Answer these questions.

15. What three things does a prescription tell you?
16. Doctors and medicines do not heal you; they only help to heal. How then do you get well?

Reviewing What You Have Learned

1. True or false? Liquids in the stomach kill many germs.
2. White blood cells destroy germs by
   a. making toxins.
   b. sending a HELP call.
   c. eating them.
3. Dead or weakened disease germs are used to make a ———.
4. We do not get the same disease the second time because we are ——— to it.
5. God made your body in a way that
   a. most germs cannot enter it.
   b. most germs are fought with antibodies.
   c. most germs are killed with a fever.

Extra Activities

1. Ask your teacher or parents if you may visit someone who is sick. You could make your own get-well card to give the sick person. First, fold a sheet of white paper once or twice; then draw or paste a cheerful picture on the outside, and write a short Bible verse on the inside.
2. Ask your parents if you can see some prescription medicine bottles that are in your home. Find the three things that a prescription tells. Why are these three things important for the doctor to give?
3. Read about some very useful medicines by looking up "Antibiotic" and "Sulfa Drugs" in an encyclopedia. Tell or write what you learned.

Lesson 4

Protection From Disease

New Words

antiseptic (an'·ti·sep'·tik), an ointment or solution used to kill germs to prevent a wound from becoming infected.

carrier, a person or thing that passes a disease to others.

contagious (kən·tā'·jəs), easily spread around to others.

infection (in·fek'·shən), a sore or sickness because of germs.

sanitation (san'·i·tā'·shen), the prevention of disease by practicing safe garbage disposal and careful food handling.

Contagious diseases can cause death. Have you ever wished that you lived long ago during pioneer times? Then forests were still full of bears, panthers, and other wildlife. The land was less crowded, and the air was much cleaner.

But life was not always better long ago. Children were much more in danger of dying from diseases. For example, only 200 years ago, one out of every three children did not live to grow up.

One reason for this was the lack of vaccines and other medicines. Doctors did not have medicines to fight contagious diseases as they do today. A *contagious* disease is any disease that spreads from one person to the next. Measles, chicken pox, and whooping cough are all contagious diseases. Small pox and diphtheria were once dreaded diseases. Many died from these diseases. Today these contagious diseases are so rare that you probably do not know anyone who had them.

How do you get a contagious disease? You get the flu, for example, by being near someone with the flu. This person is a *carrier* of the flu germs. When that person coughs or sneezes, he sends small droplets onto his hands or into the air. These droplets are sure to have some flu germs in them. You get the germs from the carrier by touching him, touching something he has touched, or even by breathing air in a room where he has been. Some of them stick to the inside of your throat and start multiplying until you become sick. Now you are the carrier of flu germs. You pass them on to someone else, and so it goes on and on.

Animals can also be carriers. Flies and mosquitoes, dogs, cats, mice, and rats are all known to be carriers of disease. Some lands are troubled with terrible, deadly diseases spread by insects and other animals.

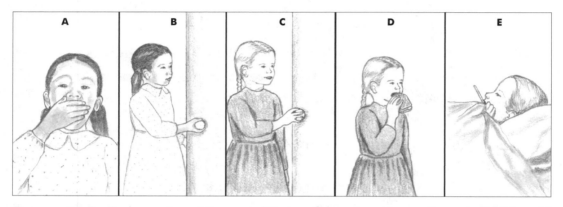

Persons with the flu are carriers of flu germs. What could have been done so the second child would not have become sick?

──────────── **Test Your Reading (Group A)** ────────────

Choose the right answer.

1. Years ago, many children did not live to be grown up because
   a. their parents did not care for them.
   b. they did not have medicines for deadly diseases.
   c. the diseases were more contagious in those days.
2. If you have a contagious disease, then
   a. you got the germs from someone.
   b. you did not have the right diet.
   c. you were in the cold air too long.
3. Which of the following diseases is rare today?
   a. chicken pox
   b. flu
   c. small pox

4. If you are a carrier of a disease, then you
   a. are immune to the disease.
   b. can give the disease to others.
   c. can easily get the disease.
5. A bite from a cat can be very serious because
   a. it may be carrying a deadly disease.
   b. the wounds from cats take a long time to heal.
   c. cats can bite very deep.

What can you do to avoid getting a contagious disease? In the Old Testament, God told His people to wash and be clean. He knew that they would not have as much problem with disease if they had clean practices. Even in a day with many medicines, you will be less likely to get sick if you practice good health habits. Practice the following rules both to stay healthy and to be polite to those around you.

Good Health Habits

1. Use a handkerchief to cover your nose and mouth when you sneeze or cough.
2. Wash your hands with soap before handling food and after using the restroom.
3. Use your own comb, toothbrush, and drinking glass.
4. Wear clean clothes, and take a bath at least twice a week.
5. Wash your hair at least once a week.

Follow the rules below to avoid giving your disease to others.

Rules During Sickness

1. Be extra careful to follow the "Good Health Habits."
2. Always keep tissues or handkerchiefs handy to catch coughs and sneezes.
3. Wash your hands often with soap.
4. Stay away from others, especially babies and other sick people.

In Lesson 2 you learned that your skin is a God-given protection from germs. Whenever a part of your skin is cut or burned, that part is an open door to germs. The germs cause signs of *infection,* such as pain, swelling, and redness.

For a deep cut or serious burn, you need to see a doctor. But you can doctor small wounds yourself. To treat a wound, wash it carefully and apply a clean, dry bandage. You might also want to put a mild *antiseptic* liquid or first-aid cream on the wound or bandage. An antiseptic keeps germs from growing.

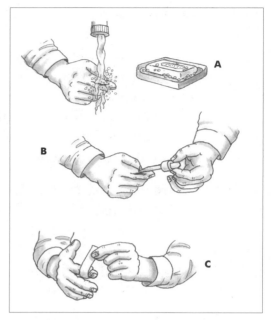

First aid for a wound: Clean the wound, kill the germs, and bandage it to keep it clean.

Test Your Reading (Group B)

Study the list of "Good Health Habits." Then supply the missing words from memory.

6. Use a ——— to cover your nose and mouth when you ——— or cough.
7. Wash your hands with ——— before handling food and after using the ———.
8. Use your ——— comb, ———, and drinking glass.
9. Wear ——— clothes, and take a bath at least ——— ——— ———.
10. ——— your hair at least ——— ——— ———.

Answer the following questions.

11. When should you be especially careful to practice good health habits?
12. What are three signs that a wound has become infected with germs?
13. Why should you put an antiseptic on a wound?

How does our community protect us from disease? When you have good health habits, you are doing your part to protect yourself from germs. But there are some important things that you cannot do by yourself. For example, how can you make sure that your drinking water is not polluted with germs? How can you make sure that the meat and milk on your table did not come from a sick cow? You cannot tell just by looking at your water, milk, or meat.

For these problems, the community works together for protection from disease. This is called *sanitation.* Providing clean water, milk, and food is a part of sanitation. Another important part is properly getting rid of garbage and sewage. You are practicing sanitation for your family when you help to wash the dishes in hot, soapy water. Sanitation is cleanliness that helps to keep germs from multiplying or spreading.

Some community workers make laws to help keep our water from being polluted with sewage. They also make laws to help keep our milk and food clean. A farmer's milk

must pass regular tests if he wants to sell it. A chicken slaughterhouse or soup cannery must also pass regular inspections and follow strict rules of cleanliness. All those who handle food must keep it as clean and germfree as possible, or they are not allowed to sell it. It is important that everyone obeys the sanitation laws.

How are these men promoting sanitation?

Why is it necessary to handle garbage properly? Flies, mice, and rats all thrive at open garbage dumps. Wherever these animal carriers go, they take many germs along and spread diseases. Because of this, garbage is usually buried at a landfill. In large cities, some garbage is burned and the heat energy is changed into electricity. Some garbage such as cardboard, plastic, and glass is used again, or recycled, instead of being wasted.

Many communities in other lands do not have enough money to have good sanitation. As a result, the people have much disease and many health problems. Many young children in such places do not live long. As we have opportunity, let us share with those who are not blessed as we are. Let us thank God for His goodness to us.

─────── **Test Your Reading (Group C)** ───────

Write *true* if the statement is true. Write *false* if the statement is not true.

14. If you practice good health habits, you can be just as healthy when others are careless as when others are careful.
15. Your water may have germs in it even if it looks clean.
16. Sanitation laws are made to make it hard for the farmers to sell milk.
17. Sanitation is the name used for a community that does not have any sickness.
18. A bakery would need to practice better sanitation than a woodworking shop.
19. Burying or burning garbage helps to have less carriers of disease germs.
20. Recycled garbage is a wasteful use of what we throw away.

Reviewing What You Have Learned

1. True or false? Any kind of antibody will fight any kind of germ.
2. A doctor makes his diagnosis after he knows your
   a. white-cell count.
   b. symptoms.
   c. prescription.
3. "A ——— heart doeth good like a medicine."
4. We need more rest when we are sick because
   a. our bodies work hard to fight germs.
   b. antibodies cannot be made while we work.
   c. medicines work best while we rest.
5. Men use chemicals to make ——— that can help us get well.

Extra Activities

1. Ask your teacher or parents if you may visit a cannery, slaughter-house, or dairy farm. Find out how sanitation is being practiced in these places. If you live on a dairy farm, ask your father what sanitation laws must be obeyed. Write a report of these laws, or give an oral report to the class.

2. Take this little test just to see how much you know about disease.

   For each sentence, write *true* if you think it is true, and *false* if you think it is not true. Ask your teacher for the correct answers.

   a. You get one kind of vitamin from being outside in the sunshine.

   b. A person taking cancer treatments should increase his vitamin intake.

   c. Some kinds of bacteria are living inside your body right now.

   d. Cancer is a contagious disease.

   e. Some people get sick from dust and cat hair.

   f. White corpuscles will attack and break up a splinter in your finger.

   g. A newborn baby is immune to many diseases.

   h. The sick who receive loving care need less pain medicine than those who are ignored.

   i. The medicine called penicillin is made from molds that grow on bread.

   j. Most mosquitoes drink human blood and spread disease.

Lesson 5

Do You Remember?

Match each word on the right with its meaning on the left.
1. Tiny plants and animals that cause disease
2. High body temperature
3. Any signs of sickness
4. Disease-fighting blood cells
5. Used to treat a disease
6. Directions for medicine
7. Those who spread germs
8. Sickness from germs

a. carriers
b. fever
c. germs
d. infection
e. medicine
f. prescription
g. symptoms
h. white blood cells

For each blank, write the missing word from the word box.

antibodies	germs	sanitation
antiseptic	immune	vaccine
contagious	minerals	vitamins
diagnosis		

9–10. Scurvy and similar diseases are found where people do not get enough ——— and ———.
11. We cannot see disease ——— except with a microscope.
12–13. A ——— causes you to become ——— to a disease without getting it.
14. Mumps ——— watch for and fight against only mumps germs.
15. A doctor wants to know the symptoms of a person's disease in order to make his ———.
16. To avoid getting infection in cuts and sores, you may put an ——— on it.
17. Any disease that spreads from one person to the next is ———.
18. Providing pure water, clean food, and proper waste disposal are important parts of ———.

Decide whether each sentence is true or not true, and write *true* or *false*.

19. Antibodies are blood cells that fight germs by eating them.
20. All germs make us sick if they get inside our bodies.
21. Measles are a symptom of fever.
22. A person's body may fight germs for weeks before getting well again.
23. The sick who trust God get well faster than those who worry.
24. Cards and visits help the sick get well.
25. One way God helps to heal us is by the work of doctors and medicines.
26. Most disease germs spread from animals to people.

Choose the best ending for each sentence, and write the correct letter on your paper.

27. These foods have plenty of vitamins and minerals:
    a. candy and cookies.
    b. potato chips and chocolate cake.
    c. carrots and oatmeal bread.
28. Some diseases caused by germs are
    a. colds and chicken pox.
    b. mumps and fever.
    c. flu and scurvy.
29. You are protected from many germs by
    a. cuts in your skin.
    b. the inside of the lungs.
    c. stomach liquids.
30. It is easiest for your body to destroy whooping cough germs
    a. when it has fought them before.
    b. when it is fighting flu viruses.
    c. when it has not fought them before.
31. Being immune to chicken pox means that you will not
    a. get any chicken pox germs inside your body again.
    b. become sick with chicken pox again.
    c. need chicken pox antibodies again.

32. A sick person needs
    a. plenty of liquids and rest.
    b. large meals and proper medicine.
    c. cheerfulness and hard work.
33. Some good foods for a sick person are
    a. cake and ice cream.
    b. soup and toast.
    c. steak and cherry pie.
34. Our food supply is kept clean mainly by
    a. adding chemicals to kill germs.
    b. dumping garbage in faraway ditches.
    c. having workers obey laws for cleanliness.

Write the correct answers.
35–36. Write two things that germs do inside your body when you become sick.
37–38. In what two ways can you become immune to a disease such as measles?
39–43. After studying the five "Good Health Habits," write them from memory.
44–47. After studying the four "Rules During Sickness," write them from memory.
48–50. What are three good ways to get rid of garbage?

Unit Five

God Made Light

"Where is the way where light dwelleth?" (Job 38:19).

Light is very common. Why will you be studying a unit of science about ordinary light? After all, you turn it on in the morning. The sun gives you light during the day. You turn off the light at night. You have known about light since you were a little child.

But there is much for you to learn about light. In this unit you will learn what makes light hot or cold, why light can bounce or bend, what makes a rainbow, how eyeglasses help people, what happens inside your eyes, and why you need two eyes.

If you study this unit so well that you get every answer right on the test, you will know only a little about light. Even a wise man like Job did not know all about light. God asked him a hard question, "Where is the way where light dwelleth?" (Job 38:19). Job did not know the answer. God did not expect Job to answer. God knew that He Himself was the only one who knows everything about light.

Light is from God. Like every good and perfect gift, light "is from above, and cometh down from the Father of lights" (James 1:17).

Lesson 1

"Let There Be Light"

New Words

light, the form of energy by which we can see.

luminous (lü′·mə·nəs), giving off its own light.

ray, a single line of light.

shadow, the dark area formed when an object stops the light coming from a source.

spectrum (spek′·trəm), the band of colors formed when white light is separated into its parts.

Let's think back to a time long, long ago. It was the very first day of the earth. What a strange earth it was! There were no leafy trees or singing birds or busy people. You could not have seen anything, for there was no *light.* Everything was as dark as the blackest midnight.

God created light. On the first day of Creation, God said, "LET THERE BE LIGHT" and there was light! (Genesis 1:3). What a wonderful thing God created that day. We like light, and we know that God liked it. The Bible says, "And God saw the light, that it was good" (Genesis 1:4).

Many years later, Job knew that the light was good. He knew that we need light to see where we are going. In thinking about what God does to great men, Job said, "They grope in the dark without light" (Job 12:25). Job knew how important light is in our everyday life.

You know that God created light so that we could see. He also created light to give us heat. We get some light and heat from fire when we burn wood or other fuels. But most of our light and heat comes from a much greater fire. In fact, this fire is a million times larger than the whole earth. It is the sun.

What are luminous objects? God created the sun as our most important source of light. We say the sun is *luminous* because it gives off its own light. The moon is not luminous because it cannot make light. Moonlight is simply sunlight that has bounced off the moon and down to the earth.

Can you think of other things that are luminous? The stars are luminous, for they are burning just like the sun. Flames are luminous, whether on candles, in oil lamps, or in fireplaces. Sometimes heated wires become luminous. For example, a common electric light bulb gives you light because the wire inside is very hot.

Not all luminous things are hot. For example, what "fire" does a firefly use for its light? Maybe you have caught one and watched its yellow-green light blink—blink—blink. Why doesn't the firefly feel hot when it lights up? God made the firefly's body give off cold light: it gives off light without becoming hot. Glowworms and some deep-sea fishes also make cold light.

Whether cold or hot, an object that gives off its own light is luminous.

What makes the light bulb filament luminous?

Cold light from a firefly

Test Your Reading (Group A)

Choose the best answer.
1. God made light on the
   a. first day.   b. second day.   c. third day.
2. Light was created when God
   a. made the sun.
   b. lighted a fire.
   c. said the word.

3. We need light in order to
    a. know who is calling.
    b. know where to walk.
    c. know a surface is rough.
4. Sunlight gives us
    a. heat.   b. rain.   c. air.
5. Something luminous makes its own
    a. food.   b. heat.   c. light.
6. Which one is luminous?
    a. the moon   b. a star   c. a dragonfly
7. Cold light is
    a. light from a luminous object that is not hot.
    b. light from the sun in the winter.
    c. light from a luminous object very far away.
8. The name *firefly* is not best because
    a. a firefly is not always luminous.
    b. a firefly is luminous without heat.
    c. a firefly is luminous while it flies.

How does light travel? When you turn on a lamp in a dark room, how does the light get from the bulb to your eyes? The light moves from the light bulb in straight lines, or **rays.** The rays leave the light bulb in all directions so that there is light in every part of the room.

Light travels in straight lines. When you see a classmate on the other side of the room, you know that he is in the direction you see him because light is reflected from him to you in straight lines. Since light rays are straight, if you put your hand between the light and the wall, the rays do not bend around the edge of your hand. Your hand makes a **shadow** on the wall. Shadows are made because light rays are straight.

What are these rays of light that come from luminous objects? Only God can answer that question fully.

Why does light make shadows?

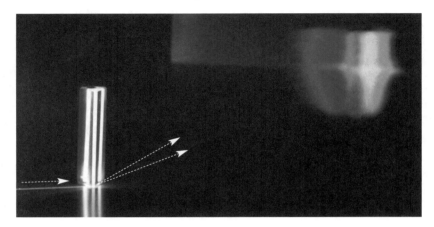

A prism separates sunlight into the colors of the spectrum.

Light is very common; we use it every day, but it is a very great mystery that shows the wisdom of God.

What is the spectrum? The light we get from the sun can be separated into many colors. Sunlight is actually made of the colors red, orange, yellow, green, blue, and purple—the colors of the rainbow. The colors in the order of the rainbow make up the *spectrum.*

In sunlight the colors of the spectrum are all mixed together. This mixture of light we call white. But when the rays of sunlight pass through raindrops, they separate into a lovely spectrum. Then you say, "Come look at the rainbow!"

Raindrops are not the only things that make light separate into its spectrum. A wedge-shaped glass called a prism will do the same thing. The scales of a fish and the wings of a dragonfly also give off rainbow colors. God has made His world very beautiful with light and color.

Test Your Reading (Group B)

Write the missing words.

9. A ray of light travels in a ——— line.

10. Light fills a room with light because rays travel in all ———.

11. A shadow is formed because light cannot ——— around the edge of an object.

12. All the colors found in sunlight are called the ———.

13. The colors of the spectrum are red, ———, yellow, ———, blue, and purple.

14. A rainbow is formed when sunlight passes through ———.

Answer the following questions.

15. Jesus said that men put a candle on a candlestick "and it giveth light unto all that are in the house." What about the travel of light makes this true?

16. What about the way light travels helps us know where to pitch a ball?

17. How is a prism like the wings of a dragonfly?

Extra Activities

1. You can make your own little rainbow to see the spectrum. Go outside during a sunny morning or afternoon, when the sun is not high in the sky. Get a garden hose, and stand with your back to the sun. Spray the water in a fine mist into the air. Through the mist you will see the spectrum.

   Materials needed:
   - garden hose
   - nozzle (to spray in a fine mist)

2. See whether or not light travels in straight lines. Cut a hole the size of a dime in the middle of two pieces of paper. Hold the papers about a foot apart as shown in the drawing.

   Look through the holes at a number on a clock or calendar. How must the holes be placed in order to see the number? What does this tell you about light?

Materials needed:
- 2 pieces of paper
- scissors
- clock or calendar

3. Make a pinhole viewer. You may be surprised at what light can do. Cut out most of one side of a cereal box as shown in the picture.

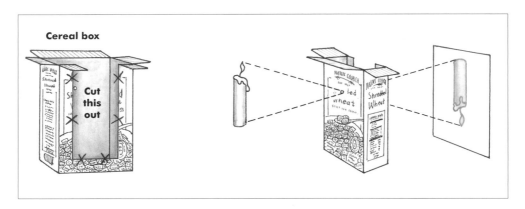

Use a pencil or nail to punch a "pinhole" about this size (o) into the other side of the box. Turn the pencil around a few times to smooth the edges of the hole.

In a darkened room, set up a lighted candle and the box as shown in the picture. Hold a sheet of white paper about eight inches behind the pinhole so that you see the flame's image. What is different about the image on the paper? Can you explain why it is turned this way? (Hint: Remember that light travels in straight lines.)

Move the paper farther away. How does this change the picture of the flame? Why?

Materials needed:
- cereal box
- scissors
- pencil or nail

- a darkened room
- candle
- sheet of white paper

Lesson 2

Reflecting Light

New Words

absorb, to take in instead of reflecting.

mirror, a coated glass in which one's image may be seen.

reflect, to cause light to bounce off.

Let's pretend you have never before seen your own face. Then for the very first time, someone gives you a *mirror*! What would you do?

You would probably look and look in the mirror. Is that face really yours? You might be surprised to see that you look very much like your big brother—the same brown eyes and straight nose. You blink your eyes and wiggle your nose. The face in the mirror blinks and wiggles too.

If you really had never seen a mirror before, you would want to keep it as a treasure. But to you, mirrors are so common that you may not think much about them. Of course, you need a mirror to comb your hair. You know that the driver of a car needs a rear-view mirror to drive safely. What is so special about a mirror?

A rear-view mirror is necessary for safe driving.

Light can be reflected. A mirror shows us something very important about light. Light can be bounced, or *reflected.* Right now, light is reflecting off this page and into your eyes. Look all around you. Light is bouncing off everything in the room and into your eyes. Reflected light allows you to see the things around you.

What if light could not be

reflected? Then you could only see when you looked right at something luminous, such as a lamp or the sun. Everything else would be dark. That would be like having night all the time.

Light-colored objects reflect light. All objects reflect light, but there is a big difference in how much light is reflected. One thing may reflect very little light, while another reflects nearly all the light that falls on it. What makes the difference?

It depends partly on the color of the object. The lighter in color an object is, the more light it reflects. For example, pink and white reflect much light.

Dark colors, such as black and brown, reflect little light. Instead, they take in, or **absorb,** most of the light that falls on them. The light energy that is absorbed changes to heat energy.

How can knowing which colors reflect and absorb light be a help to you? On cold winter mornings, you can choose dark-colored clothes. They help you feel warmer because they absorb light and change it to heat. On the other hand, you can wear light-colored clothes during the summertime. They help you feel cooler because they reflect light.

—————— **Test Your Reading (Group A)** ——————

Answer *true* if the sentence is true; answer *false* if the sentence is not true.

1. You can see yourself in a mirror because mirrors are luminous.
2. We see objects that are not luminous because they reflect light.
3. A good meaning for *reflect* would be "to pass through."
4. Light that is not reflected is changed to heat.
5. A good meaning for *absorb* would be "to take in."
6. A white coat would help you be warmer on a cold, sunny day than a brown coat would.
7. Dark colors absorb more light than light colors do.

Smooth objects make mirrors. The smoother an object is, the better you can see yourself when you look at it. You may have seen yourself when looking at the side of a very shiny car. Very smooth materials reflect light rays so evenly that you can see your face in them. Mirrors, shiny metal, and still water are such materials.

Rough surfaces scatter light. If you shine a flashlight on a mirror, it will make a spot somewhere on the wall. If you shine a flashlight on a sheet of paper, the light will be scattered around the room. Only shiny surfaces make mirrors.

Light that is reflected off a mirror bounces back in an equal way. If you shine a flashlight straight at a mirror, the light will be reflected straight back. But if you shine a flashlight at a slant from the side, the light will bounce off in an equal slant away from the flashlight. You know that if you throw a ball slanted at the floor, it will bounce away from you at an equal slant. This is the same equal way light bounces off a mirror. This is a very orderly way God made light to be reflected.

Mirrors are not always flat. Sometimes mirrors are curved inward to fit around a light. The headlights of a car and the searchlights in an airport are made this way. Because of reflection, the lights inside these curved mirrors seem much brighter than they would be by themselves. Some

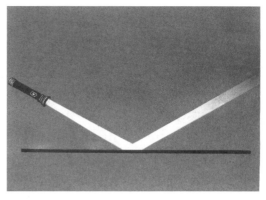

Light leaves a mirror at the same slant that it strikes the mirror.

rear-view mirrors on cars are curved outward. This lets the driver see a much wider view than with a flat mirror.

What you see in a mirror is backward. Did you know that you see yourself backward in a mirror? You are so used to seeing yourself in a mirror that what you see seems turned right to you. To see

What word is written on the front of this fire department truck? Look at it in a mirror to find out.

how you really look to other people, you must look at a photograph of yourself.

How can you tell that mirrors make things look backward? Just try reading this book or threading a needle while looking at a mirror. Maybe you have seen an ambulance with the name written backward on the front.

The name is written backward so that a driver in front can read it right when he looks in his rear-view mirror. See the picture on page 143.

God made light rays behave in this orderly way. He planned how light would reflect from a mirror.

———— Test Your Reading (Group B) ————

Find the right choice that completes the sentence.

8. Still water
9. Rough surfaces
10. Rear-view mirrors
11. Mirrors curved inward
12. Mirrors curved outward

a. give a wide view.
b. are flat or curved outward.
c. reflects light like a mirror.
d. make lights seem brighter.
e. scatter light.

Find the right choice that completes the sentence.

13. A bouncing ball
14. Flat mirrors
15. Reflected light
16. Headlights
17. A backward word

f. enters and leaves a mirror at the same slant.
g. use mirrors that are curved inward.
h. make things look backward.
i. will look right in a mirror.
j. shows the equal way light reflects.

Reviewing What You Have Learned

1. A luminous object makes its own ———.
2. True or false? A spectrum is one of the colors of the rainbow.
3. A ray travels
    a. around corners.
    b. in a straight line.
    c. to its source.
4. The sun gives us light and ———.
5. True or false? God created light on the first day of Creation.

Extra Activities

1. Try this activity using reflection. While looking only at a large mirror, write your name and address on a piece of paper. How fast can you write "backward"?

     Next, put three dots like this on your paper. Looking only at the mirror, quickly connect them with straight lines. Does it look easy? Try it!

   Materials needed:
   - pencil
   - paper
   - large mirror

2. What is the blackest black of all? You can find out. Get a shoebox with its lid and the blackest cloth scrap or paper that you can find. Cut a hole the size of a penny in one end of the box. Cut another hole the same size in the black material. Glue the material to the outside of the box so that its hole is on top of the hole in the box. Put the lid on the shoebox. Now look; which is blackest—the material or the hole? Next, get a mirror and carefully look at the black dot in the center of your eye. Can you explain what makes it so black?

   Materials needed:
   - shoebox
   - black cloth or paper
   - scissors
   - glue
   - mirror

3. You can make light turn a corner! Cut holes in the side of a cracker box as shown in the picture.

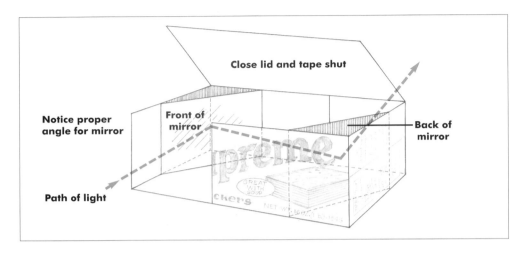

Close lid and tape shut

Notice proper angle for mirror

Front of mirror

Back of mirror

Path of light

Tape the mirrors across the corners. They must be set at just the proper slant to reflect the light into your eye. Also tape any cracks in the box so that it does not fall apart when you hold it upright.

Now you have made a little periscope! Peek around a corner with it. Use it to help you find your friends when you play hide-and-seek. Ask your teacher to tell you how periscopes are used today.

Materials needed:
- cracker box
- scissors
- 2 pocket mirrors
- tape

Lesson 3

Bending Light

New Words

concave (kon·kāv′), being curved inward so that the thinnest part of the lens is at the center.

convex (kon′·veks′), being curved outward so that the thickest part of the lens is at the center.

focus (fō′·kəs), the point where light rays are brought together.

lens, a piece of glass or other transparent material that has a curved surface to focus or scatter light.

transparent (trans·par′·ənt), being clear, like water or glass, so that objects can be seen through it.

Your last lesson told what light does when it meets an object it cannot pass through. It is either reflected or absorbed. If light meets a shiny, smooth cake pan, much is reflected off the cake pan. If light meets a dark, fuzzy blanket, much is absorbed and changed to heat.

God was wise to make light rays that can be both reflected and absorbed. Both of these ways are helpful to us. Reflected light allows us to see objects that are not luminous. Absorbed light from the sun warms the earth where we live.

When do light rays bend?

Light can pass through some materials like glass and clear plastic. When light rays enter a clear material, they bend. Does that sound strange? You learned in the first lesson that light travels in *straight* lines.

Yes, light rays do travel in straight lines most of the time. But when they meet anything clear, or **transparent,** such as glass or water, they bend. The light changes direction a little as it enters or leaves the transparent material.

You can easily see that light bends. Look at the picture of the

Put a straight edge along the pencil to see where it is "broken" by water.

Light that bends does more interesting things. Sometimes you may be riding in a car on a hot day and see "pools of water" on the highway ahead. But the "water" always disappears before you get there. The hot air above the highway made the light bend and caused you to see something that was not there.

A rainbow is caused by bending light. When sunlight passes through the transparent raindrops, it bends and makes all the colors of the spectrum to appear.

pencil in a dish of water. Why does it look bent? It is because the light rays bend sideways when they go from the water into the air.

─────────── Test Your Reading (Group A) ───────────

Choose the best answer.

1. When light rays meet an object they cannot pass through, they will either
   a. be absorbed or bent.
   b. be bounced back or bent.
   c. be changed to heat or reflected.

2. An example of a transparent object is
   a. a door.
   b. a window.
   c. a sheet of paper.

3. When light enters water, it will
   a. change direction a little.
   b. slant back equal to the slant coming in.
   c. move in a curve through the water.

4. You can tell that light bends if you
   a. look at your hand through a window glass.
   b. look at a stick held into water.
   c. look at a tree in the distance.

5. A wet-looking road may not be wet on a
   a. cold day.
   b. dry day.
   c. hot day.
6. You can see a rainbow because sunlight
   a. is reflected by the clouds.
   b. is absorbed by the rain.
   c. is bent by water.

Bending light is useful. A carefully shaped glass is called a *lens.* A lens bends light to do useful things for us. One such lens is a magnifying glass. It makes small things look large. With a magnifying glass, we can examine a flower, an ant, or our fingerprints much better than with just our eyes. We can learn new things about our world because light bends while passing through a magnifying glass.

A magnifying glass is a convex lens. A *convex* lens is thickest at the center. One or both of its sides

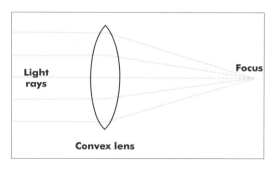

are curved outward. All convex lenses make things look larger.

A convex lens always brings light rays closer together. It bends them toward one spot called the *focus.* If you hold a magnifying glass in front of a white sheet of

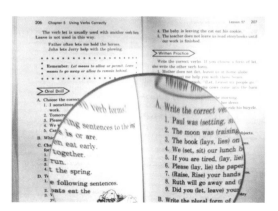

A view through a magnifying glass

The magnifying glass must be just the right distance to make the picture be in focus. Notice that the picture is upside-down.

paper, it will make a picture of the windows in your classroom if you hold it the right distance away. If you are too close or too far away, the picture will be fuzzy and blurred. But if you have the distance just right, the picture will be in focus.

A *concave* lens is just the opposite of a convex lens. One or both of its sides curve inward, so it is thinnest at the center. A concave lens spreads light rays apart.

A view through a concave lens

A concave lens makes things look smaller. You can see this if you get a pair of eyeglasses. (Most children who wear glasses have concave lenses.) If you hold the glasses in front of this book, the letters will look smaller.

In the next lesson, you can learn about some important uses of both convex and concave lenses.

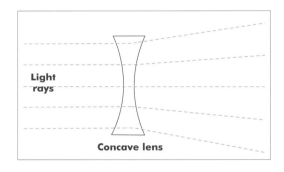

Light rays

Concave lens

———————— Test Your Reading (Group B) ————————

Write the missing words.

7. A glass with curved sides made to bend light in a useful way is called a ———.

8. A magnifying glass makes things look ———.

9. The thickest part of a convex lens is at the ———.

10. A convex lens brings light rays to a point called the ———.

11. A picture can be made on a piece of white paper with a magnifying glass if it is at the right ———.

12. Things look smaller when seen through a ——— lens.

13. The sides of a concave lens are curved ———.

14. A concave lens causes light rays to ——— apart.

Reviewing What You Have Learned

1. Which group has only luminous objects in it?
    a. fire, fireflies, shiny pan
    b. stars, raindrops, glowworms
    c. sun, light bulbs, candle flame
2. True or false? All objects reflect some light.
3. When light is absorbed by an object, it is changed into
    a. ray energy.
    b. heat energy.
    c. reflected energy.
4. A white shirt will ——— much light.
5. ——— are useful because they reflect light rays so evenly.

Extra Activities

1. Try this with lenses! You need a binocular and a straight line across the floor. Mark it with a string unless the floor already has straight lines in its design. Stand at one end of the string or line. Use the lenses in your binocular by looking through the widest end (the "wrong" end). Look down at your feet. Do they look small and far-away? Now, still watching your feet through the binocular, try walk-ing on the line to the other end. (Do you think it is easy? Try walking up a stairway, but be ready to grab the railing!)

    Materials needed:
    *   binocular
    *   string or line on floor

2. Watch what a convex lens can do to the view from your window. Is it a sunny day? If so, today is a good day for this experiment.

    Darken the other windows and switch off the lights. Get a mag-nifying glass and a sheet of white paper. Hold them a few feet away from the window, with the magnifying glass between the paper and the window. (**NEVER** try to look at the sun through the magnifying glass, or you could hurt your eyes.) Move the magnifying glass slowly back and forth until you see a clear image of the landscape on the paper. Which way is the image turned? Can you tell what causes it?

Materials needed:

- magnifying glass
- sheet of white paper

3. Did you know that bending light can make you see a penny where it isn't? Try it.

Ask someone to be your helper. Put a penny in a mug that has sides that are not transparent, then slowly back away. Stop as soon as you no longer see the penny.

Now ask your helper to slowly pour some water into the mug while you watch. What do you see? Can you tell what happened?

Materials needed:

- penny
- mug
- water

Lesson 4

Using Lenses

New Words

eyepiece, the lens that you look through in a microscope or telescope.

microscope (mī′·krə·skōp′), a device with lenses that make tiny things look larger.

telescope, a device with lenses that make stars and other faraway objects seem nearer and larger.

Lenses are used in eyeglasses. Look around at all the people in the room. How many are wearing glasses? Perhaps you are wearing glasses yourself. If you are, your sight is being helped by lenses.

You need concave lenses if you are nearsighted. Without them, you can see only nearby objects clearly.

Faraway objects look blurry. Look at the first picture on this page to see what a nearsighted person would see.

On the other hand, you need convex lenses if you are farsighted. Without them, you can only see faraway objects clearly. Nearby objects are out of focus. The picture below

The view of a person who is nearsighted

The view of a person who is farsighted

shows what a farsighted person would see.

Lenses help us see very small things. Men have learned much about God's wonderful world by using lenses. For example, we have learned that our blood is made of very tiny red and white cells. We have learned that we get strep throat and whooping cough because of very tiny germs. Germs are so tiny that thousands of them could fit on the period at the end of this sentence. The details of snowflakes can be seen and photographed (page 33). There are many kinds of tiny animals in a drop of muddy water from the bottom of a stream.

How did lenses teach us these things? They have been used to make the *microscope,* which makes tiny things look much larger. The word *microscope* is made of two parts. *Micro* means "small," and *scope* means "to see." A microscope helps us "to see small."

A very strong magnifying glass is a simple microscope. But microscopes usually have several lenses spaced a certain distance apart. With these lenses working together, a microscope makes something small look much bigger than it would with only one lens.

You remember from the last

lesson that when using a magnifying glass to make a picture on a paper, you move it back and forth to focus the picture. You use a microscope in much the same way. When you turn the knob, the lenses move up and down. What you see is in focus when the lenses are positioned so that you can see the object clearly. The microscope is then in focus.

The lens or group of lenses at the top of the microscope is called the *eyepiece.* It is called the eyepiece because that is where you put your eye to look into the microscope.

Below the eyepiece is the other lens or group of lenses. It is placed above the small object you want to

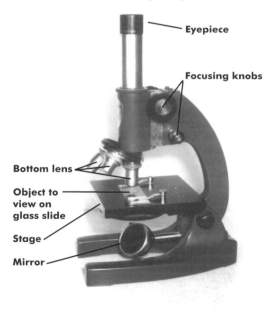

A microscope

see through the microscope. When the lenses in the eyepiece and the lenses below are in focus, you can see a sharp image that is dozens or hundreds of times bigger than the real object.

With the microscope, a Christian can see the very small wonders God has created. These wonders show how wise God is and how carefully He can make even things too small for us to see with our eyes alone.

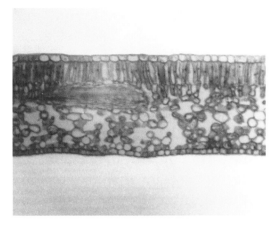

With a microscope, the cells of a leaf can be seen.

──────── Test Your Reading (Group A) ────────

Answer the following questions.

1. What kind of lenses does a person need who cannot see distant things clearly?
2. When would a person need glasses that are thickest in the center?
3. What do the two parts of the word *microscope* mean?
4. On a microscope, what is the name of the place where you look in?
5. If you look in a microscope and what you see is blurred, what must you do to see clearly?
6. What are two examples of things that men have learned with the use of the microscope?
7. What special use would a godly man make of the microscope?

Lenses help us see distant things. Do you ever use a binocular (also called field glasses) to watch wild birds and animals? The binocular helps you clearly see things that are far away. Actually, a binocular is two telescopes in one.

The word *telescope* is made of

Why would a bird watcher use a binocular?

two parts. *Tele* means "far off," and *scope* means "to see." The telescope helps us "to see far off."

All **telescopes** use lenses to make faraway things look nearer and larger. For example, with a good telescope, you can see the mountains on the moon and the four biggest moons around the planet Jupiter. Thousands of star islands called galaxies have been discovered through the telescope.

A telescope works much like a microscope. It has lenses or groups of lenses spaced just the right distance apart. The one set of lenses in the eyepiece is made the same as the eyepiece of a microscope. But the lenses in the other set are different. They are much wider than those in a microscope. The largest telescope of this kind has a lens that is 40 inches (1 meter) wide.

Today even larger telescopes use

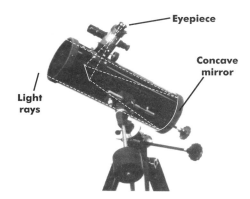

A telescope that focuses light with a mirror

mirrors instead of lenses. These mirrors can be made much wider than lenses. One large telescope in California has a mirror that is over 16 feet (5 meters) across!

You learned in this lesson that we use lenses in eyeglasses, binoculars, microscopes, and telescopes. There are many more uses for lenses. They are used in cameras and copiers. Lenses help doctors, dentists, and scientists do their work.

Although men have done much with lenses, we must remember to give God the praise He deserves. He made the materials used in glass and plastic lenses. He also gave man a good mind to learn how to make lenses. The things we learn by using lenses should help us honor God and praise His Name.

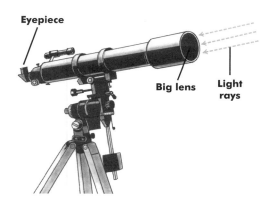

A telescope that focuses light with a large lens

—————— Test Your Reading (Group B) ——————

Choose the best ending for each sentence below.

8. *Telescope* means
9. A binocular is
10. A telescope eyepiece is
11. The lenses of a telescope are
12. A blurred view is
13. The telescope lens where light comes in is
14. Some very big telescopes use
15. Lenses are also used in

a. spaced the right distance apart.
b. cameras and copiers.
c. mirrors instead of big lenses.
d. like that of a microscope.
e. "to see far off."
f. two telescopes in one.
g. bigger than in a microscope.
h. out of focus.

Answer the following questions.

16. What are two wonders of creation in the sky that can be seen only with a telescope?
17. What two kinds of people use lenses in their work?
18. In what two ways did God make the microscope and the telescope?

Reviewing What You Have Learned

1. Which one will absorb the most light?
   a. a black shirt   b. a dark blue shirt   c. a gray shirt
2. Lenses thicker at the center than at the edge are ———.
3. True or false? Concave lenses scatter light.
4. When a light ray travels at a slant into a transparent material, it is
   a. focused.   b. reflected.   c. bent.
5. Raindrops can change light into a
   a. ray.   b. spectrum.   c. reflection.

Extra Activities

1. Borrow a pair of bifocal eyeglasses from someone. (Older people are more likely to have bifocals than younger people.) Be sure to handle the glasses very carefully. Look at a newspaper or coin and then at a calendar on the wall. Do you see that each half of the glasses has two kinds of lenses in it? How are the two kinds different from each other? Are they both concave, both convex, or is there one of each? How can you tell?

Materials needed:
- bifocal eyeglasses

2. If tonight is a clear night, use a telescope or binocular to look at the moon and stars. Find the mountains and craters on the moon, and notice how many more stars you can see this way than you could with your naked eye.

Materials needed:
- telescope or binocular

3. Make your own "microscope with two lenses."

Place a pencil on either side of a postage stamp as shown in the picture.

Lay clear plastic wrap across the pencils, keeping it stretched out. With an eyedropper or a drinking straw, carefully place one drop of water on the plastic wrap above the stamp. Take care not to wet the area around it.

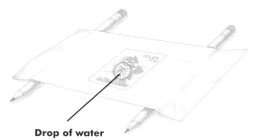

Drop of water

Look through the drop at the stamp. Does the stamp look bigger at that spot? Now hold a magnifying glass above the drop and look through both of them. How does the stamp look now?

Materials needed:
- stamp
- 2 pencils
- clear plastic wrap
- water
- eyedropper
- magnifying glass

Lesson 5

Our Eyes

New Words

cornea (kôr′·nē·ə), the clear, outer covering on the front of the eyeball.

iris (ī′·ris), the colored part of the eye that controls the amount of light entering the eye.

optic nerve (op′·tik), the cord of nerves that sends messages from the eye to the brain.

pupil, the black opening in the iris where light enters the eye.

retina (ret′·i·nə), the back inside surface of the eyeball where images form.

What would you do without your eyes? Your eyes can receive messages from trillions of miles away when they see stars. They can also see the six points of a tiny snowflake held just inches from your eyes. Sight is one of the five valuable senses God gave to you.

When you see something, the reflected light travels into your eye and a "sight message" is sent to your brain in an instant. In this lesson we shall pretend to make just one sight message travel very slowly so that we can keep up with it. We shall follow its path through your eye and into your brain. Then you can better understand how you see.

How do we see? Do you see this letter A? How did it get to your brain? First, the light reflected off this page and came straight to your clear cornea. The *cornea* is a transparent covering over the front of the eye. If you look at the side of another person's eye, you can see

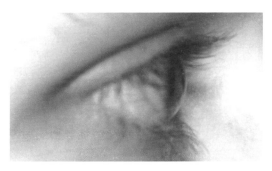

The cornea is the bulging, transparent covering on the front of the eye.

the bulging shape of the clear cornea.

After the light passed through the cornea, it traveled through a watery liquid to your iris. The *iris* is the colored circle in your eye. If you say you have brown eyes, you mean that your irises are brown.

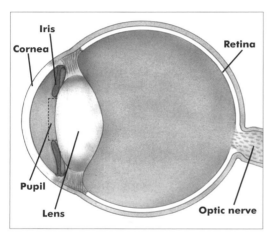

The parts of the eye

In the middle of your iris is a black dot called the pupil. The *pupil* is simply a hole or an opening in your iris where light can go through. If you read the letter A in bright light, your iris makes the pupil small and blocks out most of the light. But if you read the A in dim light, your iris opens to make a large pupil. This allows more light to enter your eye so you can see

clearly in dim light. God made the iris so it could adjust the amount of light all by itself.

After entering the pupil, the light passed through a convex lens just behind it. This lens focuses the light so that you can see clearly. Like the iris, it can adjust itself by changing its shape. The eye is a marvelous display of God's handiwork.

The light from the lens is focused sharply on the back "wall" of the inside of the eye called the *retina.* Your lens causes the A to be focused upside down on your retina. The retina is made of special cells that respond to light. The millions of cells of the retina record the total picture of what you see in front of you.

After the image of the A formed on your retina, the light cells sent the sight message up to your brain through a cord of nerves called the *optic nerve.* The optic nerve sped the message to your brain. Your brain did not mind that the A was upside-down, for it knows that all sight messages come that way. It simply turned the A right side up and told you, "That is an A." Then you were all finished seeing that A.

Actually, all this happened in only $^1/_{10}$ *of a second*!

While you read this lesson, many thousands of sight messages whiz from the page to your eye to your brain just as the **A** did. Sight is a great gift from God to you. We must thank Him for our eyes and praise Him for the wonderful way He made them.

—————— **Test Your Reading (Group A)** ——————

Use the names for eye parts given in the box to match with each of the following descriptions and the parts of the drawing. Each word is used more than once.

cornea	lens	pupil
iris	optic nerve	retina

1. It is the colored part of your eye.
2. It is the transparent covering of the eye.
3. It has cells that respond to light.
4. It speeds sight messages from the eye to the brain.
5. It controls the amount of light that enters the eye.
6. It focuses images by changing its size.
7. It is the black dot in your eye.
8. It is a cord of nerves.
9. It is a wall where upside-down images form.
10. It is convex like a magnifying glass.

11.   12.   13.   14.   15.   16.

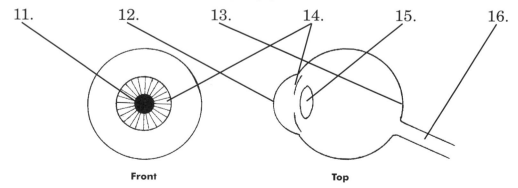

Front   Top

Answer the following questions.

17.   What happens to the eye to help you see in dim light?

18.   How did the eye get its design to be able to work so well?

Two eyes are better than one. You have learned how a sight message goes from one eye to your brain. But why do you need two at the same time? When you use both eyes, you can see a wider area around you than with only one eye. Also with two eyes, you can judge distances better. Since your eyes are a little over two inches apart, each eye sees a view that is just a little different. God has made your brain to be able to take the differences from your two eyes and tell you which objects are near and which are far.

Sometimes persons have had one eye injured so that it goes blind. They are glad that they had two eyes so they still have one eye to see. Sight is a very valuable gift from God. Be very careful that you do not lose your sight.

How did God protect your eyes? God not only gave you eyes to see, but He also provided protection for them so that you can keep on seeing. He gave you eyebrows and eyelashes to catch dust or dirt so it does not enter your eyes. He gave you corneas at the front of your eyes to act as transparent shields for the tender inner parts of the eyes.

If some dirt gets into your eye, you immediately start blinking to get it out. Tears form in your eyes to wash it away. If something comes flying toward you, your eyelids blink to protect your eyes. God made your eyelids close so quickly that you hardly think before you shut them.

Any hard knocks or bumps could seriously damage your soft eyeballs. In order to protect them, God gave you bony eye sockets like walls around the eyeballs. These strong eye sockets can stand much harder blows than your eyes can.

How can you use your eyes wisely? Even with all these protections, your eyes can still be hurt. God wants you to use your eyes wisely by doing your part to protect them. You can be a good steward of your eyes by keeping sharp objects and strong chemicals away from them. You must protect your eyes with a shield or with goggles to keep them from being hit by flying bits of matter from grinders, lawn mowers, or other machines that can throw things. You must not stare at the sun or other bright lights.

You use your eyes wisely when you use them to do good things to please God, who gave them to you. You make good use of your eyes when you read the Bible and other

How does this picture show wise use of our eyes?

good books. You make good use of your eyes when you do work that is helpful to others.

Job talked about a good use for his eyes. He said, "I was eyes to the blind" (Job 29:15). Do you think he stopped to help a blind person find his way? Do you think he gave blind people food and clothes? We do not know exactly what Job did, but we do know that he was kind to blind people. We can also be "eyes" to a blind person by helping him in any way we can. We use our eyes wisely when we help people who are blind.

You should not use your eyes to learn or do wrong things. You should be so thankful for the gift of sight that you want to use the gift only as it pleases God.

————— Test Your Reading (Group B) —————

Write the following lists of things about your eyes.

19. List three reasons why it is good that God gave you two eyes instead of one.
20. Explain five ways God provided protection for your eyes when He made you.
21. List three things that are harmful to your eyes.
22. List three good things you can do with your eyes. (Job tells us about one of them.)

Reviewing What You Have Learned

1. Mirrors are useful because they
   a. absorb light.   b. bend light.   c. reflect light.

2. A convex lens brings light rays to a point called the ———.
3. Glasses use ——— to correct eye problems.
4. The lenses on a microscope can be moved to
   a. reflect light.   b. focus light.   c. absorb light.
5. True or false? A telescope has two sets of lenses that must be spaced just right.

Extra Activities

1. Try a test on yourself. Put a chalkboard eraser underneath a chair across the room. Ask someone to time how long it takes you to start from your desk, get the eraser, and return to your desk. Then time how long it takes you to do the same thing blindfolded. How much difference is there in the amount of time? This helps to show how much you depend on your eyes.

   Materials needed:
   - clock or stopwatch
   - scarf or other blindfold

2. Take another test. Find out if your two eyes really are better than one. Close your eyes while a classmate holds a pencil upright not far away. Then open only one eye and quickly touch the top of the pencil with one finger. Could you do it? Try it again; then try it using both eyes. Which was easier?

   Materials needed:
   - pencil

3. You can watch your irises at work. All you need is a dark room and a mirror. First, look at the mirror to notice how small your pupils are right now. Next, ask someone to time you for five minutes while you stay in the dark room. When the time is up, turn on the light while you are looking at the mirror and *immediately* watch the pupils of your eyes in the mirror. What happens? Why?

   Materials needed:
   - dark room
   - mirror

Lesson 6

Do You Remember?

Match each letter to the correct word group.

1. A line of light
2. Rainbow colors
3. A looking glass
4. To bounce off
5. Making light of its own
6. A lens that is thin at the center
7. Being clear
8. Where light could not reach
9. The colored part of the eye
10. A black opening in the eye

a. concave
b. convex
c. iris
d. luminous
e. mirror
f. pupil
g. ray
h. reflect
i. shadow
j. spectrum
k. transparent

For each blank, write the missing word from the word box.

cornea	lens	optic nerve
eyepiece	light	retina
focus	microscope	telescope
heat		

11. We need ——— in order to see.
12. Light that is absorbed changes to ——— energy.
13. A curved glass made to bend light is called a ———.
14. A fuzzy, blurry image is out of ———.
15. Small things look larger when seen through a ———.
16. Faraway things look nearer when seen through a ———.
17. We look into the ——— of a microscope to see small things.
18. Your ——— protects the front of your eye.
19. The convex lens in your eye focuses light onto your ———.
20. Your ——— speeds each sight message to your brain.

Choose the best answer for each sentence.

21. God created light on the
    a. third day.
    b. second day.
    c. first day.
22. Something luminous that God created is
    a. the sun.
    b. the moon.
    c. the sky.
23. Which reflects the most light?
    a. a black shingle roof
    b. a shiny tin roof
    c. a gray slate roof
24. Which absorbs the most light?
    a. a green dress
    b. a gray dress
    c. a black dress
25. A mirror image is always
    a. upside-down.
    b. backward.
    c. slanted.
26. A transparent material will
    a. allow light to pass through it.
    b. cause light to bounce off.
    c. change most of the light to heat.
27. When a slanting light ray goes from the air into water,
    a. it is absorbed.
    b. it is reflected.
    c. it is bent.
28. A convex lens brings light rays to a point called
    a. the spectrum.
    b. the contact.
    c. the focus.

Write *true* if the sentence is true; write *false* if it is not true.

29. Light gives us heat when it is reflected.
30. Light travels in rays from the sun.
31. Sunlight is made of many colors.
32. You can sometimes see your reflection in a rough board.
33. The slant that light strikes a mirror is the same slant that it bounces off in the opposite direction.
34. A microscope must be focused to be able to see clearly.
35. A concave lens brings light rays closer together.
36. Lenses in eyeglasses can correct poor vision.
37. The lenses of a telescope must be spaced a certain distance apart in order to focus properly.
38. Your eyes are a marvelous display of God's wisdom.

Copy and finish the sentences.

39. The iris lets just enough ———.
40. Both the iris and the lens of the eye can ———.
41. We need two eyes so that we can ———.
42. Eyelids, eyelashes, and tears protect the eyes from ———.
43. Bony eye sockets protect the eyes from ———.

Write the correct answers.

44–45. Write two ways in which mirrors are useful.
46. Name something that man can see with the microscope that he cannot see without it.
47. Name something that man can see with the telescope that he cannot see without it.
48–50. Name three main ways we can use our eyes wisely.

Unit Six

Electricity Is From God

It is dark and the night is warm. You are asleep. A bright flash fills your bedroom, and you are startled out of your sleep. For several seconds you lie frozen, afraid to move. The bright light is followed by a loud crack and the echoing boom of thunder. It frightens you, and maybe you wish there was not anything like a thunderstorm. But wait! Do not be afraid. This is a display of the greatness of our God. That bright light and loud boom is

"He directeth . . . his lightning unto the ends of the earth" (Job 37:3).

made by a huge spark of electricity, much greater than men have ever made.

Think about Job. Three of his friends told him that the reason he was sick was because he had sinned. It was not because of Job's sin, but because he needed to learn how great God is and how small he was. After these three friends talked, Elihu, another man, spoke. He told Job to think about the greatness of God. As he talked, it seems that a thunderstorm came up, because he asked Job "to hear attentively the noise of [God's] mouth [thunder]. . . . He directeth . . . his lightning unto the ends of the earth." A little later he said that "God thundereth marvellously with his voice" (Job 37:1–5). After Elihu finished talking, God talked to Job out of a whirlwind and Job listened.

So when the lightning flashes and the thunder is loud, do not be afraid. Be like Job. Think about the greatness of God, and listen to God speak.

What does this have to do with electricity? Lightning is electricity—a giant electric spark of about 100 million volts. Only God can make such a giant spark!

Lesson 1

Parts of a Circuit

New Words

appliance (ə·plī′·əns), a machine or light that uses the electricity in an electric circuit.

battery, one or more cells that contain special chemicals that make an electric current.

circuit (sėr′·kit), the complete circle or path for an electric current to travel in.

conductor (kən·duk′·tər), a material that carries electricity.

insulator (in′·sə·lā′·tər), a material that will not carry electricity and will not allow electricity to pass through.

switch, a part of an electric circuit used to turn the flow of electricity on or off.

When you turn on a light switch in a dark room, can you see what turns the light on? Can you hear anything happening? No; you turn on the switch, and immediately there is light.

Something happened that you could not hear or see. It is the wonder of electricity. We use it so often to turn on lights, fry bacon, drill holes, and feed cows that we may forget that this is a work of our great God.

Electricity moves. First, think of a very small thing, so small that you would not be able to see it even in a microscope. These very small things are called electrons, from which we get the word *electricity*. The moving of these electrons through a wire is what gives us electricity. Since no one can actually see electrons, we shall use something that we can see to help explain them.

Think of a garden hose. We connect the garden hose to a faucet. When we turn the faucet on, water is pushed through the hose by a pump and you see water coming out the other end. Electricity is like that. A battery is like

How is electricity like water in a garden hose? How is it different?

a pump that moves electrons. The wire is like the garden hose. The electrons are like the water. The switch is like the faucet. This helps explain how electricity flows through a wire.

But the garden hose does not explain everything about electricity. The water comes out the end of the hose. But electrons in a wire do not work this way. You cannot hook the end of one wire to a battery and have electrons running out the other end.

Electrons move around in a circle. Let us add one more thing to our garden hose picture. If we hook the end of the garden hose to the pump, there will be a complete circle and the water will continue to go around and around.

Electrons flow in a current like this. The wires must make a complete circle, from the battery, to the light bulb, and back to the battery again. We call this a *circuit.* One wire carries the electrons to the light bulb, and another wire carries the electrons back to the battery. The electrons will move in a wire only if there is a path to carry them back to where they started.

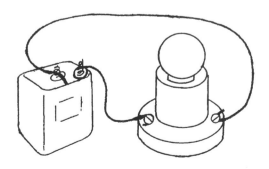

Why must two wires connect the battery and the light bulb?

Electrons move through a circuit of wire as water moves through a garden hose. But the wire does not have a hole through it like the garden hose. The electrons move through solid wire. This is a wonder of electricity, planned and created by God.

Conductors and insulators. Electricity will only move in certain kinds of materials called *conductors. Conduct* means "to carry." Any material that will carry electricity is called a conductor. Some good conductors God has given us are iron, aluminum, copper, and tin.

There are also many materials that will not conduct electricity, such as wood, plastic, glass, and rubber. Materials that do not conduct electricity are called *insulators.* They insulate electricity, or keep the electricity from going through, much as your clothes insulate you when they do not let the cold go through in the wintertime.

Rubber or plastic is the insulating material that covers the cords and wires of the electric machines that you use. To use electricity safely, you must have both conductors and insulators. You can see how wise God is to give us everything we need so that we can use electricity.

──────── Test Your Reading (Group A) ────────

Choose the best answer for each.
1. Electricity is a wonder from God because
   a. only God can make an electric circuit.
   b. electricity works in a way that only God could create and plan.
   c. we can only see electricity at work in lightning that God makes.
2. A circuit means
   a. a path for flowing electrons that comes back to where it started.
   b. the insulating material that covers the outside of a conductor.
   c. the moving electrons inside a wire.
3. All of the following are conductors except
   a. copper.
   b. plastic.
   c. aluminum.

4. An insulator is a material that
   a. keeps a wire warm.
   b. does not let electrons pass through it.
   c. carries electrons well.

5. Which of the following would make a good insulator?
   a. rubber
   b. steel
   c. tin

Answer the following questions.

6. A garden hose is like what part of an electric circuit?

7. Why do we need two wires connected to a light bulb to make it work?

The source of electricity.
Every circuit must have four parts: a source, conductors, an appliance, and a switch. You have already read about conductors. Conductors can carry electricity, but they cannot make the electrons move. We must have a source, something that produces electricity. One source of electricity is a *battery.* Special chemicals in the battery work together to produce electric current. All batteries must have two places to connect wires. Flashlight batteries have flat conducting surfaces at each end that conductors touch to complete the circuit.

Another source of electricity is a generator. A generator looks very much like a big electric

Electric power plants have large generators that are the source of electricity for many homes, schools, and businesses.

motor. The generators that make the electricity for your home and school are taller than a man. Every generator, big or small, must have two places to connect wires: one for the electrons to go out and another for the electricity to come back through the circuit.

Appliances use electricity. The electricity that flows through a wire must be used. If it is not used, the electrons will go too fast and make the wire hot. This could start a fire and be dangerous. Something must use this electricity, such as a light bulb, a toaster, a refrigerator, a drill, or

An electric drill is one kind of appliance.

a computer. These are called appliances. An *appliance* uses the electricity to do something helpful for us. An appliance keeps the wire from becoming too hot. There must be an appliance in every electric circuit.

Turning it on and off. One more thing that is needed in an

electric circuit is a *switch.* A very simple example of a switch is a knife switch. When the blade of the switch is up, the circuit is open, and the electricity cannot flow. The electrons do not move, and the light (or other appliance) is off. When the blade of the switch is put down, it touches the metal of the other part and closes the circuit. The electrons can flow, and

Which knife switch makes a closed circuit? Which makes an open circuit?

the light will come on. The light switches in your house do not look like a knife switch, but they do the same thing.

An electric circuit needs four parts: a source, conductors, a switch, and an appliance. If any part is missing, it will not work, or it will be dangerous.

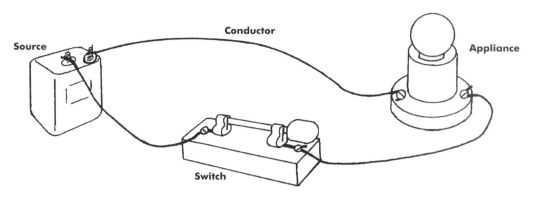

A complete electric circuit

Electricity is a wonder God created. Sometimes He shows us what electricity is like with the giant spark of lightning. At other times when electricity is running machines or lighting light bulbs, we know that moving electrons are making them work. Only God can make electricity possible.

―――――――― **Test Your Reading (Group B)** ――――――――

Write the missing words.

8. A ――― produces electricity with special chemicals.
9. Both a battery and a generator must have ――― places to connect wires.
10. The part of an electric circuit that uses the electricity is the ―――.
11. To stop the flow of electricity, the ――― must be open.
12. God shows us what electricity is like with ―――.

Answer the following questions.

13. What is the source of the electricity that you use in your house?
14. What are the four parts of an electric circuit?
15. Why would it be dangerous to have a circuit without an appliance?

For each number, choose the correct letter from the drawing on page 175.

16. Carries the electricity from one place to another
17. Provides the source of electricity
18. Uses the electricity

19. Makes a place to stop and start the flow of electricity

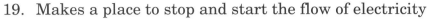

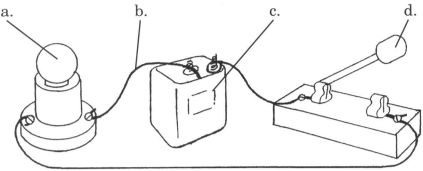

Extra Activities

1. Examine a flashlight to find the four parts of an electric circuit. Notice how the one end of the battery is touching the bottom of the bulb. How does the other end of the battery connect with the light bulb? Try to find out how the switch opens and closes the circuit.

   Materials needed:
   - a flashlight

2. Make a conductor tester. On a 4″ x 8″ board, drive in long nails on each side of two flashlight batteries laid end to end. Put one nail at each end to make electrical contact with the battery. Wedge some aluminum foil between the nail and the flat end of the battery to make good contact. Remove 1″ of insulation from the ends of 3 six-inch pieces of wire. Fold a two-inch square of aluminum foil in half twice the same way to make a piece ½″ wide and 2″ long. Place the aluminum strip flat on the board, and fasten it with a thumbtack about ¼″ from one of the ends. Before pushing the thumbtack tight, wrap one of the ends of wire around it.

   Wrap the end of another wire around the base of a flashlight bulb to make contact. Fasten the wire with thumbtacks so that the end of the light bulb is touching the aluminum foil strip. Wrap the other end of the wire around the nail at one end of the batteries.

   Connect one end of the third wire to the opposite battery nail. Your circuit will be connected in this order: wire, nail at one end of battery, batteries, nail at other end of batteries, wire, light bulb base, end of light bulb held against aluminum strip, wire under tack pushed into aluminum strip. This leaves two free ends of wire to act as a switch. Touch them together. The light bulb should light.

Now use the two free ends of wire to test if materials are conductors or insulators. Place the two free ends on a material but not touching each other. How will you know if the material is a conductor? Test many things, and make lists of conductors and insulators. Try wood, paper, coins, carbon (lead from a lead pencil), rainwater, well water, salt water, sugar water, wet soil, and many other things. For a solution that does not light the bulb, you can tell if it is conducting electricity by seeing if tiny bubbles form on one of the wires in the solution. Test a metal filing cabinet. Try a spot where there is no paint. Explain the results. **WARNING: NEVER CONNECT YOUR TESTER TO ELECTRICITY FROM AN ELECTRICAL OUTLET.**

Materials needed:
- board about 4″ x 8″
- 2 dry cell batteries
- about 6 fourpenny or sixpenny nails
- hammer
- aluminum foil
- about 18″ of insulated bell wire
- several thumbtacks
- flashlight bulb (for use with 2-cell flashlight)
- various materials to test

Lesson 2

Different Circuits

New Words

parallel circuit (par′·ə·lel′), an electric circuit that has more than one appliance and has more than one path for the electricity to follow.

resistance (ri·zis′·təns), that which slows down the flow of electricity in a circuit.

series circuit (sir′·ēz), an electric circuit that has more than one appliance but only one path for the electricity to follow.

Electricity must flow in a complete circuit. You learned this in Lesson 1. Do you remember the example of a battery, wires, switch, and light that we used in Lesson 1? In order for the light bulb to come on, the wire must go from the battery to the light and back to the battery again. This is an example of a very simple circuit.

Now suppose we want to make more than one light bulb to light. Shall we get another battery, another set of wires, and another light and switch? No, we do not need to. We can use the same battery and only add the light to the circuit. But we can choose from two kinds of circuits.

Making a series circuit. One kind of circuit is called a *series circuit. Series* means "one after the other." Below is a drawing of how the series circuit is wired. The wire connects each part of the circuit one after the other.

Since there is a complete circuit, both light bulbs will light. The electricity goes through a wire from the

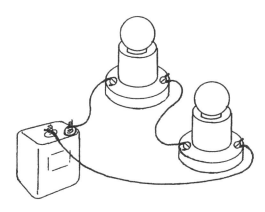

Two bulbs wired in series

battery, through the first light bulb, then through the second light bulb, and then back to the battery. Each bulb lights as the electricity passes through it.

But there is a problem of wiring lights in series. If one of the light bulbs burns out, the circuit is broken and the other light will go out also. If several bulbs in a shop would be in series and one would burn out, all the lights would go out.

Making a parallel circuit. Instead of using a series circuit, we could use a ***parallel circuit***. *Parallel* means "side by side." Below is a drawing that shows how two lights would be wired in a parallel circuit. The circuit divides, and the electricity goes through each bulb side by side. Then the circuit comes back together again.

The circuit is complete through each bulb, and both light bulbs will light. The electricity from the battery can go two ways. Some goes

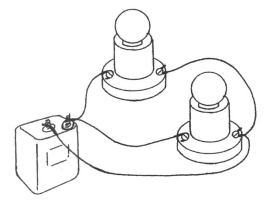

Two bulbs wired in parallel

through the one light bulb and back to the battery, and some goes through the other light bulb and back to the battery. Really, we have two circuits in one. We call this kind of circuit a parallel circuit.

The parallel circuit does not have the problem of the series circuit. Since each light bulb has its own circuit, if one bulb burns out, the other light bulb will still light. This makes it possible to have many light bulbs on one circuit and to have light even though one of them is burned out.

———————— **Test Your Reading (Group A)** ————————

Study the following circuits carefully. Decide whether the circuit is *series* or *parallel*. Write the answer for each picture.

1.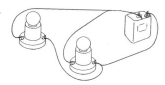

2.

3.

4.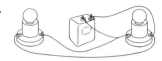

5.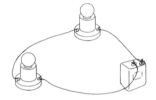

6.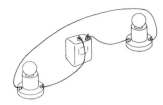

7.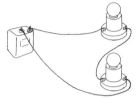

8.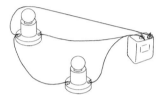

Choose the best ending.

9. The word *series* means

    a. side by side.   b. one after the other.   c. more than one.

10. You would know that two light bulbs are wired in parallel if

    a. the other went out when you unscrewed one.

    b. they both went out when you opened the switch.

    c. the other stayed on when you unscrewed one.

Switches must be wired in series. From these descriptions of the two kinds of circuits, you may say that the parallel circuit is the best. If it is the best, why do we need the series circuit? There are some places where we must use series wiring. For example, switches must be in series.

You remember that a switch turns the electricity on or off. To make the electricity stop in all the lights, it must be put somewhere between the battery and the first light of a series circuit or where the wires divide in a parallel circuit. Then if the switch is off, no electricity can flow to either of the two lights.

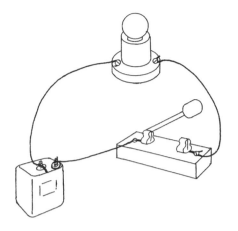

Switches are wired in series.

Wiring a switch in parallel is dangerous. If the switch was in parallel with the lights, all the current would go through the switch. The circuit would then have no appliance. This would be very dangerous since the wire would get hot and could start a fire!

Resistance—slowing electricity down. As we studied in

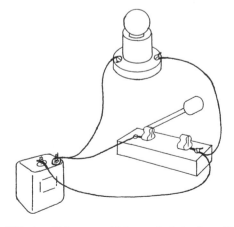

What will happen if the switch is closed?

Lesson 1, every electric circuit must have an appliance to use the electricity. An appliance slows the electricity down and keeps it from flowing too fast and making the wires hot. This is called resistance. *Resistance* is anything in an electric circuit that slows the electricity down. Appliances give resistance in a circuit. The wires of a circuit also give some resistance.

To understand resistance in a wire, let us think again of water in a garden hose. As the water flows through the hose, some of the water is slowed down by rubbing against the side of the hose. This is resistance. If we made the garden hose smaller, more of the water would touch the sides of the hose and the hose would have more resistance. If the hose were made larger, it would have less resistance and the water would move more easily. A wire is like the garden hose. A small, thin wire has a lot of resistance. A large, thick wire has little resistance.

The length of a wire also makes a difference on the amount of resistance. Just as a long garden hose has much resistance to the flow of water, the longer a wire, the more resistance it has to electricity. The shorter the wire, the less resistance. If only a small amount of electricity is needed, a long, thin wire will work. But if a strong motor that uses much electricity is being used, we need to use a thick wire and to make it as short as possible.

An understanding of circuits and resistance helps us use electricity in the best and safest way.

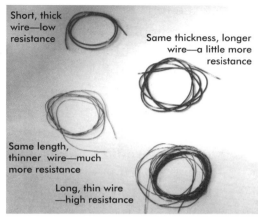

What makes each wire have more resistance than the one above it?

Test Your Reading (Group B)

Look at the switches in these drawings. Some of the switches are wired correctly, and some are wired incorrectly. Write either *correct* or *incorrect* for each drawing.

11.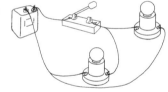

12.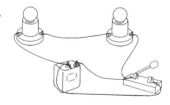

13.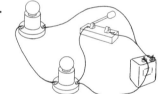

14.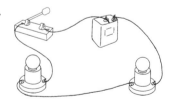

Answer *true* if the statement is true and *false* if the statement is not true.

15. A switch should be wired in series with the lights of a circuit.
16. A short wire has more resistance than a long wire.
17. A thin wire has more resistance than a thick wire.
18. If you want to send electricity for many miles, it would be best to use a thick wire.

Answer the following questions.

19. Why should a switch not be wired in parallel?
20. What two things make a wire have a high resistance?
21. Which would have more resistance—two light bulbs in series or two light bulbs in parallel? Hint: Two bulbs in series would be like hooking two garden hoses end to end. Two bulbs in parallel would be like using a Y connector and hooking two hoses to the same faucet.

A Y connector on a faucet

Reviewing What You Have Learned

1. Which one does not allow electricity to flow?
   a. appliance   b. conductor   c. insulator
2. A source of electricity, conductors, an appliance, and a switch are needed to make a ———.
3. True or false? Generators produce electricity.
4. Which one uses electricity?
   a. appliance   b. conductor   c. insulator
5. Which set has only materials that will conduct electricity?
   a. glass, copper   b. aluminum, tin   c. iron, rubber

Extra Activities

1. Use batteries and flashlight bulbs to make both series and parallel circuits. With your light bulb circuits, answer the following questions.
   a. What happens to the other bulb of the series circuit if one is taken out?
   b. What happens to the other bulb of the parallel circuit if one is taken out?
   c. Which lights are brighter—the ones in the series circuit or the ones in the parallel circuit?
   d. At what three places can you put a switch in the series circuit?

    e. At what two places can you put a switch in the parallel circuit?

Materials needed:
- 2 batteries
- 4 flashlight bulbs
- insulated bell wire

2. Draw a wiring diagram for the switch, four lights, and two outlets in a room. On a sheet of paper, copy the following drawing of a room with the parts of the circuit. Pretend that the lines on the left side are two wires coming from a source. Then use other lines (wires) to connect the parts so that the lights are in parallel and are all turned on and off by the switch. Then connect the outlets in parallel so that they are on all of the time. Ask your teacher to check your work.

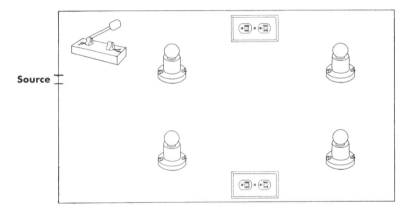

3. Take a tour with your teacher of your school building to see how it is supplied with electricity. Find out where the electricity enters the building. Where is the electric meter that measures how much electricity gets used? Where is the "panel box," where the different circuits are divided? Where are the circuit breakers? What part of the circuit are they? By counting the circuit breakers, you can find out how many circuits are in your school. Are there any three-way switches in your school? Three-way switches allow you to turn a light on or off at more than one place. Often there are three-way switches at the top and bottom of stairsteps.

Lesson 3

Electricity Is Useful

New Words

electromagnet (i·lek′·trō·mag′·nit), a magnet that is made by passing electricity through wire that is wrapped around an iron center.

fluorescent light (flu·res′·ənt), a tube that makes light when electricity travels through a gas.

heating element, a special wire that gives off heat when electricity travels through it.

incandescent light (in′·kən·des′·ənt), a bulb that makes light when electricity travels through a wire.

motor, a machine that uses electricity in electromagnets to make a center shaft turn and make power that can do work.

What would it be like to live without electricity? Just think. We would have no electric lights to turn on with a switch. We would have no freezers or refrigerators to keep our food cold. In the barn or shop, there would be no milk pumps, electric drills, or grinders. There would be no telephones. This is the way your great-grandparents lived.

Electricity is a wonder God created. It is a wonder because of how it works and because of the many useful things it can do.

Electricity can make light. In the first two lessons, we used a light bulb as an appliance in our examples to help explain how circuits work. How does a light bulb use electricity to make light? Do you remember resistance? In most appliances, we do not want wires to have much resistance because we do not want them to become hot. But in an electric light bulb, a wire with much resistance is used. When electricity travels through it, the electricity makes the wire very hot. The wire becomes so hot that it glows and gives off a yellow light. Such electric lights are called *incandescent lights.* Most of our

What makes the wire inside a light bulb give off light?

houses are lighted with incandescent light bulbs.

Another kind of electric light is the *fluorescent light,* which looks like a white, glass tube. Inside this tube is a special kind of gas. As electricity travels through the gas, the gas gives off special rays. These rays make the coating on the inside of the tube to glow white. Fluorescent tubes do not get as hot as incandescent bulbs. They give off more light and whiter light than incandescent bulbs. For these reasons, fluorescent lights are better for schools and big buildings. Perhaps your schoolroom is lighted with fluorescent lights.

Electricity can make heat. An electric stove and a heater use electricity to make heat. Electricity travels through a special wire called a *heating element.* The heating element becomes hot enough to cook food or to heat a room. To get more heat from a heating element, more electricity needs to travel through it. The different settings of the dial of your mother's kitchen stove allow different amounts of electricity to pass through the heating element. This makes different temperatures.

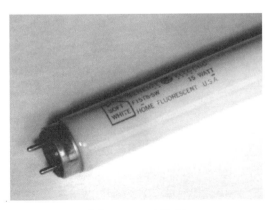

A fluorescent light

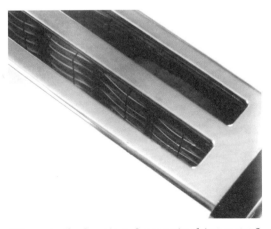

Where is the heating element in this toaster?

Test Your Reading (Group A)

On a piece of paper, write *incandescent, fluorescent,* or *heating element* for each of these descriptions.

1. Special rays from gases make a white light with little heat.
2. Its resistance makes a special wire get hot enough to give off light.
3. It is a good kind of light to use in a school or large building.
4. The resistance of a special wire makes heat to cook food.
5. It becomes very hot but does not give off light.
6. It produces much heat along with the light it makes.
7. It has a coating that makes its light white.
8. It is called a light bulb.
9. It can be found in an electric stove.

Electricity can make magnetism. To do so is simple. Take a piece of metal, such as a nail, for an iron center. Wrap 20 feet (6 meters) of thin, insulated wire around the nail. Put the wrapped wire in series with a battery and a switch. Turn the switch on, and you have an ***electromagnet.*** Pick up paper clips, pens, or thumbtacks. When you want to drop your load, turn off the switch; and paper clips or thumbtacks drop to the table.

This electromagnet is very small and will pick up only a few light things. Huge electromagnets, with bigger iron centers and more wraps of wire and more electricity, are used to move iron cargo from trucks to a ship, or to carry tons of scrap metal from one place to another in a scrapyard. All it takes is an electromagnet, electricity, and a closed switch. Such a machine can be very useful.

Electricity can make motion. Electromagnets are used in many machines. In an electric bell, an electromagnet pulls an arm against the metal gong to make a ding. Electric bells ring in our telephones. Your school may have electric bells to tell you when to start school or come in from recess. Electric

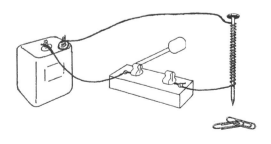

What will need to be done to make the electromagnet pick up the paper clips?

buzzers work like electric bells except that they do not have the metal bell to make the noise. All you hear is the arm moving rapidly back and forth, making a buzzing sound.

Another machine that uses electromagnets is an electric *motor.* When you look at a

What can all of these electrical appliances do?

running electric motor, all you see turning is the short shaft that comes out the end. But what makes it turn? The shaft inside the motor is covered with many electromagnets that turn with the shaft. Electric motors make power to run drills, vacuum cleaners, clocks, water pumps, and many other appliances that have parts that move.

How useful electricity is! It can make light and heat. When used in electromagnets, it can lift, pull, and turn things. By giving us electricity, God has given us a wonderful kind of energy. We can do many things with machines, which our grandparents needed to do by hand. We must use this good gift carefully and wisely.

———————— Test Your Reading (Group B) ————————

Choose the letter that would make a good ending.

10. The center of an electromagnet
11. Scrap metal can be moved
12. Electromagnets produce motion
13. The sound of a buzzer
14. Water pumps, drills, and clocks
15. The arm of an electric bell
16. More turns of wire
17. Useful electricity
18. The wire of an electromagnet

a. strikes a gong to make a noise.
b. make a stronger electromagnet.
c. is wound on an iron center.
d. is a gift from God.
f. is made by a moving arm.
g. is made of iron.
h. are run with electric motors.
i. in an electric motor.
e. with an electromagnet.

Answer the following questions.

19. Besides a source and a switch, what two things do you need to make an electromagnet?
20. How can the load carried by an electromagnet be dropped?
21. Is an electromagnet the source, conductor, appliance, or switch of an electric circuit?

Reviewing What You Have Learned

1. Electricity must have a complete ———— to flow.
2. Which wire will give the greatest resistance to electricity?
   a. a long, thin wire
   b. a short, thick wire
   c. a long, thick wire
3. True or false? Switches are wired in series.
4. In parallel wiring, the electricity
   a. flows through the appliances one after the other.
   b. flows back and forth between two appliances.
   c. divides and flows through the appliances side by side.
5. True or false? The conductor part of a circuit has no resistance to the flow of electricity.

Extra Activities

1. Do research into how a fluorescent light is made and works. What is the gas inside the tube? What is the white coating? What does this white coating do? Why must a special box called a ballast be used? What does the starter do?
2. Make an electromagnet. Number 26 insulated wire works well for this. Winding wire with thin insulation that can be bought at an electrical supply store or a motor winding shop is best. Wrap 10 feet (3 meters) of insulated wire around a heavy nail or small bolt. Connect it to a dry cell battery or toy transformer. Be sure to scrape off the insulation from the end of the wire when making a connection. Touch the other end of the wire against the source for only a little so the wire does not become too hot. Try to lift some paper clips with your electromagnet. Now add another 10 feet (3 meters) of wire to

your electromagnet (after connecting the ends together). Again test the electromagnet. Why is it stronger? Why does it not get as warm? Another 10 feet (3 meters) will make the electromagnet even better. Be sure the insulation is removed when you make a splice. Twist the wires tightly together. **WARNING: NEVER CONNECT WHAT YOU MAKE TO AN ELECTRICAL OUTLET.**

Materials needed:
- 30 feet (9 meters) of #26 insulated wire
- heavy nail or small bolt
- dry cell battery
- paper clips
- wire pliers

3. The father of someone in the class may have a worn-out electric drill that he will allow to be torn apart. Take out the screws, and remove the shields. Find the electromagnets. Find the switch. Find the brushes that send electricity into the turning part. Can you find why the electric drill will not work? **WARNING: DO NOT PLUG THE DRILL INTO AN ELECTRICAL OUTLET.**

Lesson 4

Using Electricity Safely

New Words

fuse (fyüz), a part of an electric circuit that melts when the electricity becomes too much.

receptacle (ri·sep′·tə·kəl), a thing with two or three holes into which a plug can be put to get electricity for an appliance.

shock, what you feel when electricity travels through your body.

short circuit, an electric circuit that has no appliance.

Electricity is a wonder given by God. It lets us do many things faster and better than we could if we did not have it. But just as it is with all other wonderful things God has made, we must be careful how we use it. We have already given some hints that electricity can be dangerous. In this lesson we shall learn how we can use it safely.

Appliances—using electricity safely. An appliance is necessary to use the electricity. In a circuit without an appliance, so much electricity will flow through the wire that it can become hot enough to start a fire. A circuit without an appliance is called a

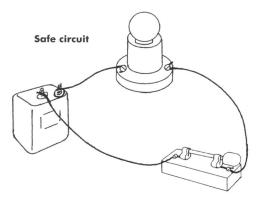
Safe circuit

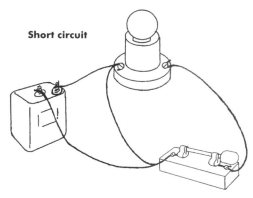
Short circuit

Electricity takes the path of least resistance. If a wire will complete the circuit, most of the electricity will go through the wire instead of the appliance.

short circuit. Short circuits are very dangerous. Not only can they start a fire, but they can melt the wire or ruin the source. Never make an electric circuit without some kind of appliance.

Receptacles—getting electricity safely. A *receptacle,* sometimes called an outlet, has two or three holes into which a plug can be put to get electricity. A receptacle is not needed to make a complete circuit, but it makes an easy and safe connection between a source and an appliance.

There are two safety rules for using a receptacle. First, never put anything into a receptacle except a plug that is made to fit it. It is dangerous to put wires without plugs, paper clips, toys, and fingers into a receptacle. Sometimes receptacles have special covers to keep small

children from putting something in them. Second, always remove a cord from a receptacle by pulling on the plug only. Never pull on the cord. Pulling on the cord can pull the wires loose inside the plug. If the wires touch each other, there will be a circuit without an appliance—a short circuit.

Cords—carrying electricity safely. Electric cords must also be used carefully. All electric cords have at least two wires inside. But they are kept separate with insulation. As long as the insulation keeps the two wires separated, the cord is safe. But if this insulation becomes broken or worn, the two wires can touch each other. Then the electricity will no longer travel all the way to the appliance and back again. Instead, it will jump across where the two wires touch,

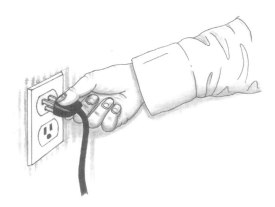

Always remove a cord from a receptacle by taking hold of the plug.

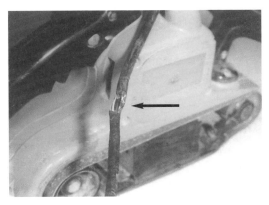

An unsafe cord in need of replacement or repair

and there will be a short circuit. The place in a circuit where the wires touch and cause a short circuit is sometimes called a short.

To keep the insulation on electric cords in good condition, do not run over them with vehicles and machinery. Keep them away from hot things, such as light bulbs, and from moving parts of machinery, such as belts. When not in use, extension cords should be coiled neatly and hung up. These rules will not only keep the cord safe to use, but also help you be a good steward of what you have.

Never touch the prongs of a plug or the bare wires in a cord when it is plugged in. Your body is a conductor. So is the ground. When electricity passes through your body and completes a circuit, you feel what we call a ***shock.*** A small amount of electricity may only make you jump and say "Ow," but a large amount could kill you. You may also be shocked if you touch only one bare wire and the ground itself or a conductor that leads to the ground, such as a metal water pipe or water in a sink. Never touch bare wires unless you know there is no electricity in them. If you do not know, do not touch them!

——————— **Test Your Reading (Group A)** ———————

In the following sentences, the underlined words make the statements false. Write the word or words that will make each statement true.

1. Electricity is a wonderful gift from God, but it must be used <u>carelessly</u>.
2. A short circuit does not have <u>a switch</u>.
3. A short circuit can start a <u>shock</u> when the wire becomes very hot.
4. Always take hold of the <u>cord</u> when removing it from a receptacle.
5. You should put a <u>wire</u> into a receptacle.
6. Inside a damaged plug or cord, the wires can come <u>apart</u> to cause a short circuit.
7. When two wires get together to cause a short circuit, it is sometimes called a <u>shock</u>.
8. Keep cords <u>against</u> moving belts and hot light bulbs.
9. Running over a cord or walking on it is <u>good</u> for it.
10. Since your body is <u>an insulator</u>, you can get shocked if you touch bare electric wires.

11. A shock may only make you jump, or it can <u>please</u> you.
12. You can be shocked if you touch one bare wire and a <u>plastic</u> water pipe.

Fuses—protecting an electric circuit. You learned earlier that a short circuit is dangerous because too much electricity flows through the wire. An appliance is necessary to use the electricity safely. As more appliances are added to the circuit, more electricity will flow through the wire. If too many appliances are on a circuit, however, the wire will get dangerously hot. Something is needed that will stop the electricity in these cases. A *fuse* is just what is needed in the circuit.

A simple kind of fuse is made of a special wire that will get hot and melt when too much electricity flows through the wire. When the fuse wire melts, it breaks the circuit

Fuses

Circuit breakers

Safety switches for electrical circuits

and stops the flow of electricity. This protects the rest of the wires in the circuit from becoming too hot. A circuit needs a fuse to make it safe. When a fuse burns out, fix the problem and replace the fuse.

Circuits in modern buildings often use special switches called circuit breakers to do the same thing as fuses. When they break a circuit, they can be reset like turning a switch on.

A third wire—carrying current away safely. It is possible to get shocked even if you do not touch a bare electric wire. Sometimes an appliance has a bad place in its wiring that lets some of the current stray out to the case. Then if a person touches the outside of the appliance and the ground itself or a material that conducts electricity to the ground, he completes the circuit and gets shocked.

Because of this danger, appliances often have a third prong on their plugs. The receptacle has a third place for that prong to go. This prong with its special wire connects the outside case of the appliance with the ground and the source.

Then if any electricity strays out to the case, it will go safely back to the source through the third wire instead of going through someone who touches the case.

Electricity is a wonderful gift from God. The way it works is marvelous. The many things it can do for us makes it very useful. As with any gift from God, we must use electricity wisely and safely. We must thank God for electricity.

What is the third prong for?

————————— Test Your Reading (Group B) —————————

Choose the best answer.

13. A fuse is really a special kind of
    a. source.
    b. appliance.
    c. switch.

14. Besides a short circuit, another way to have too much electricity flow is
    a. not having a source in the circuit.
    b. having too many appliances in a circuit.
    c. having the switch wired in series.

15. The purpose of a fuse is to stop the electricity
    a. before the wire gets too hot.
    b. before someone gets a bad shock.
    c. before the insulation on the wires becomes worn too badly.

16. The third prong on a plug
    a. allows the cord to carry more electricity.
    b. prevents a short circuit from happening.
    c. protects the one who uses the appliance from getting shocked.

Answer the following questions.

17. What needs to be done if a fuse burns out?

18. What do some circuits have instead of a fuse that has the same purpose as a fuse?
19. What three places does the third wire connect?
20. What are two reasons we should praise God for electricity?

Reviewing What You Have Learned

1. True or false? An appliance gives resistance to the flow of electricity.
2. Electromagnets are useful because they can
   a. heat things.
   b. light things.
   c. move things.
3. The ———— light bulb gives off much heat.
4. The wire in an electromagnet must be
   a. thin and shiny.
   b. insulated.
   c. high resistance.
5. If one light in a circuit with ———— wiring burns out, the other light will not go out.

Extra Activities

1. With your teacher's help, learn how to replace a worn-out plug on an extension cord or appliance cord. It will be best for you to learn using a light 2-wire cord and a 2-prong plug. Be sure the cord is not plugged into a receptacle. Cut the old plug off. Some replacement plugs are made to fasten on to the wire without removing the insulation. Follow the instructions carefully that come with the plug.

   If the plug has screw fasteners, follow these instructions: Remove the insulation from ¾″ of the end of each wire. Lay the end of the wire on a board, and cut away from yourself in removing the insulation. Twist the strands of wire tightly. Wrap the wire around each screw in the same direction each screw is tightened. Be sure the two wires (or any strands of the two wires) do not touch after they are tightened under the screws. Have your teacher inspect your work before you plug the cord into a receptacle. (Even professional electricians have inspectors check their work.)

Materials needed:
- light, 2-wire cord
- wire clippers
- knife
- board
- 2-prong plug
- screwdriver

2. **WARNING: THIS ACTIVITY SHOULD BE DONE ONLY WITH YOUR PARENT'S OR TEACHER'S SUPERVISION.** Use a neon light electrical tester to find which of the two slots of a receptacle is hot and which leads to the ground. Use a light extension cord that is long enough to go from a receptacle to some metal water pipes. Before plugging the extension cord into the receptacle, put one end of the tester into one of the slots of the extension cord. Hold the other end of the tester against a bare place on a metal water pipe. Have a friend plug in the extension cord. If the tester lights, you have the hot wire. If it does not light, you have the side of the circuit that is grounded. Go to the main electric box, or transformer, and try to find where it is grounded. The ground wire will disappear into the ground or be fastened to a rod driven into the ground.

A neon light electrical tester

Materials needed:
- neon light electrical tester
- extension cord

Lesson 5

Do You Remember?

Choose the correct letter from the list at the right to match with each phrase on the left.

1. A place in the wall to get electricity
2. Any material that stops electricity
3. Uses electricity
4. Turns the flow of electricity on or off
5. Makes light with a hot wire
6. Any material that will carry electricity
7. A white tube with a special gas
8. Protects a circuit

a. appliance
b. conductor
c. fluorescent light
d. fuse
e. heating element
f. incandescent light
g. insulator
h. receptacle
i. switch

From the word box, find and write a word for each blank.

battery	motor	series
circuit	parallel	shock
electromagnet	resistance	short circuit

9. When electricity can return to the source without being used by an appliance, it is a ———.
10. When electricity travels through you, you feel a ———.
11. Electricity must flow through each bulb one after the other when they are wired in ———.
12. Slowing electricity down in a wire or appliance is called ———.
13. A ——— is one kind of source of electricity.
14. An ——— can lift things when electricity is passed through a wire that is wrapped around an iron center.
15. Electricity must have a complete ———, or it will not flow.
16. With ——— wiring, each bulb will light even if one of the others is missing or is burned out.

Choose the best answer for each sentence.

17. Aluminum, copper, and tin are all good
    a. conductors.
    b. heating elements.
    c. insulators.

18. Heating elements are used to
    a. move parts in a machine.
    b. lift heavy objects.
    c. cook food.

19. A fuse
    a. is a source of electricity in a circuit.
    b. is a switch in a circuit.
    c. is an appliance in a circuit.

20. If we wanted to keep electricity from passing from one wire to another, we would separate them with
    a. an insulator.   b. a conductor.   c. an appliance.

21. A switch
    a. uses electricity in a circuit.
    b. turns the flow of electricity on and off.
    c. keeps the wires in a circuit from getting too hot.

22. All of the following are parts of a complete circuit **except**
    a. a source.
    b. the insulation.
    c. an appliance.

23. If we wanted to put lights in a school building, it would be best to use
    a. fluorescent lights.
    b. incandescent bulbs.
    c. heating elements.

24. Which of the following has the most resistance?
    a. a short, thin wire
    b. a long, thin wire
    c. a short, thick wire

25. All the following are true for series wiring except
    a. If one bulb is removed, all the others will go out.
    b. The electricity divides and then comes together again.
    c. Switches are wired in series.
26. When removing a cord from a receptacle, take hold of
    a. the plug.   b. the receptacle.   c. the cord.
27. Electricity must make a complete circuit
    a. without being used by an appliance.
    b. so the electrons will be able to flow.
    c. so that it must be used over again.
28. Which of the following would be the best insulator?
    a. water   b. aluminum   c. glass
29. Which of the following do **not** use electromagnets?
    a. buzzers
    b. heating elements
    c. motors

Write *true* if the sentence is true; write *false* if it is not true.
30. There can be a short circuit in an electric cord if the two wires touch each other.
31. Man, not God, should get the praise for modern electrical machines.
32. A heating element is useful because it uses electricity to make motion.
33. A third wire is a safe place for electricity to go that strays out of a circuit.
34. A battery and a generator are both appliances.
35. Plugs are the only thing that should be put in a receptacle.
36. Appliances use electricity to make light, heat, or motion.
37. If a circuit with bulbs is not complete, then only a few of the bulbs will light.
38. It will not hurt electric cords to run over them with cars or machinery.
39. If lights are wired in parallel, the switch must also be wired in parallel.

Write *parallel* if the drawing shows a parallel circuit. Write *series* if it is a series circuit.

40.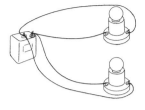

43.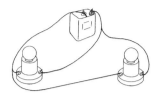

41.

44.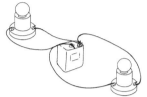

42.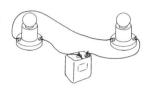

In which of the following circuits is the switch placed correctly? Write *right* if it is correct and *wrong* if it is not correct.

45.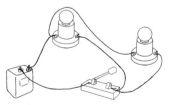

47.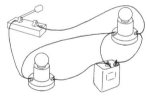

46.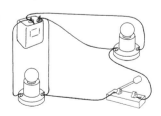

Answer the following question.

48–50. What are three safety rules to remember when we work with electricity?

Unit Seven

God Gave Us Plants

"And God said, Let the earth bring forth grass, the herb yielding seed, and the fruit tree yielding fruit after his kind, whose seed is in itself, upon the earth: and it was so" (Genesis 1:11).

What a wonderful thing is a seed! You can plant bean seeds or corn seeds or flower seeds in moist soil, and what happens? Soon tiny plants pop up and grow bigger and wider and taller. After a while you have great big plants just from tiny, little seeds. And these big plants make more tiny seeds to grow more plants.

Who would have ever thought of all this except God? Who could have ever done it except God? Just think of all the different colors and sizes and shapes of plants in the world. Think of the vegetables and mushrooms, the berries and fruit trees, the huge forest trees, the flowering and evergreen bushes, the spring bulbs, the grasses and mosses, and the waving fields of corn and wheat. God thought of each one and made it, or you would not see it today.

In this unit you will study groups of plants and how they are alike. You will learn names for the parts of plants. You will see that each part has an important work to do for the good of the whole plant. You will learn how a plant makes food. You will also see that there are other ways of raising new plants besides planting seeds.

God wisely created the plants for our good and His glory. Studying this unit should give us a greater reverence for God.

Lesson 1

Seed-Producing Plants

New Words

annual (an′·yü·əl), one of a group of plants that lives only one year.

biennial (bī·en′·ē·əl), one of a group of plants that lives two years.

conifer (kon′·ə·fər), a cone-bearing bush or tree that has needlelike leaves year around.

perennial (pə·ren′·ē·əl), one of a group of plants that lives more than two years.

We eat seeds from seed-producing plants. "And there came a messenger unto Job, and said, The oxen were plowing" (Job 1:14). Why do you think Job's oxen were plowing? Why do farmers today plow the soil?

Job, like farmers today, plowed the soil before planting seeds of grain. Both wheat and barley were grains grown in Job's time (Job 31:40). Wheat and barley were eaten by people and animals.

Today people all over the world still eat more grain than anything else. Grain does not spoil easily and is one of the cheapest foods. The most common kinds of grain are rice, wheat, and corn. You eat grain whenever you eat foods such as bread, breakfast cereal, noodles, and corn chips.

Grains are really seeds. But what is a seed? It is a tiny plant inside a tough coating. The coating protects the living plant inside. It can stay alive for months or even years. Once, some wheat seeds sprouted that were 30 years old!

Along with the tiny plant in the

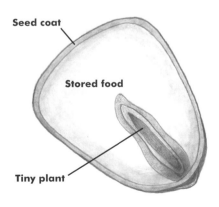

Corn seed

seed, there is some food for the plant to use when it sprouts. This stored food is what makes seeds so valuable for man and animals to eat.

Each year many new seeds sprout to produce new plants. The plants produce more seeds. The plants then die, but the seeds can be used to make new plants the next year. God planned it this way so that there are always plenty of plants on the earth. Plants are very important because every person and animal on earth gets its food from them. Even meat eaters, such as lions, depend on plants because they eat animals that eat plants.

Flowering plants are one group of seed-producing plants. Your family garden or flower beds are full of flowering plants. Most kinds of grass and many bushes and trees are flowering plants. Even thistles and prickly beggar ticks are flowering plants. Just because we might not call their flowers pretty does not mean they are not flowers.

Flowering plants can be put into two groups. The one group produces one-part seeds that have only one seed leaf. This group includes plants such as lilies, tulips, cattails,

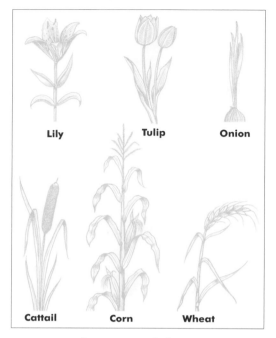

One-part-seed plants

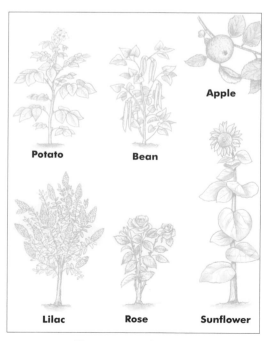

Two-part-seed plants

onions, and all grasses. Corn, wheat, and other grains are kinds of grasses, so of course, they are one-part-seed plants. The leaves of one-part-seed plants are narrow and bladelike. We talk about a blade of grass.

The other group of flowering plants has two-part seeds. You may have noticed when you shelled beans that the seeds can split in half. These two halves are the first leaves that come above the ground when the seeds sprout. Most vegetables and flowers that you plant have two-part seeds. Lilacs, roses, flowering bushes, and many trees belong to this group. Two-part-seed plants usually have broad, flat leaves.

───────── Test Your Reading (Group A) ─────────

Complete the following chart to tell if the plants have one- or two-part seeds and if their leaves are blade or broad.

Plant	Seeds	Leaves
	one-part / two-part	*blade / broad*
1. wheat	a. ───	b. ───
2. lilac	a. ───	b. ───
3. bean	a. ───	b. ───
4. corn	a. ───	b. ───

Answer the following questions.
5. What is most of the grain used for that is raised by farmers?
6. Every year many plants die. How did God plan that there would be more plants the next year?
7. What three things make up a seed?

The conifers are another group of seed-producing plants. *Conifers* make their seeds in cones instead of flowers. Pine, cedar, fir, and redwood trees are conifers. So are many kinds of shrubs planted in lawns and around buildings. These plants are also called evergreens because they stay green all year long.

It is not hard to tell conifers apart from flowering plants. Conifers have needlelike leaves, but flowering plants have blade or broad leaves. Another difference is the place where seeds are made. Conifers produce seeds in between the scales of their cones.

Leaves and cones of a spruce tree

But flowering plants produce seeds inside fruits. These fruits grow after the flowers die.

How long do seed-producing plants live? Some plants live only one year. They are called *annuals.* Many vegetable plants, such as peas, radishes, and sweet corn, are annuals. They grow, flower, produce seeds, and die all in one season.

Flowers such as marigolds, zinnias, and geraniums are also annuals. These bright flowers are favorites for flower beds.

Other plants, called *biennials,* live for two years. Some garden plants, such as beets and carrots, are biennials. The first year they store up food in their roots. The next year they use up the food while producing flowers and seeds. Of course, a gardener does not want a carrot's flowers or seeds. He wants the fat roots, so he digs up the roots the first year. Some other biennials in the garden are parsley and turnip plants.

The plants that live for more than two years are called *perennials.* Can you think of some perennial plants? Trees and bushes are perennials. Flowers such as

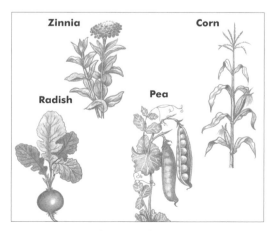

Annual plants

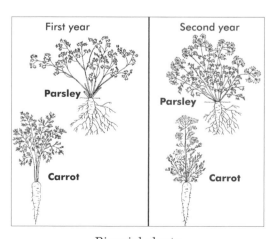

Biennial plants

lilies, tulips, and daffodils, which come up year after year, are also perennials. Raspberries and strawberries are perennial garden plants.

God has given us many different kinds of seed plants on the earth. Some have flowers, and others have cones. Some have blade leaves, some have broad leaves, and others have needle leaves. Some have one-part seeds, and some have two-part seeds. Some live one year, some live two years, and others live many years.

With so many kinds of plants, we are sure to find one for whatever we need. Many plants like corn and beans are good for food. Some large grasses make good weaving material. Both broadleaf trees and conifers are used to make lumber and paper. Of course, we plant some plants just to enjoy their pretty flowers and leaves. Plants are indeed a wonderful gift from God!

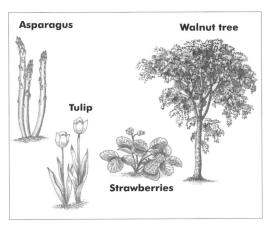

Asparagus
Walnut tree
Tulip
Strawberries

Perennial plants

Test Your Reading (Group B)

Tell whether the following plants are *annual, biennial,* or *perennial.*

8. carrots
9. strawberries
10. turnips
11. peas
12. maple trees
13. marigolds

Tell whether the following are *conifers* or *flowering plants.*

14. pine trees
15. maple trees
16. oak trees
17. fir trees

Write the missing words.

18. Conifers produce their seeds between scales in ——.
19. The conifers are ——, since they do not lose their leaves during the winter.
20. The leaves of conifers are shaped like ——.
21. A plant that produces a store of food in the roots one year and flowers and seeds the next year is called a ——.
22. Every year the farmer must sow seeds to get crops of corn, wheat, or soybeans because they are —— plants.
23. A —— plant like the apple tree will stay alive for 20 or more years.
24. God created many different kinds of —— from which we get food, paper, lumber, and beauty.

Extra Activities

1. Study both one-part and two-part seeds. Maybe your parents have leftover corn, bean, and pea seeds from last year. It will make it easier to take the seeds apart if they are soaked overnight. Can you find the tiny seed plant in each? Can you see the two parts of the two-part seeds? Put some seeds between wet cloths in a warm place for several days. Study the sprouts.

   Materials needed:
   - corn, bean, and pea seeds
   - 2 cloths

2. If you live near a woods with conifer trees, you could ask for permission to hunt for cones there. You might also get a small twig with needles along with each cone.

   Then make a display for your classroom. Place the cones and twigs on a shelf or table, and label each pair neatly. You may need a tree guide or an encyclopedia to help you.

3. Ask your mother if you may look at food labels in her cupboards or refrigerator. Try to find out which kinds of plants were used to make the foods. Make a list of one-part-seed plants and two-part-seed plants that you find. Which list is longer? You may need a dictionary to understand some words.

Lesson 2

Roots and Stems

New Words

absorb, to take in and make a part of itself.

bud, a small swelling at the tip of a stem that becomes a new stem, leaf, or flower.

cell, one of many tiny parts that make up each living thing.

root hair, one of many hairlike growths from the root of a plant.

sap, the liquid of water and minerals that flows through the stems of plants.

stem, the part of a plant from which flowers and leaves grow.

"His roots shall be dried up beneath, and above shall his branch be cut off" (Job 18:16). Does this make you think of a strong, healthy plant? Of course not. A plant without roots or branches will quickly die.

Plants are made of cells. Roots and stems are made of many tiny *cells.* In fact, anything alive is made of many cells. Your body is made of billions of cells, each too tiny to see without a microscope.

The size of a plant or animal depends on the number of cells it has. For example, the cells in a tall pine tree are hardly larger than those in a fern, but the pine tree has billions more of them.

Most of the cells in a plant have a boxlike shape. Although they may look alike, they do not all have the same job to do. Some of them store food, while others are lined up like a pipe to pass the food throughout the plant. All cells can grow and split to make new cells, but some

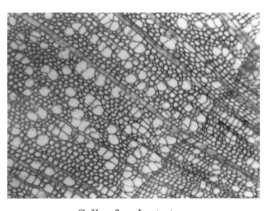

Cells of a plant stem

are able to multiply themselves much faster than the others.

For example, think of the roots of a maple tree. At the tip of each root are the cells that multiply quickly. They make the roots grow, pushing deeper and deeper into the soil.

Roots are important to plants. Roots always grow downward just as deep as they need to be to get enough water. A maple tree on a hill will usually have deeper roots than one beside a stream.

These roots fasten the plant firmly to the ground. You know how tightly roots can cling if you have ever pulled weeds in a garden. Those roots can make you work hard!

The root parts just behind the fast-growing tips are covered with many fine *root hairs.* One maple tree has billions of them. If the root hairs of one tree were all lined up end to end, the line would be

Root hairs on radish seedlings

hundreds of miles long.

Each root hair is like a tiny mouth that drinks, or *absorbs,* water and minerals from the soil. They all keep taking in water and minerals, which become the liquid *sap* inside the maple tree.

The sap travels from the root hairs to the larger part of the roots. Next, the sap reaches the main stem, which is the tree trunk. The trunk sends the sap on up to the smaller branches. Every branch and leaf receives sap.

——————— Test Your Reading (Group A) ———————

Choose the best ending for each sentence, and write the letter on your paper.

1. All living things are made of tiny
   a. buds.
   b. cells.
   c. minerals.

2. The plant part that grows downward and toward water is
   a. the stem.
   b. the bud.
   c. the root.
3. The cells of a root grow and split to make new cells fastest
   a. at the tip of the root.
   b. in the middle of the root.
   c. on the outside of the root.
4. A root hair absorbs water and minerals. This means that it
   a. takes them inside the plant.
   b. stores them for later use.
   c. sends them through the stem.
5. A plant without roots will quickly die because
   a. there is nothing to hold up the stem.
   b. the plant cannot get water or minerals.
   c. the sap will run out of the bottom of the stem.
6. Besides the work of absorbing, roots also help the plant by
   a. fastening it to the soil.
   b. making food for the plant.
   c. giving an upward push to the stems.

A stem is very important to a plant. You have just read how a *stem* or trunk helps to spread sap throughout a maple tree. All stems help to spread sap. They also spread the food a plant makes. God made this whole system work perfectly so that the whole plant gets all the food, water, and minerals it needs.

Stems also support the flowers of a plant and hold the leaves into the sunlight. The woody stems of

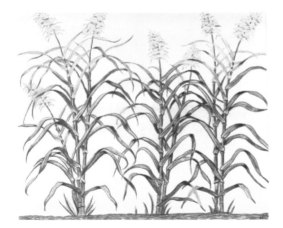

Sugar cane stalks can be up to 25 feet tall. The stems are a major source of sugar.

trees are very strong so that giant trees can stand stormy weather.

Some stems also provide storage space for food. The stems of sugar cane contain much sugar and are a major source of the sugar we buy in stores. Potatoes also store food in their stems. These potato stems that we eat grow underground.

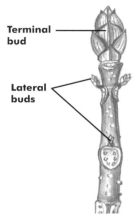

The bud on the end of a stem is called a terminal bud. *Terminal* means "end." The buds on the side of a stem are called lateral buds. *Lateral* means "side."

The underground stems of the potato plant are a good source of food.

Where a plant grows. You have already read how the cells at the tip of a root multiply quickly to make the root grow. The cells at the tip of a stem also multiply quickly to make the plant grow. The tip of a stem is called the *bud.* Some buds grow out the side of the stem to become stems, leaves, or flowers.

Many plants grow mainly at two places: at the root tips and at the buds. The plant grows taller or longer because of the cells multiplying in these two places. But some plants have fast-growing cells at a third place, around the stem. A tree trunk, for example, grows wider because of a special layer of fast-growing cells beneath the bark. As these cells grow, they make the rings inside the trunk that tell you how old a tree is. The tree makes a new ring every year. If you count the rings on a freshly-cut tree stump, you can tell how old it is.

Only God can make a plant. Since you have now finished reading this lesson, do you understand all about plants? Could you explain how the cells grow? Do you know how the sap rises? No, of course you cannot understand it all.

Not even Job could understand how God did it all. He did not know what to say when God asked, "Who hath divided a watercourse . . . to cause it to rain on the earth . . . and to cause the bud of the tender herb to spring forth?" (Job 38:25–27). But Job understood enough to humble himself before God. We should also learn enough to make us more amazed at our wonderful, wise Creator.

—————— Test Your Reading (Group B) ——————

Answer *true* if the statement is true. Answer *false* if the statement is false.

7. Stems make sap for the plant.
8. The leaves are held in the sunlight by the stems.
9. Some plants store food in stems that are underground.
10. When you eat a potato, you are eating one of the roots of a plant.
11. The cells of a bud grow fast like the cells of a root tip.
12. From a bud may come a new root.

Answer the following questions.

13. What part of the plant are you eating when you eat a potato?
14. What is the reason for the rings on a tree stump?
15. How can you tell how old a tree is when it is cut down?

Reviewing What You Have Learned

1. ———— have needles and cones.
2. An annual plant lives
   a. one year.   b. two years.   c. many years.
3. True or false? Two-part-seed plants have broad leaves.
4. A corn seed is an example of a
   a. one-part-seed plant.
   b. two-part-seed plant.
   c. many-part-seed plant.
5. True or false? A seed is a tiny plant with some stored food inside a tough coating.

Extra Activities

1. You can see the work of a stem. Get some red or blue liquid food coloring and a stalk of celery with a few leaves on it. Celery that is

nearly white works best. Daffodils will also work. You will also need a small jar or cup of water.

First, put a few drops of the food coloring into the water. Then trim off the bottom of the celery stalk. Stand it on end in the colored water. Set the jar on a sunny windowsill for a few hours.

Now look at the celery stalk. Do you see any change? What does it show you about the work of a stem?

Materials needed:
- red or blue liquid food coloring
- stalk of celery with leaves
- small jar
- knife

2. Does a plant take in water through its leaves or its roots? You can see for yourself by doing this experiment. You need some aluminum foil and two plants that are nearly alike. (It could be two small seedlings recently sprouted.)

Carefully fit the aluminum foil around the bottom of one plant. Arrange it so that no water can get to the soil. Sprinkle some water over the leaves of this plant every day. (Do this outdoors or over a sink to avoid a mess.) Water the other plant as usual, being careful not to wet the leaves.

After a few days, compare the two plants. Which one is getting the water it needs? Do these plants receive water through their roots or their leaves?

Materials needed:
- aluminum foil
- two potted plants

3. Go to a woods where tree stumps can be found. Look for one that was cut recently. Count the rings to find out how old the tree was. Someone may be able to bring a piece of a freshly cut log to school. Put needles with little flags in the ring of the year most of you were born, the year the school was built, and the years of other historical events. The rings of a tree can tell you about the weather in past years. A thin ring tells that the weather was dry. Read more about what the rings tell in an encyclopedia.

Lesson 3

Leaves Make Food

New Words

chlorophyll (klôr′·ə·fil), the green material that makes food in a plant cell.

transpiration (tran′·spə·rā′·shən), giving off water into the air from a leaf.

vein (vān), branching or parallel lines seen on a leaf.

Can you make your own food? What if you were to wake up one morning, feeling very hungry. "I want some breakfast," you tell your mother.

"Here is water," she answers, "and you have lots of air. Now use the water and air to make your own breakfast."

Could you make food from air and water? Of course not. But green plants do it again and again. They make food for themselves, for us, and for the animals.

You know why we need food. But why do plants need it? Plants need food for many of the same reasons we do. They need food in order to stay alive, to grow, and to do their work.

How does a plant make its own food? Plants are able to use

air and water to make food. They also need two more things: **chlorophyll** and light. The plant has green chlorophyll inside its cells. That is what makes plants look green.

Chlorophyll gets its power from light. For most plants, the light is sunlight. But electric lights can be used for indoor plants.

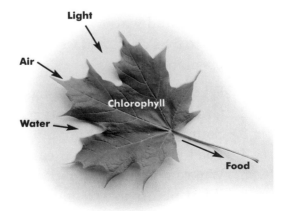

A green leaf is a food factory for itself, animals, and man.

Each leaf is like a busy factory with millions of chlorophyll workers. The food factories get busy each morning when the sun comes up. As soon as sunshine strikes the leaves, the chlorophyll starts catching it and making food. The brighter the sunshine, the faster the food is made. In the evening as the sunlight fades, food making is slower and slower. Finally, the leafy factories shut down for the night.

In places where the climate is warm the year around, the plants make food the year around. But in places with cold seasons, food making stops during the winter.

Where does a plant store its food? While the leaves of a plant are making food, the plant is using some of it and storing the rest away. The food can be stored in almost any part of a plant. For example, potato plants store food in their underground stems. Carrot and beet plants store food in their roots. Cauliflower and broccoli plants store food in their flowers. Corn and wheat plants store food in their seeds. Tomato plants, berry plants, and fruit trees all store food in their fruits.

So whatever you eat, you are eating the stored food of a plant. The apple you eat is made by the work of about 50 busy apple leaves. One peach is made by about 30 peach leaves, and a bunch of bananas is made by about 12 banana leaves.

———————— Test Your Reading (Group A) ————————

Match each letter to the correct number.

     a. air and water   d. light   f. at night
     b. to live, grow, and work   e. chlorophyll   g. sun
     c. plants

1. Why living things need food
2. Green food-making material in leaves
3. Source of food-making light
4. Food making in plants cannot happen
5. Where man and animals get their food
6. What plants use to make food
7. The power used by plants to make food

Match the plant with where it stores its food.

8. carrot   a. underground stems

9. corn   b. roots

10. tomato   c. flowers

11. potato   d. seeds

12. cauliflower   e. fruit

What happens to the water in plants? Whenever leaves are busy making food, some water is used to make the food, but some is given off into the air. This is called *transpiration.* On a warm day, the leaves of a birch tree may give off over 70 gallons (265 liters) of water through transpiration. Some people believe that transpiration keeps a plant from overheating in bright sunlight, much like sweating keeps you from getting too hot.

Transpiration takes place mostly on the underside of a leaf. The water comes out of holes that are much too tiny for you to see without a microscope. A single leaf has many thousands of them.

At night, guard cells close the holes. But during the day, while the "food factory" is busy, the guard cells keep the holes open. They let the right amount of water pass out of each opening. They also let air come inside the leaf. In this way the guard cells control the transpiration of each leaf and of the whole plant.

The plant must not lose too much water, or it will wilt. Every cell needs water to keep the right amount of pressure. The water pressure keeps the stems and leaves stiff.

You have often seen plants without enough pressure in their cells. Whenever you pick flowers, you know that they will wilt. The cells lose water from transpiration, and they are not getting more water from the roots. Then the flowers and

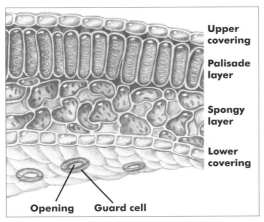

The guard cells control the air and water that enter and leave the leaf. Look at the photograph at the top of page 155. Can you find the four layers of leaf cells?

What is wrong with these petunia plants? What could be done to help them?

leaves soon hang down because they lose pressure inside their cells. If you put the stems in water, the cells keep some of their pressure. Then the flowers will not wilt quite as fast.

How can leaves help us know the kinds of plants? Sap flows through a leaf in its *veins.* You can see the veins easily on the underside of a large leaf. They look like patterns of lines on the leaf.

You can tell whether a plant has a one-part seed or a two-part seed just by looking at the veins on its leaves. If the leaf has one main vein in the center joined to smaller and smaller veins branching in all directions, that plant has a two-part seed. But if the veins all run side by side in one direction, that plant has a one-part seed. We say the veins of a one-part-seed plant are parallel because they run side by side. The veins of a two-part-seed plant are branching.

God made leaves with many interesting shapes. Many are shaped like feathers, but some are shaped like hearts, arrows, or flower petals. Oak and maple leaves look like fancy cutouts.

God also arranged leaves on

Leaves of two-part-seed plants have branching veins.

Leaves of one-part-seed plants have parallel veins.

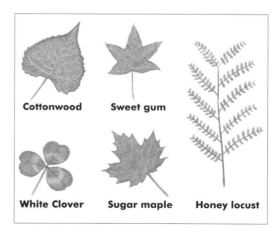

Cottonwood   Sweet gum

White Clover   Sugar maple   Honey locust

God made leaves with a variety of interesting shapes.

their stems in different ways. A maple or an oak leaf has only one large blade, but a hickory leaf is made of a number of small blades, or leaflets. On the hickory leaf, the leaflets are fastened to the stem across from each other. But the leaflets of a willow leaf are fastened at different places on the stem.

These are only a few examples of the many interesting ways in which God designed leaves. If you notice such things carefully, you can soon tell trees and many other plants apart by their leaves. You can walk through a woods and say, "This is a birch tree" or "This is a jack-in-the-pulpit." Plants will become like friends to you.

The jack-in-the-pulpit has two sets of three leaves.

———— Test Your Reading (Group B) ————

Finish each sentence with the correct ending.

13. During transpiration, a plant ———.
14. Guard cells decrease the transpiration of a plant by ———.
15. A plant needs enough water inside each cell to keep up good ———.
16. After you pick a flower, it will wilt because ———.
17. The lines on a leaf are called ———.
18. A one-part-seed plant has parallel veins, but a two-part-seed plant has veins that are ———.
19. Learning leaf shapes and the ways leaves are arranged on the stems helps you to ———.

Reviewing What You Have Learned

1. Flowering plants with one-part seeds have
   a. broad leaves.   b. bladelike leaves.   c. needlelike leaves.

2. All living things are made of ———.
3. Root hairs
   a. support and anchor a plant.
   b. carry water, minerals, and food.
   c. absorb water and minerals.
4. A ——— becomes a new stem or flower.
5. True or false? The stem of a plant can carry sap and store food.

Extra Activities

1. Make a leaf collection. You could use only tree leaves from a woods, or leaves from the plants in your yard and garden. It may be helpful to carry along a notebook, pencil, and tape as you gather the leaves. If there are several similar leaves, write the name of the plant, and tape the leaf right beside it to avoid getting mixed up. If you cannot name many of the plants, you could ask your parents to help you, or else get a book on tree or wildflower identification from a library.

   Make a poster with each leaf neatly labeled. If you have identified several different kinds of oak or pine trees, group them together on your poster.

2. Gather some leaves, and make a leaf memory game. For a quick one, cut out 20 cards large enough to hold the largest leaf you have gathered. On 10 of them, tape 10 different kinds of tree leaves. On the other 10 cards, write the names of the trees.

   Play this game just like the Memory game. Take turns picking up two cards at a time, trying to match each leaf with its name. The one who matches the most sets is the winner.

3. You can see how important sunlight is to a plant. Go outside and look for a large stone, board, or other object on top of the grass. Lift it and look at the grass underneath. Compare this grass with the other grass nearby.

Lesson 4

Flowers, Fruits, and Seeds

New Words

petal (pet′·əl), one of a set of colored parts inside the sepals of a flower.

pistil (pis′·təl), the part of a flower that makes plant eggs and seeds.

pollen (pol′·ən), fine powder from the stamen of a flower.

reproduce (rē′·prə·düs′), to produce offspring like itself.

sepal (sē′·pəl), one of a set of green, leaflike parts that cover a flower bud.

stamen (stā′·mən), the part of a flower that makes the pollen.

Will you help to tend a garden this summer? If so, perhaps you could pick a bunch of sweet corn flowers. Or how about picking some tomato flowers for your mother? Would she like that? No, your mother hardly wants you to pick these flowers, for then they cannot do their work.

What kind of work can a flower do? A tomato blossom helps to make a tomato with tomato seeds inside. Not every flower can produce a vegetable, but each kind makes seeds that can grow into new plants. In other words, flowers make seeds to *reproduce* again and again.

This work of making seeds is very important indeed. If plants were to stop making seeds for just one season, most living things and people would starve to death. Seeds are made in flowers. Flowers have four special parts: the **sepals, petals, stamens,** and **pistils.** Look at the drawing of a flower, and find each of these parts.

Before a rosebud opens, all you

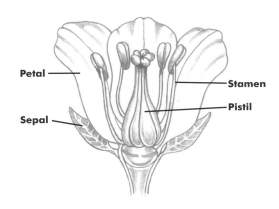

Parts of a flower

can see is its **sepals.** They protect the tender flower parts until the bud is ready to open. Then the sepals spread apart. Sepals usually look like little green leaves.

Inside the sepals is a circle of **petals.** God made petals in all kinds of bright colors that we enjoy. One-part-seed plants, such as irises, have petals and sepals in multiples of three (3, 6, 9, etc.). Two-part-seed plants, such as petunias, have petals in multiples of four or five.

Inside the circle of petals are the **stamens.** They usually look like stiff strings with little balls on top. The job of a stamen is to make many tiny grains of **pollen.** The pollen is made and stored in the little balls on top of the stringlike stamens.

A **pistil** is found at the very center of the flower. It looks like a tiny tube. The job of a pistil is to make little plant eggs at the bottom of the tube. It takes both the pollen and a plant egg to make a seed.

─────────── **Test Your Reading (Group A)** ───────────

Choose the best ending for each sentence.

1. Seeds allow flowering plants
2. Seeds are made
3. A flower needs sepals
4. A one-part-seed plant
5. A two-part-seed plant
6. The work of a stamen is
7. The work of a pistil is

a. may have 5 petals.
b. to make plant eggs.
c. to produce pollen.
d. may have 6 petals.
e. by eggs and pollen.
f. to reproduce again and again.
g. to protect the tender bud.

What are the numbered parts of this flower?

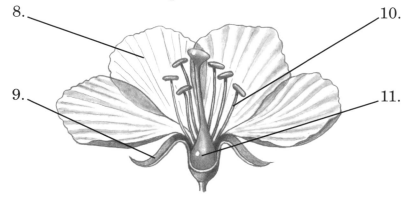

8.
9.
10.
11.

How does pollen get to the pistil? Each kind of flower needs its own kind of pollen in order to make seeds. So how does the right kind of pollen get to each pistil? God planned several ways for this to happen. In some plants, the pollen from the stamens falls onto the pistil of that same flower. This may happen whenever the wind shakes the plant a little. This is what happens to cause the pollen of corn to fall from the tassel (the stamens) onto the silk (the pistils) of the ear. In other flowers, the stamens and pistils never ripen at the same time. So the wind carries the pollen between the flowers. Trees, shrubs, and grasses have large, feathery tips to catch the fine pollen blowing around.

The pollen of tulips, roses, lilacs, and other pretty flowers is carried by insects. Some of these flowers also make sweet-smelling nectar when their pollen is ripe. Their sweet smells and bright colors make it easy for the insects to find them. Bees, for example, like to drink the nectar from the flowers and eat the rich pollen. As a bee goes in and out of a flower, the pollen sticks to its fuzzy body. Some pollen from one flower is sure to brush off on the next one. In this way, much pollen is spread around from flower to flower.

The bees do not know that they are spreading pollen. And the flowers do not know that they are feeding the bees. But God knows. He made it all work together in His wonderful plan.

After the pollen gets to a pistil,

The stamen (tassel) and pistil (silk) are at different places on a corn plant.

What is the bee doing for itself? What is the bee doing for the plant? Who designed that they help each other?

it unites with the plant eggs. Each egg starts growing into a seed. Meanwhile, the flower petals dry up and fall off. Their work is done. All that is left is the very center part of the flower. This center will grow into fruit that holds the seeds. The fruit and the seeds grow together. We eat the fruit of some plants, like the peach and pumpkin. We eat the seeds of other plants, like the beans and corn.

How are wild seeds scattered? You help to plant seeds in the garden. But how do all the wild seeds in the woods and meadows get planted? God has planned several ways for seeds to be scattered and planted in the wild.

The wind scatters many lightweight seeds. Dandelion and milkweed seeds, for example, are so light and fluffy that a little wind sends them sailing off. Maple and pine tree seeds have little wings to help them fly away with the wind.

Some seeds float on water. They fall into streams or rivers that carry them to new homes.

Some seeds travel with people or animals. They have tiny hooks or barbs to grab at anything that passes by. No doubt you yourself have helped to spread such seeds when you have taken a walk

How will the plant be helped if these seeds are pulled off and thrown away?

through a woods. You see those prickly burs and beggar ticks as just a bother and pick them off your clothes and drop them on the ground, but you are really helping to fulfill God's design for them to be scattered and planted.

How does a seed grow into a plant? In Lesson 1, you learned that a seed is a tiny plant inside a tough outer coating. Besides this, a seed always holds a small supply of food for the baby plant.

When a seed falls into the ground, it soaks up water. The seed swells until the outer coat splits apart. Inside, a tiny stem and root start growing and using the stored food inside the seed. The food supply lasts long enough for the plant to grow its first leaves. Then the leaves start their normal job of making food in sunlight for the plant.

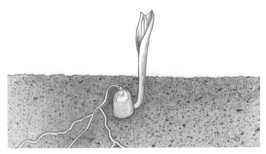

How does a corn seed know when to grow?

The new plant keeps on growing and making food. After a while, it makes flowers, fruit, and new seeds. In this way, all the flowering plants reproduce themselves year after year just as God in His great wisdom planned for them.

———————— Test Your Reading (Group B) ————————

Choose the best answer.

12. The pollen from the corn tassel gets to the silk of the ear when
    a. insects carry the pollen on their fuzzy bodies.
    b. drops of rain carry the pollen down.
    c. the wind shakes the tassel and the pollen falls down.

13. The main purpose of the petals and sweet nectar is to
    a. attract insects.
    b. encourage people to plant the flowers in their gardens.
    c. please us with beautiful sights and smells.

14. When you throw down a prickly bur, you are
    a. helping to carry pollen from the stamen to the pistil.
    b. keeping a plant from reproducing.
    c. helping a plant to spread.

15. Besides a tiny new plant, a seed contains
    a. a poison to keep animals from eating it.
    b. food for the new plant.
    c. something to keep the seed from rotting.

Answer the following questions.

16. Why do farmers with orchards like to see plenty of bees flying in the spring?

17. Why do the flowers and the bees help each other if they do not know that they are being helpful?

18. What two non-living things help to scatter seeds?

19. Why do the seeds not grow until they are put into the ground?

Reviewing What You Have Learned

1. True or false? Roots grow away from water.
2. Sap and food flow through a plant's
   a. guard cells.   b. buds.   c. veins.
3. ———— gives a plant its pressure so it can stand up.
4. During transpiration, a plant
   a. takes in water from the air.
   b. gives off water into the air.
   c. holds the water it gets from the air.
5. Chlorophyll needs ———— before it can make food from air and water.

Extra Activities

1. The next time you see an apple, look at the core end opposite the stem. There you see the dried-up remains of the pistil and stamens.
2. Make a seed collection. You could collect some seeds we eat, such as rice and dried beans. You could collect some seeds we throw away, such as watermelon and apple seeds or peach and cherry pits. You could also collect seeds from nearby trees and wild seeds, such as milkweed, cocklebur, and beggar tick seeds.

   Write the name of each seed on a slip of paper. Fasten each seed with its paper on posterboard or a bulletin board. You may need to ask your teacher or parents to help you.
3. Add pressed flowers to make your leaf collection (page 220) even more attractive. Or make pretty greeting cards from pressed flowers.

   You will need to find some pretty flowers that are not too thick. Tulips, petunias, and roses are not suitable for pressing. But violets, impatiens, and buttercups are fine choices.

   Spread the flowers out inside an old telephone book or newspaper. Put it in a dry place out of the way, and lay heavy books on top. Wait for a week or two. Then ask your teacher to help you make the card.

Lesson 5

Plants Can Multiply

New Words

bulb, a rounded, underground bud that grows into a plant such as a tulip or onion plant.

grafting, causing part of one plant to grow on another plant.

pruning, trimming buds or branches from vines or trees to get better fruit.

rooting, to cause to develop roots by placing the end of a stem in water or wet soil.

tuber (tü′·bər), a potato or other vegetable that is part of a thick underground stem.

Have you ever planted rose or tulip seeds? Or did you try apple, potato, or strawberry seeds? If you have ever raised plants from these seeds, you must be an unusual gardener. These seeds take longer to produce flowers or fruit than bean, corn, and marigold seeds do. In fact, if you were to plant some kinds of tulip seeds, you might have to wait seven years to see the first tulips!

Most gardeners can easily raise annual plants, such as peas, lettuce, and zinnias, from seeds. Some perennial flowers are not too hard to raise from seeds, either. But the best and fastest way to raise most perennial plants is by planting buds, stems, or other plant parts.

Some plants can multiply from bulbs. You raise tulips by planting tulip bulbs. A *bulb* is a rounded, underground bud. Inside is a tiny plant with plenty of stored food. On one end of the bud is a fast-growing tip. Here the plant cells multiply themselves quickly if

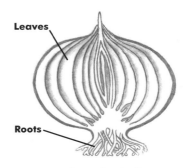

An onion bulb

the bulb is in warm, moist soil. Next, leaves and stems pop out from the tip of the bulb, and soon you see a tall tulip plant. Growing a tulip from a seed is much slower.

Onions are also grown from bulbs. The layers of the onion bulb are actually the lower ends of leaves.

Some plants can multiply from cuttings. What does your mother do when she wants a new houseplant or rosebush? She cuts off the top part of a few healthy stems. Then she puts the ends that were cut into a jar of water. For a rosebush or shrub, she might put the stems in wet soil. Then she tends the little cuttings for a few weeks, making sure they have enough water. Some of them may wither and die, but a few will likely grow their own roots. At last she is ready to plant her new plants into the soil where she wants them. She

got some whole new plants by ***rooting*** some cuttings. Rooting is one way of multiplying plants without planting seeds.

Some plants multiply from underground stems. Many plants will multiply themselves without your help. They have underground stems and roots that keep spreading and sending up new shoots. Ferns, irises, and blueberries are only a few of the many plants that multiply in this way.

You have likely seen grass plants that spread and multiply. When you see newly planted grass, it looks thin and uneven. You can see many patches of brown soil. But soon the spreading stems make the grass thicker and thicker. It becomes a lush, green carpet that hides all the soil.

Some plants have special underground stems called tubers. A ***tuber*** is a thick underground

Willow trees can be easily multiplied by rooting.

Irises spread by stems that grow underground.

stem that stores food. It also grows buds that can start new plants.

The common white potato is one kind of tuber. The potato plant stores extra food inside its tubers, the potatoes. If you want this food, you eat a potato. If you do not eat it, the potato buds will!

The potato buds are the eyes of the potato. Whenever you see those white stems growing out of a potato, you know that the buds are eating. The potato becomes small and wrinkled because the buds are using up its stored food and water. Then you wish the buds would not grow.

But when you plant cut-up potatoes in your garden, you are glad

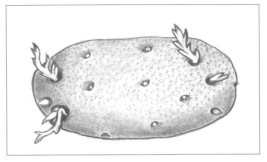

What can be done to a potato to make separate potato plants?

that the buds grow. One bud can grow into a whole new plant that produces six big potatoes. Tubers with buds can produce new potato plants much faster than seeds can. God planned this way for potato plants to multiply.

—————— Test Your Reading (Group A) ——————

Write the missing words.

1. Many plants are multiplied by planting parts of the plant because this is easier than growing them from ———.

2. A tulip is easily grown by planting a ———, which is an underground bud.

3. A new violet plant can be started by putting a ——— of a stem in water for several weeks.

4. When a stem grows roots to make a complete plant, that method of multiplying is called ———.

5. One grass plant can spread to cover a large area by sending up new shoots from ——— stems.

6. When you eat a potato, you are really eating food stored in a thick underground stem called a ———.

7. When potatoes are being cut into pieces for planting, each piece needs to have at least one ———, sometimes called an eye.

Some plants multiply from runners. God planned that strawberry plants could multiply themselves too. But instead of growing underground stems, they grow long stems above the ground. These long stems, called runners, produce many new strawberry plants.

If a runner lies on moist soil, it sends down tiny roots. The roots start sending sap upward to tiny new leaves. The new leaves soon start making their own food. Before long, the new plant could stay alive even if you were to cut it off from its parent plant. By next year it will be ready to produce juicy strawberries. It will also start sending runners in all directions to start more strawberry plants.

Ivy plants and some grasses also have spreading stems above the ground. They multiply the same way as the strawberry plant does.

Fruit trees are multiplied by grafting. If you plant a Red Delicious apple seed, you will get an apple tree that produces wild apples, not Red Delicious apples. Special fruit trees, such as Red Delicious, are multiplied by *grafting*. Although a number of different ways are used to do grafting, we shall describe only one. This kind of grafting is used to multiply special fruit trees and roses.

After these five steps are done, only the kind of branches and fruit grow on that tree that are like the tree from which the bud was taken. So if the bud came from a Red Delicious apple tree, the fruit from the graft will be Red Delicious. This is the way such special

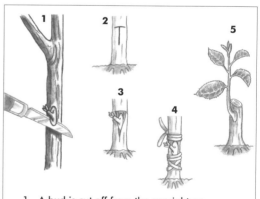

1. A bud is cut off from the special tree.
2. A slit is cut in the bark of a little tree.
3. The bud is pushed into the slit.
4. The bud is tied in place.
5. After the bud produces a leafy branch, the branches already on the little tree are cut off.

A strawberry plant can spread with runners.

Steps of grafting

apple trees are multiplied.

A strong, healthy fruit tree or grapevine will not produce large, perfect fruits unless it receives regular pruning. ***Pruning*** is cutting off unnecessary buds or branches from a plant. This causes it to produce better fruit. If the tree has too much fruit, it is best to thin the fruit by removing some of it. A well-pruned and well-thinned peach tree will produce fewer peaches than an unpruned tree, but the peaches will be larger.

When an unpruned fruit tree is loaded with fruit, one or more large limbs may break off. This weakens the whole tree. But a well-pruned tree has branches that are thinned out. They are spaced so that they are unlikely to crack or break.

Seeds, bulbs, cuttings, underground stems, runners, and grafting are wonderful ways that God planned for plants to multiply. We cannot help but say what Job did about God's world: "I know that thou canst do every thing" (Job 42:2).

Well-pruned apple trees   Young peaches needing to be thinned   Same branch well-thinned

———————— Test Your Reading (Group B) ————————

Write *true* if the statement is true. Write *false* if the statement is false.

8. A runner is a long stem above the ground that can grow roots if it lies on the ground.
9. If you cut a runner, the new plant at the end of the runner will die.
10. If you have a tree that gives apples that you like, you can have more trees with that kind of apples by planting its seeds.
11. Grafting is done when the bud from one tree is pushed into a slit in the bark of another tree.

12. After the graft produces a leafy branch, if the other branches of the tree are not cut off, the tree will give two kinds of fruit.
13. A fruit tree that gives only small fruit needs to be pruned.
14. A well-pruned tree will produce such big fruit that the branches will likely crack and break.

Reviewing What You Have Learned

1. A two-part-seed plant has
   a. branching veins in its leaves.
   b. veins that are side by side in its leaves.
   c. one vein in each leaf.
2. Stems
   a. fasten plants to the ground.
   b. carry water, minerals, and food.
   c. absorb water and minerals.
3. True or false? Guard cells control the transpiration of a plant.
4. A ——— makes pollen.
5. Flowering plants reproduce by making ———.

Extra Activities

1. If garden space is available, you might enjoy keeping a small berry patch of your own. Perhaps you could get some strawberry or raspberry starts from some friends or from your own family garden.

   Most gardeners with berry plants a few years old would be happy to have you dig up some starts because berry plants soon become too thick anyway. You might ask your parents or a gardener friend for tips on planting the starts. (For example, ask how deep and how far apart to plant them.)
2. Ask your teacher or parents to help you start some plants from cuttings as described in this lesson. Most kinds of vines are easy to start from cuttings, as well as geranium and begonia plants.
3. Read about grafting in the Bible. Find Romans 11:17–24, and read it several times. Ask your father or minister to help you understand the meaning of these verses. Write a few paragraphs about what you learned.

Lesson 6

Do You Remember?

Match each word on the right with a phrase on the left.

1. Has cones and needles
2. Lives one year
3. Lives two years
4. Lives more than two years
5. Absorbs water and minerals
6. Green food-making material

a. annual
b. biennial
c. chlorophyll
d. conifer
e. perennial
f. root hair

From the word box, find and write a word for each blank.

absorb	pruning	rooting
grafting	reproduce	transpiration
pollen		

7. A plant can ——— water and minerals from the soil.
8. A tree gives off many gallons of water through ———.
9. God caused most plants to ——— by producing seeds.
10. Bees and other insects spread ——— for many flowers.
11. Houseplants are often multiplied by ——— cut stems.
12. Special kinds of fruit trees are multiplied by ———.
13. Grapevines need regular ——— to produce good grapes.

Decide whether each sentence is true, and write *true* or *false*.

14. Most evergreens are plants with broad leaves that produce flowers, seeds, and fruit.
15. Roots fasten a plant to the ground and absorb water.
16. The wind spreads the pollen for pretty, sweet-smelling flowers.
17. Grass plants multiply by their spreading roots and underground stems.

Choose the best answer.

18. All living things are made of countless tiny
    a. seeds.
    b. buds.
    c. cells.

19. Leaves get the power for food making from
    a. water.
    b. light.
    c. heat.

20. The pressure a plant needs comes from the
    a. minerals in the soil.
    b. air inside its stem.
    c. water within its cells.

21. A tulip plant grows from a special underground bud called a
    a. bulb.
    b. tuber.
    c. stoma.

22. A tuber is an underground stem with buds, such as
    a. a potato.
    b. an onion.
    c. a radish.

23. Strawberry plants multiply by their
    a. fast-growing bulbs.
    b. long runners.
    c. underground stems.

Write the missing words.

24. The —— of a plant grow downward toward water.
25. A radish —— carries sap, stores food, and supports the leaves.
26. You can tell many trees apart by the shapes of their ——.
27. The —— of a lily make tiny grains of pollen.
28. A rose has a —— that makes plant eggs.
29. Pollen unites with the —— to make seeds.
30. The pistil of a flower becomes the —— that holds the seeds.
31. Every —— has a tough coating, stored food, and a tiny plant.

32. Guard cells control ———— by changing the size of the holes on the underside of a leaf.

Draw this picture.

33–38. Draw a picture of a large flower with these plant parts labeled neatly: *stem, veins, sepal, petal, pistil, stamen.*

Write the answers.

39. What are the leaves like of a one-part-seed plant?

40. What are the leaves like of a two-part-seed plant?

41. How many petals do the flowers have of a one-part-seed plant?

42. How many petals do the flowers have of a two-part-seed plant?

43–45. How do seeds travel away from the parent plants? Write three ways.

46–50. Write the five steps of grafting as given in the last lesson.

Index

Italics indicates vocabulary words and the pages on which the definitions are found. Illustrations are also indexed.

$$\int u \sin u \, du = \sin u - u \cos u. \qquad \int u^n \sin u \, du = -u^n \cos u + n \int u^{n-1} \cos u \, du.$$

$$\int u \cos u \, du = \cos u + u \sin u. \qquad \int u^n \cos u \, du = u^n \sin u - n \int u^{n-1} \sin u \, du.$$

$$\int e^{au} \sin nu \, du = \frac{e^{au}(a \sin nu - n \cos nu)}{a^2 + n^2}. \qquad \int e^{au} \cos nu \, du = \frac{e^{au}(a \cos nu + n \sin nu)}{a^2 + n^2}.$$

$$\int \sin au \sin bu \, du = -\frac{\sin(a + b)u}{2(a + b)} + \frac{\sin(a - b)u}{2(a - b)}, \qquad a^2 \neq b^2.$$

$$\int \cos au \cos bu \, du = \frac{\sin(a + b)u}{2(a + b)} + \frac{\sin(a - b)u}{2(a - b)}, \qquad a^2 \neq b^2.$$

$$\int \sin au \cos bu \, du = -\frac{\cos(a + b)u}{2(a + b)} - \frac{\cos(a - b)u}{2(a - b)}, \qquad a^2 \neq b^2.$$

$$\int \sinh u \, du = \cosh u. \qquad \int \cosh u \, du = \sinh u.$$

$$\Gamma(t) = \int_0^\infty e^{-u} u^{t-1} \, du, \quad t > 0; \qquad \Gamma(\tfrac{1}{2}) = \sqrt{\pi}; \quad \text{and} \quad \Gamma(n + 1) = n!, \text{ if } n \text{ is a positive integer.}$$

$\tan x = -(\cos x)\, \ln(\sec x + \tan x)$

SOME POWER SERIES EXPANSIONS

$$f(x) = f(a) + (x - a)f'(a) + \frac{(x - a)^2}{2!} f''(a) + \cdots + \frac{(x - a)^n}{n!} f^{(n)}(a) + \cdots \qquad \text{(Taylor series)}$$

$$e^x = \sum_{n=0}^\infty \frac{x^n}{n!} \qquad \sin x = \sum_{n=0}^\infty \frac{(-1)^n x^{2n+1}}{(2n + 1)!} \qquad \cos x = \sum_{n=0}^\infty \frac{(-1)^n x^{2n}}{(2n)!}$$

$$(1 - x)^{-1} = \sum_{n=0}^\infty x^n \qquad (1 - x)^{-2} = \sum_{n=0}^\infty (n + 1)x^n \qquad \ln(1 - x) = -\sum_{n=1}^\infty \frac{x^n}{n}$$

$$\tan x = x + \tfrac{1}{3}x^3 + \tfrac{2}{15}x^5 + \tfrac{17}{315}x^7 + \tfrac{62}{2835}x^9 + \cdots$$

$$\arctan x = \sum_{n=0}^\infty (-1)^n \frac{x^{2n+1}}{2n + 1}$$

$$\arcsin x = x + \frac{x^3}{2 \cdot 3} + \frac{1 \cdot 3}{2 \cdot 4 \cdot 5} x^5 + \frac{1 \cdot 3 \cdot 5}{2 \cdot 4 \cdot 6 \cdot 7} x^7 + \cdots$$

$$J_0(x) = \sum_{k=0}^\infty \frac{(-1)^k x^{2k}}{(k!)^2 2^{2k}} \qquad J_1(x) = \sum_{k=0}^\infty \frac{(-1)^k x^{2k+1}}{k!(k + 1)! 2^{2k+1}} \qquad J_n(x) = \sum_{k=0}^\infty \frac{(-1)^k x^{2k+n}}{k! \Gamma(n + k + 1) 2^{2k+n}}$$

Note: An arbitrary constant is to be added to each formula.

Fundamentals of Differential Equations

SECOND EDITION

R. KENT NAGLE

EDWARD B. SAFF

University of South Florida

The Benjamin/Cummings Publishing Company, Inc.

Redwood City, California ▪ Fort Collins, Colorado ▪ Menlo Park, California
Reading, Massachusetts ▪ New York ▪ Don Mills, Ontario ▪ Wokingham, U.K.
Amsterdam ▪ Bonn ▪ Sydney ▪ Singapore ▪ Tokyo ▪ Madrid ▪ San Juan

Editor-in-Chief: Sally Elliott
Sponsoring Editor: Lisa J. Moller
Production Coordinator: Janet Vail
Text Design: Ellen Schmutz and Richard Kharibian
Cover Design: Richard Kharibian
Composition: Syntax International

Supplements

The *Student Solution Manual to accompany Fundamentals of Differential Equations, Second Edition (30256)* contains detailed, worked-out solutions to selected exercises in the text.

If the Student Solutions Manual is not in stock at your bookstore, ask the manager to order a copy for you.

The *Instructor's Guide (30255)* contains notes to the instructor and answers to the even-numbered problems.

Library of Congress Cataloging-in-Publication Data

Nagle, R. Kent.
    Fundamentals of differential equations.

    Includes index.
    1. Differential equations.   I. Saff, E. B., 1944–
II. Title.
QA371.N24   1989   515.3′5   88-7392
ISBN 0-8053-0254-9

CDEFGHIJ-VH-93210

The Benjamin/Cummings Publishing Company, Inc.
390 Bridge Parkway
Redwood City, California 94065

To our families,
   who endured our late nights,
   soothed our anxieties,
   and shared our enthusiasm.

Sandy   **Loretta**
Kevin, Jeffrey   Lisa, Tracy, Alison

Preface

The appearance of this second edition is the result of the warm reception that our original text received. As authors we naturally appreciate positive feedback. But our primary concern is with the improvement of the text. Therefore, we have attempted to incorporate into this new edition many of the constructive comments that we received. We are grateful to our readers for their suggestions and encourage future communications.

IMPROVEMENTS IN THE SECOND EDITION

The most substantial change is the inclusion of a chapter on *partial differential equations*, which covers the method of separation of variables, Fourier series, the Heat equation, the Wave equation, and Laplace's equation. Examples in two and three variables are included. The new chapter appears in place of the chapter on existence and uniqueness Theory.

More material on *numerical methods* now appears in Sections 1.3, 3.5, 3.6, 3.7, 5.6, and 9.5. As before, these sections are optional. Of particular interest are the code recommendations in Section 3.7, the treatment of difference equations in Section 5.5, and the numerical methods for second order equations in Section 5.6. We have also included several problems and projects throughout the text that are to be done using a microcomputer. These problems and projects are denoted by the symbol at left.

Since they were well received in the first edition, we have included more *projects* and *applications* in the second edition. For example, we have added projects on the stability of numerical methods, period doubling and chaos, transmission of information, and the matrix Laplace transform method. New problems appear concerning difference equations, combat models, Airy's equation, and other applications.

OUR GOAL

While an introductory course in differential equations is a mainstay of undergraduate curricula in the sciences and engineering, the flavor of such a course varies considerably because of departmental requirements, instructors' tastes, and students' mathematical maturities and backgrounds. Our goal has been to write a flexible *one-semester* text that spans a variety of topics in the basic theory as well as applications of differential equations. At the same time we have striven to make the text "user friendly" through various design features.

WILL STUDENTS LIKE THIS TEXT?

Perhaps a more fundamental question is: Will students read a substantial part of the text? Certainly they will grapple with the assigned problems and seek inspiration from the detailed examples presented. This is true with any course. However, we have observed that students beyond the calculus level tend to rely less on lectures for details and more on the written word. This is especially true in a course like differential equations where illustrative examples often involve many steps and a variety of calculations. Also, it has been our pleasant experience that students in differential equations occasionally want to "set out on their own" in the sense of tackling more intriguing problems—particularly those relating to applications. For these reasons we have included the following features:

Procedure Boxes   Optional step-by-step procedure boxes shaded in color provide a convenient summary and a readily accessible reference.

Worked Examples   A substantial number of worked-out examples illustrate the various difficulties one might encounter in carrying out the procedures. Introductory examples are treated in greater detail. For easy identification, examples are set off by triangles ▶◀.

Projects   At the end of each chapter are projects relating to the material covered in the chapter. A project might involve a more challenging application, delve deeper into the theory, or introduce more advanced topics in differential equations. Classroom testing of the text has shown that many students regard the project experience as a valuable pre-professional activity.

Numerical Algorithms   Several numerical methods for approximating solutions to differential equations are presented along with program outlines that are easily implemented on a microcomputer. These methods are introduced early in the text so that teachers and/ or students can use them for numerical experimentation and for tackling complicated applications.

Computer Graphics   Most of the figures in the text were generated on a microcomputer with a flatbed printer/plotter. Computer graphics not only ensure greater accuracy in the illustrations, they demonstrate the use of numerical experimentation in studying the behavior of solutions.

Historical Footnotes   Throughout the text historical footnotes are set off by colored daggers (†). These footnotes typically provide the name of the person who developed the technique, the date, and the context of the original research.

Chapter Summary and Review Problems   Each chapter contains a set of review problems along with a synopsis of the major concepts presented.

Differential equations is a subject area where students rarely question applicability. Rather, the applications are a great source of motivation—particularly if they are cast in a modern setting. The following features relate to these aspects of the text:

Motivating Problem   Most chapters begin with a discussion of a problem from physics or engineering that motivates the topic presented and illustrates the methodology.

Modern Applications   Aside from standard applications such as Newtonian mechanics, electric circuits, and population models, we have included material on mathematical modeling, aquaculture, pollution, heating and cooling of buildings, combat models, frequency response modeling, and difference equations.

WILL INSTRUCTORS LIKE THIS TEXT?

Of course student contentment, as addressed above, is an important factor in an instructor's evaluation of a text. But before the concert can begin, we must be sure to have the right score! So let's remark on the content and the level of the text.

Prerequisites   While some universities make *linear algebra* a prerequisite for differential equations, many schools (especially engineering) only require calculus. With this in mind, we have designed the text so that only Chapter 6 (Higher Order Linear Differential Equations) and Chapter 10 (Matrix Methods for Linear Systems) require more than high school linear algebra. Moreover, Chapter 10 contains a review section on matrices and vectors as well as specific references for the deeper results used from the theory of linear algebra. We have also written Chapter 9 (Systems of Differential Equations and Their Applications) so as to give an introduction to systems of differential equations—including methods of solving, applications, numerical procedures, and phase plane analysis—that does not require a background in linear algebra.

Choice of Applications   Because of syllabus constraints, some courses will have little or no time for sections (such as those in Chapters 3, 5, and 9) that exclusively deal with applications. Therefore, we have made the sections in these chapters almost completely independent of each other. To afford the instructor even greater flexibility, we have built in a variety of applications in the exercises for the theoretical sections. In addition, we have included several projects that deal with such applications as aquaculture and cleaning up the Great Lakes.

Power Series   Power series solutions is a topic that occasionally causes student anxiety. Possibly, this is due to inadequate preparation in calculus where the more subtle subject of convergent series is (not infrequently) covered at a rapid pace. Our solution has been to provide a thorough treatment of power series solutions that also includes a review of their properties as well as a discussion of real analytic functions. Unlike many texts, we have provided an extensive section on the *method of Frobenius* (Section 8.6) and two sections on the various methods for finding a second linearly independent solution.

While we have given considerable space to power series solutions, we have also taken great care to allow for the instructor who only wishes to give a basic introduction to the topic. *An introduction to solving differential equations using power series and the method of Frobenius can be accomplished by covering the materials in Section 8.3, Section 8.6, and part of Section 8.7.*

Laplace Transforms   We provide a detailed chapter on Laplace transforms since this is a recurring topic for engineers. Our treatment emphasizes discontinuous forcing terms and includes a section on the Dirac delta function.

Linear Theory   We have developed the theory of linear differential equations in a gradual manner. In Chapter 4 (Linear Second Order Equations) we present the basic theory for linear second order equations and discuss various techniques for solving these equations. Higher order equations are briefly mentioned in this chapter. A more detailed discussion of linear higher order differential equations is given in Chapter 6 (Higher Order Linear Differential Equations). For a beginning course emphasizing methods of solution, the presentation in Chapter 4 is sufficient and Chapter 6 can be skipped.

Without doubt the instructor will also want to examine the following aspects of the text:

Proofs   While more pragmatic students may balk at proofs, most instructors regard these justifications as an essential ingredient in a textbook on differential equations. As with any text at this level, certain details in the proofs must be omitted. When this occurs, we flag the instance and refer readers to either a problem in the exercises or to another text. For convenience, the end of a proof is marked by the symbol ■ ■ ■.

Exercises   An abundance of exercises is graduated in difficulty from straightforward, routine problems to more challenging ones. Deeper theoretical questions, along with applications, usually occur toward the end of exercise sets.

Optional Sections   We have made several sections optional—these are denoted by a star. These sections can be omitted without affecting the logical development of the material. As mentioned earlier, the sections in Chapters 3, 5, and 9 are almost completely independent of each other.

Length of Text   If this book is designed for a one-semester (or two-quarter) course, why is it longer than some of its competitors? The length of any text is a difficult optimization problem. The price of flexibility and readability as afforded by optional sections, extensive exercise sets, a variety of applications, and detailed examples must be weighed against factors such as production and consumer costs, terseness, usability, and willingness to accept a restricted point of view. Our approach has been to provide enough cloth so that instructors can tailor the course to their own needs.

As a rough guide in designing a syllabus related to the text, we provide three sample syllabi that can be used for a 15-week course that meets three hours per week: the first emphasizes methods and applications, the second theory and methods, and the third methods and partial differential equations. Chapters 1, 2, and 4 provide the core for any course. The rest of the chapters are, for the most part, independent of each other.

Week	Methods and Applications Sections	Theory and Methods Sections	Methods and Partial Differential Equations Sections
1	1.1, 1.2, 1.3	1.1, 1.2, 2.2	1.1, 1.2, 2.2
2	2.2, 2.3	2.3, 2.4	2.3, 2.4
3	2.4, 2.6, 3.1	2.6, 4.2	4.2, 4.3
4	3.2, 3.5	4.3, 4.4, 4.5	4.4, 4.5
5	4.2, 4.3, 4.5	4.6, 4.7	4.6, 4.7
6	4.6, 4.7	4.8, 4.9	4.8, 4.9
7	4.8, 4.9	4.11, 6.2	5.1, 5.2, 5.3
8	5.1, 5.2, 5.3	6.3, 6.4	7.2, 7.3
9	7.2, 7.3	6.5, 8.3	7.4, 7.5
10	7.4, 7.5	8.4, 8.5	7.6, 8.2
11	7.6, 8.2	8.6	8.3, 8.6
12	8.3, 8.6	8.7, 10.2	8.7, 9.2
13	8.7, 9.2	10.3, 10.4	9.4, 11.2
14	9.3, 9.4	10.5	11.3, 11.4
15	9.5	10.6	11.5, 11.6, 11.7

ACKNOWLEDGMENTS

The staging of this text involved considerable behind-the-scenes activity. We want to thank Frank Glaser (California State Polytechnic University, Pomona) for many of the historical footnotes. We are indebted to Herbert E. Rauch (Lockheed Research Laboratory) for help with Section 3.3 on heating and cooling of buildings, Project B in Chapter 3 on aquaculture, and other application problems. Our appreciation goes to George Fix and R. Kannan (University of Texas, Arlington) for their useful suggestions concerning Section 3.7. We give special thanks to Richard H. Elderkin (Pomona College), Jerrold Marsden (University of California, Berkeley), T. G. Proctor (Clemson University), and Philip W. Schaefer (University of Tennessee) who read and reread the manuscript for the first edition making numerous suggestions that greatly improved the book. We also extend thanks to the many people who reviewed the manuscripts for the first and second editions:

David Bindschadler	Wayne State University
Gary Bogar	Montana State University
Bruce Edwards	University of Florida
David Ellis	San Francisco State University
Ronald Guenther	Oregon State University
Johnny Henderson	Auburn University

D. V. Ho	Georgia Institute of Technology
Nicholas D. Kazarinoff	SUNY at Buffalo
Kenneth Larsen	Brigham Young University
James Leffew	University of South Florida
Reza Malek-Madani	U. S. Naval Academy
Greg Maybury	Parkland College
Robert O'Malley, Jr.	Rensselaer Polytechnic Institute
John Omg	University of Wisconsin, Milwaukee
James R. Retherford	Louisiana State University
Klaus Schmidt	University of Utah
Kathleen M. Shannon	Stockton State College
Ralph Showalter	University of Texas, Austin
Jon C. Snader	University of South Florida
A. David Snider	University of South Florida
Jet Wimp	Drexel University

We are grateful for the suggestions and encouragement we received from our students here at the University of South Florida, especially William Albrecht, Mark Clark, Jessica Craig, Kurt Van Etten, William Hughes, David Kaplan, Laura Kneeberg, Brian Melloy, Rocky Rathgeber, Mehrdad Simkani, and Zachariah Sinkala who helped us obtain correct answers to the problems. We also thank Clive Taylor for his help in obtaining correct answers. The credit for the computer graphics goes to Hao Nguyen who never complained when we asked him to redo a graph. While several typists including Mary Baroli, Selma Canas, Carol Crosson, Jo Ann Dennison, and Loretta Saff were extremely helpful, the majority of the typing was done by Sandy Nagle who spent many late nights typing and retyping the manuscript. To Sandy we give our heartfelt thanks.

Finally, we want to thank the staff at Benjamin/Cummings for their dedicated assistance. Special kudos go to sponsoring editors Sally Elliott and Lisa Moller and production coordinator Janet Vail.

R. Kent Nagle
Edward B. Saff
Tampa, Florida
1989

Contents

*Denotes optional sections that can be deleted without compromising the logical flow.

3

Mathematical Models and Numerical Methods Involving First Order Equations   83

4

Linear Second Order Equations   152

7   *Laplace Transforms*   326

8   *Series Solutions of Linear Differential Equations*   402

Introduction

1.1 Background

In the sciences and engineering, mathematical models are developed to aid in the understanding of physical phenomena. These models often yield an equation that contains some derivatives of an unknown function. Such an equation is referred to as a **differential equation.** Two examples of models developed in calculus are the free fall of a body and the decay of a radioactive substance.

In the case of free fall, an object is dropped from a certain height above the ground and falls under the force of gravity.[†] Newton's second law, which states that an object's mass times its acceleration equals the total force acting on it, can be applied to the falling object. This leads to the equation

$$m \frac{d^2 h}{dt^2} = -mg,$$

where m is the mass of the object, h is its height above the ground, $d^2 h/dt^2$ is its acceleration, g is the gravitational constant, and $-mg$ is the force due to gravity.

Fortunately, the above equation is easy to solve for h. All we have to do is cancel

---

[†] We are assuming here that gravity is the *only* force acting on the object and that this force is constant. More general models would take into account other forces, such as air resistance.

the *m*'s and integrate twice with respect to *t*. That is,

$$\frac{d^2h}{dt^2} = -g,$$

so

$$\frac{dh}{dt} = -gt + c_1,$$

and

$$h = \frac{-gt^2}{2} + c_1 t + c_2.$$

The constants of integration, c_1 and c_2, can be determined if we know the initial height and the initial velocity of the object. We then have a formula for the height of the object at time *t*.

In the case of radioactive decay, we begin from the premise that the rate of decay is proportional to the amount of radioactive substance present. This leads to the equation

$$\frac{dA}{dt} = -kA, \qquad k > 0,$$

where $A\,(>0)$ is the unknown amount of radioactive substance present at time *t* and *k* is the proportionality constant. To solve this equation we write it in the form

$$\frac{1}{A}\,dA = -k\,dt$$

and integrate to obtain

$$\ln A = \int \frac{1}{A}\,dA = \int -k\,dt = -kt + C_1.$$

Solving for *A* yields

$$A = e^{\ln A} = e^{-kt}e^{C_1} = Ce^{-kt},$$

where *C* is the new constant e^{C_1}. The constants *C* and *k* can be determined if the initial amount of radioactive substance and the half-life of the substance are given. We then have a formula for the amount of radioactive substance at any future time *t*.

Even though the above examples were easily solved by methods learned in calculus, they do give us some insight into the study of differential equations. First of all, **integration** is an important tool in solving differential equations. Second, we do not expect to get a unique solution to a differential equation since there will be arbitrary "constants of integration." Third, we will find applications of differential equations when the model deals with **rates of change** of one variable with respect to another.

Differential equations arise in a variety of subject areas, which include not only the physical sciences but also such diverse fields as economics, medicine, psychology, and operations research. To list all the occurrences would be a Herculean task, so we shall limit the discussion to a few specific examples.

1. A classical application of differential equations is found in the study of an electric circuit consisting of resistors, inductors, and capacitors, which is driven by an electromotive force. Here an application of Kirchhoff's laws[†] leads to the equation

   (1) $$L\frac{d^2q}{dt^2} + R\frac{dq}{dt} + \frac{1}{C}q = E(t),$$

   where L is the inductance, R is the resistance, C is the capacitance, $E(t)$ is the electromotive force, $q(t)$ is the charge, and t is the time.

2. In the study of the gravitational equilibrium of a star, an application of Newton's law of gravity and of the Stefan-Boltzmann law for gases leads to the equilibrium equation

   (2) $$\frac{1}{r^2}\frac{d}{dr}\left(\frac{r^2}{\rho}\frac{dP}{dr}\right) = -4\pi\rho G,$$

   where P is the sum of the gas kinetic pressure and the radiation pressure, r is the distance from the center of the star, ρ is the density of matter, and G is the gravitational constant.

3. In psychology, one model of the learning of a task involves the equation

   (3) $$\frac{dy/dt}{y^{3/2}(1-y)^{3/2}} = \frac{2p}{\sqrt{n}}.$$

   Here the variable y represents the state of the learner or the learner's skill level as a function of time t. The constants p and n depend on the individual learner and the nature of the task.

4. In the study of vibrating strings and the propagation of waves, we find the partial differential equation

   (4) $$\frac{\partial^2 u}{\partial t^2} - \frac{\partial^2 u}{\partial x^2} = 0,^{††}$$

[†] We will discuss the applications of Kirchhoff's laws in Sections 5.4 and 9.1.

[††] *Historical Footnote:* This partial differential equation was first discovered by Jean le Rond d'Alembert (1717–1783) in 1747.

where t represents time, x the location along the string, and u the displacement of the string, which is a function of time and location.

To begin our study of differential equations we need some common terminology. If an equation involves the derivative of one variable with respect to another, then the former is called a **dependent variable** and the latter is an **independent variable.** Thus, in the equation

(5) $$\frac{d^2x}{dt^2} + a\frac{dx}{dt} + kx = 0,$$

t is the independent variable and x is the dependent variable. We refer to a and k as **parameters** or **coefficients** in equation (5). In the equation

(6) $$\frac{\partial u}{\partial x} - \frac{\partial u}{\partial y} = x - 2y,$$

x and y are independent variables and u is a dependent variable.

A differential equation involving ordinary derivatives with respect to a single independent variable is called an **ordinary differential equation.** A differential equation involving partial derivatives with respect to more than one independent variable is a **partial differential equation.** Notice that equation (5) is an ordinary differential equation, whereas equation (6) is a partial differential equation.

The **order** of a differential equation is the order of the highest-order derivatives present in the equation. Equation (5) is a second order equation because d^2x/dt^2 is the highest order derivative present. Equation (6) is a first order equation because only first order partial derivatives occur.

It will be useful to classify ordinary differential equations as being either linear or nonlinear. A **linear** differential equation is any equation that can be written in the form

(7) $$a_n(x)\frac{d^n y}{dx^n} + a_{n-1}(x)\frac{d^{n-1} y}{dx^{n-1}} + \cdots + a_1(x)\frac{dy}{dx} + a_0(x)y = F(x),$$

where $a_n(x), a_{n-1}(x), \ldots, a_0(x)$ and $F(x)$ depend only on the independent variable x, not on y. If an ordinary differential equation is not linear, then we call it **nonlinear.** For example,

$$\frac{d^2y}{dx^2} + y = x^2$$

is a linear second order ordinary differential equation, whereas

$$\frac{d^2y}{dx^2} + \sin y = 0$$

is nonlinear because of the sin y term. The equation

$$\frac{d^2y}{dx^2} - y\frac{dy}{dx} = \cos x$$

is nonlinear because of the $y\,dy/dx$ term.

EXERCISES 1.1

Listed below are some differential equations along with the field or problem area in which they arise. Classify each as an ordinary differential equation (ODE) or a partial differential equation (PDE), give the order, and indicate the independent and dependent variables. If the equation is an ordinary differential equation, indicate whether the equation is linear or nonlinear.

1. $5\dfrac{d^2x}{dt^2} + 2\dfrac{dx}{dt} + 9x = 2\cos 3t$ ODE, 2ND ORDER, LINEAR, X IS DED   t IS IND.
   (mechanical vibrations, electrical circuits, seismology).

2. $y\left[1 + \left(\dfrac{dy}{dx}\right)^2\right] = C$, where C is a constant   ORD, 1ST ORDER, NON-LINEAR   Y IS DEP, X IS IND.
   (brachistochrone problem,† calculus of variations).

3. $8\dfrac{d^4y}{dx^4} = x(1 - x)$ ODE, 4TH ORDER, Y IS DED   X IS IND, LINEAR
   (deflection of beams).

4. $\dfrac{\partial^2 u}{\partial x^2} + \dfrac{\partial^2 u}{\partial y^2} = 0$ PARTIAL, 2ND ORDER
   (Laplace's equation, potential theory, electricity, heat, aerodynamics).

5. $\dfrac{dy}{dx} = \dfrac{y(2 - 3x)}{x(1 + 3y)}$ ODE, 1ST ORDER, Y IS DED   X IS IND, NONLINEAR.
   (competition between two species, ecology).

6. $\dfrac{dx}{dt} = k(4 - x)(1 - x)$, where k is a constant   ORD, X IS IND   t IS DEP, 1ST, NON-LINEAR
   (chemical reaction rates).

7. $\dfrac{d^2y}{dx^2} - 2x\dfrac{dy}{dx} + 2py = 0$, where p is a constant   ODE, 2ND ORDER, Y IS DEP, X IS IND, LINEAR
   (Hermite's equation, quantum mechanics, harmonic oscillator).

8. $x\dfrac{d^2y}{dx^2} + \dfrac{dy}{dx} + xy = 0$ ORD, 2ND ORDER, LINEAR   Y IS DEP, X IS IND.
   (aerodynamics, stress analysis).

---

† *Historical Footnote:* In 1630 Galileo formulated the brachistochrone problem (βραχιστος = shortest, χρονος = time), that is, to determine a path down which a particle will fall from one given point to another in the shortest time. It was reproposed by John Bernoulli in 1696 and solved by him the following year.

9. $-\pi(y \tan \alpha)^2 \dfrac{dy}{dt} = 12(2gy)^{1/2}$, where α, g are constants   *[handwritten: ODE, Y IS DEP, t IS IND, NONLIN, 1ST ORDER]*

(liquid flow from a container).

10. $\dfrac{dp}{dt} = kp(P - p)$, where k, P are constants   *[handwritten: 1ST ORD, t IS IND, P IS DEP, NON-LIN.]*

(logistic curve, epidemiology, economics).

11. $\dfrac{\partial N}{\partial t} = \dfrac{\partial^2 N}{\partial r^2} + \dfrac{1}{r}\dfrac{\partial N}{\partial r} + kN$, where k is a constant   *[handwritten: PDE, 2ND ORD, t AND r IND, N IS DEP]*

(nuclear fission).

12. $\dfrac{d^2 y}{dx^2} - \varepsilon(1 - y^2)\dfrac{dy}{dx} + 9y = 0$, where ε is a constant   *[handwritten: ORD., 2ND NON-LIN.]*

(Van der Pol's equation, triode vacuum tube).

13. $x\dfrac{d^2 y}{dx^2} + 2\dfrac{dy}{dx} + x(y^2 - C)^{3/2} = 0$, where C is a constant   *[handwritten: ODE, 2ND ORDER, Y IS DEP, X IS IND, NON-LIN.]*

(white dwarf equation, gravitational potential in degenerate stars).

14. $\sqrt{1 - \alpha y}\,\dfrac{d^2 y}{dx^2} + 2x\dfrac{dy}{dx} = 0$, where α is a constant   *[handwritten: ORD, 2ND, NON-LIN]*

(Kidder's equation, flow of gases through a porous medium).

1.2 Solutions and Initial Value Problems

Any nth order ordinary differential equation can be expressed in the general form

(1) $\qquad F\left(x, y, \dfrac{dy}{dx}, \ldots, \dfrac{d^n y}{dx^n}\right) = 0,$

where F is a function of the independent variable x, the dependent variable y, and the derivatives of y up to order n; that is, $x, y, \ldots, d^n y/dx^n$. We assume that x lies in an interval I that can be any of the usual intervals (a, b), $[a, b]$, $[a, b)$, and so on. In many cases we can solve equation (1) for $d^n y/dx^n$. This allows us to write our differential equation in the form

(2) $\qquad \dfrac{d^n y}{dx^n} = f\left(x, y, \dfrac{dy}{dx}, \ldots, \dfrac{d^{n-1} y}{dx^{n-1}}\right).$

EXPLICIT SOLUTION

Definition 1.   A function $\phi(x)$ that when substituted for y in equation (1) [or (2)] satisfies the equation for all x in the interval I is called an **explicit solution** to the equation on I.

▶ **Example 1**   Show that $\phi(x) = e^{3x}$ is an explicit solution to

(3) $\dfrac{dy}{dx} = 3y$

on the interval $(-\infty, \infty)$.

Solution   The function $\phi(x) = e^{3x}$ and its derivative $d\phi/dx = 3e^{3x}$ are defined on $(-\infty, \infty)$. When we substitute them into equation (3), we find

$$3e^{3x} = (3)(e^{3x}),$$

which is true for all x in $(-\infty, \infty)$. Hence $\phi(x) = e^{3x}$ is an explicit solution to (3) on $(-\infty, \infty)$. ◀

▶ **Example 2**   Show that $\phi(x) = x^2 - x^{-1}$ is an explicit solution to

(4) $y''(x) - \dfrac{2}{x^2}\, y(x) = 0$.

Solution   The functions $\phi(x) = x^2 - x^{-1}$, $\phi'(x) = 2x + x^{-2}$, and $\phi''(x) = 2 - 2x^{-3}$ are defined for all $x \neq 0$. Substitution of $\phi(x)$ for $y(x)$ in equation (4) gives

$$(2 - 2x^{-3}) - \frac{2}{x^2}(x^2 - x^{-1}) = (2 - 2x^{-3}) - (2 - 2x^{-3}) = 0.$$

Since this is valid for any $x \neq 0$, the function $\phi(x) = x^2 - x^{-1}$ is an explicit solution to (4) on $(-\infty, 0)$ and on $(0, \infty)$. ◀

▶ **Example 3**   Show that for *any* choice of the constants c_1 and c_2, the function

(5) $\phi(x) = c_1 e^{-x} + c_2 e^{2x}$

is an explicit solution to

(6) $y'' - y' - 2y = 0$.

Solution   With $\phi(x)$ as defined in (5), we compute $\phi'(x) = -c_1 e^{-x} + 2c_2 e^{2x}$ and $\phi''(x) = c_1 e^{-x} + 4c_2 e^{2x}$. Substitution of ϕ, ϕ', and ϕ'' for y, y', and y'' in equation (6) yields

$$(c_1 e^{-x} + 4c_2 e^{2x}) - (-c_1 e^{-x} + 2c_2 e^{2x}) - 2(c_1 e^{-x} + c_2 e^{2x})$$
$$= (c_1 + c_1 - 2c_1)e^{-x} + (4c_2 - 2c_2 - 2c_2)e^{2x} = 0.$$

Since equality holds for all x in $(-\infty, \infty)$, then $\phi(x) = c_1 e^{-x} + c_2 e^{2x}$ is an explicit solution to (6) on the interval $(-\infty, \infty)$ for any choice of the constants c_1 and c_2. ◀

As we shall see in Chapter 2, the methods for solving differential equations do not always yield an explicit solution for the equation. We may have to settle for a solution that is defined implicitly.

IMPLICIT SOLUTION

Definition 2.   A relation $G(x, y) = 0$ is said to be an **implicit solution** to equation (1) on the interval I if it defines one or more explicit solutions on I.

▶ **Example 4**   Show that

(7) $y^2 - x^3 + 8 = 0$

is an implicit solution to

(8) $\dfrac{dy}{dx} = \dfrac{3x^2}{2y}$

on the interval $(2, \infty)$.

Solution   When we solve (7) for y we obtain $y = \pm\sqrt{x^3 - 8}$. Let's try $\phi(x) = \sqrt{x^3 - 8}$ to see if it is an explicit solution. Since $d\phi/dx = 3x^2/2\sqrt{x^3 - 8}$, both ϕ and $d\phi/dx$ are defined on $(2, \infty)$. Substituting them into (8) yields

$$\frac{3x^2}{2\sqrt{x^3 - 8}} = \frac{3x^2}{2(\sqrt{x^3 - 8})},$$

which is valid for all x in $(2, \infty)$. Hence relation (7) is an implicit solution to (8) on $(2, \infty)$. ◀

▶ **Example 5**   Show that

(9) $x + y + e^{xy} = 0$

is an implicit solution to

(10) $(1 + xe^{xy})\dfrac{dy}{dx} + 1 + ye^{xy} = 0.$

Solution   First, we observe that we are unable to solve (9) directly for y in terms of x alone. However, for (9) to hold, we realize that any change in x requires a change in y, so we expect the relation (9) to define implicitly at least one function $y(x)$. This is difficult to show directly but can be rigorously verified using the **implicit function theorem**[†] of advanced calculus, which guarantees that such a function $y(x)$ exists that is also differentiable (see Problem 30).

Once we know that y is a differentiable function of x, we can use the technique of implicit differentiation. Indeed, from (9) we obtain

$$1 + \frac{dy}{dx} + e^{xy}\left(y + x\frac{dy}{dx}\right) = 0$$

or

$$(1 + xe^{xy})\frac{dy}{dx} + 1 + ye^{xy} = 0,$$

which is identical to the differential equation (10). Thus relation (9) is an implicit solution to (10) on some interval guaranteed by the implicit function theorem. ◀

▶ **Example 6**   Verify that $4x^2 - y^2 = C$, where C is an arbitrary constant, gives a one-parameter family of implicit solutions to

(11) $y\dfrac{dy}{dx} - 4x = 0$

and graph several of these solution curves.

Solution   When we implicitly differentiate the equation $4x^2 - y^2 = C$ with respect to x, we find

$$8x - 2y\frac{dy}{dx} = 0,$$

which is equivalent to (11). In Figure 1.1 on page 10 we have sketched the implicit solutions for $C = 0, \pm 1, \pm 4$. The curves are hyperbolas with common asymptotes $y = \pm 2x$. Notice that the implicit solution curves (with C arbitrary) fill the entire plane and are nonintersecting for $C \neq 0$. For $C = 0$, the implicit solution gives rise to the two explicit solutions $y = 2x$, $y = -2x$, both of which pass through the origin. ◀

For brevity, we hereafter use the term *solution* to mean either an explicit or an implicit solution.

As we shall see later in the text, the methods for solving nth order differential equations involve n arbitrary constants. In most cases we will be able to determine the n constants if we know the n values $y(x_0), y'(x_0), \ldots, y^{(n-1)}(x_0)$.

[†] See *Vector Calculus*, Second Edition, by J. E. Marsden and A. J. Tromba, W. H. Freeman and Company, San Francisco, 1981, p. 232.

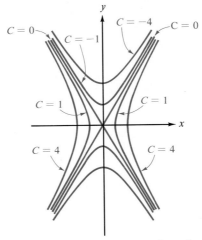

Figure 1.1 Implicit solutions $4x^2 - y^2 = C$

INITIAL VALUE PROBLEM

Definition 3.   By an **initial value problem** for an nth order differential equation

$$F\left(x, y, \frac{dy}{dx}, \ldots, \frac{d^n y}{dx^n}\right) = 0$$

we mean: Find a solution to the differential equation on an interval I that satisfies at x_0 the n initial conditions

$$y(x_0) = y_0,$$

$$\frac{dy}{dx}(x_0) = y_1,$$

$$\vdots$$

$$\frac{d^{n-1} y}{dx^{n-1}}(x_0) = y_{n-1},$$

where $x_0 \in I$ and $y_0, y_1, \ldots, y_{n-1}$ are given constants.

In the case of a first order equation, the initial conditions reduce to the single equation

$$y(x_0) = y_0,$$

and in the case of a second order equation the initial conditions have the form

$$y(x_0) = y_0, \qquad \frac{dy}{dx}(x_0) = y_1.$$

The terminology *initial conditions* comes from mechanics, in which $y(x_0) = y_0$ usually represents the location of an object at time x_0 and $dy(x_0)/dx = y_1$ gives the velocity of the object at time x_0.

▶ **Example 7**   Show that $\phi(x) = \sin x - \cos x$ is a solution to the initial value problem

(12) $$\frac{d^2y}{dx^2} + y = 0; \qquad y(0) = -1, \qquad \frac{dy}{dx}(0) = 1.$$

Solution   Observe that $\phi(x) = \sin x - \cos x$, $d\phi/dx = \cos x + \sin x$, and $d^2\phi/dx^2 = -\sin x + \cos x$ are all defined on $(-\infty, \infty)$. Substituting into the differential equation in (12) gives

$$(-\sin x + \cos x) + (\sin x - \cos x) = 0,$$

which holds for all $x \in (-\infty, \infty)$. Hence $\phi(x)$ is a solution to the differential equation in (12) on $(-\infty, \infty)$. When we check the initial conditions, we find

$$\phi(0) = \sin 0 - \cos 0 = -1,$$

$$\frac{d\phi}{dx}(0) = \cos 0 + \sin 0 = 1,$$

which meets the requirements of (12). Therefore, $\phi(x)$ is a solution to the given initial value problem. ◀

▶ **Example 8**   As shown in Example 3, the function $\phi(x) = c_1 e^{-x} + c_2 e^{2x}$ is a solution to

(13) $$\frac{d^2y}{dx^2} - \frac{dy}{dx} - 2y = 0,$$

for any choice of the constants c_1 and c_2. Determine c_1 and c_2 so that the initial conditions

$$y(0) = 2 \quad \text{and} \quad \frac{dy}{dx}(0) = -3$$

are satisfied.

Solution   To determine the constants c_1 and c_2, we first compute $d\phi/dx$ to get $d\phi/dx = -c_1 e^{-x} + 2c_2 e^{2x}$. Substituting in our initial conditions gives the following system of equations:

$$\begin{cases} \phi(0) = c_1 e^0 + c_2 e^0 = 2, \\ \dfrac{d\phi}{dx}(0) = -c_1 e^0 + 2c_2 e^0 = -3, \end{cases} \quad \text{or} \quad \begin{cases} c_1 + c_2 = 2, \\ -c_1 + 2c_2 = -3. \end{cases}$$

Adding the last two equations yields $3c_2 = -1$, so $c_2 = -\frac{1}{3}$. Since $c_1 + c_2 = 2$, we find $c_1 = \frac{7}{3}$. Hence the solution to the initial value problem is $\phi(x) = \frac{7}{3}e^{-x} - \frac{1}{3}e^{2x}$. ◄

We now state an existence and uniqueness theorem for first order initial value problems.

EXISTENCE AND UNIQUENESS OF SOLUTION

Theorem 1.   Given the initial value problem

$$\frac{dy}{dx} = f(x, y), \qquad y(x_0) = y_0,$$

assume that f and $\partial f/\partial y$ are continuous functions in a rectangle

$$R = \{(x, y): a < x < b, c < y < d\}$$

that contains the point (x_0, y_0). Then the initial value problem has a unique solution $\phi(x)$ in some interval $x_0 - h < x < x_0 + h$, where h is a positive number.

The preceding theorem tells us two things. First, when an equation satisfies the hypotheses of Theorem 1, we are assured that a solution to the initial value problem exists. Naturally it is important to know whether the equation we are trying to solve actually has a solution before we spend too much time trying to solve it. Second, when the hypotheses are satisfied, there is a **unique** solution to the initial value problem. This uniqueness tells us that if we can find a solution, then it is the *only* solution for the initial value problem. Graphically, the theorem says that there is only one solution curve that passes through the point (x_0, y_0). Notice that the existence and uniqueness of the solution holds only in some neighborhood of x_0. Unfortunately, the theorem does not tell us the size of this neighborhood but only that it has a positive radius denoted by h.

Even in the *applications* of differential equations, existence and uniqueness are points of significance. In particular, if our initial value problem represents a mathematical model for a physical situation, then we certainly expect to have a solution, because physically "something does happen." Moreover, we expect a unique solution, because if we repeat our experiment under identical conditions, we expect to observe the same results.[†]

The proof of Theorem 1 involves converting the initial value problem into an integral equation and then using Picard's method to generate a sequence of successive approximations that converge to the solution. The conversion to an integral equation and Picard's method are discussed in Project B at the end of this chapter. A detailed discussion and proof of the theorem are given in Chapter 11 of the expanded version of this text, entitled *Fundamentals of Differential Equations and Boundary Value Problems.*

▶ **Example 9**   For the initial value problem

(14) $$\frac{dy}{dx} = x^2 - xy^3, \qquad y(1) = 6,$$

does Theorem 1 imply the existence of a unique solution?

Solution   Here $f(x, y) = x^2 - xy^3$ and $\partial f/\partial y = -3xy^2$. Since both of these functions are continuous in any rectangle containing the point $(1, 6)$, the hypotheses of Theorem 1 are satisfied. It then follows from Theorem 1 that the initial value problem (14) has a unique solution in an interval about $x = 1$ of the form $(1 - h, 1 + h)$, where h is some positive number. ◀

▶ **Example 10**   For the initial value problem

(15) $$\frac{dy}{dx} = 3y^{2/3}, \qquad y(2) = 0,$$

does Theorem 1 imply the existence of a unique solution?

Solution   Here $f(x, y) = 3y^{2/3}$ and $\partial f/\partial y = 2y^{-1/3}$. Unfortunately, $\partial f/\partial y$ is not continuous or even defined when $y = 0$. Consequently, there is no rectangle containing $(2, 0)$ in which both f and $\partial f/\partial y$ are continuous. Since the hypotheses of Theorem 1 do not hold,

---

[†] At least this is the case when we are considering a deterministic model, as opposed to a probabilistic model.

we cannot use Theorem 1 to determine whether the initial value problem does or does not have a unique solution. It turns out that this initial value problem does *not* have a unique solution. We refer the reader to Problem 29 for the details. ◀

In Example 10, suppose the initial condition is changed to $y(2) = 1$. Then, since f and $\partial f/\partial y$ are continuous in the rectangle $R = \{(x, y): 0 < x < 10, 0 < y < 5\}$, which contains $(2, 1)$, it follows from Theorem 1 that this *new* initial value problem has a unique solution in some interval about $x = 2$.

EXERCISES 1.2

1. (a) Show that $\phi(x) = x^2$ is an explicit solution to

$$x \frac{dy}{dx} = 2y$$

on the interval $(-\infty, \infty)$.
   (b) Show that $\phi(x) = e^x - x$ is an explicit solution to

$$\frac{dy}{dx} + y^2 = e^{2x} + (1 - 2x)e^x + x^2 - 1$$

on the interval $(-\infty, \infty)$.
   (c) Show that $\phi(x) = x^2 - x^{-1}$ is an explicit solution to $x^2 d^2y/dx^2 = 2y$ on the interval $(0, \infty)$.

2. (a) Show that $y^2 + x - 3 = 0$ is an implicit solution to $dy/dx = -1/2y$ on the interval $(-\infty, 3)$.
   (b) Show that $xy^3 - xy^3 \sin x = 1$ is an implicit solution to

$$\frac{dy}{dx} = \frac{(x \cos x + \sin x - 1)y}{3(x - x \sin x)}$$

on the interval $(0, \pi/2)$.

In Problems 3 through 8 determine whether the given function is a solution to the given differential equation.

3. $y = \sin x + x^2$, $\dfrac{d^2y}{dx^2} + y = x^2 + 2.$

4. $y = e^{2x} - 3e^{-x}$, $\dfrac{d^2y}{dx^2} - \dfrac{dy}{dx} - 2y = 0.$

5. $x = 2e^{3t} - e^{2t}$, $\dfrac{d^2x}{dt^2} - x\dfrac{dx}{dt} + 3x = -2e^{2t}.$

6. $x = \cos 2t$, $\dfrac{dx}{dt} + tx = \sin 2t.$

7. $x = \cos t - 2 \sin t$, $x'' + x = 0$.

8. $y = 3 \sin 2x + e^{-x}$, $y'' + 4y = 5e^{-x}$.

In Problems 9 through 13 determine whether the given relation is an implicit solution to the differential equation. Assume that the relationship does define y implicitly as a function of x and use implicit differentiation.

9. $x^2 + y^2 = 4$, $\dfrac{dy}{dx} = \dfrac{x}{y}$.

10. $y - \ln y = x^2 + 1$, $\dfrac{dy}{dx} = \dfrac{2xy}{y - 1}$.

11. $e^{xy} + y = x - 1$, $\dfrac{dy}{dx} = \dfrac{e^{-xy} - y}{e^{-xy} + x}$.

12. $x^2 - \sin(x + y) = 1$, $\dfrac{dy}{dx} = 2x \sec(x + y) - 1$.

13. $\sin y + xy - x^3 = 2$, $y'' = \dfrac{6xy' + (y')^3 \sin y - 2(y')^2}{3x^2 - y}$.

14. Show that $\phi(x) = c_1 \sin x + c_2 \cos x$ is a solution to $d^2y/dx^2 + y = 0$ for any choice of the constants c_1 and c_2. Thus $c_1 \sin x + c_2 \cos x$ is a two-parameter family of solutions to the differential equation.

15. Show that $\phi(x) = Ce^{3x} + 1$ is a solution to $dy/dx - 3y = -3$ for any choice of the constant C. Thus $Ce^{3x} + 1$ is a one-parameter family of solutions to the differential equation. Graph several of the solution curves using the same coordinate axes.

16. Verify that $x^2 + cy^2 = 1$, where c is an arbitrary nonzero constant, is a one-parameter family of implicit solutions to

$$\frac{dy}{dx} = \frac{xy}{x^2 - 1}$$

and graph several of the solution curves using the same coordinate axes.

17. Verify that $\phi(x) = 2/(1 - ce^x)$, where c is an arbitrary constant, is a one-parameter family of solutions to

$$\frac{dy}{dx} = \frac{y(y - 2)}{2}.$$

Graph the solution curves corresponding to $c = 0, \pm1, \pm2$ using the same coordinate axes.

18. Movable Singular Points. Show that for any choice of the constant C, the function $\phi(x) = (C - x)^{-1}$ is a solution to $dy/dx = y^2$ on the interval (C, ∞) and on $(-\infty, C)$. Moreover, this solution becomes unbounded as x approaches C. (Observe that there is no clue from the differential equation $dy/dx = y^2$ itself that the solution $\phi(x)$ will become unbounded at $x = C$.)

19. Show that the equation $(dy/dx)^2 + y^2 + 3 = 0$ has no (real-valued) solution.

20. Determine for which values of m the function $\phi(x) = e^{mx}$ is a solution to the given equation.

(a) $\dfrac{d^2y}{dx^2} + 6\dfrac{dy}{dx} + 5y = 0.$

(b) $\dfrac{d^3y}{dx^3} + 3\dfrac{d^2y}{dx^2} + 2\dfrac{dy}{dx} = 0.$

21. Determine for which values of m the function $\phi(x) = x^m$ is a solution to the given equation.

(a) $x^2\dfrac{d^2y}{dx^2} + x\dfrac{dy}{dx} - y = 0.$

(b) $x^2\dfrac{d^2y}{dx^2} - x\dfrac{dy}{dx} - 5y = 0.$

22. The function $\phi(x) = c_1 e^{-x} + c_2 e^{2x}$ is a solution to

$$\frac{d^2y}{dx^2} - \frac{dy}{dx} - 2y = 0$$

for any choice of the constants c_1 and c_2. Determine c_1 and c_2 so that each of the following initial conditions is satisfied.

(a) $y(0) = 2, \quad y'(0) = 1.$

(b) $y(1) = 1, \quad y'(1) = 0.$

In Problems 23 through 28 determine whether Theorem 1 implies that the given initial value problem has a unique solution.

23. $\dfrac{dy}{dx} = x^3 - y^3, \qquad y(0) = 6.$

24. $\dfrac{dy}{dx} - xy = \sin^2 x, \qquad y(\pi) = 5.$

25. $\dfrac{dy}{dx} + \cos y = \sin x, \qquad y(\pi) = 0.$

26. $\dfrac{dy}{dx} = \dfrac{x}{y}, \qquad y(1) = 0.$

27. $y\dfrac{dy}{dx} - 4x = 0, \qquad y(0) = 0 \qquad \text{(see Figure 1.1)}.$

28. $y\dfrac{dy}{dx} - 4x = 0, \qquad y(2) = -\pi.$

29. For the initial value problem (15) of Example 10, show that $\phi_1(x) \equiv 0$ and $\phi_2(x) = (x - 2)^3$ are solutions. Hence the initial value problem does not have a *unique* solution.

30. Implicit Function Theorem. *Let $G(x, y)$ have continuous first partial derivatives in the rectangle $R = \{(x, y)\colon a < x < b, c < y < d\}$ containing the point (x_0, y_0). If $G(x_0, y_0) = 0$ and $G_y(x_0, y_0) \neq 0$, then there exists a differentiable function $y = \phi(x)$, defined in some interval $I = (x_0 - h, x_0 + h)$, that satisfies $G(x, \phi(x)) = 0$ for all $x \in I$.*

The implicit function theorem gives conditions under which the relationship $G(x, y) = 0$ defines y implicitly as a function of x. Use the implicit function theorem to show that the relationship $x + y + e^{xy} = 0$, given in Example 5, defines y implicitly as a function of x near the point $(0, -1)$.

★ *1.3* *Direction Fields and the Approximation Method of Euler*[†]

The existence and uniqueness theorems that we discussed in the preceeding sections certainly have great value, but they stop short of telling us anything about the *nature* of the solution to a differential equation. For practical reasons we may need to know the value of the solution at a certain point or the intervals where the solution is increasing or the points where the solution attains a maximum value. Certainly knowing an explicit representation (a formula) for the solution would be a considerable help in answering these questions. However, for many of the differential equations that the reader is likely to encounter in "real-world" applications, it will be impossible to find such a formula. Moreover, even if we are lucky enough to obtain an implicit solution, it may be difficult to use this relationship to determine an explicit form. Thus we must rely on other methods that help us to analyze and approximate the solution.

One technique that is useful in visualizing (graphing) the solutions to a differential equation is to sketch the direction field for the equation. To describe this method we need to make a general observation. Namely, a first order equation

(1) $$\frac{dy}{dx} = f(x, y)$$

specifies a slope at each point in the plane where f is defined; in other words, it gives the direction that a solution to the equation must have at each point. A plot of the directions associated with various points in the plane is called the **direction field** for the differential equation. Since the direction field gives the "flow of solutions," it facilitates the drawing of any particular solution (such as the solution to an initial value problem). In Figure 1.2 on page 18, we have sketched the direction field for the equation

(2) $$\frac{dy}{dx} = x^2 - y$$

and indicated in color several solutions of (2).

A systematic way to construct the direction field for the equation $y' = f(x, y)$ is to first determine all the points in the xy-plane that are associated with the same slope c; that is, all the points where $f(x, y) = c$. Such a locus is called an **isocline.** For equation (2), the isoclines are just the parabolas $x^2 - y = c$. Once the isoclines are determined, we draw short segments along them with slope equal to the corresponding value of c. This procedure is called the **method of isoclines.**

▶ *Example 1*   Use the method of isoclines to sketch the solution to the initial value problem

(3) $$\frac{dy}{dx} = x - y, \qquad y(0) = 1.$$

[†] This optional section will be particularly appropriate in courses emphasizing numerical techniques.

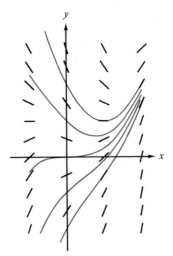

Figure 1.2 Direction field and solutions to
$dy/dx = x^2 - y$

Solution   We first determine the isoclines. These are the curves

$$x - y = c$$

which, of course, are just straight lines. In Figure 1.3(a) we have sketched (in color) several of these isoclines and indicated the corresponding value for c. We have also drawn short

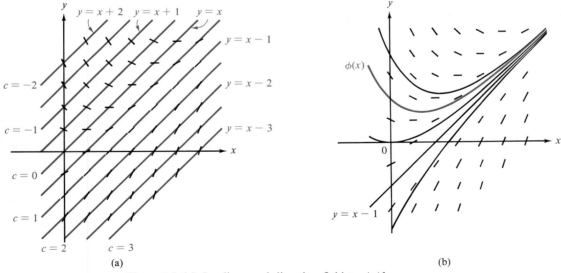

(a)   (b)

Figure 1.3 (a) Isoclines and direction field to $dy/dx = x - y$
(b) Direction field and solutions to $dy/dx = x - y$

segments (hash marks) with the appropriate slope along each isocline. Enough of the isoclines were drawn so that we can make a rough sketch (see Figure 1.3(b)) of the particular solution $\phi(x)$ to (3). Beginning at (0, 1), the solution is decreasing with slope $c = -1$. When the solution reaches and crosses the line $y = x$, it must have zero slope. After crossing the line $y = x$, the solution begins to increase. As it nears the line $y = x - 1$, its slope tends to 1, and the solution appears to approach this line asymptotically from above. ◄

   When we use the direction field method to sketch a particular solution, we try to visualize the intermediate directions between the isoclines we have drawn. If we follow a finite number of these directions, the sketch becomes a polygonal curve or chain of line segments (see Figure 1.4). This polygonal curve is, visually speaking, an approximation to the solution. Moreover, it is possible to quantify this method, so that we obtain numerical approximations to the solution at specified points. This is the so-called method of Euler (or tangent line method), which we now make precise.
   Let's assume that the initial value problem

(4) $y' = f(x, y), \qquad y(x_0) = y_0$

has a unique solution $\phi(x)$ in some interval centered at x_0. Let $h > 0$ be fixed, and consider the equally spaced points[†]

$$x_n := x_0 + nh, \qquad n = 0, 1, 2, \ldots.$$

We can construct values y_n that approximate the solution values $\phi(x_n)$ as follows. At the point (x_0, y_0), the slope of the solution to (4) is given by $dy/dx = f(x_0, y_0)$. Hence the tangent line to the solution curve at the initial point (x_0, y_0) is

(5) $y = y_0 + (x - x_0)f(x_0, y_0).$

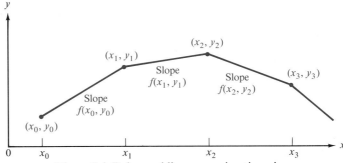

Figure 1.4 Polygonal line approximation given by Euler's method

---

[†] The symbol := means "is defined to be."

Using (5) as a linear approximation to $\phi(x)$, we find that for the point $x_1 = x_0 + h$,

$$\phi(x_1) \approx y_1 := y_0 + hf(x_0, y_0).$$

Next, starting at the point (x_1, y_1), we construct the line with slope given by the direction field at the point (x_1, y_1); that is, with slope equal to $f(x_1, y_1)$. If we follow this line[†] (namely, $y = y_1 + (x - x_1)f(x_1, y_1)$) in stepping from x_1 to $x_2 = x_1 + h$, we arrive at the approximation

$$\phi(x_2) \approx y_2 := y_1 + hf(x_1, y_1).$$

Repeating the process (as illustrated in Figure 1.4 on page 19), we get

$$\phi(x_3) \approx y_3 := y_2 + hf(x_2, y_2),$$
$$\phi(x_4) \approx y_4 := y_3 + hf(x_3, y_3), \quad \text{etc.}$$

This simple procedure is called **Euler's method** and can be summarized by the recursive formulas

(6) $\qquad x_{n+1} = x_n + h,$

(7) $\qquad y_{n+1} = y_n + hf(x_n, y_n), \qquad n = 0, 1, 2, \ldots.$

▶ *Example 2* Use Euler's method with step size $h = 0.1$ to approximate the solution to the initial value problem

(8) $\qquad y' = x\sqrt{y}, \qquad y(1) = 4$

at the points $x = 1.1, 1.2, 1.3, 1.4,$ and 1.5.

Solution Here $x_0 = 1$, $y_0 = 4$, $h = 0.1$, and $f(x, y) = x\sqrt{y}$. Thus the recursive formula (7) for y_n is

$$y_{n+1} = y_n + hf(x_n, y_n) = y_n + (0.1)x_n\sqrt{y_n}.$$

Substituting $n = 0$, we get

$$x_1 = x_0 + 0.1 = 1 + 0.1 = 1.1,$$
$$y_1 = y_0 + (0.1)x_0\sqrt{y_0} = 4 + (0.1)(1)\sqrt{4} = 4.2.$$

[†] Since y_1 is an approximation to $\phi(x_1)$, we cannot assert that this line is tangent to the solution curve $y = \phi(x)$.

Putting $n = 1$ yields

$$x_2 = x_1 + 0.1 = 1.1 + 0.1 = 1.2,$$

$$y_2 = y_1 + (0.1)x_1\sqrt{y_1} = 4.2 + (0.1)(1.1)\sqrt{4.2} = 4.42543.$$

Continuing in this manner we obtain the results listed in Table 1.1. For comparison we have included the exact value (to five decimal places) of the solution $\phi(x) = (x^2 + 7)^2/16$ to (8), which can be obtained using separation of variables (see Section 2.2). ◄

TABLE 1.1 COMPUTATIONS FOR
$y' = x\sqrt{y}, y(1) = 4$

n	x_n	Euler's Approximation	Exact Value
0	1	4	4
1	1.1	4.2	4.21276
2	1.2	4.42543	4.45210
3	1.3	4.67787	4.71976
4	1.4	4.95904	5.01760
5	1.5	5.27081	5.34766

Given the initial value problem (4) and a specific point x, how can Euler's method be used to approximate $\phi(x)$? Starting at x_0 we can take one giant step that lands on x, or we can take several smaller steps to arrive at x. If we wish to take n steps, then we set $h = (x - x_0)/n$, so that the step size h and the number of steps n are related in a specific way. It is expected that the more steps we take, the better will be the approximation. But it should be kept in mind that more steps mean more computations and hence greater roundoff error.

► *Example 3*   Use Euler's method to approximate the solution to the initial value problem

(9) $y' = y,$ $y(0) = 1$

at $x = 1$. Take $n = 1, 2, 4, 8,$ and 16.

Remark   We know that the solution to (9) is just $\phi(x) = e^x$, so Euler's method will generate algebraic approximations to the transcendental number e.

Solution Here $f(x, y) = y$, $x_0 = 0$, and $y_0 = 1$. The recursive formula for Euler's method is

(10) $\qquad y_{j+1} = y_j + hy_j = (1 + h)y_j.$

To obtain approximations at $x = 1$ with n steps, we take the step size $h = 1/n$. For $n = 1$ we have

$$\phi(1) \approx y_1 = (1 + 1)(1) = 2.$$

For $n = 2$, $\phi(x_2 = 1) \approx y_2$. In this case we get

$$y_1 = (1 + 0.5)(1) = 1.5,$$
$$\phi(1) \approx y_2 = (1 + 0.5)(1.5) = 2.25.$$

For $n = 4$, $\phi(x_4 = 1) \approx y_4$, where

$$y_1 = (1 + 0.25)(1) = 1.25,$$
$$y_2 = (1 + 0.25)(1.25) = 1.5625,$$
$$y_3 = (1 + 0.25)(1.5625) = 1.95313,$$
$$\phi(1) \approx y_4 = (1 + 0.25)(1.95313) = 2.44141.$$

(In the above computations we have rounded to five decimal places.) Similarly, taking $n = 8$ and 16, we obtain even better estimates for $\phi(1)$. These approximations are shown in Table 1.2. ◄

How good (or bad) is Euler's method? In judging a numerical scheme, we must begin with two fundamental questions. Does the method converge? And, if so, what is the rate of

TABLE 1.2 EULER'S METHOD FOR
$y' = y$, $y(0) = 1$

n	h	Approximation for $\phi(1) = e$
1	1.0	2.0
2	0.5	2.25
4	0.25	2.44141
8	0.125	2.56578
16	0.0625	2.63793

convergence? These important issues are discussed in Section 3.5 (see also Problems 18 and 19).

EXERCISES 1.3

In Problems 1 through 6 draw the isoclines with their direction markers and sketch several solution curves, including the curve satisfying the given initial conditions.

1. $dy/dx = 2x$, $y(0) = -1$.

2. $dy/dx = y$, $y(0) = 1$.

3. $dy/dx = -x/y$, $y(0) = 4$.

4. $dy/dx = x/y$, $y(0) = -1$.

5. $dy/dx = x + y$, $y(0) = 1$.

6. $dy/dx = y(2 - y)$, $y(0) = 3$. [Hint: For each $c < 1$ the isocline $y(2 - y) = c$ consists of two horizontal lines, which can be obtained using the quadratic formula.]

In many of the problems below it will be helpful to have a calculator or microcomputer available. The reader may also find it convenient to write a program for solving initial value problems using Euler's method. (Remember, all trigonometric calculations are done in radians.)

In Problems 7 through 10 use Euler's method to approximate the solution to the given initial value problem at the points $x = 0.1, 0.2, 0.3, 0.4,$ and 0.5 using steps of size 0.1 ($h = 0.1$).

7. $dy/dx = -x/y$, $y(0) = 4$
(cf. Problem 3).

8. $dy/dx = x/y$, $y(0) = -1$
(cf. Problem 4).

9. $dy/dx = x + y$, $y(0) = 1$
(cf. Problem 5).

10. $dy/dx = y(2 - y)$, $y(0) = 3$
(cf. Problem 6).

11. Use Euler's method with step size $h = 0.1$ to approximate the solution to the initial value problem

$$y' = x - y^2, \qquad y(1) = 0$$

at the points $x = 1.1, 1.2, 1.3, 1.4,$ and 1.5.

12. Use Euler's method with step size $h = 0.5$ to approximate the solution to the initial value problem

$$y' = \frac{1}{x}(y^2 + y), \qquad y(1) = 1$$

at the points $x = 1.5, 2.0, 2.5,$ and 3.0.

13. Use Euler's method to approximate the solution to the initial value problem

$$y' = 1 + x \sin(xy), \qquad y(0) = 0$$

at $x = 1$. Take $n = 1, 2, 4,$ and 8.

14. Use Euler's method to approximate the solution to the initial value problem

$$y' = 1 - \sin y, \qquad y(0) = 0$$

at $x = \pi$. Take $n = 1, 2, 4,$ and 8.

15. Use Euler's method with $h = 0.1$ to approximate the solution to the initial value problem

$$y' = \frac{1}{x^2} - \frac{y}{x} - y^2, \qquad y(1) = -1$$

on the interval $1 \le x \le 2$. Compare these approximations with the actual solution $y = -1/x$ by graphing the polygonal line approximation and the actual solution on the same coordinate system.

16. Use Euler's method with $h = 0.1$ to approximate the solution to the initial value problem

$$y' = x - y, \qquad y(0) = 0$$

on the interval $0 \le x \le 1$. Compare these approximations with the actual solution $y = e^{-x} + x - 1$ by graphing the polygonal line approximation and the actual solution on the same coordinate system.

17. Use Euler's method with $n = 20$ to approximate the solution to the initial value problem

$$y' = 1 + y^2, \qquad y(0) = 0$$

at $x = 1$. Compare the approximation with the actual solution $y = \tan x$ evaluated at $x = 1$.

18. In Example 3 we approximated the transcendental number e by using Euler's method to solve the initial value problem

$$y' = y, \qquad y(0) = 1.$$

Show that the Euler approximation y_n obtained by using the step size $1/n$ is given by the formula

$$y_n = \left(1 + \frac{1}{n}\right)^n, \qquad n = 1, 2, \dots.$$

Recall from calculus that

$$\lim_{n \to \infty} \left(1 + \frac{1}{n}\right)^n = e,$$

and hence Euler's method converges (theoretically) to the correct value.

19. Prove that the rate of convergence for Euler's method in Problem 18 is like $1/n$ by showing that

$$\lim_{n \to \infty} \frac{e - y_n}{1/n} = \frac{e}{2}.$$

[Hint: Use L'Hôpital's rule and the Maclaurin expansion for $\ln(1 + t)$.]

TABLE 1.3		

Method	Approximation of $\phi(1)$	Approximation of $\phi(3)$
Euler's method using steps of size 0.1		
Euler's method using steps of size 0.01		
Taylor polynomial of degree 2		
Taylor polynomial of degree 5		
Exact value of $\phi(x)$ to nearest thousandth		

B. PICARD'S APPROXIMATION METHOD

The initial value problem

(1) $\qquad y'(x) = f(x, y), \qquad y(x_0) = y_0$

can be expressed as an **integral** equation. This is obtained by integrating both sides of (1) with respect to x from $x = x_0$ to $x = x_1$:

(2) $\qquad \displaystyle\int_{x_0}^{x_1} y'(x)\,dx = y(x_1) - y(x_0) = \int_{x_0}^{x_1} f(x, y(x))\,dx.$

Substituting $y(x_0) = y_0$ and solving for $y(x_1)$ gives

(3) $\qquad \displaystyle y(x_1) = y_0 + \int_{x_0}^{x_1} f(x, y(x))\,dx.$

If we use t instead of x as the variable of integration, we can let $x = x_1$ be the upper limit of integration. Equation (3) then becomes

(4) $\qquad \displaystyle y(x) = y_0 + \int_{x_0}^{x} f(t, y(t))\,dt.$

Equation (4) can be used to generate successive approximations of a solution to (1). Let the function $\phi_0(x)$ be an initial guess or approximation of a solution to (1); then a new approximation is given by

$$\phi_1(x) := y_0 + \int_{x_0}^{x} f(t, \phi_0(t))\,dt,$$

where we have replaced $y(t)$ by the approximation $\phi_0(t)$ in the argument of f. In a similar fashion we can use $\phi_1(x)$ to generate a new approximation $\phi_2(x)$, and so on. In general, we obtain the $(n + 1)$st approximation from the relation

(5) $$\phi_{n+1}(x) := y_0 + \int_{x_0}^{x} f(t, \phi_n(t))\, dt.$$

This procedure is called **Picard's method,**† and under certain assumptions on f and $\phi_0(x)$, the sequence $\{\phi_n(x)\}$ is known to converge to a solution to (1). These assumptions and the proof of convergence are given in Chapter 11 of *Fundamentals of Differential Equations and Boundary Value Problems*.

Without further information about the solution to (1), it is common practice to take $\phi_0(x) \equiv y_0$.

(a) Use Picard's method with $\phi_0(x) \equiv 1$ to obtain the next four successive approximations of the solution to

(6) $$y'(x) = y(x), \qquad y(0) = 1.$$

Show, in general, that these approximations are just the partial sums of the Maclaurin series for the actual solution e^x.

(b) Use Picard's method with $\phi_0(x) \equiv 0$ to obtain the next three successive approximations of the solution to the nonlinear problem

(7) $$y'(x) = x - [y(x)]^2, \qquad y(0) = 0.$$

(c) In Problem 29 in Exercises 1.2 we showed that the initial value problem

(8) $$y'(x) = 3[y(x)]^{2/3}, \qquad y(2) = 0$$

does not have a unique solution. Show that Picard's method beginning with $\phi_0(x) \equiv 0$ converges to the solution $y(x) \equiv 0$, whereas Picard's method beginning with $\phi_0(x) = x - 2$ converges to the second solution $y(x) = (x - 2)^3$. [Hint: For the guess $\phi_0(x) = x - 2$, show that $\phi_n(x)$ has the form $c_n(x - 2)^{r_n}$, where $c_n \to 1$ and $r_n \to 3$ as $n \to \infty$.]

---

† *Historical Footnote:* This approximation method is a by-product of the famous Picard-Lindelöf existence theorem formulated at the end of the nineteenth century.

First Order Differential Equations

2.1 Introduction: Motion of a Falling Body

An object falls through the air toward the Earth. Assuming that the only forces acting on the object are gravity and air resistance, determine the velocity of the object as a function of time.

Newton's second law states that force is equal to mass times acceleration, assuming the mass is constant. We can express this by the equation

$$m \frac{dv}{dt} = F,$$

where F represents the total force on the object, m is the mass of the object, and dv/dt is the acceleration. Here we have expressed acceleration as the derivative of velocity with respect to time, dv/dt.

Near the Earth's surface the force due to gravity is just the weight of the object. This force can be expressed by mg, where g is the acceleration due to gravity. There is no general law that exactly determines the air resistance acting on the object, since this force seems to depend upon the velocity of the object, the density of the air, and the shape of the object, among other things. However, in some instances air resistance can be reasonably represented by $-kv$, where k is a positive constant depending on the density of the air and the shape of the object. We use the minus sign because air resistance is a force that opposes the motion.

Applying Newton's law we obtain the first order differential equation

(1)
$$m\frac{dv}{dt} = mg - kv.$$

This equation may be solved using **separation of variables** (this method is discussed more fully in Section 2.2). Treating dv and dt as differentials, we separate the variables to obtain

$$\frac{dv}{mg - kv} = \frac{dt}{m}.$$

Integrating, we find

$$\int \frac{1}{mg - kv}\, dv = \int \frac{1}{m}\, dt$$

$$-\frac{1}{k}\ln(mg - kv) = \frac{t}{m} + C,$$

where C is a "constant of integration." The last equation can be solved for v to obtain

(2)
$$v = \frac{mg}{k} - \frac{1}{k}e^{-kC}e^{-kt/m},$$

which is called a **general solution** to the differential equation because, as we shall see in Section 2.4, every solution to (1) can be expressed in the form given in (2).

In a specific case we would be given the values of m, g, and k. To determine the constant C in the general solution, we can use the initial velocity of the object v_0. That is, we solve the **initial value problem**

$$m\frac{dv}{dt} = mg - kv, \qquad v(0) = v_0.$$

Substituting $v = v_0$ and $t = 0$ into the general solution to the differential equation, we can

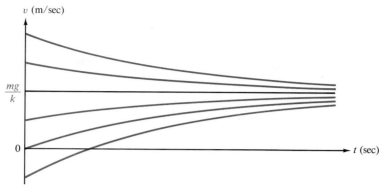

Figure 2.1 Graph of $v(t)$ for six different initial velocities v_0. ($g = 9.8$ m/sec^2, $m/k = 5$ sec)

solve for C. With this value for C, the solution to the initial value problem is

$$(3) \qquad v = \frac{mg}{k} + \left(v_0 - \frac{mg}{k} \right) e^{-kt/m}.$$

The preceding formula gives the velocity of the object falling through the air as a function of time if the initial velocity of the object is v_0. In Figure 2.1 we have sketched the graph of $v(t)$ for various values of v_0. It appears from Figure 2.1 that the velocity $v(t)$ approaches *mg/k regardless of the initial velocity v_0.* (This is easy to see from formula (3) by letting $t \to \infty$.) The constant mg/k is referred to as the **limiting velocity** of the object.

From this model for a falling body we can make certain observations. Since $e^{-kt/m}$ rapidly tends to zero, the velocity is approximately the weight, mg, divided by the coefficient of air resistance, k. Thus, in the presence of air resistance, the heavier the object, the faster it will fall. Similarly, the less air resistance, the faster an object will fall. These observations certainly agree with our experience.

Many other physical problems,[†] when given a mathematical formulation, lead to first order differential equations or initial value problems. Several of these are discussed in Chapter 3. In this chapter we shall learn how to recognize and obtain solutions for different types of first order equations. We begin by studying separable equations, then exact equations, and then linear equations. The methods for solving these are the most basic. In the last two sections we illustrate how devices such as integrating factors, substitutions, and transformations can be used to transform a special type of equation into either a separable, exact, or linear equation that we can solve.

[†] The physical problem just discussed leads to other mathematical models. For example, more precise models would take into account the variations in the gravitational field of the Earth.

2.2 *Separable Equations*

A simple class of differential equations that can be solved using integration is the class of separable equations.

SEPARABLE EQUATION

Definition 1.   If the right-hand side of the equation

(1) $$\frac{dy}{dx} = f(x, y)$$

can be expressed as a function that depends only on x times a function that depends only on y, then the differential equation is called **separable.**[†]

Thus (1) is separable if it can be written in the form

(2) $$\frac{dy}{dx} = g(x)p(y).$$

For example, the equation

$$\frac{dy}{dx} = \frac{2x + xy}{y^2 + 1}$$

is separable, since

$$\frac{2x + xy}{y^2 + 1} = x\,\frac{2 + y}{y^2 + 1} = g(x)p(y).$$

However, the equation

$$\frac{dy}{dx} = 1 + xy$$

admits no such factorization of the right-hand side and so is not separable.
To obtain solutions to the separable equation (2), we first write it in the form

(3) $$h(y)\,\frac{dy}{dx} = g(x),$$

[†] *Historical Footnote:* A procedure for solving separable equations was implicitly discovered by Gottfried Leibniz in 1691. The explicit technique called separation of variables was formalized by John Bernoulli in 1694.

where[†] $h(y) := 1/p(y)$. Letting $H(y)$ and $G(x)$ denote antiderivatives (indefinite integrals) of $h(y)$ and $g(x)$, respectively, that is

$$H'(y) = h(y), \qquad G'(x) = g(x),$$

then equation (3) becomes

(4) $$H'(y)\frac{dy}{dx} = G'(x).$$

Now let $y(x)$ be a solution to equation (4). Recalling the chain rule for differentiation, we then have

$$\frac{d}{dx}H(y(x)) = \frac{d}{dx}G(x).$$

In other words, $H(y(x))$ and $G(x)$ are two functions of x that have the same derivative; thus they must differ by a constant. That is,

(5) $$H(y(x)) = G(x) + C,$$

which defines the solution $y(x)$ *implicitly*.

This procedure can be considerably streamlined by treating dy and dx as differentials.

METHOD FOR SOLVING SEPARABLE EQUATIONS

To solve the equation

$$h(y)\frac{dy}{dx} = g(x),$$

multiply by dx to obtain

$$h(y)dy = g(x)\,dx.$$

Then integrate both sides:

$$\int h(y)\,dy = \int g(x)\,dx,$$
$$H(y) = G(x) + C.$$

The last equation is the implicit solution previously obtained in equation (5).

[†] The symbol := means "is defined to be."

▶ **Example 1**   Solve

(6) $$\frac{dy}{dx} = \frac{x - 5}{y^2}.$$

Solution   Following the streamlined approach, we separate the variables and rewrite (6) in the form

$$y^2 \, dy = (x - 5) \, dx.$$

Integrating, we have

$$\int y^2 \, dy = \int (x - 5) \, dx$$

$$\frac{y^3}{3} = \frac{x^2}{2} - 5x + C,$$

and solving this last equation for y gives

$$y = \left(\frac{3x^2}{2} - 15x + 3C \right)^{1/3}.$$

Since C is a constant of integration that can be any real number, $3C$ can also be any real number. Replacing $3C$ by the single symbol K, we then have

(7) $$y = \left(\frac{3x^2}{2} - 15x + K \right)^{1/3}.$$

If we wish to abide by the custom of letting C represent an arbitrary constant, we can go one step further and use C instead of K in the final answer. ◀

As Example 1 attests, separable equations are among the easiest to solve. However, the procedure does require a facility for computing integrals. Many of the procedures to be discussed later in the text also require a familiarity with the techniques of integration. For the student who requires it, a brief table of integrals can be found on the inside front cover.

▶ **Example 2**   Solve the initial value problem

(8) $$\frac{dy}{dx} = \frac{y - 1}{x + 3}, \qquad y(-1) = 0.$$

Solution   Separating the variables and integrating gives

(9)
$$\frac{dy}{y-1} = \frac{dx}{x+3},$$

$$\int \frac{dy}{y-1} = \int \frac{dx}{x+3},$$

(10) $\ln|y-1| = \ln|x+3| + C.$

At this point we can either solve for y explicitly (retaining the constant C) or use the initial condition to first determine C and then solve explicitly for y. Let's try the first approach.
Exponentiating equation (10), we have

$$e^{\ln|y-1|} = e^{\ln|x+3|+C} = e^C e^{\ln|x+3|},$$

$$|y-1| = e^C|x+3| = C_1|x+3|,$$

where $C_1 := e^C$. Now, depending on the values of y, we have $|y-1| = \pm(y-1)$; and similarly, $|x+3| = \pm(x+3)$. Thus (11) can be written as

$$y - 1 = \pm C_1(x+3) \quad \text{or} \quad y = 1 \pm C_1(x+3),$$

where the choice of sign depends upon the values of x and y. Since C_1 is an arbitrary positive constant (recall that $C_1 = e^C > 0$), we can replace $\pm C_1$ by C, where C now represents an arbitrary nonzero constant. We then obtain

(12) $y = 1 + C(x+3).$

Finally, we determine C such that the initial condition $y(-1) = 0$ is satisfied. Putting $x = -1$ and $y = 0$ in equation (12) gives

$$0 = 1 + C(-1+3) = 1 + 2C,$$

and so $C = -\frac{1}{2}$. Thus the solution to the initial value problem is

(13) $y = 1 - \frac{1}{2}(x+3) = -\frac{1}{2}(x+1).$

Alternative Approach.   The second approach is to first set $x = -1$ and $y = 0$ in equation (10) and then solve for C. In this case we obtain

$$\ln|0-1| = \ln|-1+3| + C,$$

$$0 = \ln 1 = \ln 2 + C,$$

and so $C = -\ln 2$. Thus, from (10), the solution y is given implicitly by

(14) $\ln(1 - y) = \ln(x + 3) - \ln 2,$

where we have replaced $|y - 1|$ by $1 - y$ and $|x + 3|$ by $x + 3$ since we are interested in x and y near the initial values $x = -1$, $y = 0$ (for such values, $y - 1 < 0$ and $x + 3 > 0$). Solving equation (14) for y, we find

$$\ln(1 - y) = \ln(x + 3) - \ln 2 = \ln\left(\frac{x + 3}{2}\right),$$

$$1 - y = \frac{x + 3}{2},$$

$$y = 1 - \tfrac{1}{2}(x + 3) = -\tfrac{1}{2}(x + 1),$$

which agrees with the solution (13) found by the first method. ◀

▶ *Example 3*   Solve

(15) $\dfrac{dy}{dx} = \dfrac{6x^5 - 2x + 1}{\cos y + e^y}.$

Solution   Separating variables and integrating, we find

$$(\cos y + e^y)\,dy = (6x^5 - 2x + 1)\,dx,$$
$$\int (\cos y + e^y)\,dy = \int (6x^5 - 2x + 1)\,dx,$$
$$\sin y + e^y = x^6 - x^2 + x + C.$$

At this point we reach an impasse. We would like to solve for y explicitly, but we are unable to do so. This is often the case in solving first order equations. Consequently, when we say "solve the equation," we must on occasion be content if only an implicit form of the solution has been found. ◀

As we shall see in the next section, first order differential equations are often written in the differential form

(16) $M(x, y)\,dx + N(x, y)\,dy = 0.$

Such an equation is separable if both M and N are separable; that is, if each can be expressed as a function that depends only on x times a function that depends only on y (see Problem 28).

EXERCISES 2.2

In Problems 1 through 6 determine whether the given differential equation is separable.

1. $\dfrac{dy}{dx} = y^3 + y.$

2. $\dfrac{dy}{dx} = \sin(x + y).$

3. $\dfrac{dy}{dx} = \dfrac{3e^{x+y}}{x^2 + 2}.$

4. $\dfrac{ds}{dt} = t \ln(s^{2t}) + 8t^2.$

5. $s^2 + \dfrac{ds}{dt} = \dfrac{s + 1}{st}.$

6. $(xy^2 + 3y^2)\,dy - 2x\,dx = 0.$

In Problems 7 through 16 solve the equation.

7. $\dfrac{dy}{dx} = \dfrac{x^2 - 1}{y^2}.$

8. $\dfrac{dy}{dx} = \dfrac{1}{xy^3}.$

9. $\dfrac{dy}{dx} = 3x^2 y.$

10. $\dfrac{dy}{dx} = y(2 + \sin x).$

11. $\dfrac{dy}{dx} = 3x^2(1 + y^2).$

12. $\dfrac{dy}{dx} + y^2 = y.$

13. $x\dfrac{dv}{dx} = \dfrac{1 - 4v^2}{3v}.$

14. $\dfrac{dy}{dx} = \dfrac{\sec^2 y}{1 + x^2}.$

15. $y \sin x \, e^{\cos x}\, dx + y^{-1}\, dy = 0.$

16. $(x + xy^2)\,dx + e^{x^2} y\, dy = 0.$

In Problems 17 through 26 solve the initial value problem.

17. $x^2\, dx + 2y\, dy = 0, \qquad y(0) = 2.$

18. $\dfrac{dy}{dx} = 8x^3 e^{-2y}, \qquad y(1) = 0.$

19. $\dfrac{dy}{dx} = y \sin x, \qquad y(\pi) = -3.$

20. $\dfrac{dy}{dx} = \dfrac{3x^2 + 4x + 2}{2y + 1}, \qquad y(0) = -1.$

21. $\dfrac{dy}{dx} = 2\sqrt{y + 1}\,\cos x, \qquad y(\pi) = 0.$

22. $y' = x^3(1 - y), \qquad y(0) = 3.$

23. $\dfrac{dy}{dx} = (1 + y^2)\tan x, \qquad y(0) = \sqrt{3}.$

24. $\dfrac{dy}{dx} = 2x\cos^2 y, \qquad y(0) = \pi/4.$

25. $\dfrac{dy}{dx} = x^2(1 + y), \qquad y(0) = 3.$

26. $\sqrt{y}\, dx + (1 + x)\, dy = 0, \qquad y(0) = 1.$

27. Solutions Not Expressible in Terms of Elementary Functions. As discussed in calculus, certain indefinite integrals (antiderivatives) such as $\int e^{x^2}\, dx$ cannot be expressed in finite terms using elementary functions. When such an integral is encountered while solving a differential equation, it is often helpful to use definite integration (integrals with variable upper limit). For example, consider the initial value problem

$$\frac{dy}{dx} = e^{x^2} y^2, \qquad y(2) = 1.$$

Dividing both sides by y^2 and integrating from $x = 2$ to $x = x_1$ gives

$$\int_2^{x_1} y^{-2}(x)\frac{dy}{dx}\,dx = -y^{-1}(x_1) + y^{-1}(2) = \int_2^{x_1} e^{x^2}\,dx.$$

If we let t be the variable of integration and replace x_1 by x and $y(2)$ by 1, then we can express the solution to the initial value problem by

$$y(x) = \left\{ 1 - \int_2^x e^{t^2}\,dt \right\}^{-1}.$$

Use definite integration to find an explicit solution to the initial value problems in (a)–(c).

(a) $dy/dx = e^{x^2}$, $y(0) = 0$.
(b) $dy/dx = e^{x^2}y^{-2}$, $y(0) = 1$.
(c) $dy/dx = \sqrt{1 + \sin x}\,(1 + y^2)$, $y(0) = 1$.
(d) Use Simpson's rule (see Appendix B) to help approximate the solution to part (b) at $x = 0.5$ to three decimal places.

28. **Differential Form.**   Show that equation (16) represents a separable equation if both functions $M(x, y)$ and $N(x, y)$ can be expressed as a function that depends only on x times a function that depends only on y.

29. **Uniqueness Questions.**   In our discussion in Chapter 1 we indicated that in applications most *initial value problems* will have a unique solution. In fact, the existence of unique solutions was so important that we stated an existence and uniqueness theorem, Theorem 1, page 12. The method for separable equations will give us a solution, but it may not give us all the solutions. To see this, consider the equation $dy/dx = y^{1/3}$.

(a) Use the method of separation of variables to show that

$$y = \left(\frac{2x}{3} + C \right)^{3/2}$$

is a solution.
(b) Show that the initial value problem $dy/dx = y^{1/3}$ with $y(0) = 0$ is satisfied for $C = 0$ by $y = (2x/3)^{3/2}$.
(c) Now show that the constant function $y \equiv 0$ also satisfies the initial value problem given in part (b). Hence this initial value problem does not have a unique solution.
(d) Finally, show that the conditions of Theorem 1 on page 12 are not satisfied.

30. **Formal Solutions.**   The method of separation of variables usually produces an implicit solution to the equation, which in certain cases can be solved to obtain an explicit solution. This problem illustrates that the method actually gives expressions that "formally" satisfy the equation, but some care is required when choosing the arbitrary constant if one is, in fact, going to obtain an implicit solution.

(a) Solve the equation $x + y\,dy/dx = 0$ using separation of variables to get an expression of the form $x^2 + y^2 = C$.

(b) Show that when $C = -1$, there are no real values for x and y that satisfy $x^2 + y^2 = C$.

(c) While C was an arbitrary constant of integration, show that it is only for $C > 0$ that we obtain an implicit relationship between x and y.

31. **Division by Zero.** In developing our method of separation of variables, we tacitly assumed, when we divided by $p(y)$ to obtain equation (3), that $p(y) \neq 0$. This assumption may cause us to lose solutions.

(a) For the equation

$$\frac{dy}{dx} = (x - 3)(y + 1)^{2/3},$$

use separation of variables to derive the solution

$$y = -1 + (x^2/6 - x + C)^3.$$

(b) Show that $y \equiv -1$ satisfies the original equation

$$dy/dx = (x - 3)(y + 1)^{2/3}.$$

(c) Show that there is no choice of the constant C that will make the solution in part (a) yield the solution $y \equiv -1$. Thus we lost the solution $y \equiv -1$ when we divided by $(y + 1)^{2/3}$.

32. **Interval of Definition.** By looking at an initial value problem $dy/dx = f(x, y)$ with $y(x_0) = y_0$, it is not always possible to determine the domain of the solution $y(x)$ or the interval over which the function $y(x)$ satisfies the differential equation.

(a) Solve the equation $dy/dx = xy^3$.

(b) Give explicitly the solutions to the initial value problem with $y(0) = 1$; $y(0) = \frac{1}{2}$; $y(0) = 2$.

(c) Determine the domains of the solutions in part (b).

(d) As found in part (c), the domains of the solutions depend upon the initial conditions. For the initial value problem $dy/dx = xy^3$ with $y(0) = a$, $a > 0$, show that as $a \to 0^+$, the domain approaches the whole real line $(-\infty, \infty)$, and as $a \to +\infty$, the domain shrinks to a single point.

(e) Sketch the solutions to the initial value problem $dy/dx = xy^3$ with $y(0) = a$ for $a = \pm\frac{1}{2}$, ± 1, and ± 2.

33. **Mixing.** Suppose a brine containing 3 kg of salt per liter (L) runs into a tank initially filled with 400 L of water containing 20 kg of salt. If the brine enters at 10 L/min, the mixture is kept uniform by stirring, and the mixture flows out at the same rate, find the amount of salt in the tank after 10 min (see Figure 2.2 on page 40). [Hint: Let A denote the number of kilograms of salt in the tank at t minutes after the process begins, and use the fact that

rate of increase in A = rate of input − rate of exit.

A further discussion of mixing problems is given in Section 3.2.]

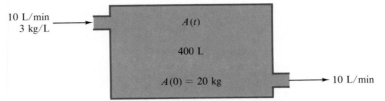

Figure 2.2 Schematic representation of a mixing problem

34. **Newton's Law of Cooling.**   According to Newton's law of cooling, if an object at temperature T is immersed in a medium having the constant temperature M, then the rate of change of T is proportional to the difference of temperature $M - T$. This gives the differential equation

$$dT/dt = k(M - T).$$

   (a) Solve the differential equation for T.
   (b) A thermometer reading $100°$ is placed in a medium having a constant temperature of $70°$. After 6 min the thermometer reads $80°$. What is the reading after 20 min?

(Further applications of Newton's law of cooling appear in Section 3.3.)

35. Blood plasma is stored at $40°$. Before the plasma can be used, it must be $90°$. When the plasma is placed in an oven at $120°$, it takes 45 min for the plasma to warm to $90°$. Assume that Newton's law of cooling (Problem 34) applies and that the cooling constant k is independent of M, the temperature of the oven. How long will it take the plasma to warm to $90°$ if the oven temperature is set at **(a)** $100°$, **(b)** $140°$, **(c)** $80°$?

2.3 *Exact Equations*

The first order differential equation

(1) $$\frac{dy}{dx} = f(x, y)$$

may also be expressed in the differential form

(2) $$M(x, y)\, dx + N(x, y)\, dy = 0.$$

For example, the equation

(3) $$\frac{dy}{dx} = \frac{3x^2 - y}{x - 1}$$

can be expressed as

(4) $(y - 3x^2)\,dx + (x - 1)\,dy = 0,$

where $M(x, y) = y - 3x^2$ and $N(x, y) = x - 1$. There are other ways of expressing equation (3) in differential form, such as

$$\left(\frac{y - 3x^2}{x - 1}\right)dx + dy = 0.$$

To solve equation (2), it is helpful to know whether the left-hand side is a **total differential.** Recall that the total differential $dF(x, y)$ of a function $F(x, y)$ of two variables is defined by

$$dF(x, y) := \frac{\partial F}{\partial x}(x, y)\,dx + \frac{\partial F}{\partial y}(x, y)\,dy,$$

where dx and dy are arbitrary increments. For example, if $F(x, y) = \sin(xy)$, then

$$dF(x, y) = y\,\cos(xy)\,dx + x\,\cos(xy)\,dy.$$

EXACT DIFFERENTIAL FORM

Definition 2.   The differential form

(5) $M(x, y)\,dx + N(x, y)\,dy$

is said to be **exact** in a rectangle R if there is a function $F(x, y)$ such that

(6) $\dfrac{\partial F}{\partial x}(x, y) = M(x, y)$ and $\dfrac{\partial F}{\partial y}(x, y) = N(x, y)$

for all (x, y) in R. That is, the total differential of $F(x, y)$ satisfies

$$dF(x, y) = M(x, y)\,dx + N(x, y)\,dy.$$

If $M(x, y)\,dx + N(x, y)\,dy$ is an exact differential form, then the equation

$$M(x, y)\,dx + N(x, y)\,dy = 0$$

is called an **exact equation.**

For example, the equation $y\,dx + x\,dy = 0$ is exact, since

$$d(xy) = y\,dx + x\,dy$$

is the total differential of $F(x, y) = xy$.

Solving exact equations is a simple matter once the function $F(x, y)$ of (6) is found. If we treat y as a function of x on some interval I, the equation $dF(x, y) = 0$ is equivalent to $\dfrac{d}{dx} F(x, y(x)) = 0$ for x in I. Hence $F(x, y(x)) = C$. In other words, the solutions of

$$dF(x, y) = 0$$

are given implicitly by

$$F(x, y) = C.$$

Like indefinite integrals, the function $F(x, y)$ satisfying conditions (6) is not uniquely determined, since we can always add an arbitrary constant K to $F(x, y)$. Because we are ultimately interested in the solution to the equation $dF = 0$, we can absorb the constant K in with the constant C and still express the solution by $F(x, y) = C$. Hence we need only find one function $F(x, y)$ whose total differential dF is $M\,dx + N\,dy$ in order to solve an exact differential equation.

▶ **Example 1**   Show that the equation

(7) $$(y - 3x^2)\,dx + (x - 1)\,dy = 0$$

is exact and find its solutions.

Solution   If we regroup the terms in (7) as follows:

$$(y\,dx + x\,dy) - 3x^2\,dx - dy = 0,$$

then we see that this equation can be written in the form

$$d(xy) - d(x^3) - dy = 0,$$
$$d(xy - x^3 - y) = 0.$$

Hence $F(x, y) = xy - x^3 - y$ satisfies

$$\frac{\partial F}{\partial x}(x, y) = y - 3x^2 = M(x, y),$$

$$\frac{\partial F}{\partial y}(x, y) = x - 1 = N(x, y),$$

and so (7) is exact. Furthermore, the solutions of (7) are given implicitly by $xy - x^3 - y = C$ or explicitly by $y = (x^3 + C)/(x - 1)$. ◀

In the preceding example we were able to see a regrouping of the terms that made it easy for us to recognize a function $F(x, y)$ whose total differential was $M(x, y)\,dx + N(x, y)\,dy$. Unfortunately, for other equations it may not be simple to determine $F(x, y)$ by inspection.

Consider the equation

$$(3y + x)\,dx + 2x\,dy = 0.$$

For this equation no amount of regrouping helps, since (as we shall soon see) it is *not* an exact equation. What we really need is a test to determine whether an equation is exact, and if it is exact, then a procedure for finding the function $F(x, y)$. These needs are met by the following theorem.

TEST FOR EXACTNESS

Theorem 1. Suppose the first partial derivatives of $M(x, y)$ and $N(x, y)$ are continuous in a rectangle R. Then

$$M(x, y)\,dx + N(x, y)\,dy = 0$$

is an exact equation in R if and only if

(8)
$$\frac{\partial M}{\partial y}(x, y) = \frac{\partial N}{\partial x}(x, y)$$

for all (x, y) in R.[†]

Proof   There are two parts to the theorem. First, if the equation is exact, then condition (8) is satisfied. Second, if condition (8) is satisfied, then the equation is exact. We will prove the first part and indicate the proof of the second, leaving the details for the exercises.

($\Rightarrow$) Assume that $M\,dx + N\,dy = 0$ is exact. Then there is a function $F(x, y)$ satisfying

(9)
$$\frac{\partial F}{\partial x}(x, y) = M(x, y) \quad \text{and} \quad \frac{\partial F}{\partial y}(x, y) = N(x, y).$$

Using these equations to compute $\partial M / \partial y$ and $\partial N / \partial x$, we obtain

$$\frac{\partial M}{\partial y}(x, y) = \frac{\partial^2 F}{\partial y\,\partial x}(x, y) \qquad \text{and} \qquad \frac{\partial N}{\partial x}(x, y) = \frac{\partial^2 F}{\partial x\,\partial y}(x, y).$$

[†] *Historical Footnote:* This theorem was proven by Leonhard Euler in 1734.

Since the first partial derivatives of M and N are continuous in R, the same must be true for the second order mixed partial derivatives of F. From calculus we recall that the continuity of these mixed partial derivatives implies that they are equal. Hence,

$$\frac{\partial M}{\partial y} = \frac{\partial^2 F}{\partial y\, \partial x} = \frac{\partial^2 F}{\partial x\, \partial y} = \frac{\partial N}{\partial x}$$

in R. Consequently, if $M\,dx + N\,dy = 0$ is exact, then condition (8) is satisfied.

Before proceeding with the second part of the proof, let's derive a formula for the function $F(x, y)$ satisfying the equations (9). Holding y constant, we integrate the first equation in (9) with respect to x to obtain

(10) $F(x, y) = \int M(x, y)\, dx + g(y).$

Notice that instead of using C to represent the constant of integration, we have written $g(y)$. This is because y is held fixed while integrating with respect to x, and so our "constant" may well depend on y. To determine $g(y)$, we differentiate both sides of (10) with respect to y to obtain

(11) $\dfrac{\partial F}{\partial y}(x, y) = \dfrac{\partial}{\partial y} \int M(x, y)\, dx + \dfrac{\partial}{\partial y} g(y).$

As g is a function of y alone, we can write $\partial g/\partial y = g'(y)$, and solving (11) for $g'(y)$ gives

$$g'(y) = \frac{\partial F}{\partial y}(x, y) - \frac{\partial}{\partial y} \int M(x, y)\, dx.$$

Since $\partial F/\partial y = N$, this last equation becomes

(12) $g'(y) = N(x, y) - \dfrac{\partial}{\partial y} \int M(x, y)\, dx.$

Notice that although the right-hand side of (12) indicates a possible dependence on x, the appearances of this variable must cancel because the left-hand side, $g'(y)$, depends only on y. By integrating (12) we can determine $g(y)$ up to a numerical constant and therefore we can determine the function $F(x, y)$ up to a numerical constant from the functions $M(x, y)$ and $N(x, y)$.

($\Leftarrow$) Suppose now that condition (8) holds. We will show that $M\,dx + N\,dy = 0$ is exact by actually exhibiting a function $F(x, y)$ that satisfies $\partial F/\partial x = M$ and $\partial F/\partial y = N$. Fortunately, we needn't look too far for such a function. The discussion in the first part of the proof suggests (10) as a candidate, where $g'(y)$ is given by (12). Namely, we define $F(x, y)$ by

(13) $$F(x, y) := \int_{x_0}^{x} M(t, y)\, dt + g(y),$$

where (x_0, y_0) is a fixed point in the rectangle R and $g(y)$ is determined, up to a numerical constant, by the equation

(14) $$g'(y) := N(x, y) - \frac{\partial}{\partial y} \int_{x_0}^{x} M(t, y)\, dt.$$

Before proceeding, we must address an extremely important question concerning the definition of $F(x, y)$. That is, how can we be sure (in this portion of the proof) that $g'(y)$, as given in equation (14), is really a function of just y? To show that the right-hand side of (14) is independent of x—i.e., that the appearances of the variable x cancel—all we need do is show that its partial derivative with respect to x is zero. This is where condition (8) is utilized. We leave to the reader this computation and the verification that $F(x, y)$ satisfies conditions (6) (see Problems 29 and 30). ■ ■ ■

Theorem 1 suggests the following procedure for solving equation (2). If the equation is not separable, then compute $\partial M / \partial y$ and $\partial N / \partial x$. If $\partial M / \partial y = \partial N / \partial x$, then the equation is exact and all we must do is determine an appropriate function $F(x, y)$. Let's review the process.

METHOD FOR SOLVING EXACT EQUATIONS

(a) If $M\, dx + N\, dy = 0$ is exact, then $\partial F / \partial x = M$. Integrate this last equation with respect to x to get

(15) $$F(x, y) = \int M(x, y)\, dx + g(y).$$

(b) To determine $g(y)$, take the partial derivative with respect to y of both sides of equation (15) and substitute N for $\partial F / \partial y$. We can now solve for $g'(y)$.

(c) Integrate $g'(y)$ to obtain $g(y)$ up to a numerical constant. Substituting $g(y)$ into equation (15) gives $F(x, y)$.

(d) The solution to $M\, dx + N\, dy = 0$ is given implicitly by

(16) $$F(x, y) = C.$$

▶ **Example 2** Solve

(17) $$(2xy - \sec^2 x)\, dx + (x^2 + 2y)\, dy = 0.$$

Solution   Here $M(x, y) = 2xy - \sec^2 x$ and $N(x, y) = x^2 + 2y$. Since

$$\frac{\partial M}{\partial y} = 2x = \frac{\partial N}{\partial x},$$

equation (17) is exact. To find $F(x, y)$, we begin by integrating M with respect to x:

(18) $F(x, y) = \int (2xy - \sec^2 x)\, dx + g(y)$

$$= x^2 y - \tan x + g(y).$$

Next we take the partial derivative of (18) with respect to y and substitute $x^2 + 2y$ for N:

$$\frac{\partial F}{\partial y}(x, y) = N(x, y),$$

$$x^2 + g'(y) = x^2 + 2y.$$

Thus $g'(y) = 2y$, and since the choice of the constant of integration is not important, we can take $g(y) = y^2$. Hence, from (18), we have $F(x, y) = x^2 y - \tan x + y^2$, and the solution to equation (17) is given implicitly by $x^2 y - \tan x + y^2 = C$. ◄

Remark   The procedure for solving exact equations requires several steps. As a check on our work, we observe that when we solve for $g'(y)$, we must obtain a function that is independent of x. If this is not the case, then we have erred either in our computation of $F(x, y)$ or in computing $\partial M/\partial y$ or $\partial N/\partial x$.

In the construction of $F(x, y)$ we can first integrate $N(x, y)$ with respect to y to get

(19) $F(x, y) = \int N(x, y)\, dy + h(x)$

and then proceed to find $h(x)$. We illustrate this alternative method in the next example.

► ***Example 3***   Solve

(20) $(1 + e^x y + x e^x y)\, dx + (x e^x + 2)\, dy = 0.$

Solution   Here $M = 1 + e^x y + x e^x y$ and $N = x e^x + 2$. Since

$$\frac{\partial M}{\partial y} = e^x + x e^x = \frac{\partial N}{\partial x},$$

equation (20) is exact. If we now integrate $N(x, y)$ with respect to y, we obtain

$$F(x, y) = \int (xe^x + 2)\, dy + h(x) = xe^x y + 2y + h(x).$$

When we take the partial derivative with respect to x and substitute for M, we get

$$\frac{\partial F}{\partial x}(x, y) = M(x, y)$$

$$e^x y + xe^x y + h'(x) = 1 + e^x y + xe^x y.$$

Thus $h'(x) = 1$, and so we take $h(x) = x$. Hence $F(x, y) = xe^x y + 2y + x$, and the solution to equation (20) is given implicitly by $xe^x y + 2y + x = C$. In this case, we can solve explicitly for y to obtain $y = (C - x)/(2 + xe^x)$. ◀

Since we can use either procedure for finding $F(x, y)$, it may be worthwhile to consider each of the integrals $\int M(x, y)\, dx$ and $\int N(x, y)\, dy$. If one is easier to evaluate than the other, this would be sufficient reason for us to use one method over the other. (The skeptical reader should try solving equation (20) by first integrating $M(x, y)$.)

▶ **Example 4** Show that

(21) $(x + 3x^3 \sin y)\, dx + (x^4 \cos y)\, dy = 0$

is *not* exact, but that multiplying this equation by the factor x^{-1} yields an exact equation. Use this fact to solve (21).

Solution   In equation (21), $M = x + 3x^3 \sin y$ and $N = x^4 \cos y$. Since

$$\frac{\partial M}{\partial y} = 3x^3 \cos y \neq 4x^3 \cos y = \frac{\partial N}{\partial x},$$

then (21) is not exact. When we multiply equation (21) by the factor x^{-1}, we obtain

(22) $(1 + 3x^2 \sin y)\, dx + (x^3 \cos y)\, dy = 0.$

For this new equation, $M = 1 + 3x^2 \sin y$ and $N = x^3 \cos y$. If we test for exactness we now find that

$$\frac{\partial M}{\partial y} = 3x^2 \cos y = \frac{\partial N}{\partial x},$$

and hence (22) *is* exact. Upon solving (22) we find that the solution is given implicitly by $x + x^3 \sin y = C$. Since equations (21) and (22) differ only by a factor of x, then any solution to one will be a solution for the other whenever $x \neq 0$. Hence the solution to equation (21) is given implicitly by $x + x^3 \sin y = C$. ◀

In the preceding example the function $\mu = x^{-1}$ is called an **integrating factor** for equation (21). In general, any factor $\mu(x, y)$ that changes a nonexact equation into an exact equation is called an integrating factor. We discuss integrating factors in more detail in Sections 2.4 and 2.5 (see also Problems 27 and 28).

EXERCISES 2.3

In Problems 1 through 6 determine whether the given equation is separable, exact, neither, or both.

1. $(6xy - \cos x)\, dx + (3x^2)\, dy = 0$.

2. $(ye^{xy} + 2x)\, dx + (xe^{xy} - 2y)\, dy = 0$.

3. $[\cos(x - y) + 1]\, dx + [\cos(x - y) + 2y]\, dy = 0$.

4. $x\, dx + (\sin y + x^2 \sin y)\, dy = 0$.

5. $[\arctan y + \cos(x + 2y)]\, dx + \left[\dfrac{x}{1 + y^2} + 2\cos(x + 2y) + y\right] dy = 0$.

6. $\sec^2 x\, dx + \sqrt{1 - y}\, dy = 0$.

In Problems 7 through 18 determine whether the equation is exact. If it is exact, then solve it.

7. $(2xy + 3)\, dx + (x^2 - 1)\, dy = 0$.

8. $(2x + y)\, dx + (x - 2y)\, dy = 0$.

9. $(1/y)\, dx - (2y - x/y^2)\, dy = 0$.

10. $(1 + \ln y)\, dt + (t/y)\, dy = 0$.

11. $(\cos x \cos y + 2x)\, dx - (\sin x \sin y + 2y)\, dy = 0$.

12. $(e^x \sin y - 3x^2)\, dx + (e^x \cos y + y^{-2/3}/3)\, dy = 0$.

13. $\cos \theta\, dr - (r \sin \theta - e^\theta)\, d\theta = 0$.

14. $(ye^{xy} - 1/y)\, dx + (xe^{xy} + x/y^2)\, dy = 0$.

15. $e^t(y - t)\, dt + (1 + e^t)\, dy = 0$.

16. $\left(2x + \dfrac{y}{1 + x^2 y^2}\right) dx + \left(\dfrac{x}{1 + x^2 y^2} - 2y\right) dy = 0$.

17. $[2x + y^2 - \cos(x + y)]\, dx + [2xy - \cos(x + y) - e^y]\, dy = 0$.

18. $\left[\dfrac{2}{\sqrt{1 - x^2}} + y \cos(xy)\right] dx + [x \cos(xy) - y^{-1/3}]\, dy = 0$.

In Problems 19 through 24 solve the initial value problem.

19. $(e^x y + 1)\, dx + (e^x - 1)\, dy = 0$, $\quad y(1) = 1$.

20. $(ye^{xy} - 1/y)\, dx + (xe^{xy} + x/y^2)\, dy = 0$, $\quad y(0) = 1$.

21. $(e^t y + te^t y)\, dt + (te^t + 2)\, dy = 0$, $\quad y(0) = -1$.

22. $(1/x + 2y^2 x)\, dx + (2yx^2 - \cos y)\, dy = 0$, $\quad y(1) = \pi$.

23. $(y^2 \sin x)\, dx + (1/x - y/x)\, dy = 0$, $\quad y(\pi) = 1$.

24. $(\tan y - 2)\, dx + (x \sec^2 y + 1/y)\, dy = 0$, $\quad y(0) = 1$.

25. For each of the following equations find the most general function $N(x, y)$ so that the equation is exact.

   (a) $[y \cos(xy) + e^x]\, dx + N(x, y)\, dy = 0$.

   (b) $(ye^{xy} - 4x^3 y + 2)\, dx + N(x, y)\, dy = 0$.

26. For each of the following equations find the most general function $M(x, y)$ so that the equation is exact.

(a) $M(x, y) \, dx + (\sec^2 y - x/y) \, dy = 0.$

(b) $M(x, y) \, dx + (\sin x \cos y - xy - e^{-y}) \, dy = 0.$

27. **Integrating Factors.**   Consider the equation   SEC. 2.5   YOU NEED THIS !

$$(y^2 + 2xy) \, dx - x^2 \, dy = 0.$$

(a) Show that this equation is not exact.

(b) Show that multiplying both sides of the equation by y^{-2} yields a new equation that is exact; that is, show that y^{-2} is an integrating factor.

(c) Use the solution of the resulting exact equation to solve the original equation.

(d) Were any solutions "lost" in the process?   LOOK AT SEP. 24. FIRST.

28. Consider the equation

$$(5x^2 y + 6x^3 y^2 + 4xy^2) \, dx + (2x^3 + 3x^4 y + 3x^2 y) \, dy = 0.$$

(a) Show that the equation is not exact.

(b) Find an integrating factor of the form $x^n y^m$ by multiplying the equation by $x^n y^m$ and determining values for n and m that make the resulting equation exact.

(c) Use the solution of the resulting exact equation to solve the original equation.

29. Using condition (8), show that the right-hand side of (14) is independent of x by showing that its partial derivative with respect to x is zero. [Hint: Since the partial derivatives of M are continuous, Leibniz's theorem allows you to interchange the operations of integration and differentiation.]

30. Verify that $F(x, y)$ as defined by (13) and (14) satisfies conditions (6).

31. **Orthogonal Trajectories.**   The geometric problem of finding a family of curves (orthogonal trajectories) that intersects a given family of curves orthogonally at each point occurs frequently in engineering. For example, we may be given the lines of force and want to find the equation for the equipotential lines. Consider the family of curves described by $F(x, y) = k$, where k is a parameter.

(a) Using implicit differentiation, show that for each curve in the family its slope is given by

$$\frac{dy}{dx} = -\frac{\partial F}{\partial x} \bigg/ \frac{\partial F}{\partial y}.$$

(b) Using the fact that the slope of a curve that is orthogonal (perpendicular) to a given curve is just the negative reciprocal of the slope of the given curve, show that the curves orthogonal to the family $F(x, y) = k$ satisfy the differential equation

$$\frac{\partial F}{\partial y}(x, y) \, dx - \frac{\partial F}{\partial x}(x, y) \, dy = 0.$$

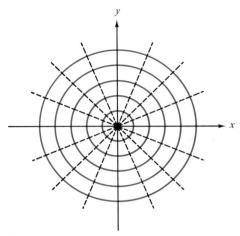

Figure 2.3 Orthogonal trajectories for concentric circles are lines through the center

(c) Using the preceding differential equation, show that the orthogonal trajectories to the family of circles $x^2 + y^2 = k$ are just straight lines through the origin (see Figure 2.3).

32. Use the method in Problem 31 to find the orthogonal trajectories for each of the given family of curves. Sketch the family of curves along with their orthogonal trajectories.

  (a) $xy = k$. (b) $2x^2 + y^2 = k$. (c) $x^2 - y^2 = k$.

33. Use the method in Problem 31 to find the orthogonal trajectories for each of the given family of curves.

  (a) $y = kx^4$. (b) $y = e^{kx}$. (c) $y^2 = kx$.

[Hint: First express the family in the form $F(x, y) = k$.]

2.4 Linear Equations

A type of first order differential equation that occurs frequently in applications is the linear equation. Recall from Section 1.1 that a **linear first order equation** is an equation that can be expressed in the form

(1) $$a_1(x)\frac{dy}{dx} + a_0(x)y = b(x),$$

where $a_1(x)$, $a_0(x)$, and $b(x)$ depend only on the independent variable x, not on y.
  For example, the equation

$$x^2 \sin x - (\cos x)y = (\sin x)\frac{dy}{dx}$$

is linear since it can be rewritten in the form

$$(\sin x)\frac{dy}{dx} + (\cos x)y = x^2 \sin x.$$

However, the equation

$$y\frac{dy}{dx} + (\sin x)y^3 = e^x + 1$$

is not linear, because it cannot be put in the form of equation (1). This is due to the presence of the y^3 and $y\,dy/dx$ terms.

In this section we assume that the functions $a_1(x)$, $a_0(x)$, and $b(x)$ are continuous on an interval and that $a_1(x) \neq 0$ on that interval. Then, on dividing by $a_1(x)$, we can rewrite equation (1) in the **standard form**

$$(2) \qquad \frac{dy}{dx} + P(x)y = Q(x),$$

where $P(x)$ and $Q(x)$ are continuous functions on the interval.

Let's express equation (2) in the differential form

$$(3) \qquad [P(x)y - Q(x)]\,dx + dy = 0.$$

If we test this equation for exactness, we find $\partial M/\partial y = P(x)$ and $\partial N/\partial x = 0$. Consequently, equation (3) is exact only when $P(x) \equiv 0$. While this is disappointing news, it is no cause for despair, for it turns out that an **integrating factor** μ, which depends only on x, can be easily obtained for the general equation (3).[†]

So let's multiply (3) by a function $\mu(x)$ and try to determine $\mu(x)$ so that the resulting equation

$$(4) \qquad [\mu(x)P(x)y - \mu(x)Q(x)]\,dx + \mu(x)\,dy = 0$$

is exact. From the equations

$$\frac{\partial M}{\partial y}(x,\,y) = \mu(x)P(x) \quad \text{and} \quad \frac{\partial N}{\partial x}(x,\,y) = \frac{d\mu}{dx}(x),$$

we see that (4) is exact if μ satisfies the differential equation

$$(5) \qquad \frac{d\mu}{dx}(x) = P(x)\mu(x).$$

[†] *Historical Footnote:* This method was discovered by Gottfried Leibniz in 1694.

Fortunately, (5) is separable and, for *any* antiderivative $\int P(x)\,dx$, has the solution

$$(6) \qquad \mu(x) = \exp\left(\int P(x)\,dx\right),$$

which is our desired integrating factor. With this choice, we can, of course, proceed to solve equation (4) by the method discussed in Section 2.3. However, there is a shorter path to finding the solution, which we now describe.

Returning to equation (2), we multiply by $\mu(x)$ defined in (6) to obtain

$$(7) \qquad \mu(x)\frac{dy}{dx} + P(x)\mu(x)y = \mu(x)Q(x).$$

We know from (5) that $P(x)\mu(x) = d\mu/dx$, and so (7) can be written in the form

$$\underbrace{\mu(x)\frac{dy}{dx} + \frac{d\mu}{dx}(x)y} = \mu(x)Q(x),$$

$$(8) \qquad \frac{d}{dx}(\mu(x)y) \quad = \mu(x)Q(x),$$

where we have made use of the product rule for differentiation. Integrating (8) with respect to x gives

$$\mu(x)y = \int \mu(x)Q(x)\,dx + C,$$

and solving for y yields

$$(9) \qquad y = \mu(x)^{-1}\left(\int \mu(x)Q(x)\,dx + C\right),$$

where $\mu(x)^{-1} = \exp(-\int P(x)\,dx)$. The function $y(x)$ given by equation (9) is referred to as the **general solution** to equation (2).

The above discussion suggests the following theorem.

EXISTENCE AND UNIQUENESS OF SOLUTION

Theorem 2. Suppose $P(x)$ and $Q(x)$ are continuous on an interval (a, b) that contains the point x_0. Then for any choice of initial value y_0, there exists a unique solution $y(x)$ on (a, b) to the initial value problem

$$(10) \qquad \frac{dy}{dx} + P(x)y = Q(x), \qquad y(x_0) = y_0.$$

In fact, the solution is given by (9) for a suitable value of C.

The proof of Theorem 2 is based on the previous discussion, that led to equation (9). (See Problems 32 and 33 for the details.) Like Theorem 1 of Chapter 1, Theorem 2 is an existence and uniqueness theorem. It asserts that the initial value problem (10) *always has a solution* on the interval (a, b) *for any choice of initial value* y_0. Furthermore, the initial value problem (10) has *only one solution* on (a, b) for a given value y_0. Theorem 2 does differ from Theorem 1 on page 12 in that for the linear initial value problem (10) we have the existence and uniqueness of the solution on the *whole* interval (a, b), rather than on some smaller interval about x_0.

We can summarize the method for solving linear equations as follows:

METHOD FOR SOLVING LINEAR EQUATIONS

(a) Write the equation in the standard form

$$\frac{dy}{dx} + P(x)y = Q(x).$$

(b) Calculate the integrating factor $\mu(x)$ by the formula

$$\mu(x) = \exp\left(\int P(x)\, dx \right).$$

(c) Multiply the equation in standard form by $\mu(x)$ and, recalling that the left-hand side is just $\dfrac{d}{dx}(\mu(x)y)$, obtain

$$\underbrace{\mu(x)\frac{dy}{dx} + P(x)\mu(x)y}_{} = \mu(x)Q(x),$$

$$\frac{d}{dx}(\mu(x)y) \qquad = \mu(x)Q(x).$$

(d) Integrate the last equation and solve for y by dividing by $\mu(x)$.

▶ **Example 1**   Find the general solution to

(11) $$\frac{dy}{dx} + 2y = 3e^x.$$

Solution   This linear equation is in standard form with $P(x) = 2$, and so

$$\mu(x) = \exp\left(\int P(x)\, dx \right) = \exp\left(\int 2\, dx \right) = e^{2x}.$$

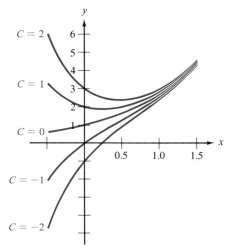

Figure 2.4 Graph of $y = e^x + Ce^{-2x}$ for five values of the constant C

Multiplying equation (11) by e^{2x} yields

$$e^{2x}\frac{dy}{dx} + 2e^{2x}y = 3e^{3x},$$

$$\frac{d}{dx}(e^{2x}y) = 3e^{3x}.$$

Next, we integrate both sides of the last equation and find

$$e^{2x}y = \int 3e^{3x}\,dx = e^{3x} + C.$$

Solving this equation for y gives the general solution

(12) $y = e^x + Ce^{-2x}.$

Since $P(x) = 2$ and $Q(x) = 3e^x$ are continuous for all real x, this solution is valid for all real x. In Figure 2.4 we have sketched solutions for various values of the constant C in (12). ◄

▶ **Example 2**   Solve the initial value problem

(13) $\dfrac{1}{x}\dfrac{dy}{dx} - \dfrac{2y}{x^2} = x\cos x,$ $y\left(\dfrac{\pi}{2}\right) = 3.$

Solution To put this linear equation in standard form, we multiply by x to obtain

(14) $$\frac{dy}{dx} - \frac{2}{x} y = x^2 \cos x.$$

Here $P(x) = -2/x$, and so

$$\int P(x)\, dx = \int \frac{-2}{x}\, dx = -2 \ln|x|.$$

Thus an integrating factor is

$$\mu(x) = e^{-2 \ln|x|} = e^{\ln(x^{-2})} = x^{-2}.$$

Multiplying equation (14) by $\mu(x)$ yields

$$\underbrace{x^{-2} \frac{dy}{dx} - 2x^{-3}y}_{} = \cos x,$$

$$\frac{d}{dx}(x^{-2}y) \quad = \cos x.$$

We now integrate both sides and solve for y to find

$$x^{-2}y = \int \cos x\, dx = \sin x + C.$$

(15) $$y = x^2 \sin x + Cx^2.$$

Substituting $x = \pi/2$ and $y = 3$ into equation (15) and solving for C gives

$$3 = \frac{\pi^2}{4} \sin \frac{\pi}{2} + \frac{\pi^2}{4} C,$$

$$3 = \frac{\pi^2}{4} + \frac{\pi^2}{4} C;$$

so $C = (12/\pi^2) - 1$. Thus the solution to the initial value problem is given by

$$y = x^2 \sin x + \left(\frac{12}{\pi^2} - 1 \right) x^2,$$

and since $P(x) = -2/x$ and $Q(x) = x^2 \cos x$ are continuous on the interval $(0, \infty)$, this solution is valid on $(0, \infty)$. ◀

The theory of linear differential equations is an important branch of mathematics not only because these equations occur in applications, but because of the elegant structure associated with them. For example, first order linear equations always have a general solution given by equation (9). Some further properties of first order linear equations are described in Problems 26 and 27. Higher order linear equations will be treated in Chapters 4, 6, and 8.

EXERCISES 2.4

In Problems 1 through 8 classify the equation as separable, exact, or linear. Notice that some equations may have more than one classification.

1. $(x^{10/3} - 2y) \, dx + x \, dy = 0.$ L

2. $(ye^{xy} + 2x) \, dx + (xe^{xy} - 2y) \, dy = 0.$

3. $(x^2 y + x^4 \cos x) \, dx - x^3 \, dy = 0.$ L

4. $\sqrt{-2y - y^2} \, dx + (3 + 2x - x^2) \, dy = 0.$

5. $y^2 \, dx + (2xy + \cos y) \, dy = 0.$ E, L

6. $xy \, dx + dy = 0.$

7. $(3r - \theta - 1) \, d\theta + \theta \, dr = 0.$ E

8. $[2x + y \cos(xy)] \, dx + [x \cos(xy) - 2y] \, dy = 0.$

In Problems 9 through 18 obtain the general solution to the equation.

9. $\dfrac{dy}{dx} - y = e^{3x}.$

10. $\dfrac{dy}{dx} = \dfrac{y}{x} + 2x + 1.$

11. $\dfrac{dy}{dx} = x^2 e^{-4x} - 4y.$

12. $x\dfrac{dy}{dx} + 2y = x^{-3}.$

13. $\dfrac{dr}{d\theta} + r \tan \theta = \sec \theta.$

14. $(t + y + 1) \, dt - dy = 0.$

15. $y\dfrac{dx}{dy} + 2x = 5y^3.$

16. $(x^2 + 1)\dfrac{dy}{dx} + xy = x.$

17. $x\dfrac{dy}{dx} + 3y + 2x^2 = x^3 + 4x.$

18. $(x^2 + 1)\dfrac{dy}{dx} = x^2 + 2x - 1 - 4xy.$

In Problems 19 through 24 solve the initial value problem.

19. $\dfrac{dy}{dx} - \dfrac{y}{x} = xe^x, \qquad y(1) = e - 1.$

20. $\dfrac{dy}{dx} + 4y - e^{-x} = 0, \qquad y(0) = \dfrac{4}{3}.$

21. $\sin x \dfrac{dy}{dx} + y \cos x = x \sin x, \qquad y\left(\dfrac{\pi}{2}\right) = 2.$

22. $\dfrac{dy}{dx} + \dfrac{3y}{x} + 2 = 3x, \qquad y(1) = 1.$

23. $x^3\dfrac{dy}{dx} + 3x^2 y = x, \qquad y(2) = 0.$

24. $\cos x\dfrac{dy}{dx} + y \sin x = 2x \cos^2 x, \qquad y\left(\dfrac{\pi}{4}\right) = \dfrac{-15\sqrt{2}\,\pi^2}{32}.$

25. Solve the equation

$$\dfrac{dy}{dx} = \dfrac{1}{e^{4y} + 2x}.$$

26. Constant Multiples of Solutions.

(a) Show that $y = e^{-x}$ is a solution of the linear equation

(16) $$\frac{dy}{dx} + y = 0,$$

and $y = x^{-1}$ is a solution of the nonlinear equation

(17) $$\frac{dy}{dx} + y^2 = 0.$$

(b) Show that for any constant C, Ce^{-x} is a solution of equation (16), while Cx^{-1} is a solution of equation (17) only when $C = 0$ or 1.

(c) Show that for any linear equation of the form

$$\frac{dy}{dx} + P(x)y = 0,$$

if $\hat{y}(x)$ is a solution, then for any constant C, the function $C\hat{y}(x)$ is also a solution.

27. Solutions Not Expressible in Terms of Elementary Functions. Solve the following initial value problems using definite integration (see Problem 27 in Exercises 2.2).

(a) $$\frac{dy}{dx} + 2xy = 1, \qquad y(2) = 1.$$

(b) $$\frac{dy}{dx} + \frac{\sin 2x}{2(1 + \sin^2 x)}\, y = 1, \qquad y(0) = 0.$$

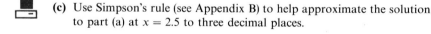

(c) Use Simpson's rule (see Appendix B) to help approximate the solution to part (a) at $x = 2.5$ to three decimal places.

28. Bernoulli Equations. The equation

(18) $$\frac{dy}{dx} + 2y = xy^{-2},$$

is an example of a Bernoulli equation. (Further discussion of Bernoulli equations appears in Section 2.6.)

(a) Show that the substitution $v = y^3$ reduces equation (18) to the equation

(19) $$\frac{dv}{dx} + 6v = 3x.$$

(b) Solve equation (19) for v; then make the substitution $v = y^3$ to obtain the solution to equation (18).

29. Discontinuous Coefficients. As we will see in Chapter 3, there are times when the coefficient $P(x)$ in a linear equation may not be continuous, but

may have a jump discontinuity. Fortunately, we may still obtain a reasonable solution. For example, consider the initial value problem

$$\frac{dy}{dx} + P(x)y = x, \qquad y(0) = 1,$$

where

$$P(x) := \begin{cases} 1, & 0 \le x \le 2, \\ 3, & x > 2. \end{cases}$$

(a) Find the general solution for $0 \le x \le 2$.
(b) Choose the constant in the solution of part (a) so that the initial condition is satisfied.
(c) Find the general solution for $x > 2$.
(d) Now choose the constant in the general solution from part (c) so that
the solution from part (b) and the solution from part (c) agree at $x = 2$.
By patching the two solutions together we are able to obtain a continuous function that satisfies the differential equation except at $x = 2$,
where its derivative is undefined.
(e) Sketch the graph of the solution from $x = 0$ to $x = 5$.

30. Discontinuous Forcing Terms. There are times when the forcing term $Q(x)$
in a linear equation may not be continuous, but may have a jump discontinuity. Fortunately, we may still obtain a reasonable solution using the procedure discussed in Problem 29. Use this procedure to find the continuous
solution to the initial value problem

$$\frac{dy}{dx} + 2y = Q(x), \qquad y(0) = 0,$$

where

$$Q(x) := \begin{cases} 2, & 0 \le x \le 3, \\ -2, & x > 3. \end{cases}$$

Sketch the graph of the solution from $x = 0$ to $x = 7$.

31. Singular Points. Those values of x for which $P(x)$ in equation (2) is not
defined are called **singular points** of the equation. For example, $x = 0$ is a
singular point of the equation $xy' + 2y = 3x$, since when the equation is
written in the standard form $y' + (2/x)y = 3$, we see that $P(x) = 2/x$ is not
defined at $x = 0$. On an interval containing a singular point the questions
of the existence and uniqueness of a solution are left unanswered since
Theorem 2 does not apply. To show the possible behavior of solutions near
a singular point consider the following equations.

(a) Show that $xy' + 2y = 3x$ has only one solution defined at $x = 0$. Then
show that the initial value problem for this equation with initial condition $y(0) = y_0$ has a unique solution when $y_0 = 0$ and no solution
when $y_0 \ne 0$.

(b) Show that $xy' - 2y = 3x$ has an infinite number of solutions defined at $x = 0$. Then show that the initial value problem for this equation with initial condition $y(0) = 0$ has an infinite number of solutions.

32. Existence. Under the assumptions of Theorem 2, we will show that equation (9) gives a solution to equation (2) on (a, b). We can then choose the constant C in equation (9) so that the initial value problem (10) has a solution.

(a) Show that since $P(x)$ is continuous on (a, b), then $\mu(x)$ defined in (6) is a positive, continuous function satisfying $d\mu/dx = P(x)\mu(x)$ on (a, b).

(b) Since

$$\frac{d}{dx} \int \mu(x)Q(x)\,dx = \mu(x)Q(x),$$

verify that y given in equation (9) satisfies equation (2) by differentiating both sides of equation (9).

(c) Show that when we let $\int \mu(x)Q(x)\,dx$ be the antiderivative whose value at x_0 is 0, (i.e., $\int_{x_0}^{x} \mu(t)Q(t)\,dt$), then by choosing C to be $y_0\mu(x_0)$, the initial condition $y(x_0) = y_0$ is satisfied.

33. Uniqueness. Under the assumptions of Theorem 2, we will show that the initial value problem (10) has only one solution. Let $y_1(x)$ and $y_2(x)$ be solutions to (10).

(a) Show that $\hat{y}(x) = y_1(x) - y_2(x)$ satisfies the initial value problem

$$\frac{dy}{dx} + P(x)y = 0, \qquad y(x_0) = 0.$$

(b) Let $\mu(x)$ be the integrating factor defined in equation (6). Show that

$$\frac{d}{dx}(\mu(x)\hat{y}(x)) = 0,$$

and thus $\mu(x)\hat{y}(x) = C$, for some constant C.

(c) Since $\hat{y}(x_0) = 0$ and $\mu(x) > 0$ for x in (a, b), show that $\hat{y}(x) = 0$ for all x in (a, b). Hence $y_1(x) = y_2(x)$ for all x in (a, b).

34. Mixing. Suppose a brine containing 2 kg of salt per liter runs into a tank initially filled with 500 L of water containing 50 kg of salt. The brine enters the tank at a rate of 5 L/min. The mixture, kept uniform by stirring, is flowing out at the rate of 5 L/min (see Figure 2.5 on page 60).

(a) Find the concentration, in kilograms per liter, of salt in the tank after 10 min. [Hint: Let A denote the number of kilograms of salt in the tank at t minutes after the process begins, and use the fact that

rate of increase in A = rate of input − rate of exit.

A further discussion of mixing problems is given in Section 3.2.]

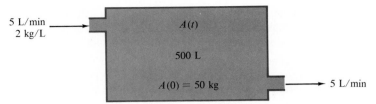

5 L/min
2 kg/L

$A(t)$

500 L

$A(0) = 50$ kg

5 L/min

Figure 2.5 Mixing problem with equal flow rates

(b) After 10 min a leak develops in the tank and an additional liter per minute of mixture flows out of the tank (see Figure 2.6). What will be the concentration, in kilograms per liter, of salt in the tank after 20 min? [Hint: Use the method discussed in Problems 29 and 30.]

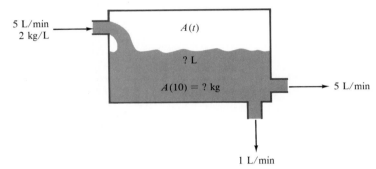

5 L/min
2 kg/L

$A(t)$

? L

$A(10) = ?$ kg

5 L/min

1 L/min

Figure 2.6 Mixing problem with unequal flow rates

35. Secretion of Hormones. The secretion of hormones into the blood is often a periodic activity. If a hormone is secreted on a 24-hr cycle, then the rate of change of the level of the hormone in the blood may be represented by the initial value problem

$$\frac{dx}{dt} = \alpha - \beta \cos \frac{\pi t}{12} - kx, \qquad x(0) = x_0,$$

where $x(t)$ is the amount of the hormone in the blood at time t, α is the average secretion rate, β is the amount of variation in the secretion, and k is a positive constant reflecting the rate at which the body removes the hormone from the blood. If $\alpha = \beta = 1$, $k = 2$, and $x_0 = 10$, solve for $x(t)$.

★ 2.5 *Special Integrating Factors*

In solving linear equations written in differential form, we found a multiplier μ that made the resulting equation exact. Do such multiplicative factors μ exist for other classes of differential equations? If so, how are they computed? The present section is devoted to these questions.[†]

INTEGRATING FACTOR

Definition 3. If the equation

(1) $M(x, y)\,dx + N(x, y)\,dy = 0$

is not exact, but the equation

(2) $\mu(x, y)M(x, y)\,dx + \mu(x, y)N(x, y)\,dy = 0,$

which results from multiplying equation (1) by the function $\mu(x, y)$, is exact, then $\mu(x, y)$ is called an **integrating factor** of the equation (1).

▶ *Example 1*   Show that $\mu(x, y) = xy^2$ is an integrating factor for

(3) $(2y - 6x)\,dx + (3x - 4x^2 y^{-1})\,dy = 0.$

Use this integrating factor to solve the equation.

Solution   We leave it for the reader to show that (3) is not exact. Multiplying (3) by $\mu(x, y) = xy^2$, we obtain

(4) $(2xy^3 - 6x^2 y^2)\,dx + (3x^2 y^2 - 4x^3 y)\,dy = 0.$

For this equation we have $M = 2xy^3 - 6x^2 y^2$ and $N = 3x^2 y^2 - 4x^3 y$. Since

$$\frac{\partial M}{\partial y}(x, y) = 6xy^2 - 12x^2 y = \frac{\partial N}{\partial x}(x, y),$$

equation (4) is exact, and so $\mu(x, y) = xy^2$ is indeed an integrating factor of equation (3).
    Let us now solve equation (4) using the procedure of Section 2.3. To find $F(x, y)$ we begin by integrating M with respect to x:

$$F(x, y) = \int (2xy^3 - 6x^2 y^2)\,dx + g(y) = x^2 y^3 - 2x^3 y^2 + g(y).$$

[†] *Historical Footnote:* A general theory of integrating factors was developed by Alexis Clairaut in 1739. Leonhard Euler also studied classes of equations that could be solved using a specific integrating factor.

When we take the partial derivative with respect to y and substitute for N, we find

$$\frac{\partial F}{\partial y}(x, y) = N(x, y)$$

$$3x^2y^2 - 4x^3y + g'(y) = 3x^2y^2 - 4x^3y.$$

Thus $g'(y) = 0$, and so we can take $g(y) \equiv 0$. Hence $F(x, y) = x^2y^3 - 2x^3y^2$, and the solution to equation (4) is given implicitly by

(5) $\qquad x^2y^3 - 2x^3y^2 = C.$

While equations (3) and (4) have essentially the same solutions, *it is possible to lose or gain solutions when multiplying by* $\mu(x, y)$. In this case $y \equiv 0$ is a solution of equation (4) but not of equation (3). The extraneous solution arises because when we multiply (3) by $\mu = xy^2$ to obtain (4), we are actually multiplying both sides of (3) by zero if $y \equiv 0$. This gives us $y \equiv 0$ as a solution to (4), while it is not a solution to (3). ◄

How do we find an integrating factor? If $\mu(x, y)$ is an integrating factor of (1) with continuous first partial derivatives, then testing (2) for exactness we must have

(6) $\qquad \dfrac{\partial}{\partial y}\left[\mu(x, y)M(x, y)\right] = \dfrac{\partial}{\partial x}\left[\mu(x, y)N(x, y)\right].$

By use of the product rule, this reduces to the equation

(7) $\qquad M\dfrac{\partial \mu}{\partial y} - N\dfrac{\partial \mu}{\partial x} = \left(\dfrac{\partial N}{\partial x} - \dfrac{\partial M}{\partial y}\right)\mu.$

But solving the partial differential equation (7) for μ is usually more difficult than solving the original equation (1). There are, however, two important exceptions.

Let's assume equation (1) has an integrating factor that depends only on x; that is, $\mu = \mu(x)$. In this case equation (7) reduces to the separable equation

(8) $\qquad \dfrac{d\mu}{dx} = \left\{\dfrac{\partial M/\partial y - \partial N/\partial x}{N}\right\}\mu,$

where $(\partial M/\partial y - \partial N/\partial x)/N$ is just a function of x. In a similar fashion, if equation (1) has an integrating factor that depends only on y, then equation (7) reduces to the separable equation

(9) $\qquad \dfrac{d\mu}{dy} = \left\{\dfrac{\partial N/\partial x - \partial M/\partial y}{M}\right\}\mu,$

where $(\partial N/\partial x - \partial M/\partial y)/M$ is a function of just y.

We can reverse the above argument. In particular, if $(\partial M/\partial y - \partial N/\partial x)/N$ is a function that depends only on x, then we can solve the separable equation (8) to obtain the integrating factor

$$\mu(x) = \exp\left(\int \left\{\frac{\partial M/\partial y - \partial N/\partial x}{N}\right\} dx\right)$$

for equation (1). We summarize these observations in the following theorem.

SPECIAL INTEGRATING FACTORS

Theorem 3. If $(\partial M/\partial y - \partial N/\partial x)/N$ is continuous and depends only on x, then

(10) $\qquad \mu(x) = \exp\left(\int \left\{\frac{\partial M/\partial y - \partial N/\partial x}{N}\right\} dx\right)$

is an integrating factor for equation (1).
    If $(\partial N/\partial x - \partial M/\partial y)/M$ is continuous and depends only on y, then

(11) $\qquad \mu(y) = \exp\left(\int \left\{\frac{\partial N/\partial x - \partial M/\partial y}{M}\right\} dy\right)$

is an integrating factor for equation (1).

Theorem 3 suggests the following procedure:

METHOD FOR FINDING SPECIAL INTEGRATING FACTORS

If $M\,dx + N\,dy = 0$ is neither separable nor linear, compute $\partial M/\partial y$ and $\partial N/\partial x$. If $\partial M/\partial y = \partial N/\partial x$, then the equation is exact. If it is not exact, consider

(12) $\qquad \dfrac{\partial M/\partial y - \partial N/\partial x}{N}.$

If (12) is a function of just x, then an integrating factor is given by formula (10). If not, consider

(13) $\qquad \dfrac{\partial N/\partial x - \partial M/\partial y}{M}.$

If (13) is a function of just y, then an integrating factor is given by formula (11).

▶ *Example 2*   Solve

(14) $(2x^2 + y)\,dx + (x^2y - x)\,dy = 0.$

Solution   A quick inspection shows that equation (14) is neither separable nor linear. We also note that

$$\frac{\partial M}{\partial y} = 1 \neq (2xy - 1) = \frac{\partial N}{\partial x}.$$

Since (14) is not exact, we compute

$$\frac{\partial M/\partial y - \partial N/\partial x}{N} = \frac{1 - (2xy - 1)}{x^2y - x} = \frac{2(1 - xy)}{-x(1 - xy)} = \frac{-2}{x}.$$

Since we obtain a function of only x, an integrating factor for (14) is given by formula (10). That is,

$$\mu(x) = \exp\left(\int \frac{-2}{x}\,dx\right) = x^{-2}.$$

When we multiply (14) by $\mu = x^{-2}$ we get the exact equation

$$(2 + yx^{-2})\,dx + (y - x^{-1})\,dy = 0.$$

Solving this equation, we ultimately derive the implicit solution

(15) $2x - yx^{-1} + \dfrac{y^2}{2} = C.$

Notice that the solution $x \equiv 0$ was lost in multiplying by $\mu = x^{-2}$. Hence (15) and $x \equiv 0$ are solutions to equation (14). ◀

There are many differential equations that are not covered by Theorem 3 but for which an integrating factor nevertheless exists. The major difficulty, however, is in finding an explicit formula for these integrating factors, which in general will depend on both x and y.

EXERCISES 2.5

In Problems 1 through 6 identify the equation as separable, linear, exact, or having an integrating factor that is a function of either x alone or y alone.

1. $(2x + yx^{-1})\,dx + (xy - 1)\,dy = 0.$

2. $(2y^3 + 2y^2)\,dx + (3y^2x + 2xy)\,dy = 0.$

3. $(y^2 + 2xy)\,dx - x^2\,dy = 0.$

4. $(2x + y)\,dx + (x - 2y)\,dy = 0.$

5. $(2y^2x - y)\,dx + x\,dy = 0$.

6. $(x^2 \sin x + 4y)\,dx + x\,dy = 0$.

In Problems 7 through 12 solve the equation.

7. $(3x^2 + y)\,dx + (x^2y - x)\,dy = 0$.

8. $(2xy)\,dx + (y^2 - 3x^2)\,dy = 0$.

9. $(2xy^3 + 1)\,dx + (3x^2y^2 - y^{-1})\,dy = 0$.

10. $(y^2 + 2xy)\,dx - x^2\,dy = 0$.

11. $(x^4 - x + y)\,dx - x\,dy = 0$.

12. $(2y^2 + 2y + 4x^2)\,dx + (2xy + x)\,dy = 0$.

In Problems 13 and 14 find an integrating factor of the form $x^n y^m$ and solve the equation.

13. $(2y^2 - 6xy)\,dx + (3xy - 4x^2)\,dy = 0$.

14. $(12 + 5xy)\,dx + (6xy^{-1} + 3x^2)\,dy = 0$.

15. Show that if $(\partial N/\partial x - \partial M/\partial y)/(xM - yN)$ depends only on the product xy, that is

$$\frac{\partial N/\partial x - \partial M/\partial y}{xM - yN} = H(xy),$$

then the equation $M(x, y)\,dx + N(x, y)\,dy = 0$ has an integrating factor of the form $\mu(xy)$. Give the general formula for $\mu(xy)$.

16. If $xM(x, y) + yN(x, y) \equiv 0$, find the solution to the equation

$$M(x, y)\,dx + N(x, y)\,dy = 0.$$

17. Orthogonal Trajectories. Use the method described in Problem 31 of Exercises 2.3 to show that the orthogonal trajectories to the family of curves $x^2 + y^2 = kx$, k a parameter, satisfy

$$(2yx^{-1})\,dx + (y^2x^{-2} - 1)\,dy = 0.$$

Find the orthogonal trajectories by solving the above equation. Sketch the family of curves, along with their orthogonal trajectories. [Hint: Look for an integrating factor of the form $x^m y^n$.]

★ 2.6 Substitutions and Transformations

When the equation

$$M(x, y)\,dx + N(x, y)\,dy = 0$$

is not a separable, exact, or linear equation, it may still be possible to transform it into one that we know how to solve. This, in fact, was our approach in Section 2.5, where we used an integrating factor to transform our original equation into an exact equation.

In this section we study four types of equations that can be transformed into either a separable or linear equation by means of a suitable substitution or transformation.

express (6) in the derivative form

(7) $$\frac{dy}{dx} = \frac{xy + y^2 + x^2}{x^2} = \frac{y}{x} + \left(\frac{y}{x}\right)^2 + 1,$$

then we see that the right-hand side of (7) is a function of just y/x. Thus equation (6) is homogeneous.

Now let $v = y/x$ and recall that $dy/dx = v + x(dv/dx)$. With these substitutions equation (7) becomes

$$v + x\frac{dv}{dx} = v + v^2 + 1.$$

The above equation is separable, and, on separating the variables and integrating, we obtain

$$\int \frac{1}{v^2 + 1}\, dv = \int \frac{1}{x}\, dx,$$

$$\arctan v = \ln|x| + C.$$

Hence

$$v = \tan(\ln|x| + C).$$

Finally, we substitute y/x for v and solve for y to get

$$y = x\,\tan(\ln|x| + C)$$

as an explicit solution to equation (6). ◀

EQUATIONS OF THE FORM dy/dx = G(ax + by)

When the right-hand side of the equation $dy/dx = f(x, y)$ can be expressed as a function of $ax + by$, where a and b are constants, that is

$$\frac{dy}{dx} = G(ax + by),$$

then the substitution

$$z = ax + by$$

transforms the equation into a separable one. The method is illustrated in the next example.

▶ **Example 2**   Solve

(8) $$\frac{dy}{dx} = y - x - 1 + (x - y + 2)^{-1}.$$

Solution   Since the right-hand side can be expressed as a function of $x - y$, that is,

$$y - x - 1 + (x - y + 2)^{-1} = -(x - y) - 1 + [(x - y) + 2]^{-1},$$

let $z = x - y$. To solve for dy/dx we differentiate $z = x - y$ with respect to x to obtain $dz/dx = 1 - dy/dx$, and so $dy/dx = 1 - dz/dx$. Substituting into (8) yields

$$1 - \frac{dz}{dx} = -z - 1 + (z + 2)^{-1},$$

or

$$\frac{dz}{dx} = (z + 2) - (z + 2)^{-1}.$$

Solving this separable equation, we obtain

$$\int \frac{z + 2}{(z + 2)^2 - 1} \, dz = \int dx,$$

$$\frac{1}{2} \ln|(z + 2)^2 - 1| = x + C_1,$$

from which it follows that

$$(z + 2)^2 = Ce^{2x} + 1.$$

Finally, replacing z by $x - y$ yields

$$(x - y + 2)^2 = Ce^{2x} + 1$$

as an implicit solution to equation (8). ◀

BERNOULLI EQUATIONS

> ### BERNOULLI EQUATION
>
> **Definition 5.**   A first order equation that can be written in the form
>
> (9) $$\frac{dy}{dx} + P(x)y = Q(x)y^n,$$
>
> where $P(x)$ and $Q(x)$ are continuous on an interval (a, b) and n is a real number, is called a **Bernoulli equation.**[†]

Notice that when $n = 0$ or 1, equation (9) is also a linear equation and can be solved by the method discussed in Section 2.4. For other values of n, the substitution

$$v = y^{1-n}$$

transforms the Bernoulli equation into a linear equation as we now show.

Dividing equation (9) by y^n yields

(10) $$y^{-n}\frac{dy}{dx} + P(x)y^{1-n} = Q(x).$$

Taking $v = y^{1-n}$, we find via the chain rule that

$$\frac{dv}{dx} = (1 - n)y^{-n}\frac{dy}{dx},$$

and so equation (10) becomes

$$\frac{1}{1 - n}\frac{dv}{dx} + P(x)v = Q(x).$$

Since $1/(1 - n)$ is just a constant, the last equation is indeed linear.

[†] *Historical Footnote:* This equation was proposed for solution by James Bernoulli in 1695. It was solved by his brother John Bernoulli. (James and John were two of eight mathematicians in the Bernoulli family.) In 1696 Gottfried Leibniz showed that the Bernoulli equation can be reduced to a linear equation by making the substitution $v = y^{1-n}$.

▶ *Example 3* Solve

$$(11) \qquad \frac{dy}{dx} - 5y = -\frac{5}{2} xy^3.$$

Solution This is a Bernoulli equation with $n = 3$, $P(x) = -5$, and $Q(x) = -5x/2$. To transform (11) into a linear equation, we first divide by y^3 to obtain

$$y^{-3} \frac{dy}{dx} - 5y^{-2} = -\frac{5}{2} x.$$

Next we make the substitution $v = y^{-2}$. Since $dv/dx = -2y^{-3} \, dy/dx$, the transformed equation is

$$-\frac{1}{2} \frac{dv}{dx} - 5v = -\frac{5}{2} x,$$

$$(12) \qquad \frac{dv}{dx} + 10v = 5x.$$

Equation (12) is linear, so we can solve is for v using the method discussed in Section 2.4. When we do this, it turns out that

$$v = \frac{x}{2} - \frac{1}{20} + Ce^{-10x}.$$

Substituting $v = y^{-2}$ gives the solution

$$y^{-2} = \frac{x}{2} - \frac{1}{20} + Ce^{-10x}.$$

Not included in the last equation is the solution $y \equiv 0$ that was lost in the process of dividing (11) by y^3. ◀

EQUATIONS WITH LINEAR COEFFICIENTS

We have used various substitutions for y to transform the original equation into a new equation that we could solve. In some cases we must transform *both* x and y into new variables, say u and v. This is the situation for **equations with linear coefficients,** that is, equations of the form

$$(13) \qquad (a_1 x + b_1 y + c_1) \, dx + (a_2 x + b_2 y + c_2) \, dy = 0,$$

where the a_i's, b_i's, and c_i's are constants. We leave it as an exercise to show that when $a_1 b_2 = a_2 b_1$, equation (13) can be put in the form $dy/dx = G(ax + by)$, which we solved via the substitution $z = ax + by$.

Before considering the general case when $a_1 b_2 \neq a_2 b_1$, let's first look at the special situation when $c_1 = c_2 = 0$. Equation (13) then becomes

$$(a_1 x + b_1 y)\, dx + (a_2 x + b_2 y)\, dy = 0,$$

which can be rewritten in the form

$$\frac{dy}{dx} = -\frac{a_1 x + b_1 y}{a_2 x + b_2 y} = -\frac{a_1 + b_1(y/x)}{a_2 + b_2(y/x)}.$$

Since this equation is homogeneous, we can solve it using the method discussed earlier in this section.

The above discussion suggests the following procedure for solving (13). If $a_1 b_2 \neq a_2 b_1$, then we seek a translation of axes of the form

$$x = u + h \quad \text{and} \quad y = v + k,$$

where h, k are constants, that will change $a_1 x + b_1 y + c_1$ into $a_1 u + b_1 v$ and change $a_2 x + b_2 y + c_2$ into $a_2 u + b_2 v$. Some elementary algebra shows that such a transformation exists if the system of equations

(14)
$$\begin{aligned} a_1 h + b_1 k + c_1 &= 0, \\ a_2 h + b_2 k + c_2 &= 0 \end{aligned}$$

has a solution. This is assured by the assumption $a_1 b_2 \neq a_2 b_1$, which is geometrically equivalent to assuming that the two lines described by the system (14) intersect. Now if (h, k) satisfies (14), then the substitutions $x = u + h$ and $y = v + k$ transform equation (13) into the homogeneous equation

(15)
$$\frac{dv}{du} = -\frac{a_1 u + b_1 v}{a_2 u + b_2 v} = -\frac{a_1 + b_1(v/u)}{a_2 + b_2(v/u)},$$

which we know how to solve.

▶ **Example 4**   Solve

(16)
$$(-3x + y + 6)\, dx + (x + y + 2)\, dy = 0.$$

Solution   Since $a_1 b_2 = (-3)(1) \neq (1)(1) = a_2 b_1$, we will use the translation of axes $x = u + h$, $y = v + k$, where h and k satisfy the system

$$-3h + k + 6 = 0,$$
$$h + k + 2 = 0.$$

Solving the above system for h and k gives $h = 1$, $k = -3$. Hence, we let $x = u + 1$ and $y = v - 3$. Since $dy = dv$ and $dx = du$, substituting in equation (16) for x and y yields

$$(-3u + v)\, du + (u + v)\, dv = 0,$$

or

$$\frac{dv}{du} = \frac{3 - (v/u)}{1 + (v/u)}.$$

The above equation is homogeneous, so we let $z = v/u$. Then $dv/du = z + u(dz/du)$, and, substituting for v/u, we obtain

$$z + u\frac{dz}{du} = \frac{3 - z}{1 + z}.$$

Separating variables gives

$$\int \frac{z + 1}{z^2 + 2z - 3}\, dz = -\int \frac{1}{u}\, du,$$

$$\frac{1}{2}\ln|z^2 + 2z - 3| = -\ln|u| + C_1,$$

from which it follows that

$$z^2 + 2z - 3 = Cu^{-2}.$$

When we substitute back in for z, u, and v, we find

$$(v/u)^2 + 2(v/u) - 3 = Cu^{-2},$$
$$v^2 + 2uv - 3u^2 = C,$$
$$(y + 3)^2 + 2(x - 1)(y + 3) - 3(x - 1)^2 = C.$$

This last equation gives an implicit solution to (16). ◀

EXERCISES 2.6

In Problems 1 through 8 identify the equation as homogeneous, Bernoulli, linear coefficients, or of the form $y' = G(ax + by)$.

1. $(y - 4x - 1)^2\, dx - dy = 0.$

2. $(x^2 - y^2)\, dx + 2xy\, dy = 0.$

3. $(3x - y - 6)\, dx + (x + y + 2)\, dy = 0.$

4. $dy/dx + y/x = x^3 y^2.$

5. $(ye^{-2x} + y^3)\, dx - e^{-2x}\, dy = 0.$

6. $x\, dy - y\, dx = \sqrt{xy}\, dx.$

7. $(x - y - 2)\, dx + (x + y)\, dy = 0.$

8. $\cos(x + y)\, dy = \sin(x + y)\, dx.$

Use the method discussed under "Homogeneous Equations" to solve Problems 9 through 16.

9. $(x^2 + y^2)\, dx + 2xy\, dy = 0.$

10. $(xy + y^2)\, dx - x^2\, dy = 0.$

11. $(y^2 - xy)\, dx + x^2\, dy = 0.$

12. $(3x^2 - y^2)\, dx + (xy - x^3 y^{-1})\, dy = 0.$

13. $\dfrac{dy}{dx} = \dfrac{y^2 + x\sqrt{x^2 + y^2}}{xy}.$

14. $\dfrac{dy}{dx} = \dfrac{x\sec(y/x) + y}{x}.$

15. $\dfrac{dy}{dx} = \dfrac{x^2 - y^2}{3xy}.$

16. $\dfrac{dy}{dx} = \dfrac{y(\ln y - \ln x + 1)}{x}.$

Use the method discussed under "Equations of the Form $dy/dx = G(ax + by)$" to solve Problems 17 through 20.

17. $dy/dx = \sqrt{x + y} - 1.$

18. $dy/dx = (x - y + 5)^2.$

19. $dy/dx = (x + y + 2)^2.$

20. $dy/dx = \sin(x - y).$

Use the method discussed under "Bernoulli Equations" to solve Problems 21 through 28.

21. $\dfrac{dy}{dx} - y = e^{2x}y^3.$

22. $\dfrac{dy}{dx} + \dfrac{y}{x} = x^2 y^2.$

23. $\dfrac{dy}{dx} = \dfrac{2y}{x} - x^2 y^2.$

24. $\dfrac{dy}{dx} + \dfrac{y}{(x - 2)} = 5(x - 2)y^{1/2}.$

25. $\dfrac{dy}{dx} + y^3 x + \dfrac{y}{x} = 0.$

26. $\dfrac{dy}{dx} + y = e^x y^{-2}.$

27. $\dfrac{dy}{dx} = \dfrac{y^2 + 2xy}{x^2}.$

28. $\dfrac{dy}{dx} + y^3 x + y = 0.$

Use the method discussed under "Equations with Linear Coefficients" to solve Problems 29 through 32.

29. $(-3x + y - 1)\, dx + (x + y + 3)\, dy = 0.$

30. $(x + y - 1)\, dx + (y - x - 5)\, dy = 0.$

31. $(2x + y + 4)\, dx + (x - 2y - 2)\, dy = 0.$

32. $(2x - y)\, dx + (4x + y - 3)\, dy = 0.$

In Problems 33 through 40 solve the equation given in:

33. Problem 1.

34. Problem 2.

35. Problem 3.

36. Problem 4.

37. Problem 5.

38. Problem 6.

39. Problem 7.

40. Problem 8.

41. Use the substitution $v = x - y + 2$ to solve equation (8).

42. Use the substitution $y = vx^2$ to solve

$$\frac{dy}{dx} = \frac{2y}{x} + x \cos(y/x^2).$$

43. (a) Show that the equation $dy/dx = f(x, y)$ is homogeneous if and only if $f(tx, ty) = f(x, y)$. [Hint: Let $t = 1/x$.]

(b) A function $H(x, y)$ is called **homogeneous of order n** if $H(tx, ty) = t^n H(x, y)$. Show that the equation

$$M(x, y)\,dx + N(x, y)\,dy = 0$$

is homogeneous if $M(x, y)$ and $N(x, y)$ are both homogeneous of the same order.

44. Show that equation (13) reduces to an equation of the form

$$\frac{dy}{dx} = G(ax + by),$$

when $a_1 b_2 = a_2 b_1$. [Hint: If $a_1 b_2 = a_2 b_1$, then $a_2/a_1 = b_2/b_1 = k$, so that $a_2 = ka_1$ and $b_2 = kb_1$.]

45. Ecological Systems. In modeling ecological systems, there often arise coupled equations of the form

$$\frac{dy}{dt} = ax + by,$$

$$\frac{dx}{dt} = \alpha x + \beta y,$$

where a, b, α, and β are constants. The quantities x and y represent the populations at time t of two competing species. In this problem we wish to determine the relationship between x and y rather than the individual populations as functions of t. For this purpose, divide the first equation by the second to obtain

(17) $$\frac{dy}{dx} = \frac{ax + by}{\alpha x + \beta y}.$$

This new equation is homogeneous, so we can solve it via the substitution $v = y/x$. We refer to the solutions of (17) as **integral curves** (see Section 9.6). Determine the integral curves for the system

$$\frac{dy}{dt} = -4x - y,$$

$$\frac{dx}{dt} = 2x - y.$$

46. Riccati Equation. An equation of the form

(18) $$\frac{dy}{dx} = P(x)y^2 + Q(x)y + R(x)$$

is called a generalized Riccati equation.[†]

(a) If one solution, say $u(x)$, of (18) is known, show that the substitution $v = y - u$ reduces (18) to a Bernoulli equation.

(b) Given that $u(x) = x$ is a solution to

$$\frac{dy}{dx} = x^3(y - x)^2 + \frac{y}{x},$$

use the result of part (a) to find all the other solutions to this equation. (The particular solution $u(x) = x$ can be found by inspection or by using a Taylor series method.)

47. Guerrilla Combat Model[††]. In modeling a pair of guerrilla forces in combat, the following system arises

$$\frac{dy}{dt} = -axy,$$

$$\frac{dx}{dt} = -bxy,$$

where $x(t)$ and $y(t)$ are the strengths of opposing forces at time t and a and b are positive constants. The terms $-axy$ and $-bxy$ represent the *combat loss rate* for the troops y and x, respectively. This model assumes no reinforcements.

(a) Show that x and y satisfy the equation

$$\frac{dy}{dx} = \frac{a}{b}.$$

(b) Let $y(0) = y_0$ and $x(0) = x_0$. Solving the equation in part (a), derive the **linear combat law**

$$by - ax = c,$$

where $c = by_0 - ax_0$.

(c) Use the linear combat law to show that the y troops win if $c > 0$ and lose if $c < 0$.

[†] *Historical Footnote:* Count Jacopo Riccati studied a particular case of this equation in 1724 during his investigation of curves whose radii of curvature depend only on the variable y and not the variable x.

[††] For a discussion of combat models see *Differential Equation Models*, M. Braun, C. S. Coleman, and D. A. Drew, eds., Springer-Verlag, New York, 1983, Chapter 8.

48. Mixed Combat Model. In modeling a conflict between a guerrilla force and a conventional force, the following system arises

$$\frac{dy}{dt} = -ax,$$

$$\frac{dx}{dt} = -bxy,$$

where $x(t)$ is the strength of the guerrilla force, $y(t)$ is the strength of the conventional force at time t, and a and b are positive constants. The terms $-ax$ and $-bxy$ represent the *combat loss rate* for troops y and x, respectively. This model assumes no reinforcements.

(a) Show that x and y satisfy the equation

$$\frac{dy}{dx} = \frac{a}{by}.$$

(b) Let $y(0) = y_0$ and $x(0) = x_0$. Solving the equation in part (a), derive the **parabolic combat law**

$$by^2 - 2ax = c,$$

where $c = by_0^2 - 2ax_0$.

(c) Use the parabolic combat law to show that the y troops win if $c > 0$ and lose if $c < 0$.

Chapter Summary

In this chapter we have discussed various types of first order differential equations. The most important were the separable, exact, and linear equations. Their principal features and method of solution are outlined below.

Separable Equations: $dy/dx = g(x)p(y)$.
Separate the variables and integrate.

Exact Equations: $dF(x, y) = 0$.
Solutions are given implicitly by $F(x, y) = C$. If $\partial M/\partial y = \partial N/\partial x$, then $Mdx + Ndy = 0$ is exact and F is given by

$$F = \int M\,dx + g(y), \quad \text{where} \quad g'(y) = N - \frac{\partial}{\partial y}\int M\,dx,$$

or

$$F = \int N\,dy + h(x), \quad \text{where} \quad h'(x) = M - \frac{\partial}{\partial x}\int N\,dy.$$

Linear Equations: $dy/dx + P(x)y = Q(x)$.
The integrating factor $\mu = \exp(\int P(x)\,dx)$ reduces the equation to $d(\mu y)/dx = \mu Q$, so that $\mu y = \int \mu Q\,dx + C$.

When an equation is not separable, exact, or linear, it may be possible to find an integrating factor or perform a substitution that will enable us to solve the equation.

Special Integrating Factors: $\mu M\,dx + \mu N\,dy = 0$ is exact.
If $(\partial M/\partial y - \partial N/\partial x)/N$ depends only on x, then

$$\mu(x) = \exp\left(\int \left\{\frac{\partial M/\partial y - \partial N/\partial x}{N}\right\}dx\right)$$

is an integrating factor. If $(\partial N/\partial x - \partial M/\partial y)/M$ depends only on y, then

$$\mu(y) = \exp\left(\int \left\{\frac{\partial N/\partial x - \partial M/\partial y}{M}\right\}dy\right)$$

is an integrating factor.

Homogeneous Equations: $dy/dx = G(y/x)$.
Let $v = y/x$. Then $dy/dx = v + x(dv/dx)$, and the transformed equation in the variables v and x is separable.

Equations of the Form: $dy/dx = G(ax + by)$.
Let $z = ax + by$. Then $dz/dx = a + b(dy/dx)$, and the transformed equation in the variables z and x is separable.

Bernoulli Equations: $dy/dx + P(x)y = Q(x)y^n$.
For $n \neq 0$ or 1, let $v = y^{1-n}$. Then $dv/dx = (1-n)y^{-n}(dy/dx)$, and the transformed equation in the variables v and x is linear.

Linear Coefficients: $(a_1x + b_1y + c_1)\,dx + (a_2x + b_2y + c_2)\,dy = 0$.
For $a_1b_2 \neq a_2b_1$, let $x = u + h$ and $y = v + k$, where h and k satisfy

$$a_1h + b_1k + c_1 = 0,$$
$$a_2h + b_2k + c_2 = 0.$$

Then the transformed equation in the variables u and v is homogeneous.

REVIEW PROBLEMS

In Problems 1 through 30 solve the equation.

1. $\dfrac{dy}{dx} = \dfrac{e^{x+y}}{y - 1}$. $e^x e^y$

   SEP.

2. $\dfrac{dy}{dx} - 4y = 32x^2$.

   LINEAR

$$\int 3\ln x = e^{x}$$

$$\frac{\partial M}{\partial y} = 2x = \frac{\partial N}{\partial x}$$

3. $(2xy - 3x^2)\,dx + (x^2 - 2y^{-3})\,dy = 0.$ EXACT

   EXACT **5.** $[\sin(xy) + xy\cos(xy)]\,dx + [1 + x^2\cos(xy)]\,dy = 0.$

SEP, **6.** $2xy^3\,dx - (1 - x^2)\,dy = 0.$

LIN, **8.** $\dfrac{dy}{dx} + \dfrac{2y}{x} = 2x^2y^2.$

CAN'T DO **10.** $[1 + (1 + x^2 + 2xy + y^2)^{-1}]\,dx + [y^{-1/2} + (1 + x^2 + 2xy + y^2)^{-1}]\,dy = 0.$

C.D, **11.** $\dfrac{dy}{dx} = 1 + \cos^2(x - y).$

LIN **13.** $\dfrac{dy}{dx} - \dfrac{y}{x} = x^2\sin 2x.$

15. $\dfrac{dy}{dx} = 2 - \sqrt{2x - y + 3}.$

17. $\dfrac{dy}{dx} + 2y = y^2.$

19. $(x^2 - 3y^2)\,dx + 2xy\,dy = 0.$

21. $(y - 2x - 1)\,dx + (x + y - 4)\,dy = 0.$

23. $(y - x)\,dx + (x + y)\,dy = 0.$

25. $y(x - y - 2)\,dx + x(y - x + 4)\,dy = 0.$

27. $(3x - y - 5)\,dx + (x - y + 1)\,dy = 0.$

29. $(4xy^3 - 9y^2 + 4xy^2)\,dx + (3x^2y^2 - 6xy + 2x^2y)\,dy = 0.$

30. $\dfrac{dy}{dx} = (x + y + 1)^2 - (x + y - 1)^2.$

4. $\dfrac{dy}{dx} + \dfrac{3y}{x} = x^2 - 4x + 3.$ LINEAR,

$$dy + 3y = (x^3 - 4x + 3)\,dx$$
$$\frac{dy}{dx} + 3y = x^3 - 4x + 3$$

7. $x^3y^2\,dx + x^4y^{-6}\,dy = 0.$ SEP

9. $(x^2 + y^2)\,dx + 3xy\,dy = 0.$

C.D **12.** $(y^3 + 4e^xy)\,dx + (2e^x + 3y^2)\,dy = 0.$

LIN **14.** $\dfrac{dy}{dx} - \dfrac{y}{x - 1} = x^2 + 2.$

LIN **16.** $\dfrac{dy}{dx} + y\tan x + \sin x = 0.$

18. $\dfrac{dy}{dx} = (2x + y - 1)^2.$

20. $\dfrac{dy}{dx} + \dfrac{y}{x} = -4xy^{-2}.$

22. $(2x - 2y - 8)\,dx + (x - 3y - 6)\,dy = 0.$

EXACT **24.** $(\sqrt{y/x} + \cos x)\,dx + (\sqrt{x/y} + \sin y)\,dy = 0.$

SEP. **26.** $\dfrac{dy}{dx} + xy = 0.$

28. $\dfrac{dy}{dx} = \dfrac{x - y - 1}{x + y + 5}.$

$$\frac{1}{y} = v, \qquad x_y = \frac{1}{y} = v, \qquad \frac{1}{v} + v = y$$

In Problems 31 through 40 solve the initial value problem.

HOMOGENEOUS

31. $(x^3 - y)\,dx + x\,dy = 0,$ $y(1) = 3.$

HOMOGENEOUS **32.** $\dfrac{dy}{dx} = \left(\dfrac{x}{y} + \dfrac{y}{x}\right),$ $y(1) = -4.$

33. $(x + y + 3)\,dx + dy = 0,$ $y(0) = 1.$

34. $\dfrac{dy}{dx} - \dfrac{2y}{x} = x^2\cos x,$ $y(\pi) = 2.$

35. $(2y^2 + 4x^2)\,dx - xy\,dy = 0,$ $y(1) = -2.$

36. $[2\cos(2x + y) - x^2]\,dx + [\cos(2x + y) + e^y]\,dy = 0,$ $y(1) = 0.$

37. $(2x - y)\,dx + (x + y - 3)\,dy = 0,$ $y(0) = 2.$

38. $\sqrt{y}\,dx + (x^2 + 4)\,dy = 0,$ SEP. $y(0) = 4.$

BERN **39.** $\dfrac{dy}{dx} - \dfrac{2y}{x} = x^{-1}y^{-1},$ $y(1) = 3.$

40. $\dfrac{dy}{dx} - 4y = 2xy^2,$ $y(0) = -4.$

Projects for Chapter 2

A. THE SNOWPLOW PROBLEM

EXTRA CREDIT FOR TEST

To apply the techniques discussed in this chapter to real-world problems, it is necessary to "translate" these problems into questions that can be answered mathematically. The process of reformulating a real-world problem as a mathematical one often requires making certain simplifying assumptions. To illustrate this, consider the following snowplow problem.

> One morning it began to snow very hard and continued snowing steadily throughout the day. A snowplow set out at 9:00 A.M. to clear a road, clearing 2 mi by 11:00 A.M. and an additional mile by 1:00 P.M. *At what time did it start snowing?*

To solve this problem, you can make two physical assumptions concerning the rate at which it is snowing and the rate at which the snowplow can clear the road. Since it is snowing steadily, it is reasonable to assume that it is snowing at a constant rate. From the data given (and from our experience) the snowplow moves slower, the deeper the snow. With this in mind, assume that the rate (in mi/hr) at which a snowplow can clear a road is inversely proportional to the depth of the snow.

B. ANALYTIC FUNCTIONS AND ORTHOGONAL TRAJECTORIES

A complex-valued function $f(z)$ of the complex variable $z = x + iy$, where $i = \sqrt{-1}$, can be written in the form $f(z) = u(x, y) + iv(x, y)$, where u and v are real-valued functions. If $f(z)$ has a derivative at each point of a region $\mathcal{D}$, then $f(z)$ is said to be **analytic**[†] in $\mathcal{D}$. For example, any polynomial function of z is analytic in the whole plane. It is known that the real and imaginary parts of an analytic function satisfy the **Cauchy-Riemann equations**

$$\frac{\partial u}{\partial x} = \frac{\partial v}{\partial y}, \qquad \frac{\partial u}{\partial y} = -\frac{\partial v}{\partial x}.$$

(a) For an analytic function $f(z) = u(x, y) + iv(x, y)$, show that the level curves

$$u(x, y) = \text{constant}$$

are orthogonal trajectories (see Problem 31, Exercises 2.3) for the level curves

$$v(x, y) = \text{constant}. \qquad \text{[Hint: Use the Cauchy-Riemann equations.]}$$

(b) Let $v(x, y) = y - 2xy$. Find $u(x, y)$ so that $f(z) = u(x, y) + iv(x, y)$ satisfies the Cauchy-Riemann equations. [Hint: Start with $\partial u/\partial x = \partial v/\partial y = 1 - 2x$.] Now use the result of part (a) to determine the orthogonal trajectories of the family of curves $y - 2xy = C$.

(c) The function $f(z) = z + 1/z$ is analytic for $z \neq 0$. Using complex arithmetic, write $f(z)$ in the form $u(x, y) + iv(x, y)$ and show that the level curve $v(x, y) = 0$ consists of the x-axis and the unit circle $x^2 + y^2 = 1$.

[†] For a discussion of analytic functions of a complex variable see, for example, *Fundamentals of Complex Analysis,* by E. B. Saff and A. D. Snider, Prentice-Hall, Inc., Englewood Cliffs, New Jersey, 1976.

(d) The level curves $v(x, y) = C$ from part (c) that lie outside the unit circle can be interpreted as the stream lines of a fluid flow around a cylindrical obstacle. Sketch these level curves for various values of C. [Hint: Solve for x in terms of y and C and plot points.]

C. ASYMPTOTIC BEHAVIOR OF SOLUTIONS TO LINEAR EQUATIONS

To illustrate how the asymptotic behavior of the forcing term $Q(x)$ affects the solution to a linear equation, consider the equation

(1) $$\frac{dy}{dx} + ay = Q(x),$$

where the constant a is positive and $Q(x)$ is continuous on $(0, \infty)$.

(a) Show that the general solution to equation (1) can be written in the form

(2) $$y(x) = y(x_0)e^{-a(x - x_0)} + e^{-ax} \int_{x_0}^{x} e^{at}Q(t)\,dt,$$

where x_0 is a nonnegative constant.

(b) If $|Q(x)| \le k$ for $x \ge x_0$, where k and x_0 are nonnegative constants, show that

$$|y(x)| \le |y(x_0)|e^{-a(x - x_0)} + \frac{k}{a}[1 - e^{-a(x - x_0)}]$$

for $x \ge x_0$.

(c) Let $z(x)$ satisfy the same equation as (1) but with forcing function $\tilde{Q}(x)$, that is,

$$\frac{dz}{dx} + az = \tilde{Q}(x),$$

where $\tilde{Q}(x)$ is continuous on $(0, \infty)$. Show that if

$$|\tilde{Q}(x) - Q(x)| \le K \quad \text{for} \quad x \ge x_0,$$

then

$$|z(x) - y(x)| \le |z(x_0) - y(x_0)|e^{-a(x - x_0)} + \frac{K}{a}[1 - e^{-a(x - x_0)}]$$

for $x \ge x_0$.

(d) Now show that if $Q(x) \to \beta$ as $x \to \infty$, then any solution $y(x)$ of equation (1) satisfies $y(x) \to \beta/a$ as $x \to \infty$. [Hint: Take $\tilde{Q}(x) \equiv \beta$ and $z(x) \equiv \beta/a$ in part (c).]

(e) As an application of part (d), suppose that a brine solution containing $q(t)$ kilograms of salt per liter at time t runs into a tank of water at a fixed rate and that the mixture, kept uniform by stirring, flows out at the same rate. Given that $q(t) \to \beta$ as $t \to \infty$, use the result of part (d) to determine the limiting concentration of the salt in the tank as $t \to \infty$ (see Problem 34, Exercises 2.4).

D. CLAIRAUT EQUATIONS AND
SINGULAR SOLUTIONS

An equation of the form

(3) $$y = x\frac{dy}{dx} + f\left(\frac{dy}{dx}\right),$$

where f is a continuously differentiable function, is called a **Clairaut equation.**[†] Interest in these equations is due to the fact that (3) has a one-parameter family of solutions that consist of *straight lines*. Furthermore, the **envelope** of this family—that is, the curve whose tangent lines are given by the family—is also a solution to (3) and is called the **singular solution.**
  To solve a Clairaut equation:

  (a) Differentiate equation (3) with respect to x and simplify to show that

(4) $$\left[x + f'\left(\frac{dy}{dx}\right)\right]\frac{d^2y}{dx^2} = 0.$$

  (b) From (4), conclude that $dy/dx = c$ or $f'(dy/dx) = -x$. Assume that $dy/dx = c$ and substitute back into (3) to obtain the family of *straight-line solutions*

  $$y = cx + f(c).$$

  (c) Show that another solution to (3) is given parametrically by

  $$x = -f'(p),$$
  $$y = f(p) - pf'(p),$$

where the parameter $p = dy/dx$. This solution is the *singular solution.*

  (d) Use the above method to find the family of straight-line solutions and the singular solution to the equation

  $$y = x\left(\frac{dy}{dx}\right) + 2\left(\frac{dy}{dx}\right)^2.$$

Sketch several of the straight-line solutions along with the singular solution on the same coordinate system. Observe that the straight-line solutions are all tangent to the singular solution.

  (e) Repeat part (d) for the equation

  $$x\left(\frac{dy}{dx}\right)^3 - y\left(\frac{dy}{dx}\right)^2 + 1 = 0.$$

[†] *Historical Footnote:* These equations were studied by Alexis Clairaut in 1734.

Mathematical Models and Numerical Methods Involving First Order Equations

3.1 Mathematical Modeling

Adopting the Babylonian practices of careful measurement and detailed observations, the ancient Greeks sought to comprehend nature by logical analysis. Aristotle's convincing arguments that the world was not flat, but spherical, led the intellectuals of that day to ponder the question: What is the circumference of the Earth? And it was astonishing that Eratosthenes managed to obtain a fairly accurate answer to this problem without having to set foot beyond the ancient city of Alexandria. His method involved certain assumptions and simplifications: The Earth is a perfect sphere, the Sun's rays travel parallel paths, the city of Syene was 5000 stadia due south of Alexandria, etc. With these idealizations, Eratosthenes created a mathematical context in which the principles of geometry could be applied.

Today, as scientists seek to further our understanding of nature and as engineers seek, on a more pragmatic level, to find answers to technical problems, the technique of representing our "real world" in mathematical terms has become an invaluable tool. This process of mimicking reality by using the language of mathematics is known as **mathematical modeling.**

Formulating problems in mathematical terms has several benefits. First, it requires that we clearly state our premises. Real-world problems are often complex, involving several different and possibly interrelated processes. Before mathematical treatment can proceed, one must determine which variables are significant and which can be ignored. Often, for the relevant variables, relationships are postulated in the form of laws, formulas, theories, etc. These assumptions constitute the **idealizations** of the model.

Mathematics contains a wealth of theorems and techniques for making logical deductions and manipulating equations. Hence it provides a context in which analysis can take place free of any preconceived notions of the outcome. It is also of great practical importance that mathematics provides a format for obtaining numerical answers via a computer.

The process of building an effective mathematical model takes skill, imagination, and objective evaluation. Certainly an exposure to several existing models that illustrate various aspects of modeling can lead to a better feel for the process. Several excellent books and articles are devoted exclusively to the subject.[†] In this chapter we concentrate on examples of models that involve first order differential equations. In studying these and in building your own models, the following broad outline of the process may be helpful.

FORMULATE THE PROBLEM

Here you must pose the problem in such a way that it can be "answered" mathematically. This requires an understanding of the problem area as well as the mathematics. At this stage you may need to spend time talking with nonmathematicians and reading the relevant literature.

DEVELOP THE MODEL

There are two things to be done here. First you must decide which variables are important and which are not. The former are then classified as independent variables or dependent variables. The unimportant variables are those that have very little or no effect on the process. (For example, in studying the motion of a falling body, its color is usually of little interest.) The independent variables are those whose effect is significant and that will serve as input for the model.[††] For the falling body, its shape, mass, initial position, initial velocity, and time from release are possible independent variables. The dependent variables are those that are affected by the independent variables and that are important to solving the problem. Again for a falling body, its velocity, location, and time of impact are all possible dependent variables.

Second, you must determine or specify the relationships (e.g., a differential equation) that exist among the relevant variables. This requires a good background in the area and insight into the problem. You may begin with a crude model; then, based upon testing, refine the model as needed. For example, you might begin by ignoring any friction acting on the falling body. Then, if necessary to obtain a more acceptable answer, try to take into account any frictional forces that may affect the motion.

[†] See, for example, *Mathematical Modeling,* edited by J. G. Andrews and R. R. McLone, Butterworths, London, 1976, or *An Introduction to Mathematical Modeling,* by Edward A. Bender, John Wiley and Sons, New York, 1978.

[††] In the mathematical formulation of the model, certain of the independent variables may be called **parameters.**

TEST THE MODEL

Before attempting to "verify" a model by comparing its output with experimental data, the following questions should be considered:

Are the assumptions reasonable?

Are the physical dimensions of the variables correct?

Is the model internally consistent in the sense that equations do not contradict one another?

Do the relevant equations have solutions?

How difficult is it to obtain the solutions?

Do the solutions provide an answer for the problem being studied?

When possible, try to validate the model by comparing its predictions with any experimental data. Begin with rather simple predictions that involve little computation or analysis. Then, as the model is refined, check to see that the accuracy of the model's predictions are acceptable to you. In some cases validation is impossible or socially, politically, economically, or morally unreasonable. For example, how does one validate a model that predicts when our sun will die out?

Each time the model is used to predict the outcome of a process and hence solve a problem, it represents a further test of the model that may lead to further refinements or simplifications. In many cases a model is simplified to give a quicker or less expensive answer—provided, of course, that sufficient accuracy is maintained.

One should always keep in mind that a model is *not* reality, but only a representation of reality. The more refined models *may* provide an understanding of the underlying processes of nature. For this reason applied mathematicians strive for better, more refined models. Still, the real test of a model is its ability to find an acceptable answer for the posed problem.

In this chapter we discuss various models that involve differential equations. In Section 3.2, Compartmental Analysis, and Section 3.4, Newtonian Mechanics, we consider two general models that result from interpreting the derivative as a rate of change of one variable with respect to another. Section 3.3 describes a model for the heating and cooling of a building. Sections 3.5 and 3.6 contain a brief introduction to some numerical techniques for solving first order initial value problems. This will enable us to study more realistic models that cannot be solved using the techniques of Chapter 2.

3.2 *Compartmental Analysis*

Many complicated processes can be broken down into distinct stages and the entire system modeled by describing the interactions between the various stages. Such systems are called **compartmental** and are graphically depicted by **block diagrams.** In this section we study the basic unit of these systems, a single compartment, and analyze some simple processes that can be handled by such a model.

Figure 3.1 Schematic representation of a one-compartment system

The basic one-compartment system consists of a function $x(t)$ that represents the amount of a substance in the compartment at time t, an input rate at which the substance enters the compartment, and an output rate at which the substance leaves the compartment (see Figure 3.1).

Since the derivative of x with respect to t can be interpreted as the rate of change in the amount of the substance in the compartment with respect to time, the one-compartment system suggests

(1) $$\frac{dx}{dt} = \textbf{input rate} - \textbf{output rate,}$$

as a mathematical model for the process.

MIXING PROBLEMS

A problem for which the one-compartment system provides a useful representation is the mixing of fluids in a tank. Let $x(t)$ represent the amount of a substance in a tank (compartment) at time t. In order to use the compartmental analysis model we must be able to determine the rates at which this substance enters and leaves the tank. In mixing problems, one is often given the rate at which a fluid containing the substance flows into the tank along with the concentration of the substance in that fluid. Hence multiplying the flow rate (volume/time) by the concentration (amount/volume) yields the input rate (amount/time).

The output rate of the substance is usually more difficult to determine. If we are given the exit rate of the mixture of fluids in the tank, then how do we determine the concentration of the substance in this mixture? One simplifying assumption that we might make is that the concentration is kept uniform in the mixture. Then, we can compute the concentration of the substance in the mixture by dividing the amount $x(t)$ by the volume of the mixture in the tank at time t. Multiplying this concentration by the exit rate of the mixture then gives the desired output rate of the substance. This model is used in the next two examples.

▶ **Example 1** Consider a large tank holding 1000 L of water into which a brine solution of salt begins to flow at a constant rate of 6 L/min. The solution inside the tank is kept well stirred and is flowing out of the tank at a rate of 6 L/min. If the concentration of salt in the brine entering the tank is 1 kg/L, determine when the concentration of salt in the tank will reach $\frac{1}{2}$ kg/L (see Figure 3.2).

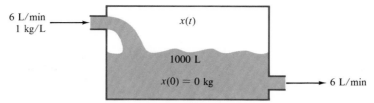

6 L/min
1 kg/L

$x(t)$

1000 L

$x(0) = 0$ kg

6 L/min

Figure 3.2 Mixing problem with equal flow rates

Solution   We can view the tank as a compartment containing salt. If we let $x(t)$ denote the amount of salt in the tank at time t, we can determine the concentration of salt in the tank by dividing $x(t)$ by the volume of fluid in the tank at time t. We use the mathematical model described by equation (1) to solve for $x(t)$.

First we must determine the rate at which salt enters the tank. We are given that brine flows into the tank at a rate of 6 L/min. Since the concentration of this brine is 1 kg/L, we conclude that the input rate of salt into the tank is

(2)   (6 L/min)(1 kg/L) = 6 kg/min.

We must now determine the output rate of salt from the tank. Since the brine solution in the tank is kept well stirred, let's assume that the concentration of salt in the tank is uniform. That is, the concentration of salt in any part of the tank at time t is just $x(t)$ divided by the volume of fluid in the tank. Since the tank initially contains 1000 L and the rate of flow into the tank is the same as the rate of flow out, the volume is a constant 1000 L. Hence the output rate of salt is

(3) $(6 \text{ L/min})\left(\dfrac{x(t)}{1000} \text{ kg/L}\right) = \dfrac{3x(t)}{500} \text{ kg/min.}$

Since the tank initially contained just water, we set $x(0) = 0$. Substituting the rates in (2) and (3) into equation (1) then gives the initial value problem

(4) $\dfrac{dx}{dt} = 6 - \dfrac{3x}{500}, \qquad x(0) = 0,$

as a mathematical model for the mixing problem.

The equation in (4) is separable (and linear) and easy to solve. Using the initial condition $x(0) = 0$ to evaluate the arbitrary constant, we obtain

(5) $x(t) = 1000(1 - e^{-3t/500}).$

Thus the concentration of salt in the tank at time t is

(6) $\dfrac{x(t)}{1000} = 1 - e^{-3t/500} \text{ kg/L.}$

To determine when the concentration of salt is $\frac{1}{2}$ kg/L, we set the right-hand side of (6) equal to $\frac{1}{2}$ and solve for t. This gives

$$1 - e^{-3t/500} = \frac{1}{2} \quad \text{or} \quad e^{-3t/500} = \frac{1}{2},$$

and hence

$$t = \frac{500 \ln 2}{3} \approx 115.52 \text{ min.}$$

Consequently the concentration of salt in the tank will be $\frac{1}{2}$ kg/L after 115.52 min. ◀

From equation (5) we observe that the amount of salt in the tank steadily increases and has the limiting value

$$\lim_{t \to \infty} x(t) = \lim_{t \to \infty} 1000(1 - e^{-3t/500}) = 1000 \text{ kg.}$$

Thus, the limiting concentration of salt in the tank is 1 kg/L, which is the same as the concentration of salt in the brine flowing into the tank. This certainly agrees with our expectations!

It might be interesting to see what would happen to the concentration if the flow rate into the tank is greater than the flow rate out.

▶ **Example 2**   For the mixing problem described in Example 1, assume now that the brine leaves the tank at a rate of 5 L/min instead of 6 L/min, with all else being the same (see Figure 3.3). Determine the concentration of salt in the tank as a function of time.

Solution   Since the difference between the rate of flow into the tank and the rate of flow out is $6 - 5 = 1$ L/min, the amount of fluid in the tank after t minutes is $(1000 + t)$ L. Hence the rate at which salt leaves the tank is

(7) $(5 \text{ L/min}) \left[\dfrac{x(t)}{1000 + t} \text{ kg/L} \right] = \dfrac{5x(t)}{1000 + t} \text{ kg/min.}$

Using (7) in place of (3) for the output rate gives the initial value problem

(8) $\dfrac{dx}{dt} = 6 - \dfrac{5x}{1000 + t}, \qquad x(0) = 0,$

as a mathematical model for the mixing problem.

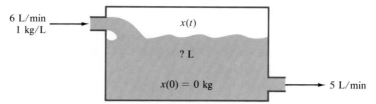

Figure 3.3 Mixing problem with unequal flow rates

Since the equation in (8) is linear, we can use the procedure outlined on page 53 to solve for $x(t)$. The integrating factor is $\mu(t) = (1000 + t)^5$. Thus

$$\frac{d}{dt}\left[(1000 + t)^5 x\right] = 6(1000 + t)^5,$$

$$(1000 + t)^5 x = (1000 + t)^6 + c,$$

(9) $$x(t) = (1000 + t) + c(1000 + t)^{-5}.$$

Using the initial condition $x(0) = 0$, we find $c = -(1000)^6$, and thus the solution to (8) is

(10) $$x(t) = (1000 + t) - (1000)^6(1000 + t)^{-5}.$$

From (10) we see that the concentration of salt in the tank at time t is

(11) $$\frac{x(t)}{1000 + t} = 1 - (1000)^6(1000 + t)^{-6} \text{ kg/L.} \blacktriangleleft$$

As in Example 1, the concentration given by (11) approaches 1 kg/L as $t \to \infty$. However, in Example 2 the volume of fluid in the tank becomes unbounded, and when the tank begins to overflow, the model in (8) is no longer appropriate.

For mixing problems, the one-compartment model is extremely useful. The only assumption made that is the least bit questionable is that the well-stirred mixture in the tank has a uniform concentration. Even with stirring, the salt entering the tank at the top has a delayed effect on the concentration of the brine leaving at the bottom. It is more realistic to assume that the concentration of brine leaving the tank at time t is equal to the average concentration at an earlier instant, say at time $t - t_0$, where t_0 is a positive constant. The original problem would now be described by the initial value problem

(12) $$x'(t) = 6 - \frac{3}{500} x(t - t_0), \qquad x(t) = 0 \quad \text{for} \quad t \in [-t_0, 0].$$

Equations such as the one in (12) are called **delay differential equations** due to the "delay" in the argument of $x(t - t_0)$. These equations are discussed further in the projects at the end of this chapter (see Project A).

POPULATION MODELS

How does one predict the growth of a population? If we are interested in a single population, we can think of the species as being contained in a compartment (a Petrie dish, an island, a country, etc.) and study the growth process as a one-compartment system.

Let $p(t)$ be the population at time t. While the population is always an integer, it is usually large enough so that very little error is introduced in assuming that $p(t)$ is a continuous function. We now need to determine the growth (input) rate and the death (output) rate for the population.

Let's consider a population of bacteria that reproduce by simple cell division. In our model we assume that the growth rate is proportional to the population present. This assumption is consistent with observations of bacteria growth. As long as there are sufficient space and ample food supply for the bacteria, we can also assume that the death rate is zero. (Remember that in cell division, the parent cell does not die, but becomes two new cells.) Hence a mathematical model for a population of bacteria is

$$(13) \qquad \frac{dp}{dt} = kp, \qquad p(0) = p_0,$$

where $k > 0$ is the proportionality constant for the growth rate and p_0 is the population at time $t = 0$. The equation in (13) is separable, and solving the initial value problem for $p(t)$ gives

$$(14) \qquad p(t) = p_0 e^{kt}.$$

The mathematical model in (13) is called the **Malthusian** or **exponential law** of population growth. It has been used to study not only colonies of bacteria, but also the population growth of small mammals over short time intervals, and has even been applied in certain studies of human populations.

To test the Malthusian model, let's apply it to the demographic history of the United States.

▶ **Example 3** In 1790 the population of the United States was 3.93 million, and in 1800 the population was 5.31 million. Using the Malthusian model, estimate the population of the United States as a function of time.

Solution   If we set $t = 0$ to be the year 1790, then by formula (14), we have

$$(15) \qquad p(t) = (3.93)e^{kt},$$

where $p(t)$ is the population in millions. To determine k, we observe that in 1800, when $t = 10$ years, we have

$$(16) \qquad p(10) = 5.31 = (3.93)e^{10k}.$$

Solving (16) for k yields

$$k = \frac{\ln(5.31) - \ln(3.93)}{10} \approx 0.0301,$$

and substituting this value in equation (15), we find

(17) $\qquad p(t) = (3.93)e^{(0.0301)t}.$ ◀

In Table 3.1 we have listed the United States population as given by the U.S. Bureau of the Census, and the population predicted by the Malthusian model using equation (17).

		Malthusian	**Logistic**
Year	**U.S. Census**	**(Example 3)**	**(Example 4)**
1790	3.93	3.93	3.93
1800	5.31	5.31	5.30
1810	7.24	7.18	7.13
1820	9.64	9.70	9.58
1830	12.87	13.10	12.82
1840	17.07	17.70	17.07
1850	23.19	23.92	22.60
1860	31.44	32.32	29.70
1870	39.83	43.67	38.65
1880	50.16	59.01	49.69
1890	62.95	79.73	62.95
1900	75.99	107.73	78.37
1910	91.97	145.57	95.64
1920	105.71	196.69	114.21
1930	122.78	265.77	133.28
1940	131.67	359.11	152.00
1950	151.33	485.24	169.56
1960	179.32	655.66	185.35
1970	203.21	885.93	199.01
1980	226.50	1197.08	210.46

TABLE 3.1 A COMPARISON OF THE MALTHUSIAN AND LOGISTIC MODELS WITH U.S. CENSUS DATA (POPULATION IS GIVEN IN MILLIONS)

Looking at Table 3.1 we see that the predictions based on the Malthusian model are in reasonable agreement with the census data until about 1870. After 1870 the predicted population is too large, and the Malthusian model is unacceptable.

Let's take a closer look at our assumptions. The premise that the growth rate of the population is proportional to the size of the population seems reasonable, but our assumption of a zero death rate is certainly wrong. Assuming that people die of natural causes, we might expect the death rate also to be proportional to the size of the population. This gives

$$\frac{dp}{dt} = kp - k_1 p = (k - k_1)p,$$

where $k > 0$ is the proportionality constant for the birth rate and $k_1 > 0$ is the proportionality constant for the death rate. Notice, however, that our inclusion of death by natural causes gives the same (faulty) mathematical model that we had before.

What about premature deaths due to malnutrition, inadequate medical supplies, communicable diseases, violent crimes, etc.? Since these factors involve a competition within the population, we might assume that the death rate is proportional to the number of two-party interactions. For a population of size p, there are $p(p-1)/2$ such interactions. Thus we will assume that the death rate due to intraspecies competition is

$$k_2 \frac{p(p-1)}{2},$$

where k_2 is the proportionality constant. This leads to the model

(18) $$\frac{dp}{dt} = ap - bp^2, \qquad p(0) = p_0,$$

where $a = k - k_1 + k_2/2$ and $b = k_2/2$.

The equation (18) is separable and can be solved using partial fractions:

$$\int \frac{1}{p(a - bp)} \, dp = \int dt,$$

$$\frac{1}{a} \int \frac{1}{p} \, dp - \frac{1}{a} \int \frac{-b}{a - bp} \, dp = \int dt,$$

$$\frac{1}{a} \ln|p| - \frac{1}{a} \ln|a - bp| = t + c_1,$$

$$\ln \left| \frac{p}{a - bp} \right| = at + c_2,$$

$$\frac{p}{a - bp} = c_3 e^{at}.$$

Solving for p we have

(19)
$$p(t) = \frac{ac_3 e^{at}}{bc_3 e^{at} + 1} = \frac{ac_3}{bc_3 + e^{-at}}.$$

Using the initial condition in (18), we find

$$c_3 = \frac{p_0}{a - bp_0}, \quad \text{if} \quad p_0 \neq 0 \quad \text{or} \quad a/b.$$

Thus, on substituting for c_3 and simplifying, we get

(20)
$$p(t) = \frac{ap_0}{bp_0 + (a - bp_0)e^{-at}}.$$

The equation in (18) is called the **logistic equation** and (20) the **logistic function.** In Figure 3.4, we have sketched the graph of this function, which is called the **logistic curve.** The logistic model for population growth was first developed by P. F. Verhulst around 1840.

An important property of the logistic function is that

$$\lim_{t \to \infty} p(t) = \frac{a}{b} \quad \text{if} \quad p_0 > 0.$$

Consequently, we see that any population following the logistic model will remain **bounded.** Moreover, when the initial population p_0 is greater than the ratio a/b, the population will decrease toward a/b, and when the initial population is less than a/b, it will increase toward a/b as illustrated in Figure 3.4.

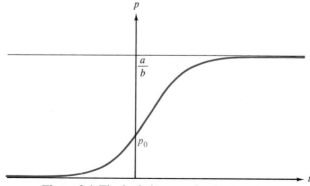

Figure 3.4 The logistic curve for $0 < p_0 < a/b$

In deriving the solution given in (20), we excluded the two cases when $p_0 = a/b$ or 0. These two populations are referred to as **equilibrium populations.** This terminology follows from the observation that when $p(t) \equiv a/b$ (or 0), then

$$0 \equiv \frac{dp}{dt} \text{ and } ap - bp^2 = p(a - bp) \equiv 0.$$

Hence, $p(t) \equiv a/b$ (or 0) are constant solutions to (18). Notice that the graph of these equilibrium populations are the horizontal asymptotes of the logistic curve in Figure 3.4.

Let's test the logistic model on the population growth of the United States.

▶ **Example 4**   Taking the 1790 population of 3.93 million as the initial population and given the 1840 and 1890 populations of 17.07 and 62.95 million, respectively, use the logistic model to estimate the population at time t.

Solution   With $t = 0$ corresponding to the year 1790, we know that $p_0 = 3.93$. We must now determine the parameters a, b in equation (20). For this purpose we use the given facts that $p(50) = 17.07$ and $p(100) = 62.95$; that is,

(21) $$17.07 = \frac{3.93a}{3.93b + (a - 3.93b)e^{-50a}},$$

(22) $$62.95 = \frac{3.93a}{3.93b + (a - 3.93b)e^{-100a}}.$$

Equations (21) and (22) are two nonlinear equations in the two unknowns a, b. To solve such a system we would usually resort to a numerical approximation scheme such as Newton's method. However, for the case at hand, it is possible to find the solutions directly because the data is given at times t_1 and t_2 with $t_2 = 2t_1$. Indeed, from equation (21), we find that

$$3.93b = \frac{(3.93 - 17.07e^{-50a})a}{17.07(1 - e^{-50a})},$$

and substituting this expression into (22) leads to a linear equation in $x := e^{-50a}$ (see Problem 10). Carrying out the algebra, we ultimately find that

(23) $$a = 0.0304667 \quad \text{and} \quad b = 0.0001214.$$

Thus the logistic model for the given data is

(24) $$p(t) = \frac{0.1197340}{0.0004771 + (0.0299896)e^{-(0.0304667)t}}. \quad ◀$$

The model (24) predicts a limit on the future population of the United States, namely,

$$\lim_{t \to \infty} p(t) = \frac{a}{b} = \frac{0.0304667}{0.0001214} \approx 251 \text{ million.}$$

In Table 3.1 we have also listed the U.S. population as predicted by the logistic function in (24). As you can see, these predictions are in better agreement with the census data. We have still not considered the effect of major wars, immigration, social and technological changes, etc. A more refined population model would take these into account as well as the number of females in various age groups, especially the number of females of child-bearing age. Some sophisticated models are probabilistic in nature and involve what are called **Markov chains.**

WILL NOT BE ON TEST #1

EXERCISES 3.2

1. A brine solution of salt flows at a constant rate of 8 L/min into a large tank that initially held 100 L of brine solution in which was dissolved 5 kg of salt. The solution inside the tank is kept well stirred and flows out of the tank at the same rate. If the concentration of salt in the brine entering the tank is 0.5 kg/L, determine the amount of salt in the tank after t minutes. When will the concentration of salt in the tank reach 0.2 kg/L?

2. A brine solution of salt flows at a constant rate of 6 L/min into a large tank that initially held 50 L of brine solution in which was dissolved 5 kg of salt. The solution inside the tank is kept well stirred and flows out of the tank at the same rate. If the concentration of salt in the brine entering the tank is 0.5 kg/L, determine the amount of salt in the tank after t minutes. When will the concentration of salt in the tank reach 0.3 kg/L?

3. A nitric acid solution flows at a constant rate of 6 L/min into a large tank that initially held 200 L of a 0.5% nitric acid solution. The solution inside the tank is kept well stirred and flows out of the tank at a rate of 8 L/min. If the solution entering the tank is 20% nitric acid, determine the amount of nitric acid in the tank after t minutes. When will the percentage of nitric acid in the tank reach 10%?

4. A brine solution of salt flows at a constant rate of 4 L/min into a large tank that initially held 100 L of water. The solution inside the tank is kept well stirred and flows out of the tank at a rate of 3 L/min. If the concentration of salt in the brine entering the tank is 0.2 kg/L, determine the amount of salt in the tank after t minutes. When will the concentration of salt in the tank reach 0.1 kg/L?

5. A swimming pool whose volume is 10,000 gallons (gal) contains water that is 0.01% chlorine. Starting at $t = 0$, city water containing 0.001% chlorine is pumped into the pool at a rate of 5 gal/min, and the pool water flows out at the same rate. What is the percentage of chlorine in the pool after 1 hr? When will the pool water be 0.002% chlorine?

6. The air in a small room 12 ft by 8 ft by 8 ft is 3% carbon monoxide. Starting at $t = 0$, fresh air containing no carbon monoxide is blown into the room at a rate of 100 ft^3/min. If air in the room flows out through a vent at the same rate, when will the air in the room be 0.01% carbon monoxide?

7. Blood carries a drug into an organ at a rate of 3 cm^3/sec and leaves at the same rate. The organ has a liquid volume of 125 cm^3. If the concentration of the drug in the blood entering the organ is 0.2 g/cm^3, what is the concentration of the drug in the organ at time t if there was no trace of the drug initially? When will the concentration of the drug in the organ reach 0.1 g/cm^3?

8. Water flows into Lake Magdalene from Sweetwater Creek at a rate of 300 gal/min. Lake Magdalene contains about 100 million gal of water. The spraying of nearby orange groves has caused the concentration of pesticides in the lake to reach 0.000035, or. 35 parts per million. If pesticides are banned, how long will it be before the concentration of pesticides in Lake Magdalene is below 10 parts per million? (Assume that Sweetwater Creek contains no pesticides and the volume of Lake Magdalene stays constant.)

9. In 1970 the Department of Natural Resources released 1000 splake (a crossbreed of fish) into a lake. In 1977 the population of splake in the lake was estimated to be 3000. Using a Malthusian law for population growth, estimate the population of splake in the lake in 1980. What would the estimate be for the year 1991 using the Malthusian law?

10. For the logistic curve (20), assume that $p_1 := p(t_1)$ and $p_2 := p(t_2)$ are given with $t_2 = 2t_1 (t_1 > 0)$. Show that

$$a = \frac{1}{t_1} \ln\left[\frac{p_2(p_1 - p_0)}{p_0(p_2 - p_1)}\right], \qquad b = \frac{a}{p_1}\left[\frac{p_1^2 - p_0 p_2}{p_1 p_2 - 2p_0 p_2 + p_0 p_1}\right].$$

[Hint: Solve, separately, the equations $p_1 = p(t_1)$ and $p_2 = p(t_2)$ for bp_0 and set the answers equal.] Use these formulas to verify the numerical values given in (23).

11. In Problem 9, suppose we have the additional information that the population of splake in 1984 was estimated to be 5000. Use a logistic model to estimate the population of splake in the year 1991. What is the predicted limiting population? [Hint: Use the formulas in Problem 10.]

12. In 1970 the population of alligators on the Kennedy Space Center grounds was estimated to be just 300. In 1980 the population had grown to an estimated 1500. Using a Malthusian law for population growth, estimate the alligator population on the Kennedy Space Center grounds in the year 2000.

13. In Problem 12, suppose we have the additional information that the population of alligators on the grounds of the Kennedy Space Center in 1975 was estimated to be 1200. Use a logistic model to estimate the population of alligators in the year 2000. What is the predicted limiting population? [Hint: Use the formulas in Problem 10.]

14. A population model used in actuarial predictions is based on the **Gompertz equation**

(25) $$\frac{dP}{dt} = P(a - b \ln P),$$

where a and b are constants.

(a) Solve the Gompertz equation for $P(t)$.
(b) If $P(0) = P_0 > 0$, give a formula for $P(t)$ in terms of a, b, P_0, and t.
(c) Describe the behavior of $P(t)$ as $t \to \infty$. [Hint: Consider cases for $b > 0$ and $b < 0$.]

15. A snowball melts in such a way that the rate of change in its volume is proportional to its surface area. If the snowball was initially 4 in. in diameter and after 30 min its diameter is 3 in., when will its diameter be 2 in.? Mathematically speaking, when will the snowball disappear?

16. Suppose that the snowball in Problem 15 melts so that the rate of change in its *diameter* is proportional to its surface area. With the same given data, when will its diameter be 2 in.? Mathematically speaking, when will the snowball disappear?

In Problems 17 through 19 assume that the rate of decay of a radioactive substance is proportional to the amount of the substance present. The half-life of a radioactive substance is the time it takes for one-half of the substance to disintegrate.

17. If initially there are 50 grams (g) of a radioactive substance and after 3 days there are only 10 g remaining, what percentage of the original amount remains after 4 days?

18. If initially there are 300 g of a radioactive substance and after 5 years there are 200 g remaining, how much time must elapse before only 10 g remain?

19. Carbon dating is often used to determine the age of a fossil. For example, a humanoid skull was found in a cave in South Africa along with the remains of a campfire. Archaeologists believe the age of the skull to be the same age as the campfire. It is determined that only 2% of the original amount of carbon-14 remains in the burnt wood of the campfire. Estimate the age of the skull if the half-life of carbon-14 is about 5600 years.

3.3 Heating and Cooling of Buildings

Our goal is to formulate a mathematical model that describes the 24-hr temperature profile inside a building as a function of the outside temperature, the heat generated inside the building, and the furnace heating or air conditioning cooling. From this model we would like to answer the following three questions:

(a) How long does it take to change the building temperature substantially?

(b) How does the building temperature vary during spring and fall when there is no furnace heating or air conditioning?

(c) How does the building temperature vary in summer when there is air conditioning or in the winter when there is furnace heating?

A natural approach to modeling the temperature inside a building is to use compartmental analysis. If we let $T(t)$ represent the temperature inside the building at time t and view the building as a single compartment, then the rate of change in the temperature is just the difference between the rate at which the temperature increases and the rate at which the temperature decreases.

We will consider three main factors affecting the temperature inside the building. The first factor is the heat produced by people, lights, and machines inside the building. This causes a rate of increase in temperature that we will denote by $H(t)$. The second factor is the heating (or cooling) supplied by the furnace (or air conditioning). This rate of increase (or decrease) in temperature will be represented by $U(t)$. In general, the additional heating rate $H(t)$ and the furnace (or air conditioning) rate $U(t)$ are described in terms of energy per unit time (such as British thermal units per hour). However, by multiplying by the heat capacity of the building (in units of degrees temperature change per heat energy) we can express the two quantities $H(t)$ and $U(t)$ in terms of temperature per unit time.

The third factor is the effect of the outside temperature $M(t)$ on the temperature inside the building. Experimental evidence has shown that this factor can be modeled using **Newton's law of cooling,** which states that there is a rate of change in the temperature $T(t)$ that is proportional to the difference between the outside temperature $M(t)$ and the inside temperature $T(t)$. That is, the rate of change in the building temperature due to $M(t)$ is

$$K[M(t) - T(t)].$$

The positive constant K depends on the physical properties of the building, such as the number of doors and windows and the type of insulation, but K does not depend on M, T, or t. Hence, when the outside temperature is greater than the inside temperature, then $M(t) - T(t) > 0$, and there is an increase in the rate of change of the building temperature due to $M(t)$. On the other hand, when the outside temperature is less than the inside temperature, then $M(t) - T(t) < 0$, and there is a decrease in this rate of change.

Summarizing, we find

(1) $$\frac{dT}{dt} = K[M(t) - T(t)] + H(t) + U(t),$$

where the additional heating rate $H(t)$ is always nonnegative and $U(t)$ is positive for furnace heating and negative for air conditioner cooling. A more detailed model of the temperature dynamics of the building could involve more variables to represent different temperatures in different rooms or zones. Such an approach would use compartmental analysis, with the rooms as different compartments. (See Section 9.4.)

Since equation (1) is linear, it can be solved using the method discussed in Section 2.4. Rewriting (1) in the standard form

(2) $$\frac{dT}{dt}(t) + P(t)T(t) = Q(t),$$

where

(3) $$P(t) := K,$$

(4) $$Q(t) := KM(t) + H(t) + U(t),$$

we find that the integrating factor is

(5) $$\mu(t) = \exp\left(\int K\,dt\right) = e^{Kt}.$$

To solve (2), multiply each side by e^{Kt} and integrate:

(6) $$e^{Kt}\frac{dT}{dt}(t) + Ke^{Kt}T(t) = e^{Kt}Q(t),$$

$$e^{Kt}T(t) = \int e^{Kt}Q(t)\,dt + C.$$

Solving for $T(t)$ gives

(7) $$T(t) = e^{-Kt}\left\{\int e^{Kt}[KM(t) + H(t) + U(t)]\,dt + C\right\}.$$

▶ *Example 1* Suppose that, at the end of the day (at time t_0), when people leave the building, the outside temperature stays constant at M_0, the additional heating rate H inside the building is zero, and the furnace/air conditioner rate U is zero. Determine $T(t)$, given the initial condition $T(t_0) = T_0$.

Solution With $M = M_0$, $H = 0$, and $U = 0$, equation (7) becomes

$$T(t) = e^{-Kt}\left\{\int e^{Kt}KM_0\,dt + C\right\} = e^{-Kt}[M_0e^{Kt} + C]$$

$$= M_0 + Ce^{-Kt}.$$

Setting $t = t_0$ and using the initial value T_0 of the temperature, we find that the constant C is $(T_0 - M_0)\exp(Kt_0)$. Hence,

(8) $$T(t) = M_0 + (T_0 - M_0)e^{-K(t - t_0)}. \quad ◀$$

When $M_0 < T_0$, the solution in (8) decreases exponentially from the initial temperature T_0 to the final temperature M_0. To determine a measure of the time it takes for the temperature to change "substantially," let's consider the simple linear equation $dA/dt = -\alpha A$, whose solutions have the form $A(t) = A(0)e^{-\alpha t}$. Now as $t \to \infty$, the function $A(t)$ either decays exponentially ($\alpha > 0$) or grows exponentially ($\alpha < 0$). In either case, the time it takes for $A(t)$ to change from $A(0)$ to $A(0)/e$ ($\approx 0.368\ A(0)$) is just $1/\alpha$, because

$$A\left(\frac{1}{\alpha}\right) = A(0)e^{-\alpha(1/\alpha)} = \frac{A(0)}{e}.$$

The quantity $1/|\alpha|$, which is independent of $A(0)$, is called the **time constant** for the equation. For linear equations of the more general form $dA/dt = -\alpha A + g(t)$, we again refer to $1/|\alpha|$ as the time constant.

Returning to Example 1, we see that the temperature $T(t)$ satisfies the equations

$$\frac{dT}{dt}(t) = -KT(t) + KM_0, \qquad \frac{d(T - M_0)}{dt}(t) = -K[T(t) - M_0]$$

for M_0 a constant. In either case, the time constant is just $1/K$, which represents the time it takes for the temperature difference $T - M_0$ to change from $T_0 - M_0$ to $(T_0 - M_0)/e$. We also call $1/K$ the **time constant for the building** (without heating or air conditioning). A typical value for the time constant of a building is 2 to 4 hr, but the time constant can be much shorter if windows are open or if there is a fan circulating air, or it can be much longer if the building is well insulated.

In the context of Example 1, we can use the notion of time constant to answer our initial question (a): The building temperature changes exponentially with a time constant of $1/K$. An answer to question (b) about the temperature inside the building during spring and fall is given in the next example.

▶ *Example 2*   Find the building temperature $T(t)$ if the additional heating rate $H(t)$ is equal to the constant H_0, there is no heating or cooling ($U(t) \equiv 0$), and the outside temperature M varies as a sine wave over a 24-hr period, with its minimum at $t = 0$ (midnight) and its maximum at $t = 12$ (noon); that is,

$$M(t) = M_0 - B \cos \omega t,$$

where B is a positive constant and $\omega = 2\pi/24 = \pi/12$ radians/hr. (This could be the situation during the spring or fall when there is neither furnace heating nor air conditioning.)

Solution   The function $Q(t)$ in (4) is now

$$Q(t) = K(M_0 - B \cos \omega t) + H_0.$$

If we set $B_0 := M_0 + H_0/K$, then

(9) $$Q(t) = K(B_0 - B \cos \omega t),$$

where KB_0 represents the daily average value of $Q(t)$; that is,

$$KB_0 = \frac{1}{24} \int_0^{24} Q(t)\, dt.$$

When the forcing function $Q(t)$ in equation (9) is substituted into the expression for the temperature in equation (7), the result (after using integration by parts) is

$$T(t) = e^{-Kt} \left\{ \int e^{Kt}(KB_0 - KB \cos \omega t)\, dt + C \right\}$$

(10) $\qquad T(t) = B_0 - BF(t) + Ce^{-Kt},$

where

(11) $\qquad F(t) := \dfrac{\cos \omega t + (\omega/K) \sin \omega t}{1 + (\omega/K)^2}.$

The constant C is chosen so that at midnight $(t_0 = 0)$ the value of the temperature T is equal to some initial temperature T_0. Thus,

$$C = T_0 - B_0 + BF(0) = T_0 - B_0 + \frac{B}{1 + (\omega/K)^2}. \quad \blacktriangleleft$$

Notice that the third term in solution (10) involving the constant C tends to zero exponentially. The constant term B_0 in (10) is equal to $M_0 + H_0/K$ and represents the daily average temperature inside the building (neglecting the exponential term). When there is no additional heating rate inside the building $(H_0 = 0)$, this average temperature is equal to the average outside temperature M_0. The term $BF(t)$ in (10) represents the sinusoidal variation of temperature inside the building responding to the outside temperature variation. Since $F(t)$ in (11) can be written in the form

$$F(t) = [1 + (\omega/K)^2]^{-1/2} \cos(\omega t - \alpha),$$

where $\tan \alpha = \omega/K$ (see Problem 15), the sinusoidal variation inside the building lags behind the outside variation by α hours. Furthermore, the magnitude of the variation inside the building is slightly less, by a factor of $[1 + (\omega/K)^2]^{-1/2}$, than the outside variation. The angular frequency of variation ω is $\pi/12$ radians/hr (which is about $\frac{1}{4}$). Typical values for the dimensionless ratio ω/K lie between $\frac{1}{2}$ and 1. For this range, the lag between inside and outside temperature is approximately 1.8 to 3 hr and the magnitude of the inside variation is between 89% and 71% of the variation outside. Figure 3.5 on page 102 shows the 24-hr sinusoidal variation of the outside temperature for a typical moderate day as well as the temperature variations inside the building for a dimensionless ratio ω/K of unity, which corresponds to a time constant $1/K$ of approximately 4 hr. In sketching the latter curve, we have assumed that the exponential term has died out.

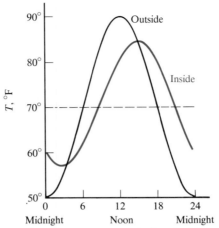

Figure 3.5 Temperature variation inside and outside an unheated building

---

▶ *Example 3*   Suppose that, in the building of Example 2, a simple thermostat is installed that is used to compare the actual temperature inside the building with a desired temperature T_D. If the actual temperature is below the desired temperature, the furnace supplies heating; otherwise it is turned off. If the actual temperature is above the desired temperature, the air conditioner supplies cooling; otherwise it is off. (In practice there is some dead zone around the desired temperature in which the temperature difference is not sufficient to activate the thermostat, but that is to be ignored here.) Assuming that the amount of heating or cooling supplied is proportional to the difference in temperature—that is,

$$U(t) = K_U[T_D - T(t)],$$

where K_U is the (positive) proportionality constant—find $T(t)$.

Solution   If the proportional control $U(t)$ is substituted directly into the differential equation (1) for the building temperature, we get

(12) $$\frac{dT(t)}{dt} = K[M(t) - T(t)] + H(t) + K_U[T_D - T(t)].$$

A comparison of equation (12) with the first order linear differential equation (2) shows that for this example the quantity P is equal to $K + K_U$, while the quantity $Q(t)$ representing the forcing function includes the desired temperature T_D. That is,

$$P = K + K_U,$$

$$Q(t) = KM(t) + H(t) + K_U T_D.$$

When the additional heating rate is a constant H_0 and the outside temperature M varies as a sine wave over a 24-hr period in the same way as it did in Example 2, the forcing function is

$$Q(t) = K(M_0 - B\cos\omega t) + H_0 + K_U T_D.$$

The function $Q(t)$ has a constant term and a cosine term just as in equation (9), and this equivalence becomes more apparent after the following substitution:

(13) $\qquad Q(t) = K_1(B_2 - B_1\cos\omega t),$

where

(14) $\qquad \omega := \dfrac{2\pi}{24} = \dfrac{\pi}{12}, \qquad\qquad K_1 := K + K_U,$

(15) $\qquad B_2 := \dfrac{K_U T_D + KM_0 + H_0}{K_1}, \qquad B_1 := \dfrac{BK}{K_1}.$

The expressions for the constant P and the forcing function $Q(t)$ of equation (13) are the same as the expressions in Example 2, except that the constants K, B_0, and B are replaced, respectively, by the constants K_1, B_2, and B_1. Hence, the solution to the differential equation (12) will be the same as the temperature solution in Example 2, except that the three constant terms are changed. Thus,

(16) $\qquad T(t) = B_2 - B_1 F_1(t) + C\exp(-K_1 t),$

where

(17) $\qquad F_1(t) := \dfrac{\cos\omega t + (\omega/K_1)\sin\omega t}{1 + (\omega/K_1)^2}.$

The constant C is chosen so that at time $t_0 = 0$ the value of the temperature T equals T_0. Thus,

$$C = T_0 - B_2 + B_1 F_1(0). \blacktriangleleft$$

In the above example the time constant for equation (12) is $1/P = 1/K_1$, where $K_1 = K + K_U$. Here $1/K_1$ is referred to as the **time constant for the building with heating and air conditioning.** For a typical heating and cooling system K_U is somewhat less than 2, and for a typical building the constant K is between $\frac{1}{2}$ and $\frac{1}{4}$, so the sum gives a value for K_1 of about 2. Hence, the time constant for the building with heating and air conditioning is about $\frac{1}{2}$ hr.

When the heating or cooling is turned on, it takes about 30 min for the exponential term in (16) to die off. If we neglect this exponential term, the average temperature inside the building is B_2. Since K_1 is much larger than K, it follows from (15) that B_2 is nearly T_D, the desired temperature. In other words, after a certain period of time, the temperature inside the building is nearly T_D, with a small sinusoidal variation. (The outside average M_0 and inside heating rate H_0 have only a small effect.) Thus, to save energy, the heating or cooling system may be left off during the night. When it is turned on in the morning, it will take roughly 30 min for the inside of the building to attain the desired temperature. These observations provide an answer to the question regarding the temperature inside the building during summer and winter that was posed at the beginning of this section.

The assumption made in Example 3 that the amount of heating or cooling is $U(t) = K_u[T_D - T(t)]$ may not always be suitable. We have used it here and in the exercises to illustrate the use of the time constant. More adventuresome students may want to experiment with other models for $U(t)$, especially if they have available the numerical techniques discussed in Sections 3.5 and 3.6.

EXERCISES 3.3

1. On a hot Saturday morning while people are working, the air conditioner keeps the temperature inside the building at 75°F. At noon the air conditioner is turned off and the people go home. The temperature outside is a constant 95°F the rest of the afternoon. If the time constant for the building is 4 hr, what will be the temperature inside the building at 2:00 P.M.? At 6:00 P.M.? When will the temperature inside the building reach 80°F?

2. On a mild Saturday morning while people are working, the furnace keeps the temperature inside the building at 21°C. At noon the furnace is turned off and the people go home. The temperature outside is a constant 12°C the rest of the afternoon. If the time constant for the building is 3 hr, when will the temperature inside the building reach 16°C? If some windows are left open and the time constant drops to 2 hr, when will the temperature inside reach 16°C?

3. A warehouse is being built that will have neither heating nor cooling. Depending upon the amount of insulation, the time constant for the building may range from 1 to 5 hr. To illustrate the effect insulation will have on the temperature inside the warehouse, assume that the outside temperature varies as a sine wave, with a minimum of 60°F at 2:00 A.M. and a maximum of 90°F at 2:00 P.M. Assuming that the exponential term (which involves the initial temperature T_0) has died off, what is the lowest temperature inside the building if the time constant is 1 hr? If the time constant is 5 hr? What is the highest temperature inside the building if the time constant is 1 hr? If it is 5 hr?

4. A garage with no heating or cooling has a time constant of 2 hr. If the outside temperature varies as a sine wave with a minimum of 50°F at 2:00 A.M. and a maximum of 80°F at 2:00 P.M., determine the times at which the building reaches its lowest temperature and its highest temperature, assuming that the exponential term has died off.

5. During the summer the temperature inside a van reaches 130°F while the outside temperature is a constant 95°F. When the driver gets into the van, she turns on the air conditioner with the thermostat set at 60°F. If the time constant for the van is $1/K = 2$ hr and for the van with its air conditioning system is $1/K_1 = \frac{1}{3}$ hr, when will the temperature inside the van reach 80°F?

6. Early Monday morning the temperature in the lecture hall has fallen to 40°F, the same as the temperature outside. At 7:00 A.M. the janitor turns on the furnace with the thermostat set at 70°F. The time constant for the building is $1/K = 2$ hr and for the building along with its heating system is $1/K_1 = \frac{1}{2}$ hr. Assuming that the outside temperature remains constant, what will be the temperature inside the lecture hall at 8:00 A.M.? When will the temperature inside the lecture hall reach 65°F?

7. A solar hot water heating system consists of a hot water tank and a solar panel. The tank is well insulated and has a time constant of 64 hr. The solar panel generates 2000 Btu/hr during the day, and the tank has a heat capacity of 2°F per thousand Btu. If the water in the tank is initially 110°F and the room temperature outside the tank is 80°F, what will be the temperature in the tank after 12 hr of sunlight?

8. In Problem 7, if a larger tank with a heat capacity of 1°F per thousand Btu and a time constant of 72 hr is used instead (with all other factors being the same), what would be the temperature in the tank after 12 hr?

9. A hot cup of coffee initially at 95°C cools to 80°C in 5 min while sitting in a room of temperature 21°C. Using just Newton's law of cooling, determine when the temperature of the coffee will be a nice 50°C?

10. A cold beer initially at 35°F warms up to 40°F in 3 min while sitting in a room of temperature 70°F. How warm will the beer be if left out for 20 min?

11. A white wine at room temperature 70°F is chilled in ice (32°F). If it takes 15 min for the wine to chill to 60°F, how long will it take for the wine to reach 56°F?

12. A red wine is brought up from the wine cellar, which is a cool 10°C, and left to breathe in a room of temperature 23°C. When will the temperature of the wine reach 18°C if it takes 10 min for the wine to reach 15°C?

13. **Stefan's law** of radiation states that the rate of change of temperature of a body at T degrees Kelvin in a medium at M degrees Kelvin is proportional to $M^4 - T^4$. That is,

$$\frac{dT}{dt} = k(M^4 - T^4),$$

where k is a positive constant. Solve this equation using separation of variables. Explain why Newton's law and Stefan's law are nearly the same when T is close to M and M is constant. [Hint: Factor $M^4 - T^4$.]

14. Two friends sit down to talk and enjoy a cup of coffee. When the coffee is served, the impatient friend immediately adds a teaspoon of cream to his coffee. The relaxed friend waits 5 min before adding a teaspoon of cream (which has been kept at a constant temperature). The two now begin to drink their coffee. *Who has the hotter coffee?* Assume that the cream is cooler than the air and use Newton's law of cooling.

15. Show that $C_1 \cos \omega t + C_2 \sin \omega t$ can be written in the form $A \cos(\omega t - \alpha)$, where $A = \sqrt{C_1^2 + C_2^2}$ and $\tan \alpha = C_2/C_1$. [Hint: Use a standard trigonometric identity with $C_1 = A \cos \alpha, C_2 = A \sin \alpha$.] Use this fact to verify the alternate representation of $F(t)$ discussed in Example 2.

3.4 *Newtonian Mechanics*

Mechanics is the study of the motion of objects and the effect of forces acting on these objects. It is the foundation of several branches of physics and engineering. **Newtonian** or **classical mechanics** deals with the motion of **ordinary** objects; that is, objects that are large compared to an atom and slow moving compared with the speed of light. A model for Newtonian mechanics can be based on **Newton's laws of motion:**[†]

1. When a body is subject to no resultant external force, it moves with a constant velocity.

2. When a body is subject to one or more external forces, the time rate of change of the body's momentum is equal to the vector sum of the external forces acting on it.

3. When one body interacts with a second body, the force of the first body on the second is equal in magnitude, but opposite in direction, to the force of the second body on the first.

Experimental results for more than two centuries verify that these laws are extremely useful for studying the motion of ordinary objects in an **inertial reference frame;** that is, a reference frame in which an undisturbed body moves with a constant velocity. It is Newton's second law, which applies only to inertial reference frames, that enables us to formulate the equations of motion for a moving body. We can express Newton's second law by

(1) $$\frac{dp}{dt} = F\left(t, x, \frac{dx}{dt}\right),$$

where $F(t, x, dx/dt)$ is the resultant force on the body at time t, location x, and velocity dx/dt, and $p(t)$ is the momentum of the body at time t. The momentum is the product of the mass of the body and its velocity, that is,

$$p(t) = m(t)v(t).$$

In most applications the mass remains constant, so we can express Newton's second law as

(2) $$m\frac{dv}{dt} = ma = F(t, x, dx/dt),$$

where $v = dx/dt$ is the velocity and $a = dv/dt$ is the acceleration of the body at time t. Observe that equation (2) will be a first order equation in $v(t)$ provided that F does not depend upon x.

[†] For a discussion of Newton's laws of motion see *University Physics,* by F. W. Sears, M. W. Zemansky, and H. D. Young, Addison-Wesley Publishing Co., Reading, Massachusetts, Sixth Edition, 1982.

To apply Newton's laws of motion to a problem in mechanics, the following general procedure may be useful.

PROCEDURE FOR NEWTONIAN MODELS

(a) Determine *all* relevant forces acting on the object being studied. It is helpful to draw a simple diagram of the object that depicts these forces.

(b) Choose an appropriate axis or coordinate system in which to represent the motion of the object and the forces acting on it. Keep in mind that this coordinate system must be an inertial reference frame.

(c) Apply Newton's second law as expressed in equation (1) or equation (2), whichever is appropriate, to determine the equations of motion for the object.

In this section we consider examples in which the motion of the object lies in one dimension and Newton's second law gives rise to a first order differential equation. We use either of two systems of units: the British system or the meter-kilogram-second (MKS) system. The various units in these systems are summarized in Table 3.2, along with approximate values for the Earth's gravitational constant.

TABLE 3.2 MECHANICAL UNITS IN THE BRITISH AND METRIC SYSTEMS

Unit	British System	MKS System
Distance	feet ft	meters m
Mass	slugs	kilograms kg
Time	seconds sec	seconds sec
Force	pounds lb	newtons N
g (Earth)	32 ft/sec^2	9.81 m/sec^2

▶ *Example 1* An object of mass m is given an initial downward velocity v_0 and allowed to fall under the influence of gravity. Assuming that the gravitational force is constant and the force due to air resistance is proportional to the velocity of the object, determine the equation of motion for this object.

Solution We are told that there are two forces acting on the object: a constant force due to the downward pull of gravity and a force due to air resistance that is proportional to the velocity of the object and acts in opposition to the motion of the object. Hence the

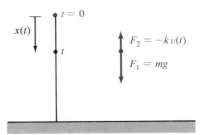

Figure 3.6 Forces on a falling object

motion of the object will take place along a vertical axis. On this axis we choose the origin to be the point where the object was initially dropped and let $x(t)$ denote the distance the object has fallen in time t (see Figure 3.6).

The forces acting on the object can be expressed in terms of this axis. The force due to gravity is

(3) $F_1 = mg,$

where g is the gravitational constant near the Earth (see Table 3.2). The force due to air resistance is

(4) $F_2 = -kv(t) = -kx'(t),$

where $k\ (>0)$ is the proportionality constant and the negative sign is present because air resistance acts in opposition to the motion of the object. Hence the net force acting on the object (see Figure 3.6) is

(5) $F = F_1 + F_2 = mg - kv(t).$

We now apply Newton's second law by substituting (5) into (2) to obtain

(6) $m\dfrac{dv}{dt} = mg - kv.$

Since the initial velocity of the object is v_0, a model for the velocity of the falling body is expressed by the initial value problem

(7) $m\dfrac{dv}{dt} = mg - kv, \qquad v(0) = v_0,$

where g is the gravitational constant and k is the proportionality constant for air resistance.

The model (7) is the same as the one we obtained in Section 2.1. Using separation of variables (as we did previously), we get

(8) $v(t) = \dfrac{mg}{k} + \left(v_0 - \dfrac{mg}{k}\right)e^{-kt/m}.$

Since we have taken $x = 0$ when $t = 0$, we can determine the equation of motion of the object by integrating $v = dx/dt$ with respect to t. Thus, from (8) we obtain

$$(9) \qquad x(t) = \int v(t)\, dt = \frac{mg}{k}t - \frac{m}{k}\left(v_0 - \frac{mg}{k}\right)e^{-kt/m} + c,$$

and setting $x = 0$ when $t = 0$, we find

$$0 = -\frac{m}{k}\left(v_0 - \frac{mg}{k}\right) + c,$$

$$(10) \qquad c = \frac{m}{k}\left(v_0 - \frac{mg}{k}\right).$$

Hence the equation of motion is

$$(11) \qquad x(t) = \frac{mg}{k}t + \frac{m}{k}\left(v_0 - \frac{mg}{k}\right)(1 - e^{-kt/m}). \ \blacktriangleleft$$

In Figure 3.7 we have sketched the graphs of the velocity and the position as functions of t. Observe that the velocity $v(t)$ approaches the horizontal asymptote $v = mg/k$ as $t \to \infty$, and that the position $x(t)$ asymptotically approaches the line

$$x = \frac{mg}{k}t - \frac{m^2g}{k^2} + \frac{m}{k}v_0$$

as $t \to +\infty$. The value mg/k of the horizontal asymptote for $v(t)$ is called the **limiting.or terminal velocity** of the object.

Now that we have obtained the equation of motion for a falling object with air resistance proportional to v, we can answer a variety of questions.

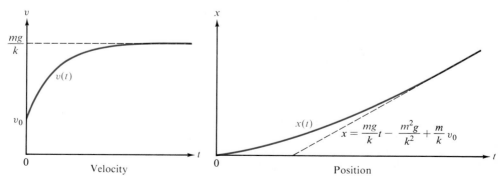

Figure 3.7 Graphs of the position and velocity of a falling object

▶ *Example 2*   An object of mass 3 kg is released from rest 500 m above the ground and allowed to fall under the influence of gravity. Assuming that the gravitational force is constant— that is, $g = 9.81$ m/sec²—and the force due to air resistance is proportional to the velocity of the object with proportionality constant $k = 3$ kg/sec, determine when the object will strike the ground.

Solution   We can use the model discussed in Example 1 with $v_0 = 0$, $m = 3$, $k = 3$, and $g = 9.81$. From (11), the equation of motion in this case is

(12) $$x(t) = \frac{(3)(9.81)}{(3)} t - \frac{(3)^2(9.81)}{(3)^2} (1 - e^{-3t/3}) = (9.81)t - (9.81)(1 - e^{-t}).$$

Since the object is released 500 m above the ground, we can determine when the object strikes the ground by setting $x(t) = 500$ and solving for t. Thus we put

$$500 = (9.81)t - 9.81 + (9.81)e^{-t}$$

or

(13) $$t + e^{-t} = \frac{509.81}{9.81} = 51.97,$$

where we have rounded the computations to two decimal places. Unfortunately this equation cannot be solved explicitly for t. We might try to approximate t using Newton's approximation method (see Appendix A), but in this case it is not necessary. Since e^{-t} will be very small for t near $51.97 (e^{-51.97} \approx 10^{-22})$, we simply ignore the term e^{-t} and obtain as our approximation $t = 51.97$ sec.   ◀

▶ *Example 3*   A parachutist whose weight (actually mass) is 75 kg drops from a helicopter hovering 4000 m above the ground and falls toward the earth under the influence of gravity. Assume that the gravitational force is constant and that the force due to air resistance is proportional to the velocity of the parachutist, with the proportionality constant $k_1 = 15$ kg/sec when the chute is closed and with constant $k_2 = 105$ kg/sec when the chute is open. If the chute does not open until 1 min after the parachutist leaves the helicopter, after how many seconds will she hit the ground?

Solution   Since we are only interested in when the parachutist will hit the ground and not where, we consider only the vertical component of her descent. For this we need to use two equations—one to describe the motion before the chute opens and the other to apply after it opens. Before the chute opens, the model is the same as in Example 1 with $v_0 = 0$, $m = 75$ kg, $k = k_1 = 15$ kg/sec, and $g = 9.81$ m/sec². If we let $x_1(t)$ be the distance the parachutist has fallen in t seconds and let $v_1 = dx_1/dt$, then substituting into equations

(8) and (11) we have

(14)　　　$v_1(t) = \dfrac{(75)(9.81)}{15}(1 - e^{-(15/75)t})$

　　　　　　$= (49.05)(1 - e^{-0.2t}),$

and

(15)　　　$x_1(t) = \dfrac{(75)(9.81)}{15}t - \dfrac{(75)^2(9.81)}{(15)^2}(1 - e^{-(15/75)t})$

　　　　　　$= 49.05t - 245.25(1 - e^{-0.2t}).$

Hence, after 1 min, when $t = 60$, the parachutist is falling at a rate

(16)　　　$v_1(60) = (49.05)(1 - e^{-0.2(60)}) = 49.05$ m/sec,

and has fallen

(17)　　　$x_1(60) = (49.05)(60) - (245.25)(1 - e^{-0.2(60)}) = 2697.75$ m.

(In these and other computations for this problem we round our answers to two decimal places.)

Now when the chute opens, the parachutist is $4000 - 2697.75$ or 1302.25 m above the ground and traveling at a velocity of 49.05 m/sec. To determine the equation of motion after the chute opens, let $x_2(t)$ denote the position of the parachutist t seconds after the chute opens, taking $x_2(0) = 0$ at $x_1(60)$ (see Figure 3.8). Since the forces acting on the parachutist are the same as those acting on the object in Example 1, we can again use equations

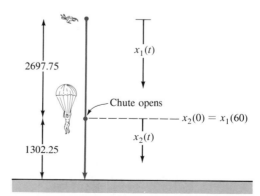

Figure 3.8 The fall of the parachutist

(8) and (11). With $v_0 = 49.05$, $m = 75$, $k = k_2 = 105$, and $g = 9.81$, we find from (11)

$$
(18) \qquad x_2(t) = \frac{(75)(9.81)}{105} t + \frac{75}{105} \left[49.05 - \frac{(75)(9.81)}{105} \right] (1 - e^{-(105/75)t})
$$

$$
= 7.01t + 30.03(1 - e^{-1.4t}).
$$

Now to determine when the parachutist will hit the ground, we just set $x_2(t) = 1302.25$, the height the parachutist was above the ground when her parachute opened. This gives

$$
7.01t + 30.03 - 30.03e^{-1.4t} = 1302.25
$$

$$
(19) \qquad t - 4.28e^{-1.4t} - 181.49 = 0.
$$

Again we cannot solve (19) explicitly for t. However, since $e^{-1.4t}$ is very small for t near 181.49, we ignore the exponential term and obtain $t = 181.49$. Hence, the parachutist will strike the earth 181.49 sec after the parachute opens, or 241.49 sec after dropping from the helicopter. ◄

In the computation for t in equation (19), we found that the exponential $e^{-1.4t}$ was negligible. Consequently, ignoring the corresponding exponential term in equation (8), we see that the parachutist's velocity at impact is

$$
(20) \qquad \frac{mg}{k_2} = \frac{(75)(9.81)}{105} = 7.01 \text{ m/sec},
$$

which is the limiting velocity for her fall with the chute open.

EXERCISES 3.4

1. An object of mass 5 kg is released from rest 1000 m above the ground and allowed to fall under the influence of gravity. Assuming that the force due to air resistance is proportional to the velocity of the object with proportionality constant $k = 50$ kg/sec, determine the equation of motion of the object. When will the object strike the ground?

2. A 400-lb object is released from rest 500 ft above the ground and allowed to fall under the influence of gravity. Assuming that the force in pounds due to air resistance is $-10v$, where v is the velocity of the object in ft/sec, determine the equation of motion of the object. When will the object hit the ground?

3. If the object in Problem 1 has a mass of 500 kg instead of 5 kg, when will it strike the ground? [Hint: Here the exponential term is too large to ignore. Use Newton's method to approximate the time t when the object strikes the ground (see Appendix A).]

4. If the object in Problem 2 is released from rest 30 ft above the ground instead of 500 ft, when will it strike the ground? [Hint: Use Newton's method to solve for t.]

5. An object of mass 5 kg is given an initial downward velocity of 50 m/sec and then allowed to fall under the influence of gravity. Assume that the force in newtons (N) due to air resistance is $-10v$, where v is the velocity of the object in m/sec. Determine the equation of motion of the object. If the object is initially 500 m above the ground, determine when the object will strike the ground.

6. An object of mass 8 kg is given an upward initial velocity of 20 m/sec and then allowed to fall under the influence of gravity. Assume that the force in newtons due to air resistance is $-16v$, where v is the velocity of the object in m/sec. Determine the equation of motion of the object. If the object is initially 100 m above the ground, determine when the object will strike the ground.

7. A parachutist whose weight (mass) is 75 kg drops from a helicopter hovering 2000 m above the ground and falls toward the ground under the influence of gravity. Assume that the force due to air resistance is proportional to the velocity of the parachutist, with the proportionality constant $k_1 = 30$ kg/sec when the chute is closed and $k_2 = 90$ kg/sec when the chute is open. If the chute does not open until the velocity of the parachutist reaches 20 m/sec, after how many seconds will she reach the ground?

8. A parachutist whose weight (mass) is 100 kg drops from a helicopter hovering 3000 m above the ground and falls under the influence of gravity. Assume that the force due to air resistance is proportional to the velocity of the parachutist, with the proportionality constant $k_3 = 20$ kg/sec when the chute is closed and $k_4 = 100$ kg/sec when the chute is open. If the chute does not open until 30 sec after the parachutist leaves the helicopter, after how many seconds will he hit the ground? If the chute does not open until 1 min after he leaves the helicopter, after how many seconds will he hit the ground?

9. An object of mass 100 kg is released from rest from a boat into the water and allowed to sink. While gravity is pulling the object down, a buoyancy force of $\frac{1}{40}$ times the weight of the object is pushing the object up (weight = mg). If we assume that water resistance exerts a force on the object that is proportional to the velocity of the object, with proportionality constant 10 kg/sec, find the equation of motion of the object. After how many seconds will the velocity of the object be 70 m/sec?

10. An object of mass 2 kg is released from rest from a platform 30 m above the water and allowed to fall under the influence of gravity. After the object strikes the water, it begins to sink with gravity pulling down and a buoyancy force pushing up. Assuming that the force of gravity is constant, that the buoyancy force is $\frac{1}{2}$ the weight (weight = mg), and that the force due to air resistance or water resistance is proportional to the velocity, with proportionality constant $k_1 = 10$ kg/sec in the air and $k_2 = 100$ kg/sec in the water, find the equation of motion of the object. What is the velocity of the object 1 min after it is released?

11. In Example 1 we solved for the velocity of the object as a function of time (equation (8)). In some cases it is useful to have an expression, independent

of t, that relates v and x. Find this relation for the motion in Example 1. [Hint: Let $v(t) = V(x(t))$, then $dv/dt = (dV/dx)V$.]

12. When the velocity v of an object is very large, the magnitude of the force due to air resistance is proportional to v^2 with the force acting in opposition to the motion of the object. If a shell of mass m is shot upward with an initial velocity v_0 from an initial height x_0 and the magnitude of the force due to air resistance is kv^2, $k > 0$, then show that $v(t)$ and $x(t)$ are given by

$$v(t) = \frac{ae^{\alpha t} - b}{c + de^{\alpha t}},$$

$$x(t) = \frac{a}{\alpha d} \ln|c + de^{\alpha t}| + \frac{b}{\alpha c} \ln|d + ce^{-\alpha t}| + x_0$$

$$- \frac{ac + bd}{\alpha cd} \ln|c + d|,$$

where

$$a := \sqrt{\frac{mg}{k}} \left(\sqrt{\frac{mg}{k}} + v_0 \right), \qquad b := \sqrt{\frac{mg}{k}} \left(\sqrt{\frac{mg}{k}} - v_0 \right),$$

$$c := \sqrt{\frac{mg}{k}} - v_0, \qquad d := \sqrt{\frac{mg}{k}} + v_0, \qquad \alpha := 2\sqrt{\frac{kg}{m}}.$$

13. A shell of mass 2 kg is shot upward with an initial velocity of 200 m/s. The magnitude of the force on the shell due to air resistance is $|v|/20$. When will the shell reach its maximum height above the ground? What is the maximum height?

14. An object of mass m is released from rest and falls under the influence of gravity. If the magnitude of the force due to air resistance is kv^n, where k and n are positive constants, find the limiting velocity of the object (assuming this limit exists). [Hint: Argue that the existence of a (finite) limiting velocity implies that $dv/dt \to 0$ as $t \to \infty$.]

15. A rotating flywheel is being turned by a motor that exerts a constant torque T. A retarding torque due to friction is proportional to the angular velocity ω. If the moment of inertia of the flywheel is I and its initial angular velocity is ω_0, find the equation for the angular velocity ω as a function of time. [Hint: Use Newton's second law for rotational motion, that is, moment of inertia × angular acceleration = torque.]

16. Find the equation for the angular velocity ω in Problem 15, assuming that the retarding torque is proportional to $\sqrt{\omega}$.

17. In Problem 16 let $I = 50$ kg-m^2 and let the retarding torque be $5\sqrt{\omega}$ N-m. If the motor is turned off with the angular velocity at 225 rad/sec, determine how long it will take for the flywheel to come to rest.

18. When an object moves on a surface, it encounters a resistance force called **friction.** This force has a magnitude of μN, where μ is the **coefficient of**

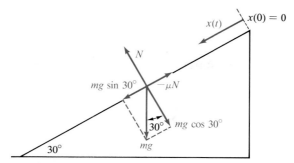

Figure 3.9 Forces on an object on an inclined plane

friction and N is the magnitude of the normal force that the surface applies to the object. Friction acts in opposition to motion, but cannot initiate motion. Suppose that an object of mass 30 kg is released from the top of an inclined plane that is inclined 30° to the horizontal (see Figure 3.9). Assume that the gravitational force is constant, air resistance is negligible, and the coefficient of friction $\mu = 0.2$. Determine the equation of motion for the object as it slides down the plane. If the top surface of the plane is 5 m long, what is the velocity of the object when it reaches the bottom?

19. An object of mass 60 kg starts from rest at the top of a 45° inclined plane. Assume that the coefficient of friction is 0.05 (see Problem 18). If the force due to air resistance is proportional to the velocity of the object, say $-3v$, find the equation of motion of the object. How long will it take the object to reach the bottom of the inclined plane if the incline is 10 m long?

20. Recall that an object will not move down an inclined plane until the component of the gravitational force down the incline is greater than the force due to friction (see Problem 18). If μ is the coefficient of friction and α is the angle at which the plane is inclined, determine the critical angle α_0 for which an object will begin to move down the plane if $\alpha > \alpha_0$ but will not move if $\alpha < \alpha_0$.

21. A sailboat has been running (on a straight course) under a light wind at 1 m/sec. Suddenly the wind picks up, blowing hard enough to apply a constant force of 600 N to the sailboat. The only other force acting on the boat is water resistance that is proportional to the velocity of the boat. If the proportionality constant for water resistance is $k = 100$ kg/sec and the mass of the sailboat is 50 kg, find the equation of motion of the sailboat. What is the maximum velocity of the sailboat under this wind?

22. In Problem 21 it is observed that when the velocity of the sailboat reaches 5 m/sec, the boat begins to rise out of the water and "plane." When this happens, the proportionality constant for the water resistance drops to $k_0 = 60$ kg/sec. Now find the equation of motion of the sailboat. What is the maximum velocity of the sailboat under this wind as it is planing?

23. Sailboats A and B each have a mass of 60 kg and cross the starting line at the same time on the first leg of a race. Each has an initial velocity of

2 m/sec. The wind applies a constant force of 650 N to each boat, and the force due to water resistance is proportional to the velocity of the boat. For sailboat A, the proportionality constants are $k_1 = 80$ kg/sec before planing when the velocity is less than 5 m/sec, and $k_2 = 60$ kg/sec when the velocity is above 5 m/sec. For sailboat B, the proportionality constants are $k_3 = 100$ kg/sec before planing when the velocity is less than 6 m/sec and $k_4 = 50$ kg/sec when the velocity is above 6 m/sec. If the first leg of the race is 500 m long, which sailboat will be leading at the end of the first leg?

24. Rocket Flight. A rocket having initial mass m_0 kg is launched vertically from the surface of the Earth. The rocket expels gas at a constant rate of α kg/sec and at a constant velocity of β m/sec relative to the rocket. Assume that the gravitational field is a constant g kg/sec^2. Since the mass is not constant, Newton's second law, which states that force is equal to the time rate of change of the momentum, leads to the equation.

$$(m_0 - \alpha t)\frac{dv}{dt} - \alpha\beta = -g(m_0 - \alpha t),$$

where $v = dx/dt$ is the velocity of the rocket, x is its height above the surface of the Earth, and $m_0 - \alpha t$ is the mass of the rocket at t seconds after launch. If the initial velocity is zero, solve the above equation to determine the velocity of the rocket and its height above ground for $0 \leq t < m_0/\alpha$.

3.5 *Improved Euler's Method*

While the analytical techniques presented in Chapter 2 were useful for the variety of mathematical models presented earlier in this chapter, **the majority of the differential equations encountered in applications cannot be solved either implicitly or explicitly.** This is especially true of higher order equations and systems of equations, which we study in later chapters. In this section and the next, we discuss methods for obtaining a numerical *approximation* of the solution to an initial value problem for a first order differential equation. Our goal is to develop algorithms that you can use with a calculator or microcomputer. We describe the rationale behind each method, but leave the more detailed discussion to texts on numerical analysis.[†]

Consider the initial value problem

(1) $\qquad y' = f(x, y) \qquad y(x_0) = y_0.$

To guarantee that (1) has a unique solution, we assume that f and $\partial f/\partial y$ are continuous in a rectangle $R := \{(x, y): a < x < b, c < y < d\}$ containing (x_0, y_0). It follows from Theorem 1

[†] See, for example, *Elements of Numerical Analysis*, by P. Henrici, John Wiley and Sons, Inc., New York, 1964, or *Numerical Analysis*, Third Edition, by R. L. Burden and J. D. Faires, Prindle, Weber & Schmidt, Boston, 1985.

in Chapter 1 that the initial value problem (1) has a unique solution $\phi(x)$ in some interval $x_0 - \delta < x < x_0 + \delta$, where δ is a positive number. Since δ is not known a priori, there is no assurance that the solution will exist at a particular point $x (\neq x_0)$, even if x is in the interval (a, b). However, if $\partial f / \partial y$ is continuous and *bounded*[†] on the vertical strip

$$S := \{(x, y): a < x < b, \; -\infty < y < \infty\},$$

then it turns out that (1) has a unique solution on the whole interval (a, b). In describing numerical methods we will assume that this last condition is satisfied and that f possesses as many continuous partial derivatives as needed.

In the optional Section 1.3 we used the method of isoclines to motivate a scheme for approximating the solution to the initial value problem (1). This scheme, called **Euler's method,** is one of the most basic and so it is worthwhile to discuss its advantages, disadvantages, and possible improvements. We begin with a derivation of Euler's method that is somewhat different from that presented in Section 1.3.

Let $h > 0$ be fixed (h is called the **step size**), and consider the equally spaced points

(2) $\qquad x_n := x_0 + nh, \qquad n = 0, 1, 2, \dots .$

Our goal is to obtain an approximation to the solution $\phi(x)$ of the initial value problem (1) at those points x_n that lie in the interval (a, b). Namely, we will describe a method that generates values $y_0, y_1, y_2, \dots$ that approximate $\phi(x)$ at the respective points $x_0, x_1, x_2, \dots$; that is,

(3) $\qquad y_n \approx \phi(x_n), \qquad n = 0, 1, 2, \dots .$

Of course, the first "approximant" y_0 is exact, since $y_0 = \phi(x_0)$ is given. Thus we must describe how to compute $y_1, y_2, \dots .$

For Euler's method we begin by integrating both sides of equation (1) from x_n to x_{n+1} to obtain

(4) $\qquad \phi(x_{n+1}) - \phi(x_n) = \int_{x_n}^{x_{n+1}} \phi'(t) \, dt = \int_{x_n}^{x_{n+1}} f(t, \phi(t)) \, dt,$

where we have substituted $\phi(x)$ for y. Solving for $\phi(x_{n+1})$, we have

(5) $\qquad \phi(x_{n+1}) = \phi(x_n) + \int_{x_n}^{x_{n+1}} f(t, \phi(t)) \, dt.$

Without knowing $\phi(t)$, we cannot integrate $f(t, \phi(t))$. Hence, we must approximate the integral in (5). Assuming we have already found $y_n \approx \phi(x_n)$, the simplest approach is to approximate the area under the function $f(t, \phi(t))$ by the rectangle with base $[x_n, x_{n+1}]$ and height $f(x_n, \phi(x_n))$ (see Figure 3.10 on page 118). This gives

$$\phi(x_{n+1}) \approx \phi(x_n) + (x_{n+1} - x_n) f(x_n, \phi(x_n)).$$

[†] A function $g(x, y)$ is bounded on S if there exists a number M such that $|g(x, y)| \leq M$ for all (x, y) in S.

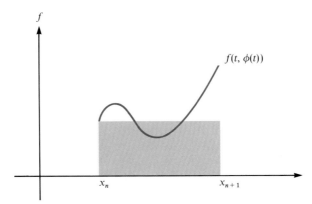

Figure 3.10 Approximation by a rectangle

Substituting h for $x_{n+1} - x_n$ and the approximation y_n for $\phi(x_n)$, we arrive at the numerical scheme

(6) $\qquad y_{n+1} = y_n + hf(x_n, y_n), \qquad n = 0, 1, 2, \ldots,$

which is Euler's method.

Starting with the given value y_0, we use (6) to compute $y_1 = y_0 + hf(x_0, y_0)$, then use y_1 to compute $y_2 = y_1 + hf(x_1, y_1)$, etc. Several examples of Euler's method can be found in Section 1.3.

As discussed in Section 1.3, if we wish to use Euler's method to approximate the solution to the initial value problem (1) at a particular value of x, say $x = c$, then we must first determine a suitable step size h so that $x_0 + nh = c$ for some integer n. For example, we can take $n = 1$ and $h = c - x_0$ in order to arrive at the approximation after just one step:

$$\phi(c) = \phi(x_0 + h) \approx y_1.$$

If, instead, we wish to take 10 steps ($n = 10$) in Euler's method, we choose $h = (c - x_0)/10$ and ultimately obtain

$$\phi(c) = \phi(x_0 + 10h) = \phi(x_{10}) \approx y_{10}.$$

In general, depending on the size of h, we will get different approximations to $\phi(c)$. It is reasonable to expect that as h gets smaller (or, equivalently, as n gets larger), then the Euler approximations approach the exact value $\phi(c)$. On the other hand, as h gets smaller, the number (and cost) of computations increases and hence so do machine errors that arise from round-off. Thus, it is important to analyze how the error in the approximation scheme varies with h.

If Euler's method is used to approximate the solution $\phi(x) = e^x$ to the problem

(7) $\qquad y' = y, \qquad y(0) = 1,$

at $x = 1$, then we obtain approximations to the constant $e = \phi(1)$. It turns out that these approximations take a particularly simple form that enables us to compare the error in the approximation with the step size h. Indeed, setting $f(x, y) = y$ in (6) yields

$$y_{n+1} = y_n + hy_n = (1 + h)y_n, \qquad n = 0, 1, 2, \ldots .$$

Since $y_0 = 1$, we get

$$y_1 = (1 + h)y_0 = 1 + h$$
$$y_2 = (1 + h)y_1 = (1 + h)(1 + h) = (1 + h)^2$$
$$y_3 = (1 + h)y_2 = (1 + h)(1 + h)^2 = (1 + h)^3,$$

and, in general,

(8) $$\qquad y_n = (1 + h)^n, \qquad n = 0, 1, 2, \ldots .$$

For the problem in (7) we have $x_0 = 0$; so to obtain approximations at $x = 1$, we must set $nh = 1$. That is, h must be the reciprocal of an integer ($h = 1/n$). Replacing n by $1/h$ in (8), we see that Euler's method gives the (familiar) approximation $(1 + h)^{1/h}$ to the constant e. In Table 3.3 we have computed this approximation for $h = 1, 10^{-1}, 10^{-2}, 10^{-3}, 10^{-4}$, along with the corresponding errors

$$e - (1 + h)^{1/h}.$$

From the second and third columns in Table 3.3 we see that the approximation gains roughly one decimal place in accuracy as h decreases by a factor of 10. That is, the error is roughly proportional to h. This observation is further confirmed by the entries in the last column of Table 3.3. In fact, using methods of calculus (see Problem 19, Section 1.3,

TABLE 3.3 EULER'S APPROXIMATIONS TO
$e = 2.71828 \ldots$

h	Euler's Approximation $(1 + h)^{1/h}$	Error $e - (1 + h)^{1/h}$	Error $\dfrac{}{h}$
1	2.00000	0.71828	0.71828
10^{-1}	2.59374	0.12454	1.24539
10^{-2}	2.70481	0.01347	1.34680
10^{-3}	2.71692	0.00136	1.35799
10^{-4}	2.71815	0.00014	1.35910

page 24) it can be shown that

(9) $$\lim_{h \to 0} \frac{\text{error}}{h} = \lim_{h \to 0} \frac{e - (1 + h)^{1/h}}{h} = \frac{e}{2} \approx 1.35914.$$

The general situation is similar: When Euler's method is used to approximate the solution to the initial value problem (1), the error in the approximation is at worst a constant times the step size h. Moreover, in view of (9), this is the best one can say.

Numerical analysts have a convenient notation for describing the convergence behavior of a numerical scheme. For fixed x, we denote by $y(x; h)$ the approximation to the solution $\phi(x)$ of (1) obtained via the scheme when using a step size of h. We say that the numerical scheme **converges** at x if

(10) $$\lim_{h \to 0} y(x; h) = \phi(x).$$

In other words, as the step size h decreases to zero, the approximations approach the exact value $\phi(x)$. The rate at which $y(x; h)$ tends to $\phi(x)$ is often expressed in terms of a suitable power of h. If the error $\phi(x) - y(x; h)$ tends to zero like a constant times h^p, we write

(11) $$\phi(x) - y(x; h) = O(h^p),$$

and say that the method is of order p. Of course, the higher the power p, the faster is the rate of convergence.

As seen from our earlier discussion, the rate of convergence of Euler's method is $O(h)$; that is, *Euler's method is of order $p = 1$.* This means that to have an error less than 10^{-2} generally requires more than 100 steps ($n > 10^2$). Thus Euler's method converges too slowly to be of practical use.

How can we improve Euler's method? To answer this, let's return to the derivation expressed in formulas (4)–(6), and analyze the "errors" that were introduced to get the approximation. A crucial step in the process was to approximate the integral

$$\int_{x_n}^{x_{n+1}} f(t, \phi(t)) \, dt$$

by using a rectangle (recall Figure 3.10). This step gives rise to what is called the local truncation error in the method. From calculus we know that a better (more accurate) approach to approximating the integral is to use a trapezoid; that is, to apply the trapezoidal rule (see Figure 3.11). This gives

$$\int_{x_n}^{x_{n+1}} f(t, \phi(t)) \, dt \approx \frac{h}{2} \left[f(x_n, \phi(x_n)) + f(x_{n+1}, \phi(x_{n+1})) \right]$$

which leads to the numerical scheme

(12) $$y_{n+1} = y_n + \frac{h}{2} \left[f(x_n, y_n) + f(x_{n+1}, y_{n+1}) \right], \qquad n = 0, 1, 2, \dots.$$

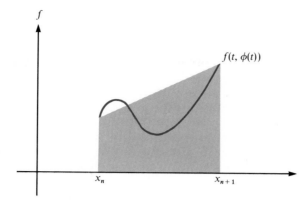

f

$f(t, \phi(t))$

x_n $\qquad$ x_{n+1}

Figure 3.11 Approximation by a trapezoid

We call equation (12) the **trapezoid scheme.** It is an example of an **implicit method;** that is, unlike Euler's method, equation (12) gives only an implicit formula for y_{n+1}. Assuming that we have already computed y_n, some root-finding technique such as Newton's method (see Appendix A) might be needed to compute y_{n+1}. Despite the inconvenience of working with an implicit method, the trapezoid scheme has two advantages over Euler's method. First, it is a method of order $p = 2$; that is, it converges at a rate that is proportional to h^2 and hence is faster than Euler's method. Second, as illustrated in Project F, the trapezoid scheme has the desirable feature of being **stable.**

Can we somehow modify the trapezoid scheme in order to obtain an explicit method? One idea is to first get an estimate (say, y_{n+1}^*) of the value y_{n+1} using Euler's method and then use formula (12) with y_{n+1} replaced by y_{n+1}^* on the right-hand side. This two-step process is an example of a **predictor-corrector method.** That is, we predict y_{n+1} using Euler's method and then use that value in (12) to obtain a "more correct" approximation. Setting $y_{n+1} = y_n + hf(x_n, y_n)$ in the right-hand side of (12), we obtain

(13) $\qquad y_{n+1} = y_n + \dfrac{h}{2} \left[f(x_n, y_n) + f(x_n + h, y_n + hf(x_n, y_n)) \right], \qquad n = 0, 1, \ldots,$

where $x_{n+1} = x_n + h$. This explicit scheme is referred to as the **improved Euler's method.**

▶ *Example 1*   Compute the improved Euler's method approximation to the solution $\phi(x) = e^x$ of

$$y' = y, \qquad y(0) = 1$$

at $x = 1$ using step sizes of $h = 1, 10^{-1}, 10^{-2}, 10^{-3}, 10^{-4}$.

Solution   The starting values are $x_0 = 0$ and $y_0 = 1$. Since $f(x, y) = y$, formula (13) becomes

$$y_{n+1} = y_n + \dfrac{h}{2} \left[y_n + (y_n + hy_n) \right] = y_n + hy_n + \dfrac{h^2}{2} y_n,$$

that is,

(14) $\qquad y_{n+1} = \left(1 + h + \dfrac{h^2}{2}\right) y_n.$

Since $y_0 = 1$, we see inductively that

$$y_n = \left(1 + h + \dfrac{h^2}{2}\right)^n, \qquad n = 0, 1, 2, \dots.$$

To obtain approximations at $x = 1$, we must have $1 = x_0 + nh = nh$, and so $n = 1/h$. Hence the improved Euler's approximations to $e = \phi(1)$ are just

$$\left(1 + h + \dfrac{h^2}{2}\right)^{1/h}.$$

In Table 3.4 we have computed this approximation for the specified values of h, along with the corresponding errors

$$e - \left(1 + h + \dfrac{h^2}{2}\right)^{1/h}.$$

Comparing the entries of this table with those of Table 3.3, we observe that the improved Euler's method converges much more rapidly than the original Euler's method. In fact, from the first few entries in the second and third columns of Table 3.4, it appears that the approximation gains two decimal places in accuracy each time h is decreased by a factor of 10. In other words, the error is roughly proportional to h^2 (see the last column of the table and also Problem 4). The entries in the last two rows of the table must be regarded with caution. Indeed, when $h = 10^{-3}$ or $h = 10^{-4}$, the true error is so small that the calculator used rounded this error to zero. The entries in color in the last column are inaccurate due to the loss of significant figures in the calculator arithmetic. ◄

TABLE 3.4 IMPROVED EULER'S APPROXIMATION TO $e = 2.71828\dots$

h	Approximation $\left(1 + h + \dfrac{h^2}{2}\right)^{1/h}$	Error	Error $\dfrac{}{h^2}$
1	2.50000	0.21828	21.828
10^{-1}	2.71408	0.00420	0.4201
10^{-2}	2.71824	0.00004	0.4496
10^{-3}	2.71828	0.00000	0.5430
10^{-4}	2.71828	0.00000	0.0000

As the preceding example suggests, the improved Euler's method converges at the rate $O(h^2)$ and, indeed, it can be proved that, in general, *this method is of order $p = 2$*.

A step-by-step outline for an algorithm that implements the improved Euler's method is given below. Notice that it halves the size of h in going from one approximation to the next. For binary arithmetic and certain extrapolation methods (see Project E), it is more convenient to use powers of 2 rather than powers of 10.

IMPROVED EULER'S METHOD ALGORITHM

Purpose To approximate the solution to the initial value problem

$$y' = f(x, y), \qquad y(x_0) = y_0,$$

at $x = c$.

INPUT x_0, y_0, c
ε (tolerance)
M (maximum number of iterations)

Step 1 Set $z = y_0$

Step 2 For $m = 0$ to M do Steps $3 - 9^{\dagger}$

Step 3 Set $h = (c - x_0)2^{-m}$, $x = x_0$, $y = y_0$

Step 4 For $i = 1$ to 2^m do Steps 5 and 6

Step 5 Set

$$F = f(x, y)$$
$$G = f(x + h, y + hF)$$

Step 6 Set

$$x = x + h$$
$$y = y + \frac{h}{2}(F + G)$$

Step 7 Print h, y

Step 8 If $|y - z| < \varepsilon$, go to Step 12

Step 9 Set $z = y$

Step 10 Print "$\phi(c)$ is approximately"; y; "but may not be within the tolerance"; ε

Step 11 Go to Step 13

Step 12 Print "$\phi(c)$ is approximately"; y; "with tolerance"; ε

Step 13 Stop

OUTPUT Approximations of the solution to the initial value problem at $x = c$ using 2^m steps.

---

† To save time, one can start with $m = K < M$ rather than with $m = 0$.

Notice that one of the inputs to this algorithm is the "tolerance." In practice we want to estimate $\phi(x)$ to some desired accuracy, say with a permissible error of ε. To save time and money, we will want to stop the algorithm when we suspect that our estimate is within ε of $\phi(x)$. One such procedure is to terminate the computations when

(15) $\qquad \left| y(c; (c - x_0)2^{-m}) - y(c; (c - x_0)2^{-(m-1)}) \right| < \varepsilon,$

where $y(x; h)$ denotes the approximation of $\phi(x)$ using step size h. The preceding algorithm repeatedly uses the improved Euler's method to approximate $\phi(c)$, halving the step size with each iteration. When two successive iterations differ by less than ε, the process terminates. Using $y(c; (c - x_0)2^{-m})$ to approximate $\phi(c)$, inequality (15) simulates the **absolute error**

$$\left| y(c; (c - x_0)2^{-m}) - \phi(c) \right|.$$

If one desires a stopping procedure that simulates the **relative error** $\left| [y(c; (c - x_0)2^{-m}) - \phi(c)]/\phi(c) \right|$, then replace Step 8 by

$\qquad$ Step 8′ $\quad$ If $\left| \dfrac{y - z}{z} \right| < \varepsilon$, go to Step 12.

▶ **Example 2** $\quad$ Use the algorithm for improved Euler's method to approximate the solution to the initial value problem

(16) $\qquad y' = x + 2y, \qquad y(0) = 0.25,$

at $x = 2$. For a tolerance of $\varepsilon = 0.001$, use a stopping procedure based on the absolute error.

Solution $\quad$ The starting values are $x_0 = 0$, $y_0 = 0.25$. Since we are computing the approximations for $c = 2$, the initial value for h in Step 3 of the algorithm is

$$h = (2 - 0)2^{-0} = 2.$$

For equation (16) we have $f(x, y) = x + 2y$, and so the numbers F and G in Step 5 are

$$F = x + 2y$$
$$G = (x + h) + 2(y + hF) = x + 2y + h(1 + 2x + 4y),$$

and Step 6 becomes

$$x = x + h$$
$$y = y + \frac{h}{2}(F + G) = y + \frac{h}{2}(2x + 4y) + \frac{h^2}{2}(1 + 2x + 4y).$$

Thus, with $x_0 = 0$, $y = 0.25$, and $h = 2$, we get for the first approximation

$$y = 0.25 + (0 + 1) + 2(1 + 1) = 5.25.$$

To describe the further outputs of the algorithm, we use the notation $y(2; h)$ for the approximation obtained with step size h. Thus $y(2; 2) = 5.25$, and we find from the algorithm

$$y(2; 1) = 11.25000 \qquad y(2; 2^{-5}) = 25.98132$$
$$y(2; 2^{-1}) = 18.28125 \qquad y(2; 2^{-6}) = 26.03172$$
$$y(2; 2^{-2}) = 23.06067 \qquad y(2; 2^{-7}) = 26.04468$$
$$y(2; 2^{-3}) = 25.12012 \qquad y(2; 2^{-8}) = 26.04797$$
$$y(2; 2^{-4}) = 25.79127 \qquad y(2; 2^{-9}) = 26.04880.$$

Since $\left| y(2; 2^{-9}) - y(2; 2^{-8}) \right| = 0.00083$, which is less than $\varepsilon = 0.001$, we stop. The exact solution to (16) is $\phi(x) = \frac{1}{2}(e^{2x} - x - \frac{1}{2})$, and so we have determined that

$$\phi(2) = \frac{1}{2}(e^4 - \frac{5}{2}) \approx 26.04880. \blacktriangleleft$$

In the next section we discuss methods with higher rates of convergence than either Euler's or the improved Euler's methods.

EXERCISES 3.5

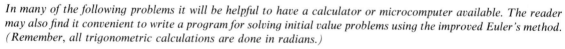

In many of the following problems it will be helpful to have a calculator or microcomputer available. The reader may also find it convenient to write a program for solving initial value problems using the improved Euler's method. (Remember, all trigonometric calculations are done in radians.)

1. Show that when Euler's method is used to approximate the solution of the initial value problem

$$y' = 5y, \qquad y(0) = 1,$$

at $x = 1$, then the approximation with step size h is $(1 + 5h)^{1/h}$.

2. Show that when Euler's method is used to approximate the solution of the initial value problem

$$y' = -\frac{1}{2}y, \qquad y(0) = 3,$$

at $x = 2$, then the approximation with step size h is

$$3\left(1 - \frac{h}{2}\right)^{2/h}$$

3. Show that when the trapezoid scheme given in formula (12) is used to approximate the solution $\phi(x) = e^x$ of

$$y' = y, \qquad y(0) = 1,$$

at $x = 1$, then we get

$$y_{n+1} = \left(\frac{1 + h/2}{1 - h/2}\right) y_n, \qquad n = 0, 1, 2, \ldots,$$

which leads to the approximation

$$\left(\frac{1 + h/2}{1 - h/2}\right)^{1/h}$$

for the constant e. Compute this approximation for $h = 1$, 10^{-1}, 10^{-2}, 10^{-3}, and 10^{-4} and compare your results with those in Tables 3.3 and 3.4.

4. In Example 1, the improved Euler's method approximation to e with step size h was shown to be

$$\left(1 + h + \frac{h^2}{2}\right)^{1/h}$$

First prove that error $:= e - (1 + h + h^2/2)^{1/h}$ approaches zero as $h \to 0$. Then use L'Hôpital's rule to show that

$$\lim_{h \to 0} \frac{\text{error}}{h^2} = \frac{e}{6} \approx 0.45304.$$

Compare this constant with the entries in the last column of Table 3.4.

5. Show that when the improved Euler's method is used to approximate the solution of the initial value problem

$$y' = 4y, \qquad y(0) = \tfrac{1}{3},$$

at $x = \tfrac{1}{2}$, then the approximation with step size h is

$$\tfrac{1}{3}(1 + 4h + 8h^2)^{1/(2h)}.$$

6. Since the integral $y(x) := \int_0^x f(t)\,dt$ with variable upper limit satisfies (for continuous f) the initial value problem

$$y' = f(x), \qquad y(0) = 0,$$

any numerical scheme that is used to approximate the solution at $x = 1$ will give an approximation to the definite integral

$$\int_0^1 f(t)\,dt.$$

Derive a formula for this approximation of the integral   using **(a)** Euler's method **(b)** Trapezoid scheme. **(c)** Improved Euler's method.

7. Use formula (13) for the improved Euler's method with step size $h = 0.1$ to approximate the solution to the initial value problem

$$y' = x - y^2, \qquad y(1) = 0,$$

at the points $x = 1.1, 1.2, 1.3, 1.4$, and 1.5.

8. Use formula (13) for the improved Euler's method with step size $h = 0.5$ to approximate the solution to the initial value problem

$$y' = \frac{1}{x}(y^2 + y), \qquad y(1) = 1,$$

at the points $x = 1.5, 2.0, 2.5$, and 3.0.

9. Use the improved Euler's method with step size $h = 0.2$ to approximate the solution to

$$y' = x + 3\cos(xy), \qquad y(0) = 0,$$

at the points $x = 0, 0.2, 0.4, \ldots, 2.0$. Use your answers to make a rough sketch of the solution on $[0, 2]$.

10. Use the improved Euler's method with step size $h = 0.1$ to approximate the solution to

$$y' = 4\cos(x + y), \qquad y(0) = 1,$$

at the points $x = 0, 0.1, 0.2, \ldots, 1.0$. Use your answers to make a rough sketch of the solution on $[0, 1]$.

11. Use the algorithm for the improved Euler's method to approximate the solution to

$$y' = 1 + x\sin(xy), \qquad y(0) = 0,$$

at $x = 1$. For a tolerance of $\varepsilon = 0.01$, use a stopping procedure based on the absolute error.

12. Use the algorithm for the improved Euler's method to approximate the solution to

$$y' = 1 - \sin y, \qquad y(0) = 0,$$

at $x = \pi$. For a tolerance of $\varepsilon = 0.01$, use a stopping procedure based on the absolute error.

13. Use the algorithm for the improved Euler's method to approximate the solution to

$$y' = 1 - y + y^3, \qquad y(0) = 0,$$

at $x = 1$. For a tolerance of $\varepsilon = 0.003$, use a stopping procedure based on the absolute error.

14. Use the algorithm for the improved Euler's method to approximate the solution to

$$y' = 1 + y^2, \qquad y(0) = 0,$$

at $x = 1.2$. For a tolerance of $\varepsilon = 0.1$, use a stopping procedure based on the absolute error.

15. Redo Problem 13 for a tolerance of $\varepsilon = 0.003$ using a stopping procedure based on the relative error.

16. Redo Problem 14 for a tolerance of $\varepsilon = 0.1$ using a stopping procedure based on the relative error.

17. Use Euler's method (6) with $h = 0.1$ to approximate the solution to the initial value problem

$$y' = -20y, \qquad y(0) = 1,$$

on the interval $0 \le x \le 1$ (that is, at $x = 0, 0.1, \ldots, 1.0$). Compare your answers with the actual solution $y = e^{-20x}$. What went wrong? Next, try the step size $h = 0.025$ and also $h = 0.2$. What conclusions can you draw concerning the choice of step size?

18. Local versus Global Error. In deriving formula (6) for Euler's method, a rectangle was used to approximate the area under a curve (see Figure 3.10). With $g(t) := f(t, \phi(t))$, this approximation can be written as

$$\int_{x_n}^{x_{n+1}} g(t)\, dt \approx hg(x_n), \qquad \text{where} \quad h = x_{n+1} - x_n.$$

(a) Show that if g has a continuous derivative that is bounded in absolute value by B, then the rectangle approximation has error $O(h^2)$, that is, for some constant M,

$$\left| \int_{x_n}^{x_{n+1}} g(t)\, dt - hg(x_n) \right| \le Mh^2.$$

This is called the *local truncation error* of the scheme. [Hint: Write

$$\int_{x_n}^{x_{n+1}} g(t)\, dt - hg(x_n) = \int_{x_n}^{x_{n+1}} [g(t) - g(x_n)]\, dt.$$

Next, using the mean value theorem, show that $|g(t) - g(x_n)| \le B|t - x_n|$. Now integrate to obtain the error bound $(B/2)h^2$.]

(b) In applying Euler's method, local truncation errors occur in each step of the process and are propagated throughout the further computations. Show that the *sum* of the local truncation errors in part (a) that arise after n steps is $O(h)$. This is the *global error*, which is the same as the convergence rate of Euler's method.

19. In Section 3.2 we discussed the logistic equation

$$\frac{dp}{dt} = ap - bp^2, \qquad p(0) = p_0$$

and its use in modeling population growth. A more general model might involve the equation

(17) $$\frac{dp}{dt} = ap - bp^r, \qquad p(0) = p_0,$$

where $r > 1$. To see the effect of changing the parameter r in (17), take $a = 3$, $b = 1$, and $p_0 = 1$. Now use the improved Euler's method with $h = 0.25$ to approximate the solution to (17) on the interval $0 \le t \le 5$ for $r = 1.5, 2$, and 3.

20. In Example 1 of Section 3.4 we modeled the velocity of a falling body by the initial value problem

$$m\frac{dv}{dt} = mg - kv, \qquad v(0) = v_0,$$

under the assumption that the force due to air resistance is $-kv$. However, in certain cases the force due to air resistance behaves more like $-kv^r$, where r (>1) is some constant. This leads to the model

(18) $$m\frac{dv}{dt} = mg - kv^r, \qquad v(0) = v_0.$$

To study the effect of changing the parameter r in (18), take $m = 1$, $g = 9.81$, $k = 2$, and $v_0 = 0$. Now use the improved Euler's method with $h = 0.2$ to approximate the solution to (18) on the interval $0 \le t \le 5$ for $r = 1.0, 1.5$, and 2.0.

21. In Section 3.3 we modeled the temperature inside a building by the initial value problem

(19) $$\frac{dT}{dt} = K[M(t) - T(t)] + H(t) + U(t), \qquad T(t_0) = T_0,$$

where M is the temperature outside the building, T is the temperature inside the building, H is the additional heating rate, U is the furnace heating or air conditioner cooling rate, K is a positive constant, and T_0 is the initial temperature at time t_0. In a typical model, $t_0 = 0$ (midnight), $T_0 = 65°F$, $H(t) = 0.1$, $U(t) = 1.5[70 - T(t)]$, and $M(t) = 75 - 20\cos(\pi t/12)$. The constant K is usually between $\frac{1}{4}$ and $\frac{1}{2}$, depending on such things as insulation. To study the effect of insulating this building, consider the typical building described above and use the improved Euler's method with $h = \frac{2}{3}$ to approximate the solution to (19) on the interval $0 \le t \le 24$ (1 day) for $K = 0.2, 0.4$, and 0.6.

3.6 Higher Order Numerical Methods: Taylor and Runge-Kutta

In Sections 1.3 and 3.5 we discussed a simple numerical procedure, Euler's method, for obtaining a numerical approximation of the solution $\phi(x)$ to the initial value problem

(1) $y' = f(x, y), \qquad y(x_0) = y_0.$

Euler's method is easy to implement because it just involves linear approximations to the solution $\phi(x)$. But it suffers from slow convergence, being a method of order 1; that is, the error is $O(h)$. Even the improved Euler's method discussed in Section 3.5 has order of only 2. In this section we present numerical methods that have faster rates of convergence. These include **Taylor methods,** which are natural extensions of the Euler procedure, and **Runge-Kutta methods,** which are the more popular schemes for solving initial value problems because they have fast rates of convergence and are easy to program.

As in the previous section we assume that f and $\partial f / \partial y$ are continuous and bounded on the vertical strip $\{(x, y): a < x < b, \ -\infty < y < \infty\}$ and that f possesses as many continuous partial derivatives as needed.

Let $\phi_n(x)$ be the exact solution of the related initial value problem

(2) $\phi_n' = f(x, \phi_n) \qquad \phi_n(x_n) = y_n.$

The Taylor series for $\phi_n(x)$ about the point x_n is

$$\phi_n(x) = \phi_n(x_n) + h\phi_n'(x_n) + \frac{h^2}{2!}\,\phi_n''(x_n) + \cdots,$$

where $h = x - x_n$. Since ϕ_n satisfies (2), we can write this series in the form

(3) $\phi_n(x) = y_n + hf(x_n, y_n) + \dfrac{h^2}{2!}\,\phi_n''(x_n) + \cdots.$

Observe that the recursive formula for y_{n+1} in Euler's method is obtained by truncating the Taylor series after the linear term. For a better approximation, we will use more terms in the Taylor series. This requires that we express the higher order derivatives of the solution in terms of the function $f(x, y)$.

If y satisfies $y' = f(x, y)$, we can compute y'' by using the chain rule:

(4) $y'' = \dfrac{\partial f}{\partial x}(x, y) + \dfrac{\partial f}{\partial y}(x, y)y'$

$\qquad\quad = \dfrac{\partial f}{\partial x}(x, y) + \dfrac{\partial f}{\partial y}(x, y)f(x, y)$

$\qquad\quad =: f_2(x, y).$

In a similar fashion, define f_3, f_4, etc., that correspond to the expressions for $y'''(x)$, $y^{(4)}(x)$, etc. If we truncate the expansion in (3) after the h^p term, then, with the above notation, the recursive formulas for the **Taylor method of order** p are

(5) $\qquad x_{n+1} = x_n + h,$

(6) $\qquad y_{n+1} = y_n + h f(x_n, y_n) + \dfrac{h^2}{2!} f_2(x_n, y_n) + \cdots + \dfrac{h^p}{p!} f_p(x_n, y_n).$

As before, $y_n \approx \phi(x_n)$, where $\phi(x)$ is the solution to the initial value problem (1). It can be shown[†] that **the Taylor method of order** p **has the rate of convergence** $O(h^p)$.

▶ **Example 1** Determine the recursive formulas for the Taylor method of order 2 for the initial value problem

(7) $\qquad y' = \sin(xy), \qquad y(0) = \pi.$

Solution We must compute $f_2(x, y)$ as defined in (4). Since $f(x, y) = \sin(xy)$,

(8) $\qquad \dfrac{\partial f}{\partial x}(x, y) = y \cos(xy), \qquad \dfrac{\partial f}{\partial y}(x, y) = x \cos(xy).$

Substituting into (4) we have

(9) $\qquad f_2(x, y) = \dfrac{\partial f}{\partial x}(x, y) + \dfrac{\partial f}{\partial y}(x, y) f(x, y)$

$\qquad\qquad = y \cos(xy) + x \cos(xy) \sin(xy)$

$\qquad\qquad = y \cos(xy) + \dfrac{x}{2} \sin(2xy).$

Hence, using (9), the recursive formulas (5) and (6) are

(10) $\qquad x_{n+1} = x_n + h,$

(11) $\qquad y_{n+1} = y_n + h \sin(x_n y_n) + \dfrac{h^2}{2}\left[y_n \cos(x_n y_n) + \dfrac{x_n}{2} \sin(2x_n y_n) \right],$

where $x_0 = 0$, $y_0 = \pi$ are the starting values. ◀

[†] See P. Henrici, *Elements of Numerical Analysis*, John Wiley and Sons, Inc., New York, 1964, Chapter 14.

The difficulty in employing higher order Taylor methods is the tedious computation of the partial derivatives needed to determine f_p; these computations grow exponentially with p. Fortunately, this difficulty can be circumvented by using one of the **Runge-Kutta methods.**[†]

Observe that the general Taylor method has the form

(12) $y_{n+1} = y_n + hF(x_n, y_n; h),$

where the choice of F depends on p. In particular (cf. (6)), for

(13) $p = 1,$ $F = T_1(x, y; h) := f(x, y),$

(14) $p = 2,$ $F = T_2(x, y; h) := f(x, y) + \dfrac{h}{2}\left[\dfrac{\partial f}{\partial x}(x, y) + \dfrac{\partial f}{\partial y}(x, y)f(x, y)\right].$

The idea behind the Runge-Kutta method of order 2 is to choose F in (12) of the form

(15) $F = K_2(x, y; h) := f(x + \alpha h, y + \beta h f(x, y)),$

where the constants α, β are to be selected so that (12) has the rate of convergence $O(h^2)$. The advantage here is that K_2 is computed by two evaluations of the original function $f(x, y)$ and does not involve the derivatives of $f(x, y)$.

To ensure $O(h^2)$ convergence, we compare this new scheme with the Taylor method of order 2 and require

(16) $T_2(x, y; h) - K_2(x, y; h) = O(h^2),$ as $h \to 0.$

That is, we choose α, β so that the Taylor expansions for T_2 and K_2 agree through terms of order h. For (x, y) fixed, when we expand $K_2 = K_2(h)$ as given in (15) about $h = 0$, we find

(17) $K_2(h) = K_2(0) + \dfrac{dK_2}{dh}(0)\, h + O(h^2)$

$= f(x, y) + \left[\alpha \dfrac{\partial f}{\partial x}(x, y) + \beta \dfrac{\partial f}{\partial y}(x, y)f(x, y)\right]h + O(h^2),$

where the expression in brackets for dK_2/dh follows from the chain rule. Comparing (17) with (14), we see that for T_2 and K_2 to agree through terms of order h, we must have $\alpha = \beta = \frac{1}{2}$. Thus

(18) $K_2(x, y; h) = f\left(x + \dfrac{h}{2}, y + \dfrac{h}{2}f(x, y)\right).$

[†] *Historical Footnote:* These methods were developed by C. Runge in 1895 and W. Kutta in 1901.

The Runge-Kutta method we have derived is called the **midpoint method** and it has the recursive formulas

(19) $$x_{n+1} = x_n + h,$$

(20) $$y_{n+1} = y_n + hf\left(x_n + \frac{h}{2}, y_n + \frac{h}{2}f(x_n, y_n)\right).$$

By construction, the midpoint method has the same rate of convergence as the Taylor method of order 2; that is, $O(h^2)$. This is the same rate as the improved Euler's method.

In a similar fashion one can work with the Taylor method of order 4, and after some elaborate calculations, obtain the **classical** or **fourth order Runge-Kutta method.** The recursive formulas for this method are

(21)
$$x_{n+1} = x_n + h,$$
$$y_{n+1} = y_n + \tfrac{1}{6}(k_1 + 2k_2 + 2k_3 + k_4),$$

where

$$k_1 = hf(x_n, y_n),$$

$$k_2 = hf\left(x_n + \frac{h}{2}, y_n + \frac{k_1}{2}\right),$$

$$k_3 = hf\left(x_n + \frac{h}{2}, y_n + \frac{k_2}{2}\right),$$

$$k_4 = hf(x_n + h, y_n + k_3).$$

The fourth order Runge-Kutta method is one of the more popular methods because its rate of convergence is $O(h^4)$ and it is easy to program. When combined with extrapolation (see Project E), it produces very accurate approximations.

A program outline for the fourth order Runge-Kutta method is given in the box on page 134. In this algorithm (as in the improved Euler's algorithm) the step sizes are successively halved, and a stopping procedure is included that compares the two approximations $y(x; h)$ and $y(x; h/2)$ for $\phi(x)$. In particular, if ε is the prescribed tolerance, then the computations end when these consecutive approximations differ by less than ε.

▶ *Example 2*   Use the fourth order Runge-Kutta algorithm outlined on the next page to approximate the solution $\phi(x)$ of the initial value problem

(22) $$y' = y, \qquad y(0) = 1$$

at $x = 1$ with a tolerance of 0.001.

FOURTH ORDER RUNGE-KUTTA ALGORITHM

Purpose   To approximate the solution to the initial value problem

$$y' = f(x, y), \qquad y(x_0) = y_0$$

at $x = c$.

INPUT x_0, y_0, c
ε (tolerance)
M (maximum number of iterations)

Step 1   Set $z = y_0$

Step 2   For $m = 0$ to M do Steps 3–9[†]

Step 3   Set $h = (c - x_0)2^{-m}, \quad x = x_0, \quad y = y_0$

Step 4   For $i = 1$ to 2^m do Steps 5 and 6

Step 5   Set

$$k_1 = hf(x, y)$$
$$k_2 = hf\left(x + \frac{h}{2}, y + \frac{k_1}{2}\right)$$
$$k_3 = hf\left(x + \frac{h}{2}, y + \frac{k_2}{2}\right)$$
$$k_4 = hf(x + h, y + k_3)$$

Step 6   Set

$$x = x + h$$
$$y = y + \tfrac{1}{6}(k_1 + 2k_2 + 2k_3 + k_4)$$

Step 7   Print h, y

Step 8   If $|z - y| < \varepsilon$ go to Step 12

Step 9   Set $z = y$

Step 10   Print "$\phi(c)$ is approximately,"; y; "but may not be within the tolerance"; ε

Step 11   Go to Step 13

Step 12   Print "$\phi(c)$ is approximately,"; y; "with tolerance"; ε

Step 13   STOP

OUTPUT   Approximations of the solution to the initial value problem at $x = c$, using 2^m steps.

[†] To save time, one can start with $m = K < M$ rather than with $m = 0$.

Solution The inputs are $x_0 = 0$, $y_0 = 1$, $c = 1$, $\varepsilon = 0.001$, and $M = 100$ (say). Since $f(x, y) = y$, the formulas in Step 5 of the algorithm become

$$k_1 = hy, \qquad k_2 = h\left(y + \frac{k_1}{2}\right), \qquad k_3 = h\left(y + \frac{k_2}{2}\right), \qquad k_4 = h(y + k_3).$$

The initial value for h in Step 3 is

$$h = (1 - 0)2^{-0} = 1.$$

Thus, in Step 5, we compute

$$k_1 = (1)(1) = 1, \qquad k_2 = (1)(1 + 0.5) = 1.5,$$
$$k_3 = (1)(1 + 0.75) = 1.75, \qquad k_4 = (1)(1 + 1.75) = 2.75,$$

and, in Step 6, we get for the first approximation

$$\begin{aligned} y &= y_0 + \tfrac{1}{6}(k_1 + 2k_2 + 2k_3 + k_4) \\ &= 1 + \tfrac{1}{6}[1 + 2(1.5) + 2(1.75) + 2.75] \\ &= 2.70833, \end{aligned}$$

where we have rounded to five decimal places. Since

$$|z - y| = |y_0 - y| = |1 - 2.70833| = 1.70833 > \varepsilon,$$

we return to Step 3 and set $h = 0.5$.

Doing Steps 5 and 6 for $i = 1$ and 2, we ultimately obtain (for $i = 2$) the approximation

$$y = 2.71735.$$

Since $|z - y| = |2.70833 - 2.71735| = 0.00902 > \varepsilon$, we return to Step 3 and set $h = 0.25$. This leads to the approximation

$$y = 2.71821,$$

so that

$$|z - y| = |2.71735 - 2.71821| = 0.00086,$$

which is less than $\varepsilon = 0.001$. Hence $\phi(1) = e \approx 2.71821$. ◀

In the previous example we were able to obtain a better approximation for $\phi(1) = e$ with $h = 0.25$ than we obtained in Section 3.5 using Euler's method with $h = 0.001$ (see Table 3.3) and roughly the same accuracy as we obtained in Section 3.5 using the improved Euler's method with $h = 0.01$ (see Table 3.4).

▶ *Example 3*   Use the fourth order Runge-Kutta method (21) to approximate the solution $\phi(x)$ of the initial value problem

(23) $y' = y^2$, $y(0) = 1$

at $x = 2$ using $h = 0.25$.

Solution   Here the starting values are $x_0 = 0$ and $y_0 = 1$. Since $f(x, y) = y^2$, we use formulas (21) with

$$k_1 = h(y_n)^2, \qquad k_2 = h\left(y_n + \frac{k_1}{2}\right)^2,$$

$$k_3 = h\left(y_n + \frac{k_2}{2}\right)^2, \qquad k_4 = h(y_n + k_3)^2.$$

For $h = 0.25$, we have $n = 8$. From the preceding formulas, we find

$y_1 = 1.33322$,

$y_2 = 1.99884$,

$y_3 = 3.97238$,

$y_4 = 32.82820$,

$y_5 = 4.09664 \times 10^{11}$,

$y_6 = $ overflow.

What happened? Fortunately the equation in (23) is separable, and, solving for $\phi(x)$, we obtain $\phi(x) = (1 - x)^{-1}$. It is now obvious where the problem lies; the true solution $\phi(x)$ is not defined at $x = 1$. If we had been more cautious, we would have realized that $\partial f/\partial y = 2y$ is *not* bounded for all y. Hence the existence of a unique solution is not guaranteed for all x between 0 and 2, and in this case the method does *not* converge. ◀

▶ *Example 4*   Use the fourth order Runge-Kutta algorithm to approximate the solution $\phi(x)$ of the initial value problem

(24) $y' = x - y^2$, $y(0) = 1$

at $x = 2$ with a tolerance of 0.0001.

Solution   This time we check to see whether $\partial f/\partial y$ is bounded. Here $\partial f/\partial y = -2y$, which is certainly unbounded in any vertical strip. However, let's consider the qualitative behavior

		TABLE 3.5 FOURTH ORDER RUNGE-KUTTA APPROXIMATION FOR $\phi(2)$		
m	h	Approximation for $\phi(2)$	$\lvert y(2; 2^{-m+1}) - y(2; 2^{-m+2})\rvert$
0	2.0	-8.33334	
1	1.0	1.27504	9.60838
2	0.5	1.25170	0.02334
3	0.25	1.25132	0.00038
4	0.125	1.25132	0.00000

of the solution $\phi(x)$. The solution curve starts at $(0, 1)$, where $\phi'(0) = 0 - 1 < 0$, so $\phi(x)$ begins decreasing and continues to decrease until it crosses the curve $y = \sqrt{x}$. After crossing this curve, $\phi(x)$ begins to increase, since $\phi'(x) = x - \phi^2(x) > 0$. As $\phi(x)$ increases, it remains below the curve $y = \sqrt{x}$, because if the solution were to get "close" to the curve $y = \sqrt{x}$, then the slope of $\phi(x)$ would approach zero, so that overtaking the function $\sqrt{x}$ is impossible.

The above argument shows that $\phi(x)$ exists for $x > 0$, and since it exists, we feel reasonably sure that the fourth order Runge-Kutta method will give a good approximation of the true solution $\phi(x)$. Proceeding with the algorithm, we use the starting values $x_0 = 0$ and $y_0 = 1$. Since $f(x, y) = x - y^2$, the formulas in Step 5 become

$$k_1 = h(x - y^2), \qquad\qquad k_2 = h\left[\left(x + \frac{h}{2}\right) - \left(y + \frac{k_1}{2}\right)^2\right],$$

$$k_3 = h\left[\left(x + \frac{h}{2}\right) - \left(y + \frac{k_2}{2}\right)^2\right], \qquad k_4 = h[(x + h) - (y + k_3)^2].$$

In Table 3.5 we give the approximations $y(2; 2^{-m+1})$ for $\phi(2)$ for $m = 0, 1, 2, 3,$ and 4. The algorithm stops at $m = 4$ since

$$\lvert y(2; 0.125) - y(2; 0.25)\rvert = 0.00000.$$

Hence $\phi(2) \approx 1.25132$, with a tolerance of 0.0001. ◀

EXERCISES 3.6

As in Exercises 3.5, the reader will find it helpful to have a microcomputer available.

1. Determine the recursive formulas for the Taylor method of order 2 for the initial value problem

$$y' = \cos(x + y), \qquad y(0) = \pi.$$

2. Determine the recursive formulas for the Taylor method of order 2 for the initial value problem

$$y' = xy - y^2, \qquad y(0) = -1.$$

3. Determine the recursive formulas for the Taylor method of order 4 for the initial value problem

$$y' = x - y, \qquad y(0) = 0.$$

4. Determine the recursive formulas for the Taylor method of order 4 for the initial value problem

$$y' = x^2 + y, \qquad y(0) = 0.$$

5. Use the Taylor methods of orders 2 and 4 with $h = 0.25$ to approximate the solution to the initial value problem

$$y' = x + 1 - y, \qquad y(0) = 1$$

at $x = 1$. Compare these approximations to the actual solution $y = x + e^{-x}$ evaluated at $x = 1$.

6. Use the Taylor methods of orders 2 and 4 with $h = 0.25$ to approximate the solution to the initial value problem

$$y' = 1 - y, \qquad y(0) = 0$$

at $x = 1$. Compare these approximations to the actual solution $y = 1 - e^{-x}$ evaluated at $x = 1$.

7. Use the fourth order Runge-Kutta method (21) with $h = 0.25$ to approximate the solution to the initial value problem

$$y' = 2y - 6, \qquad y(0) = 1$$

at $x = 1$. Compare this approximation to the actual solution $y = 3 - 2e^{2x}$ evaluated at $x = 1$.

8. Use the fourth order Runge-Kutta method (21) with $h = 0.25$ to approximate the solution to the initial value problem

$$y' = 1 + y^2, \qquad y(0) = 0$$

at $x = 1$.

9. Use the fourth order Runge-Kutta method (21) with $h = 0.5$ and $h = 0.25$ to approximate the solution to the initial value problem

$$y' = x^2 - y^2, \qquad y(0) = 1$$

at $x = 1$.

10. Use the fourth order Runge-Kutta method (21) with $h = 0.5$ and $h = 0.25$ to approximate the solution to the initial value problem

$$y' = \frac{2y}{1+x}, \qquad y(0) = 1$$

at $x = 1$.

11. Use the fourth order Runge-Kutta method (21) with $h = 0.25$ to approximate the solution to the initial value problem

$$y' = x + 1 - y, \qquad y(0) = 1$$

at $x = 1$. Compare this approximation with the one obtained in Problem 5 using the Taylor method of order 4.

12. Use the fourth order Runge-Kutta method (21) with $h = 0.25$ to approximate the solution to the initial value problem

$$y' = 1 - y, \qquad y(0) = 0$$

at $x = 1$. Compare this approximation with the one obtained in Problem 6 using the Taylor method of order 4.

13. Use the fourth order Runge-Kutta algorithm to approximate the solution to the initial value problem

$$y' = 1 - xy, \qquad y(1) = 1$$

at $x = 2$. For a tolerance of $\varepsilon = 0.001$, use a stopping procedure based on the absolute error.

14. Use the fourth order Runge-Kutta algorithm to approximate the solution to the initial value problem

$$y' = y \cos x, \qquad y(0) = 1$$

at $x = \pi$. For a tolerance of $\varepsilon = 0.01$, use a stopping procedure based on the absolute error.

15. Use the fourth order Runge-Kutta method (21) with $h = 0.1$ to approximate the solution to

$$y' = \cos(5y) - x; \qquad y(0) = 0,$$

at the points $x = 0, 0.1, 0.2, \ldots, 3.0$. Use your answers to make a rough sketch of the solution on $[0, 3]$.

16. Use the fourth order Runge-Kutta method (21) with $h = 0.1$ to approximate the solution to

$$y' = 3 \cos(y - 5x); \qquad y(0) = 0,$$

at the points $x = 0, 0.1, 0.2, \ldots, 4.0$. Use your answers to make a rough sketch of the solution on $[0, 4]$.

17. The Taylor method of order 2 can be used to approximate the solution to the initial value problem

$$y' = y, \qquad y(0) = 1$$

at $x = 1$. Show that the approximation y_n obtained by using the Taylor method of order 2 with the step size $1/n$ is given by the formula

$$y_n = \left(1 + \frac{1}{n} + \frac{1}{2n^2}\right)^n, \qquad n = 1, 2, \dots.$$

Since the solution to the initial value problem is $y = e^x$, then y_n is an approximation to the constant e.

18. If the Taylor method of order p is used in Problem 17, show that

$$y_n = \left(1 + \frac{1}{n} + \frac{1}{2n^2} + \frac{1}{6n^3} + \cdots + \frac{1}{p!n^p}\right)^n, \qquad n = 1, 2, \dots.$$

19. **Fluid Flow.**   In the study of the nonisothermal flow of a Newtonian fluid between parallel plates the equation

$$\frac{d^2y}{dx^2} + x^2 e^y = 0, \qquad x > 0$$

was encountered. By a series of substitutions this equation can be transformed into the first order equation

$$\frac{dv}{du} = u\left(\frac{u}{2} + 1\right)v^3 + \left(u + \frac{5}{2}\right)v^2.$$

Use the fourth order Runge-Kutta algorithm to approximate $v(3)$ if $v(t)$ satisfies $v(2) = 0.1$. For a tolerance of $\varepsilon = 0.0001$, use a stopping procedure based on the relative error.

20. **Chemical Reactions.**   The reaction between nitrous oxide and oxygen to form nitrogen dioxide is given by the balanced chemical equation $2NO + O_2 = 2NO_2$. At high temperatures the dependence of the rate of this reaction on the concentrations of NO, O_2, and NO_2 is complicated. However, at $25°C$ the rate at which NO_2 is formed obeys the law of mass action and is given by the rate equation

$$\frac{dx}{dt} = k(\alpha - x)^2\left(\beta - \frac{x}{2}\right),$$

where $x(t)$ denotes the concentration of NO_2 at time t, k is the rate constant, α is the initial concentration of NO, and β is the initial concentration of O_2. At $25°C$, the constant k is 7.13×10^3 (liter)^2/(mole)^2(second). Let $\alpha = 0.0010$ mole/L, $\beta = 0.0041$ mole/L, and $x(0) = 0$ mole/L. Use the fourth order Runge-Kutta algorithm to approximate $x(10)$. For a tolerance of $\varepsilon = 0.000001$, use a stopping procedure based on the relative error.

21. Transmission Lines. In studying the electric field that is induced by two nearby transmission lines, an equation of the form

$$\frac{dz}{dx} + g(x)z^2 = f(x)$$

arises. Let $f(x) = 5x + 2$ and $g(x) = x^2$. If $z(0) = 1$, use the fourth order Runge-Kutta algorithm to approximate $z(1)$. For a tolerance of $\varepsilon = 0.0001$, use a stopping procedure based on the absolute error.

3.7 Some Available Codes for Initial Value Problems

Before describing some commercially available codes for solving initial value problems, we must first introduce multistep methods and the concept of step size control.

In the previous two sections we discussed numerical methods for solving initial value problems for a first order differential equation. These techniques are examples of **one-step methods** because the approximation y_{n+1} of $y(x_{n+1})$ is obtained using the differential equation and the previous approximation y_n of $y(x_n)$. More generally, we can use **multistep methods.** For such schemes the differential equation and the previous k approximations

$$y_n, \, y_{n-1}, \, \ldots, \, y_{n-(k-2)}, \, y_{n-(k-1)}$$

are used to obtain the approximation y_{n+1}. (In this case the method is called a **k-step method.**)

A two-step method that is easy to derive is based on Simpson's rule for approximating integrals (see Appendix B). Let y_n be the approximation of the solution $y(x)$ to the initial value problem

(1) $\qquad y' = f(x, y), \qquad y(x_0) = y_0$

at $x_n = x_0 + nh$, where $h > 0$ is the step size. If we integrate both sides of the equation in (1) from x_{n-1} to x_{n+1}, then we have

(2) $\qquad y(x_{n+1}) - y(x_{n-1}) = \int_{x_{n-1}}^{x_{n+1}} f(x, y(x)) \, dx.$

We now approximate the integral in (2) using Simpson's rule. This gives

$$y(x_{n+1}) - y(x_{n-1}) \approx \frac{h}{3} \left[f(x_{n-1}, y(x_{n-1})) + 4f(x_n, y(x_n)) + f(x_{n+1}, y(x_{n+1})) \right].$$

Substituting the approximations y_{n-1}, y_n, and y_{n+1} for $y(x_{n-1})$, $y(x_n)$, and $y(x_{n+1})$, respectively, we obtain the numerical scheme

(3) $\qquad y_{n+1} - y_{n-1} = \frac{h}{3} \left[f(x_{n-1}, y_{n-1}) + 4f(x_n, y_n) + f(x_{n+1}, y_{n+1}) \right].$

This method is called **Simpson's rule.** As you can see, it is an implicit, two-step method. Starting with y_0 and y_1, formula (3) determines y_2; knowing y_1 and y_2 we again use (3) to determine y_3; etc. Formula (3) can also be used in a predictor-corrector procedure, where y_{n+1}^*, a predicted value for y_{n+1}, is used in the right-hand side of (3) to obtain a "corrected" estimate y_{n+1}.

Multistep methods were introduced by J. C. Adams prior to the Runge-Kutta methods. In fact, two important classes of multistep methods are the explicit Adams methods called the **Adams-Bashford methods** and the implicit Adams methods called the **Adams-Moulton methods.** Like the Runge-Kutta methods, there exist Adams methods with different orders of convergence.

A disadvantage of the multistep methods is that they are more susceptible to instability. (Stability is discussed in Project F and Example 4, Section 5.5.) From a programming viewpoint, the multistep methods also have the disadvantage of not being self-starting; that is, the first k approximations $y_0, y_1, \dots, y_{k-1}$ are needed in a k-step method in order to determine y_k. Therefore, one must use some other method to generate the starting values $y_1, y_2, \dots, y_{k-1}$ (recall that y_0 is given). This means the Runge-Kutta formulas are easier to code. However, the Runge-Kutta formulas require several evaluations of the function $f(x, y)$ at each step, whereas the multistep formulas require only one evaluation of $f(x, y)$ at each stage. This makes the multistep methods less expensive (and faster) when the function $f(x, y)$ is complicated. For a discussion of multistep methods, we refer the reader to the texts *Numerical Initial Value Problems in Ordinary Differential Equations*, by C. W. Gear, Prentice-Hall, 1971, and *Discrete Variable Methods in Ordinary Differential Equations*, by P. Henrici, John Wiley and Sons, 1962.

In practice, one is confronted with the problem of approximating the solution to within a desired tolerance and obtaining this approximation as inexpensively or as quickly as possible. This is seldom achieved using a *constant* step size h. To illustrate the problem, consider the periodic function $y(x)$ whose graph is given in Figure 3.12. (The solutions to the "Brusselator" equation, which models a chemical reaction that possesses periodic solutions, have graphs similar to the one in Figure 3.12.) If we are trying to approximate $y(x)$, then, over most of its period, we can use a step size h that is relatively large. However, at the "spike," we must take h to be very small or else we will miss the spike entirely or poorly approximate the values of y on the spike. Therefore, it is advantageous to be able to control the step size h.

Much work has been done on writing codes that vary the step size h. These codes can choose h at each step so that the local error is within the given tolerance; shorten the step size, if necessary, to keep the error within tolerance; and decide what the next step size should be. The codes using multistep methods can vary the order of approximation by shifting from one type of multistep method to another. This allows them to begin with a one-step method, which resolves the difficulty of determining the starting values $y_1, y_2, \dots, y_{k-1}$ in a k-step method. Even when using a code with variable step size and order strategies, it is important to use whatever information one might have to assist in approximating the solution on those intervals where it is changing rapidly.

Because of the considerable effort involved in developing and testing codes for numerically solving initial value problems, a scientist or engineer will often use one of the commercially available packages for "real life" applications. We now briefly describe four such

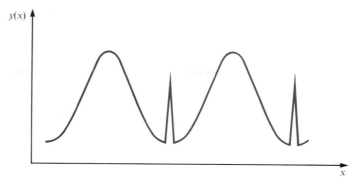

Figure 3.12 Periodic function with spike

codes: three codes using multistep methods with variable order and step size strategies and one fixed order Runge-Kutta method with a variable step size strategy.

DEABM was developed by L. F. Shampine and H. A. Watts and is a modification of the code **DE** that is described in the book *Computer Solution of Ordinary Differential Equations, the Initial Value Problem,* by L. F. Shampine and M. K. Gordon, Freeman and Company, San Francisco, 1975. This code uses a predictor-corrector approach involving the Adams methods. In this program the step size is adjusted to maintain accuracy in the intervals where the solution varies rapidly and the order is changed to maintain accuracy over the intervals where the solution is slowly varying.

EPISODE is a code that is also based on the Adams methods. It is available from the National Energy Software Center, Building 221, Argonne National Laboratory, 9700 South Cass Avenue, Argonne, IL 60439. This method uses a different strategy for varying the order than does **DEABM** and tends to change order less frequently.

LSODE is another code based on the Adams methods. It is an improvement of the code **DIFSUB,** which was developed by C. W. Gear, and is also available from Argonne National Laboratory, where **EPISODE** can be obtained. Its step size and order strategies are similar to **EPISODE.**

DOPRI8 is a one-step method that uses an eighth order Runge-Kutta formula with a seventh order error estimate and step size control. The formulas were obtained by P. J. Prince and J. R. Dormand. The code is given in the appendix to the book *Solving Ordinary Differential Equations I—Nonstiff Problems,* by E. Hairer, S. P. Nørsett, and G. Wanner, which is published by Springer-Verlag, Berlin, 1987.

RECOMMENDATIONS

In the just-mentioned book by Hairer, Nørsett, and Wanner, the authors make the following recommendations concerning which code to use. For tolerances between 10^{-3} and 10^{-12}, where the function $f(x, y)$ is inexpensive to evaluate, they recommend using **DOPRI8,** since it is less expensive and faster. When it is costly to evaluate $f(x, y)$, the multistep codes **DEABM, EPISODE,** and **LSODE** are preferred. For tolerances smaller than 10^{-15}, such as 10^{-18}, a method using extrapolation techniques (see Project E) should be considered.

Projects for Chapter 3

A. DELAY DIFFERENTIAL EQUATIONS

In our discussion of mixing problems in Section 3.2, we encountered the initial value problem

(1) $x'(t) = 6 - \dfrac{3}{500} x(t - t_0),$ $x(t) = 0$ for $t \in [-t_0, 0],$

where t_0 is a positive constant. The equation in (1) is an example of a **delay differential equation.** These equations differ from the usual differential equations by the presence of the shift $(t - t_0)$ in the argument of the unknown function $x(t)$. In general these equations are more difficult to work with than regular differential equations, but quite a bit is known about them.[†]

   (a) Show that the simple linear delay differential equation

(2) $u'(t) = au(t - b),$

where a and b are constants, has a solution of the form $u = Ce^{st}$, for any constant C, provided that s satisfies the transcendental equation $s = ae^{-bs}$.

   (b) A solution to (2) for $t > 0$ can also be found using the **method of steps.** Assume that $u(t) = f(t)$ for $-b \le t \le 0$. For $0 \le t \le b$, equation (2) becomes

$$u'(t) = au(t - b) = af(t - b),$$

and so

$$u(t) = \int_0^t af(v - b)\, dv + u(0).$$

Now that we know $u(t)$ on $[0, b]$, we can repeat this procedure to obtain

$$u(t) = \int_b^t au(v - b)\, dv + u(b)$$

for $b \le t \le 2b$. This process can be continued indefinitely.
   Use the method of steps to show that the solution to the initial value problem

$$u'(t) = u(t - 1),   u(t) = 1   \text{ on }   [-1, 0]$$

is given by

$$u(t) = \sum_{k=0}^{n} \frac{[t - (k - 1)]^k}{k!},   n - 1 \le t \le n,$$

where n is a nonnegative integer. (This problem can also be solved using Laplace transforms.)

[†] See, for example, *Differential-Difference Equations,* by R. Bellman and K. L. Cooke, Academic Press, New York, 1963, or *Ordinary and Delay Differential Equations,* by R. D. Driver, Springer-Verlag, New York, 1977.

(c) Use the method of steps to compute the solution to the initial value problem given in (1) on the interval $0 \leq t \leq 10$ for $t_0 = 2$.

B. AQUACULTURE

Aquaculture is the art of cultivating the plants and animals indigenous to water. In the example considered here, it is assumed that a batch of catfish are raised in a pond. We are interested in determining the best time for harvesting the fish so that the cost per pound for raising the fish is minimized.

A differential equation describing the growth of fish may be expressed as

$$(3) \qquad \frac{dW}{dt} = KW^{\alpha},$$

where $W(t)$ is the weight of the fish at time t, and K and α are empirically determined growth constants. The functional form of this relationship is similar to that of the growth models for other species. Modeling the growth rate or metabolic rate by a term like W^{α} is a common assumption. Biologists often refer to equation (3) as the **allometric equation.** It can be supported by plausibility arguments such as growth rate depending on the surface area of the gut (which varies like $W^{2/3}$) or depending on the volume of the animal (which varies like W).

(a) Solve equation (3) when $\alpha \neq 1$.

(b) The solution obtained in part (a) grows large without bound, but in practice there is some limiting maximum weight W_{MAX} for the fish. This limiting weight may be included in the differential equation describing growth by inserting a dimensionless variable S that can range between 0 and 1 and involves an empirically determined dimensionless parameter μ. Namely, we now assume

$$(4) \qquad \frac{dW}{dt} = KW^{\alpha}S,$$

where $S := 1 - (W/W_{MAX})^{\mu}$. When $\mu = 1 - \alpha$, equation (4) has a closed form solution.

Solve equation (4) when $K = 12$, $\alpha = \frac{2}{3}$, $\mu = \frac{1}{3}$, $W_{MAX} = 64$ (ounces), and $W(0) = 1$ (ounce). The constants are given for t measured in months.

(c) The differential equation describing the total cost in dollars $C(t)$ of raising a fish for t months has one constant term K_1 that specifies the cost per month (due to costs such as interest, depreciation, and labor) and a second constant K_2 that multiplies the growth rate (because the amount of food consumed by the fish is approximately proportional to the growth rate). That is,

$$(5) \qquad \frac{dC}{dt} = K_1 + K_2 \frac{dW}{dt}.$$

Solve equation (5) when $K_1 = 0.5$, $K_2 = 0.1$, $C(0) = 1.1$ (dollars), and $W(t)$ is as determined in part (b).

(d) Sketch the curve obtained in part (b) that represents the weight of the fish as a function of time. Next, sketch the curve obtained in part (c) that represents the total cost of raising the fish as a function of time.

(e) To determine the optimal time for harvesting the fish, sketch the ratio $C(t)/W(t)$. This ratio represents the total cost per ounce as a function of time. When this ratio reaches its minimum—that is, when the total cost per ounce is at its lowest—this is the optimal time to harvest the fish. Determine this optimal time to the nearest month.

C. CURVE OF PURSUIT

An interesting geometric model arises when one tries to determine the path of a pursuer chasing its prey. This path is called a *curve of pursuit*. These problems were analyzed using methods of calculus circa 1730 (more than two centuries after Leonardo da Vinci had considered them). The simplest problem is to find the curve along which a vessel moves in pursuing another vessel that flees along a straight line, assuming that the speeds of the two vessels are constant.

Let's assume vessel A, traveling at a speed α, is pursuing vessel B, which is traveling at a speed β. In addition, assume that vessel A begins (at time $t = 0$) at the origin and pursues vessel B, which begins at the point $(b, 0)$, $b > 0$, and travels up the line $x = b$. After t hours, vessel A is located at the point $P = (x, y)$ and vessel B is located at the point $Q = (b, \beta t)$ (see Figure 3.13). The goal is to describe the locus of points P; that is, to find y as a function of x.

(a) Since vessel A is pursuing vessel B, then at the time t, vessel A must be heading right at vessel B. That is, the tangent line to the curve of pursuit at P must pass through the point Q (see Figure 3.13). For this to be true, show that

(6)
$$\frac{dy}{dx} = \frac{y - \beta t}{x - b}.$$

(b) Since we know the speed at which vessel A is traveling, we know that the distance it travels in time t is αt. This distance is also the length of the pursuit curve from $(0, 0)$ to (x, y). Using the arclength formula from calculus, show that

(7)
$$\alpha t = \int_0^x \sqrt{1 + [y'(u)]^2}\, du.$$

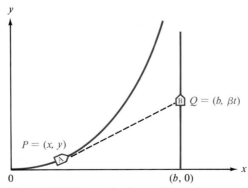

Figure 3.13 The path of vessel A as it pursues vessel B

Solving for t in equations (6) and (7), conclude that

(8)
$$\frac{y - (x - b)(dy/dx)}{\beta} = \frac{1}{\alpha} \int_0^x \sqrt{1 + [y'(u)]^2}\, du.$$

(c) Differentiating both sides of (8) with respect to x, derive the first order equation

(9)
$$(x - b)\frac{dw}{dx} = -\frac{\beta}{\alpha}\sqrt{1 + w^2},$$

where $w := dy/dx$.

(d) Using separation of variables and the initial conditions $x = 0$ and $w = dy/dx = 0$ when $t = 0$, show that

(10)
$$\frac{dy}{dx} = w = \frac{1}{2}\left[\left(1 - \frac{x}{b}\right)^{-\beta/\alpha} - \left(1 - \frac{x}{b}\right)^{\beta/\alpha}\right].$$

(e) For $\alpha > \beta$, that is, the pursuing vessel A travels faster than the vessel B that is being pursued, use equation (10) and the initial conditions $x = 0$ and $y = 0$ when $t = 0$ to derive the curve of pursuit

(11)
$$y = \frac{b}{2}\left[\frac{(1 - x/b)^{1 + \beta/\alpha}}{1 + \beta/\alpha} - \frac{(1 - x/b)^{1 - \beta/\alpha}}{1 - \beta/\alpha}\right] + \frac{b\alpha\beta}{\alpha^2 - \beta^2}.$$

(f) Find the location where vessel A intercepts vessel B if $\alpha > \beta$.

(g) Show that if $\alpha = \beta$, then the curve of pursuit is given by

$$y = \frac{b}{2}\left\{\frac{1}{2}\left[\left(1 - \frac{x}{b}\right)^2 - 1\right] - \ln\left(1 - \frac{x}{b}\right)\right\}.$$

Will vessel A ever reach vessel B?

D. A LINEAR DIFFERENCE EQUATION

The linear first order difference equation

(12)
$$y_{n+1} = ay_n + b, \qquad n = 0, 1, 2, \ldots,$$

where $a \neq 0$ and b are constants, arises in such applications as computing simple and compound interest and amortizations. One seeks a sequence $\{y_n\}_{n=0}^{\infty}$ that satisfies relation (12) with y_0 a prescribed "initial condition."

(a) After computing $y_1, y_2, y_3,$ and y_4, deduce the general formula

(13)
$$y_n = a^n y_0 + b(1 + a + \cdots + a^{n-1}), \qquad n = 1, 2, 3, \ldots.$$

(b) Show that when $a \neq 1$, we can express y_n in the form

(14) $\qquad y_n = a^n(y_0 - y^*) + y^*, \qquad n = 1, 2, 3, \dots,$

where $y^* := b/(1 - a)$.

(c) By considering separately the various cases, describe the behavior (as $n \to \infty$) of the solution sequence $\{y_n\}_{n=0}^{\infty}$. For example, show that when $0 < a < 1$ and $y_0 < y^*$, then the sequence increases monotonically to the limit y^*. [Hint: There are up to ten cases corresponding to the different assumptions on a, b, and y_0.]

E. EXTRAPOLATION

When precise information about the *form* of the error in an approximation method is known, a technique called **extrapolation** can be used to improve the rate of convergence.

Suppose the approximation method converges with rate $O(h^p)$ as $h \to 0$ (cf. Section 3.5). From theoretical considerations assume we know, more precisely, that

(15) $\qquad y(x; h) = \phi(x) + h^p a_p(x) + O(h^{p+1}),$

where $y(x; h)$ is the approximation to $\phi(x)$ using step size h and $a_p(x)$ is some function that is independent of h (typically we do not know a formula for $a_p(x)$, only that it exists). Our goal is to obtain approximations that converge at the *faster* rate $O(h^{p+1})$.

We start by replacing h by $h/2$ in (15) to get

(16) $\qquad y(x; h/2) = \phi(x) + \dfrac{h^p}{2^p} a_p(x) + O(h^{p+1}).$

If we multiply both sides of (16) by 2^p and subtract equation (15), we find

(17) $\qquad 2^p y(x; h/2) - y(x; h) = (2^p - 1)\phi(x) + O(h^{p+1}).$

Solving for $\phi(x)$ yields

$$\phi(x) = \frac{2^p y(x; h/2) - y(x; h)}{2^p - 1} + O(h^{p+1}).$$

Hence

(18) $\qquad y^*(x; h/2) := \dfrac{2^p y(x; h/2) - y(x; h)}{2^p - 1}$

has a rate of convergence of $O(h^{p+1})$.

(a) Assuming $y^*(x; h/2) = \phi(x) + h^{p+1} a_{p+1}(x) + O(h^{p+2})$, show that

(19) $\qquad y^{**}(x; h/4) := \dfrac{2^{p+1} y^*(x; h/4) - y^*(x; h/2)}{2^{p+1} - 1}$

has a rate of convergence of $O(h^{p+2})$.

(b) Assuming $y^{**}(x; h/4) = \phi(x) + h^{p+2}a_{p+2}(x) + O(h^{p+3})$, show that

$$(20) \qquad y^{***}(x; h/8) := \frac{2^{p+2}y^{**}(x; h/8) - y^{**}(x; h/4)}{2^{p+2} - 1}$$

has a rate of convergence of $O(h^{p+3})$.

(c) The results of using Euler's method (with $h = 1, \frac{1}{2}, \frac{1}{4}, \frac{1}{8}$) to approximate the solution to the initial value problem

$$y' = y, \qquad y(0) = 1,$$

at $x = 1$ are given in Table 1.2, page 22. For Euler's method, the extrapolation procedure applies with $p = 1$. Use the results of Table 1.2 to find an approximation to $e = y(1)$ by computing $y^{***}(1, \frac{1}{8})$. [Hint: Compute $y^*(1; \frac{1}{2})$, $y^*(1; \frac{1}{4})$, and $y^*(1; \frac{1}{8})$; then compute $y^{**}(1; \frac{1}{4})$ and $y^{**}(1; \frac{1}{8})$.]

(d) Table 1.2 also contains Euler's approximation for $y(1)$ when $h = \frac{1}{16}$. Use this additional information to compute the next step in the extrapolation procedure; that is, compute $y^{****}(1, \frac{1}{16})$.

F. STABILITY OF NUMERICAL METHODS

Numerical methods are often tested on simple initial value problems of the form

$$(21) \qquad y' + \lambda y = 0, \qquad y(0) = 1, \qquad (\lambda = \text{constant}),$$

which has the solution $\phi(x) = e^{-\lambda x}$. Notice that, for each $\lambda > 0$, the solution $\phi(x)$ tends to zero as $x \to \infty$. Thus a desirable property for any numerical scheme that generates approximations $y_0, y_1, y_2, y_3, \ldots$ to $\phi(x)$ at the points $0, h, 2h, 3h, \ldots$ is that, for $\lambda > 0$,

$$(22) \qquad y_n \to 0 \quad \text{as} \quad n \to \infty.$$

For single-step linear methods, property (22) is called **absolute stability.**

(a) Show that for $x_n = nh$, Euler's method applied to the initial value problem (21) yields the approximations

$$y_n = (1 - \lambda h)^n, \qquad n = 0, 1, 2, \ldots,$$

and deduce that this method is absolutely stable only when $0 < \lambda h < 2$. (This means that for a given $\lambda > 0$, we must choose the step size h sufficiently small in order for property (22) to hold.) Furthermore, show that for $h > 2/\lambda$, the error $y_n - \phi(x_n)$ grows large exponentially!

(b) Show that for $x_n = nh$, the trapezoid scheme of Section 3.5 applied to problem (21) yields the approximations

$$y_n = \left(\frac{1 - \dfrac{\lambda h}{2}}{1 + \dfrac{\lambda h}{2}} \right)^n, \qquad n = 0, 1, 2, \ldots,$$

and deduce that this scheme is absolutely stable for all $\lambda > 0, h > 0$.

(c) Show that the improved Euler's method applied to problem of (21) is absolutely stable for $0 < \lambda h < 2$.

Multistep Methods When multistep numerical methods are used, instability problems may arise that cannot be circumvented by simply choosing the step size h sufficiently small. This is due to the fact that multistep methods yield "extraneous solutions," which may dominate the calculations. To illustrate what can happen, consider the two-step method

(23) $$y_{n+1} = y_{n-1} + 2hf(x_n, y_n), \qquad n = 1, 2, \ldots,$$

for the equation $y' = f(x, y)$.

(d) Show that for the initial value problem

(24) $$y' + 2y = 0, \qquad y(0) = 1,$$

the recurrence formula (23), with $x_n = nh$, becomes

(25) $$y_{n+1} + 4hy_n - y_{n-1} = 0.$$

Equation (25), which is called a **difference equation,** can be solved by using an approach that is similar to solving linear differential equations with constant coefficients. Namely, we try a solution of the form $y_n = r^n$, where r is a constant to be determined.

(e) Show that substituting $y_n = r^n$ in (25) leads to the "characteristic equation"

$$r^2 + 4hr - 1 = 0,$$

which has roots

$$r_1 = -2h + \sqrt{1 + 4h^2} \quad \text{and} \quad r_2 = -2h - \sqrt{1 + 4h^2}.$$

By analogy with the theory for second order differential equations, it can be shown (see Section 5.5) that a general solution of (25) is

(26) $$y_n = c_1 r_1^n + c_2 r_2^n,$$

where c_1 and c_2 are arbitrary constants. Thus the difference equation (25) has two linearly independent solutions, whereas the differential equation (24) has only one—namely, $\phi(x) = e^{-2x}$.

(f) Show that for each $h > 0$,

$$\lim_{n \to \infty} r_1^n = 0, \quad \text{but} \quad \lim_{n \to \infty} |r_2^n| = \infty.$$

Hence the term r_1^n behaves like the solution $\phi(x_n) = e^{-2x_n}$ as $n \to \infty$. However, the extraneous solution r_2^n grows large without bound.

(g) Applying the scheme of (23) to the initial value problem (24) requires two starting values y_0, y_1. The exact values are $y_0 = 1$, $y_1 = e^{-2h}$. However, regardless of the choice of starting values and the size of h, the term $c_2 r_2^n$ will eventually dominate the full solution to the recurrence equation as x_n increases. Illustrate this instability by taking $y_0 = 1$, $y_1 = e^{-2h}$, and using a calculator or microcomputer to compute $y_2, y_3, \ldots, y_{100}$ from the recurrence formula (25) for (i) $h = 0.5$ (ii) $h = 0.05$.

G. PERIOD DOUBLING AND CHAOS

In the study of dynamical systems the phenomena of *period doubling* and *chaos* are observed. These phenomena can be seen when one uses a numerical scheme to approximate the solution to an initial value problem for a nonlinear differential equation such as the following logistic model for population growth:

(27)
$$\frac{dp}{dt} = 10p(1 - p), \qquad p(0) = 0.1$$

(see Section 3.2).

      (a) Solve the initial value problem (27) and show that $p(t)$ approaches 1 as t approaches infinity.

      (b) Show that using Euler's method (see Sections 1.3 and 3.5) with step size h to approximate the solution to (27) gives

(28)
$$p_{n+1} = (1 + 10h)p_n - (10h)p_n^2, \qquad p_0 = 0.1.$$

      (c) For $h = 0.18$, 0.23, 0.25, and 0.3, show that the first 40 iterations of (28) appear to: converge to 1 when $h = 0.18$; jump between 1.18 and 0.69 when $h = 0.23$; jump between 1.23, 0.54, 1.16, and 0.70 when $h = 0.25$; and display no discernible pattern when $h = 0.3$.

      The transitions from convergence to jumping between two numbers, then four numbers, etc., are called **period doubling.** The phenomenon displayed when $h = 0.3$ is referred to as **chaos.** This transition from period doubling to chaos as h increases is frequently observed in dynamical systems.

      Our concern is with the instabilities of the numerical procedure when h is not chosen small enough. Fortunately, the instability observed for Euler's method—the period doubling and chaos—was immediately recognized because we know that this type of behavior is not expected of a solution to the logistic equation. Consequently, if we had tried Euler's method with $h = 0.23$, 0.25, or 0.3 to numerically solve (27), we would have realized that h was not chosen small enough.

      The situation for the fourth order Runge-Kutta method (see Section 3.6) is more troublesome. It may happen that for a certain choice of h period doubling occurs, but it is also possible that for other choices of h the numerical solution actually converges to a limiting value that is *not* the limiting value for any solution to the logistic equation in (27).

      (d) Approximate the solution to (27) by computing the first 60 iterations of the fourth order Runge-Kutta method using the step size $h = 0.3$. Repeat with $h = 0.325$ and $h = 0.35$. Which values of h (if any) do you feel are giving the "correct" approximation to the solution? Why?

Linear Second Order Equations

4.1 Introduction: The Simple Pendulum

A simple pendulum consists of a mass m suspended by a cable of length l and negligible mass (see Figure 4.1). If the cable is always straight and the mass is free to swing in a vertical plane, find the period of oscillation.

We can use Newton's law to determine the equation that governs the motion of the pendulum. If we can solve this equation, then we can find the period of oscillation.

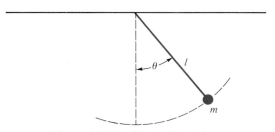

Figure 4.1 The Simple Pendulum

152

Newton's second law states that

(1) $\mathbf{F} = m\mathbf{a},$

where $\mathbf{F}$ is the net (total) force vector applied to the mass m and $\mathbf{a}$ is the acceleration vector of the mass. Since the mass travels along a circle with radius l, we shall see that the net force $\mathbf{F}$ is a vector acting along (tangent to) this circle. Furthermore the acceleration can be expressed as d^2s/dt^2, where s is the arclength that gives the position of the mass on its circular path.

There are two forces acting on the pendulum. One force is the weight of the mass pulling down and the second is the tension pulling back up the cable. In Figure 4.2 let AB denote the cable with A the point where the cable is attached and B the end where the mass m is attached. Let AC denote the vertical line through A and let θ be the angle between AB and AC.

The force exerted by the weight mg of the mass at B has two components: a component $\mathbf{F}_1$ along the straight line through AB and a component $\mathbf{F}_2$ perpendicular to AB and in a downward direction tangent to the path of the pendulum. The magnitude of the force $\mathbf{F}_1$ is just

$$|\mathbf{F}_1| = mg \cos \theta,$$

and the magnitude of the force $\mathbf{F}_2$ is

$$|\mathbf{F}_2| = |mg \sin \theta|.$$

Now the tension $\mathbf{T}$ on the cable is equal in magnitude but opposite in direction to the component $\mathbf{F}_1$. Hence $\mathbf{F}_1$ and $\mathbf{T}$ cancel each other. Therefore, the resulting force acting on the pendulum is the force $\mathbf{F}_2$, which is tangent to the path of the pendulum and toward the vertical AC. Let's agree to take $\theta > 0$ for B to the right of C. Then, relative to θ, we can set

(2) $\mathbf{F}_2 = -mg \sin \theta.$

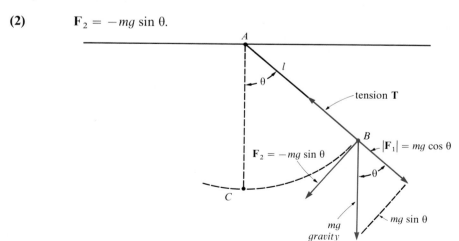

Figure 4.2 Forces on the simple pendulum

Since arclength $s = l\theta$, the acceleration of the mass along the tangent to the path at B is just

(3) $$\frac{d^2s}{dt^2} = l\frac{d^2\theta}{dt^2}.$$

Finally, applying Newton's second law, we have

$$m\frac{d^2s}{dt^2} = \mathbf{F}_2$$

$$ml\frac{d^2\theta}{dt^2} = -mg\sin\theta,$$

which reduces to

(4) $$\frac{d^2\theta}{dt^2} + \frac{g}{l}\sin\theta = 0.$$

Equation (4), which governs the motion of the simple pendulum, is an example of a nonlinear equation. In most cases one cannot find a solution to a nonlinear equation, and even when a solution is found it often cannot be expressed using elementary functions. (Two special cases are discussed in Section 4.11.) In practice, when one encounters a nonlinear equation, it is helpful to study the **linearization** of the equation. This is an approximation of the nonlinear equation by a linear one. In our case, we observe that for θ small, $\sin\theta \approx \theta$. Using this approximation in equation (4), we obtain the linear equation

(5) $$\frac{d^2\theta}{dt^2} + \frac{g}{l}\theta = 0.$$

Because of the difficulty in solving the pendulum equation (4), we focus instead on its linearization (5). For small oscillations of the pendulum we expect that the period as determined from (5) will be a good approximation to the actual period.

To solve equation (5) we observe that we are looking for a function $\theta(t)$ with the property that its second derivative is just a negative constant times itself. Recalling that this property holds for sine and cosine functions, we are led to guess that our desired function has the form

(6) $$\theta(t) = \cos\omega t \quad \text{or} \quad \theta(t) = \sin\omega t,$$

for some suitable choice of the constant ω. Substituting $\theta(t) = \cos\omega t$ into equation (5) gives

$$-\omega^2\cos\omega t + \frac{g}{l}\cos\omega t = 0,$$

or

(7) $$\left(\frac{g}{l} - \omega^2\right)\cos \omega t = 0.$$

Hence, if we choose $\omega = \sqrt{g/l}$, then $\theta(t) = \cos(\sqrt{g/l}\,t)$ is a solution. Similarly, substituting $\theta(t) = \sin \omega t$, we again find $\omega = \sqrt{g/l}$. Therefore, both

(8) $$\theta_1(t) = \cos\left(\sqrt{\frac{g}{l}}\,t\right) \quad \text{and} \quad \theta_2(t) = \sin\left(\sqrt{\frac{g}{l}}\,t\right)$$

are solutions to (5). In fact, because (5) is a *linear* differential equation, a short computation shows that any function of the form

(9) $$\theta(t) = c_1\cos\left(\sqrt{\frac{g}{l}}\,t\right) + c_2\sin\left(\sqrt{\frac{g}{l}}\,t\right),$$

where c_1 and c_2 are arbitrary constants, is also a solution to (5) (see Section 4.2). Moreover (as we shall see in Section 4.3), every solution to (5) must be of the form (9).

If we are given the initial angular displacement $\theta(0)$ and initial angular velocity $\theta'(0)$, then we can determine c_1 and c_2 in equation (9). However, to calculate the period of oscillation, it is not necessary to know c_1 and c_2. It is clear from (9) that since the period of $\cos \omega t$ and $\sin \omega t$ is $2\pi/\omega$, then the period of oscillation P is

(10) $$P = \frac{2\pi}{\sqrt{g/l}} = 2\pi\sqrt{\frac{l}{g}}.$$

This formula provides an approximation to the period of oscillation for the pendulum.

The motion described by equation (9) is called **simple harmonic motion.** We will study this motion in Section 5.1 in connection with mechanical vibrations. The nonlinear equation (4) that governs the motion of the simple pendulum is studied in more detail in Projects D and E. Linearization of nonlinear problems is discussed in Project C.

In this chapter we concentrate on the theory of linear second order equations and methods for solving them.

4.2 *Linear Differential Operators*

Recall that a **second order** differential equation is an equation of the form

(1) $$F\left(x, y, \frac{dy}{dx}, \frac{d^2y}{dx^2}\right) = 0.$$

For example,

(2) $$(x^3 - 1)\frac{d^2y}{dx^2} - x\frac{dy}{dx} + \sin y + e^x = 0$$

is a second order equation. In general, such equations are very difficult to solve. However, for special types of these equations, substitutions are known that transform the original equation into one that can be solved by elementary functions, elliptic functions, Painlevé transcendents, or some other type of special function. A class of second order equations for which an extensive theory exists, and that arises quite frequently in applications, is the class of linear equations.

A **linear** second order equation is an equation that can be written in the form

(3) $$a_2(x)\frac{d^2y}{dx^2} + a_1(x)\frac{dy}{dx} + a_0(x)y = b(x),$$

where $a_0(x)$, $a_1(x)$, $a_2(x)$, and $b(x)$ are continuous functions of x on an interval I. When a_0, a_1, and a_2 are constants, we say that the equation has **constant coefficients;** otherwise it has **variable coefficients.**

For now we are interested only in those linear equations for which $a_2(x) \neq 0$ on I. In this case we can rewrite (3) in the **standard form**

(4) $$\frac{d^2y}{dx^2} + p(x)\frac{dy}{dx} + q(x)y = g(x),$$

where $p(x) := a_1(x)/a_2(x)$, $q(x) := a_0(x)/a_2(x)$, and $g(x) := b(x)/a_2(x)$ are continuous on I.

Associated with equation (4) is the equation

(5) $$\frac{d^2y}{dx^2} + p(x)\frac{dy}{dx} + q(x)y = 0,$$

which is obtained from (4) by replacing $g(x)$ with zero. We say that (4) is a **nonhomogeneous** equation and that (5) is the corresponding **homogeneous** equation. Here the meaning of *homogeneous* is not related to the use of the term for first order equations but is used more in the sense of a homogeneous system of linear equations as studied in linear algebra.

Let's consider the expression on the left-hand side of equation (5), which, for convenience, we now write with prime notation:

(6) $$y''(x) + p(x)y'(x) + q(x)y(x).$$

Given any function y with a continuous second derivative on the interval I, then (6) generates a new function that we will denote by $L[y]$. That is,

(7) $$L[y] := y'' + py' + qy.$$

What we have done is to associate with each function y the function $L[y]$.

The term *function,* in its general sense, means a mapping that associates with each element in its domain a unique element in its range. Thus L can be interpreted as a function that is defined *on a set of functions.* Its domain is the collection of functions with a continuous second derivative; its range consists of continuous functions; and the rule of correspondence is given by (7). To avoid confusion, such mappings are called **operators.** Since L involves differentiation, we refer to L as a **differential operator.**

The image of a function y under the operator L is the function $L[y]$. If we wish to evaluate this image function at some point x, we write $L[y](x)$.

For example, let $p(x) = x$ and $q(x) = x - 1$; then

(8) $L[y](x) = y''(x) + xy'(x) + (x - 1)y(x).$

If $y_1(x) = x^3$, we get

(9) $L[y_1](x) = 6x + x(3x^2) + (x - 1)x^3 = x^4 + 2x^3 + 6x.$

Thus L maps the function x^3 to the function $x^4 + 2x^3 + 6x$. If $y_2(x) = \sin 2x$, then we similarly find from (8)

(10) $L[y_2](x) = -4 \sin 2x + x(2 \cos 2x) + (x - 1) \sin 2x$
$= x \sin 2x - 5 \sin 2x + 2x \cos 2x.$

The differential operator L defined by (7) has two very important properties that are extensions of the familiar facts that "the derivative of the sum is the sum of the derivatives" and "the derivative of a constant times a function is the constant times the derivative of the function."

LINEARITY OF THE DIFFERENTIAL OPERATOR L

Lemma 1.   Let $L[y] := y'' + py' + qy$. If y_1 and y_2 are any two functions with continuous second derivatives on the interval I, and if c is any constant, then

(11) $L[y_1 + y_2] = L[y_1] + L[y_2],$

(12) $L[cy_1] = cL[y_1].$

In (11) and (12) equality is meant in the sense of equal functions on I.

Proof On I we have

$$L[y_1 + y_2] = (y_1 + y_2)'' + p(y_1 + y_2)' + q(y_1 + y_2)$$
$$= (y_1'' + y_2'') + p(y_1' + y_2') + q(y_1 + y_2).$$

On regrouping, this gives

$$L[y_1 + y_2] = (y_1'' + py_1' + qy_1) + (y_2'' + py_2' + qy_2)$$
$$= L[y_1] + L[y_2],$$

which verifies property (11). We leave the proof of property (12) for the exercises (see Problem 28). ∎

An operator that satisfies properties (11) and (12) for any constant c and any functions y_1 and y_2 in its domain is called a **linear operator.** If (11) or (12) fails to hold, the operator is **nonlinear.**

As we have shown in Lemma 1, the operator L defined by (7) is linear. We now give an example of a nonlinear operator.

▶ *Example 1*   Show that the operator T defined by

(13) $T[y](x) := y''(x) + \sin(y(x))$,

where y is any function whose second derivative is continuous for all real x, is nonlinear.

Solution   To see that T is a nonlinear operator, it suffices to show that property (12) is *not always* satisfied. Let's choose $y_1(x) = x$. Since $y_1''(x) \equiv 0$, we have

$$T[cy_1](x) = \sin(cx), \qquad cT[y_1](x) = c \sin x.$$

But, in general, $\sin(cx) \neq c \sin x$ (take, for example, $c = 2$ and $x = \pi/2$), so property (12) is violated. Hence T is a nonlinear operator.   ◀

The linearity of the differential operator L in (7) can be used to prove the following theorem concerning homogeneous equations.

LINEAR COMBINATIONS OF SOLUTIONS

Theorem 1.   Let y_1 and y_2 be solutions to the homogeneous equation

(14) $y'' + py' + qy = 0$.

Then any linear combination $c_1 y_1 + c_2 y_2$ of y_1 and y_2, where c_1 and c_2 are constants, is also a solution to (14).

Proof If we let $L[y] := y'' + py' + qy$, then $L[y_1] = 0$ and $L[y_2] = 0$, since y_1 and y_2 are solutions to (14). Using the linearity of L as expressed in properties (11) and (12), we have

$$L[c_1y_1 + c_2y_2] = L[c_1y_1] + L[c_2y_2]$$
$$= c_1L[y_1] + c_2L[y_2]$$
$$= 0 + 0 = 0.$$

Thus $c_1y_1 + c_2y_2$ is a solution to equation (14). ∎

▶ **Example 2** Given that $y_1(x) = e^{2x} \cos 3x$ and $y_2(x) = e^{2x} \sin 3x$ are solutions to the homogeneous equation

(15) $y'' - 4y' + 13y = 0,$

find a solution to (15) that satisfies the initial conditions

(16) $y(0) = 2$ and $y'(0) = -5.$

Solution As a consequence of Theorem 1, any linear combination

(17) $y(x) = c_1e^{2x} \cos 3x + c_2e^{2x} \sin 3x,$

with c_1 and c_2 arbitrary constants, will be a solution to (15). Thus we try to select c_1 and c_2 so as to satisfy the initial conditions. On differentiating (17) we find

(18) $y'(x) = c_1(2e^{2x} \cos 3x - 3e^{2x} \sin 3x) + c_2(2e^{2x} \sin 3x + 3e^{2x} \cos 3x).$

Substituting (17) and (18) into the initial conditions (16) yields the system of equations

$$c_1 = 2, \qquad 2c_1 + 3c_2 = -5,$$

whose solution is given by $c_1 = 2$, $c_2 = -3$. Hence, the solution to (15) that satisfies conditions (16) is

$$y(x) = 2e^{2x} \cos 3x - 3e^{2x} \sin 3x. \quad ◀$$

As was the case for linear first order equations, the initial value problem for linear second order equations also has a unique solution.

EXISTENCE AND UNIQUENESS OF SOLUTION

Theorem 2. Suppose $p(x)$, $q(x)$, and $g(x)$ are continuous on an interval (a, b) that contains the point x_0. Then, for any choice of the initial values y_0 and y_1, there exists a unique solution $y(x)$ on the whole interval (a, b) to the initial value problem

(19) $$\frac{d^2y}{dx^2} + p(x)\frac{dy}{dx} + q(x)y = g(x);$$

(20) $$y(x_0) = y_0, \qquad y'(x_0) = y_1.$$

The proof of this theorem is more complicated than the proof of Theorem 2 in Section 2.4 for linear first order equations; it is given in Chapter 11 of the extended version of this text, *Fundamentals of Differential Equations and Boundary Value Problems.*

▶ **Example 3**   Determine the largest interval for which Theorem 2 ensures the existence and uniqueness of a solution to the initial value problem

(21) $$\frac{d^2y}{dx^2} + \frac{1}{x-3}\frac{dy}{dx} + \sqrt{x}\, y = \ln x;$$

$$y(1) = 3, \qquad y'(1) = -5.$$

Solution   Here $p(x) = 1/(x-3)$, $q(x) = \sqrt{x}$, $g(x) = \ln x$, and $x_0 = 1$. Now $p(x)$ is continuous for $x \neq 3$, and both $q(x)$ and $g(x)$ are continuous for $x > 0$. Hence the largest open interval containing $x_0 = 1$ for which $p(x)$, $q(x)$, and $g(x)$ are simultaneously continuous is the interval $(0, 3)$. From Theorem 2 we can conclude that the initial value problem (21) has a unique solution on the interval $(0, 3)$.   ◀

Let D denote differentiation with respect to x and D^2 differentiation with respect to x twice. That is, $D := dy/dx$, $D^2y := d^2y/dx^2$. In general, let $D^n y := d^n y/dx^n$. Using this notation,[†] we can express L as defined in (7) by

(22) $$L[y] = D^2y + p\,Dy + qy = (D^2 + p\,D + q)y.$$

For example, if

(23) $$L[y] = y'' + 4y' + 3y,$$

[†] *Historical Footnote:* The symbol D was introduced by the French mathematician F. J. Servois. The notion of a symbolic operation dates from B. Brisson in 1808, and was extended by Augustin Cauchy in 1827.

then we can write L in the form

(24) $\qquad L[y] = D^2 y + 4Dy + 3y = (D^2 + 4D + 3)y.$

When p and q are constants, we can even treat $D^2 + pD + q$ as a polynomial in D and factor it. This is illustrated in the next example.

▶ **Example 4** Show that the operator $D^2 + 4D + 3$ is the same as the product $(D + 1)(D + 3)$, where by *product* we mean the composition of operators.

Solution For an arbitrary twice-differentiable function y, we have

$$
\begin{aligned}
(D + 1)(D + 3)y &= (D + 1)[(D + 3)y] = (D + 1)[y' + 3y] \\
&= D[y' + 3y] + 1[y' + 3y] = (y'' + 3y') + (y' + 3y) \\
&= y'' + 4y' + 3y = (D^2 + 4D + 3)y.
\end{aligned}
$$

Hence $(D + 1)(D + 3) = D^2 + 4D + 3.$ ◄

Further discussion of the algebra of differential operators is given in Problems 32–36.

EXERCISES 4.2

In Problems 1 through 8 determine whether the equation is linear or nonlinear. If it is linear, classify it as being homogeneous or nonhomogeneous, with constant coefficients or with variable coefficients.

1. $\dfrac{d^2 y}{dx^2} - x\dfrac{dy}{dx} + y = 0.$

2. $y'' + (1 - x)y' + xy = \sin x.$

3. $xy'' - yy' = \sin x.$

4. $3\dfrac{d^2 y}{dx^2} + \dfrac{dy}{dx} = 2y.$

5. $t^2 \dfrac{d^2 x}{dt^2} = t\dfrac{dx}{dt} + 4x - \ln t.$

6. $\dfrac{d^2 \theta}{dx^2} = \tan \theta.$

7. $y'' + y = \tan x.$

8. $y'' + 3y' - y^{1/2} = x^2.$

9. Let $L[y](x) = y''(x) - 4y'(x) + 3y(x)$. Compute:

    (a) $L[x^2]$.
    (b) $L[e^{3x}]$.
    (c) $L[e^{rx}]$, $\ r$ a constant.

10. Let $L[y](x) = x^2 y''(x) - 3xy'(x) - 5y(x)$. Compute:

    (a) $L[\cos x]$.
    (b) $L[x^{-1}]$.
    (c) $L[x^r]$, $\ r$ a constant.

11. Show that T defined by

$$T[y](x) := y''(x) - y'(x) + y^2(x),$$

where y is any function whose second derivative is continuous for all real x, is a nonlinear operator.

12. Show that T defined by

$$T[y](x):= y''(x) + \{y'(x)y^2(x)\}^{1/3}$$

is a nonlinear operator.

13. Given that $y_1(x) = e^{2x} \cos x$ and $y_2(x) = e^{2x} \sin x$ are solutions to the homogeneous equation

$$y'' - 4y' + 5y = 0,$$

find solutions to this equation that satisfy the following initial conditions:

(a) $y(0) = 1, \quad y'(0) = -1.$ **(b)** $y(\pi) = 4e^{2\pi}, \quad y'(\pi) = 5e^{2\pi}.$

14. Given that $y_1(x) = e^{2x}$ and $y_2(x) = e^{-x}$ are solutions to the homogeneous equation

$$y'' - y' - 2y = 0,$$

find solutions to this equations that satisfy the following initial conditions:

(a) $y(0) = -1, \quad y'(0) = 4.$ **(b)** $y(0) = 3/2, \quad y'(0) = 0.$

In Problems 15 through 18 use Theorem 2 to discuss the existence and uniqueness of a solution to the differential equation satisfying the initial conditions $y(1) = y_0$, $y'(1) = y_1$, where y_0 and y_1 are real constants.

15. $x^2 y'' + y = \cos x.$ **16.** $x(x-3)y'' + 2xy' - y = x^2.$

17. $e^x y'' - \dfrac{y'}{x-3} + y = \ln x.$ **18.** $(1 + x^2)y'' + xy' - y = \tan x.$

In Problems 19 through 22 determine whether Theorem 2 applies. If it applies, then discuss what conclusions can be drawn. If it does not apply, explain why.

19. $y'' + yy' = x^2 - 1; \qquad y(0) = 1, \qquad y'(0) = -1.$

20. $x^2 y'' + xy' + y = \cos x; \qquad y(0) = 1, \qquad y'(0) = 0.$

21. $(1 - x)y'' + xy' - 2y = \sin x; \qquad y(0) = 1, \qquad y'(0) = 1.$

22. $y'' + xy' - x^2 y = 0; \qquad y(0) = 0, \qquad y(1) = 0.$

In Problems 23 through 26 express the given operator L using the differential operator D.

23. $L[y]:= y'' - 3y' + 2y.$ **24.** $L[y]:= x^2 y'' - xy' + y.$

25. $L[y]:= y'' + xy.$ **26.** $L[y]:= 2y'' + y' - y.$

27. Let L be defined by $L[y]:= (D^2 - xD + 2)y$. Compute:

(a) $L[x^2].$ **(b)** $L[\cos x].$

28. Complete the proof of Lemma 1 by verifying that the differential operator L defined by (7) satisfies property (12).

29. Show that the integro-differential operator L defined by

$$L[y](x) := \int_0^1 (x - t)^2 y(t)\, dt + x^2 y'(x),$$

for any function y having a continuous derivative on $[0, 1]$, is linear; that is, that L satisfies properties (11) and (12).

30. Boundary Value Problems. When the values of a solution to a differential equation are specified at two different points, these conditions are called **boundary conditions.** (In contrast, initial conditions specify the values of a function and its derivative at the same point.) Given that every solution to

(25) $y'' + y = 0$

is of the form

$$y(x) = c_1 \cos x + c_2 \sin x,$$

where c_1 and c_2 are arbitrary constants, show that:

(a) there is a unique solution to (25) that satisfies the boundary conditions $y(0) = 2$ and $y(\pi/2) = 0$;
(b) there is no solution to (25) that satisfies $y(0) = 2$ and $y(\pi) = 0$;
(c) there are infinitely many solutions to (25) that satisfy $y(0) = 2$ and $y(\pi) = -2$.

31. Let $y = \phi(x)$ be the solution to the initial value problem

$$y'' + x^2 y' + e^x y = x - 1; \qquad y(0) = 1, \qquad y'(0) = -1.$$

Assuming that the differential equation can be repeatedly differentiated, determine $\phi''(0)$, $\phi'''(0)$, and $\phi^{(4)}(0)$.

32. Differential Operators with Constant Coefficients. Let A and B represent two linear differential operators with constant coefficients; that is,

$$A := a_2 D^2 + a_1 D + a_0 \quad \text{and} \quad B := b_2 D^2 + b_1 D + b_0,$$

where $a_0, a_1, a_2, b_0, b_1,$ and b_2 are constants. We define the **sum** $A + B$ by

$$(A + B)[y] := A[y] + B[y]$$

and the **product** AB by

$$(AB)[y] := A[B[y]].$$

Notice that the product AB is the composite operator obtained by applying first B, then A. We say two operators A and B are **equal** if $A[y] = B[y]$ for all functions y with the necessary derivatives. With these definitions, verify the following properties.

(a) Commutative laws: $A + B = B + A,$ $AB = BA.$
(b) Associative laws: $(A + B) + C = A + (B + C),$ $(AB)C = A(BC).$
(c) Distributive law: $A(B + C) = AB + AC.$

33. Let $A = (D - 1)$, $B = (D + 2)$, and $y = x^3$. Compute:

(a) $A[y]$.   (b) $B[A[y]]$.   (c) $B[y]$.
(d) $A[B[y]]$.   (e) AB.   (f) $(AB)[y]$.

34. Verify, as in Example 4, each of the following operator equations:

(a) $(D - 1)(D + 6) = D^2 + 5D - 6.$
(b) $(D + 1)(2D^2 - 1) = 2D^3 + 2D^2 - D - 1.$

35. Factor the following differential operators:

(a) $D^2 + 3D - 4.$ (b) $D^2 + D - 6.$
(c) $2D^2 + 9D - 5.$ (d) $D^2 - 2.$

36. Let $A = (xD - 1)$ and $B = (D + 1)$. Show for the function $y = x$ that $(AB)[y] \neq (BA)[y]$. Hence, for operators with **variable** coefficients, the commutative law need not hold.

4.3 Fundamental Solutions of Homogeneous Equations

In this section we discuss those properties of homogeneous equations that help us obtain *all* solutions of these equations. First, let's examine the particular equation

$$(1) \qquad L[y] = \frac{d^2y}{dx^2} - y = 0.$$

It is easy to verify that the two functions $y_1 = e^x$ and $y_2 = e^{-x}$ are solutions to this homogeneous equation. Furthermore, since L is linear, we know from Theorem 1 in Section 4.2 that $c_1 e^x + c_2 e^{-x}$ is also a solution, for any choice of constants c_1 and c_2. The question is, can all solutions of (1) be represented by

$$c_1 e^x + c_2 e^{-x},$$

with appropriate choices for c_1 and c_2? As we now show, the answer lies in applying the existence and uniqueness theorem (Theorem 2, page 160).

Let $\phi(x)$ be a solution to (1) and let x_0 be a fixed real number. If we can choose c_1 and c_2 so that

$$(2) \qquad c_1 e^{x_0} + c_2 e^{-x_0} = \phi(x_0),$$

$$(3) \qquad c_1 e^{x_0} - c_2 e^{-x_0} = \phi'(x_0),$$

then, since $\phi(x)$ and $c_1 e^x + c_2 e^{-x}$ satisfy the same initial conditions at x_0, the uniqueness conclusion of Theorem 2 guarantees that $\phi(x) = c_1 e^x + c_2 e^{-x}$ for all x.

To solve the system (2)–(3) for c_1, we add the two equations and then divide by $2e^{x_0}$ to obtain

(4) $$c_1 = \frac{\phi(x_0) + \phi'(x_0)}{2e^{x_0}}.$$

Subtracting (3) from (2) and dividing by $2e^{-x_0}$ gives

(5) $$c_2 = \frac{\phi(x_0) - \phi'(x_0)}{2e^{-x_0}}.$$

Notice that since e^{x_0} and e^{-x_0} are never zero, we can always carry out the above procedure for finding c_1 and c_2. Thus, by uniqueness, we have

$$\phi(x) = c_1 e^x + c_2 e^{-x}$$

for all x, where c_1 and c_2 are given in (4) and (5).

We have shown that every solution of (1) can be expressed as a linear combination of two particular solutions of (1). A similar result holds for general linear homogeneous equations, provided that the two solutions y_1 and y_2 satisfy a certain property.

REPRESENTATION OF SOLUTIONS (HOMOGENEOUS CASE)

Theorem 3.   Let y_1 and y_2 denote two solutions on (a, b) of

(6) $$y'' + p(x)y' + q(x)y = 0,$$

where p and q are continuous on (a, b). If at some point x_0 in (a, b) these solutions satisfy

(7) $$y_1(x_0)y_2'(x_0) - y_1'(x_0)y_2(x_0) \neq 0,$$

then every solution of (6) on (a, b) can be expressed in the form

(8) $$y(x) = c_1 y_1(x) + c_2 y_2(x),$$

where c_1 and c_2 are constants.

The linear combination of y_1 and y_2 in (8), written with arbitrary constants c_1 and c_2, is referred to as a **general solution** to (6).

Proof of Theorem 3   Let $\phi(x)$ be any solution to (6). As before, we consider the system

(9) $c_1 y_1(x_0) + c_2 y_2(x_0) = \phi(x_0),$

(10) $c_1 y_1'(x_0) + c_2 y_2'(x_0) = \phi'(x_0),$

where x_0 is a point at which (7) holds. To solve for c_1, multiply (9) by $y_2'(x_0)$, multiply (10) by $y_2(x_0)$, and subtract to obtain

$$c_1[y_1(x_0)y_2'(x_0) - y_1'(x_0)y_2(x_0)] = \phi(x_0)y_2'(x_0) - \phi'(x_0)y_2(x_0).$$

Because of condition (7), the expression in brackets is not zero. Hence,

$$c_1 = \frac{\phi(x_0)y_2'(x_0) - \phi'(x_0)y_2(x_0)}{y_1(x_0)y_2'(x_0) - y_1'(x_0)y_2(x_0)}.$$

Similarly, we find

$$c_2 = \frac{\phi'(x_0)y_1(x_0) - \phi(x_0)y_1'(x_0)}{y_1(x_0)y_2'(x_0) - y_1'(x_0)y_2(x_0)}.$$

With these choices for c_1 and c_2, the functions $c_1 y_1 + c_2 y_2$ and ϕ are solutions to (6) that satisfy the same initial conditions. Hence they must be the same function on (a, b), according to the uniqueness result in Theorem 2. ∎∎∎

Since the expression on the left-hand side of (7) plays an important role in the theory, we adopt the following terminology.

WRONSKIAN

Definition 1.   For any two differentiable functions y_1 and y_2, the function

(11) $W[y_1, y_2](x) := y_1(x)y_2'(x) - y_1'(x)y_2(x)$

is called the **Wronskian** of y_1 and y_2.[†]

A convenient way of writing the Wronskian $W[y_1, y_2]$, which will generalize to higher order linear equations, is in terms of the determinant

(12) $W[y_1, y_2](x) = \begin{vmatrix} y_1(x) & y_2(x) \\ y_1'(x) & y_2'(x) \end{vmatrix}.$

[†] *Historical Footnote:* The Wronskian was named after the Polish mathematician H. Wronski (1778–1853).

FUNDAMENTAL SOLUTION SET

Definition 2. A pair of solutions $\{y_1, y_2\}$ of $y'' + py' + qy = 0$ on (a, b) is called a **fundamental solution set** if

(13) $\qquad W[y_1, y_2](x_0) \neq 0$

at some x_0 in (a, b).[†]

For example, the solutions $y_1 = e^x$, $y_2 = e^{-x}$ of the differential equation (1) form a fundamental solution set for this equation on $(-\infty, \infty)$, since

$$W[y_1, y_2](x) = e^x(-e^{-x}) - e^x e^{-x} = -2 \neq 0$$

for any x.

Using the terminology of Definition 2, Theorem 3 can be summarized as follows.

PROCEDURE FOR SOLVING HOMOGENEOUS EQUATIONS

To determine all solutions to $y'' + py' + qy = 0$:

(a) Find two solutions y_1, y_2 that form a fundamental solution set.

(b) A general solution is

(14) $\qquad y(x) = c_1 y_1(x) + c_2 y_2(x),$

where c_1 and c_2 are arbitrary constants.

▶ *Example 1* Given that $y_1(x) = \cos 3x$ and $y_2(x) = \sin 3x$ are solutions to

(15) $\qquad y'' + 9y = 0$

on $(-\infty, \infty)$, find a general solution to (15).

Solution First we verify that $\{\cos 3x, \sin 3x\}$ is a fundamental solution set. Since we are given that both $y_1(x) = \cos 3x$ and $y_2(x) = \sin 3x$ are solutions to (15) (the reader can quickly verify this), we need show only that $W[y_1, y_2](x) \neq 0$ for some x in $(-\infty, \infty)$.

[†] *Historical Footnote:* Lazarus Fuchs introduced the terminology *fundamental system* in 1866.

Substituting y_1 and y_2 into formula (11) yields

$$W[y_1, y_2](x) = (\cos 3x)(3\cos 3x) - (-3\sin 3x)(\sin 3x)$$

$$= 3(\cos^2 3x + \sin^2 3x)$$

$$= 3 \neq 0.$$

Thus $\{\cos 3x, \sin 3x\}$ forms a fundamental solution set, and a general solution to (15) is

$$y(x) = c_1 \cos 3x + c_2 \sin 3x. \blacktriangleleft$$

It is easy to see that a fundamental solution set always exists for equation (6). Indeed, let $x_0 \in (a, b)$ and take $y_1(x)$ and $y_2(x)$ to be the solutions to (6) that satisfy the initial conditions

$$y_1(x_0) = 1, \qquad y_2(x_0) = 0,$$

$$y_1'(x_0) = 0, \qquad y_2'(x_0) = 1.$$

Then $W[y_1, y_2](x_0) = 1 \neq 0$, and so $\{y_1, y_2\}$ is a fundamental solution set.

There is another method that can be used to determine quickly whether a pair of solutions form a fundamental solution set. To describe this test, we need to recall some basic facts about **vectors** (directed line segments) in the plane.

A planar vector is prescribed by an ordered pair of real numbers, say (u_1, u_2). Recall that vector addition is done componentwise as is scalar multiplication; that is,

$$(u_1, u_2) + (v_1, v_2) = (u_1 + v_1, u_2 + v_2), \qquad c(u_1, u_2) = (cu_1, cu_2).$$

Two vectors are parallel (point in the same or opposite directions) if and only if one vector is a scalar multiple of the other. This is equivalent to saying that there exist two constants c_1, c_2 *not both zero* such that

$$c_1(u_1, u_2) + c_2(v_1, v_2) = (0, 0).$$

Parallel vectors are said to be **linearly dependent,** whereas two nonparallel vectors are **linearly independent.**

These notions also apply to functions.

LINEAR DEPENDENCE OF FUNCTIONS

Definition 3. Two functions y_1 and y_2 are said to be **linearly dependent on an interval *I*** if there exist constants c_1 and c_2, not both zero, such that

$$c_1 y_1(x) + c_2 y_2(x) = 0$$

for all x in I. If two functions are not linearly dependent, they are said to be **linearly independent.**

The preceding definition extends in a natural way to sets of more than two functions: this is studied in Chapter 6. **In the case of just two functions, linear dependence on I is equivalent to one function being a constant multiple of the other function on I** (see Problem 14).

▶ *Example 2*   Determine whether the following pairs of functions y_1 and y_2 are linearly dependent on $(-5, 5)$:

(a) $y_1(x) = e^{3x}$, $y_2(x) = x + 1$.

(b) $y_1(x) = \sin 2x$, $y_2(x) = \cos x \sin x$.

Solution   (a) A glance at the functions $y_1(x) = e^{3x}$ and $y_2(x) = x + 1$ indicates that neither is a constant multiple of the other. Indeed, if a constant c exists such that

$$e^{3x} = c(x + 1) \quad \text{for all } x \text{ in } (-5, 5),$$

then we arrive at a contradiction by setting $x = 0$ and $x = 1$:

$$e^0 = c(0 + 1) \Rightarrow c = 1,$$
$$e^3 = c(1 + 1) \Rightarrow c = e^3/2 \neq 1.$$

Hence e^{3x} and $x + 1$ are linearly independent.

(b) Since $y_1(x) = \sin 2x = 2 \sin x \cos x$, we see that $y_1(x) = 2y_2(x)$. Hence y_1 and y_2 are linearly dependent on $(-5, 5)$. ◀

CONDITION FOR LINEAR DEPENDENCE OF SOLUTIONS

Theorem 4.   Let y_1, y_2 be solutions to $y'' + py' + qy = 0$ on (a, b), and let $x_0 \in (a, b)$. Then y_1 and y_2 are linearly dependent on (a, b) if and only if the initial vectors[†]

$$\begin{bmatrix} y_1(x_0) \\ y_1'(x_0) \end{bmatrix} \quad \text{and} \quad \begin{bmatrix} y_2(x_0) \\ y_2'(x_0) \end{bmatrix}$$

are linearly dependent.

Remark   Although not explicitly mentioned, we assume in Theorem 4 and in subsequent results that the coefficient functions p and q are continuous.

[†] Here and in later discussions we represent planar vectors in column rather than row form.

Proof of Theorem 4   ($\Rightarrow$) Assume that y_1 and y_2 are linearly dependent. Then one of these functions is a constant multiple of the other, say $y_1 = cy_2$ on (a, b). Thus $y_1' = cy_2'$, and we have

$$\begin{bmatrix} y_1(x_0) \\ y_1'(x_0) \end{bmatrix} = \begin{bmatrix} cy_2(x_0) \\ cy_2'(x_0) \end{bmatrix} = c\begin{bmatrix} y_2(x_0) \\ y_2'(x_0) \end{bmatrix}.$$

Since one initial vector is a constant multiple of the other, they are linearly dependent.
  ($\Leftarrow$) Assume now that the initial vectors are linearly dependent, say

$$\begin{bmatrix} y_1(x_0) \\ y_1'(x_0) \end{bmatrix} = c\begin{bmatrix} y_2(x_0) \\ y_2'(x_0) \end{bmatrix}.$$

This implies that the functions y_1 and cy_2 satisfy the same initial conditions; that is,

$$y_1(x_0) = cy_2(x_0) \quad \text{and} \quad y_1'(x_0) = cy_2'(x_0).$$

Since y_1 and cy_2 are solutions to the same initial value problem, by the uniqueness property they must be the same function on (a, b). Thus y_1 is a constant multiple of y_2 on (a, b); that is, y_1 and y_2 are linearly dependent on (a, b). ∎

  A simple algebraic test for the linear independence of two column vectors

(16) $$\begin{bmatrix} u_1 \\ u_2 \end{bmatrix} \quad \text{and} \quad \begin{bmatrix} v_1 \\ v_2 \end{bmatrix}$$

is to compute the determinant

$$\begin{vmatrix} u_1 & v_1 \\ u_2 & v_2 \end{vmatrix} = u_1v_2 - v_1u_2.$$

The vectors (16) are linearly independent if and only if this determinant is not zero. Using this fact, we obtain the following consequence of Theorem 4.

FUNDAMENTAL SETS AND LINEAR INDEPENDENCE

Corollary 1.   Let y_1, y_2 be solutions to $y'' + py' + qy = 0$ on (a, b). Then $\{y_1, y_2\}$ is a fundamental solution set on (a, b) if and only if the functions y_1 and y_2 are linearly independent on (a, b).

Proof   Let $x_0 \in (a, b)$. Theorem 4, restated in terms of linear *in*dependence, asserts that the two solutions y_1 and y_2 are linearly independent on (a, b) if and only if the initial vectors

$$\begin{bmatrix} y_1(x_0) \\ y_1'(x_0) \end{bmatrix} \quad \text{and} \quad \begin{bmatrix} y_2(x_0) \\ y_2'(x_0) \end{bmatrix}$$

are linearly independent. By the determinant test, this last condition is equivalent to

$$W[y_1, y_2](x_0) = \begin{vmatrix} y_1(x_0) & y_2(x_0) \\ y_1'(x_0) & y_2'(x_0) \end{vmatrix} \neq 0,$$

which, by Definition 2, is the same as saying that $\{y_1, y_2\}$ is a fundamental solution set.   ▮▮▮

Notice that in the proof of Corollary 1, the point x_0 was taken *arbitrarily* in (a, b). In other words, if x_1 is another point in (a, b), then the linear independence of two solutions y_1 and y_2 on (a, b) is also equivalent to the condition $W[y_1, y_2](x_1) \neq 0$. Thus, whenever linear independence on (a, b) holds for these solutions, we must have $W[y_1, y_2](x) \neq 0$ for *every* x in (a, b). On the other hand, if y_1 and y_2 are linearly dependent on (a, b), then $W[y_1, y_2](x) \equiv 0$ on (a, b). We summarize these observations in the following result.

A PROPERTY OF THE WRONSKIAN OF SOLUTIONS

Corollary 2.   Let y_1, y_2 be solutions to $y'' + py' + qy = 0$ on (a, b). Then the Wronskian $W[y_1, y_2](x)$ of the two solutions is either identically zero or never zero on (a, b). Furthermore, the Wronskian of two **solutions** is identically zero if and only if the solutions are linearly dependent.

▶ **Example 3**   Show that $y_1(x) = x^{-1}$ and $y_2(x) = x^3$ are solutions to

(17) $x^2 y'' - xy' - 3y = 0$

on the interval $(0, \infty)$ and give a general solution.

Solution   The verification that y_1 and y_2 are solutions to (17) is straightforward. Substituting $y = x^{-1}$ and $y = x^3$ in (17) gives, respectively, the identities

$$x^2(2x^{-3}) - x(-x^{-2}) - 3(x^{-1}) = 0 \quad \text{and} \quad x^2(6x) - x(3x^2) - 3(x^3) = 0.$$

Furthermore, the solution functions x^{-1} and x^3 are linearly independent on $(0, \infty)$ (neither is a constant multiple of the other on $(0, \infty)$). Hence, by Corollary 1, $\{x^{-1}, x^3\}$ is a fundamental solution set on $(0, \infty)$, and so a general solution is

$$y(x) = c_1 x^{-1} + c_2 x^3. \quad \blacktriangleleft$$

▶ **Example 4** Can the function $w(x) = 3(x - 1)^2$ be the Wronskian on $(0, 2)$ for some homogeneous linear second order equation (with p and q continuous)?

Solution Since $w(x) = 0$ only for $x = 1$, then by Corollary 2, $w(x)$ cannot be such a Wronskian on any open interval containing $x = 1$. ◀

If two differentiable functions are linearly independent on I, can their Wronskian be identically zero? Surprisingly, the answer is yes. The reader can verify (see Problem 18) that the Wronskian of the functions $y_1(x) = x^3$ and $y_2(x) = |x^3|$ is identically zero on $(-\infty, \infty)$; yet these functions are certainly linearly independent on $(-\infty, \infty)$ because one is not a constant multiple of the other for all x in $(-\infty, \infty)$. Does this example contradict Corollary 2? No, because Corollary 2 refers only to functions $y_1(x)$ and $y_2(x)$ that are solutions to the **same** homogeneous linear second order differential equation. What we can conclude from Corollary 2 is that $y_1(x) = x^3$ and $y_2(x) = |x^3|$ cannot be solutions to the same equation on $(-\infty, \infty)$.

A useful representation of the Wronskian, known as **Abel's identity,**[†] is given in the next theorem. We leave its proof as an exercise (see Problem 20).

ABEL'S IDENTITY

Theorem 5. Let y_1, y_2 be solutions to $y'' + py' + qy = 0$ on (a, b) and let $x_0 \in (a, b)$. Then

(18) $$W[y_1, y_2](x) = C \exp\left(-\int_{x_0}^{x} p(t)\, dt \right)$$

where C is a constant that depends upon y_1 and y_2.

The properties of the Wronskian and linear independence can be extended to sets of n functions $y_1(x), \ldots, y_n(x)$. This is done in Chapter 6, where we consider higher order linear equations. Although the proofs in Chapter 6 are a bit more complicated, the ideas are essentially the same as in the case of linear second order equations.

In Sections 4.5 and 4.6 we concentrate on methods for actually finding a pair of functions that form a fundamental solution set.

[†] *Historical Footnote:* Abel's identity was derived by Niels Abel in 1827.

EXERCISES 4.3

In Problems 1 through 6 determine whether the functions y_1 and y_2 are linearly dependent on $(0, 1)$. Also compute the Wronskian $W[y_1, y_2](x)$.

1. $y_1(x) = e^{3x}$, $y_2(x) = e^{-4x}$.

2. $y_1(x) = e^{-x} \cos 2x$, $y_2(x) = e^{-x} \sin 2x$.

3. $y_1(x) = xe^{2x}$, $y_2(x) = e^{2x}$.

4. $y_1(x) = x^2 \cos(\ln x)$, $y_2(x) = x^2 \sin(\ln x)$.

5. $y_1(x) = \sin^2 x + \cos^2 x$, $y_2(x) = 3$.

6. $y_1(x) = 0$, $y_2(x) = e^x$.

In Problems 7 through 12: (a) verify that the functions y_1 and y_2 are linearly independent solutions of the given differential equation; (b) find a general solution to the given differential equation; (c) find the solution that satisfies the given initial conditions.

7. $y'' - 5y' + 6y = 0$; $y_1(x) = e^{2x}$, $y_2(x) = e^{3x}$; $y(0) = -1$, $y'(0) = -4$.

8. $y'' - 5y' = 0$; $y_1(x) = 2$, $y_2(x) = e^{5x}$; $y(0) = 2$, $y'(0) = 5$.

9. $y'' - 2y' + 5y = 0$; $y_1(x) = e^x \cos 2x$, $y_2(x) = e^x \sin 2x$; $y(0) = 2$, $y'(0) = 0$.

10. $y'' - y = 0$; $y_1(x) = \cosh x$, $y_2(x) = \sinh x$; $y(0) = 1$, $y'(0) = -1$.

11. $x^2 y'' - 2y = 0$; $y_1(x) = x^2$, $y_2(x) = x^{-1}$; $y(1) = -2$, $y'(1) = -7$.

12. $xy'' - (x + 2)y' + 2y = 0$; $y_1(x) = e^x$, $y_2(x) = x^2 + 2x + 2$; $y(1) = 0$, $y'(1) = 1$.

13. Consider the differential equation

(19) $y'' + 5y' - 6y = 0$.

(a) Show that $S_1 := \{e^x, e^x - e^{-6x}\}$ is a fundamental solution set for (19).

(b) Show that $S_2 := \{e^x, 3e^x + e^{-6x}\}$ is another fundamental solution set for (19).

(c) Verify that $\phi(x) = e^{-6x}$ is a solution to (19); then express ϕ as a linear combination of functions in S_1. Likewise, express ϕ as a linear combination of functions in S_2.

14. Prove that two functions are linearly dependent on an interval I if and only if one is a constant times the other on I.

15. Determine whether the following functions can be the Wronskians on $(-1, 1)$ for some homogeneous linear second order equation (with p and q continuous).

(a) $w(x) = -3e^{-2x}$.

(b) $w(x) = x^2$.

(c) $w(x) = (x + 1)^{-1}$.

(d) $w(x) \equiv 0$.

16. Show that two column vectors $\begin{bmatrix} u_1 \\ u_2 \end{bmatrix}$ and $\begin{bmatrix} v_1 \\ v_2 \end{bmatrix}$ are linearly independent if and only if the determinant

$$\begin{vmatrix} u_1 & v_1 \\ u_2 & v_2 \end{vmatrix} \neq 0.$$

17. Let y_1 and y_2 be two functions defined on $(-\infty, \infty)$:

(a) (True or False) If y_1 and y_2 are linearly dependent on the interval $[a, b]$, then y_1 and y_2 are linearly dependent on the smaller interval $[c, d] \subset [a, b]$.

(b) (True or False) If y_1 and y_2 are linearly dependent on the interval $[a, b]$, then y_1 and y_2 are linearly dependent on the larger interval $[C, D] \supset [a, b]$.

18. Let $y_1(x) = x^3$ and $y_2(x) = |x^3|$. Are y_1 and y_2 linearly independent on the interval:

   (a) $[0, \infty)$?   **(b)** $(-\infty, 0]$?   **(c)** $(-\infty, \infty)$?
   (d) Compute the Wronskian $W[y_1, y_2](x)$ on the interval $(-\infty, \infty)$.

19. Use Abel's identity (18) in Theorem 5 to determine (up to a constant multiple) the Wronskian of two solutions on $(0, \infty)$ to

$$xy'' + (x - 1)y' + 3y = 0.$$

20. Prove Theorem 5 by completing the following steps:

   (a) Show that the Wronskian W satisfies the equation $W' + p(x)W = 0$.
   (b) Solve the linear equation in part (a) using an appropriate integrating factor.

21. Prove that if y_1 and y_2 are linearly independent solutions of $y'' + py' + qy = 0$ on (a, b), then they cannot both be zero at the same point x_0 in (a, b).

22. Show that if y_1 and y_2 are linearly independent solutions of $y'' + py' + qy = 0$ on (a, b), then they cannot both have an extremum at the same point x_0 in (a, b).

23. Normal Form.   Show that the substitution $y(x) = u(x)v(x)$, where

$$v(x) := \exp\left(-\frac{1}{2}\int p(x)\,dx\right),$$

transforms the differential equation

$$y'' + p(x)y' + q(x)y = 0,$$

into an equation of the form

$$u'' + f(x)u = 0.$$

The last equation is called the **normal form** of a homogeneous linear second order equation.

★ 4.4 Reduction of Order

As we found in the previous section, a general solution to a linear second order homogeneous equation is given by a linear combination of two linearly independent solutions. But what can be done if a method for solving such an equation produces (apart from a multiplicative constant) only *one* nontrivial solution? It seems reasonable that knowing one solution should help us to find a second linearly independent solution. This is, in fact, the case. We can use the known solution to reduce a homogeneous linear second order equation to a separable first order equation—a type that we discussed in Section 2.2. This method is referred to as **reduction of order.**[†]

Let f be a nontrivial solution to the homogeneous equation

(1) $y'' + p(x)y' + q(x)y = 0.$

Since we want a second solution that is linearly independent of f, let's try to find a solution of the form

(2) $y(x) = v(x)f(x),$

where the nonconstant function v is to be determined. Differentiating the product vf, we have

$$y' = vf' + v'f,$$
$$y'' = vf'' + 2v'f' + v''f.$$

Substituting these expressions into (1) yields

$$(vf'' + 2v'f' + v''f) + p(vf' + v'f) + qvf = 0,$$

or, on regrouping,

(3) $(f'' + pf' + qf)v + fv'' + (2f' + pf)v' = 0.$

Since f is a solution to (1), the factor in front of v is zero. Thus (3) reduces to

(4) $fv'' + (2f' + pf)v' = 0.$

This is a separable first order equation in the variable $w = v'$. Indeed, on substituting w for v' in (4), we have

$$fw' + (2f' + pf)w = 0.$$

Then, separating the variables and integrating gives

$$\int \frac{dw}{w} = -2 \int \frac{f'}{f}\, dx - \int p\, dx,$$
$$\ln w = \ln(f^{-2}) - \int p\, dx,$$
$$w = f^{-2} e^{-\int p\, dx}.$$

[†] *Historical Footnote:* The method for the reduction of order is credited to Jean le Rond d'Alembert circa 1760.

If we replace w by v' in the last equation and integrate, we find

(5) $$v = \int \frac{e^{-\int p(x)\,dx}}{[f(x)]^2}\,dx.$$

Here a second linearly independent solution is $y(x) = v(x)f(x)$, where $v(x)$ is given in equation (5).

The above discussion can be summarized as follows.

REDUCTION OF ORDER PROCEDURES

Given a nontrivial solution $f(x)$ to $y'' + py' + qy = 0$, a second linearly independent solution $y(x)$ can be determined in either of the following ways.

1. Set $y(x) = v(x)f(x)$ and substitute for y, y', and y'' in the given equation. This gives a separable equation for v'. Solve for v' and integrate v' to obtain v. The desired second solution is given by $v(x)f(x)$.

2. The solution $y(x)$ can also be obtained by plugging $p(x)$ and $f(x)$ directly into the **reduction of order formula:**

(6) $$y(x) = f(x) \int \frac{e^{-\int p(x)\,dx}}{[f(x)]^2}\,dx.$$

Caution: If the equation is $a_2(x)y'' + a_1(x)y' + a_0(x)y = 0$, then it must first be put in the form $y'' + p(x)y' + q(x)y = 0$.

The first procedure is more work, but we only have to remember the substitution $y = v(x)f(x)$. The second procedure is much easier, but we must remember the reduction of order formula. In the next example we illustrate both of these methods.

▶ **Example 1** Given that $f(x) = e^x$ is a solution to

(7) $$y'' - 2y' + y = 0,$$

determine a second linearly independent solution.

Solution Let $y = v(x)f(x) = ve^x$. Then

$$y' = ve^x + v'e^x,$$
$$y'' = ve^x + 2v'e^x + v''e^x.$$

Substituting these representations into (7) gives

$$(ve^x + 2v'e^x + v''e^x) - 2(ve^x + v'e^x) + ve^x = 0,$$

which simplifies to $v'' = 0$. Hence $v = c_1 x + c_2$. Since we want y to be linearly independent of e^x, we must take $c_1 \neq 0$; so let $c_1 = 1$ and $c_2 = 0$. Then a second linearly independent solution is

$$y = vf = xe^x.$$

The alternative approach is to use the reduction of order formula given by equation (6). In this example $p(x) = -2$ and $f(x) = e^x$. Hence

$$-\int p(x)\, dx = \int 2\, dx = 2x + c.$$

We will take $c = 0$. Now

$$y(x) = f(x) \int \frac{e^{-\int p(x)\, dx}}{[f(x)]^2}\, dx = e^x \int \frac{e^{2x}}{(e^x)^2}\, dx$$

$$= e^x \int dx = e^x(x + C).$$

Again, we set $C = 0$. This gives us the same linearly independent solution, $y = xe^x$. ◄

► **Example 2** Given that $f(x) = x$ is a solution to

(8) $\qquad y'' - 2xy' + 2y = 0,$

determine a second linearly independent solution.

Solution Here $p(x) = -2x$, and so

$$-\int p(x)\, dx = \int 2x\, dx = x^2,$$

where we have taken the constant of integration to be zero. The reduction of order formula in (6) gives

(9) $\qquad y(x) = x \int \frac{e^{x^2}}{x^2}\, dx$

as a second linearly independent solution. Unfortunately, we are not able to evaluate the integral in (9) in terms of elementary functions. One alternative is to write $y(x)$ in terms of a definite integral, say,

$$y(x) = x \int_1^x \frac{e^{t^2}}{t^2} \, dt.$$

Then $y(x)$ can be approximated for various values of x by using a numerical integration method such as Simpson's rule (see Problem 17). Another approach is to obtain a **power series expansion** for the solution in (9). This can be derived as follows.

Recall that the Maclaurin expansion for e^x is

$$e^x = 1 + x + \frac{x^2}{2!} + \frac{x^3}{3!} + \cdots + \frac{x^n}{n!} + \cdots.$$

Hence, the expansion for e^{x^2} is just

$$e^{x^2} = 1 + x^2 + \frac{x^4}{2!} + \frac{x^6}{3!} + \cdots + \frac{x^{2n}}{n!} + \cdots.$$

Substituting this series for e^{x^2} into (9) and assuming we can integrate term by term, we obtain

$$y(x) = x \int x^{-2} \left\{ 1 + x^2 + \frac{x^4}{2} + \cdots + \frac{x^{2n}}{n!} + \cdots \right\} dx$$

$$= x \int \left\{ x^{-2} + 1 + \frac{x^2}{2} + \cdots + \frac{x^{2n-2}}{n!} + \cdots \right\} dx$$

$$= x \left\{ -x^{-1} + x + \frac{x^3}{6} + \cdots + \frac{x^{2n-1}}{n!(2n-1)} + \cdots \right\},$$

where we have taken the constant of integration to be zero. Hence

$$(10) \qquad y(x) = -1 + x^2 + \frac{x^4}{6} + \cdots + \frac{x^{2n}}{n!(2n-1)} + \cdots. \ \blacktriangleleft$$

In the last example we did not bother to justify the use of term-by-term integration to obtain equation (10). Such questions are addressed in Chapter 8.

EXERCISES 4.4

In Problems 1 through 6 a differential equation and a nontrivial solution $f(x)$ are given. Find a second linearly independent solution.

1. $y'' - 3y' + 2y = 0;$ $\quad f(x) = e^x$.

2. $y'' + 2y' - 15y = 0;$ $\quad f(x) = e^{3x}$.

3. $x^2 y'' + 6xy' + 6y = 0,$ $\quad x > 0;$ $\quad f(x) = x^{-2}$.

4. $x^2 y'' - 2xy' - 4y = 0,$ $\quad x > 0;$ $\quad f(x) = x^{-1}$.

5. $xy'' - (x + 1)y' + y = 0,$ $x > 0;$ $f(x) = e^x.$

6. $xy'' + (1 - 2x)y' + (x - 1)y = 0,$ $x > 0;$ $f(x) = e^x.$

7. The reduction of order procedure can be used, more generally, to reduce a homogeneous linear nth order equation to a homogeneous linear $(n - 1)$th order equation. For the equation

$$xy''' - xy'' + y' - y = 0,$$

which has $f(x) = e^x$ as a solution, use the substitution $y(x) = v(x)f(x)$ to reduce this third order equation to a homogeneous linear second order equation in the variable $w = v'$.

8. The equation

$$xy''' + (1 - x)y'' + xy' - y = 0$$

has $f(x) = x$ as a solution. Use the substitution $y(x) = v(x)f(x)$ to reduce this third order equation to a homogeneous linear second order equation in the variable $w = v'$.

9. Given that $f(x) = x$ is a solution to

$$y'' - xy' + y = 0:$$

(a) Obtain an integral representation for a second linearly independent solution.

(b) Using the integral representation from part (a), obtain a Maclaurin series expansion for this solution.

10. Given that $f(x) = x$ is a solution to

$$(1 - x^2)y'' - 2xy' + 2y = 0, \qquad -1 < x < 1:$$

(a) Obtain an integral representation for a second linearly independent solution.

(b) Using the integral representation from part (a), obtain a Maclaurin series expansion for this solution. [Hint: $(1 - x)^{-1} = 1 + x + x^2 + \cdots .$]

(c) Use partial fractions to evaluate the integral in part (a), and give a general solution to the differential equation.

11. The reduction of order formula (6) can also be derived from Abel's identity [formula (18) of Section 4.3]. Let $f(x)$ be a nontrivial solution to (1) and let $y(x)$ be a second linearly independent solution. Show that

$$\left(\frac{y}{f}\right)' = \frac{W[f, y]}{f^2},$$

and then use Abel's identity for the Wronskian $W[f, y]$ to obtain the reduction of order formula.

12. Verify, by direct substitution, that the power series (10) is a solution to the differential equation (8).

13. In quantum mechanics the study of the Schrödinger equation for the case of a harmonic oscillator leads to a consideration of **Hermite's equation,**

$$y'' - 2xy' + \lambda y = 0,$$

where λ is a parameter. Use the reduction of order formula to obtain an integral representation of a second linearly independent solution to Hermite's equation for the given value of λ and corresponding solution $f(x)$.

(a) $\lambda = 4$, $f(x) = 1 - 2x^2$.   **(b)** $\lambda = 6$, $f(x) = 3x - 2x^3$.

14. In quantum mechanics the study of the Schrödinger equation for the hydrogen atom leads to a consideration of **Laguerre's equation,**

$$xy'' + (1 - x)y' + \lambda y = 0, \qquad x > 0,$$

where λ is a parameter. Use the reduction of order formula to obtain an integral representation of a second linearly independent solution to Laguerre's equation for the given value of λ and corresponding solution $f(x)$.

(a) $\lambda = 1$, $f(x) = x - 1$.   **(b)** $\lambda = 2$, $f(x) = x^2 - 4x + 2$.

15. In mathematical physics, many problems with spherical symmetry involve the study of **Legendre's equation,**

$$(1 - x^2)y'' - 2xy' + \lambda(\lambda + 1)y = 0, \qquad -1 < x < 1,$$

where λ is a parameter. Use the reduction of order formula to obtain an integral representation of a second linearly independent solution to Legendre's equation for the given value of λ and corresponding solution $f(x)$.

(a) $\lambda = 1$, $f(x) = x$.   **(b)** $\lambda = 2$, $f(x) = 3x^2 - 1$.
(c) $\lambda = 3$, $f(x) = 5x^3 - 3x$.

16. For equation (8) we showed in Example 2 that

$$f(x) = x \quad \text{and} \quad h(x) = -1 + x^2 + \frac{x^4}{6} + \cdots + \frac{x^{2n}}{n!(2n - 1)} + \cdots$$

are two linearly independent solutions. Show that the solution to the initial value problem

$$(11) \qquad y'' - 2xy' + 2y = 0; \qquad y(0) = -2, \qquad y'(0) = -1$$

is given by $y(x) = 2h(x) - f(x)$. Obtain an approximation for the solution to the initial value problem (11) at $x = 1$ by using the first five nonzero terms of the power series for $h(x)$.

17. In Example 2 we showed that a solution to equation (8) is given by

$$g(x) = x \int_1^x \frac{e^{t^2}}{t^2}\, dt.$$

(a) Show that this solution satisfies $g(1) = 0$, $g'(1) = e$.

(b) Using Simpson's rule (see Appendix B), approximate the solution to the initial value problem

$$y'' - 2xy' + y = 0; \qquad y(1) = 0, \qquad y'(1) = e,$$

at $x = 2$.

18. In Example 2 we showed that

$$f(x) = x, \qquad g(x) = x \int_1^x \frac{e^{t^2}}{t^2}\, dt,$$

and

$$h(x) = -1 + x^2 + \frac{x^4}{6} + \cdots + \frac{x^{2n}}{n!(2n-1)} + \cdots$$

are all solutions to equation (8). Hence, by the representation theorem for homogeneous equations, we know that $h(x)$ can be expressed as a linear combination of $f(x)$ and $g(x)$. This representation can be determined as follows:

(a) Using integration by parts, show that

$$g(x) = ex - e^{x^2} + 2x \int_1^x e^{t^2}\, dt.$$

(b) Prove that

$$h(x) = g(x) + \left(2 \int_0^1 e^{t^2}\, dt - e\right) f(x).$$

4.5 Homogeneous Linear Equations with Constant Coefficients

Let's consider the homogeneous linear second order differential equation with constant coefficients

(1) $ay'' + by' + cy = 0,$

where $a\,(\neq 0)$, b, and c are real constants. Since constant functions are everywhere continuous, Theorem 2 guarantees that equation (1) has solutions defined for all x in $(-\infty, \infty)$.

If we can find two linearly independent solutions to (1), say y_1 and y_2, then we can express a general solution in the form

$$y = c_1 y_1 + c_2 y_2,$$

where c_1 and c_2 are arbitrary constants.

A look at equation (1) tells us that a solution of (1) must have the property that a constant times its second derivative plus a constant times its first derivative plus a constant times itself must sum to zero. This suggests that we try to find a solution of the form $y = e^{rx}$, since derivatives of e^{rx} are just constants times e^{rx}. If we substitute $y = e^{rx}$ into (1), we obtain

$$ar^2 e^{rx} + bre^{rx} + ce^{rx} = 0,$$

$$e^{rx}(ar^2 + br + c) = 0.$$

Because e^{rx} is never zero, we can divide by it to obtain

(2) $ar^2 + br + c = 0.$

Consequently, $y = e^{rx}$ is a solution to (1) if and only if r satisfies equation (2). Equation (2) is called the **auxiliary equation** associated with the homogeneous equation (1).

Now the auxiliary equation is just a quadratic, and its roots are

(3) $$r_1 = \frac{-b + \sqrt{b^2 - 4ac}}{2a} \quad \text{and} \quad r_2 = \frac{-b - \sqrt{b^2 - 4ac}}{2a}.$$

When the discriminant, $b^2 - 4ac$, is positive, the roots r_1 and r_2 are real and distinct; if $b^2 - 4ac = 0$, the roots are real and equal; and when $b^2 - 4ac < 0$, the roots are complex conjugate numbers. We consider the case of complex roots in the next section.

DISTINCT REAL ROOTS

If the auxiliary equation has distinct real roots r_1 and r_2, then $e^{r_1 x}$ and $e^{r_2 x}$ are linearly independent solutions to (1). Therefore, a general solution of (1) is

$$y(x) = c_1 e^{r_1 x} + c_2 e^{r_2 x},$$

where c_1 and c_2 are arbitrary constants.

▶ **Example 1**   Find a general solution to

(5) $y'' + 5y' - 6y = 0.$

Solution The auxiliary equation associated with (5) is

(6) $\quad r^2 + 5r - 6 = (r - 1)(r + 6) = 0,$

which has the roots $r_1 = 1$, $r_2 = -6$. Thus $\{e^x, e^{-6x}\}$ is a fundamental solution set for equation (5), and so a general solution is

$$y(x) = c_1 e^x + c_2 e^{-6x}. \blacktriangleleft$$

▶ *Example 2* Solve the initial value problem

(7) $\quad y'' + 2y' - y = 0; \qquad y(0) = 0, \qquad y'(0) = -1.$

Solution Here the auxiliary equation is

(8) $\quad r^2 + 2r - 1 = 0.$

Using the quadratic formula, we find that the roots of this equation are

$$r_1 = -1 + \sqrt{2} \quad \text{and} \quad r_2 = -1 - \sqrt{2}.$$

Consequently, a general solution to the equation in (7) is

(9) $\quad y(x) = c_1 e^{(-1+\sqrt{2})x} + c_2 e^{(-1-\sqrt{2})x},$

where c_1 and c_2 are arbitrary constants. To find the particular solution that satisfies the initial conditions given in (7), we first differentiate y as given in (9), then plug y and y' into the initial conditions of (7). This gives

(10)
$$y(0) = c_1 e^0 + c_2 e^0,$$
$$y'(0) = (-1 + \sqrt{2})c_1 e^0 + (-1 - \sqrt{2})c_2 e^0,$$

or

(11)
$$0 = c_1 + c_2,$$
$$-1 = (-1 + \sqrt{2})c_1 + (-1 - \sqrt{2})c_2.$$

Solving system (11) yields $c_1 = -\sqrt{2}/4$ and $c_2 = \sqrt{2}/4$. Thus,

(12) $\quad y(x) = -\dfrac{\sqrt{2}}{4} e^{(-1+\sqrt{2})x} + \dfrac{\sqrt{2}}{4} e^{(-1-\sqrt{2})x}$

is the desired solution. ◀

When the roots of the auxiliary equation (2) are equal, that is, $r_1 = r_2 = r$, then, unlike the previous case, we get only one nontrivial solution, namely $y = e^{rx}$. Of course, constant multiples of this function are also solutions, but they are of no help in finding a second **linearly independent** solution. We can resolve this shortcoming by using the reduction of order method discussed in Section 4.4. When we apply this procedure to the case of a repeated root r, we find that a second linearly independent solution is just xe^{rx}; that is, x times the original solution e^{rx}. We leave the verification of this fact to the exercises (see Problem 26).

REPEATED ROOT

If the auxiliary equation has a repeated root r, then two linearly independent solutions to (1) are e^{rx} and xe^{rx}, and a general solution is

(13) $y(x) = c_1 e^{rx} + c_2 x e^{rx},$

where c_1 and c_2 are arbitrary constants.

▶ **Example 3** Find a general solution to

(14) $y'' + 4y' + 4y = 0.$

Solution The auxiliary equation for (14) is

$$r^2 + 4r + 4 = (r + 2)^2 = 0.$$

Since $r = -2$ is a double root, two linearly independent solutions are e^{-2x} and xe^{-2x}. These give

(15) $y(x) = c_1 e^{-2x} + c_2 x e^{-2x}$

as a general solution. ◀

The method we have described for solving homogeneous linear second order equations with constant coefficients applies to any order (even first order) homogeneous linear equations with constant coefficients. We give a detailed treatment of such higher order equations in Chapter 6. For now, we shall be content to illustrate the method by means of an example. We remark that, in general, a homogeneous linear nth order equation has a fundamental solution set consisting of n linearly independent solutions.

▶ **Example 4** Find a general solution to

(16) $y''' + 3y'' - y' - 3y = 0.$

Solution　If we try to find solutions of the form $y = e^{rx}$, then, as with second order equations, we are led to finding roots of the auxiliary equation

$$(17) \qquad r^3 + 3r^2 - r - 3 = 0.$$

We observe that $r = 1$ is a root of the above equation, and dividing the polynomial on the left-hand side of (17) by $r - 1$ leads to the factorization

$$(r - 1)(r^2 + 4r + 3) = (r - 1)(r + 1)(r + 3) = 0.$$

Hence the roots of the auxiliary equation are 1, -1, and -3, and so three solutions of (16) are e^x, e^{-x}, and e^{-3x}. For now we assume that these form a fundamental solution set. (A discussion of linear independence for sets containing more than two functions is given in Section 6.2.) A general solution to (16) is then

$$(18) \qquad y(x) = c_1 e^x + c_2 e^{-x} + c_3 e^{-3x}. \quad \blacktriangleleft$$

　　In the last example we can actually verify that (18) is a "general solution" by showing, as we did in the proof of Theorem 3 on page 165 that every solution to equation (16) can be written in the form (18) for a suitable choice of constants c_1, c_2, and c_3. For this verification, we need a generalization of the existence and uniqueness theorem to linear third order equations (see Section 6.2).
　　In the general case of a homogeneous linear nth order equation with constant coefficients, the auxiliary equation is a polynomial equation of order n. The fundamental theorem of algebra[†] states that a polynomial equation of order n has n roots, some of which may be complex. Unfortunately, a result from Galois theory by Abel and Ruffini[††] also states that for arbitrary polynomial equations of order greater than four, there does *not* exist a formula involving radicals for determining the roots of the equation. Thus, when $n > 4$, we will usually have to rely on numerical techniques for approximating the roots (see Problem 30).

EXERCISES 4.5

In Problems 1 through 12 find a general solution to the given differential equation.

1. $y'' + y' - 2y = 0.$
2. $y'' + 5y' + 6y = 0.$
3. $y'' - 8y' + 16y = 0.$
4. $y'' + 6y' + 9y = 0.$
5. $y'' + y' - y = 0.$
6. $y'' - 5y' + 6y = 0.$
7. $7y' + 10y = 0.$
8. $y'' - y' - 11y = 0.$
9. $6y'' + y' - 2y = 0.$
10. $4y'' - 4y' + y = 0.$
11. $4y'' + 20y' + 25y = 0.$
12. $3y'' + 11y' - 7y = 0.$

In Problems 13 through 20 solve the given initial value problem.

13. $y'' + y' = 0;$　$y(0) = 2,$　$y'(0) = 1.$
14. $y'' + 2y' - 8y = 0;$　$y(0) = 3,$　$y'(0) = -12.$

[†] See, for example, *Elements of Abstract Algebra*, by Richard A. Dean, John Wiley and Sons, Inc., New York, 1966, Section 4.6.

[††] Ibid., Section 10.5.

15. $y'' + 2y' + y = 0$; $y(0) = 1$, $y'(0) = -3$.
16. $y'' - 4y' + 3y = 0$; $y(0) = 1$, $y'(0) = \frac{1}{3}$.
17. $y'' - 2y' - 2y = 0$; $y(0) = 0$, $y'(0) = 3$.
18. $y'' - 6y' + 9y = 0$; $y(0) = 2$, $y'(0) = \frac{25}{3}$.
19. $y'' - 4y' + 4y = 0$; $y(1) = 1$, $y'(1) = 1$.
20. $y'' - 4y' - 5y = 0$; $y(-1) = 3$, $y'(-1) = 9$.

In Problems 21 through 23 find a general solution to the given third order differential equation.

21. $y''' - 6y'' - y' + 6y = 0$.   22. $y''' + y'' - 6y' + 4y = 0$.   23. $y''' + 2y'' - 4y' - 8y = 0$.

24. Solve the initial value problem

$$y''' - y' = 0;   \quad y(0) = 2,   \quad y'(0) = 3,   \quad y''(0) = -1.$$

25. **(a)** Show that the **Cauchy-Euler equation,**

$$ax^2 \frac{d^2y}{dx^2} + bx \frac{dy}{dx} + cy = 0,   \quad x > 0,$$

is transformed into the constant coefficient equation

$$a \frac{d^2y}{dt^2} + (b - a) \frac{dy}{dt} + cy = 0$$

by the change of variables $x = e^t$. [Hint: Show that $x\, dy/dx = dy/dt$ and $x^2\, d^2y/dx^2 = d^2y/dt^2 - dy/dt$.]
(b) Use the result of part (a) to find a general solution to

$$x^2 \frac{d^2y}{dx^2} + 2x \frac{dy}{dx} - 6y = 0,   \quad x > 0.$$

(c) Find a general solution to

$$x^2 \frac{d^2y}{dx^2} + 5x \frac{dy}{dx} + 4y = 0,   \quad x > 0.$$

26. When $b^2 - 4ac = 0$, the roots of the auxiliary equation (2) are equal; that is, $r_1 = r_2 = r = -b/2a$. Hence $f(x) = e^{(-b/2a)x}$ is a solution to (1). Use the reduction of order formula (6) of Section 4.4 to derive $xe^{(-b/2a)x}$ as a second linearly independent solution to (1).

27. Suppose the auxiliary equation (2) has a repeated root r. Then, on dividing by a, equation (1) can be written in the equivalent form

$$(D - r)^2 y = y'' - 2ry' + r^2 y = 0,$$

where D is the differential operator d/dx.

(a) Show that for any twice differentiable function u,

$$(D - r)^2[e^{rx}u] = e^{rx} D^2u,$$

and hence the problem of solving $(D - r)^2 y = 0$ reduces to that of solving $D^2 u = 0$, where $y = e^{rx}u$.

(b) Use the result of part (a) to show that e^{rx} and xe^{rx} are linearly independent solutions of $(D - r)^2 y = 0$.

28. Let $L[y] := ay'' + by' + c$, where $b^2 - 4ac = 0$.

(a) Show that $L[e^{rx}](x) = a(r - r_0)^2 e^{rx}$, where $r_0 = -b/2a$.

(b) Show that $L[(\partial/\partial r)e^{rx}] = (\partial/\partial r)L[e^{rx}]$, and thus

$$L[xe^{rx}](x) = 2a(r - r_0)e^{rx} + ax(r - r_0)^2 e^{rx}.$$

(c) Use the results of parts (a) and (b) to show that $e^{r_0 x}$ and $xe^{r_0 x}$ are linearly independent solutions to (1).

29. The suspension in an automobile can be modeled as a vibrating spring with damping due to the shock absorbers. This leads to the equation

$$mx''(t) + bx'(t) + kx(t) = 0,$$

where m is the mass of the automobile, b is the damping constant of the shocks, k is the spring constant, and $x(t)$ is the vertical displacement of the automobile at time t. In the next section we will find that the solution of a homogeneous linear second order equation with constant coefficients oscillates when the auxiliary equation has complex roots. If the mass of an automobile is 1000 kilograms (kg) and the spring constant is 3000 kg/sec^2, determine the minimum value for the damping constant in kilograms per second that will provide a smooth, vibration-free (theoretically!) ride. If we replace the springs with heavy duty ones having twice the spring constant, how does this minimum value for b change?

30. Find a general solution to

$$3y''' + 18y'' + 33y' - 19y = 0$$

by using Newton's method or some other numerical procedure to approximate the roots of the auxiliary equation.

4.6 Auxiliary Equations with Complex Roots

The *simple harmonic equation* $y'' + y = 0$, so-called because of its relation to the fundamental vibration of a musical tone, has as solutions $y_1(x) = \cos x$ and $y_2(x) = \sin x$. Notice that the auxiliary equation associated with the harmonic equation is $r^2 + 1 = 0$ which has imaginary roots $r = \pm i$, where i denotes $\sqrt{-1}$.[†] In the previous section, we expressed the solutions to a linear second order equation with constant coefficients in terms of exponential functions. To see how the trigonometric functions arise from complex exponential functions, we use Euler's formula, which is discussed below.

When $b^2 - 4ac < 0$, the roots of the auxiliary equation

(1) $ar^2 + br + c = 0$

associated with the homogeneous equation

(2) $ay'' + by' + cy = 0$

are the complex conjugate numbers

$$r_1 = \alpha + i\beta \quad \text{and} \quad r_2 = \alpha - i\beta \qquad (i = \sqrt{-1}),$$

where α, β are the real numbers

(3) $\alpha = -\dfrac{b}{2a} \quad \text{and} \quad \beta = \dfrac{\sqrt{4ac - b^2}}{2a}.$

As in the previous section, we would like to assert that the functions $e^{r_1 x}$ and $e^{r_2 x}$ are solutions to the equation (2). This is, in fact, the case, but before we can proceed we need to address some fundamental questions. For example, if $r_1 = \alpha + i\beta$ is a complex number, what do we mean by the expression $e^{(\alpha + i\beta)x}$? If we assume that the law of exponents applies to complex numbers, then

(4) $e^{(\alpha + i\beta)x} = e^{\alpha x + i\beta x} = e^{\alpha x} e^{i\beta x}.$

We now need only clarify the meaning of $e^{i\beta x}$.

For this purpose, let's assume that the Maclaurin series for e^z is the same for complex numbers z as it is for real numbers. Recalling that $i^2 = -1$, then for θ real we have

$$e^{i\theta} = 1 + (i\theta) + \frac{(i\theta)^2}{2!} + \cdots + \frac{(i\theta)^n}{n!} + \cdots$$

$$= 1 + i\theta - \frac{\theta^2}{2!} - \frac{i\theta^3}{3!} + \frac{\theta^4}{4!} + \frac{i\theta^5}{5!} + \cdots$$

$$= \left(1 - \frac{\theta^2}{2!} + \frac{\theta^4}{4!} + \cdots\right) + i\left(\theta - \frac{\theta^3}{3!} + \frac{\theta^5}{5!} + \cdots\right).$$

[†] Engineers frequently use the symbol j to denote $\sqrt{-1}$.

Recognizing the series expansions for the real and imaginary parts to be Maclaurin series for cos θ and sin θ, respectively, we can simplify the above expansion to

(5) $e^{i\theta} = \cos \theta + i \sin \theta,$

which is known as **Euler's formula.**[†]

When Euler's formula (with θ = βx) is used in equation (4), we find

(6) $e^{(\alpha + i\beta)x} = e^{\alpha x}(\cos \beta x + i \sin \beta x),$

which expresses the complex function $e^{(\alpha + i\beta)x}$ in terms of familiar real functions. Having made sense out of $e^{(\alpha + i\beta)x}$, we can now show (see Problem 30) that

(7) $\dfrac{d}{dx} e^{(\alpha + i\beta)x} = (\alpha + i\beta)e^{(\alpha + i\beta)x}.$

In general, if $z(x)$ is a complex-valued function of the real variable x, we can write

$$z(x) = u(x) + iv(x),$$

where $u(x)$ and $v(x)$ are real-valued functions. The derivatives of $z(x)$ are then given by

$$\frac{dz}{dx} = \frac{du}{dx} + i\frac{dv}{dx}, \qquad \frac{d^2z}{dx^2} = \frac{d^2u}{dx^2} + i\frac{d^2v}{dx^2}.$$

With this background, we next show that the complex-valued solution $e^{(\alpha + i\beta)x}$ gives rise to two linearly independent *real-valued* solutions.

REAL SOLUTIONS DERIVED FROM COMPLEX SOLUTIONS

Lemma 2.   Let $z(x) = u(x) + iv(x)$ be a solution to equation (2), where a, b, and c are real numbers. Then $u(x)$ and $v(x)$ are real-valued solutions of (2).

Proof   By assumption, $az'' + bz' + cz = 0$, and hence

$$a(u'' + iv'') + b(u' + iv') + c(u + iv) = 0$$

$$(au'' + bu' + cu) + i(av'' + bv' + cv) = 0.$$

[†] *Historical Footnote:* This formula first appeared in Leonhard Euler's monumental two-volume *Introductio in Analysin Infinitorum* (1748).

But a complex number is zero if and only if its real and imaginary parts are both zero. Thus we must have

$$au'' + bu' + cu = 0 \quad \text{and} \quad av'' + bv' + cv = 0,$$

which means that both $u(x)$ and $v(x)$ are real-valued solutions of (2). ∎

When we apply Lemma 2 to the solution

(8) $$e^{(\alpha + i\beta)x} = e^{\alpha x} \cos \beta x + i e^{\alpha x} \sin \beta x$$

we obtain the following.

COMPLEX CONJUGATE ROOTS

If the auxiliary equation has complex conjugate roots $\alpha \pm i\beta$, then two linearly independent solutions to (2) are

(9) $$e^{\alpha x} \cos \beta x \quad \text{and} \quad e^{\alpha x} \sin \beta x,$$

and a general solution is

(10) $$y(x) = c_1 e^{\alpha x} \cos \beta x + c_2 e^{\alpha x} \sin \beta x,$$

where c_1 and c_2 are arbitrary constants.

In the preceding discussion we glossed over some important details concerning complex numbers and complex-valued functions. In particular, further analysis is required to justify the use of the law of exponents, Euler's formula, and even the fact that the derivative of e^{rx} is re^{rx} when r is a complex constant.[†] Readers who feel uneasy about our conclusions can easily check the answer by substituting it into (2).

The reader may also be wondering what would have happened if we had worked with the function $e^{(\alpha - i\beta)x}$ instead of $e^{(\alpha + i\beta)x}$. We leave it as an exercise to verify that $e^{(\alpha - i\beta)x}$ gives rise to the same general solution (10).

▶ **Example 1**   Find a general solution to

(11) $$y'' + 2y' + 4y = 0.$$

[†] For a detailed treatment of these topics see, for example, *Fundamentals of Complex Analysis*, by E. B. Saff and A. D. Snider, Prentice-Hall, Inc., Englewood Cliffs, New Jersey, 1976.

Solution The auxiliary equation is

(12) $r^2 + 2r + 4 = 0,$

which has roots

(13) $r = \dfrac{-2 \pm \sqrt{4 - 16}}{2} = \dfrac{-2 \pm \sqrt{-12}}{2} = -1 \pm i\sqrt{3}.$

Hence with $\alpha = -1$, $\beta = \sqrt{3}$, a general solution for (11) is

(14) $y(x) = c_1 e^{-x} \cos(\sqrt{3}x) + c_2 e^{-x} \sin(\sqrt{3}x).$ ◀

▶ *Example 2*   In the study of a vibrating spring with damping, we are led to an initial value problem of the form

(15) $mx''(t) + bx'(t) + kx(t) = 0;$ $x(0) = x_0,$ $x'(0) = v_0,$

where m is the mass of the spring system, b is the damping constant, k is the spring constant, x_0 is the initial displacement, v_0 is the initial velocity, and $x(t)$ is the displacement from equilibrium of the spring system at time t (see Figure 4.3). Determine the equation of motion for this spring system when $m = 36$ kg, $b = 12$ kg/sec, $k = 37$ kg/sec^2, $x_0 = 70$ centimeters (cm), and $v_0 = 10$ cm/sec. Also find $x(10)$, the displacement after 10 sec.

Solution The equation of motion is given by $x(t)$, the solution of the initial value problem (15) for the specified values of m, b, k, x_0, and v_0, That is, we seek the solution to

(16) $36x'' + 12x' + 37x = 0;$ $x(0) = 70,$ $x'(0) = 10.$

The auxiliary equation for (16) is

(17) $36r^2 + 12r + 37 = 0,$

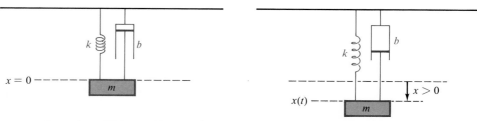

System in equilibrium position   System in motion

Figure 4.3 Vibrating spring with damping

which has roots

(18) $r = \dfrac{-12 \pm \sqrt{144 - 4(36)(37)}}{72} = \dfrac{-12 \pm 12\sqrt{1 - 37}}{72} = -\dfrac{1}{6} \pm i.$

Hence with $\alpha = -\frac{1}{6}$, $\beta = 1$, the displacement $x(t)$ can be expressed in the form

(19) $x(t) = c_1 e^{-t/6} \cos t + c_2 e^{-t/6} \sin t.$

We can find c_1 and c_2 by substituting $x(t)$ and $x'(t)$ into the initial conditions given in (16). Differentiating (19), we get a formula for $x'(t)$:

(20) $x'(t) = \left(-\dfrac{c_1}{6} + c_2 \right) e^{-t/6} \cos t + \left(-c_1 - \dfrac{c_2}{6} \right) e^{-t/6} \sin t.$

Substituting into the initial conditions now results in the system

$$c_1 = 70,$$

(21)

$$-\dfrac{c_1}{6} + c_2 = 10.$$

Upon solving (21), we find $c_1 = 70$ and $c_2 = \frac{65}{3}$. With these values, the equation of motion is

(22) $x(t) = 70e^{-t/6} \cos t + \frac{65}{3}e^{-t/6} \sin t,$

and

$$x(10) = 70e^{-5/3} \cos 10 + \tfrac{65}{3}e^{-5/3} \sin 10$$

$$\approx -13.32 \text{ cm. } \blacktriangleleft$$

If the constants a, b, and c in (2) are complex numbers, then the roots r_1, r_2 of the auxiliary equation (1) are, in general, complex numbers, but not necessarily complex conjugates of each other. If $r_1 \neq r_2$, then a general solution is

$$y(x) = c_1 e^{r_1 x} + c_2 e^{r_2 x},$$

where c_1 and c_2 are now arbitrary *complex-valued* constants.

We remark that a complex differential equation can be regarded as a system of two real differential equations, since we can always work separately with its real and imaginary parts. Such systems are discussed in Chapters 9 and 10.

EXERCISES 4.6 ————————————————————————

In Problems 1 through 8 the auxiliary equation for the given differential equation has complex roots. Find a general solution.

1. $y'' + y = 0.$

2. $y'' + 4y = 0.$

3. $y'' - 6y' + 10y = 0.$

4. $y'' - 10y' + 26y = 0.$

5. $y'' + 4y' + 6y = 0.$

6. $y'' - 4y' + 7y = 0.$

7. $4y'' + 4y' + 6y = 0.$

8. $4y'' - 4y' + 26y = 0.$

In Problems 9 through 20 find a general solution.

9. $y'' + 4y' + 8y = 0.$

10. $y'' - 8y' + 7y = 0.$

11. $y'' + 10y' + 25y = 0.$

12. $y'' + 7y = 0.$

13. $y'' + 2y' + 5y = 0.$

14. $y'' - 2y' + 26y = 0.$

15. $y'' - 3y' - 11y = 0.$

16. $y'' + 10y' + 41y = 0.$

17. $y'' - y' + 7y = 0.$

18. $2y'' + 13y' - 7y = 0.$

19. $3y'' + 4y' + 9y = 0.$

20. $9y'' - 12y' + 4y = 0.$

In Problems 21 through 27 solve the given initial value problem.

21. $y'' + 2y' + 2y = 0;$ $y(0) = 2,$ $y'(0) = 1.$

22. $y'' + 2y' + 17y = 0;$ $y(0) = 1,$ $y'(0) = -1.$

23. $y'' - 4y' + 2y = 0;$ $y(0) = 0,$ $y'(0) = 1.$

24. $y'' + 9y = 0;$ $y(0) = 1,$ $y'(0) = 1.$

25. $y'' - 2y' + y = 0;$ $y(0) = 1,$ $y'(0) = -2.$

26. $y'' - 4y' + 5y = 0;$ $y(0) = 1,$ $y'(0) = 6.$

27. $y'' - 2y' + 2y = 0;$ $y(\pi) = e^\pi,$ $y'(\pi) = 0.$

28. To see the effect of changing the parameter b in the initial value problem

$$y'' + by' + 4y = 0; \qquad y(0) = 1, \qquad y'(0) = 0,$$

solve the problem for $b = 5$, 4, and 2 and sketch the solutions.

29. Find a general solution to the following third order equations.

(a) $y''' - y'' + y' + 3y = 0.$ **(b)** $y''' + 2y'' + 5y' - 26y = 0.$

30. Using the representation for $e^{(\alpha + i\beta)x}$ in (6), verify the differentiation formula (7).

31. Verify, by directly substituting into equation (2), that $e^{\alpha x} \cos \beta x$ and $e^{\alpha x} \sin \beta x$, where α, β are given in (3), are solutions to equation (2).

32. Vibrating Spring without Damping. A vibrating spring without damping can be modeled by the initial value problem (15) in Example 2 by taking $b = 0$.

(a) If $m = 10$ kg, $k = 250$ kg/sec^2, $x_0 = 30$ cm, and $v_0 = -10$ cm/sec, find the equation of motion for this undamped vibrating spring.

(b) When the equation of motion is of the form displayed in (10), the motion is said to be **oscillatory** with **frequency** $\beta/2\pi$. Find the frequency of oscillation for the spring system of part (a).

33. Vibrating Spring with Damping. Using the model for a vibrating spring with damping discussed in Example 2:

(a) Find the equation of motion for the vibrating spring with damping if $m = 10$ kg, $b = 60$ kg/sec, $k = 250$ kg/sec^2, $x_0 = 30$ cm, and $v_0 = -10$ cm/sec.

(b) Find the frequency of oscillation for the spring system of part (a). [Hint: See the definition of frequency given in Problem 32(b).]

(c) Comparing the results of Problems 32 and 33, what effect does the damping have on the frequency of oscillation? What other effects does it have on the solution?

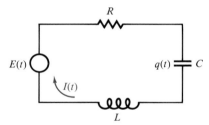

Figure 4.4 RLC series circuit

34. RLC Series Circuit. In the study of an electrical circuit consisting of a resistor, capacitor, inductor, and an electromotive force (see Figure 4.4), we are led to an initial value problem of the form

$$(23) \qquad L\frac{dI}{dt} + RI + \frac{q}{C} = E(t); \qquad q(0) = q_0, \qquad I(0) = I_0,$$

where L is the inductance in henrys, R is the resistance in ohms, C is the capacitance in farads, $E(t)$ is the electromotive force in volts, $q(t)$ is the charge in coulombs on the capacitor at time t, and $I = dq/dt$ is the current in amperes. Find the current at time t if the charge on the capacitor is initially zero, the initial current is zero, $L = 10$ henrys, $R = 20$ ohms, $C = (6260)^{-1}$ farads, and $E(t) = 100$ volts. [Hint: Differentiate both sides of the differential equation in (23) to obtain a homogeneous linear second order equation for $I(t)$. Then use (23) to determine dI/dt at $t = 0$.]

35. Swinging Door. The motion of a swinging door with an adjustment screw that controls the amount of friction on the hinges is governed by the initial value problem

$$I\theta'' + b\theta' + k\theta = 0; \qquad \theta(0) = \theta_0, \qquad \theta'(0) = v_0.$$

where θ is the angle that the door is open, I is the moment of inertia of the door about its hinges, $b > 0$ is a damping constant that varies with the amount of friction on the door, $k > 0$ is the spring constant associated with the swinging door, θ_0 is the initial angle that the door is opened, and v_0 is the initial angular velocity imparted to the door. If I and k are fixed, determine for which values of b the door will *not* continually swing back and forth when closing.

4.7 Superposition and Nonhomogeneous Equations

The differential operator L defined by

$$(1) \qquad L[y](x) := y'' + p(x)y' + q(x)y$$

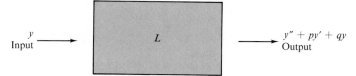

Figure 4.5 Black box diagram for L

can be viewed as a "black box" with input the function $y(x)$ and output the function on the right-hand side of (1) (see Figure 4.5).

Suppose the input functions $y_1(x)$ and $y_2(x)$ yield, respectively, the output functions $g_1(x)$ and $g_2(x)$; that is,

$$L[y_1](x) = g_1(x), \qquad L[y_2](x) = g_2(x).$$

Then, since L is a linear operator, an input consisting of the linear combination $c_1 y_1(x) + c_2 y_2(x)$ produces the output $c_1 g_1(x) + c_2 g_2(x)$ in the same combination. Stated in terms of solutions to differential equations, we have the following result.

SUPERPOSITION PRINCIPLE

Theorem 6. Let y_1 be a solution of the differential equation

$$L[y](x) = g_1(x)$$

and let y_2 be a solution of

$$L[y](x) = g_2(x),$$

where L is a linear differential operator. Then for any constants c_1 and c_2, the function $c_1 y_1 + c_2 y_2$ is a solution to the differential equation

$$L[y](x) = c_1 g_1(x) + c_2 g_2(x).$$

▶ **Example 1**   Given that $y_1(x) = -x/3 - \frac{2}{9}$ is a solution to

(2) $y'' + 2y' - 3y = x,$

and $y_2(x) = e^{2x}/5$ is a solution to

(3) $y'' + 2y' - 3y = e^{2x},$

find a solution to

(4) $y'' + 2y' - 3y = 4x - 5e^{2x}.$

Solution   Let $L[y] := y'' + 2y' - 3y$. We are given that

$$L[y_1](x) = g_1(x) = x \quad \text{and} \quad L[y_2](x) = g_2(x) = e^{2x}.$$

Since we can express

$$4x - 5e^{2x} = 4g_1(x) - 5g_2(x),$$

then, by the superposition principle, the function

$$4y_1(x) - 5y_2(x) = 4\left(\frac{-x}{3} - \frac{2}{9}\right) - 5\left(\frac{e^{2x}}{5}\right)$$

$$= \frac{-4x}{3} - \frac{8}{9} - e^{2x}$$

is a solution to equation (4). ◀

If we combine the superposition principle with the representation theorem for solutions of homogeneous equations, we can prove that *all* solutions of a *non*homogeneous equation can be found if we know just one solution and a general solution to the corresponding homogeneous equation.

REPRESENTATION OF SOLUTIONS (NONHOMOGENEOUS CASE)

Theorem 7.   Let $y_p(x)$ be a particular solution to the nonhomogeneous equation

(5) $y'' + p(x)y' + q(x)y = g(x),$

on the interval (a, b) and let $y_1(x)$, $y_2(x)$ be linearly independent solutions on (a, b) of the corresponding homogeneous equation

(6) $y'' + p(x)y' + q(x)y = 0.$

Then every solution of (5) on the interval (a, b) can be expressed in the form

(7) $y(x) = y_p(x) + c_1 y_1(x) + c_2 y_2(x).$

The linear combination of y_p, y_1, and y_2 in (7), written with arbitrary constants c_1 and c_2, is referred to as a **general solution** to (5).

Proof of Theorem 7   Let $\phi(x)$ be any solution to (5). Since both $\phi(x)$ and $y_p(x)$ are solutions to (5), the superposition principle states that the difference $\phi(x) - y_p(x)$ is a solution to the homogeneous equation (6). It then follows from Theorem 3 of Section 4.3 that

$$\phi(x) - y_p(x) = c_1 y_1(x) + c_2 y_2(x)$$

for suitable constants c_1 and c_2. Since the last equation is equivalent to (7) (with $\phi(x)$ in place of $y(x)$), the theorem is proved.   ∎

PROCEDURE FOR SOLVING NONHOMOGENEOUS EQUATIONS

To solve $y'' + py' + qy = g$:

(a) Determine a general solution, $c_1 y_1 + c_2 y_2$, of the corresponding homogeneous equation.

(b) Find a particular solution, y_p, of the given nonhomogeneous equation.

(c) A general solution of the given equation is the sum of a particular solution and a general solution to the homogeneous equation; that is,

$$y = y_p + c_1 y_1 + c_2 y_2.$$

▶ **Example 2**   Given that $y_p(x) = x^2$ is a particular solution to

(8) $y'' - y = 2 - x^2,$

find a general solution of (8).

Solution   The corresponding homogeneous equation,

(9) $y'' - y = 0,$

has the associated auxiliary equation $r^2 - 1 = 0$. Since $r = \pm 1$ are the roots of this equation, a general solution to (9) is $c_1 e^x + c_2 e^{-x}$. Combining this with the particular solution $y_p(x) = x^2$ of the nonhomogeneous equation (8), we find that a general solution to (8) is

$$y(x) = x^2 + c_1 e^x + c_2 e^{-x}. \quad ◀$$

In Sections 4.8 and 4.9 we study two methods for actually finding a particular solution to a nonhomogeneous linear second order differential equation.

EXERCISES 4.7

In Problems 1 through 10 a nonhomogeneous equation and a particular solution are given. Find a general solution for the equation.

1. $y'' + y' = 1,$ $\quad y_p(x) = x.$

2. $y'' - y = x,$ $\quad y_p(x) = -x.$

3. $y'' - y' - 2y = 1 - 2x,$ $\quad y_p(x) = x - 1.$

4. $\dfrac{d^2x}{dt^2} - 4\dfrac{dx}{dt} + 3x = -2e^t,$ $\quad x_p(t) = te^t.$

5. $y'' + 2y' + 4y - 4\cos 2x = 0,$ $\quad y_p(x) = \sin 2x.$

6. $\dfrac{d^2y}{dx^2} + y = 5e^{2x},$ $\quad y_p(x) = e^{2x}.$

7. $\dfrac{d^2\theta}{dt^2} - \dfrac{d\theta}{dt} + \theta = \sin t,$ $\quad \theta_p(t) = \cos t.$

8. $y'' + 5y' + 6y = 6x^2 + 10x + 2 + 12e^x,$ $\quad y_p(x) = e^x + x^2.$

9. $y'' = 2y + 2\tan^3 x,$ $\quad y_p(x) = \tan x.$

10. $y'' = 2y' - y + 2e^x,$ $\quad y_p(x) = x^2 e^x.$

11. Given that $y_1(x) = \cos x$ is a solution to

$$y'' - y' + y = \sin x,$$

and $y_2(x) = e^{2x}/3$ is a solution to

$$y'' - y' + y = e^{2x},$$

find solutions to the following differential equations:

(a) $y'' - y' + y = 5\sin x.$
(b) $y'' - y' + y = \sin x - 3e^{2x}.$
(c) $y'' - y' + y = 4\sin x + 18e^{2x}.$

12. Let $L[y]:= y'' + 2y' + 4y,$ $y_1(x):= \frac{1}{4}\sin 2x,$ and $y_2(x):= x/4 - \frac{1}{8}.$ Verify that $L[y_1](x) = \cos 2x$ and $L[y_2](x) = x.$ Now use the superposition principle to find solutions to the following differential equations:

(a) $L[y](x) = x + \cos 2x.$
(b) $L[y](x) = 2x - 3\cos 2x.$
(c) $L[y](x) = 11x - 12\cos 2x.$
(d) $L[y](x) = 0.$

13. Let $L[y]:= y'' - 2y,$ $y_1(x):= (\tan x)/2,$ $y_2(x):= -x/2,$ and $y_3(x):= -\frac{1}{2}.$ Verify that $L[y_1](x) = \tan^3 x,$ $L[y_2](x) = x,$ and $L[y_3](x) = 1.$ Now use the superposition principle to find solutions to the following differential equations.

(a) $L[y](x) = \tan^3 x - 1.$
(b) $L[y](x) = x - 2.$
(c) $L[y](x) = 2\tan^3 x + 3x - 4.$
(d) $L[y](x) = (x - \tan^3 x)/4.$

14. The reduction of order procedure (see Section 4.4) can also be applied to the nonhomogeneous equation

$$y'' + p(x)y' + q(x)y = g(x).$$

Using the substitution $y = v(x)f(x)$, where $f(x)$ is a nontrivial solution to the corresponding homogeneous equation, reduce the nonhomogeneous equation to a linear first order equation that can be solved by the methods of Section 2.4. Use this procedure to find a general solution to

$$y'' + x^{-1}y' - 4x^{-2}y = 1 - x^{-3}, \qquad x > 0,$$

given that $f(x) = x^2$ is a solution to the corresponding homogeneous equation.

15. There is another type of reduction of order procedure that can be applied to equations of the form $L[y](x) = g(x)$, provided that L is a differential operator that can be written as the product of first order factors. To illustrate this method consider the equation

(10) $L[y](x) := y'' - y' - 2y = e^x.$

Notice that $L[y] = (D^2 - D - 2)y$ can be written as $L[y] = (D+1)(D-2)y$. Let $v = (D-2)y$ and observe that solving (10) is equivalent to solving the two first order equations

(11) $(D+1)v = e^x,$

(12) $(D-2)y = v,$

which, in turn, can be solved using the method discussed in Section 2.4. Carry out this procedure by completing the following steps.

(a) Solve equation (11) for v.
(b) Now substitute the v obtained in part (a) into equation (12) and solve for y. This gives a general solution to (10).

16. Use the method of Problem 15 to find a general solution to

$$y'' + 6y' + 5y = 10x + 5.$$

4.8 *Method of Undetermined Coefficients*

In this section we give a simple procedure for finding a particular solution to a nonhomogeneous linear equation with constant coefficients when the nonhomogeneous term $g(x)$ is of a special type. To motivate the procedure, let's first look at a few examples.

▶ *Example 1*   Find a particular solution to

(1) $L[y](x) := y'' + 3y' + 2y = 3x + 1.$

Solution   We want to find a function $y_p(x)$ such that $L[y_p](x) = 3x + 1$. Notice that if L is applied to any linear function $y_p = Ax + B$, we obtain the linear function

$$L[y_p](x) = 0 + 3A + 2(Ax + B) = 2Ax + (3A + 2B).$$

Let's therefore try to solve the equation

$$2Ax + (3A + 2B) = 3x + 1$$

for the constants A and B. Since two polynomials are equal when their corresponding coefficients are equal, we set

$$2A = 3,$$
$$3A + 2B = 1.$$

Solving this system gives $A = \frac{3}{2}$ and $B = -\frac{7}{4}$. Thus the function

$$y_p(x) = \frac{3}{2}x - \frac{7}{4}$$

is a particular solution to equation (1) since $L[y_p](x) = 3x + 1$. ◀

Throughout this section, L denotes a linear differential operator with **constant coefficients.** For such operators, Example 1 suggests the following method for finding a particular solution to the equation

$$L[y](x) = p_n(x),$$

where $p_n(x)$ is a polynomial of degree n. Let

$$y_p(x) = A_n x^n + \cdots + A_1 x + A_0$$

and solve

(2) $L[y_p](x) = p_n(x)$

for the coefficients $A_0, A_1, \ldots, A_n$. This procedure involves solving $n + 1$ linear equations in the $n + 1$ unknowns $A_0, \ldots, A_n$ and usually has a solution. The technique is called the **method of undetermined coefficients.**†

---

† *Historical Footnote:* This method was developed by Leonhard Euler in his theory of the motion of the moon in 1753.

▶ *Example 2*   Find a particular solution to

(3) $L[y](x) := y'' + 3y' + 2y = e^{3x}.$

Solution   Here we seek a function y_p such that $L[y_p](x) = e^{3x}$. If we try $y_p(x) = Ae^{3x}$, where A is a constant, then

$$L[y_p](x) = 9Ae^{3x} + 3(3Ae^{3x}) + 2(Ae^{3x}) = 20Ae^{3x}.$$

Setting $20Ae^{3x} = e^{3x}$ and solving for A gives $A = \frac{1}{20}$. Hence

$$y_p(x) = \frac{e^{3x}}{20}$$

is a particular solution to equation (3) since $L[y_p](x) = e^{3x}$.   ◀

The method of undetermined coefficients will also work for equations of the form

$$L[y](x) = ae^{\alpha x},$$

where a and α are given constants. Here we would try

$$y_p(x) = Ae^{\alpha x}$$

and solve $L[y_p](x) = ae^{\alpha x}$ for the unknown coefficient A.

▶ *Example 3*   Find a particular solution to

(4) $L[y](x) := y'' - y' - y = \sin x.$

Solution   This time we seek a function y_p that satisfies $L[y_p](x) = \sin x$. Our initial action might be to try letting $y_p(x) = A \sin x$, in which case we get

$$L[y_p](x) = -2A \sin x - A \cos x.$$

However, since the right-hand side of (4) involves only sin x, this choice of solution would force A (and hence y_p) to be zero, which is absurd!
    Instead, to compensate for the cos x term, let's try

$$y_p(x) = A \cos x + B \sin x,$$

so that

$$L[y_p](x) = (-2A - B) \cos x + (A - 2B) \sin x.$$

Then setting

$$(-2A - B)\cos x + (A - 2B)\sin x = \sin x$$

and equating the coefficients of $\cos x$ and of $\sin x$ leads to the system of equations

$$-2A - B = 0,$$
$$A - 2B = 1.$$

Solving for A and B yields $A = \frac{1}{5}$ and $B = -\frac{2}{5}$. Hence

$$y_p(x) = \tfrac{1}{5}\cos x - \tfrac{2}{5}\sin x$$

is a particular solution to equation (4). ◀

More generally, for an equation of the form

$$L[y](x) = a\cos \beta x + b\sin \beta x,$$

the method of undetermined coefficients suggests that we try

$$y_p(x) = A\cos \beta x + B\sin \beta x$$

and solve $L[y_p](x) = a\cos \beta x + b\sin \beta x$ for the unknowns A and B.

▶ **Example 4**   Find a particular solution to

(5) $$L[y](x):= y'' + y' = 5.$$

Solution   Since the right-hand side of (5) is the constant polynomial $p_0(x) \equiv 5$, Example 1 suggests that we let $y_p(x) = A$ and set $L[y_p](x) = 5$. But then we get

$$L[y_p](x) = 0 \neq 5.$$

This unfortunate circumstance occurs because any constant function is a solution to the corresponding homogeneous equation $L[y](x) = 0$. To circumvent this difficulty, we temporarily abandon the method of undetermined coefficients and observe that we can integrate both sides of equation (5) to obtain the linear first order equation

(6) $$y' + y = 5x + c_1,$$

where c_1 is an arbitrary constant. Using the method of Section 2.4 for solving linear first order equations, we find that

(7) $y(x) = 5x - 5 + c_1 + c_2 e^{-x}$

is a general solution to equation (6) and hence to equation (5).
    Notice that with $c_1 = 5$ and $c_2 = 0$ in (7), we get

(8) $y_p(x) = 5x$

as a particular solution to equation (5). This suggests that in our original attempt to use undetermined coefficients we should have taken

        $y_p(x) = Ax$

instead of $y_p = A$. Indeed, with $y_p = Ax$, setting $L[y_p](x) = 5$ immediately gives $A = 5$, and we again obtain (8). ◄

    In the preceding example the trial choice for y_p did not work, because it was a solution to the corresponding homogeneous equation. However, when we replaced y_p by the new function $\hat{y}_p = xy_p$, we were able to find a particular solution to the nonhomogeneous equation. Consequently the procedure of undetermined coefficients must be modified as follows.
    If any term in the trial expression for y_p is a solution to the corresponding homogeneous equation, then replace y_p by $x^s y_p$, where s is the smallest nonnegative integer such that no term in $x^s y_p$ is a solution to the corresponding homogeneous equation.

► **Example 5**   Determine the form of a particular solution to

(9) $y'' - y' - 12y = e^{4x}$.

Solution   The auxiliary equation for the corresponding homogeneous equation

(10) $y'' - y' - 12y = 0$

has the roots $r_1 = 4$ and $r_2 = -3$. A general solution for (10) is therefore

(11) $y_h(x) = c_1 e^{4x} + c_2 e^{-3x}$.

Now, since the right-hand side of (9) is e^{4x}, we first let $y_p = Ae^{4x}$. Because e^{4x} is a solution to equation (10), however, we replace this choice by $y_p = Axe^{4x}$. Since xe^{4x} is not a solution to equation (10), there exists a particular solution to (9) of the form

(12) $y_p(x) = Axe^{4x}$. ◄

TABLE 4.1 THE FORM OF A PARTICULAR SOLUTION $y_p(x)$ OF $L[y](x) = g(x)$ WHEN $L[y]$ HAS CONSTANT COEFFICIENTS

Type	$g(x)$	$y_p(x)$
(I)	$p_n(x) = a_n x^n + \cdots + a_1 x + a_0$	$x^s P_n(x) = x^s\{A_n x^n + \cdots + A_1 x + A_0\}$
(II)	$ae^{\alpha x}$	$x^s A e^{\alpha x}$
(III)	$a \cos \beta x + b \sin \beta x$	$x^s\{A \cos \beta x + B \sin \beta x\}$
(IV)	$p_n(x)e^{\alpha x}$	$x^s P_n(x) e^{\alpha x}$
(V)	$p_n(x) \cos \beta x + q_m(x) \sin \beta x,$ where $q_m(x) = b_m x^m + \cdots + b_1 x + b_0$	$x^s\{P_N(x) \cos \beta x + Q_N(x) \sin \beta x\},$ where $Q_N(x) = B_N x^N + \cdots + B_1 x + B_0$ and $N = \max(n, m)$
(VI)	$ae^{\alpha x} \cos \beta x + be^{\alpha x} \sin \beta x$	$x^s\{Ae^{\alpha x} \cos \beta x + Be^{\alpha x} \sin \beta x\}$
(VII)	$p_n(x)e^{\alpha x} \cos \beta x + q_m(x)e^{\alpha x} \sin \beta x$	$x^s e^{\alpha x}\{P_N(x) \cos \beta x + Q_N(x) \sin \beta x\},$ where $N = \max(n, m)$

The nonnegative integer s is chosen to be the smallest integer so that no term in the particular solution $y_p(x)$ is a solution to the corresponding homogeneous equation $L[y](x) = 0$.

As our examples illustrate, when the nonhomogeneous term $g(x)$ is a polynomial, an exponential, a sine, or a cosine function, the function $g(x)$ itself suggests the form of the particular solution $y_p(x)$. In fact, we can expand the list of functions $g(x)$ for which the method of undetermined coefficients can be applied to include products of these functions as well. In Table 4.1 we have listed the various forms for $g(x)$ and the corresponding forms for the particular solution $y_p(x)$. In using the table, the reader is reminded to choose s as the smallest nonnegative integer such that no term in y_p is a solution to the corresponding homogeneous equation. For linear second order equations, s will be either 0, 1, or 2. An incorrect choice for s leads to an inconsistent system of equations.

▶ *Example 6* Using Table 4.1, find the form for a particular solution y_p to

(13) $y'' + 2y' - 3y = g(x),$

where $g(x)$ equals

(a) $7 \cos 3x,$ (b) $5e^{-3x},$ (c) $x^2 \cos \pi x,$ (d) $2xe^x \sin x - e^x \cos x,$
(e) $x^2 e^x + 3xe^x,$ (f) $\tan x.$

Solution   The auxiliary equation for the corresponding homogeneous equation,

(14) $y'' + 2y' - 3y = 0,$

has roots $r_1 = 1$ and $r_2 = -3$. Thus a general solution for (14) is

(15) $y_h(x) = c_1 e^x + c_2 e^{-3x}.$

(a) Referring to Table 4.1, the function $g(x) = 7 \cos 3x$ is of Type III (with $a = 7, b = 0, \beta = 3$). Hence y_p has the form

(16) $y_p(x) = A \cos 3x + B \sin 3x,$

since no term in (16) is a solution to (14).

(b) The function $g(x) = 5e^{-3x}$ is of Type II, and so y_p has the form $x^s A e^{-3x}$. Here we take $s = 1$ since e^{-3x} is a solution to equation (14) and xe^{-3x} is not. Thus

$$y_p(x) = Axe^{-3x}.$$

(c) The function $g(x) = x^2 \cos \pi x$ is of Type V, with $p_2(x) = x^2$, $q_0(x) \equiv 0$. Since $N = \max\{2, 0\} = 2,$

(17) $y_p(x) = (A_2 x^2 + A_1 x + A_0) \cos \pi x + (B_2 x^2 + B_1 x + B_0) \sin \pi x,$

where we have taken $s = 0$ because no term in (17) is a solution to the homogeneous equation.

(d) The function $g(x) = 2xe^x \sin x - e^x \cos x$ is of Type VII, with $p_0(x) = -1$ and $q_1(x) = 2x$. For these polynomials, $N = \max\{0, 1\} = 1$, so

$$x^s e^x\{(A_1 x + A_0) \cos x + (B_1 x + B_0) \sin x\}$$

is the form for the particular solution. Since none of the terms $e^x x \cos x$, $e^x \cos x$, $e^x x \sin x$, and $e^x \sin x$ is a solution of the homogeneous equation (14), we set $s = 0$ and obtain

$$y_p(x) = e^x\{(A_1 x + A_0) \cos x + (B_1 x + B_0) \sin x\}.$$

(e) Here $g(x) = x^2 e^x + 3xe^x = (x^2 + 3x)e^x$ is of Type IV with $p_2(x) = x^2 + 3x$. Thus

$$y_p(x) = x(A_2 x^2 + A_1 x + A_0)e^x,$$

where we have taken $s = 1$ since the term $A_0 e^x$ in

$$(A_2 x^2 + A_1 x + A_0)e^x$$

is a solution to equation (14).

(f) Unfortunately, $g(x) = \tan x$ is not one of the forms for which the method of undetermined coefficients can be used. In Section 4.9 we discuss a different method that can handle such nonhomogeneous terms. ◄

Let's summarize:

METHOD OF UNDETERMINED COEFFICIENTS

To determine a particular solution to $L[y] = g$:

(a) Check that the linear equation has constant coefficients and that the nonhomogeneous term $g(x)$ is one of the types suitable for the method.

(b) Solve the corresponding homogeneous equation $L[y](x) = 0$.

(c) Based on the form of the nonhomogeneous term $g(x)$, determine the appropriate form of the particular solution $y_p(x)$. Remember that no term in the trial expression for $y_p(x)$ may be a solution to the corresponding homogeneous equation.

(d) Since we want $L[y_p](x) = g(x)$, set the corresponding coefficients from both sides of this equation equal to each other to form a system of linear equations.

(e) Solve this system of linear equations for the coefficients of $y_p(x)$.

If we combine the method of undetermined coefficients with the superposition principle, we can solve for $y_p(x)$ when $g(x)$ is a finite *sum* of terms like those listed in Table 4.1.

► **Example 7**   Find a general solution to the equation

(18) $y'' - y = 2e^{-x} - 4xe^{-x} + 10 \cos 2x.$

Solution   We first solve the associated homogeneous equation $y'' - y = 0$ and obtain as a general solution $y_h(x) = c_1 e^x + c_2 e^{-x}$.

Notice that the right-hand side of (18) is not one of the forms given in Table 4.1, but is the sum of two such forms. This suggests that we use the superposition principle and consider separately the equations

(19) $y'' - y = 2e^{-x} - 4xe^{-x}$

and

(20) $y'' - y = 10 \cos 2x.$

A particular solution to equation (19) has the form $y_q(x) = x^s(A_1x + A_0)e^{-x}$. Since A_0e^{-x} is a solution to the corresponding homogeneous equation, we take $s = 1$. Then

$$y_q(x) = (A_1x^2 + A_0x)e^{-x}.$$

Substituting y_q for y in (19) gives

(21) $-4A_1xe^{-x} + (2A_1 - 2A_0)e^{-x} = -4xe^{-x} + 2e^{-x}.$

When we equate the coefficients of xe^{-x} and e^{-x} on both sides of equation (21), we obtain the system

$$-4A_1 = -4,$$
$$2A_1 - 2A_0 = 2.$$

Solving, we find $A_1 = 1$ and $A_0 = 0$; thus

$$y_q(x) = x^2e^{-x}$$

is a particular solution to (19).

Next, consider equation (20). A particular solution to this equation has the form

$$y_r(x) = A \cos 2x + B \sin 2x$$

(here we can take $s = 0$). Substituting y_r for y in (20) gives

(22) $-5A \cos 2x - 5B \sin 2x = 10 \cos 2x,$

which yields $A = -2$ and $B = 0$. Thus

$$y_r(x) = -2 \cos 2x.$$

It follows from the superposition principle that a particular solution to the original equation (18) is given by the sum $y_q + y_r$; that is,

$$y_p(x) = x^2e^{-x} - 2 \cos 2x.$$

Hence a general solution to equation (18), given by the sum of the general solution to the corresponding homogeneous equation and a particular solution, is

$$y(x) = c_1e^x + c_2e^{-x} + x^2e^{-x} - 2 \cos 2x. \blacktriangleleft$$

Success in applying the method of undetermined coefficients lies in the ability to guess the form of a particular solution. As we have seen, when L is a second order linear differential operator with constant coefficients, there is a class of functions $g(x)$ for which the choice of the form of a particular solution to the equation $L[y](x) = g(x)$ is quite easy to determine. This class consists of functions of the form

$$p_n(x)e^{\alpha x} \cos \beta x + q_m(x)e^{\alpha x} \sin \beta x,$$

where $p_n(x)$ and $q_m(x)$ are polynomials. The method works because when we apply the operator L to a function of this form we get back a function of the same type. As you might have guessed, these functions are themselves solutions of some (higher order) homogeneous linear differential equation with constant coefficients. We verify in Chapter 6 that the method of undetermined coefficients applies to such functions.

EXERCISES 4.8

In Problems 1 through 16 find a particular solution to the differential equation.

1. $y'' + 2y' - y = 10.$

2. $y'' + 2y = -8.$

3. $y'' + y = 5e^{2x}.$

4. $y'' - y = 3e^{-2x}.$

5. $2y' + y = 3x^2 + 10x.$

6. $y'' - y' - 2y = -2x^3 - 3x^2 + 8x + 1.$

7. $y'' + y' + y = 2 \cos 2x - 3 \sin 2x.$

8. $y'' - y' + 9y = 3 \sin 3x.$

9. $y'' - 5y' + 6y = xe^x.$

10. $y'' + 2y' - 8y = xe^{-x} + e^{-x}.$

11. $y'' - y = x \sin x.$

12. $y'' + y = 2^x.$

13. $y'' - 2y' + y = 8e^x.$

14. $y'' - 4y' = x^2 - 1.$

15. $y'' - 6y' + 9y = x^2 + e^x.$

16. $y'' - 4y' - 5y = 2e^{-x}.$

In Problems 17 through 30 find a general solution to the differential equation.

17. $y'' - y = -11x + 1.$

18. $y'' + y = 7x + 5.$

19. $y'' + y' - 2y = x^2 - 2x + 3.$

20. $y'' - 2y' - 3y = 3x^2 - 5.$

21. $y'' - 3y' + 2y = e^x \sin x.$

22. $y'' + 4y = \sin x - \cos x.$

23. $y'' + 2y' + 2y = e^{-x} \cos x.$

24. $y'' + 6y' + 10y = 10x^4 + 24x^3 + 2x^2 - 12x + 18.$

25. $y'' - 4y' + 4y = xe^{2x}.$

26. $y'' - 7y' = x^2.$

27. $y'' + 4y' + 5y = e^{-x} - \sin 2x.$

28. $y'' - 3y = x^2 - e^x.$

29. $y'' + y' + y = \cos x - x^2 e^x.$

30. $y'' - 2y' - 35y = 13 \sin x - e^{3x} + 1.$

In Problems 31 through 40 find the solution to the initial value problem.

31. $y' - y = 1, \qquad y(0) = 0.$

32. $y'' = 6x; \qquad y(0) = 3, \qquad y'(0) = -1.$

33. $y'' + y = 2e^{-x}; \qquad y(0) = 0, \qquad y'(0) = 0.$

34. $y'' + 9y = 27; \qquad y(0) = 4, \qquad y'(0) = 6.$

35. $y'' - y' - 2y = \cos x - \sin 2x; \qquad y(0) = -\frac{7}{20}, \qquad y'(0) = \frac{1}{5}.$

36. $y'' - y = e^x - e^{-x} + 2; \qquad y(0) = 0, \qquad y'(0) = 0.$

37. $y'' + y' - 12y = e^x + e^{2x} - 1; \qquad y(0) = 1, \qquad y'(0) = 3.$

38. $y'' - 7y' + 10y = x^2 - 4 + e^x; \qquad y(0) = 3, \qquad y'(0) = -3.$

39. $y'' - y = \sin x - e^{2x}; \qquad y(0) = 1, \qquad y'(0) = -1.$

40. $y'' + 2y' + y = x^2 + 1 - e^x;$ $y(0) = 0,$ $y'(0) = 2.$

In Problems 41 through 48 determine the form of a particular solution for the differential equation.

41. $y'' + y = \sin x + x \cos x + 10^x.$

42. $y'' - y = e^{2x} + xe^{2x} + x^2 e^{2x}.$

43. $y'' - y' - 2y = e^x \cos x - x^2 + x + 1.$

44. $y'' + 5y' + 6y = \sin x - \cos 2x.$

45. $y'' - 4y' + 4y = x^2 e^{2x} - e^{2x}.$

46. $y'' - 4y' + 5y = e^{5x} + x \sin 3x - \cos 3x.$

47. $y'' - y = e^x - 7 + \cos x.$

48. $y'' + 2y' + 2y = x^2 + e^{-x} \cos x + xe^{-x} \sin x.$

In Problems 49 and 50 find a particular solution to the given third order equation.

49. $y''' - y'' + y = \sin x.$

50. $2y''' + 3y'' + y' - 4y = e^{-x}.$

51. Discontinuous Forcing Term. In certain physical models the nonhomogeneous term, or **forcing term,** $g(x)$ in the equation $L[y](x) = g(x)$ may not be continuous, but may have a jump discontinuity. If this occurs, we can still obtain a reasonable solution using the following procedure. Consider the initial value problem

$$y'' + 2y' + 5y = g(x); \quad y(0) = 0, \quad y'(0) = 0,$$

where

$$g(x) := \begin{cases} 10, & 0 \le x \le \dfrac{3\pi}{2}, \\ 0, & x > \dfrac{3\pi}{2}. \end{cases}$$

(a) Find a solution to the initial value problem for $0 \le x \le 3\pi/2.$
(b) Find a general solution for $x > 3\pi/2.$
(c) Now choose the constants in the general solution from part (b) so that the solution from part (a) and the solution from part (b) agree at $x = 3\pi/2.$ This gives us a continuous function that satisfies the differential equation except at $x = 3\pi/2.$

Problems 52–54 concern justifications for the method of undetermined coefficients.

52. Consider the nonhomogeneous equation

(23) $ay'' + by' + cy = a_n x^n + \cdots + a_1 x + a_0.$

We want to determine the form of a particular solution y_p to equation (23).
(a) Assume

(24) $y_p(x) = A_n x^n + \cdots + A_0,$

and substitute y_p into equation (23) to obtain, after simplifying,

$$cA_n x^n + (cA_{n-1} + nbA_n)x^{n-1} + \cdots + (2aA_2 + bA_1 + cA_0)$$
$$= a_n x^n + \cdots + a_0.$$

(b) Show that if $c \neq 0$, then no term in (24) is a solution to the homogeneous equation

(25) $$a y'' + b y' + c y = 0.$$

(c) Show that if $c \neq 0$, then you can solve for the constants $A_n, A_{n-1}, \ldots,$ A_0 in terms of the constants $a_n, a_{n-1}, \ldots, a_0$; hence there exists a solution to equation (23) of the form (24).

53. Consider the nonhomogeneous equation

(26) $$a y'' + b y' + c y = e^{\alpha x}(a_n x^n + \cdots + a_0).$$

We want to determine the form of a particular solution y_p to equation (26).

(a) Let $y_p(x) = e^{\alpha x} v(x)$. Substitute for y, y', and y'' in equation (26) and cancel the factor $e^{\alpha x}$ to obtain

(27) $$a v'' + (2a\alpha + b) v + (a\alpha^2 + b\alpha + c) v = a_n x^n + \cdots + a_0.$$

(b) Using the results from Problem 52, show that if $e^{\alpha x}$ is not a solution to the homogeneous equation (25), then equation (27) has a solution of the form

$$y_p(x) = e^{\alpha x}(A_n x^n + \cdots + A_0).$$

54. Annihilator Method.   The annihilator method, which is discussed in Chapter 6, can be used to justify the method of undetermined coefficients. To illustrate the annihilator approach, consider the equation

(28) $$(D - 1)(D + 1)y = y'' - y = e^{3x}.$$

(a) Show that applying $(D - 3)$ to both sides of equation (28) gives

(29) $$(D - 3)(D - 1)(D + 1)y = y''' - 3y'' - y' + 3y = 0.$$

(Since $(D - 3)e^{3x} \equiv 0$, we say that $(D - 3)$ "annihilates" e^{3x}.)

(b) If y_p satisfies equation (28), it will also satisfy equation (29). Now verify that

(30) $$c_1 e^{3x} + c_2 e^x + c_3 e^{-x}$$

is a general solution to (29) and conclude that there exists a particular solution to (28) of the form (30).

(c) Using the fact that $c_2 e^x + c_3 e^{-x}$ is a solution to the homogeneous equation

$$(D - 1)(D + 1)y = 0,$$

conclude that there must be a particular solution to (28) of the form $y_p(x) = c_1 e^{3x}$.

(d) Use the above procedure to show that there is a particular solution to

$$(D - 1)(D + 1)y = e^x$$

of the form $y_p(x) = Cxe^x$. [Hint: Use the annihilator $(D - 1)$.]

55. Forced Vibrations. A vibrating spring with damping that is under external force can be modeled by

(31) $$mx'' + bx' + kx = g(t),$$

where $m > 0$ is the mass of the spring system, $b > 0$ is the damping constant, $k > 0$ is the spring constant, $g(t)$ is the force on the system at time t, and $x(t)$ is the displacement from the equilibrium of the spring system at time t. Assume $b^2 < 4mk$.

(a) Determine the form of the equation of motion for the spring system when $g(t) = \sin \beta t$ by finding a general solution to equation (31).

(b) Discuss the long-term behavior of this system. [Hint: Consider what happens to the general solution obtained in part (a) as $t \to +\infty$.]

4.9 Variation of Parameters

We have seen that the method of undetermined coefficients is a simple procedure for determining a particular solution when the equation has constant coefficients and the non-homogeneous term is of a special type. Here we present a more general method, called **variation of parameters,**[†] which can be used to determine a particular solution. This method applies even when the coefficients of the differential equation are functions of x, *provided* we know a fundamental solution set for the corresponding homogeneous equation.

Consider the nonhomogeneous linear second order equation

(1) $$L[y](x) := y'' + p(x)y' + q(x)y = g(x),$$

where the coefficient of y'' is taken to be 1, and let $\{y_1(x), y_2(x)\}$ be a fundamental solution set for the corresponding homogeneous equation

(2) $$L[y](x) = 0.$$

Then we know that the solutions to the homogeneous equation (2) are given by

(3) $$y_h(x) = c_1 y_1(x) + c_2 y_2(x),$$

where c_1 and c_2 are constants. To find a particular solution to the nonhomogeneous equation, the idea behind variation of parameters is to replace the constants in (3) by functions

---

[†] *Historical Footnote:* The method of variation of parameters was discovered by Joseph Lagrange in 1774.

of x. That is, we seek a solution of (1) of the form

(4) $y_p(x) = v_1(x)y_1(x) + v_2(x)y_2(x).$

Since we have introduced two unknown functions, $v_1(x)$ and $v_2(x)$, it is reasonable to expect that we will need two equations involving these functions in order to determine them. Naturally, one of these two equations should come from (1). Let's therefore plug $y_p(x)$ given by (4) into (1). To accomplish this, we must first compute $y_p'(x)$ and $y_p''(x)$. From (4) we obtain

(5) $y_p' = (v_1'y_1 + v_2'y_2) + (v_1 y_1' + v_2 y_2').$

To simplify the computation and to avoid second order derivatives for the unknowns v_1, v_2 in the expression for y_p'', let us require

(6) $v_1'y_1 + v_2'y_2 = 0.$

Then (5) becomes

(7) $y_p' = v_1 y_1' + v_2 y_2',$

so

(8) $y_p'' = v_1'y_1' + v_1 y_1'' + v_2'y_2' + v_2 y_2''.$

Now, substituting y_p, y_p', and y_p'', as given in (4), (7), and (8), into (1) we find

(9) $g = L[y_p]$

$= (v_1'y_1' + v_1 y_1'' + v_2'y_2' + v_2 y_2'') + p(v_1 y_1' + v_2 y_2') + q(v_1 y_1 + v_2 y_2)$

$= (v_1'y_1' + v_2'y_2') + v_1(y_1'' + py_1' + qy_1) + v_2(y_2'' + py_2' + qy_2)$

$= (v_1'y_1' + v_2'y_2') + v_1 L[y_1] + v_2 L[y_2].$

Since y_1 and y_2 are solutions to the homogeneous equation, we have $L[y_1] = L[y_2] = 0$. Thus (9) becomes

(10) $v_1'y_1' + v_2'y_2' = g.$

If we can find v_1 and v_2 that satisfy both (6) and (10), that is,

(11)

$y_1 v_1' + y_2 v_2' = 0,$

$y_1' v_1' + y_2' v_2' = g,$

then y_p given by (4) will be a particular solution to (1). To determine v_1 and v_2, we first solve the linear system (11) for v_1' and v_2'. Algebraic manipulation or Cramer's rule immediately gives

(12) $\qquad v_1'(x) = \dfrac{-g(x)y_2(x)}{W[y_1, y_2](x)}, \qquad v_2'(x) = \dfrac{g(x)y_1(x)}{W[y_1, y_2](x)},$

where $W[y_1, y_2](x)$, which occurs in the denominator, is the Wronskian of $y_1(x)$ and $y_2(x)$. Notice that this Wronskian is never zero, because $\{y_1, y_2\}$ is a fundamental solution set. Upon integrating the equations in (12), we finally obtain

(13) $\qquad v_1(x) = \displaystyle\int \dfrac{-g(x)y_2(x)}{W[y_1, y_2](x)}\, dx, \qquad v_2(x) = \displaystyle\int \dfrac{g(x)y_1(x)}{W[y_1, y_2](x)}\, dx.$

Let's review this procedure:

METHOD OF VARIATION OF PARAMETERS

To determine a particular solution to $y'' + py' + qy = g$:

(a) Find a fundamental solution set $\{y_1(x), y_2(x)\}$ for the corresponding homogeneous equation and take

$$y_p(x) = v_1(x)y_1(x) + v_2(x)y_2(x).$$

(b) Determine $v_1(x)$ and $v_2(x)$ by using the formulas in (13) or by solving the system in (11) for $v_1'(x)$ and $v_2'(x)$ and integrating. (If the equation is $a_2(x)y'' + a_1(x)y' + a_0(x)y = b(x)$, then it must be put in the form $y'' + p(x)y' + q(x)y = g(x)$.)

(c) Substitute $v_1(x)$ and $v_2(x)$ into the expression for $y_p(x)$ to obtain a particular solution.

▶ *Example 1* Find a general solution on $(-\pi/2, \pi/2)$ to

(14) $\qquad \dfrac{d^2y}{dx^2} + y = \tan x.$

Solution Recall that a fundamental solution set for the homogeneous equation $y'' + y = 0$ is $\{\cos x, \sin x\}$. We now set

(15) $\qquad y_p(x) = v_1(x) \cos x + v_2(x) \sin x$

and referring to (11), solve the system

$$(\cos x)v_1'(x) + (\sin x)v_2'(x) = 0,$$
$$(-\sin x)v_1'(x) + (\cos x)v_2'(x) = \tan x$$

for $v_1'(x)$ and $v_2'(x)$. This gives

$$v_1'(x) = -\tan x \sin x,$$

$$v_2'(x) = \tan x \cos x = \sin x.$$

Integrating, we obtain

(16) $\quad v_1(x) = -\int \tan x \sin x \, dx = -\int \frac{\sin^2 x}{\cos x} \, dx$

$$= -\int \frac{1 - \cos^2 x}{\cos x} \, dx = \int (\cos x - \sec x) \, dx$$

$$= \sin x - \ln(\sec x + \tan x) + C_1,$$

(17) $\quad v_2(x) = \int \sin x \, dx = -\cos x + C_2.$

Since we need only one particular solution, we take both C_1 and C_2 to be zero. Hence, plugging $v_1(x)$ and $v_2(x)$ back into (15), we obtain

$$y_p(x) = [\sin x - \ln(\sec x + \tan x)] \cos x - \cos x \sin x,$$

which simplifies to

(18) $\quad y_p(x) = -(\cos x) \ln(\sec x + \tan x).$

Recall from Theorem 7 in Section 4.7 that a general solution to a nonhomogeneous equation is given by the sum of a general solution to the homogeneous equation and a particular solution. Consequently, a general solution to equation (14) on the interval $(-\pi/2, \pi/2)$ is

(19) $\quad y(x) = c_1 \cos x + c_2 \sin x - (\cos x) \ln(\sec x + \tan x). \blacktriangleleft$

In the above example, the constants C_1 and C_2 appearing in (16) and (17) were chosen to be zero. If we had retained these arbitrary constants, the ultimate effect would be just to add a solution of the homogeneous equation. Hence, leaving C_1 and C_2 arbitrary and plugging $v_1(x)$ and $v_2(x)$ back into (15) leads to the general solution given in (19).

▶ *Example 2* Find a particular solution on $(-\pi/2, \pi/2)$ to

(20) $\quad \dfrac{d^2 y}{dx^2} + y = \tan x + 3x - 1.$

Solution With $g(x) = \tan x + 3x - 1$, the variation of parameters procedure will lead to a solution of (20). But it is simpler in this case to consider separately the equations

(21) $\dfrac{d^2y}{dx^2} + y = \tan x,$

(22) $\dfrac{d^2y}{dx^2} + y = 3x - 1$

and then use the superposition principle (Theorem 6, page 195).
    In Example 1 we found that

(23) $y_q(x) = -(\cos x)\ln(\sec x + \tan x)$

is a particular solution for equation (21). For equation (22), the method of undetermined coefficients can be applied. On seeking a solution to (22) of the form $y_r(x) = Ax + B$, we quickly obtain

(24) $y_r(x) = 3x - 1.$

Finally, we apply the superposition principle to get

$$y_p(x) = y_q(x) + y_r(x)$$
$$= -(\cos x)\ln(\sec x + \tan x) + 3x - 1$$

as a particular solution for equation (20). ◀

    One important advantage the method of variation of parameters has over the method of undetermined coefficients is its applicability to linear equations whose coefficients are functions of x (see Problems 19–22). The fly in the ointment is that variation of parameters requires that we know a fundamental solution set for the corresponding homogeneous equation. For equations with variable coefficients, this set may be extremely difficult to determine.

EXERCISES 4.9

In Problems 1 through 10 find a general solution to the differential equation using the method of variation of parameters.

1. $y'' + 4y = \tan 2x.$
2. $y'' + y = \sec x.$
3. $2y'' - 2y' - 4y = 2e^{3x}.$
4. $y'' - y = 2x + 4.$
5. $y'' - 2y' + y = x^{-1}e^x.$
6. $y'' + 2y' + y = e^{-x}.$
7. $y'' + 16y = \sec 4x.$
8. $y'' + 9y = \sec^2 3x.$
9. $y'' + 4y = \csc^2 2x.$
10. $y'' + 4y' + 4y = e^{-2x}\ln x.$

In Problems 11 through 18 find a general solution to the differential equation.

11. $y'' + y = \tan x + e^{3x} - 1.$
12. $y'' + y = \tan^2 x.$
13. $y'' + 4y = \sec^4 2x.$
14. $y'' + y = \sec^3 x.$
15. $y'' + y = 3\sec x - x^2 + 1.$
16. $y'' + 5y' + 6y = 18x^2.$
17. $\frac{1}{2}y'' + 2y = \tan 2x - \frac{1}{2}e^x.$
18. $y'' - 6y' + 9y = x^{-3}e^{3x}.$

In Problems 19 through 22 find a general solution to the differential equation, given that the functions y_1 and y_2 are linearly independent solutions to the corresponding homogeneous equation for $x > 0$. Remember to put the equation in the same form as equation (1).

19. $xy'' - (x + 1)y' + y = x^2;$ $y_1 = e^x,$ $y_2 = x + 1.$

20. $x^2y'' - 4xy' + 6y = x^3 + 1;$ $y_1 = x^2,$ $y_2 = x^3.$

21. $xy'' + (5x - 1)y' - 5y = x^2 e^{-5x};$ $y_1 = 5x - 1,$ $y_2 = e^{-5x}.$

22. $xy'' + (1 - 2x)y' + (x - 1)y = xe^x;$ $y_1 = e^x,$ $y_2 = e^x \ln x.$

23. The **Bessel equation** of order one-half,

$$x^2y'' + xy' + (x^2 - \tfrac{1}{4})y = 0, \qquad x > 0,$$

has two linearly independent solutions,

$$y_1(x) = x^{-1/2} \cos x, \qquad y_2(x) = x^{-1/2} \sin x.$$

Find a general solution to the nonhomogeneous equation

$$x^2y'' + xy' + (x^2 - \tfrac{1}{4})y = x^{5/2}, \qquad x > 0.$$

24. Use the method of variation of parameters to show that

$$y(x) = c_1 \cos x + c_2 \sin x + \int_0^x \sin(x - s)f(s)\,ds$$

is a general solution to the differential equation

$$y'' + y = f(x)$$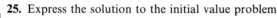

where $f(x)$ is a continuous function on $(-\infty, \infty)$. [Hint: Use the trigonometric identity $\sin(x - s) = \sin x \cos s - \sin s \cos x.$]

25. Express the solution to the initial value problem

$$y'' - y = \frac{1}{x}; \qquad y(1) = 0, \qquad y'(1) = -2$$

using definite integrals. Using Simpson's rule to approximate the integrals, find an approximation for $y(2)$.

★ *4.10 Cauchy-Euler Equations*

Until now we have concentrated on solving linear second order differential equations with constant coefficients. In this section we consider a special class of equations with **variable** coefficients.

CAUCHY-EULER EQUATIONS

Definition 4. A linear second order equation that can be expressed in the form

$$(1) \qquad ax^2 \frac{d^2y}{dx^2} + bx\frac{dy}{dx} + cy = h(x),$$

where a, b, and c are constants is called a **Cauchy-Euler equation.**[†]

For example, the differential equation

$$(2) \qquad 3x^2y'' - 2xy' + 7y = \sin x$$

is a Cauchy-Euler equation, whereas

$$(3) \qquad 2y'' - 3xy' + 11y = 3x - 1$$

is *not,* because the coefficient of y'' is 2, which is not a constant times x^2.

To solve equation (1), we first obtain two linearly independent solutions to the associated homogeneous equation. There are two methods that can be used for this purpose. The first involves the substitution $x = e^t$, which transforms equation (1) into an equation with constant coefficients. The second method involves the guess $y = x^r$, which leads to an auxiliary equation for r. In this section we demonstrate the first technique and leave the discussion of the second method for Section 8.5 (see also Problems 29–31).

▶ *Example 1* Find a general solution to

$$(4) \qquad 3x^2 \frac{d^2y}{dx^2} + 11x\frac{dy}{dx} - 3y = 0, \qquad x > 0.$$

Solution We use the substitution $x = e^t$ to transform (4) into an equation in which the new independent variable is t. Since $x = e^t$, it follows by the chain rule that

$$\frac{dy}{dt} = \frac{dy}{dx}\frac{dx}{dt} = \frac{dy}{dx}e^t = x\frac{dy}{dx};$$

and hence

$$(5) \qquad x\frac{dy}{dx} = \frac{dy}{dt}.$$

[†] *Historical Footnote:* Although work on this equation was published by Leonhard Euler in 1769 and later by Augustin Cauchy, its solution was known to John Bernoulli prior to 1700.

Differentiating (5) with respect to t, we find from the product rule that

$$\frac{d^2y}{dt^2} = \frac{d}{dt}\left(x\frac{dy}{dx}\right) = \frac{dx}{dt}\frac{dy}{dx} + x\frac{d}{dt}\left(\frac{dy}{dx}\right)$$

$$= \frac{dy}{dt} + x\frac{d^2y}{dx^2}\frac{dx}{dt} = \frac{dy}{dt} + x\frac{d^2y}{dx^2}e^t$$

$$= \frac{dy}{dt} + x^2\frac{d^2y}{dx^2}.$$

Hence

(6) $$x^2\frac{d^2y}{dx^2} = \frac{d^2y}{dt^2} - \frac{dy}{dt}.$$

Substituting into (4) the expressions for $x\,dy/dx$ and $x^2\,d^2y/dx^2$ given in (5) and (6) yields

$$3\left(\frac{d^2y}{dt^2} - \frac{dy}{dt}\right) + 11\frac{dy}{dt} - 3y = 0,$$

(7) $$3\frac{d^2y}{dt^2} + 8\frac{dy}{dt} - 3y = 0.$$

The auxiliary equation associated with (7) is

$$3r^2 + 8r - 3 = (3r - 1)(r + 3) = 0.$$

Since the roots of this equation are $\frac{1}{3}$ and -3, the general solution to (7) is

$$y(t) = c_1e^{t/3} + c_2e^{-3t} = c_1(e^t)^{1/3} + c_2(e^t)^{-3}.$$

Expressing y in terms of the original variable x, we find

(8) $$y(x) = c_1x^{1/3} + c_2x^{-3} \quad \text{for } x > 0. \blacktriangleleft$$

It turns out that the solution (8) for the special equation (4) is valid for all $x \neq 0$ even though it was derived only for $x > 0$. In general, it can be shown that if $y(x)$ is a solution to a homogeneous Cauchy-Euler equation for $x > 0$, then $\phi(x) := y(-x)$ is a solution for $x < 0$ (see Problem 21).

Using formulas (5) and (6), the reader can verify that the substitution $x = e^t$ transforms the general Cauchy-Euler equation

(9) $$ax^2\frac{d^2y}{dx^2} + bx\frac{dy}{dx} + cy = h(x), \quad x > 0$$

into the constant coefficient equation

(10) $a\dfrac{d^2y}{dt^2} + (b-a)\dfrac{dy}{dt} + cy = h(e^t).$

If the transformed function $h(e^t)$ is of the appropriate type, the method of undetermined coefficients can be applied to find a particular solution to (10) [and hence to (9)]. The next example illustrates this approach.

▶ *Example 2*   Solve the initial value problem

(11) $3x^2\dfrac{d^2y}{dx^2} + 11x\dfrac{dy}{dx} - 3y = 8 - 3\ln x;$ $y(1) = 1,$ $\dfrac{dy}{dx}(1) = \dfrac{4}{3}.$

Solution   Referring to equation (10) (or Example 1), we see that the substitution $x = e^t$ transforms (11) into

$$3\frac{d^2y}{dt^2} + (11-3)\frac{dy}{dt} - 3y = 8 - 3\ln e^t,$$

(12) $3\dfrac{d^2y}{dt^2} + 8\dfrac{dy}{dt} - 3y = 8 - 3t.$

In Example 1 we found that

$$y_1(t) = e^{t/3} \quad \text{and} \quad y_2(t) = e^{-3t}$$

are linearly independent solutions to the associated homogeneous equation. To find a particular solution to (12), notice that the nonhomogeneous term is a first order polynomial in t. Hence there exists a particular solution of the form $y_p(t) = At + B$. Substituting y_p for y in equation (12) yields

$$(8A - 3B) - 3At = 8 - 3t.$$

Equating coefficients gives the system

$$-3A = -3, \qquad 8A - 3B = 8,$$

whose solution is $A = 1$ and $B = 0$. Hence $y_p(t) = t$. A general solution to (12) can now be written as

(13) $y(t) = c_1y_1(t) + c_2y_2(t) + y_p(t) = c_1e^{t/3} + c_2e^{-3t} + t.$

Expressing (13) in terms of x, we find that a general solution to the differential equation in (11) is

(14) $y(x) = c_1 x^{1/3} + c_2 x^{-3} + \ln x, \qquad x > 0.$

It remains to determine c_1 and c_2. Computing dy/dx, we have

(15) $\dfrac{dy}{dx} = \dfrac{1}{3} c_1 x^{-2/3} - 3c_2 x^{-4} + \dfrac{1}{x}.$

With the formulas for y and dy/dx in (14) and (15), the initial conditions given in (11) lead to the system

$$y(1) = c_1 + c_2 + 0 = 1,$$

$$\frac{dy}{dx}(1) = \frac{1}{3} c_1 - 3c_2 + 1 = \frac{4}{3},$$

which yields $c_1 = 1$ and $c_2 = 0$. Thus the solution to (11) is

(16) $y(x) = x^{1/3} + \ln x, \qquad x > 0.$ ◀

   The method discussed here for second order Cauchy-Euler equations also applies to higher order Cauchy-Euler equations of the form

(17) $a_n x^n y^{(n)}(x) + a_{n-1} x^{n-1} y^{(n-1)}(x) + \cdots + a_0 y(x) = h(x),$

where $a_n, a_{n-1}, \ldots, a_0$ are real constants (see Problems 24–28).

EXERCISES 4.10

In Problems 1 through 16 find a general solution to the given differential equation for $x > 0$.

1. $x^2 y''(x) + 7xy'(x) - 7y(x) = 0.$

2. $x^2 y''(x) + 6xy'(x) + 4y(x) = 0.$

3. $x^2 y''(x) - 3xy'(x) + 4y(x) = 0.$

4. $9x^2 y''(x) + 15xy'(x) + y(x) = 0.$

5. $y''(x) - \dfrac{1}{x} y'(x) + \dfrac{5}{x^2} y(x) = 0.$

6. $x^2 y''(x) + 9xy'(x) + 17y(x) = 0.$

7. $x^2 y''(x) - 3xy'(x) + 6y(x) = 0.$

8. $xy''(x) + y'(x) = 9x^2.$

9. $xy''(x) + 3y'(x) - \dfrac{3}{x} y(x) = x^2.$

10. $x^2 y''(x) - y(x) = (\ln x)^2 - 1.$

11. $x^4 y''(x) - 6x^2 y(x) = 1 - 6x^2.$

12. $x^2 y''(x) + 3xy'(x) - 8y(x) = (\ln x)^3 - \ln x.$

13. $x^2 y''(x) + 3xy'(x) + 5y(x) = x^2$.

14. $x^2 y''(x) = xy'(x) - 10y(x) + \sin(\ln x)$.

15. $x^2 y''(x) + xy'(x) + y(x) = (\ln x)\sin(\ln x)$.

16. $x^2 y''(x) + 3xy'(x) + 4y(x) = \cos(4 \ln x)$.

In Problems 17 through 20 solve the given initial value problem.

17. $x^2 y''(x) - 4xy'(x) + 4y(x) = 0; \qquad y(1) = -2, \qquad y'(1) = -11$.

18. $x^2 y''(x) + 7xy'(x) + 5y(x) = 0; \qquad y(1) = -1, \qquad y'(1) = 13$.

19. $x^2 y''(x) - 3xy'(x) + 3y(x) = 9(\ln x)^2 + 4; \qquad y(1) = 6, \qquad y'(1) = 8$.

20. $x^2 y''(x) - 6y(x) = 8x^2 - 5x^3; \qquad y(1) = 3, \qquad y'(1) = 5$.

21. Let $y(x)$ be a solution for $x > 0$ to the *homogeneous* Cauchy-Euler equation $ax^2 y'' + bxy' + cy = 0$. Show that $\phi(x) := y(-x)$ is a solution to the equation for $x < 0$. Is the analogous statement true for the *non*homogeneous Cauchy-Euler equation?

In Problems 22 and 23 use the result of Problem 21 to find a general solution to the given differential equation for $x < 0$.

22. $x^2 y''(x) + xy'(x) - 2y(x) = 0$.

23. $2x^2 y''(x) + 7xy'(x) + 2y(x) = 0$.

24. Use the substitution $x = e^t$ to show that the third order Cauchy-Euler equation

$$ax^3 y'''(x) + bx^2 y''(x) + cxy'(x) + dy(x) = 0, \qquad x > 0$$

is equivalent to the constant coefficient equation

$$ay'''(t) + (b - 3a)y''(t) + (2a - b + c)y'(t) + dy(t) = 0.$$

In Problems 25 through 28 use the result of Problem 24 to find a general solution to the given differential equation for $x > 0$.

25. $x^3 y'''(x) - 2x^2 y''(x) + 3xy'(x) - 3y(x) = 0$.

26. $x^3 y'''(x) + x^2 y''(x) - 2xy'(x) + 2y(x) = 0$.

27. $x^3 y'''(x) + x^2 y''(x) - 8xy'(x) - 4y(x) = 0$.

28. $x^3 y'''(x) + 2x^2 y''(x) - xy'(x) + y(x) = 0$.

29. Show that the homogeneous Cauchy-Euler equation

$$ax^2 y''(x) + bxy'(x) + cy(x) = 0, \qquad x > 0$$

has a solution of the form $y = x^r$ if and only if r satisfies the auxiliary equation

$$ar^2 + (b - a)r + c = 0.$$

30. Use the result of Problem 29 to find a general solution for $x > 0$ to the following equations.

   (a) $x^2 y'' + xy' - y = 0.$ **(b)** $2x^2 y'' - xy' + y = 0.$

31. Use the result of Problem 29 to find a general solution for $x > 0$ to the equation

$$x^2 y'' - xy' + y = 0.$$

[Hint: Use the reduction of order formula (6) of Section 4.4 to find a second linearly independent solution.]

★ *4.11* *Nonlinear Equations Solvable by First Order Techniques*

Thus far our emphasis has been on second order equations that are linear. For such equations, we have given methods for finding the solutions when the equation has constant coefficients or is a Cauchy-Euler equation. There are, however, other classes of second order equations that are amenable to techniques already familiar to us.

In this section we study two types of second order equations that can be solved by reducing them to a pair of *first order equations*. This reduction is accomplished by the substitution $w = dy/dx$. The technique is especially important because it applies to certain types of nonlinear equations.

EQUATIONS WITH DEPENDENT VARIABLE MISSING

Let's consider a second order equation of the form

(1) $y'' = F(x, y'),$

where the dependent variable y is missing from the equation. If we use the substitution $w = y'$, then $y'' = w'$. Hence solving the original equation (1) is equivalent to solving the system of equations

(2) $w' = F(x, w),$

(3) $y' = w.$

Since (2) is a first order equation, we have available the methods discussed in Chapter 2 to solve it for $w(x)$. Then, substituting $w(x)$ into equation (3), we integrate with respect to x to obtain the desired solution $y(x)$.

▶ **Example 1**   Solve

(4) $2xy'' - y' + (y')^{-1} = 0, \qquad x > 0.$

Solution   Since the dependent variable y is missing in equation (4), let $w = y'$. Then, $y'' = w'$. Now substituting for y' and y'' in (4) gives the system

(5) $2xw' - w + w^{-1} = 0,$

(6) $y' = w.$

We can solve equation (5) by separation of variables:

$$2x\frac{dw}{dx} = w - \frac{1}{w} = \frac{w^2 - 1}{w},$$

and so

$$\int \frac{2w}{w^2 - 1}\,dw = \int \frac{1}{x}\,dx,$$

(7) $\ln|w^2 - 1| = \ln x + c, \qquad x > 0.$

When we solve (7) for w, we obtain

(8) $w = \pm\sqrt{1 + c_1 x},$

where $c_1 = \pm e^c$ is an arbitrary nonzero constant.
    Since $y' = w$, integrating (8) yields

$$y = \pm \int \sqrt{1 + c_1 x}\,dx,$$

(9) $y = \pm \dfrac{2}{3c_1}(1 + c_1 x)^{3/2} + c_2,$

where c_2 is an arbitrary constant.
    In the process of separating variables we divided by $w^2 - 1$. It is therefore possible that we lost a solution in dividing by zero. To check this possibility, set

$$w^2 = (y')^2 = 1$$

and solve for y to obtain

(10) $y = \pm x + c_3,$

where c_3 is an arbitrary constant. Because (10) is indeed a solution to (4) but is not a special case of (9), we list both (9) and (10) as solutions. ◄

In the above example, it is not surprising that the solution given by (9) contains two arbitrary constants. But it is disturbing that the solution given in (10) cannot be expressed using equation (9), regardless of the choice of the constants c_1 and c_2. Because of this, one should be careful when speaking about a "general solution" for a nonlinear equation.

EQUATIONS WITH INDEPENDENT VARIABLE MISSING

Now let's consider a second order equation of the form

(11) $$\frac{d^2y}{dx^2} = F\left(y, \frac{dy}{dx}\right),$$

where the independent variable x is missing from the equation. If we again use the substitution $w = dy/dx$ then, by the chain rule,

(12) $$\frac{d^2y}{dx^2} = \frac{dw}{dx} = \frac{dw}{dy}\frac{dy}{dx} = w\frac{dw}{dy}.$$

Hence solving equation (11) is equivalent to solving the system

(13) $$w\frac{dw}{dy} = F(y, w),$$

(14) $$\frac{dy}{dx} = w.$$

In equation (13), notice that y plays the role of the *independent* variable. If we can solve this first order equation, then we can determine $w(y)$. Finally, substituting $w(y)$ into (14), we obtain a separable equation that determines $y(x)$.

► **Example 2**   Solve

(15) $$2y\frac{d^2y}{dx^2} = 1 + \left(\frac{dy}{dx}\right)^2.$$

Solution   Since the independent variable x is missing in equation (15), let $w = dy/dx$ and d^2y/dx^2 be given by equation (12). When we substitute for dy/dx and d^2y/dx^2 in equation

(15), we obtain the system

(16) $$2yw\frac{dw}{dy} = 1 + w^2,$$

(17) $$\frac{dy}{dx} = w.$$

Since (16) is separable, we have

$$\int \frac{2w}{1 + w^2}\, dw = \int \frac{1}{y}\, dy$$

$$\ln(1 + w^2) = \ln|y| + c.$$

Solving this last equation for w, we get

$$w = \pm\sqrt{c_1 y - 1},$$

where c_1 is an arbitrary nonzero constant.

Substituting dy/dx for w yields

(18) $$\frac{dy}{dx} = \pm\sqrt{c_1 y - 1},$$

and, separating variables, we find

$$\pm \int (c_1 y - 1)^{-1/2}\, dy = \int dx,$$

(19) $$\pm\frac{2}{c_1}(c_1 y - 1)^{1/2} = x + c_2.$$

When we square both sides of (19), we obtain

$$4(c_1 y - 1) = c_1^2(x + c_2)^2,$$

which implies that

(20) $$y = \frac{1}{c_1} + \frac{c_1}{4}(x + c_2)^2,$$

where c_1 ($\neq 0$) and c_2 are arbitrary constants.

In the process of separating variables, we divided by y and thus may have lost the solution $y \equiv 0$. In fact, a quick check shows that $y \equiv 0$ is not a solution to (15). Thus all the solutions to equation (15) are given by (20). ◄

EXERCISES 4.11

In Problems 1 through 18 solve the differential equation.

1. $xy'' + y' = 8x$, $\quad x > 0$.

2. $x^2y'' + 2xy' = 6x - x^{-2}$, $\quad x > 0$.

3. $y'' = 4x\sqrt{y'}$.

4. $xy'' + y' = \cos x - x\sin x$, $\quad x > 0$.

5. $y'' = 1 + (y')^2$.

6. $y'' + 2x(y')^2 = 0$.

7. $y'y'' = 1$.

8. $yy'' + (y')^2 = 0$.

9. $y'' + y(y')^3 = 0$.

10. $y^2y'' = y'$.

11. $y'' + yy' = 0$.

12. $y'' + y = 0$.

13. $y'' - \left(\dfrac{2}{x}\right)y' = x^4 - 3x^3 + x^2$, $\quad x > 0$.

14. $yy'' - (y')^2 = 0$.

15. $y'' = y'e^y$.

16. $xy'' = (x + 1)y'$, $\quad x > 0$.

17. $(1 + y^2)y'' = y' + (y')^3$.

18. $x^2y'' + (y')^2 = 0$, $\quad x > 0$.

19. Suspended Cable. In the study of a cable suspended between two fixed points, one encounters the initial value problem

$$\frac{d^2y}{dx^2} = \frac{1}{a}\sqrt{1 + \left(\frac{dy}{dx}\right)^2}; \quad y(0) = a, \quad y'(0) = 0,$$

where a ($\neq 0$) is a constant. Solve this initial value problem for y. The resulting curve is called a **catenary.**

20. Newton Equation. An equation of the form

$$\frac{d^2y}{dx^2} = f(y),$$

where $f(y)$ is a continuous function for all y, is called a **Newton equation.** Derive the following implicit solution to the Newton equation:

$$\int \left(2\int f(y)\,dy + c_1\right)^{-1/2} dy = x + c_2.$$

Chapter Summary

In this chapter we discussed the theory of linear second order equations and presented methods for solving these equations. The important features and techniques are listed.

HOMOGENEOUS LINEAR EQUATIONS

$$y'' + p(x)y' + q(x)y = 0$$

Fundamental Solution Set: $\{y_1, y_2\}$.

Two solutions y_1 and y_2 to the homogeneous equation on the interval I form a fundamental solution set provided that their Wronskian,

$$W[y_1, y_2](x) := y_1(x)y_2'(x) - y_1'(x)y_2(x),$$

is different from zero for some x in I. If y_1 and y_2 are linearly independent solutions on I, then $W[y_1, y_2](x) \neq 0$ on I, and hence y_1 and y_2 form a fundamental solution set.

General Solution to Homogeneous Equation: $c_1 y_1 + c_2 y_2$.

If y_1 and y_2 are linearly independent solutions to the homogeneous equation, then a general solution is

$$y(x) = c_1 y_1(x) + c_2 y_2(x),$$

where c_1 and c_2 are arbitrary constants.

Homogeneous Equation with Constant Coefficients: $ay'' + by' + cy = 0$.

The form of a general solution for a homogeneous equation with constant coefficients depends on the roots

$$r_1 = \frac{-b + \sqrt{b^2 - 4ac}}{2a}, \qquad r_2 = \frac{-b - \sqrt{b^2 - 4ac}}{2a}$$

of the auxiliary equation

$$ar^2 + br + c = 0, \qquad a \neq 0.$$

(a) When $b^2 - 4ac > 0$, the auxiliary equation has two distinct real roots r_1 and r_2, and a general solution is

$$y(x) = c_1 e^{r_1 x} + c_2 e^{r_2 x}.$$

(b) When $b^2 - 4ac = 0$, the auxiliary equation has a repeated real root $r = r_1 = r_2$, and a general solution is

$$y(x) = c_1 e^{rx} + c_2 x e^{rx}.$$

(c) When $b^2 - 4ac < 0$, the auxiliary equation has complex conjugate roots $r = \alpha \pm i\beta$, and a general solution is

$$y(x) = c_1 e^{\alpha x} \cos \beta x + c_2 e^{\alpha x} \sin \beta x.$$

Reduction of Order Formula: $y(x) = v(x)f(x)$.

Let $f(x)$ be a nontrivial solution to the homogeneous equation. The substitution $y(x) = v(x)f(x)$ reduces the homogeneous equation to a first order equation in v'. When solved for

v' and integrated to obtain v, a second linearly independent solution $y(x)$ is given by the reduction of order formula

$$y(x) = f(x) \int \frac{e^{-\int p(x)\,dx}}{[f(x)]^2}\,dx.$$

NONHOMOGENEOUS LINEAR EQUATIONS

$$y'' + p(x)y' + q(x)y = g(x)$$

General Solution to Nonhomogeneous Equation: $y_p + c_1 y_1 + c_2 y_2$.

If y_p is any particular solution to the nonhomogeneous equation, and y_1 and y_2 are linearly independent solutions to the corresponding homogeneous equation, then a general solution is

$$y(x) = y_p(x) + c_1 y_1(x) + c_2 y_2(x),$$

where c_1 and c_2 are arbitrary constants.

Two methods for finding a particular solution y_p are those of undetermined coefficients and variation of parameters.

Undetermined Coefficients: $g(x) = e^{\alpha x} p_n(x) \begin{Bmatrix} \cos \beta x \\ \sin \beta x \end{Bmatrix}$.

If the right-hand side $g(x)$ of a nonhomogeneous equation with constant coefficients is a polynomial, an exponential of the form $e^{\alpha x}$, a trigonometric function of the form $\cos \beta x$ or $\sin \beta x$, or any product of these special types of functions, then a particular solution of an appropriate form exists. This special form is given in Table 4.1, page 204.

Variation of Parameters: $y(x) = v_1(x)y_1(x) + v_2(x)y_2(x)$.

If y_1 and y_2 are two linearly independent solutions to the corresponding homogeneous equation, then a particular solution to the nonhomogeneous equation is

$$y(x) = v_1(x)y_1(x) + v_2(x)y_2(x),$$

where

$$v_1(x) = \int \frac{-g(x)y_2(x)}{W[y_1, y_2](x)}\,dx, \qquad v_2(x) = \int \frac{g(x)y_1(x)}{W[y_1, y_2](x)}\,dx.$$

Superposition Principle: $L[y] = c_1 g_1 + c_2 g_2$.

If y_1 and y_2 are solutions to the equations

$$y'' + py' + qy = g_1 \quad \text{and} \quad y'' + py' + qy = g_2,$$

respectively, then $c_1y_1 + c_2y_2$ is a solution to the equation

$$y'' + py' + qy = c_1g_1 + c_2g_2.$$

USEFUL SUBSTITUTIONS

The following special equations can be solved using a suitable transformation.

Dependent Variable Missing: $y'' = F(x, y')$.

Let $w = y'$, so that $w' = y''$. Solving the original equation is equivalent to solving the system of equations

$$w' = F(x, w),$$

$$y' = w.$$

Independent Variable Missing: $\dfrac{d^2y}{dx^2} = F\left(y, \dfrac{dy}{dx}\right)$.

Let $w = dy/dx$, so that $d^2y/dx^2 = w\,dw/dy$. Solving the original equation is equivalent to solving the system

$$w\frac{dw}{dy} = F(y, w),$$

$$\frac{dy}{dx} = w.$$

Cauchy-Euler Equations: $ax^2\dfrac{d^2y}{dx^2} + bx\dfrac{dy}{dx} + cy = h(x), \qquad x > 0.$

Let $x = e^t$. This substitution transforms the original equation into the following constant coefficient equation in t:

$$a\frac{d^2y}{dt^2} + (b - a)\frac{dy}{dt} + cy = h(e^t).$$

REVIEW PROBLEMS _____

In Problems 1 through 28 find a general solution to the given differential equation.

1. $y'' + 8y' - 9y = 0.$

2. $49y'' + 14y' + y = 0.$

3. $4y'' - 4y' + 10y = 0.$

4. $6y'' - 11y' + 3y = 0.$

5. $9y'' - 30y' + 25y = 0.$

6. $y'' + 8y' - 14y = 0.$

7. $36y'' + 24y' + 5y = 0.$

8. $25y'' + 20y' + 4y = 0.$

9. $16y'' - 56y' + 49y = 0.$

10. $y'' + 11y = 0.$

11. $x^2y''(x) + 5y(x) = 0, \qquad x > 0.$

12. $2y''' - 3y'' - 12y' + 20y = 0.$

13. $y(y')^3 - y'' = 0.$ **14.** $y'' - 4y' + 7y = 0.$ **15.** $3y''' + 10y'' + 9y' + 2y = 0.$

16. $y''' + 10y' - 11y = 0.$ **17.** $y''' + 3y'' + 5y' + 3y = 0.$ **18.** $y^{(4)} = 120x.$

19. $4y''' + 8y'' - 11y' + 3y = 0.$ **20.** $2yy'' - (y')^2 = 1.$ **21.** $y'' - 3y' + 7y = 7x^2 - e^x.$

22. $y'' - 8y' - 33y = 546 \sin x.$ **23.** $y'' + 16y = \tan 4x.$ **24.** $10y'' + y' - 3y = x - e^{x/2}.$

25. $4y'' - 12y' + 9y = e^{5x} + e^{3x}.$ **26.** $y'' + 6y' + 15y = e^{2x} + 75.$

27. $x^2y'' + 2xy' - 2y = 6x^{-2} + 3x,$ $x > 0.$ **28.** $y'' = 5x^{-1}y' - 13x^{-2}y,$ $x > 0.$

In Problems 29 through 36 find the solution to the initial value problem.

29. $4y'' - 4y' + 5y = 0;$ $y(0) = 1,$ $y'(0) = -\frac{11}{2}.$

30. $y'' + 2y' + y = 2 \cos x;$ $y(0) = 3,$ $y'(0) = 0.$

31. $y'' - 2y' + 10y = 6 \cos 3x - \sin 3x;$ $y(0) = 2,$ $y'(0) = -8.$

32. $y'' + 4y' + 7y = 0;$ $y(0) = 1,$ $y'(0) = -2.$

33. $y''' - 12y'' + 27y' + 40y = 0;$ $y(0) = -3,$ $y'(0) = -6,$ $y''(0) = -12.$

34. $y'' + 5y' - 14y = 0;$ $y(0) = 5,$ $y'(0) = 1.$

35. $y'' + y = \sec x;$ $y(0) = 1,$ $y'(0) = 2.$

36. $9y'' + 12y' + 4y = 0;$ $y(0) = -3,$ $y'(0) = 3.$

In Problems 37 through 39 a differential equation and a nontrivial solution $f(x)$ are given. Find a general solution for the equation.

37. $xy'' + (x - 1)y' - y = 0,$ $x > 0;$ $f(x) = e^{-x}.$

38. $(x - 1)y'' - xy' + y = 0,$ $x > 1;$ $f(x) = e^x.$

39. $(1 - x^2)y'' - 2xy' + 2y = 0,$ $-1 < x < 1;$ $f(x) = x.$

40. Determine whether the statement made is *always true* or *sometimes false*.

   (a) Two differentiable functions are linearly independent on $[a, b]$ if and only if their Wronskian is not zero on $[a, b]$.

   (b) The differential operator $L[y](x) := 2y''(x) + x^2y'(x) + \dfrac{1}{x} y(x)$ defined for twice differentiable functions on $(0, \infty)$ is linear.

   (c) The initial value problem

$$xy'' + \frac{5}{x - 3} y' + 2y = \cos x;   y(1) = 6,   y'(1) = 23$$

   has a unique solution on the interval $(0, 3)$.

   (d) A general solution of $y'' + y = x$ is given by

$$y = c_1 \cos x + c_2 \sin x + c_3x,$$

   where $c_1, c_2,$ and c_3 are arbitrary constants.

Projects for Chapter 4

A. EIGENVALUE AND BOUNDARY VALUE PROBLEMS

The **eigenvalue problem** for a linear operator L is the problem of finding those real or complex values of the parameter λ, called **eigenvalues,** for which the equation $L[y] = \lambda y$ has a nontrivial ($y \neq 0$) solution *in the domain of* L.

For this project take

(1) $L[y](x) := -y''(x),$

where the domain of L is the set of functions with continuous second derivatives on $[0, \pi]$ that satisfy the boundary conditions $y(0) = y(\pi) = 0$. Then $\lambda = 1$ is an eigenvalue of L because the nontrivial function $y = \sin x$ satisfies

$$L[y](x) = -(-\sin x) = 1 \cdot \sin x = 1 \cdot y,$$

and $\sin 0 = \sin \pi = 0$.

(a) Find *all* the eigenvalues of L and the corresponding nontrivial solutions, called **eigenfunctions.**

(b) It can be shown that if λ is *not* an eigenvalue of L, then the equation

(2) $L[y](x) = \lambda y(x) + f(x),$

where $f(x)$ is continuous on $[0, \pi]$, always has a solution in the domain of L. Verify this fact for $\lambda = 2$ and $f(x) = x^2$.

(c) If λ is an eigenvalue for L, then equation (2) *may* or *may not* have a solution in the domain of L. Show that for $\lambda = 1$ and $f(x) = x$, equation (2) does *not* have a solution in the domain of L, while for $\lambda = 1$ and $f(x) = \cos x$, there exists a one-parameter family of solutions in the domain of L.

B. ASYMPTOTIC BEHAVIOR OF SOLUTIONS

In the application of linear systems theory to mechanical and electrical problems, one often encounters the equation

(3) $y'' + py' + qy = f(x),$

where p and q are positive constants with $p^2 < 4q$ and $f(x)$ is a forcing function for the system. In many cases it is important for the design engineer to know that a bounded forcing function gives rise only to bounded solutions. More specifically, how does the behavior of $f(x)$ for large values of x affect the asymptotic behavior of the solution? To answer this question:

(a) Show that the homogeneous equation associated with equation (3) has two linearly independent solutions given by

$$e^{\alpha x} \cos \beta x, \qquad e^{\alpha x} \sin \beta x,$$

where $\alpha = -p/2 < 0$ and $\beta = \frac{1}{2}\sqrt{4q - p^2}$.

(b) Let $f(x)$ be a continuous function defined on the interval $[0, \infty)$. Use the variation of parameters formula to show that any solution to (3) on $[0, \infty)$ can be expressed in the form

(4)
$$y(x) = c_1 e^{\alpha x} \cos \beta x + c_2 e^{\alpha x} \sin \beta x$$

$$-\frac{1}{\beta} e^{\alpha x} \cos \beta x \int_0^x f(t) e^{-\alpha t} \sin \beta t \, dt$$

$$+\frac{1}{\beta} e^{\alpha x} \sin \beta x \int_0^x f(t) e^{-\alpha t} \cos \beta t \, dt.$$

(c) Assuming that f is bounded on $[0, \infty)$, that is, that there exists a constant K such that $|f(t)| \le K$ for all $t \ge 0$, use the triangle inequality and other properties of the absolute value to show that $y(x)$ given in (4) satisfies

$$|y(x)| \le \{|c_1| + |c_2|\} e^{\alpha x} + \frac{2K}{|\alpha|\beta}(1 - e^{\alpha x})$$

for all $x > 0$.

(d) In a similar fashion, show that if $f_1(x)$ and $f_2(x)$ are two bounded continuous functions on $[0, \infty)$ such that $|f_1(x) - f_2(x)| \le \varepsilon$ for all $x > x_0$, and if ϕ_1 is a solution to (3) with $f = f_1$ and ϕ_2 is a solution to (3) with $f = f_2$, then

$$|\phi_1(x) - \phi_2(x)| \le M e^{\alpha x} + \frac{2\varepsilon}{|\alpha|\beta}(1 - e^{\alpha(x - x_0)})$$

for all $x > x_0$, where M is a constant that depends on ϕ_1 and ϕ_2 but not on x.

(e) Now assume that $f(x) \to F_0$ as $x \to \infty$, where F_0 is a constant. By using the result of part (d), prove that any solution ϕ to (3) must satisfy $\phi(x) \to F_0/q$ as $x \to \infty$. [Hint: Choose $f_1 = f$, $f_2 \equiv F_0$, $\phi_1 = \phi$, $\phi_2 \equiv F_0/q$.]

C. LINEARIZATION OF NONLINEAR PROBLEMS

A useful approach to analyzing a nonlinear equation is to study its **linearized equation,** which is obtained by replacing the nonlinear terms by linear approximations. For example, the nonlinear equation

(5)
$$\frac{d^2\theta}{dt^2} + \sin \theta = 0,$$

which governs the motion of a simple pendulum, has

(6) $$\frac{d^2\theta}{dt^2} + \theta = 0$$

as a linearization for small θ. (The nonlinear term $\sin\theta$ has been replaced by the linear approximation θ.)

Since a general solution to equation (5) involves Jacobi elliptic functions (see Project D), let's try to approximate the solutions. For this purpose we consider two methods: Taylor series and linearization.

(a) Derive the first six terms of the Taylor series about $t = 0$ of the solution to equation (5) with initial conditions $\theta(0) = \pi/12$, $\theta'(0) = 0$. (The Taylor series method is discussed in Project A of Chapter 1 and Section 8.2.)

(b) Solve equation (6) subject to the same initial conditions $\theta(0) = \pi/12$, $\theta'(0) = 0$.

(c) On the same coordinate axes, graph the two approximations found in parts (a) and (b).

(d) Discuss the advantages and disadvantages of the Taylor series method and the linearization method.

(e) Give a linearization for the initial value problem

$$x''(t) + 0.1[1 - x^2(t)]x'(t) + x(t) = 0; \qquad x(0) = 0.5, \qquad x'(0) = 0$$

for x small. Solve this linearized problem to obtain an approximation for the nonlinear problem.

D. SIMPLE PENDULUM

In Section 4.1 we discussed the simple pendulum consisting of a mass m suspended by a rod of length l having negligible mass and derived the nonlinear initial value problem

(7) $$\frac{d^2\theta}{dt^2} + \frac{g}{l}\sin\theta = 0; \qquad \theta(0) = \alpha, \qquad \theta'(0) = 0,$$

where g is the acceleration due to gravity and $\theta(t)$ is the angle the rod makes with the vertical at time t (see Figure 4.1). Here it is assumed that the mass is released with zero velocity at an initial angle α, $0 < \alpha < \pi$. We would like to determine the equation of motion for the pendulum and its period of oscillation.

(a) Use equation (7) and the techniques discussed in Section 4.11 to show that

$$\left(\frac{d\theta}{dt}\right)^2 = \frac{2g}{l}(\cos\theta - \cos\alpha)$$

and hence

(8) $$dt = \sqrt{\frac{l}{2g}}\frac{d\theta}{\sqrt{\cos\theta - \cos\alpha}}.$$

(b) Use the trigonometric identity

$$\cos x = 1 - 2\sin^2(x/2)$$

to express dt by

(9) $$dt = \frac{1}{2}\sqrt{\frac{l}{g}}\frac{d\theta}{\sqrt{\sin^2(\alpha/2) - \sin^2(\theta/2)}}.$$

(c) Make the change of variables

$$\sin(\theta/2) = \sin(\alpha/2)\sin\phi,$$

to rewrite dt in the form

(10) $$dt = \sqrt{\frac{l}{g}}\frac{d\phi}{\sqrt{1 - k^2\sin^2\phi}},$$

where $k := \sin(\alpha/2)$.

(d) The period $P(\alpha)$ of the pendulum is defined to be the time required for the pendulum to swing from one extreme to the other and back, that is, from α to $-\alpha$ back to α. Show that the period of oscillation is given by

(11) $$P(\alpha) = 4\sqrt{\frac{l}{g}}\int_0^{\pi/2}\frac{d\phi}{\sqrt{1 - k^2\sin^2\phi}},$$

where $k := \sin(\alpha/2)$. [Hint: The period is just four times the time it takes the pendulum to go from $\theta = 0$ to $\theta = \alpha$.]

The integral in (11) is called an **elliptic integral of the first kind** and is denoted by $F(k, \pi/2)$. As you might expect, the period of the simple pendulum depends on the length l of the rod and the initial displacement α. In fact, a check of an elliptic integral table will show that the period about doubles as the initial displacement increases from $\pi/8$ to $15\pi/16$ (for fixed l). What happens as α approaches π?

(e) To determine the equation of motion of the pendulum, we observe that as t varies from 0 to t, θ varies from α to θ, and ϕ varies from $\pi/2$ to ϕ. Integrating equation (10), show that

(12) $$t + \frac{P(\alpha)}{4} = \sqrt{\frac{l}{g}}\int_0^\phi\frac{ds}{\sqrt{1 - k^2\sin^2 s}} = \sqrt{\frac{l}{g}}F(k, \phi).$$

For fixed k, $F(k, \phi)$ has an "inverse," denoted by $\mathrm{sn}(k, u)$, that satisfies $u = F(k, \phi)$ if and only if $\mathrm{sn}(k, u) = \sin\phi$. The function $\mathrm{sn}(k, u)$ is called a **Jacobi elliptic function** and has many properties that are similar to those of the sine function. Using the Jacobi elliptic function $\mathrm{sn}(k, u)$ express the equation of motion for the pendulum in the form

(13) $$\theta = 2 \arcsin\left\{k \; \text{sn}\left(k, \sqrt{\frac{g}{l}}\left(t + \frac{P(\alpha)}{4}\right)\right)\right\},$$

where $k := \sin(\alpha/2)$.

E. PHASE PLANE DIAGRAMS AND PERIODIC SOLUTIONS

In Project D a procedure is given for computing the period of a simple pendulum in terms of elliptic integrals. That computation was based on the premise that the simple pendulum problem *has* a periodic solution.

The differential equation that governs the motion of a simple pendulum is

(14) $$\frac{d^2\theta}{dt^2} + \frac{g}{l}\sin\theta = 0,$$

where θ is the angular displacement from the vertical, l is the length of the pendulum, and g is the gravitational constant (see Figure 4.1 on page 152). To simplify the computations let's assume that $l = g$, so that equation (14) becomes

(15) $$\frac{d^2\theta}{dt^2} + \sin\theta = 0.$$

To show that equation (15) has a periodic solution, proceed as follows:

(a) Show that solving (15) is equivalent to solving the system

(16) $$\frac{d\theta}{dt} = v,$$

$$\frac{dv}{dt} = -\sin\theta.$$

(b) The **phase plane** for system (16) is the plane of the variables $v = d\theta/dt$ and θ. A solution to system (16) traces out a **path** in the $\theta v -$ phase plane. Show that this path is a solution to the differential equation

(17) $$\frac{dv}{d\theta} = -\frac{\sin\theta}{v}.$$

(c) Solve equation (17).

(d) Show that there are closed paths in the phase plane associated with the simple pendulum equation, and hence that the simple pendulum problem has periodic solutions (see Figure 4.6 on page 236).

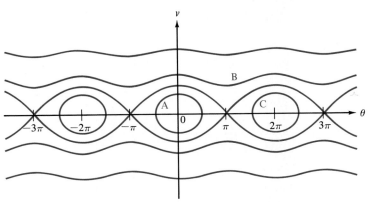

Figure 4.6 Phase plane trajectories for a simple pendulum

  (e) Give a physical interpretation of the motion of a pendulum that corresponds to the three trajectories labeled A, B, and C in Figure 4.6.

  (f) The procedure outlined in parts (a)–(d) can be used to show the existence of periodic solutions for other nonlinear equations. In particular, show that the **nonlinear spring equation**

(18) $$\frac{d^2x}{dt^2} + x + \beta x^3 = 0,$$

where $\beta > 0$ is a fixed parameter, has a nontrivial periodic solution.

Applications of Linear Second Order Differential Equations

5.1 Mechanical Vibrations and Simple Harmonic Motion

Each day we encounter many types of mechanical vibrations. The bouncing motion of an automobile due to the bumps and cracks in the pavement, the vibrations of a bridge caused by traffic and wind, and the normal flutter of an airplane wing due to the vibration of the engine and the air rushing past are some common examples. To study mechanical vibrations, we shall start with the simple mechanical system consisting of a coil spring suspended from a rigid support with a mass attached to the end of the spring.

To analyze this spring-mass system, we need to recall two laws of physics: Hooke's law and Newton's second law of motion. Hooke's law states that the spring exerts a restoring force opposite to the direction of elongation of the spring and with a magnitude directly proportional to the amount of elongation.[†] That is, the spring exerts a restoring force $\mathscr{F}$ whose magnitude is ks, where s is the amount of elongation and $k(>0)$ is the **spring constant.**

For example, if a 20-lb weight stretches a spring 6 in., then (in the ft-lb system) Hooke's law gives

(1) $\qquad 20 = |\mathscr{F}| = ks = k(\tfrac{1}{2}).$

Hence, the spring constant is $k = 40$ lb/ft.

[†] Hooke's law is a reasonable approximation until the spring is stretched to near its elastic limit.

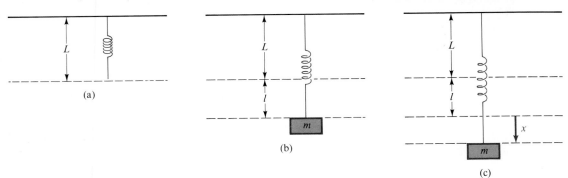

Figure 5.1 Spring **(a)** in natural position, **(b)** in equilibrium, and **(c)** in motion

In Section 3.4 we discussed Newton's second law and how to apply it to problems in mechanics. Recall that when mass remains constant, this law can be expressed as

(2) $$m\frac{d^2x}{dt^2} = ma = F(t, x, dx/dt),$$

where x is the position, dx/dt is the velocity, and d^2x/dt^2 is the acceleration of the mass at time t. Here F, the total force acting on the mass, is assumed to depend only on time, position, and velocity.

A first step in the analysis of the spring-mass system is to choose a coordinate axis in which to represent the motion of the mass. For this purpose, we observe that the spring has a certain natural length L when hanging from its support (see Figure 5.1(a)). Attaching a mass m elongates the spring, and when it comes to rest (equilibrium), the spring has been stretched an amount, say l, beyond its natural length (Figure 5.1(b)). Therefore, let's choose a vertical coordinate axis passing through the spring, with the origin at the equilibrium position of the mass. We let x denote the displacement of the mass from its equilibrium position, taking x positive when the mass is below its equilibrium position, as shown in Figure 5.1(c).

We now consider the various forces acting on the mass m.

Gravity. The force of gravity F_1 is a downward force with magnitude mg, where g is the acceleration due to gravity. Hence

$$F_1 = mg.$$

Restoring Force. The spring exerts a restoring force F_2 whose magnitude is proportional to the elongation of the spring. Referring to Figure 5.1(c), we see that the spring is stretched $x + l$ units beyond its natural length. Hence the magnitude of F_2 is $k(x + l)$, where k is the spring constant. Since the spring pulls upward (in the negative x direction), we have

$$F_2 = -k(x + l).$$

We should observe that when $x = 0$, that is, when the system is at equilibrium, the force of gravity and the force due to the spring balance each other. Thus, $mg = kl$. We can now express the restoring force as

$$F_2 = -kx - mg.$$

Damping Force. There is a damping or frictional force F_3 acting on the mass. For example, this force may be air resistance or friction due to a shock absorber. In either case we *assume* that the damping force is proportional to the magnitude of the velocity of the mass, but opposite in direction. That is,

$$F_3 = -b\frac{dx}{dt}, \qquad b > 0,$$

where b is the **damping constant** given in units of mass/time (or force-time/length). In certain circumstances a more elaborate formula for the damping force may be valid, but empirical studies show that when the velocity is small, the above expression for F_3 is a reasonable one.

External Forces. Any external forces acting on the mass (for example, a magnetic force or the forces exerted on a car by bumps in the pavement) will be denoted by $F_4 = f(t)$. For simplicity, we assume that these forces depend only on time and *not* on the location of the mass or its velocity. (We can model the vertical displacements of a car in this way if its horizontal position is known as a function of time.)

The total force F acting on the mass m is the sum of the four forces $F_1, F_2, F_3,$ and F_4:

(3) $$F(t, x, dx/dt) = mg - kx - mg - b\frac{dx}{dt} + f(t).$$

Applying Newton's second law to the system gives

$$m\frac{d^2x}{dt^2} = mg - kx - mg - b\frac{dx}{dt} + f(t),$$

which simplifies to

(4) $$m\frac{d^2x}{dt^2} + b\frac{dx}{dt} + kx = f(t).$$

When $b = 0$, the system is said to be **undamped;** otherwise it is **damped.** When $f(t) \equiv 0$, the motion is said to be **free;** otherwise the motion is **forced.** A convenient schematic representation for a simple spring-mass system with damping is given in Figure 5.2 on page 240.

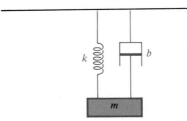

Figure 5.2 Spring-mass system with spring constant k, damping constant b, and mass m

Let's begin with the simple system in which $b = 0$ and $f(t) \equiv 0$, the so-called **undamped, free** case. In this case equation (4) reduces to

(5) $$m \frac{d^2x}{dt^2} + kx = 0,$$

and, when divided by m, becomes

(6) $$\frac{d^2x}{dt^2} + \omega^2 x = 0,$$

where $\omega = \sqrt{k/m}$. The auxiliary equation associated with (6) is $r^2 + \omega^2 = 0$, which has complex conjugate roots $\pm\omega i$. Hence a general solution to (6) is

(7) $$x(t) = C_1 \cos \omega t + C_2 \sin \omega t.$$

We can express $x(t)$ in the more convenient form

(8) $$x(t) = A \sin(\omega t + \phi)$$

by letting $C_1 = A \sin \phi$ and $C_2 = A \cos \phi$. That is,

$$A \sin(\omega t + \phi) = A \cos \omega t \sin \phi + A \sin \omega t \cos \phi$$
$$= C_1 \cos \omega t + C_2 \sin \omega t.$$

Solving for A and ϕ in terms of C_1 and C_2, we find

(9) $$A = \sqrt{C_1^2 + C_2^2} \quad \text{and} \quad \tan \phi = \frac{C_1}{C_2}.$$

It is evident from (8) that the motion of a mass in an *undamped, free* system is simply a sine wave, or what is called **simple harmonic motion.** The constant A is the **amplitude** of the motion and ϕ is the **phase angle.** The motion is periodic with **period** $2\pi/\omega$ and **natural**

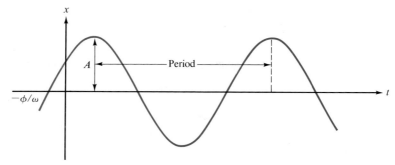

Figure 5.3 Simple harmonic motion of undamped, free vibrations

frequency $\omega/2\pi$, where $\omega = \sqrt{k/m}$. (The constant ω is the **angular frequency** for the sine function in (8).)

Observe that the amplitude and phase angle depend on the constants C_1 and C_2, which, in turn, are determined by the initial position and initial velocity of the mass. However, the period and frequency depend only on k and m and not on the initial conditions (see Figure 5.3).

▶ *Example 1*   A mass weighing 4 lb stretches a spring 3 in. after coming to rest at equilibrium. The mass is then pulled down 6 in. below the equilibrium point and given a downward velocity of $\sqrt{2}$ ft/sec. Neglecting any damping or external forces that may be present, determine the equation of motion of the mass along with its amplitude, period, and natural frequency. How long after release does the mass pass through the equilibrium position?

Solution   Since we have a case of undamped, free vibration, the equation of motion is given by (7). To find k, we observe that the 4-lb mass stretches the spring 3 in. or $\frac{1}{4}$ ft. Using Hooke's law, we have

$$4 = mg = k(\tfrac{1}{4}),$$

or $k = 16$ lb/ft. Since $g \approx 32$ ft/sec², we find $m = \frac{4}{32} = \frac{1}{8}$ slugs and so

$$\omega = \sqrt{\frac{k}{m}} = \sqrt{\frac{16}{1/8}} = 8\sqrt{2}.$$

Substituting this value for ω into (7) gives

(10) $x(t) = C_1 \cos(8\sqrt{2}t) + C_2 \sin(8\sqrt{2}t).$

Now we use the initial conditions, $x(0) = 6$ in. $= \frac{1}{2}$ ft and $x'(0) = \sqrt{2}$ ft/sec, to solve for C_1 and C_2 in (10). That is,

$$\frac{1}{2} = x(0) = C_1,$$
$$\sqrt{2} = x'(0) = 8\sqrt{2}C_2,$$

and so $C_1 = \frac{1}{2}$ and $C_2 = \frac{1}{8}$. Hence the equation of motion of the mass is

(11) $x(t) = \frac{1}{2}\cos(8\sqrt{2}t) + \frac{1}{8}\sin(8\sqrt{2}t).$

To express $x(t)$ in the alternate form (8), we set

$$A = \sqrt{C_1^2 + C_2^2} = \sqrt{(\tfrac{1}{2})^2 + (\tfrac{1}{8})^2} = \frac{\sqrt{17}}{8},$$

$$\tan \phi = \frac{C_1}{C_2} = \frac{1/2}{1/8} = 4.$$

Since both C_1 and C_2 are positive, ϕ is in the first quadrant, and so $\phi = \arctan 4$. Hence

(12) $x(t) = \dfrac{\sqrt{17}}{8}\sin(8\sqrt{2}t + \phi).$

Thus the amplitude A is $\sqrt{17}/8$ and the phase angle ϕ is $\arctan 4 \approx 1.326$. The period is $P = 2\pi/\omega = 2\pi/(8\sqrt{2}) = \sqrt{2}\pi/8$, and the natural frequency is $1/P = 8/(\sqrt{2}\pi)$.

Finally, to determine when the mass will pass through the equilibrium position, $x = 0$, we must solve the trigonometric equation

(13) $x(t) = \dfrac{\sqrt{17}}{8}\sin(8\sqrt{2}t + \phi) = 0$

for t. Equation (13) will be satisfied whenever

(14) $8\sqrt{2}t + \phi = n\pi,$

n an integer. Since $0 < \phi < \pi/2$, putting $n = 1, 2, \ldots$ in (14) determines the (positive) times t when the mass crosses its equilibrium position. The first such occurrence is when

$$8\sqrt{2}t + \phi = \pi;$$

that is,

$$t = \frac{\pi - \phi}{8\sqrt{2}} = \frac{\pi - \arctan 4}{8\sqrt{2}} \approx 0.16 \text{ sec.} \blacktriangleleft$$

EXERCISES 5.1

In the following problems take $g = 32$ ft/sec² for the British system and $g = 9.8$ m/sec² for the MKS system.

1. A mass weighing 8 lb is attached to a spring suspended from the ceiling. When the mass comes to rest at equilibrium, the spring has been stretched 6 in. The mass is then pulled down 3 in. below the equilibrium point and given an upward velocity of 0.5 ft/sec. Neglecting any damping or external forces that may be present, determine the equation of motion of the mass, along with its amplitude, period, and natural frequency. Sketch the graph of this simple harmonic motion.

2. A mass of 100 kg is attached to a spring suspended from the ceiling, causing the spring to stretch 20 cm on coming to rest at equilibrium. The mass is then pulled down 5 cm below the equilibrium point and released (zero initial velocity). Neglecting any damping or external forces that may be present, determine the equation of motion of the mass, along with its amplitude, period, and natural frequency. Sketch the graph of this simple harmonic motion.

3. A mass weighing 8 lb stretches a spring 2 ft on coming to rest at equilibrium. The mass is then lifted up 6 in. above the equilibrium point and given a downward velocity of 1 ft/sec. Determine the simple harmonic motion of the mass. How fast and in what direction will the mass be moving 10 sec after being released?

4. Show that the period of the simple harmonic motion of a mass hanging from a spring is $2\pi\sqrt{l/g}$, where l denotes the amount (beyond its natural length) that the spring is stretched when the mass is at equilibrium.

5. A mass of 5 kg is attached to a spring hanging from a ceiling, thereby stretching the spring 0.5 m on coming to rest at equilibrium. The mass is then pulled down 0.1 m below the equilibrium point and given an upward velocity of 0.1 m/sec. Determine the equation for the simple harmonic motion of the mass. When will the mass first reach its minimum height after being set in motion?

6. A mass of 5 kg is attached to a spring suspended from a ceiling, thereby stretching the spring 2 m on coming to rest at equilibrium. The mass is then lifted up 1 m above the equilibrium point and given an upward velocity of $\frac{1}{3}$ m/sec. Determine the equation for the simple harmonic motion of the mass. When will the mass first reach its maximum height after being set in motion?

7. A mass weighing 16 lb is attached to the lower end of a spring, thereby stretching the spring 2 ft on coming to rest at equilibrium. The mass is then pulled down 6 in. and given an upward velocity of $\frac{1}{2}$ ft/sec. Determine the equation for the simple harmonic motion of the mass. How long until the mass first returns to the equilibrium position?

8. A weight hanging on a spring oscillates with a period of 3 sec. After 2 lb is added, the period becomes 4 sec. Assuming that we can neglect any damping or external forces, determine how much weight was originally attached to the spring.

5.2 *Damped Free Vibrations*

In the previous section we considered vibrations in a rather idyllic setting—no external or frictional forces were assumed present—and the result was simple harmonic motion. In most applications, however, there is at least some type of frictional or damping force that plays a significant role. This force may be due to a component in the system, such as a shock absorber in a car, or to the medium that surrounds the system, such as air or some liquid.

In this section we study the effect of a damping force on free vibrations. In particular, setting $f(t) \equiv 0$ in equation (4) of Section 5.1, we consider the motion of a system that is governed by

(1) $$m \frac{d^2x}{dt^2} + b \frac{dx}{dt} + kx = 0.$$

The auxiliary equation associated with (1) is

(2) $$mr^2 + br + k = 0;$$

its roots are

(3) $$-\frac{b}{2m} \pm \frac{1}{2m} \sqrt{b^2 - 4mk}.$$

As we found in Chapter 4, the form of the solution to (1) depends on the nature of these roots and, in particular, on the discriminant $b^2 - 4mk$.

UNDERDAMPED OR OSCILLATORY MOTION ($b^2 < 4mk$)

When $b^2 < 4mk$, the discriminant $b^2 - 4mk$ is negative and there are two complex conjugate roots to the auxiliary equation (2). These roots are $\alpha \pm i\beta$, where

(4) $$\alpha := -\frac{b}{2m}, \qquad \beta := \frac{1}{2m} \sqrt{4mk - b^2}.$$

Hence a general solution to (1) is

(5) $$x(t) = e^{\alpha t}(C_1 \cos \beta t + C_2 \sin \beta t).$$

As we did with simple harmonic motion, we can express $x(t)$ in the alternate form

(6) $$x(t) = Ae^{\alpha t} \sin(\beta t + \phi),$$

where $A = \sqrt{C_1^2 + C_2^2}$ and $\tan \phi = C_1/C_2$. It is now evident that $x(t)$ is the product of an

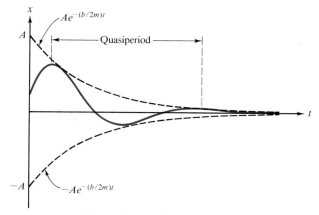

Figure 5.4 Oscillatory motion

exponential factor

$$Ae^{\alpha t} = Ae^{-(b/2m)t}$$

called the **damping factor,** and a sine factor $\sin(\beta t + \phi)$ that accounts for the oscillatory motion. Since the sine factor varies between -1 and 1 with period $2\pi/\beta$, the solution $x(t)$ varies between $-Ae^{\alpha t}$ and $Ae^{\alpha t}$ with **quasiperiod** $P = 2\pi/\beta = 4m\pi/\sqrt{4mk - b^2}$ and **quasi-frequency** $1/P$. Moreover, since b and m are positive, $\alpha = -b/2m$ is negative, and thus the damping factor tends to zero as $t \to \infty$. A graph of a typical solution $x(t)$ is given in Figure 5.4. The system is called **underdamped** because there is not enough damping present (b is too small) to prevent the system from oscillating.

We leave it for the reader to verify that as $b \to 0$ the damping factor approaches the constant A and the quasifrequency approaches the natural frequency of the simple harmonic motion corresponding to $b = 0$. It is also worth mentioning that the values of t where the graph of $x(t)$ touches the exponential curves $\pm Ae^{-\alpha t}$ are *not* the same values of t at which $x(t)$ attains its relative maximum and minimum values (see Problem 11).

CRITICALLY DAMPED MOTION ($b^2 = 4mk$)

When $b^2 = 4mk$, the discriminant $b^2 - 4mk$ is zero and the auxiliary equation has the repeated root $-b/2m$. Hence a general solution to (1) is now

(7) $x(t) = (C_1 + C_2t)e^{-(b/2m)t}$.

To understand the motion described by $x(t)$ in (7), we first consider the behavior of $x(t)$ as $t \to \infty$. Using L'Hôpital's rule,

(8) $\displaystyle\lim_{t \to \infty} x(t) = \lim_{t \to \infty} \frac{C_1 + C_2t}{e^{(b/2m)t}} = \lim_{t \to \infty} \frac{C_2}{(b/2m)e^{(b/2m)t}} = 0,$

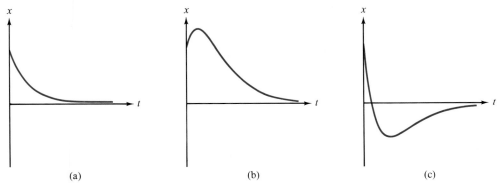

Figure 5.5 Critically damped vibrations

(recall that $b/2m > 0$). Hence, $x(t)$ dies off to zero as $t \to \infty$. Moreover, since

$$x'(t) = \left(C_2 - \frac{b}{2m} C_1 - \frac{b}{2m} C_2 t \right) e^{-(b/2m)t},$$

we see that the derivative is either identically zero (when $C_1 = C_2 = 0$) or vanishes for at most one point (when the linear factor in parentheses is zero). If the trivial solution is ignored, it follows that $x(t)$ has at most one local maximum or minimum for $t > 0$. Therefore, $x(t)$ *does not oscillate*. This leaves, qualitatively, only three possibilities for the motion of $x(t)$, depending on the initial conditions. These are illustrated in Figure 5.5. This special case when $b^2 = 4mk$ is called **critically damped** motion, since if b were any smaller, oscillation would occur.

OVERDAMPED MOTION ($b^2 > 4mk$)

When $b^2 > 4mk$, the discriminant $b^2 - 4mk$ is positive and there are two distinct real roots to the auxiliary equation (2):

(9) $$r_1 = -\frac{b}{2m} + \frac{1}{2m} \sqrt{b^2 - 4mk}, \qquad r_2 = -\frac{b}{2m} - \frac{1}{2m} \sqrt{b^2 - 4mk}.$$

Hence a general solution to (1) is

(10) $$x(t) = C_1 e^{r_1 t} + C_2 e^{r_2 t}.$$

Obviously r_2 is negative. And since $b^2 > b^2 - 4mk$ (that is, $b > \sqrt{b^2 - 4mk}$), it follows that r_1 is also negative. Therefore, as $t \to \infty$, both of the exponentials in (10) decay and $x(t) \to 0$. Moreover, since

$$x'(t) = C_1 r_1 e^{r_1 t} + C_2 r_2 e^{r_2 t} = e^{r_1 t}(C_1 r_1 + C_2 r_2 e^{(r_2 - r_1)t}),$$

it follows that $x'(t) = 0$ only when $C_1 r_1 + C_2 r_2 e^{(r_2-r_1)t} = 0$. Thus a nontrivial solution $x(t)$ can have at most one local maximum or minimum for $t > 0$. As in the case of critical damping, the motion is *nonoscillatory* and must be qualitatively like one of the three sketches in Figure 5.5. This case where $b^2 > 4mk$ is called **overdamped** motion.

▶ **Example 1**   Assume that the motion of a spring-mass system with damping is governed by

(11) $$\frac{d^2x}{dt^2} + b\frac{dx}{dt} + 25x = 0; \qquad x(0) = 1, \qquad x'(0) = 0.$$

Find the equation of motion and sketch its graph for the three cases when $b = 8$, 10, and 12.

Solution   The auxiliary equation for (11) is

(12) $$r^2 + br + 25 = 0,$$

whose roots are

(13) $$r = -\frac{b}{2} \pm \frac{1}{2}\sqrt{b^2 - 100}.$$

Case 1.   When $b = 8$, the roots (13) are $-4 \pm 3i$. This is thus a case of underdamping, and the equation of motion has the form

(14) $$x(t) = C_1 e^{-4t}\cos 3t + C_2 e^{-4t}\sin 3t.$$

Setting $x(0) = 1$ and $x'(0) = 0$ gives the system

$$C_1 = 1, \qquad -4C_1 + 3C_2 = 0,$$

whose solution is $C_1 = 1$, $C_2 = \frac{4}{3}$. To express $x(t)$ as the product of a damping factor and a sine factor (recall equation (6)), we set

$$A = \sqrt{C_1^2 + C_2^2} = \frac{5}{3}, \qquad \tan\phi = \frac{C_1}{C_2} = \frac{3}{4},$$

where ϕ is a first-quadrant angle. Then

(15) $$x(t) = \tfrac{5}{3}e^{-4t}\sin(3t + \phi),$$

where $\phi = \arctan\frac{3}{4} \approx 0.64$ (see Figure 5.6 (a) on page 248).

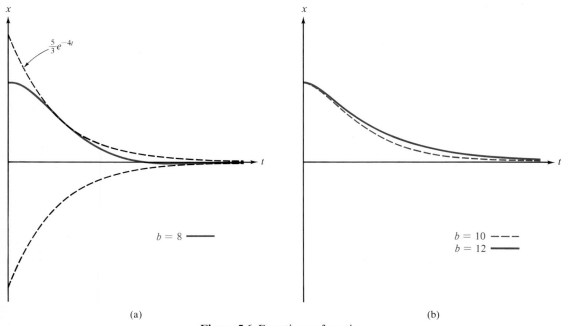

Figure 5.6 Equations of motion
for various values of b

Case 2. When $b = 10$, there is only one (repeated) root to the auxiliary equation (12), namely $r = -5$. This is a case of critical damping, and the equation of motion has the form

(16) $\qquad x(t) = (C_1 + C_2 t)e^{-5t}.$

Setting $x(0) = 1$ and $x'(0) = 0$ now gives

$$C_1 = 1, \qquad C_2 - 5C_1 = 0,$$

and so $C_1 = 1$, $C_2 = 5$. Thus

(17) $\qquad x(t) = (1 + 5t)e^{-5t}.$

The graph of $x(t)$ given in (17) is represented by the dashed line in Figure 5.6(b). Notice that $x(t)$ is zero only for $t = -\frac{1}{5}$ and hence doesn't cross the t-axis for $t > 0$.

Case 3. When $b = 12$, the roots to the auxiliary equation are $-6 \pm \sqrt{11}$. This is a case of overdamping, and the equation of motion has the form

(18) $\qquad x(t) = C_1 e^{(-6+\sqrt{11})t} + C_2 e^{(-6-\sqrt{11})t}.$

Setting $x(0) = 1$ and $x'(0) = 0$ gives

$$C_1 + C_2 = 1, \qquad (-6 + \sqrt{11})C_1 + (-6 - \sqrt{11})C_2 = 0,$$

from which we find $C_1 = (11 + 6\sqrt{11})/22$ and $C_2 = (11 - 6\sqrt{11})/22$. Hence

(19)
$$x(t) = \frac{11 + 6\sqrt{11}}{22} e^{(-6 + \sqrt{11})t} + \frac{11 - 6\sqrt{11}}{22} e^{(-6 - \sqrt{11})t}$$

$$= \frac{e^{(-6 + \sqrt{11})t}}{22} \{11 + 6\sqrt{11} + (11 - 6\sqrt{11})e^{-2\sqrt{11}t}\}.$$

The graph of this overdamped motion is represented by the solid line in Figure 5.6(b). ◀

It is interesting to observe in Example 1 that when the system is underdamped ($b = 8$), the solution goes to zero like e^{-4t}; when the system is critically damped ($b = 10$), the solution tends to zero roughly like e^{-5t}; and when the system is overdamped ($b = 12$), the solution goes to zero like $e^{(-6 + \sqrt{11})t} \approx e^{-2.68t}$. This means that if the system is underdamped, it not only oscillates, but also dies off slower than if it were critically damped. Moreover, if the system is overdamped, it again dies off slower than if it were critically damped. (This agrees with our physical intuition that the damping forces hinder the return to equilibrium.)

▶ **Example 2** An 8-lb weight is attached to a spring hanging from the ceiling. When the weight comes to rest at equilibrium, the spring has been stretched 2 ft. The damping constant b for the system is 1 lb-sec/ft. If the weight is raised 6 in. above equilibrium and given an initial upward velocity of 1 ft/sec, find the equation of motion for the weight. What is the maximum displacement above equilibrium that the weight will attain?

Solution Since an 8-lb weight stretches the spring 2 ft, Hooke's law gives $8 = k2$, and so the spring constant is $k = 4$. The 8-lb weight has mass $m = W/g$, where g is the gravitational constant 32 ft/sec^2. Thus $m = \frac{8}{32} = \frac{1}{4}$ slugs. Substituting these values for m, k, and the given value $b = 1$ into equation (1) and using the initial conditions, we obtain the initial value problem

(20)
$$\frac{1}{4} \frac{d^2x}{dt^2} + \frac{dx}{dt} + 4x = 0; \qquad x(0) = -\frac{1}{2}, \qquad x'(0) = -1;$$

the negative signs for the initial conditions reflect the facts that the initial displacement and push are *upward* (cf. Figure 5.1(c) on page 238).

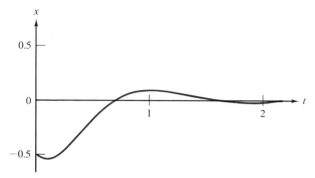

Figure 5.7 Oscillatory motion of spring in Example 2

The reader can verify that the solution to problem (20) is

(21) $$x(t) = -\frac{1}{2} e^{-2t} \cos(2\sqrt{3}\, t) - \frac{1}{\sqrt{3}} e^{-2t} \sin(2\sqrt{3}t),$$

or

(22) $$x(t) = \sqrt{\frac{7}{12}}\, e^{-2t} \sin(2\sqrt{3}\, t + \phi),$$

where $\tan \phi = \sqrt{3}/2$ and ϕ lies in the third quadrant. (See Figure 5.7 for a sketch of $x(t)$.)

To determine the maximum displacement above equilibrium, we must determine the *lowest* point on the graph of $x(t)$. Since $x(t)$ dies off exponentially, this will occur at the first positive critical point of $x(t)$. Computing $x'(t)$ from (21), setting it equal to zero, and solving gives

$$x'(t) = e^{-2t} \left\{ \frac{5}{\sqrt{3}} \sin(2\sqrt{3}t) - \cos(2\sqrt{3}t) \right\} = 0,$$

$$\frac{5}{\sqrt{3}} \sin(2\sqrt{3}t) = \cos(2\sqrt{3}t),$$

$$\tan(2\sqrt{3}t) = \frac{\sqrt{3}}{5}.$$

Thus the first positive root is

$$t = \frac{1}{2\sqrt{3}} \arctan \frac{\sqrt{3}}{5} \approx 0.096.$$

Substituting this value for t back into equation (21) or (22) gives $x(0.096) \approx -0.55$. Hence the maximum displacement above equilibrium is approximately 0.55 ft. ◄

EXERCISES 5.2

1. The motion of a spring-mass system with damping is governed by

$$x''(t) + bx'(t) + 16x(t) = 0; \qquad x(0) = 1, \qquad x'(0) = 0.$$

Find the equation of motion and sketch its graph for $b = 6$, 8, and 10.

2. The motion of a spring-mass system with damping is governed by

$$x''(t) + bx'(t) + 64x(t) = 0; \qquad x(0) = 1, \qquad x'(0) = 0.$$

Find the equation of motion and sketch its graph for $b = 10$, 16, and 20.

3. The motion of a spring-mass system with damping is governed by

$$x''(t) + 10x'(t) + kx(t) = 0; \qquad x(0) = 1, \qquad x'(0) = 0.$$

Find the equation of motion and sketch its graph for $k = 20$, 25, and 30.

4. The motion of a spring-mass system with damping is governed by

$$x''(t) + 4x'(t) + kx(t) = 0; \qquad x(0) = 1, \qquad x'(0) = 0.$$

Find the equation of motion and sketch its graph for $k = 2$, 4, and 6.

5. A 4-lb weight is attached to a spring suspended from the ceiling. When the weight comes to rest at equilibrium, the spring has been stretched 3 in. The damping constant for the system is $\frac{1}{2}$ lb-sec/ft. If the weight is raised 2 in. above equilibrium and given an initial upward velocity of $\frac{1}{2}$ ft/sec, determine the equation of motion of the weight and give its damping factor, quasiperiod, and quasifrequency.

6. A mass of 20 kg stretches a spring 98 cm on coming to rest at equilibrium. The damping constant for the system is 140 N-sec/m. If the mass is pulled 25 cm below equilibrium and given an upward velocity of 1 m/sec, when will it return to its equilibrium position?

7. A mass of 2 kg stretches a spring 49 cm on coming to rest at equilibrium. The damping constant for the system is $8\sqrt{5}$ kg/sec. If the mass is pulled 10 cm below equilibrium and given a downward velocity of 2 m/sec, what is the maximum displacement from equilibrium that it will attain?

8. An 8-lb weight stretches a spring 1 ft on coming to rest at equilibrium. The damping constant for the system is $\frac{1}{4}$ lb-sec/ft. If the weight is raised 1 ft above equilibrium and released, what is the maximum displacement below equilibrium that it will attain?

9. An 8-lb weight stretches a spring 1 ft on coming to rest at equilibrium. The damping constant for the system is 2 lb-sec/ft. If the weight is raised 6 in. above equilibrium and given an upward velocity of 2 ft/sec, when will the mass attain its maximum displacement above equilibrium?

10. A mass of 1 kg stretches a spring 9.8 cm on coming to rest at equilibrium. The damping constant for the system is 0.2 N-sec/m. If the mass is pushed

downward from the equilibrium position with a velocity of 1 m/sec, when will it attain its maximum displacement below equilibrium?

11. Show that for the underdamped system of Example 2, the times when the solution curve $x(t)$ in (22) touches the exponential curves $\pm\sqrt{7/12}e^{-2t}$ are not the same values of t for which the function $x(t)$ attains its relative extrema.

12. For an underdamped system, verify that as $b \to 0$ the damping factor approaches the constant A and the quasifrequency approaches the natural frequency $\sqrt{k/m}/2\pi$.

5.3 *Forced Vibrations*

We now consider the vibrations of a spring-mass system when an external force is applied. Of particular interest is the response of the system to a *periodic* forcing term. As a paradigm, let's investigate the effect of a cosine forcing function on the system governed by the differential equation

$$(1) \qquad m\frac{d^2x}{dt^2} + b\frac{dx}{dt} + kx = F_0 \cos \gamma t,$$

where F_0, γ are nonnegative constants and $0 < b^2 < 4mk$.

A solution to (1) has the form $x = x_h + x_p$, where x_p is a particular solution and x_h is a general solution to the corresponding homogeneous equation. We found in equation (6) of Section 5.2 that

$$(2) \qquad x_h(t) = Ae^{-(b/2m)t} \sin\left(\frac{\sqrt{4mk - b^2}}{2m} t + \phi\right),$$

where A and ϕ are constants.

To determine x_p we can use the method of undetermined coefficients (Section 4.8). From the form of the nonhomogeneous term, we know that

$$(3) \qquad x_p(t) = A_1 \cos \gamma t + A_2 \sin \gamma t,$$

where A_1, A_2 are constants to be determined. Substituting this expression into equation (1) and simplifying gives

$$(4) \qquad [(k - m\gamma^2)A_1 + b\gamma A_2] \cos \gamma t + [(k - m\gamma^2)A_2 - b\gamma A_1] \sin \gamma t = F_0 \cos \gamma t.$$

Setting the corresponding coefficients on both sides equal, we have

$$(k - m\gamma^2)A_1 + b\gamma A_2 = F_0,$$
$$-b\gamma A_1 + (k - m\gamma^2)A_2 = 0,$$

and, solving, we obtain

(5) $$A_1 = \frac{F_0(k - m\gamma^2)}{(k - m\gamma^2)^2 + b^2\gamma^2}, \qquad A_2 = \frac{F_0 b\gamma}{(k - m\gamma^2)^2 + b^2\gamma^2}.$$

Hence a particular solution to (1) is

(6) $$x_p(t) = \frac{F_0}{(k - m\gamma^2)^2 + b^2\gamma^2} \{(k - m\gamma^2)\cos\gamma t + b\gamma\sin\gamma t\}.$$

Since the expression in braces can also be written as

$$\sqrt{(k - m\gamma^2)^2 + b^2\gamma^2}\;\sin(\gamma t + \theta),$$

we can express x_p in the alternate form

(7) $$x_p(t) = \frac{F_0}{\sqrt{(k - m\gamma^2)^2 + b^2\gamma^2}}\;\sin(\gamma t + \theta),$$

where $\tan\theta = (k - m\gamma^2)/(b\gamma)$.

Combining equations (2) and (7), we have the following representation of a general solution to (1) in the case $0 < b^2 < 4mk$:

(8) $$x(t) = \underbrace{Ae^{-(b/2m)t}\sin\left(\frac{\sqrt{4mk - b^2}}{2m}\,t + \phi\right)}_{\text{transient } x_h} + \underbrace{\frac{F_0}{\sqrt{(k - m\gamma^2)^2 + b^2\gamma^2}}\;\sin(\gamma t + \theta)}_{\text{steady-state } x_p}.$$

The solution (8) is the sum of two terms. The first term, x_h, represents damped oscillation and depends only on the parameters of the system and the initial conditions. Because of the damping factor $e^{-(b/2m)t}$, this term tends to zero as $t \to \infty$. Consequently, it is referred to as a **transient** solution. The second term, x_p, in (8) is the offspring of the external forcing function $f(t) = F_0\cos\gamma t$. Like the forcing function, x_p is a sinusoid with angular frequency γ; however, x_p is out of phase with $f(t)$ (by the angle $\theta - \pi/2$), and its magnitude is different by the factor

(9) $$\frac{1}{\sqrt{(k - m\gamma^2)^2 + b^2\gamma^2}}.$$

As the transient term dies off, the motion of the spring-mass system becomes essentially that of the second term x_p. Hence this term is called the **steady-state** solution. The factor appearing in (9) is referred to as the **frequency gain** since it represents the change in the magnitude of the sinusoidal input. The frequency gain has units of length/force.

▶ *Example 1* A 10-kg mass is attached to a spring hanging from the ceiling. This causes the spring to stretch 2 m on coming to rest at equilibrium. At time $t = 0$, an external force $f(t) = 20 \cos 4t$ is applied to the system. The damping constant for the system is 3 N-sec/m. Determine the steady-state solution for the system.

Solution Since the mass m, damping constant b, and forcing term are given, we need only determine the spring constant k to obtain the differential equation that governs the system. The gravitational constant g in the MKS system is approximately 9.8 m/sec². Thus the force of gravity on the system is $mg = (10)(9.8) = 98$ N. From Hooke's law, we have $98 = k2$, and so $k = 49$ N/m. Now, substituting into equation (1), we obtain

$$(10) \qquad 10\frac{d^2x}{dt^2} + 3\frac{dx}{dt} + 49x = 20 \cos 4t,$$

where $x(t)$ is the displacement (from equilibrium) of the mass at time t.

To find the steady-state response we must produce a particular solution to (10) that is a sinusoid. We can do this using the method of undetermined coefficients, guessing a solution of the form $A_1 \cos 4t + A_2 \sin 4t$. But this is precisely how we derived equation (7). Thus we substitute directly into (7) and find

$$(11) \qquad x_p(t) = \frac{20}{\sqrt{(49 - 160)^2 + (9)(16)}} \sin(4t + \theta) \approx (0.18) \sin(4t + \theta),$$

where $\tan \theta = (49 - 160)/12 \approx -9.25$. Since the numerator, $(49 - 160)$, is negative and the denominator, 12, positive, θ is a fourth-quadrant angle. Thus

$$\theta \approx \arctan(-9.25) \approx -1.46,$$

and the steady-state solution is given approximately by

$$(12) \qquad x_p(t) = (0.18) \sin(4t - 1.46). \quad ◀$$

The above example illustrates an important point made earlier: the steady-state response (12) to the sinusoidal forcing function $20 \cos 4t$ is a sinusoid of the same frequency but different amplitude. The gain factor (see (9)) in this case is $(0.18)/20 = 0.009$ m/N.

In general, the amplitude of the steady-state solution to equation (1) depends on the angular frequency γ of the forcing function and is given by $A(\gamma) = F_0 M(\gamma)$, where

$$(13) \qquad M(\gamma) := \frac{1}{\sqrt{(k - m\gamma^2)^2 + b^2\gamma^2}} = \frac{1/m}{\sqrt{\left(\frac{k}{m} - \gamma^2\right)^2 + \left(\frac{b}{m}\right)^2 \gamma^2}}$$

is the frequency gain (see (9)). This formula is valid even when $b^2 \geq 4mk$. For a given system (m, b, and k fixed), it is often of interest to know how this system reacts to sinusoidal inputs of various frequencies (γ is a variable). For this purpose, the graph of the gain $M(\gamma)$, called the **frequency response curve** or **resonance curve** for the system, is enlightening.

In order to sketch the frequency response curve for $\gamma \geq 0$, we observe that when $\gamma = 0$, we have $M(0) = 1/k$. Also note that as $\gamma \to \infty$, the gain $M(\gamma) \to 0$. As a further aid in describing the graph, we compute from (13)

$$(14) \qquad M'(\gamma) = \frac{-\left(\dfrac{2\gamma}{m}\right)\left[\gamma^2 - \left(\dfrac{k}{m} - \dfrac{b^2}{2m^2}\right)\right]}{\left[\left(\dfrac{k}{m} - \gamma^2\right)^2 + \left(\dfrac{b}{m}\right)^2 \gamma^2\right]^{3/2}}.$$

It follows from (14) that $M'(\gamma) = 0$ if and only if

$$(15) \qquad \gamma = 0 \quad \text{or} \quad \gamma = \gamma_r := \sqrt{\frac{k}{m} - \frac{b^2}{2m^2}}.$$

Now when $b^2 > 2mk$, the term inside the radical in (15) is negative and hence $M'(\gamma) = 0$ only when $\gamma = 0$. In this case, as γ increases from zero to infinity, $M(\gamma)$ decreases from $M(0) = 1/k$ to a limit value of zero.

When $b^2 < 2mk$, then γ_r is real and positive, and it is easy to verify that $M(\gamma)$ has a *maximum* at γ_r. Substituting γ_r into (13) gives

$$(16) \qquad M(\gamma_r) = \frac{1}{b\sqrt{\dfrac{k}{m} - \dfrac{b^2}{4m^2}}}.$$

The value $\gamma_r/2\pi$ is called the **resonance frequency** for the system, and, when stimulated by an external force at this frequency, the system is said to be **at resonance.**

Observe that since we must have $b^2 < 2mk$ for resonance to occur, a system cannot be at resonance unless it is underdamped ($b^2 < 4mk$).

To illustrate the effect of the damping constant b on the resonance curve, let's consider a system in which $m = k = 1$. In this case the frequency response curves are given by

$$(17) \qquad M(\gamma) = \frac{1}{\sqrt{(1 - \gamma^2)^2 + b^2\gamma^2}},$$

and, for $b < \sqrt{2}$, the resonance frequency is $\gamma_r/2\pi = (1/2\pi)\sqrt{1 - b^2/2}$. Figure 5.8 on page 256 displays the graphs of these frequency response curves for $b = \frac{1}{4}, \frac{1}{2}, 1, \frac{3}{2}$, and 2. Observe that as $b \to 0$, the maximum magnitude of the frequency gain increases and the resonance frequency $\gamma_r/2\pi$ for the damped system approaches $1/2\pi = \sqrt{k/m}/2\pi$, the natural frequency for the undamped system

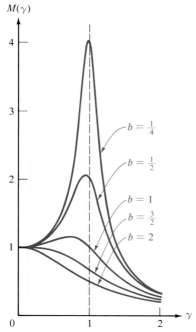

Figure 5.8 Frequency response curves for various values of b

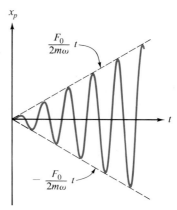

Figure 5.9 Undamped oscillation of the particular solution in (21)

To understand what is occurring, let's consider the undamped system ($b = 0$) with forcing term $F_0 \cos \gamma t$. This system is governed by

(18) $$m \frac{d^2 x}{dt^2} + kx = F_0 \cos \gamma t.$$

A general solution to (18) is the sum of a particular solution and a general solution to the homogeneous equation. In Section 5.1 we showed that the latter describes simple harmonic motion:

(19) $$x_h(t) = A \sin(\omega t + \phi), \qquad \omega := \sqrt{k/m}.$$

The formula for the particular solution given in (7) is valid for $b = 0$ provided that $\gamma \neq \omega = \sqrt{k/m}$. However, when $b = 0$ and $\gamma = \omega$, then the form we used with undetermined coefficients to derive (7) does not work, because $\cos \omega t$ and $\sin \omega t$ are solutions to the corresponding homogeneous equation. The correct form is

(20) $$x_p(t) = A_1 t \cos \omega t + A_2 t \sin \omega t,$$

which leads to the solution

(21) $$x_p(t) = \frac{F_0}{2m\omega} t \sin \omega t.$$

(The verification of (21) is left to the reader.) Hence, in the *undamped resonant case* (when $\gamma = \omega$), a general solution to (18) is

(22) $$x(t) = A \sin(\omega t + \phi) + \frac{F_0}{2m\omega} t \sin \omega t.$$

Returning to the question of resonance, observe that the particular solution in (21) oscillates between $\pm (F_0 t)/(2m\omega)$. Hence as $t \to \infty$, the maximum magnitude of (21) approaches ∞ (see Figure 5.9).

It is obvious from the above discussion that if the damping constant b is very small, the system is subject to large oscillations when the forcing function has a frequency near the resonance frequency for the system. It is these large vibrations at resonance that concern engineers. Indeed, resonance vibrations have been known to cause airplane wings to snap, bridges to collapse,[†] and (less catastrophic) wine glasses to shatter.

EXERCISES 5.3

In the following problems take $g = 32$ ft/sec^2 for the British system and $g = 9.8$ m/sec^2 for the MKS system.

1. An 8-kg mass is attached to a spring hanging from the ceiling. This causes the spring to stretch 1.96 m upon coming to rest at equilibrium. At time $t = 0$, an external force $f(t) = \cos 2t$ N is applied to the system. The damping constant for the system is 3 N-sec/m. Determine the steady-state solution for the system.

2. A mass weighing 32 lb is attached to a spring hanging from the ceiling and comes to rest at its equilibrium position. At time $t = 0$, an external force $f(t) = 3 \cos 4t$ lb is applied to the system. If the spring constant is 5 lb/ft and the damping constant is 2 lb-sec/ft, find the steady-state solution for the system.

3. A mass weighing 8 lb is attached to a spring hanging from the ceiling and comes to rest at its equilibrium position. At time $t = 0$, an external force $f(t) = 2 \cos 2t$ lb is applied to the system. If the spring constant is 16 lb/ft and the damping constant is $\frac{1}{4}$ lb-sec/ft, find the equation of motion of the mass. What is the resonance frequency for the system?

4. A 2-kg mass is attached to a spring hanging from the ceiling. This causes the spring to stretch 20 cm upon coming to rest at equilibrium. At time

---

[†] An interesting discussion of one such disaster, involving the Tacoma Narrows bridge in Washington State, can be found in *Differential Equations and Their Applications,* by M. Braun, Springer-Verlag, New York, 1978.

$t = 0$, the mass is displaced 5 cm below the equilibrium position and released. At this same instant, an external force $f(t) = 0.3 \cos t$ N is applied to the system. If the damping constant for the system is 5 N-sec/m, determine the equation of motion for the mass. What is the resonance frequency for the system?

5. Sketch the frequency response curve (13) for the system in which $m = 4$, $k = 1$, $b = 2$.

6. Sketch the frequency response curve (13) for the system in which $m = 2$, $k = 3$, $b = 3$.

7. Determine the equation of motion for an undamped system at resonance governed by

$$\frac{d^2x}{dt^2} + 9x = 2 \cos 3t; \qquad x(0) = 1, \qquad x'(0) = 0.$$

Sketch the solution.

8. Determine the equation of motion for an undamped system at resonance governed by

$$\frac{d^2x}{dt^2} + x = 5 \cos t; \qquad x(0) = 0, \qquad x'(0) = 1.$$

Sketch the solution.

9. An undamped system is governed by

$$m\frac{d^2x}{dt^2} + kx = F_0 \cos \gamma t, \qquad x(0) = x'(0) = 0,$$

where $\gamma \neq \omega := \sqrt{k/m}$.

(a) Find the equation of motion of the system.

(b) Use trigonometric identities to show that the solution can be written in the form

$$x(t) = \frac{2F_0}{m(\omega^2 - \gamma^2)} \sin\left(\frac{\omega + \gamma}{2}\right)t \sin\left(\frac{\omega - \gamma}{2}\right)t.$$

(c) When γ is near ω, then $\omega - \gamma$ is small, while $\omega + \gamma$ is relatively large compared with $\omega - \gamma$. Hence, $x(t)$ can be viewed as the product of a slowly varying sine function, $\sin[(\omega - \gamma)t/2]$, and a rapidly varying sine function, $\sin[(\omega + \gamma)t/2]$. The net effect is a sine function $x(t)$ with frequency $(\omega - \gamma)/4\pi$, whose amplitude is a sine function with frequency $(\omega + \gamma)/4\pi$. This vibration phenomenon is referred to as **beats** and is used in tuning stringed instruments. This same phenomenon in electronics is called **amplitude modulation.** To illustrate this phenomenon, sketch the curve $x(t)$ for $F_0 = 32$, $m = 2$, $\omega = 9$, and $\gamma = 7$.

10. Derive the formula for $x_p(t)$ given in (21).

5.4 *Elementary Electric Circuits*

In this section we consider the application of differential equations to an elementary electric circuit consisting of an electromotive force (e.g., a battery or generator), resistor, inductor, and capacitor in series. These circuits are called **RLC series circuits** and are represented schematically as shown in Figure 5.10.

Two physical principles governing *RLC* series circuits are (I) conservation of charge and (II) conservation of energy. These conservation laws were formulated for electric circuits by G. R. Kirchhoff in 1859 and are called **Kirchhoff's laws.** They state:

(I) The current *I* passing through each of the elements (resistor, inductor, capacitor, or electromotive force) in the series circuit must be the same.

(II) The algebraic sum of the instantaneous changes in potential (voltage drops) around a closed circuit must be zero.

In order to apply Kirchhoff's laws we obviously need to know the voltage drop across each element of the circuit. These voltage formulas are stated below (the reader can consult an introductory physics text for further details[†]).

(a) According to Ohm's law, the voltage drop E_R across a resistor is proportional to the current *I* passing through the resistor:

$$E_R = RI.$$

The proportionality constant *R* is called the **resistance.**

(b) It can be shown using Faraday's law and Lenz's law that the voltage drop E_L across an inductor is proportional to the instantaneous rate of change of the current *I*:

$$E_L = L\frac{dI}{dt}.$$

The proportionality constant *L* is called the **inductance.**

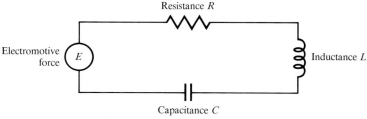

Figure 5.10 Schematic representation of an *RLC* series circuit

[†] For example, *Physics*, by Paul A. Tipler, Worth Publishers, Inc., New York, 1983.

(c) The voltage drop E_C across a capacitor is proportional to the electric charge q on the capacitor:

$$E_C = \frac{1}{C} q.$$

The proportionality constant $1/C$ is called the **elastance** and C the **capacitance.**

An electromotive force is assumed to *add* voltage or potential energy to the circuit. If we let $E(t)$ denote the voltage supplied to the circuit at time t, then Kirchhoff's conservation of energy law gives

(1) $E_L + E_R + E_C = E(t).$

Substituting into (1) the expressions for E_L, E_R, and E_C gives

(2) $L\dfrac{dI}{dt} + RI + \dfrac{1}{C} q = E(t).$

Now the current is just the instantaneous rate of change in charge; that is, $I = dq/dt$. Therefore, we can express (2) in terms of the single variable q as follows:

(3) $L\dfrac{d^2q}{dt^2} + R\dfrac{dq}{dt} + \dfrac{1}{C} q = E(t).$

In many applications we will be interested in determining the current $I(t)$. If we differentiate (3) with respect to t and substitute I for dq/dt, we obtain

(4) $L\dfrac{d^2I}{dt^2} + R\dfrac{dI}{dt} + \dfrac{1}{C} I = \dfrac{dE}{dt}.$

For an *RLC* series circuit, one is usually given the initial charge on the capacitor $q(0)$ and the initial current $I(0) = q'(0)$. These constants provide the initial conditions for equation (3). However, for equation (4), we also need to know the initial rate of change in the current, $I'(0)$. This can be obtained from equation (2) by substituting in the initial values $q(0)$, $I(0)$, and $E(0)$.

The common units and symbols used for electric circuits are listed in Table 5.1.

▶ *Example 1*   An *RLC* series circuit has an electromotive force given by $E(t) = \sin 100t$ volts, a resistor of 0.02 ohms, an inductor of 0.001 henrys, and a capacitor of 2 farads. If the initial current and the initial charge on the capacitor are both zero, determine the current in the circuit for $t > 0$.

TABLE 5.1 COMMON UNITS AND SYMBOLS USED WITH ELECTRIC CIRCUITS			
Quantity	Letter Representation	Units	Symbol Representation
Electromotive force (impressed voltage)	E	volt (V)	—◯— Generator —⊣⊢— Battery
Resistance	R	ohm (Ω)	—⋀⋀—
Inductance	L	henry (H)	—⟓⟓⟓—
Capacitance	C	farad (F)	—⊣⊢—
Charge	q	coulomb	
Current	I	ampere	

Solution   Here we have $L = 0.001$, $R = 0.02$, $C = 2$, and $E(t) = \sin 100t$. Substituting these into equation (4) for the current gives

(5) $$(0.001)\frac{d^2 I}{dt^2} + (0.02)\frac{dI}{dt} + (0.5)I = 100 \cos 100t,$$

or, equivalently,

(6) $$\frac{d^2 I}{dt^2} + 20\frac{dI}{dt} + 500I = 100{,}000 \cos 100t.$$

The homogeneous equation associated with (6) has the auxiliary equation

$$r^2 + 20r + 500 = (r + 10)^2 + (20)^2 = 0,$$

whose roots are $-10 \pm 20i$. Hence the solution to the homogeneous equation is

(7) $$I_h(t) = C_1 e^{-10t} \cos 20t + C_2 e^{-10t} \sin 20t.$$

To find a particular solution for (6), we can use the method of undetermined coefficients. Setting

$$I_p(t) = A \cos 100t + B \sin 100t$$

and carrying out the procedure in Section 4.8, we ultimately find

(8) $$A = -\frac{95}{9.425}, \qquad B = \frac{20}{9.425}.$$

Hence a particular solution to (6) is given by

$$(9) \qquad I_p(t) = -\frac{95}{9.425} \cos 100t + \frac{20}{9.425} \sin 100t.$$

Since $I = I_h + I_p$, we find from (7) and (9) that

$$(10) \qquad I(t) = e^{-10t}(C_1 \cos 20t + C_2 \sin 20t)$$

$$-\frac{95}{9.425} \cos 100t + \frac{20}{9.425} \sin 100t.$$

To determine the constants C_1 and C_2, we need the values $I(0)$ and $I'(0)$. We were given $I(0) = q(0) = 0$. To find $I'(0)$, we substitute the values for L, R, and C into equation (2) and equate the two sides at $t = 0$. This gives

$$(0.001)I'(0) + (0.02)I(0) + (0.5)q(0) = \sin 0.$$

Since $I(0) = q(0) = 0$, we find $I'(0) = 0$. Finally, using $I(t)$ in (10) and the initial conditions $I(0) = I'(0) = 0$, we obtain the system

$$I(0) = C_1 - \frac{95}{9.425} = 0,$$

$$I'(0) = -10C_1 + 20C_2 + \frac{2000}{9.425} = 0.$$

Solving this system yields $C_1 = 95/9.425$ and $C_2 = -105/18.85$. Hence the current in the *RLC* series circuit is

$$(11) \qquad I(t) = e^{-10t}\left(\frac{95}{9.425} \cos 20t - \frac{105}{18.85} \sin 20t \right)$$

$$-\frac{95}{9.425} \cos 100t + \frac{20}{9.425} \sin 100t. \ \blacktriangleleft$$

Observe that, as was the case with mechanical vibrations, the current in (11) is made up of two components. The first, I_h, is a **transient current** that tends to zero as $t \to \infty$. The second,

$$I_p(t) = -\frac{95}{9.425} \cos 100t + \frac{20}{9.425} \sin 100t,$$

is a **steady-state current** that remains. If we had chosen to solve for the charge $q(t)$ in Example 1, we would also have found that there is a **transient charge** q_h that dies off and a **steady-state charge** q_p that remains.

We leave it for the reader to verify that the steady-state solutions $q_p(t)$ and $I_p(t)$ that arise from the electromotive force $E(t) = E_0 \sin \gamma t$ are

(12) $$q_p(t) = \frac{-E_0 \cos(\gamma t + \theta)}{\sqrt{(1/C - L\gamma^2)^2 + \gamma^2 R^2}},$$

(13) $$I_p(t) = q'_p(t) = \frac{E_0 \sin(\gamma t + \theta)}{\sqrt{R^2 + [\gamma L - 1/(\gamma C)]^2}},$$

where $\tan \theta = (1/C - L\gamma^2)/(\gamma R)$. The quantity $\sqrt{R^2 + [\gamma L - 1/(\gamma C)]^2}$ is called the **impedance** of the circuit and is a function of the frequency γ of the electromotive force $E(t)$.

It should be obvious to the reader that the differential equations that describe mechanical vibrations and RLC series circuits are essentially the same. And, in fact, there is a natural identification of the parameters m, b, and k for a spring-mass system with the parameters L, R, and C that describe circuits. This is illustrated in Table 5.2. Moreover, the terms *transient, steady-state, overdamped, critically damped, underdamped,* and *resonance frequency* described in the preceding sections apply to RLC series circuits as well.

This analogy between a simple mechanical system and an elementary electric circuit extends to large-scale systems and circuits. An interesting consequence of this is the use of analog simulation and, in particular, analog computers to analyze mechanical systems. Due to size, time, and cost constraints, large-scale mechanical systems are modeled by building a corresponding electric system and then measuring the charge $q(t)$ and current $I(t)$. While such analog simulations are important, both large-scale mechanical and electric systems are currently modeled using computer simulation. This involves the numerical solution of the initial value problem governing the system. Still, the analogy between mechanical and electric systems means that basically the same computer software can be used to analyze both systems.

TABLE 5.2 ANALOGY BETWEEN MECHANICAL AND ELECTRIC SYSTEMS

Mechanical Spring-Mass System with Damping		Electric *RLC* Series Circuit	
$mx'' + bx' + kx = f(t)$		$Lq'' + Rq' + (1/C)q = E(t)$	
Displacement	x	Charge	q
Velocity	x'	Current	$q' = I$
Mass	m	Inductance	L
Damping constant	b	Resistance	R
Spring constant	k	Elastance	$1/C$
External force	$f(t)$	Electromotive force	$E(t)$

EXERCISES 5.4

1. An *RLC* series circuit has an electromotive force given by $E(t) = 20$ volts, a resistor of 100 ohms, an inductor of 4 henrys, and a capacitor of 0.01 farads. If the initial current is zero and the initial charge on the capacitor is 4 coulombs, determine the current in the circuit for $t > 0$.

2. An *RLC* series circuit has an electromotive force given by $E(t) = 40 \cos 2t$ volts, a resistor of 2 ohms, an inductor of $\frac{1}{4}$ henrys, and a capacitor of $\frac{1}{13}$ farads. If the initial current is zero and the initial charge on the capacitor is 3.5 coulombs, determine the charge on the capacitor for $t > 0$.

3. An *RLC* series circuit has an electromotive force given by $E(t) = 10 \cos 2t$ volts, a resistor of 120 ohms, an inductor of 4 henrys, and a capacitor of $(2200)^{-1}$ farads. Find the steady-state current (solution) for this circuit. What is the resonance frequency of the circuit?

4. An *LC* series circuit has an electromotive force given by $E(t) = 30 \sin 50t$ volts, an inductor of 2 henrys, and a capacitor of 0.02 farads (but no resistor). What is the current in this circuit for $t > 0$ if at $t = 0$, $I(0) = q(0) = 0$?

5. An *RLC* series circuit has an electromotive force of the form $E(t) = E_0 \cos \gamma t$ volts, a resistor of 10 ohms, an inductor of 4 henrys, and a capacitor of 0.01 farads. Sketch the frequency response curve for this circuit.

6. Show that when the electromotive force in (3) is of the form $E(t) = E_0 \sin \gamma t$, then the steady-state solutions q_p and I_p are as given in equations (12) and (13).

7. A spring-mass system with damping consists of a 7-kg mass, a spring with spring constant 3 N/m, a frictional component with damping constant 2 N-sec/m, and an external force given by $f(t) = 10 \cos 10t$ N. Using a 10-ohm resistor, construct an *RLC* series circuit that is the analog of this mechanical system in the sense that the two systems are governed by the same differential equation.

8. A spring-mass system with damping consists of a 16-lb weight, a spring with spring constant 64 lb/ft, a frictional component with damping constant 10 lb-sec/ft, and an external force given by $f(t) = 20 \cos 8t$ lb. Using an inductor of 0.01 henrys, construct an *RLC* series circuit that is the analog of this mechanical system.

9. Because of Euler's formula, $e^{i\theta} = \cos \theta + i \sin \theta$, it is often convenient to treat the electromotive forces $E_0 \cos \gamma t$ and $E_0 \sin \gamma t$ simultaneously, using $E(t) = E_0 e^{i\gamma t}$, where $i = \sqrt{-1}$. In this case equation (3) becomes

(14) $$L\frac{d^2q}{dt^2} + R\frac{dq}{dt} + \frac{1}{C}q = E_0 e^{i\gamma t}.$$

(a) Show that the steady-state solution to (14) is

$$q_p(t) = \frac{E_0}{1/C - \gamma^2 L + i\gamma R} e^{i\gamma t}.$$

[Hint: Use the method of undetermined coefficients with the guess $q_p = Ae^{i\gamma t}$, where A denotes a complex constant.]

(b) Now show that the steady-state current is

$$I_p(t) = \frac{E_0}{R + i[\gamma L + 1/(\gamma C)]} \, e^{i\gamma t}.$$

(c) Use the relation $\alpha + i\beta = \sqrt{\alpha^2 + \beta^2} \, e^{i\theta}$, where $\tan \theta = \beta/\alpha$, to show that I_p can be expressed in the form

$$I_p(t) = \frac{E_0}{\sqrt{R^2 + [\gamma L - 1/(\gamma C)]^2}} \, e^{i(\gamma t + \theta)},$$

where $\tan \theta = (1/C - L\gamma^2)/(\gamma R)$.

(d) Since the imaginary part of $e^{i\gamma t}$ is $\sin \gamma t$, then the imaginary part of the solution to (14) must be the solution to equation (3) for $E(t) = E_0 \sin \gamma t$. Verify that this is also the case for the current by showing that the imaginary part of I_p in part (c) is the same as that given in equation (13).

5.5 *Linear Difference Equations*

In this section we give a brief discussion of linear difference equations.[†] These equations occur in mathematical models of physical processes and as tools in numerical analysis. For example, a model for population dynamics under immigration involves the equation

$$P_{t+1} - P_t = aP_t + b,$$

where $P_{t+1} - P_t$ is the difference between the population at time $t + 1$ and at time t, the constant a is the difference between the average birth rate and average death rate, and b is the rate at which people immigrate to the country. First order difference equations of this type were studied in Project D in Chapter 3. Another example is the equation

$$y_{n+1} - y_{n-1} = -2hy_n,$$

which arises in the study of the stability of a numerical scheme that approximates the solution to a differential equation. Here y_n is the approximation of the solution at x_n and h is the step size.

As these examples suggest, difference equations can be thought of as discrete analogs of differential equations. In fact, the theory of linear difference equations parallels the theory of linear differential equations as discussed in Chapter 4. Using the results of that chapter as a model both for the statements of the theorems and for their proofs, we can develop a theory and devise methods for solving linear difference equations.

[†] For a more in-depth discussion of difference equations and their applications we refer the reader to *Introduction to Difference Equations* by Samuel Goldberg, Dover Publications, Inc., New York, 1986, or *Differential and Difference Equations* by Louis Brand, John Wiley and Sons, Inc., New York, 1966.

THEORY

A **kth-order linear difference equation** is an equation of the form

(1) $$a_k(n)y_{n+k} + a_{k-1}(n)y_{n+k-1} + \cdots + a_1(n)y_{n+1} + a_0(n)y_n = g_n,$$

$n = 0, 1, 2, \ldots$, where $a_k(n), \ldots, a_0(n)$, and g_n are defined for all nonnegative integers n. By a **solution** to (1) we mean a sequence of numbers $\{y_n\}_{n=0}^{\infty}$ that satisfies (1) for all integers $n \geq 0$. For example, the sequence $\{2^n\}_{n=0}^{\infty}$ is a solution to the equation

$$y_{n+2} + y_{n+1} - 6y_n = 0,$$

since

$$2^{n+2} + 2^{n+1} - (6)2^n = 2^n(4 + 2 - 6) = 0,$$

for $n = 0, 1, 2, \ldots$.
    When $a_k(n) \neq 0$ for all integers $n \geq 0$, we can solve equation (1) for y_{n+k}:

(2) $$y_{n+k} = \frac{-1}{a_k(n)}\{a_{k-1}(n)y_{n+k-1} + \cdots + a_0(n)y_n - g_n\}.$$

If we are given the first k values for $\{y_n\}$, that is, $y_0, y_1, \ldots, y_{k-1}$, then we can use equation (2) with $n = 0$ to solve uniquely for y_k. But knowing y_k then allows us to use equation (2) with $n = 1$ to determine y_{k+1} uniquely. Since we can continue this process indefinitely, we see that there is a unique solution to (1) that satisfies the given initial conditions. We summarize these observations in the following theorem.

EXISTENCE AND UNIQUENESS OF SOLUTION

Theorem 1. Let $Y_0, Y_1, \ldots, Y_{k-1}$ be given constants and assume that $a_k(n) \neq 0$ for all integers $n \geq 0$. Then, there exists a unique solution $\{y_n\}_{n=0}^{\infty}$ to (1) that satisfies the initial conditions $y_0 = Y_0, y_1 = Y_1, \ldots, y_{k-1} = Y_{k-1}$.

When $g_n = 0$ for $n \geq 0$, equation (1) becomes the **homogeneous** (or **reduced**) equation

(3) $$a_k(n)y_{n+k} + \cdots + a_0(n)y_n = 0, \qquad n = 0, 1, 2, \ldots.$$

As is the case for homogeneous differential equations, if two sequences $\{y_n\}_{n=0}^{\infty}$ and $\{z_n\}_{n=0}^{\infty}$ are solutions to the homogeneous equation (3), then so is any linear combination of these sequences (see Problem 28). In this context, by a linear combination of sequences $\{y_n\}_{n=0}^{\infty}$ and $\{z_n\}_{n=0}^{\infty}$, we mean a sequence of the form

$$\{c_1 y_n + c_2 z_n\}_{n=0}^{\infty},$$

where c_1 and c_2 are constants.

As you would probably guess, if we can find two "different" solutions $\{y_n\}_{n=0}^{\infty}$ and $\{z_n\}_{n=0}^{\infty}$ to a homogeneous linear *second* order equation

(4) $$a_2(n)y_{n+2} + a_1(n)y_{n+1} + a_0(n)y_n = 0, \qquad n = 0, 1, 2, \ldots,$$

then we can express any solution to (4) as a linear combination of these solutions. To show this (and to decide what we should mean by "different"), let $\{w_n\}_{n=0}^{\infty}$ be a solution to (4). If it is possible to choose constants c_1 and c_2 so that

(5)
$$c_1 y_0 + c_2 z_0 = w_0,$$
$$c_1 y_1 + c_2 z_1 = w_1,$$

then, since $\{w_n\}_{n=0}^{\infty}$ and $\{c_1 y_n + c_2 z_n\}_{n=0}^{\infty}$ are two solutions to (4) that satisfy the same initial conditions (5), the uniqueness conclusion of Theorem 1 gives

$$w_n = c_1 y_n + c_2 z_n, \qquad n = 0, 1, 2, \ldots.$$

A necessary and sufficient condition for (5) to have a unique solution for every w_0, w_1 is that

(6) $$\begin{vmatrix} y_0 & z_0 \\ y_1 & z_1 \end{vmatrix} = y_0 z_1 - y_1 z_0 \neq 0.$$

This is equivalent to saying that the first two terms in the sequences are not multiples of each other, that is, $(z_0, z_1) \neq c(y_0, y_1)$.

We now state the representation theorem for solutions to the homogeneous equation that we have just proved.

REPRESENTATION OF SOLUTIONS (HOMOGENEOUS CASE)

Theorem 2. Assume $a_2(n) \neq 0$ for all integers $n \geq 0$, and let $\{y_n\}_{n=0}^{\infty}$ and $\{z_n\}_{n=0}^{\infty}$ be any two solutions to (4) that satisfy the condition[†]

(7) $$y_0 z_1 - y_1 z_0 \neq 0.$$

Then, every solution $\{w_n\}_{n=0}^{\infty}$ to (4) can be expressed in the form

(8) $$w_n = c_1 y_n + c_2 z_n, \qquad n = 0, 1, 2, \ldots,$$

where c_1 and c_2 are constants.

[†] Condition (7) is similar to the condition we encountered in Chapter 4 for linear second order differential equations. There we introduced the Wronskian function and discussed its connection with linear independence. The analog of the Wronskian function is the **Casoratian** sequence, which is named for the Italian mathematician Felice Casorati (1835–1890).

A solution set $\{\{y_n\}_{n=0}^{\infty}, \{z_n\}_{n=0}^{\infty}\}$ that satisfies condition (7) is called a **fundamental solution set** for (4). The linear combination of $\{y_n\}_{n=0}^{\infty}$ and $\{z_n\}_{n=0}^{\infty}$ in (8), written with arbitrary constants c_1 and c_2, is referred to as a **general solution** to (4).

▶ **Example 1** Given that $\{2^{-n}\}_{n=0}^{\infty}$ and $\{(-3)^n\}_{n=0}^{\infty}$ are solutions to

(9) $\qquad 2y_{n+2} + 5y_{n+1} - 3y_n = 0, \qquad n = 0, 1, 2, \ldots,$

find the solution to (9) that satisfies $y_0 = 0$ and $y_1 = 1$.

Solution Since $(2^{-0})(-3) - (2^{-1})(-3)^0 = -3 - \frac{1}{2} \neq 0$, condition (7) is satisfied and so a general solution to (9) is

(10) $\qquad y_n = c_1 2^{-n} + c_2(-3)^n, \qquad n = 0, 1, 2, \ldots,$

where c_1 and c_2 are arbitrary constants. Using the initial conditions to solve for c_1 and c_2 gives the system

$$y_0 = c_1 + c_2 = 0,$$
$$y_1 = (1/2)c_1 - 3c_2 = 1,$$

whose solution is $c_1 = -c_2 = \frac{2}{7}$. Thus the solution we seek is

(11) $\qquad y_n = \left(\frac{2}{7}\right)2^{-n} - \left(\frac{2}{7}\right)(-3)^n, \qquad n = 0, 1, 2, \ldots.$ ◀

When $\{g_n\}$ is not the zero sequence, equation (1) is said to be **nonhomogeneous** (or **complete**). Using the superposition principle for linear difference equations (see Problem 29) and the representation theorem for homogeneous equations, we can prove the following representation theorem for nonhomogeneous equations. We leave its proof as an exercise (see Problem 30).

REPRESENTATION OF SOLUTIONS (NONHOMOGENEOUS CASE)

Theorem 3. Assume $a_2(n) \neq 0$ for all integers $n \geq 0$, and let $\{p_n\}_{n=0}^{\infty}$ be a particular solution to the nonhomogeneous equation

(12) $\qquad a_2(n)y_{n+2} + a_1(n)y_{n+1} + a_0(n)y_n = g_n, \qquad n = 0, 1, 2, \ldots.$

Then, every solution to (12) can be expressed in the form

(13) $\qquad w_n = p_n + c_1 y_n + c_2 z_n, \qquad n = 0, 1, 2, \ldots,$

where $\{\{y_n\}_{n=0}^{\infty}, \{z_n\}_{n=0}^{\infty}\}$ is a fundamental solution set for the corresponding homogeneous equation and c_1 and c_2 are constants.

The linear combination of $\{p_n\}_{n=0}^{\infty}$, $\{y_n\}_{n=0}^{\infty}$, and $\{z_n\}_{n=0}^{\infty}$ in (13) written with arbitrary constants c_1 and c_2 is referred to as a **general solution** to (12).

CONSTANT COEFFICIENT EQUATIONS

When a_0, a_1, and a_2 are constants, the equation

(14) $\qquad a_2 y_{n+2} + a_1 y_{n+1} + a_0 y_n = g_n, \qquad n = 0, 1, 2, \ldots$

is said to have **constant coefficients.** To find a general solution to (14), we begin with the homogeneous equation

(15) $\qquad a_2 y_{n+2} + a_1 y_{n+1} + a_0 y_n = 0, \qquad n = 0, 1, 2, \ldots .$

We assume that both a_0 and a_2 are not zero so that we have a genuine second order difference equation.

Our experience with differential equations suggests that we try to find solutions of the form $y_n = r^n$, $n = 0, 1, 2, \ldots$, where $r \neq 0$ is a fixed (real or complex) number. Substituting in (15) gives

$$a_2 r^{n+2} + a_1 r^{n+1} + a_0 r^n = r^n(a_2 r^2 + a_1 r + a_0) = 0.$$

Hence, a nontrivial solution to (15) is given by $y_n = r^n$, $n = 0, 1, 2, \ldots$, if and only if r satisfies the **auxiliary equation**

(16) $\qquad a_2 r^2 + a_1 r + a_0 = 0.$

Now the form of a fundamental solution set for (15) depends upon the type of roots to the auxiliary equation. These results are summarized in the following theorem.

FORM OF GENERAL SOLUTION TO $a_2 y_{n+2} + a_1 y_{n+1} + a_0 y_n = 0$

Theorem 4. Let r_1 and r_2 be the roots of the auxiliary equation (16), where a_2, a_1, a_0 are real constants, $a_2 \neq 0$, $a_1 \neq 0$.

(a) If r_1 and r_2 are distinct real roots, then a general solution to (15) is

(17) $\qquad y_n = c_1 r_1^n + c_2 r_2^n, \qquad n = 0, 1, 2, \ldots .$

(b) If $r_1 = r_2 = r = -a_1/(2a_2)$ is a repeated root, then a general solution to (15) is

(18) $\qquad y_n = c_1 r^n + c_2 n r^n, \qquad n = 0, 1, 2, \ldots .$

(c) If r_1 and r_2 are complex conjugate roots and we express r_1 in the polar form $r_1 = \rho e^{i\theta}$, then a general solution to (15) is

(19) $\qquad y_n = c_1 \rho^n \cos n\theta + c_2 \rho^n \sin n\theta, \qquad n = 0, 1, 2, \ldots .$

Proof   Parts (a) and (b) are analogous to the results for linear second order differential equations with constant coefficients, and so we omit their proofs. To prove part (c), we observe that if $r_1 = \rho e^{i\theta}$, then $r_1^n = \rho^n e^{in\theta}$. Using Euler's formula, we find

$$r_1^n = \rho^n \{\cos n\theta + i \sin n\theta\}, \qquad n = 0, 1, 2, \ldots.$$

If $\{r_1^n\}_{n=0}^{\infty}$ is a complex-valued solution, then the two real-valued sequences that make up the real and imaginary parts of $\{r_1^n\}_{n=0}^{\infty}$ must also be solutions. Hence, two solutions are

$$\{\rho^n \cos n\theta\}_{n=0}^{\infty} \quad \text{and} \quad \{\rho^n \sin n\theta\}_{n=0}^{\infty}.$$

Here condition (7) is $\rho \sin \theta = \text{Im}(r_1) \neq 0$. But we have assumed that r_1 is complex, and so $\text{Im}(r_1) \neq 0$. Thus, these two real-valued sequences form a fundamental solution set. ∎

▶ **Example 2**   Find a general solution to

(20) $$y_{n+2} + 6y_{n+1} + 9y_n = 0, \qquad n = 0, 1, 2, \ldots.$$

Solution   The auxiliary equation is

$$r^2 + 6r + 9 = (r + 3)^2 = 0,$$

which has roots $r_1 = r_2 = -3$. Hence, by Theorem 4, part (b), a general solution is

(21) $$y_n = c_1(-3)^n + c_2 n(-3)^n, \qquad n = 0, 1, 2, \ldots. \blacktriangleleft$$

▶ **Example 3**   Find a general solution to

(22) $$y_{n+2} + 2y_{n+1} + 5y_n = 0, \qquad n = 0, 1, 2, \ldots.$$

Solution   The auxiliary equation is

$$r^2 + 2r + 5 = (r + 1)^2 + 2^2 = 0,$$

which has roots $r = -1 \pm 2i$. Writing $r_1 = -1 + 2i$ in polar form, we find $\rho = \sqrt{(-1)^2 + 2^2} = \sqrt{5}$ and $\tan \theta = 2/(-1) = -2$. Since θ lies in the second quadrant, we have $\theta = \pi - \arctan 2 \approx 2.03$ radians. Hence, by Theorem 4, part (c), a general solution is

(23) $$y_n = c_1(\sqrt{5})^n \cos n\theta + c_2(\sqrt{5})^n \sin n\theta, \qquad n = 0, 1, 2, \ldots,$$

where $\theta = \pi - \arctan 2$. ◀

▶ *Example 4*   To approximate the solution to the initial value problem

(24) $y' = -y, \qquad y(0) = 1,$

a method based upon the center-difference formula, $y'(x) \approx [y(x + h) - y(x - h)]/2h$, leads to the difference equation

(25) $y_{n+1} = y_{n-1} - 2hy_n, \qquad n = 1, 2, 3, \ldots, \qquad y_0 = 1,$

where $h\,(>0)$ is the step size and y_n is the approximation to y at the point $x_n = nh$, $n = 0, 1, 2, \ldots$. Discuss the stability of this method, that is, compare the behavior (as $n \to \infty$) of the solutions to (25) with the solution to (24).

Solution   The exact solution to equation (24) is just $\phi(x) = e^{-x}$. For fixed $h\,(>0)$, if $x_n = nh$, then $\phi(x_n) = e^{-x} n = e^{-nh}$ and $\phi(x_n) \to 0$ as $n \to \infty$.
Equation (25) is a linear second order difference equation with auxiliary equation

$$r^2 + 2hr - 1 = 0,$$

which has roots

$$r_1 = -h + \sqrt{1 + h^2} \quad \text{and} \quad r_2 = -h - \sqrt{1 + h^2}.$$

Hence, a general solution to (25) is

$$y_n = c_1 r_1^n + c_2 r_2^n.$$

To solve for c_1 and c_2, we must know y_0 and y_1. The initial condition for the initial value problem (24) only provides $y_0 = 1$. Thus the value for y_1 must be determined by some other numerical method. This, however, is not the problem. To understand the difficulty, let's consider what happens to r_1^n and r_2^n as $n \to \infty$.
For any $h > 0$, it is easy to check that $0 < r_1 < 1$. Hence $r_1^n \to 0$ as $n \to \infty$. This is the same behavior as the exact solution $\phi(x) = e^{-x}$. But, $r_2 = -h - \sqrt{1 + h^2} < -1$, and so r_2^n diverges as $n \to \infty$. Consequently, if $c_2 \neq 0$, then $|y_n| \to \infty$.
This particular method for approximating the solution to (24) has given rise to the extraneous "solution" $c_2 r_2^n$ which exhibits larger and larger oscillations. Moreover, since y_1 can only be approximated due to truncation error (or because of round-off), the coefficient c_2, however small, will be nonzero. Hence, at some point the term $c_2 r_2^n$ will dominate the term $c_1 r_1^n$, giving rise to wild oscillations of the form $(-h - \sqrt{1 + h^2})^n$. Therefore, this method is unstable for any choice of the step size h. ◀

UNDETERMINED COEFFICIENTS

To find a solution to the nonhomogeneous equation (14), we use the analog of the **method of undetermined coefficients** discussed in Section 4.8. We can use Table 4.1 on page 204 with a minor modification. For difference equations it is more convenient to express an exponential function in the form α^n rather than $e^{\alpha t}$. (Recall $\alpha^n = e^{(\ln \alpha)n}$.) The method of undetermined coefficients is illustrated in the following example.

▶ *Example 5*   Find a general solution to

(26) $y_{n+2} - 2y_{n+1} + 2y_n = 3 \sin n,$ $n = 0, 1, 2, \ldots.$

Solution   We first solve the associated homogeneous equation

$$y_{n+2} - 2y_{n+1} + 2y_n = 0,$$

which has the auxiliary equation $r^2 - 2r + 2 = (r-1)^2 + 1^2 = 0$. The roots of the auxiliary equation are $r = 1 \pm i$. Writing $1 + i = \rho e^{i\theta}$, we find $\rho = \sqrt{1^2 + 1^2} = \sqrt{2}$ and $\theta = \arctan 1 = \pi/4$. Hence, a general solution to the homogeneous equation is

(27) $h_n = c_1(\sqrt{2})^n \cos\left(\dfrac{n\pi}{4}\right) + c_2(\sqrt{2})^n \sin\left(\dfrac{n\pi}{4}\right),$ $n = 0, 1, 2, \ldots.$

Since the nonhomogeneous term is $g_n = \sin n$, we seek a particular solution of the form

(28) $p_n = A \cos n + B \sin n,$

where the constants A and B are to be determined. Substituting this expression for p_n into (26) yields

$$A \cos(n+2) + B \sin(n+2) - 2(A \cos(n+1) + B \sin(n+1))$$
$$+ 2(A \cos n + B \sin n) = 3 \sin n, \qquad n = 0, 1, 2, \ldots.$$

Using the addition formulas for the trigonometric functions and simplifying, we have

$$[(2 + \cos 2 - 2 \cos 1)A + (\sin 2 - 2 \sin 1)B] \cos n$$
$$+ [(2 \sin 1 - \sin 2)A + (2 + \cos 2 - 2 \cos 1)B] \sin n = 3 \sin n.$$

When we set corresponding coefficients equal, we obtain the system

(29)
$$(2 + \cos 2 - 2 \cos 1)A + (\sin 2 - 2 \sin 1)B = 0,$$
$$(2 \sin 1 - \sin 2)A + (2 + \cos 2 - 2 \cos 1)B = 3,$$

which has the solution

(30)
$$A = \frac{-3(\sin 2 - 2\sin 1)}{(2 + \cos 2 - 2\cos 1)^2 + (\sin 2 - 2\sin 1)^2},$$

$$B = \frac{3(2 + \cos 2 - 2\cos 1)}{(2 + \cos 2 - 2\cos 1)^2 + (\sin 2 - 2\sin 1)^2}.$$

Thus, a general solution to (26) is

(31)
$$y_n = h_n + p_n, \qquad n = 0, 1, 2, \ldots,$$

where h_n is given by equation (27) and p_n is given by equation (28) with A and B given in (30). ◄

When one of the terms in our initial guess $\{p_n\}_{n=0}^{\infty}$ is a solution to the corresponding homogeneous equation, we must modify our guess by multiplying by n^s where s is the smallest nonnegative integer such that no term in $\{n^s p_n\}_{n=0}^{\infty}$ is a solution to the corresponding homogeneous equation.

EXERCISES 5.5

In Problems 1 through 10 find a general solution to the given homogeneous equation for $n = 0, 1, 2, \ldots$.

1. $y_{n+2} - 6y_{n+1} + 8y_n = 0.$

2. $y_{n+2} - 4y_{n+1} + 3y_n = 0.$

3. $y_{n+2} + 3y_{n+1} - y_n = 0.$

4. $y_{n+2} + 4y_{n+1} + 4y_n = 0.$

5. $y_{n+2} - 6y_{n+1} + 11y_n = 0.$

6. $y_{n+2} + 4y_{n+1} + 9y_n = 0.$

7. $y_{n+2} + 10y_{n+1} + 25y_n = 0.$

8. $4y_{n+2} + 4y_{n+1} - 3y_n = 0.$

9. $y_{n+2} - y_{n+1} + 4y_n = 0.$

10. $y_{n+2} + y_{n+1} - y_n = 0.$

In Problems 11 through 18 find a general solution to the given nonhomogeneous equation for $n = 0, 1, 2, \ldots$.

11. $y_{n+2} + y_n = n^2.$

12. $y_{n+2} + y_{n+1} - 2y_n = n - 1.$

13. $y_{n+2} - y_n = \cos 3n.$

14. $y_{n+2} - 4y_n = \sin 2n.$

15. $y_{n+2} + 6y_{n+1} + 5y_n = 2^n.$

16. $y_{n+2} + 2y_{n+1} - y_n = (-1)^n.$

17. $y_{n+2} - 4y_{n+1} + 4y_n = 2^n.$

18. $y_{n+2} - y_{n+1} - 2y_n = (-1)^n.$

In Problems 19 through 22 find a general solution to the given third order equation for $n = 0, 1, 2, \ldots$.

19. $y_{n+3} + y_{n+2} - 4y_{n+1} - 4y_n = 0.$

20. $y_{n+3} - 4y_{n+2} + 5y_{n+1} - 2y_n = 0.$

21. $y_{n+3} - 3y_{n+2} + 4y_{n+1} - 2y_n = 0.$

22. $y_{n+3} + 3y_{n+2} + 3y_{n+1} + y_n = 0.$

In Problems 23 through 27 find the solution to the initial value problem for $n = 0, 1, 2, \ldots$.

23. $y_{n+2} + 2y_{n+1} + 5y_n = 0; \qquad y_0 = 1, \qquad y_1 = -1.$

24. $y_{n+2} - 5y_{n+1} + 6y_n = 0; \qquad y_0 = 3, \qquad y_1 = -2.$

25. $y_{n+2} - 6y_{n+1} + 9y_n = 1; \qquad y_0 = 0, \qquad y_1 = 0.$

26. $y_{n+2} - 4y_{n+1} + 3y_n = 3^n$; $y_0 = 1$, $y_1 = 0$.

27. $y_{n+2} - 2y_{n+1} + y_n = n$; $y_0 = 1$, $y_1 = 3$.

28. Prove that if the two sequences $\{y_n\}_{n=0}^{\infty}$ and $\{z_n\}_{n=0}^{\infty}$ are solutions to the homogeneous equation (3), then so is any linear combination $\{c_1 y_n + c_2 z_n\}_{n=0}^{\infty}$.

29. Superposition Principle.   Let $\{y_n\}_{n=0}^{\infty}$ be a solution to the nonhomogeneous equation (1) with nonhomogeneous term g_n and $\{z_n\}_{n=0}^{\infty}$ be a solution to (1) with nonhomogeneous term h_n. Show that the sequence $\{c_1 y_n + c_2 z_n\}_{n=0}^{\infty}$ is a solution to (1) with nonhomogeneous term $c_1 g_n + c_2 h_n$.

30. Using the representation theorem for homogeneous equations and the superposition principle given in Problem 29, prove Theorem 3, the representation theorem for nonhomogeneous equations.

31. The linear multistep numerical method

$$y_{n+2} - y_{n+1} = \frac{h}{2}(3f_{n+1} - f_n), \qquad h > 0,$$

is used to approximate the solution to

$$y' = f(x, y), \qquad y(0) = y_0,$$

where $x_n := nh$, $f_n := f(x_n, y_n)$. As in Example 4, discuss the stability (as $n \to \infty$) of this method when it is applied to

$$y' = -y, \qquad y(0) = 1.$$

32. National Income Model.   P. A. Samuelson[†] developed a model for national income Y_t in period t under fixed government spending. His model involved the difference equation

$$Y_{t+2} - \alpha(1 + \beta)Y_{t+1} + \alpha\beta Y_t = 1, \qquad t = 0, 1, 2, \ldots,$$

where α is a constant called the *marginal propensity to consume* and β is a constant of proportionality called the *relation*, which is a consequence of the so–called acceleration principle of economics.

(a) Solve for the national income in the special case when $\alpha = \frac{1}{2}$, $\beta = 1$, $Y_0 = 2$, and $Y_1 = 3$.

(b) Show that as $t \to \infty$, the national income Y experiences damped oscillations that converge to $1/(1 - \alpha) = 2$. (Samuelson concluded that a fixed level of government spending will result in damped oscillations in the national income that will gradually approach the quantity $1/(1 - \alpha)$ times the level of government spending.)

[†] P. A. Samuelson, "Interactions Between the Multiplier Analysis and the Principle of Acceleration," Review of Economic Statistics, 21 (1939), 75–78.

5.6 *Numerical Methods for Second Order Equations*

The standard approach for obtaining numerical approximations of the solution to an initial value problem for a second order differential equation is first to convert the second order equation to a system of first order equations. This can be accomplished by the following reduction procedure.

Any second order initial value problem

(1) $\quad y''(t) = F(t, y, y'); \quad\quad y(t_0) = y_0, \quad\quad y'(t_0) = y_1,$

can be converted into a first order system by setting

(2) $\quad x_1(t) := y(t), \quad\quad x_2(t) := y'(t).$

With this substitution, equation (1) is equivalent to the system

(3) $\quad \begin{aligned} x_1'(t) &= y'(t) = x_2(t), \\ x_2'(t) &= y''(t) = F(t, x_1, x_2), \end{aligned}$

and the initial conditions become

(4) $\quad x_1(t_0) = y(t_0) = y_0, \quad\quad x_2(t_0) = y'(t_0) = y_1.$

▶ **Example 1** Convert the initial value problem

(5) $\quad y''(t) + 3y'(t) + 2y(t) = 0; \quad\quad y(0) = 1, \quad\quad y'(0) = 1,$

into an initial value problem for a system of first order equations.

Solution We first express the differential equation in (5) as

$$y''(t) = -3y'(t) - 2y(t).$$

Setting $x_1(t) := y(t)$, $x_2(t) := y'(t)$, we obtain

(6) $\quad \begin{aligned} x_1'(t) &= x_2(t), \\ x_2'(t) &= -3x_2(t) - 2x_1(t). \end{aligned}$

The initial conditions in (5) transform to $x_1(0) = 1$, $x_2(0) = 1$. ◀

The numerical methods for solving initial value problems for systems of first order differential equations are just extensions of techniques for solving a single first order differential equation. To see how these extensions are done, let's recall the classical Runge-Kutta method of order four, which was discussed in Section 3.6.

For the initial value problem

(7) $x' = f(t, x), \qquad x(t_0) = x_0,$

the recursive formulas for the fourth order Runge-Kutta method are

(8)
$$t_{n+1} = t_n + h, \qquad n = 0, 1, \ldots,$$
$$x_{n+1} = x_n + \tfrac{1}{6}(k_1 + 2k_2 + 2k_3 + k_4),$$

where h is the step size and

(9)
$$k_1 = hf(t_n, x_n), \qquad k_2 = hf\left(t_n + \frac{h}{2}, x_n + \frac{1}{2}k_1\right),$$
$$k_3 = hf\left(t_n + \frac{h}{2}, x_n + \frac{1}{2}k_2\right), \qquad k_4 = hf(t_n + h, x_n + k_3).$$

Now suppose that we wish to approximate the solution $x_1(t)$, $x_2(t)$ to the system

(10)
$$x_1'(t) = f_1(t, x_1, x_2),$$
$$x_2'(t) = f_2(t, x_1, x_2),$$

that satisfies the initial conditions

(11) $x_1(t_0) = a_1, \qquad x_2(t_0) = a_2.$

Let $x_{n,1}$ and $x_{n,2}$ denote approximations to $x_1(t_n)$ and $x_2(t_n)$, respectively, where $t_n = t_0 + nh$ for $n = 0, 1, 2, \ldots$. The recursive formulas for the fourth order Runge-Kutta method for the system (10)–(11) are obtained from the formulas for a single equation given in (8)–(9) by treating each of the quantities x_n, k_1, k_2, k_3, and k_4 as *vectors*. Namely, we set $\mathbf{x}_n := (x_{n,1}, x_{n,2})$, $\mathbf{k}_1 := (k_{1,1}\ k_{1,2})$, $\mathbf{k}_2 := (k_{2,1}, k_{2,2})$, etc. This approach gives the following recursive formulas for the fourth order Runge-Kutta method for system (10)–(11):

(12) $t_{n+1} := t_n + h, \, n = 0, 1, 2, \ldots$

(13) $x_{n+1,1} := x_{n,1} + \tfrac{1}{6}(k_{1,1} + 2k_{2,1} + 2k_{3,1} + k_{4,1}),$

(14) $x_{n+1,2} := x_{n,2} + \tfrac{1}{6}(k_{1,2} + 2k_{2,2} + 2k_{3,2} + k_{4,2}),$

where h is the step size and, for $i = 1$ and 2,

$$k_{1,i} := hf_i(t_n, x_{n,1}, x_{n,2}),$$

$$k_{2,i} := hf_i\left(t_n + \frac{h}{2}, x_{n,1} + \frac{1}{2}k_{1,1}, x_{n,2} + \frac{1}{2}k_{1,2}\right),$$

$$k_{3,i} := hf_i\left(t_n + \frac{h}{2}, x_{n,1} + \frac{1}{2}k_{2,1}, x_{n,2} + \frac{1}{2}k_{2,2}\right),$$

$$k_{4,i} := hf_i(t_n + h, x_{n,1} + k_{3,1}, x_{n,2} + k_{3,2}).$$

It is important to note that both $k_{1,1}$ and $k_{1,2}$ must be computed before either $k_{2,1}$ or $k_{2,2}$. Similarly, both $k_{2,1}$ and $k_{2,2}$ are needed to compute $k_{3,1}$ and $k_{3,2}$, etc.

▶ **Example 2**   Use the Runge-Kutta method with step size $h = 0.125$ to find an approximation at $t = 1$ for the solution to the initial value problem

(15) $\qquad y''(t) + 3y'(t) + 2y(t) = 0; \qquad y(0) = 1, \qquad y'(0) = 1.$

Solution   In Example 1 we showed that setting $x_1 := y$, $x_2 := y'$ reduces the initial value problem in (15) to

(16) $\qquad \begin{aligned} x_1' &= x_2; & x_1(0) &= 1, \\ x_2' &= -3x_2 - 2x_1; & x_2(0) &= 1. \end{aligned}$

Comparing this system with (10)–(11), we see that $f_1(t, x_1, x_2) = x_2$ and $f_2(t, x_1, x_2) = -3x_2 - 2x_1$. With the starting values of $t_0 = 0$, $x_{0,1} = 1$, and $x_{0,2} = 1$, we compute

$$k_{1,1} = hf_1(t_0, x_{0,1}, x_{0,2}) = hx_{0,2} = (0.125)(1) = 0.125,$$

$$k_{1,2} = hf_2(t_0, x_{0,1}, x_{0,2}) = h(-3x_{0,2} - 2x_{0,1})$$
$$= (0.125)[(-3)(1) - 2(1)] = -0.625,$$

$$k_{2,1} = hf_1\left(t_0 + \frac{h}{2}, x_{0,1} + \frac{1}{2}k_{1,1}, x_{0,2} + \frac{1}{2}k_{1,2}\right)$$

$$= h\left(x_{0,2} + \frac{1}{2}k_{1,2}\right) = (0.125)(1 - 0.3125) = 0.08594,$$

$$k_{2,2} = hf_2\left(t_0 + \frac{h}{2}, x_{0,1} + \frac{1}{2}k_{1,1}, x_{0,2} + \frac{1}{2}k_{1,2}\right)$$

$$= -3h\left(x_{0,2} + \frac{1}{2}k_{1,2}\right) - 2h\left(x_{0,1} + \frac{1}{2}k_{1,1}\right)$$

$$= -3(0.125)(1 - 0.3125) - 2(0.125)(1 + 0.0625)$$

$$= -0.52344.$$

Similarly, we find

$$k_{3,1} = hf_1\left(t_0 + \frac{h}{2}, x_{0,1} + \frac{1}{2}k_{2,1}, x_{0,2} + \frac{1}{2}k_{2,2}\right) = 0.09229,$$

$$k_{3,2} = hf_2\left(t_0 + \frac{h}{2}, x_{0,1} + \frac{1}{2}k_{2,1}, x_{0,2} + \frac{1}{2}k_{2,2}\right) = -0.53760,$$

$$k_{4,1} = hf_1(t_0 + h, x_{0,1} + k_{3,1}, x_{0,2} + k_{3,2}) = 0.05780,$$

$$k_{4,2} = hf_2(t_0 + h, x_{0,1} + k_{3,1}, x_{0,2} + k_{3,2}) = -0.44647.$$

Hence from (13) and (14), we compute

$$
\begin{aligned}
x_{1,1} &= x_{0,1} + \tfrac{1}{6}(k_{1,1} + 2k_{2,1} + 2k_{3,1} + k_{4,1}) \\
&= 1 + \tfrac{1}{6}(0.125 + 2(0.08594) + 2(0.09229) + 0.05780) \\
&= 1.08987, \\
x_{1,2} &= x_{0,2} + \tfrac{1}{6}(k_{1,2} + 2k_{2,2} + 2k_{3,2} + k_{4,2}) \\
&= 1 - \tfrac{1}{6}(0.625 + 2(0.52344) + 2(0.53760) + 0.44647) \\
&= 0.46774.
\end{aligned}
$$

Continuing the algorithm, we compute $x_{i,1}$ and $x_{i,2}$ for $i = 2, 3, \dots, 8$. These values, along with the values of the actual solution to (15), $y(t) = x_1(t) = 3e^{-t} - 2e^{-2t}$, are given in Table 5.3 (to five decimal places). We note that the $x_{i,2}$ column gives approximations for $y'(t)$ since $x_2(t) = y'(t)$. ◄

TABLE 5.3 FOURTH ORDER RUNGE-KUTTA APPROXIMATION OF THE SOLUTION TO (15) USING h = 0.125

t_i	$x_{i,1}$	$x_{i,2}$	$y(t_i) = x_1(t_i)$	$|y(t_i) - x_{i,1}|$
0.000	1.00000	1.00000	1.00000	0
0.125	1.08987	0.46774	1.08989	2×10^{-5}
0.250	1.12332	0.08977	1.12334	2×10^{-5}
0.375	1.11711	-0.17235	1.11713	2×10^{-5}
0.500	1.08381	-0.34802	1.08383	2×10^{-5}
0.625	1.03275	-0.45971	1.03277	2×10^{-5}
0.750	0.97981	-0.52453	0.97984	3×10^{-5}
0.875	0.90302	-0.55544	0.90304	2×10^{-5}
1.000	0.83295	-0.56226	0.83297	2×10^{-5}

Notice that the Runge-Kutta method as described in (12)–(14) applies to any system of two first order equations. For the second order equation (1), with the reduction procedure of setting $x_1 = y$, $x_2 = y'$, we find by comparing system (3) with system (10) that

$$f_1(t, x_1, x_2) = x_2,$$
$$f_2(t, x_1, x_2) = F(t, x_1, x_2).$$

Using these functions, we can easily modify the Runge-Kutta algorithm of Chapter 3 to obtain the following Runge-Kutta algorithm for approximating the solution to an initial value problem for a second order equation. Notice that the new procedure stops when two successive approximations for *both* the function $y = x_1$ and its derivative $y' = x_2$ differ by less than a prescribed tolerance ε, or it stops after a prescribed maximum number of iterations.

Numerical methods for higher order equations and systems are discussed in Section 9.5.

RUNGE-KUTTA ALGORITHM FOR SECOND ORDER EQUATIONS

Purpose To approximate the solution to the initial value problem

$$y'' = F(t, y, y'); \qquad y(t_0) = a_1, \qquad y'(t_0) = a_2$$

at $t = c$.

INPUT t_0, a_1, a_2, c
ε (tolerance)
M (maximum number of iterations)

Step 1 Set $z_1 = a_1$, $z_2 = a_2$

Step 2 For $n = 0$ to M do Steps 3–9

Step 3 Set $h = (c - t_0)2^{-n}$, $t = t_0$, $x_1 = a_1$, $x_2 = a_2$

Step 4 For $j = 1$ to 2^n do Steps 5 and 6

Step 5 Set $k_{1,1} = hx_2$

$$k_{1,2} = hF(t, x_1, x_2)$$

$$k_{2,1} = h\left(x_2 + \frac{1}{2}k_{1,2}\right)$$

$$k_{2,2} = hF\left(t + \frac{h}{2}, x_1 + \frac{1}{2}k_{1,1}, x_2 + \frac{1}{2}k_{1,2}\right)$$

$$k_{3,1} = h\left(x_2 + \frac{1}{2}k_{2,2}\right)$$

$$k_{3,2} = hF\left(t + \frac{h}{2}, x_1 + \frac{1}{2}k_{2,1}, x_2 + \frac{1}{2}k_{2,2}\right)$$

$$k_{4,1} = h(x_2 + k_{3,2})$$

$$k_{4,2} = hF(t + h, x_1 + k_{3,1}, x_2 + k_{3,2})$$

Step 6   Set $t = t + h$

$$x_1 = x_1 + \frac{1}{6}(k_{1,1} + 2k_{2,1} + 2k_{3,1} + k_{4,1})$$

$$x_2 = x_2 + \frac{1}{6}(k_{1,2} + 2k_{2,2} + 2k_{3,2} + k_{4,2})$$

Step 7   Print t, x_1, x_2

Step 8   If $|z_1 - x_1| < \varepsilon$ and $|z_2 - x_2| < \varepsilon$, go to Step 12

Step 9   Set $z_1 = x_1, z_2 = x_2$

Step 10   Print "$y(c)$ is approximately,"; x_1; "but may not be within the tolerance";
          ε

Step 11   Go to Step 13

Step 12   Print "$y(c)$ is approximately,"; x_1; "with tolerance"; ε

Step 13   Stop

OUTPUT   Approximations of the solution to the initial value problem at $t = c$,
          using 2^n steps.

EXERCISES 5.6

The reader will find it helpful to have a microcomputer available or access to a mainframe.

In Problems 1 through 4 use the Runge-Kutta method with $h = 0.25$ to find an approximation for the solution to the given initial value problem on the specified interval.

1. $y'' + ty' + y = 0$; $y(0) = 1$, $y'(0) = 0$ on $[0, 1]$.

2. $(1 + t^2)y'' + y' - y = 0$; $y(0) = 1$, $y'(0) = -1$ on $[0, 1]$.

3. $t^2 y'' + y = t + 2$; $y(1) = 1$, $y'(1) = -1$ on $[1, 2]$.

4. $y'' = t^2 - y^2$; $y(0) = 0$, $y'(0) = 1$ on $[0, 1]$.

5. Using the Runge-Kutta method with $h = 0.5$, approximate the solution to
the initial value problem

$$3t^2 y'' - 5ty' + 5y = 0; \qquad y(1) = 0, \qquad y'(1) = \tfrac{2}{3}$$

at $t = 8$. Compare this approximation to the actual solution $y(t) = t^{5/3} - t$.

6. Using the Runge-Kutta algorithm with the stopping procedure based on
the absolute error and a tolerance of $\varepsilon = 0.01$, approximate the solution
to the initial value problem

$$y'' = t^2 + y^2; \qquad y(0) = 1, \qquad y'(0) = 0$$

at $t = 1$.

7. Using the Runge-Kutta algorithm with the stopping procedure based on the relative error and a tolerance of $\varepsilon = 0.02$, approximate the solution to the initial value problem

$$y'' = ty^3; \qquad y(0) = 1, \qquad y'(0) = 1$$

at $t = 1$.

8. In Section 3.5 we discussed Euler's method for approximating the solution to a first order equation. Extend Euler's method to systems and give the recursive formulas in component form.

9. In Section 3.5 we discussed the improved Euler's method for approximating the solution to a first order equation. Extend this method to systems and give the recursive formulas for solving the initial value problem (1).

10. In Project E of Chapter 4 it was shown that the simple pendulum equation

$$\theta''(t) + \sin \theta(t) = 0$$

has periodic solutions when the initial displacement and velocity are small. Show that the period of the solution may depend upon the initial conditions by using the Runge-Kutta method with $h = 0.02$ to approximate the solutions to the simple pendulum problem on $[0, 4]$ for the initial conditions:

   (a) $\theta(0) = 0.1;$ $\theta'(0) = 0.$
   (b) $\theta(0) = 0.5;$ $\theta'(0) = 0.$
   (c) $\theta(0) = 1.0;$ $\theta'(0) = 0.$

[Hint: Approximate the length of time from $t = 0$ to the time of the next maximum.]

11. **Fluid Ejection.** In the design of a sewage treatment plant, the following equation arose:[†]

$$60 - H = (77.7)H'' + (19.42)(H')^2; \qquad H(0) = H'(0) = 0,$$

where H is the level of the fluid in an ejection chamber and t is the time in seconds. Use the Runge-Kutta method with $h = 0.5$ to approximate $H(t)$ over the interval $[0, 5]$.

12. **Oscillations and Nonlinear Equations.** For the initial value problem

$$x'' + (0.1)(1 - x^2)x' + x = 0; \qquad x(0) = x_0, \, x'(0) = 0$$

use the Runge-Kutta method with $h = 0.02$ to illustrate that as t increases from 0 to 20 the solution x exhibits damped oscillations with $x_0 = 1$, whereas x exhibits expanding oscillations when $x_0 = 3$.

13. **Nonlinear Spring.** The **Duffing equation**

$$y'' + y + ry^3 = 0,$$

[†] See *Numerical Solution of Differential Equations*, by William Milne, Dover Publications, Inc., New York, 1970, p. 82.

where r is a constant, is a model for the vibrations of a mass attached to a *nonlinear* spring. For this model, does the period of vibration vary as the parameter r is varied? Does the period vary as the initial conditions are varied? [Hint: Use the Runge-Kutta method with $h = 0.1$ to approximate the solutions, for $r = 1$ and 2, with initial conditions $y(0) = a$, $y'(0) = 0$ for $a = 1$, 2, and 3.]

14. **Pendulum with Varying Length.** A pendulum is formed by a mass m attached to the end of a wire that is attached to the ceiling. Assume that the length $l(t)$ of the wire varies with time in some predetermined fashion. If $\theta(t)$ is the angle between the pendulum and the vertical, then the motion of the pendulum is governed by the initial value problem

$$l^2(t)\theta''(t) + 2l(t)l'(t)\theta'(t) + gl(t)\theta(t) = 0; \qquad \theta(0) = \theta_0, \quad \theta'(0) = \theta_1,$$

where g is the gravitational constant. Assume that

$$l(t) = l_0 + l_1 \cos(\omega t - \phi),$$

where l_1 is much smaller than l_0. (This might be a model for a person on a swing, where the *pumping* action changes the distance from the center of mass of the swing to the point where the swing is attached.) To simplify the computations, take $g = 1$. Using the Runge-Kutta method with $h = 0.1$, study the motion of the pendulum when $\theta_0 = 0.5$, $\theta_1 = 0$, $l_0 = 1$, $l_1 = 0.1$, $\omega = 1$, and $\phi = 0.02$. In particular, does the pendulum ever attain an angle greater in absolute value than the initial angle θ_0? Does the total arc traversed during one-half of a swing ever exceed 1?

Projects for Chapter 5

A. FINITE-DIFFERENCE METHOD FOR BOUNDARY VALUE PROBLEMS

A classical method for numerically approximating a solution to a boundary value problem for a linear second order differential equation consists of replacing each derivative in the differential equation by a difference quotient that approximates that derivative. To illustrate this procedure, consider the linear boundary value problem

(1) $y''(x) + p(x)y'(x) + q(x)y(x) = g(x); \qquad a < x < b.$

(2) $y(a) = \alpha, \qquad y(b) = \beta,$

where p, q, and g are continuous on $[a, b]$ and α, β are given constants.

We begin by partitioning the interval $[a, b]$ into $N + 1$ subintervals of equal length h. That is, let $h := (b - a)/(N + 1)$ and for $k = 0, 1, \ldots, N + 1$ set

$$x_k := a + kh.$$

Then, $a = x_0 < x_1 < \cdots < x_N < x_{N+1} = b.$

Assuming that a solution $y(x)$ to (1)–(2) exists, our aim is to approximate $y(x)$ at the interior mesh points x_k, $k = 1, 2, \ldots, N$. At these points we know that

(3) $\qquad y''(x_k) + p(x_k)y'(x_k) + q(x_k)y(x_k) = g(x_k).$

The essence of the finite-difference method is to find difference quotients that closely approximate the derivatives $y'(x_k)$ and $y''(x_k)$ when h is small.

(a) Assuming that y has a Taylor series representation of the form

(4) $\qquad y(x) = y(x_k) + y'(x_k)(x - x_k) + \dfrac{y''(x_k)}{2}(x - x_k)^2 + \dfrac{y'''(x_k)}{3!}(x - x_k)^3 + \cdots$

$\qquad\qquad = \displaystyle\sum_{j=0}^{\infty} \dfrac{y^{(j)}(x_k)}{j!}(x - x_k)^j,$

derive the following **centered-difference formula for** $y'(x_k)$:

(5) $\qquad y'(x_k) = \dfrac{1}{2h}\left[y(x_{k+1}) - y(x_{k-1})\right] + [\text{terms involving } h^2, h^3, \ldots].$

[Hint: Work with the Taylor representations for $y(x_{k+1})$ and $y(x_{k-1})$.]

(b) Similarly, derive from (4) the following centered-difference formula for $y''(x_k)$:

(6) $\qquad y''(x_k) = \dfrac{1}{h^2}\left[y(x_{k+1}) - 2y(x_k) + y(x_{k-1})\right] + [\text{terms involving } h^2, h^3, \ldots].$

(c) If we let w_k denote the approximation (to be computed) for $y(x_k)$, $k = 1, 2, \ldots, N$ and set $w_0 = y(x_0) = \alpha$, $w_{N+1} = y(x_{N+1}) = \beta$, then from (5) and (6) we obtain the approximations

(7) $\qquad y''(x_k) \approx \dfrac{1}{h^2}(w_{k+1} - 2w_k + w_{k-1}),$

(8) $\qquad y'(x_k) \approx \dfrac{1}{2h}(w_{k+1} - w_{k-1}).$

Using the centered-difference approximations (7) and (8) in place of $y''(x_k)$ and $y'(x_k)$ in (3) yields the system of equations

(9) $\qquad \left(\dfrac{w_{k+1} - 2w_k + w_{k-1}}{h^2}\right) + p(x_k)\left(\dfrac{w_{k+1} - w_{k-1}}{2h}\right) + q(x_k)w_k = g(x_k),$

$k = 1, 2, \ldots, N$. The equations (9) represent N linear equations in the N unknowns $w_1, \ldots, w_N$. Thus, on solving (9), we obtain approximations for $y(x)$ at the interior mesh points x_k, $k = 1, \ldots, N$.

Use this method to approximate the solution to the boundary value problem

(10) $\qquad y''(x) - 4y(x) = 0; \qquad y(0) = 1, \qquad y(1) = e^{-2},$

taking $h = \frac{1}{4}$ $(N = 3)$.

Let's assume that the surface is so smooth that we can neglect any friction due to the motion of the objects along the surface. Since there are no outside forces acting on the objects, the only forces we need to consider are those due to the springs themselves. Recall that Hooke's law asserts that the force acting on an object due to a spring has magnitude proportional to the displacement of the spring from its natural length and has direction opposite to its displacement. That is, if the spring is either stretched or compressed, then it tries to return to its natural length.

To determine the equations of motion, we apply Newton's second law to each object. The 2-kg mass has a force F_1 acting on its left side due to one spring and a force F_2 acting on its right side due to the second spring. Referring to Figure 6.1 and applying Hooke's law, we see that

(1) $$F_1 = -k_1 x, \qquad F_2 = +k_2(y - x),$$

where $(y - x)$ is the net displacement of the second spring from its natural length. There is only one force acting on the 1-kg mass; namely the force due to the second spring, which is

(2) $$F_3 = -k_2(y - x).$$

Applying Newton's second law to these objects, we now obtain

$$\begin{cases} m_1 \dfrac{d^2 x}{dt^2} = F_1 + F_2 = -k_1 x + k_2(y - x), \\[2mm] m_2 \dfrac{d^2 y}{dt^2} = F_3 = -k_2(y - x), \end{cases}$$

or

(3) $$\begin{cases} m_1 \dfrac{d^2 x}{dt^2} + (k_1 + k_2)x - k_2 y = 0, \\[2mm] m_2 \dfrac{d^2 y}{dt^2} + k_2 y - k_2 x = 0. \end{cases}$$

In this problem, we know that $m_1 = 2$, $m_2 = 1$, $k_1 = 4$, and $k_2 = 2$. Substituting these values into system (3) yields

(4) $$2\frac{d^2 x}{dt^2} + 6x - 2y = 0,$$

(5) $$\frac{d^2 y}{dt^2} + 2y - 2x = 0.$$

We can reduce the preceding system to a single differential equation in x by solving (4) for y and then substituting the expression for y back into (5). (This is called the **elimination method;** see Section 9.2.) From (4) we get

(6) $$y = \frac{d^2x}{dt^2} + 3x,$$

and, substituting for y in (5), we find

(7) $$\frac{d^2}{dt^2}\left[\frac{d^2x}{dt^2} + 3x\right] + 2\left[\frac{d^2x}{dt^2} + 3x\right] - 2x = 0,$$

which simplifies to

(8) $$\frac{d^4x}{dt^4} + 5\frac{d^2x}{dt^2} + 4x = 0.$$

Notice that equation (8) is linear with constant coefficients. To solve it, let's proceed as we did with linear second order equations and try to find solutions of the form $x = e^{rt}$. Substituting e^{rt} in equation (8) gives

(9) $$(r^4 + 5r^2 + 4)e^{rt} = 0.$$

Thus we have a solution to (8), provided that r satisfies the auxiliary equation

(10) $$r^4 + 5r^2 + 4 = 0.$$

From the factorization $r^4 + 5r^2 + 4 = (r^2 + 1)(r^2 + 4)$, we see that the roots of the auxiliary equation are the complex numbers i, $-i$, $2i$, $-2i$. Using Euler's formula, it follows that

$$z_1(t) = e^{it} = \cos t + i \sin t$$

and

$$z_2(t) = e^{2it} = \cos 2t + i \sin 2t$$

are complex-valued solutions to equation (8). To obtain real-valued solutions to (8), we take the real and imaginary parts of $z_1(t)$ and $z_2(t)$. Thus four real-valued solutions are

(11)
$$x_1(t) = \cos t, \qquad x_2(t) = \sin t,$$
$$x_3(t) = \cos 2t, \qquad x_4(t) = \sin 2t.$$

Because (8) is a linear homogeneous equation, any linear combination of $x_1(t)$, $x_2(t)$, $x_3(t)$, and $x_4(t)$ will also be a solution. Hence a (general) solution to (8) is

(12) $x(t) = a_1 \cos t + a_2 \sin t + a_3 \cos 2t + a_4 \sin 2t,$

where a_1, a_2, a_3, and a_4 are arbitrary constants.

To obtain a formula for $y(t)$, we substitute the above representation for $x(t)$ into equation (6):

(13) $y(t) = \dfrac{d^2 x}{dt^2} + 3x,$

$$= -a_1 \cos t - a_2 \sin t - 4a_3 \cos 2t - 4a_4 \sin 2t$$
$$+ 3a_1 \cos t + 3a_2 \sin t + 3a_3 \cos 2t + 3a_4 \sin 2t,$$

and so

(14) $y(t) = 2a_1 \cos t + 2a_2 \sin t - a_3 \cos 2t - a_4 \sin 2t.$

In order to determine the constants a_1, a_2, a_3, and a_4, let's return to the original problem. We were told that the objects were originally displaced 3 m to the right and then released. Hence

(15) $x(0) = 3, \qquad \dfrac{dx}{dt}(0) = 0; \qquad y(0) = 3, \qquad \dfrac{dy}{dt}(0) = 0.$

On differentiating equations (12) and (14), we find

(16) $\dfrac{dx}{dt} = -a_1 \sin t + a_2 \cos t - 2a_3 \sin 2t + 2a_4 \cos 2t,$

(17) $\dfrac{dy}{dt} = -2a_1 \sin t + 2a_2 \cos t + 2a_3 \sin 2t - 2a_4 \cos 2t.$

Now, if we put $t = 0$ in the formulas for x, dx/dt, y, and dy/dt, the initial conditions (15) give the four equations

$$x(0) = a_1 + a_3 = 3, \qquad \frac{dx}{dt}(0) = a_2 + 2a_4 = 0,$$

$$y(0) = 2a_1 - a_3 = 3, \qquad \frac{dy}{dt}(0) = 2a_2 - 2a_4 = 0.$$

From this system we find $a_1 = 2$, $a_2 = 0$, $a_3 = 1$, and $a_4 = 0$. Hence the equations of motion for the two objects are

(18) $x(t) = 2 \cos t + \cos 2t,$

(19) $y(t) = 4 \cos t - \cos 2t.$

The analysis of the coupled spring-mass system illustrates that many of the techniques developed for second order linear equations have natural extensions to higher order linear equations. This chapter is devoted to exploring these generalizations.

6.2 Basic Theory of Linear Differential Equations

In this section we discuss the basic theory of linear higher order differential equations. The material is a generalization of the results we obtained in Chapter 4 for second order equations. In the statements and proofs of these results we will be using concepts usually covered in an elementary linear algebra course; namely linear dependence, determinants, and solving systems of linear equations. These concepts also arise in the matrix approach for solving systems of differential equations and are discussed in Section 10.2.

Recall that a *linear* differential equation is an equation that can be written in the form

(1) $$a_n(x)y^{(n)}(x) + a_{n-1}(x)y^{(n-1)}(x) + \cdots + a_0(x)y(x) = b(x),$$

where $a_0(x), a_1(x), \ldots, a_n(x)$, and $b(x)$ depend only on x, not y. When $a_0, a_1, \ldots, a_n$ are constants, we say that equation (1) has **constant coefficients;** otherwise it has **variable coefficients.** If $b(x) \equiv 0$, equation (1) is called **homogeneous;** otherwise it is **nonhomogeneous.**

In developing a basic theory, we assume that $a_0(x), a_1(x), \ldots, a_n(x)$, and $b(x)$ are continuous on an interval I and $a_n(x) \neq 0$ on I. Then, on dividing by $a_n(x)$, we can rewrite (1) in the **standard form**

(2) $$y^{(n)}(x) + p_1(x)y^{(n-1)}(x) + \cdots + p_n(x)y(x) = g(x),$$

where the functions $p_1(x), \ldots, p_n(x)$, and $g(x)$ are continuous on I.

For a linear higher order differential equation the initial value problem always has a unique solution.

EXISTENCE AND UNIQUENESS

Theorem 1. Suppose that $p_1(x), \ldots, p_n(x)$, and $g(x)$ are each continuous on an interval (a, b) that contains the point x_0. Then, for any choice of the initial values $y_0, y_1, \ldots, y_{n-1}$, there exists a unique solution $y(x)$ on the whole interval (a, b) to the initial value problem

(3) $$y^{(n)}(x) + p_1(x)y^{(n-1)}(x) + \cdots + p_n(x)y(x) = g(x),$$

(4) $$y(x_0) = y_0, \; y'(x_0) = y_1, \; \ldots, \; y^{(n-1)}(x_0) = y_{n-1}.$$

The proof of Theorem 1 can be found in Chapter 11 of the expanded version of this text, *Fundamentals of Differential Equations and Boundary Value Problems.*

▶ **Example 1**   For the initial value problem

(5) $x(x - 1)y''' - 3xy'' + 6x^2y' - (\cos x)y = \sqrt{x + 5}$;

(6) $y(x_0) = 1, \qquad y'(x_0) = 0, \qquad y''(x_0) = 7,$

determine the values of x_0 and the intervals (a, b) containing x_0 for which Theorem 1 guarantees the existence of a unique solution on (a, b).

Solution   Here $p_1(x) = -3/(x - 1)$, $p_2(x) = 6x/(x - 1)$, $p_3(x) = -(\cos x)/[x(x - 1)]$, and $g(x) = \sqrt{x + 5}/[x(x - 1)]$. Now $p_1(x)$ and $p_2(x)$ are continuous on every interval not containing $x = 1$, while $p_3(x)$ is continuous on every interval not containing $x = 0$ or $x = 1$. The function $g(x)$ is not defined for $x < -5$, $x = 0$, and $x = 1$, but is continuous on $(-5, 0)$, $(0, 1)$, and $(1, \infty)$. Hence the functions p_1, p_2, p_3, and g are *simultaneously* continuous on the intervals $(-5, 0)$, $(0, 1)$, and $(1, \infty)$. From Theorem 1 it follows that if we choose $x_0 \in (-5, 0)$, then there exists a unique solution to the initial value problem (5)–(6) on the whole interval $(-5, 0)$. Similarly, for $x_0 \in (0, 1)$ there is a unique solution on $(0, 1)$, and for $x_0 \in (1, \infty)$ a unique solution exists on $(1, \infty)$. ◀

If we let the left-hand side of equation (3) define the differential operator L,

(7) $$L[y] := \frac{d^n y}{dx^n} + p_1 \frac{d^{n-1}y}{dx^{n-1}} + \cdots + p_n y,$$

then we can express equation (3) in the operator form

(8) $L[y](x) = g(x).$

It is essential to keep in mind that L is a *linear* operator: it satisfies

(9) $L[y_1 + y_2] = L[y_1] + L[y_2],$

(10) $L[cy_1] = cL[y_1], \qquad c$ a constant

(see Problem 25).

As a consequence of this linearity, if $y_1, \ldots, y_m$ are solutions to the homogeneous equation

(11) $L[y](x) = 0,$

then any linear combination of these functions, $C_1 y_1 + \cdots + C_m y_m$, is also a solution to (11). Imagine now that we have found n solutions $y_1, \ldots, y_n$ to the nth order linear equation (11). Is it true that *every* solution to (11) can be represented by

(12) $C_1 y_1 + \cdots + C_n y_n$

for appropriate choices of the constants $C_1, \ldots, C_n$? The answer is yes, provided that the solutions $y_1, \ldots, y_n$ satisfy a certain property of independence that we shall now derive.

Let $\phi(x)$ be a solution to (11) on the interval (a, b) and let x_0 be a fixed number in (a, b). If it is possible to choose the constants $C_1, \ldots, C_n$ so that

$$
\begin{aligned}
C_1 y_1(x_0) \quad &+ \cdots + C_n y_n(x_0) \quad = \phi(x_0), \\
C_1 y_1'(x_0) \quad &+ \cdots + C_n y_n'(x_0) \quad = \phi'(x_0), \\
&\vdots \\
C_1 y_1^{(n-1)}(x_0) &+ \cdots + C_n y_n^{(n-1)}(x_0) = \phi^{(n-1)}(x_0),
\end{aligned}
$$

(13)

then, since $\phi(x)$ and $C_1 y_1(x) + \cdots + C_n y_n(x)$ are two solutions satisfying the same initial conditions at x_0, the uniqueness conclusion of Theorem 1 gives

(14) $\phi(x) = C_1 y_1(x) + \cdots + C_n y_n(x)$

for all x in (a, b).

The system (13) consists of n linear equations in the n unknowns $C_1, \ldots, C_n$. It has a unique solution for all possible values of $\phi(x_0), \ldots, \phi^{(n-1)}(x_0)$ if and only if the determinant of the coefficients is different from zero; that is, if and only if

(15)
$$
\begin{vmatrix}
y_1(x_0) & y_2(x_0) & \cdots & y_n(x_0) \\
y_1'(x_0) & y_2'(x_0) & \cdots & y_n'(x_0) \\
\vdots & \vdots & & \vdots \\
y_1^{(n-1)}(x_0) & y_2^{(n-1)}(x_0) & \cdots & y_n^{(n-1)}(x_0)
\end{vmatrix} \neq 0.
$$

Hence, if $y_1, \ldots, y_n$ are solutions to equation (11) and there is some point x_0 in (a, b) such that (15) holds, then every solution $\phi(x)$ to (11) is a linear combination of $y_1, \ldots, y_n$.

Before putting this observation in the form of a theorem, it is convenient to define the Wronskian of a set of n functions.

WRONSKIAN

Definition 1. Let $f_1, \ldots, f_n$ be any n functions that are $(n-1)$ times differentiable. The function

$$(16) \qquad W[f_1, \ldots, f_n](x) := \begin{vmatrix} f_1(x) & f_2(x) & \cdots & f_n(x) \\ f_1'(x) & f_2'(x) & \cdots & f_n'(x) \\ \cdot & \cdot & & \cdot \\ \cdot & \cdot & & \cdot \\ \cdot & \cdot & & \cdot \\ f_1^{(n-1)}(x) & f_2^{(n-1)}(x) & \cdots & f_n^{(n-1)}(x) \end{vmatrix}$$

is called the **Wronskian** of $f_1, \ldots, f_n$.

We now state the representation theorem for solutions to homogeneous linear differential equations that we proved above.

REPRESENTATION OF SOLUTIONS (HOMOGENEOUS CASE)

Theorem 2. Let $y_1, \ldots, y_n$ be n solutions on (a, b) of

$$(17) \qquad y^{(n)}(x) + p_1(x)y^{(n-1)}(x) + \cdots + p_n(x)y(x) = 0,$$

where $p_1, \ldots, p_n$ are continuous on (a, b). If at some point x_0 in (a, b) these solutions satisfy

$$(18) \qquad W[y_1, \ldots, y_n](x_0) \neq 0,$$

then every solution of (17) on (a, b) can be expressed in the form

$$(19) \qquad y(x) = C_1 y_1(x) + \cdots + C_n y_n(x),$$

where $C_1, \ldots, C_n$ are constants.

A set of solutions $\{y_1, \ldots, y_n\}$ satisfying (18) for some x_0 in (a, b) is called a **fundamental solution set** for (17) on (a, b). The linear combination of $y_1, \ldots, y_n$ in (19), written with arbitrary constants $C_1, \ldots, C_n$, is referred to as a **general solution** to (17).

▶ **Example 2**   Given that $y_1(x) = x$, $y_2(x) = x^2$, and $y_3(x) = x^{-1}$ are solutions to

(20) $x^3y''' + x^2y'' - 2xy' + 2y = 0$, $x > 0$,

find a general solution.

Solution   We first show that $\{y_1, y_2, y_3\}$ is a fundamental solution set for equation (20) on $(0, \infty)$. Since we are told that y_1, y_2, and y_3 satisfy (20) (the reader can easily verify this), we need only consider

$$W[y_1, y_2, y_3](x) = \begin{vmatrix} y_1(x) & y_2(x) & y_3(x) \\ y_1'(x) & y_2'(x) & y_3'(x) \\ y_1''(x) & y_2''(x) & y_3''(x) \end{vmatrix} = \begin{vmatrix} x & x^2 & x^{-1} \\ 1 & 2x & -x^{-2} \\ 0 & 2 & 2x^{-3} \end{vmatrix}.$$

Evaluating the determinant, we find after a little algebra that

$$W[y_1, y_2, y_3](x) = 6x^{-1},$$

which is not zero for $x > 0$. Thus $\{y_1, y_2, y_3\}$ is a fundamental solution set, and hence a general solution is

(21) $y(x) = C_1x + C_2x^2 + C_3x^{-1}$, $x > 0$. ◀

The important condition (18) concerning the nonvanishing of the Wronskian can also be described in terms of the linear independence of the solutions $y_1, \ldots, y_n$.

LINEAR DEPENDENCE OF FUNCTIONS

Definition 2.   The m functions $f_1, \ldots, f_m$ are said to be **linearly dependent on an interval I** if there exist constants $c_1, \ldots, c_m$, not all zero, such that

(22) $c_1 f_1(x) + \cdots + c_m f_m(x) = 0$

for all x in I. If the functions $f_1, \ldots, f_m$ are not linearly dependent on I, they are said to be **linearly independent on I**.

▶ **Example 3**   Show that the functions $f_1(x) = e^x$, $f_2(x) = e^{-2x}$, and $f_3(x) = 3e^x - 2e^{-2x}$ are linearly dependent on $(-\infty, \infty)$.

Solution   Notice that f_3 is a linear combination of f_1 and f_2:

$$f_3(x) = 3e^x - 2e^{-2x} = 3f_1(x) - 2f_2(x).$$

Therefore, we have

(23) $3f_1(x) - 2f_2(x) - f_3(x) = 0$

for all x in $(-\infty, \infty)$. Consequently, f_1, f_2, and f_3 are linearly dependent on $(-\infty, \infty)$. ◀

To prove that functions $f_1, f_2, \ldots, f_m$ are linearly *independent* on (a, b), a convenient approach is the following: *Assume* that equation (22) holds on (a, b) and show that this forces $c_1 = c_2 = \cdots = c_m = 0$.

▶ **Example 4**   Show that the functions $f_1(x) = x$, $f_2(x) = x^2$, and $f_3(x) = 1 - 2x^2$ are linearly independent on $(-\infty, \infty)$.

Solution   Assume that c_1, c_2, and c_3 are constants for which

(24) $c_1 x + c_2 x^2 + c_3(1 - 2x^2) = 0$

holds at every x. If we can prove that (24) implies $c_1 = c_2 = c_3 = 0$, then linear independence follows. Let's set $x = 0$, 1, and -1 in equation (24); these x values are, essentially, "picked out of a hat," but will get the job done. Substituting in (24) gives

$$
\begin{aligned}
c_3 &= 0 & (x = 0), \\
\textbf{(25)} \qquad c_1 + c_2 - c_3 &= 0 & (x = 1), \\
-c_1 + c_2 - c_3 &= 0 & (x = -1).
\end{aligned}
$$

When we solve this system (or compute the determinant of the coefficients), we find that the only possible solution is $c_1 = c_2 = c_3 = 0$. Consequently, the functions f_1, f_2, and f_3 are linearly independent on $(-\infty, \infty)$. ◀

The connection between linear independence and fundamental solution sets is stated in the next theorem.

LINEAR INDEPENDENCE AND FUNDAMENTAL SOLUTIONS

Theorem 3.   Let $y_1, \ldots, y_n$ be n solutions to $y^{(n)} + p_1 y^{(n-1)} + \cdots + p_n y = 0$ on (a, b). Then $\{y_1, \ldots, y_n\}$ is a fundamental solution set on (a, b) if and only if these functions are linearly independent on (a, b).

Theorem 3 is a generalization of Corollary 1 in Section 4.3. Since its proof is similar, we leave it as an exercise (see Problem 30).

As with linear second order equations, *the Wronskian of solutions is either identically zero or never zero on (a, b)*. This fact follows from the proof of Theorem 3 or from **Abel's**

identity,

(26) $$W[y_1, \ldots, y_n](x) = W[y_1, \ldots, y_n](x_0) \exp\left(-\int_{x_0}^{x} p_1(t)\,dt\right),$$

which holds for any n solutions $y_1, \ldots, y_n$ to $y^{(n)} + p_1 y^{(n-1)} + \cdots + p_n y = 0$ on (a, b). In (26), the point x_0 can be anywhere in (a, b). For a proof of Abel's identity when $n = 3$, see Problem 31.

Notice that Theorem 3 provides a simpler approach to proving that the solutions $y_1(x) = x$, $y_2(x) = x^2$, $y_3(x) = x^{-1}$ in Example 2 form a fundamental solution set. For, without having to compute a determinant, we can see (practically at a glance) that these functions are linearly independent on $(0, \infty)$.

It is useful to keep in mind that the following sets consist of functions that are linearly independent on every open interval (a, b):

$$\{1, x, x^2, \ldots, x^n\},$$

$$\{1, \cos x, \sin x, \cos 2x, \sin 2x, \ldots, \cos nx, \sin nx\},$$

$$\{e^{\alpha_1 x}, e^{\alpha_2 x}, \ldots, e^{\alpha_n x}\}, \qquad \alpha_i\text{'s distinct constants.}$$

(See Problems 27, 28.)

Recall that the **superposition principle** (Chapter 4, page 195) for linear differential operators states that if $L[y_1] = g_1$ and $L[y_2] = g_2$, then the linear combination $C_1 y_1 + C_2 y_2$ satisfies

$$L[C_1 y_1 + C_2 y_2] = C_1 g_1 + C_2 g_2.$$

If we combine this principle with the representation theorem for solutions of the homogeneous equation, we obtain the following representation theorem for nonhomogeneous equations.

REPRESENTATION OF SOLUTIONS (NONHOMOGENEOUS CASE)

Theorem 4. Let $y_p(x)$ be a particular solution to the nonhomogeneous equation

(27) $$y^{(n)}(x) + p_1(x)y^{(n-1)}(x) + \cdots + p_n(x)y(x) = g(x)$$

on the interval (a, b) and let $\{y_1, \ldots, y_n\}$ be a fundamental solution set on (a, b) for the corresponding homogeneous equation

(28) $$y^{(n)}(x) + p_1(x)y^{(n-1)}(x) + \cdots + p_n(x)y(x) = 0.$$

Then every solution of (27) on the interval (a, b) can be expressed in the form

(29) $$y(x) = y_p(x) + C_1 y_1(x) + \cdots + C_n y_n(x).$$

Proof   Let $\phi(x)$ be any solution to (27). Since both $\phi(x)$ and $y_p(x)$ are solutions to (27), the superposition principle states that the difference $\phi(x) - y_p(x)$ is a solution to the homogeneous equation (28). It then follows from Theorem 2 that

$$\phi(x) - y_p(x) = C_1 y_1(x) + \cdots + C_n y_n(x)$$

for suitable constants $C_1, \ldots, C_n$. Since the last equation is equivalent to (29) (with $\phi(x)$ in place of $y(x)$), the theorem is proved. ∎

The linear combination of $y_p, y_1, \ldots, y_n$ in (29) written with arbitrary constants $C_1, \ldots, C_n$ is, for obvious reasons, referred to as a **general solution** to (27).

▶ **Example 5**   Given that $y_p(x) = x^2$ is a particular solution to

(30) $y''' - 2y'' - y' + 2y = 2x^2 - 2x - 4$

on the interval $(-\infty, \infty)$ and that $y_1(x) = e^{-x}$, $y_2(x) = e^x$, $y_3(x) = e^{2x}$ are solutions to the corresponding homogeneous equation, find a general solution to (30).

Solution   We previously remarked that the functions e^{-x}, e^x, e^{2x} are linearly independent because the exponents -1, 1, and 2 are distinct. Since each of these functions is a solution to the corresponding homogeneous equation, then $\{e^{-x}, e^x, e^{2x}\}$ is a fundamental solution set. It now follows from the representation theorem for nonhomogeneous equations that a general solution is

(31) $y(x) = x^2 + C_1 e^{-x} + C_2 e^x + C_3 e^{2x}$. ◀

EXERCISES 6.2

In Problems 1 through 6 determine the largest interval (a, b) for which Theorem 1 guarantees the existence of a unique solution on (a, b) to the given initial value problem.

1. $xy''' - 3y' + e^x y = x^2 - 1$; $y(-2) = 1$, $y'(-2) = 0$, $y''(-2) = 2$.

2. $y''' - \sqrt{x}\, y = \sin x$; $y(\pi) = 0$, $y'(\pi) = 11$, $y''(\pi) = 3$.

3. $y''' - y'' + \sqrt{x - 1}\, y = \tan x$; $y(5) = y'(5) = y''(5) = 1$.

4. $x(x + 1)y''' - 3xy' + y = 0$; $y(-\tfrac{1}{2}) = 1$, $y'(-\tfrac{1}{2}) = y''(-\tfrac{1}{2}) = 0$.

5. $x\sqrt{x + 1}\, y''' - y' + xy = 0$; $y(\tfrac{1}{2}) = y'(\tfrac{1}{2}) = -1$, $y''(\tfrac{1}{2}) = 1$.

6. $(x^2 - 1)y''' + e^x y = \ln x$; $y(\tfrac{3}{4}) = 1$, $y'(\tfrac{3}{4}) = y''(\tfrac{3}{4}) = 0$.

In Problems 7 through 14 determine whether the given functions are linearly dependent or linearly independent on the specified interval. Also compute their Wronskian.

7. $\{e^{3x}, e^{5x}, e^{-x}\}$ on $(-\infty, \infty)$.

8. $\{x^2, x^2 - 1, 5\}$ on $(-\infty, \infty)$.

9. $\{\sin^2 x, \cos^2 x, 1\}$ on $(-\infty, \infty)$.

10. $\{\sin x, \cos x, \tan x\}$ on $(-\pi/2, \pi/2)$.

11. $\{x^{-1}, x^{1/2}, x\}$ on $(0, \infty)$.

12. $\{\cos 2x, \cos^2 x, \sin^2 x\}$ on $(-\infty, \infty)$.

13. $\{x, x^2, x^3, x^4\}$ on $(-\infty, \infty)$.

14. $\{x, xe^x, 1\}$ on $(-\infty, \infty)$.

In Problems 15 through 18 verify that the given functions form a fundamental solution set for the given differential equation and find a general solution.

15. $y''' + 2y'' - 11y' - 12y = 0;$ $\{e^{3x}, e^{-x}, e^{-4x}\}$.

16. $y''' - y'' + 4y' - 4y = 0;$ $\{e^x, \cos 2x, \sin 2x\}$.

17. $x^3 y''' - 3x^2 y'' + 6xy' - 6y = 0,$ $x > 0;$ $\{x, x^2, x^3\}$.

18. $y^{(4)} - y = 0;$ $\{e^x, e^{-x}, \cos x, \sin x\}$.

In Problems 19 through 22 a particular solution and a fundamental solution set are given for a nonhomogeneous equation and its corresponding homogeneous equation. (a) Find a general solution to the nonhomogeneous equation. (b) Find the solution that satisfies the specified initial conditions.

19. $y''' + y'' + 3y' - 5y = 2 + 6x - 5x^2;$ $y(0) = -1,$ $y'(0) = 1,$ $y''(0) = -3;$ $y_p = x^2;$ $\{e^x, e^{-x} \cos 2x, e^{-x} \sin 2x\}$.

20. $xy''' - y'' = -2;$ $y(1) = 2,$ $y'(1) = -1,$ $y''(1) = -4;$ $y_p = x^2;$ $\{1, x, x^3\}$.

21. $x^3 y''' + xy' - y = 3 - \ln x;$ $y(1) = 3,$ $y'(1) = 3,$ $y''(1) = 0;$ $y_p = \ln x;$ $\{x, x \ln x, x(\ln x)^2\}$.

22. $y^{(4)} + 4y = 5 \cos x;$ $y(0) = 2,$ $y'(0) = 1,$ $y''(0) = -1,$ $y'''(0) = -2;$ $y_p = \cos x;$ $\{e^x \cos x, e^x \sin x, e^{-x} \cos x, e^{-x} \sin x\}$.

23. Let $L[y] := y''' + y' + xy,$ $y_1(x) := \sin x,$ and $y_2(x) := x.$ Verify that $L[y_1](x) = x \sin x$ and $L[y_2](x) = x^2 + 1.$ Now use the superposition principle to find a solution to the differential equation:

   (a) $L[y] = 2x \sin x - x^2 - 1.$

   (b) $L[y] = 4x^2 + 4 - 6x \sin x.$

24. Let $L[y] := y''' - xy'' + 4y' - 3xy,$ $y_1(x) := \cos 2x,$ and $y_2(x) := -\frac{1}{3}.$ Verify that $L[y_1](x) = x \cos 2x$ and $L[y_2](x) = x.$ Now use the superposition principle to find a solution to the differential equation:

   (a) $L[y] = 7x \cos 2x - 3x.$

   (b) $L[y] = -6x \cos 2x + 11x.$

25. Prove that L defined in (7) is a linear operator by verifying that properties (9) and (10) hold for any two n-times differentiable functions y_1, y_2 on (a, b).

26. Show that a fundamental solution set always exists for equation (17). [Hint: By Theorem 1 we know that there is a unique solution for each choice of initial conditions. Choose n sets of initial conditions wisely!]

27. Show that the set of functions $\{1, x, x^2, \ldots, x^n\},$ where n is a positive integer, is linearly independent on every open interval (a, b). [Hint: Use the fact that a polynomial of degree at most n has no more than n zeros unless it is identically zero.]

28. The set of functions

$$\{1, \cos x, \sin x, \ldots, \cos nx, \sin nx\},$$

where n is a positive integer, is linearly independent on every interval (a, b). Prove this in the special case $n = 2$ and $(a, b) = (-\infty, \infty)$.

29. **(a)** Show that if $f_1, \ldots, f_m$ are linearly independent on $(-1, 1)$, then they are linearly independent on $(-\infty, \infty)$.
    (b) Give an example to show that if $f_1, \ldots, f_m$ are linearly independent on $(-\infty, \infty)$, then they need not be linearly independent on $(-1, 1)$.

30. To prove Theorem 3, proceed as follows:
    (a) Let $x_0 \in (a, b)$. Prove that the solutions $y_1, \ldots, y_n$ are linearly dependent on (a, b) if and only if the initial vectors $(y_k(x_0), y_k'(x_0), \ldots, y_k^{(n-1)}(x_0))$, $k = 1, 2, \ldots, n$, are linearly dependent.
    (b) Use the result of part (a) and the fact that *the column vectors of a matrix are linearly independent if and only if the determinant of the matrix is not zero* to complete the proof of Theorem 3.

31. To prove Abel's identity for $n = 3$ proceed as follows:
    (a) Let $W(x) := W[y_1, y_2, y_3](x)$. Use the product rule for differentiation to show

$$W'(x) = \begin{vmatrix} y_1' & y_2' & y_3' \\ y_1' & y_2' & y_3' \\ y_1'' & y_2'' & y_3'' \end{vmatrix} + \begin{vmatrix} y_1 & y_2 & y_3 \\ y_1'' & y_2'' & y_3'' \\ y_1'' & y_2'' & y_3'' \end{vmatrix} + \begin{vmatrix} y_1 & y_2 & y_3 \\ y_1' & y_2' & y_3' \\ y_1''' & y_2''' & y_3''' \end{vmatrix}.$$

(b) Show that the above expression reduces to

$$(32) \qquad W'(x) = \begin{vmatrix} y_1 & y_2 & y_3 \\ y_1' & y_2' & y_3' \\ y_1''' & y_2''' & y_3''' \end{vmatrix}.$$

(c) Since each y_i satisfies (17), show that

$$(33) \qquad y_i^{(3)}(x) = -\sum_{k=1}^{3} p_k(x) y_i^{(3-k)}(x), \qquad i = 1, 2, 3.$$

(d) Substituting the expressions in (33) into (32), show that

$$(34) \qquad W'(x) = -p_1(x) W(x).$$

(e) Deduce Abel's identity by solving equation (34).

6.3 Homogeneous Linear Equations with Constant Coefficients

In this section we discuss the homogeneous linear nth order differential equation

$$(1) \qquad a_n y^{(n)}(x) + a_{n-1} y^{(n-1)}(x) + \cdots + a_1 y'(x) + a_0 y(x) = 0,$$

where a_n ($\neq 0$), $a_{n-1}, \ldots, a_0$ are real constants.[†] Since constant functions are everywhere continuous, equation (1) has solutions defined for all x in $(-\infty, \infty)$ (recall Theorem 1 in Section 6.2). If we can find n linearly independent solutions to (1) on $(-\infty, \infty)$, say $y_1, \ldots, y_n$, then we can express a general solution to (1) in the form

(2) $\qquad y(x) = C_1 y_1(x) + \cdots + C_n y_n(x),$

with $C_1, \ldots, C_n$ as arbitrary constants.

To find these n linearly independent solutions, we shall capitalize on our previous success with second order equations. Namely, experience suggests that we begin by trying a function of the form $y = e^{rx}$.

If we let L be the differential operator defined by the left-hand side of (1), that is,

(3) $\qquad L[y] := a_n y^{(n)} + a_{n-1} y^{(n-1)} + \cdots + a_1 y' + a_0 y,$

then we can write (1) in the operator form

(4) $\qquad L[y](x) = 0.$

For $y = e^{rx}$, we find

(5) $\qquad L[e^{rx}](x) = a_n r^n e^{rx} + a_{n-1} r^{n-1} e^{rx} + \cdots + a_0 e^{rx}$

$\qquad\qquad = e^{rx}(a_n r^n + a_{n-1} r^{n-1} + \cdots + a_0) = e^{rx} P(r),$

where $P(r)$ is the polynomial $a_n r^n + a_{n-1} r^{n-1} + \cdots + a_0$. Thus e^{rx} is a solution to equation (4), provided that r is a root of the **auxiliary equation**

(6) $\qquad P(r) = a_n r^n + a_{n-1} r^{n-1} + \cdots + a_0 = 0.$

According to the fundamental theorem of algebra, the auxiliary equation has n roots (counting multiplicities), which may be either real or complex. As we mentioned in Chapter 4, there are no formulas for determining the zeros of an arbitrary polynomial of degree greater than four. However, if we can determine one zero r_1, then we can divide out the factor $r - r_1$ and be left with a polynomial of lower degree. (For convenience we have chosen most of our examples and exercises so that 0, ± 1, or ± 2 are zeros of any polynomial of degree greater than two that we must factor.) When a zero cannot be exactly determined, numerical algorithms such as Newton's method or the quotient-difference algorithm can be used to compute approximate roots of the polynomial equation.[††] Some pocket calculators even have these algorithms built in.

[†] *Historical Footnote:* In a letter to John Bernoulli dated September 15, 1739, Leonhard Euler claimed to have solved the general case of the homogeneous linear nth order equation with constant coefficients.

[††] See, for example, *Applied and Computational Complex Analysis*, by P. Henrici, Wiley-Interscience, New York, 1974, Volume 1, or *Numerical Analysis*, Second Edition, by R. L. Burden, J. D. Faires, and A. C. Reynolds, Prindle, Weber & Schmidt, Boston, 1981.

DISTINCT REAL ROOTS

If the roots $r_1, \ldots, r_n$ of the auxiliary equation (6) are real and distinct, then n solutions to equation (1) are

(7) $\qquad y_1(x) = e^{r_1 x}, y_2(x) = e^{r_2 x}, \ldots, y_n(x) = e^{r_n x}.$

As stated in the previous section, these functions are linearly independent on $(-\infty, \infty)$—a fact that we shall now officially verify. Let's assume that $c_1, \ldots, c_n$ are constants such that

(8) $\qquad c_1 e^{r_1 x} + \cdots + c_n e^{r_n x} = 0$

for all x in $(-\infty, \infty)$. Our goal is to prove that $c_1 = c_2 = \cdots = c_n = 0$.

One way to show this is to construct a linear operator L_k that annihilates (maps to zero) everything on the left-hand side of (8) except the kth term. For this purpose, we note that since $r_1, \ldots, r_n$ are the zeros of the auxiliary polynomial $P(r)$, then $P(r)$ can be factored as

(9) $\qquad P(r) = a_n(r - r_1) \cdots (r - r_n).$

Consequently, the operator $L[y] = a_n y^{(n)} + a_{n-1} y^{(n-1)} + \cdots + a_0 y$ can be expressed as the following composition:[†]

(10) $\qquad L = P(D) = a_n(D - r_1) \cdots (D - r_n).$

We now construct the polynomial $P_k(r)$ by deleting the factor $(r - r_k)$ from $P(r)$. Then we set $L_k := P_k(D)$; that is,

(11) $\qquad L_k := P_k(D) = a_n(D - r_1) \cdots (D - r_{k-1})(D - r_{k+1}) \cdots (D - r_n).$

Applying L_k to both sides of (8), we get, via linearity,

(12) $\qquad c_1 L_k[e^{r_1 x}] + \cdots + c_n L_k[e^{r_n x}] = 0.$

Also, since $L_k = P_k(D)$, we find (just as in equation (5)) that $L_k[e^{rx}](x) = e^{rx} P_k(r)$ for all r. Thus (12) can be written as

$$c_1 e^{r_1 x} P_k(r_1) + \cdots + c_n e^{r_n x} P_k(r_n) = 0,$$

which simplifies to

(13) $\qquad c_k e^{r_k x} P_k(r_k) = 0,$

[†] *Historical footnote:* The symbolic notation $P(D)$ was introduced by Augustin Cauchy in 1827.

because $P_k(r_i) = 0$ for $i \neq k$. Since r_k is not a root of $P_k(r)$, then $P_k(r_k) \neq 0$. It now follows from (13) that $c_k = 0$. But as k is arbitrary, all the constants $c_1, \ldots, c_n$ must be zero. Thus $y_1(x), \ldots, y_n(x)$ as given in (7) are linearly independent.

We have proved that, in the case of n distinct real roots, a general solution to (1) is

$$(14) \qquad y(x) = C_1 e^{r_1 x} + \cdots + C_n e^{r_n x},$$

where $C_1, \ldots, C_n$ are arbitrary constants.

▶ **Example 1** Find a general solution to

$$(15) \qquad y''' - 2y'' - 5y' + 6y = 0.$$

Solution The auxiliary equation is

$$(16) \qquad r^3 - 2r^2 - 5r + 6 = 0.$$

By inspection, we find that $r = 1$ is a root. Thus, using polynomial division, we have

$$r^3 - 2r^2 - 5r + 6 = (r - 1)(r^2 - r - 6),$$

which further factors into $(r - 1)(r + 2)(r - 3)$. Hence the roots of equation (16) are $r_1 = 1, r_2 = -2, r_3 = 3$. Since these roots are real and distinct, a general solution to (15) is

$$y(x) = C_1 e^x + C_2 e^{-2x} + C_3 e^{3x}. \quad ◀$$

COMPLEX ROOTS

If $\alpha + i\beta$ (α, β real) is a complex root of the auxiliary equation (6), then so is its complex conjugate $\alpha - i\beta$, since the coefficients of $P(r)$ are real valued (see Problem 22). If we accept complex-valued functions as solutions, then both $e^{(\alpha + i\beta)x}$ and $e^{(\alpha - i\beta)x}$ are solutions to (1). Moreover, if there are no repeated roots, then a general solution to (1) is again given by (14). To find two real-valued solutions, corresponding to the roots $\alpha \pm i\beta$, we can just take the real and imaginary parts of $e^{(\alpha + i\beta)x}$. That is, since

$$(17) \qquad e^{(\alpha + i\beta)x} = e^{\alpha x} \cos \beta x + i e^{\alpha x} \sin \beta x,$$

then two linearly independent solutions to (1) are

$$(18) \qquad e^{\alpha x} \cos \beta x, \qquad e^{\alpha x} \sin \beta x.$$

In fact, using these solutions in place of $e^{(\alpha + i\beta)x}$ and $e^{(\alpha - i\beta)x}$ in (14) preserves the linear independence of the set of n solutions. Thus, treating each of the conjugate pairs of roots in this manner, we obtain a real-valued general solution to (1).

▶ *Example 2*   Find a general solution to

(19) $y''' + y'' + 3y' - 5y = 0.$

Solution   The auxiliary equation is

(20) $r^3 + r^2 + 3r - 5 = (r - 1)(r^2 + 2r + 5) = 0,$

which has distinct roots $r_1 = 1, r_2 = -1 + 2i, r_3 = -1 - 2i$. Thus a general solution is

(21) $y(x) = C_1 e^x + C_2 e^{-x} \cos 2x + C_3 e^{-x} \sin 2x.$ ◀

REPEATED ROOTS

If r_1 is a root of multiplicity m, then the n solutions given in (7) are not even distinct, let alone linearly independent. Recall that, for a second order equation, when we had a repeated root r_1 to the auxiliary equation, we obtained two linearly independent solutions by taking $e^{r_1 x}$ and $x e^{r_1 x}$. So if r_1 is a root of (6) of multiplicity m, we might expect that m linearly independent solutions are

(22) $e^{r_1 x}, x e^{r_1 x}, x^2 e^{r_1 x}, \ldots, x^{m-1} e^{r_1 x}.$

To see that this is the case, observe that if r_1 is a root of multiplicity m, then the auxiliary equation can be written in the form

(23) $a_n (r - r_1)^m (r - r_{m+1}) \cdots (r - r_n) = 0,$

$$(r - r_1)^m \tilde{P}(r) = 0,$$

where $\tilde{P}(r) := a_n (r - r_{m+1}) \cdots (r - r_n)$ and $\tilde{P}(r_1) \neq 0$. With this notation,

(24) $L[e^{rx}](x) = e^{rx}(r - r_1)^m \tilde{P}(r)$

(see (5)). Setting $r = r_1$ in (24), we again see that $e^{r_1 x}$ is a solution.

  To find other solutions, we take the kth partial derivative with respect to r of both sides of (24):

(25) $\dfrac{\partial^k}{\partial r^k} L[e^{rx}](x) = \dfrac{\partial^k}{\partial r^k} \left[e^{rx}(r - r_1)^m \tilde{P}(r) \right].$

Carrying out the differentiation on the right-hand side of (25), the resulting expression will still have $(r - r_1)$ as a factor, provided that $k \leq m - 1$. Thus, setting $r = r_1$ in (25) gives

(26) $\dfrac{\partial^k}{\partial r^k} L[e^{rx}](x) \Big|_{r=r_1} = 0$ if $k \leq m - 1.$

Now notice that the function e^{rx} has continuous partial derivatives of all orders with respect to r and x. Hence for mixed partial derivatives of e^{rx}, it makes no difference whether the differentiation is done first with respect to x, then with respect to r, or vice versa. Since L involves derivatives with respect to x, this means we can interchange the order of differentiation in (26) to obtain

$$L\left[\frac{\partial^k}{\partial r^k}(e^{rx})\bigg|_{r=r_1}\right](x) = 0.$$

Thus

(27) $$\frac{\partial^k}{\partial r^k}(e^{rx})\bigg|_{r=r_1} = x^k e^{r_1 x}$$

will be a solution to (1) for $k = 0, 1, \ldots, m-1$. So m distinct solutions to (1), due to the root $r = r_1$ of multiplicity m, are indeed given by (22). We leave it as an exercise to show that the m functions in (22) are linearly independent on $(-\infty, \infty)$ (see Problem (23)).

If $\alpha + i\beta$ is a repeated complex root of multiplicity m, then we can replace the $2m$ complex-valued functions

$$e^{(\alpha+i\beta)x}, xe^{(\alpha+i\beta)x}, \ldots, x^{m-1}e^{(\alpha+i\beta)x},$$

$$e^{(\alpha-i\beta)x}, xe^{(\alpha-i\beta)x}, \ldots, x^{m-1}e^{(\alpha-i\beta)x}$$

by the $2m$ linearly independent real-valued functions

(28) $$e^{\alpha x}\cos\beta x, xe^{\alpha x}\cos\beta x, \ldots, x^{m-1}e^{\alpha x}\cos\beta x,$$
$$e^{\alpha x}\sin\beta x, xe^{\alpha x}\sin\beta x, \ldots, x^{m-1}e^{\alpha x}\sin\beta x.$$

Using the results of the three cases discussed above, we can obtain a set of n linearly independent solutions that yield a real-valued general solution for (1).

▶ **Example 3** Find a general solution to

(29) $$y^{(4)} - y^{(3)} - 3y'' + 5y' - 2y = 0.$$

Solution The auxiliary equation is

$$r^4 - r^3 - 3r^2 + 5r - 2 = (r-1)^3(r+2) = 0,$$

which has roots $r_1 = 1$, $r_2 = 1$, $r_3 = 1$, $r_4 = -2$. Since the root at 1 has multiplicity 3, a general solution is

(30) $y(x) = C_1e^x + C_2xe^x + C_3x^2e^x + C_4e^{-2x}.$ ◄

► **Example 4**   Find a general solution to

(31) $y^{(4)} - 8y^{(3)} + 26y'' - 40y' + 25y = 0,$

whose auxiliary equation can be factored as

(32) $r^4 - 8r^3 + 26r^2 - 40r + 25 = (r^2 - 4r + 5)^2 = 0.$

Solution   The auxiliary equation (32) has repeated complex roots: $r_1 = 2 + i$, $r_2 = 2 + i$, $r_3 = 2 - i$, and $r_4 = 2 - i$. Hence a general solution is

$$y(x) = C_1e^{2x}\cos x + C_2xe^{2x}\cos x + C_3e^{2x}\sin x + C_4xe^{2x}\sin x.$$ ◄

EXERCISES 6.3

In Problems 1 through 14 find a general solution for the differential equation.

1. $y''' - 3y'' - y' + 3y = 0.$
2. $y''' + 2y'' - 8y' = 0.$
3. $6y''' + 7y'' - y' - 2y = 0.$
4. $y''' + 2y'' - 19y' - 20y = 0.$
5. $y''' + 3y'' - 4y' - 6y = 0.$
6. $y''' + 3y'' + 28y' + 26y = 0.$
7. $y''' - y'' + 2y = 0.$
8. $y''' + 5y'' - 13y' + 7y = 0.$
9. $y''' - 9y'' + 27y' - 27y = 0.$
10. $2y''' - y'' - 10y' - 7y = 0.$
11. $y''' + 5y'' + 3y' - 9y = 0.$
12. $y^{(4)} + 4y''' + 6y'' + 4y' + y = 0.$
13. $y^{(4)} + 4y'' + 4y = 0.$
14. $y''' + 5y'' + 5y' - 11y = 0.$

In Problems 15 through 18 find a general solution to the linear homogeneous differential equation with constant coefficients whose auxiliary equation is given.

15. $(r - 1)^2(r + 3)(r^2 + 2r + 5)^2 = 0.$
16. $(r + 1)^2(r - 6)^3(r + 5)(r^2 + 1)(r^2 + 4) = 0.$
17. $(r - 1)^3(r - 2)(r^2 + r + 1)(r^2 + 6r + 10)^3 = 0.$
18. $(r + 4)(r - 3)(r + 2)^3(r^2 + 4r + 5)^2r^5 = 0.$

In Problems 19 through 21 solve the given initial value problem.

19. $y''' + 7y'' + 14y' + 8y = 0;$ $y(0) = 1,$ $y'(0) = -3,$ $y''(0) = 13.$
20. $y''' - y'' - 4y' + 4y = 0;$ $y(0) = -4,$ $y'(0) = -1,$ $y''(0) = -19.$
21. $y''' - 4y'' + 7y' - 6y = 0;$ $y(0) = 1,$ $y'(0) = 0,$ $y''(0) = 0.$

22. Let $P(r) = a_nr^n + \cdots + a_1r + a_0$ be a polynomial with real coefficients $a_n, \ldots, a_0$. Prove that if r_1 is a zero of $P(r)$, then so is its complex conju-

gate $\bar{r}_1$. [Hint: Show that $\overline{P(r)} = P(\bar{r})$, where the bar denotes complex conjugation.]

23. Show that the m functions $e^{rx}, xe^{rx}, \ldots, x^{m-1}e^{rx}$ are linearly independent on $(-\infty, \infty)$. [Hint: Show that these functions are linearly independent if and only if $1, x, \ldots, x^{m-1}$ are linearly independent.]

24. As an alternate proof that $\{e^{r_1 x}, \ldots, e^{r_n x}\}$ is linearly independent when $r_1, \ldots, r_n$ are distinct, proceed as follows:

    (a) Show that $W[e^{r_1 x}, \ldots, e^{r_n x}](x) = e^{(r_1 + \cdots + r_n)x} V(r_1, \ldots, r_n)$ where $V(r_1, \ldots, r_n)$ is the determinant of the $n \times n$ matrix whose jth column is $\mathrm{col}[1 \; r_j \; r_j^2 \ldots r_j^{n-1}]$. V is called a **Vandermonde determinant.**

    (b) Use the fact that
    $$V(r_1, \ldots, r_n) = [r_2 - r_1][(r_3 - r_1)(r_3 - r_2)] \cdots$$
    $$[(r_n - r_1) \cdots (r_n - r_{n-1})]$$
    $$= \prod_{i < j = 2}^{n} (r_j - r_i)$$

    to show that the exponential functions are linearly independent on any interval (a, b).

25. Find a general solution to
    $$y^{(4)} + 2y''' - 3y'' - y' + \tfrac{1}{2}y = 0$$

    by using Newton's method or some other numerical procedure to approximate the roots of the auxiliary equation.

26. Find a general solution to $y''' - 3y' - y = 0$ by using Newton's method or some other numerical procedure to approximate the roots of the auxiliary equation.

27. **Higher Order Cauchy-Euler Equations.** A differential equation that can be expressed in the form
    $$a_n x^n y^{(n)}(x) + a_{n-1} x^{n-1} y^{(n-1)}(x) + \cdots + a_0 y(x) = 0,$$

    where $a_n, a_{n-1}, \ldots, a_0$ are constants, is called a homogeneous **Cauchy-Euler** equation. (The second order case is discussed in Sections 4.10 and 8.5.) Use the substitution $y = x^r$ to help determine a fundamental solution set for the following Cauchy-Euler equations.

    (a) $x^3 y''' + x^2 y'' - 2xy' + 2y = 0$, $\quad x > 0$.
    (b) $x^4 y^{(4)} + 6x^3 y''' + 2x^2 y'' - 4xy' + 4y = 0$, $\quad x > 0$.
    (c) $x^3 y''' - 2x^2 y'' + 13xy' - 13y = 0$, $\quad x > 0$.
    [Hint: $x^{\alpha + i\beta} = e^{(\alpha + i\beta)\ln x} = x^\alpha \{\cos(\beta \ln x) + i \sin(\beta \ln x)\}$.]

28. Let $y(x) = Ce^{rx}$, where $C \neq 0$ and r are real numbers, be a solution to a differential equation. Suppose we cannot determine r exactly, but can only approximate it by $\tilde{r}$. Let $\tilde{y}(x) := Ce^{\tilde{r}x}$ and consider the error $y(x) - \tilde{y}(x)$.

(a) If r and $\bar{r}$ are positive, $r \neq \bar{r}$, show that the error grows exponentially large as x approaches ∞.

(b) If r and $\bar{r}$ are negative, $r \neq \bar{r}$, show that the error goes to zero exponentially as x approaches ∞.

29. On a smooth horizontal surface a mass of m_1 kg is attached to a vertical surface by a spring with spring constant k_1 N/m. Another mass of m_2 kg is attached to the first object by a spring with spring constant k_2 N/m. The objects are aligned horizontally so that the springs are their natural lengths. As we showed in Section 6.1, this coupled spring-mass system is governed by the system of differential equations

(33) $$m_1 \frac{d^2x}{dt^2} + (k_1 + k_2)x - k_2 y = 0,$$

(34) $$m_2 \frac{d^2y}{dt^2} - k_2 x + k_2 y = 0.$$

Let's assume that $m_1 = m_2 = 1$, $k_1 = 3$, and $k_2 = 2$. If both objects are displaced 1 m to the right of their equilibrium positions and then released, determine the equations of motion for the objects as follows:

(a) Show that $x(t)$ satisfies the equation

(35) $$x^{(4)}(t) + 7x''(t) + 6x(t) = 0.$$

[Hint: Solve equation (33) for y in terms of x and x'' and substitute into equation (34).]

(b) Find a general solution $x(t)$ to (35).

(c) Substitute $x(t)$ back into (33) to obtain a general solution for $y(t)$.

(d) Use the initial conditions to determine the solutions, $x(t)$ and $y(t)$, which are the equations of motion.

30. Suppose the two springs in the coupled spring-mass system discussed in Problem 29 are switched, giving the new data $m_1 = m_2 = 1$, $k_1 = 2$, and $k_2 = 3$. If both objects are now displaced 1 m to the right of their equilibrium positions and then released, determine the equations of motion of the two objects.

6.4 Annihilator Method and Undetermined Coefficients

Armed with the ability to solve homogeneous linear equations with constant coefficients, we now attack the nonhomogeneous case. For a certain family of forcing terms $g(x)$, our strategy is to transform the nonhomogeneous equation into a homogeneous one. For this purpose, the concept of an annihilator is helpful.

ANNIHILATOR

Definition 3. A linear differential operator A is said to **annihilate** a function f if

(1) $\qquad A[f](x) = 0, \quad$ all x.

That is, A annihilates f if f is a solution to the homogeneous linear differential equation (1) on $(-\infty, \infty)$.

For example, $A = D - 3$ annihilates $f(x) = e^{3x}$ since

$$(D - 3)[e^{3x}] = 3e^{3x} - 3e^{3x} = 0.$$

Also, $A = D^2 - 4D + 20$ is an annihilator of $e^{2x} \sin 4x$ since this function satisfies the equation

$$y'' - 4y' + 20y = 0.$$

From what we learned in the previous section about auxiliary equations with repeated roots, it follows that the differential operator $(D - r)^m$, m a positive integer, annihilates each of the functions

(2) $\qquad e^{rx}, \, xe^{rx}, \, \ldots, \, x^{m-1}e^{rx}.$

Moreover, the differential operator $[(D - \alpha)^2 + \beta^2]^m$ annihilates each of the functions

(3) $\qquad \begin{aligned} &e^{\alpha x} \cos \beta x, \, xe^{\alpha x} \cos \beta x, \, \ldots, \, x^{m-1}e^{\alpha x} \cos \beta x, \\ &e^{\alpha x} \sin \beta x, \, xe^{\alpha x} \sin \beta x, \, \ldots, \, x^{m-1}e^{\alpha x} \sin \beta x, \end{aligned}$

since these are the $2m$ linearly independent solutions to $[(D - \alpha)^2 + \beta^2]^m y = 0$.

In the next example we make use of the fact that linear differential operators with *constant* coefficients commute (see Exercises 4.2, Problem 32).

▶ *Example 1* Find a differential operator that annihilates

(4) $\qquad 6xe^{-4x} + 5e^x \sin 2x.$

Solution Let's consider the two functions whose sum appears in (4). Observe that $(D + 4)^2$ annihilates the function $f_1(x) := 6xe^{-4x}$. Further, $f_2(x) := 5e^x \sin 2x$ is annihilated by the operator $(D - 1)^2 + 4$. Hence the composite operator

$$A := (D + 4)^2[(D - 1)^2 + 4],$$

which is the same as the operator

$$[(D - 1)^2 + 4](D + 4)^2,$$

annihilates both f_1 and f_2. But then, by linearity, A also annihilates the sum $f_1 + f_2$. ◀

We now show how annihilators can be used to determine particular solutions to certain *non*homogeneous equations. Consider the nth order differential equation with constant coefficients

(5) $a_n y^{(n)}(x) + a_{n-1} y^{(n-1)}(x) + \cdots + a_0 y(x) = g(x),$

which can be written in the operator form

(6) $L[y](x) = g(x),$

where

$$L[y] := a_n y^{(n)} + a_{n-1} y^{(n-1)} + \cdots + a_0 y.$$

In this section we restrict our attention to nonhomogeneous terms that can be annihilated by a linear differential operator with *constant* coefficients. Assuming that A is such an annihilator of g, then applying A to both sides of (6) yields

(7) $A[L[y]](x) = A[g](x) = 0.$

Therefore, if y is a solution to (6), then y is also a solution to the *homogeneous* linear differential equation

(8) $AL[y](x) = 0$

involving the composition of the operators A and L. Since equation (8) has constant coefficients (why?), we can apply the methods of Section 6.3 to obtain its general solution. Comparing this with a general solution of $L[y] = 0$, it is then possible to determine the *form* of a particular solution to equation (6). This procedure, known as the **annihilator method,** is illustrated in the following examples.

▶ *Example 2*   Find a general solution to

(9) $y''(x) + y(x) = e^{2x} + 1.$

Solution   Since $D - 2$ annihilates e^{2x} and D annihilates 1, then $A := D(D - 2)$ annihilates $e^{2x} + 1$. Therefore, applying A to both sides of (9) yields

$$A[y'' + y] = A[e^{2x} + 1]$$

(10) $D(D - 2)(D^2 + 1)[y] = 0.$

The auxiliary equation associated with (10) is

(11) $r(r - 2)(r^2 + 1) = 0,$

which has the roots i, $-i$, 2, 0. Hence a general solution to (10) is

(12) $y(x) = C_1 \cos x + C_2 \sin x + C_3 e^{2x} + C_4.$

Now recall that a general solution to (9) is of the form $y_h + y_p$, where y_p is a particular solution to (9) and y_h is a general solution to

(13) $y''(x) + y(x) = 0.$

Since every solution to (9) is also a solution to (10), then $y_h + y_p$ must have the form displayed on the right-hand side of (12). But we recognize that $y_h(x) = C_1 \cos x + C_2 \sin x$, and so there exists a particular solution of the form

(14) $y_p(x) = C_3 e^{2x} + C_4.$

To determine the constants C_3 and C_4, we substitute y_p given by (14) into (9):

$$4C_3 e^{2x} + C_3 e^{2x} + C_4 = e^{2x} + 1,$$
$$5C_3 e^{2x} + C_4 = e^{2x} + 1.$$

Equating the coefficients of e^{2x} and setting the constant terms equal yields $C_3 = \frac{1}{5}$ and $C_4 = 1$. Thus

$$y_p(x) = \tfrac{1}{5} e^{2x} + 1,$$

and so a general solution to (9) is

(15) $y(x) = C_1 \cos x + C_2 \sin x + \tfrac{1}{5} e^{2x} + 1.$ ◀

▶ **Example 3**   Determine the form of a particular solution to

(16) $y'' - y = e^{-2x} \sin x.$

Solution   The function $g(x) = e^{-2x} \sin x$ is annihilated by the operator

(17) $A := (D + 2)^2 + 1^2 = D^2 + 4D + 5.$

If we apply A to both sides of (16), we obtain

$$A[y'' - y] = A[e^{-2x} \sin x]$$

(18) $(D^2 + 4D + 5)(D^2 - 1)[y] = 0.$

Now the auxiliary equation associated with (18) is

(19) $(r^2 + 4r + 5)(r - 1)(r + 1) = 0,$

which has roots $1, -1, -2 + i, -2 - i$. Hence a general solution to (18) is

(20) $y(x) = C_1 e^x + C_2 e^{-x} + C_3 e^{-2x} \cos x + C_4 e^{-2x} \sin x.$

Since a general solution to the corresponding homogeneous equation $y'' - y = 0$ is $y_h(x) = C_1 e^x + C_2 e^{-x}$, we see that a particular solution for (16) has the form

(21) $y_p(x) = C_3 e^{-2x} \cos x + C_4 e^{-2x} \sin x.$ ◀

The reader may already have guessed that there is a connection between the annihilator method and the method of **undetermined coefficients** discussed in Section 4.8. Indeed, in Examples 2 and 3, the forms derived for the particular solutions can also be obtained from the appropriate entries of Table 4.1, which is also reproduced on the inside back cover. The essential point is that the annihilator method can be used to *justify* the method of undetermined coefficients; that is, to derive the entries that appear in Table 4.1. This applies not only to second order, but also to higher order linear differential equations with constant coefficients.

The connection between the two methods is even more evident once one realizes that those functions for which the method of undetermined coefficients works are *exactly* those functions that are solutions to higher order linear differential equations with constant coefficients; that is, those functions $g(x)$ that are annihilated by a linear differential operator with constant coefficients. In particular, these methods work for polynomials, exponentials, sines, and cosines, and any product or sum of these functions. (Why?)

We leave it for the reader to show how the annihilator method yields various entries in Table 4.1 (see Problems 34–37). The derivation for the general case, where

$$g(x) = p_n(x)e^{\alpha x} \cos \beta x + q_m(x)e^{\alpha x} \sin \beta x,$$

p_n, q_m polynomials, is discussed in Project A at the end of this chapter.

► **Example 4**   Find the form of a particular solution to

(22) $y'''(x) - 3y''(x) + 4y(x) = xe^{2x} - \cos x,$

using (a) the method of undetermined coefficients and (b) the annihilator method.

Solution   We first solve the corresponding homogeneous equation

(23) $y'''(x) - 3y''(x) + 4y(x) = 0.$

The auxiliary equation

(24) $r^3 - 3r^2 + 4 = (r + 1)(r - 2)^2 = 0$

has a simple root at -1 and a double root at 2, and hence a general solution to (23) is

(25) $y_h(x) = C_1 e^{-x} + C_2 e^{2x} + C_3 x e^{2x}.$

(a) Using the method of undetermined coefficients, we can find the form for a particular solution y_p to equation (22) by referring to Table 4.1. The portion of y_p due to the term xe^{2x} is

(26) $x^s(A_1 x + A_0)e^{2x}.$

Since e^{2x} and xe^{2x} are solutions to the corresponding homogeneous equation (23), we take $s = 2$. That is, part of y_p has the form

(27) $(A_1 x^3 + A_0 x^2)e^{2x}.$

The portion of y_p due to $-\cos x$ has the general form

(28) $x^s(B_1 \cos x + B_2 \sin x).$

Since neither $\cos x$ nor $\sin x$ is a solution to the corresponding homogeneous equation (23), we take $s = 0$. Then (28) becomes

(29) $B_1 \cos x + B_2 \sin x.$

Combining (27) and (29), we see that for suitable constants $A_1, A_0, B_1, B_2,$

(30) $y_p(x) = (A_1 x^3 + A_0 x^2)e^{2x} + B_1 \cos x + B_2 \sin x.$

(b) To determine y_p using the annihilator method, we observe that the term xe^{2x} is annihilated by the operator $(D - 2)^2$ and the term $-\cos x$ is annihilated by $(D^2 + 1)$.

Hence the composite operator

(31) $A := (D^2 + 1)(D - 2)^2$

is an annihilator for the nonhomogeneous term $xe^{2x} - \cos x$. If we now apply A to both sides of (22), we obtain

(32)
$$A[y''' - 3y'' + 4y] = A[xe^{2x} - \cos x],$$
$$(D^2 + 1)(D - 2)^2(D + 1)(D - 2)^2[y] = 0.$$

Regrouping the factors in (32), we have

(33) $(D^2 + 1)(D - 2)^4(D + 1)[y] = 0.$

The auxiliary equation associated with (33) is

(34) $(r^2 + 1)(r - 2)^4(r + 1) = 0,$

which has roots $i, -i, 2, 2, 2, 2, -1$. Hence a general solution to (33) is

(35) $y(x) = C_1 \cos x + C_2 \sin x + (C_3 + C_4 x + C_5 x^2 + C_6 x^3)e^{2x} + C_7 e^{-x}.$

Comparing (35) with the general solution to (23) given in equation (25), we see that a particular solution for (22) is of the form

(36) $y_p(x) = C_1 \cos x + C_2 \sin x + (C_5 x^2 + C_6 x^3)e^{2x},$

which is the same, except for notation, as the form given in (30). ◀

Substituting either (30) or (36) for y_p into (22) and solving for the unknown constants yields (after some algebra) the particular solution

(37) $y_p(x) = -\frac{7}{50} \cos x + \frac{1}{50} \sin x + \frac{1}{18}(x^3 - x^2)e^{2x}.$

Hence a general solution for equation (22) is

(38) $y(x) = y_h(x) + y_p(x),$

where $y_h(x)$ and $y_p(x)$ are given in equations (25) and (37), respectively.

EXERCISES 6.4 ───────────────────────────────

In Problems 1 through 10 find a differential operator that annihilates the given function.

1. $3x^2 - 6x + 1.$

2. $x^4 - x^2 + 11.$

3. $e^{5x}.$

4. $e^{-7x}.$

5. $e^{2x} - 6e^x.$

6. $x^2 - e^x.$

7. $x^2 e^{-x} \sin 2x$.   **8.** $xe^{3x} \cos 5x$.   **9.** $x^2 e^x - x \sin 4x + x^3$.

10. $xe^{-2x} + xe^{-5x} \sin 3x$.

In Problems 11 through 20 use the annihilator method to determine the form of a particular solution for the given equation.

11. $y'' - 5y' + 6y = \cos 2x + 1$.   **12.** $y'' + 6y' + 8y = e^{3x} - \sin x$.

13. $y'' - 5y' + 6y = e^{3x} - x^2$.   **14.** $y'' - y = xe^x$.

15. $y'' + 2y' + y = x^2 - x + 1$.   **16.** $y'' - 6y' + 9y = \sin 2x + x$.

17. $y'' + 2y' + 2y = e^{-x} \cos x + x^2$.   **18.** $y'' - 6y' + 10y = e^{3x} - x$.

19. $y''' - 2y'' + y' = x - e^x$.   **20.** $y''' + 2y'' - y' - 2y = e^x - 1$.

In Problems 21 through 24 use the method of undetermined coefficients (Table 4.1, inside back cover) to determine the form of a particular solution for the given equation.

21. $y''' - 2y'' - 5y' + 6y = e^x + x^2$.   **22.** $y''' + y'' - 5y' + 3y = e^{-x} + \sin x$.

23. $y''' + 3y'' - 4y = e^{-2x}$.   **24.** $y''' + y'' - 2y = xe^x + 1$.

In Problems 25 through 30 find a general solution to the given equation.

25. $y''' - 2y'' - 5y' + 6y = e^x + x^2$.   **26.** $y''' + y'' - 5y' + 3y = e^{-x} + \sin x$.

27. $y''' + 3y'' - 4y = e^{-2x}$.   **28.** $y''' + y'' - 2y = xe^x + 1$.

29. $y''' + 4y'' + y' - 26y = e^{-3x} \sin 2x + x$.   **30.** $y''' - 3y'' + 3y' - y = e^x$.

In Problems 31 through 33 solve the given initial value problem.

31. $y''' + 2y'' - 9y' - 18y = -18x^2 - 18x + 22;$ $y(0) = -2,$ $y'(0) = -8,$ $y''(0) = -12.$

32. $y''' - 2y'' + 5y' = -24e^{3x};$ $y(0) = 4,$ $y'(0) = -1,$ $y''(0) = -5$

33. $y''' - 2y'' - 3y' + 10y = 34xe^{-2x} - 16e^{-2x} - 10x^2 + 6x + 34;$ $y(0) = 3,$ $y'(0) = 0,$ $y''(0) = 0.$

34. Use the annihilator method to show that if $a_0 \neq 0$ in equation (5) and $g(x)$ has the form

(39) $g(x) = b_m x^m + b_{m-1} x^{m-1} + \cdots + b_1 x + b_0,$

then

$$y_p(x) = B_m x^m + B_{m-1} x^{m-1} + \cdots + B_1 x + B_0$$

is the form of a particular solution to equation (5).

35. Use the annihilator method to show that if $a_0 = 0$ and $a_1 \neq 0$ in (5) and $g(x)$ has the form given in (39), then equation (5) has a particular solution of the form

$$y_p(x) = x\{B_m x^m + B_{m-1} x^{m-1} + \cdots + B_1 x + B_0\}.$$

36. Use the annihilator method to show that if $g(x)$ in (5) has the form $g(x) = Be^{\alpha x}$, then equation (5) has a particular solution of the form $y_p(x) = x^s Be^{\alpha x}$, where s is chosen to be the smallest nonnegative integer such that $x^s e^{ax}$ is not a solution to the corresponding homogeneous equation.

37. Use the annihilator method to show that if $g(x)$ in (5) has the form

$$g(x) = a \cos \beta x + b \sin \beta x,$$

then equation (5) has a particular solution of the form

(40) $y_p(x) = x^s\{A \cos \beta x + B \sin \beta x\},$

where s is chosen to be the smallest nonnegative integer such that $x^s \cos \beta x$ and $x^s \sin \beta x$ are not solutions to the corresponding homogeneous equation.

38. Referring to the coupled spring-mass system discussed in Section 6.1, suppose that an external force $E(t) = 37 \cos 3t$ is applied to the second object of mass 1 kg. The displacement functions $x(t)$ and $y(t)$ now satisfy the system

(41) $2x''(t) + 6x(t) - 2y(t) = 0,$

(42) $y''(t) + 2y(t) - 2x(t) = 37 \cos 3t.$

(a) Show that $x(t)$ satisfies the equation

(43) $x^{(4)}(t) + 5x''(t) + 4x(t) = 37 \cos 3t.$

[Hint: Solve equation (41) for y in terms of x and x'' and substitute into equation (42).]
(b) Find a general solution $x(t)$ to equation (43).
(c) Substitute $x(t)$ back into (41) to obtain a general solution for $y(t)$.
(d) If both masses are displaced 2 m to the right of their equilibrium positions and then released, find the displacement functions $x(t)$ and $y(t)$.

39. Suppose the displacement functions $x(t)$ and $y(t)$ for a coupled spring-mass system (similar to the one discussed in Problem 38) satisfy the initial value problem

(44) $x''(t) + 5x(t) - 2y(t) = 0; \qquad x(0) = x'(0) = 0,$

(45) $y''(t) + 2y(t) - 2x(t) = 3 \sin 2t; \qquad y(0) = 1, \qquad y'(0) = 0.$

Solve for $x(t)$ and $y(t)$.

40. The currents in the electric network in Figure 6.3 satisfy the system

$$\frac{1}{9} I_1 + 64 I_2'' = -2 \sin \frac{t}{24},$$

$$\frac{1}{64} I_3 + 9 I_3'' - 64 I_2'' = 0,$$

$$I_1 = I_2 + I_3,$$

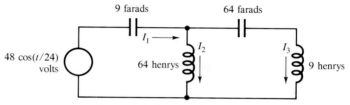

9 farads   64 farads

48 cos(t/24) volts

64 henrys   9 henrys

Figure 6.3 An electric network

where I_1, I_2, and I_3 are the currents through the different branches of the network. By completing the following steps, determine the currents if initially $I_1(0) = I_2(0) = I_3(0) = 0$, $I'_1(0) = \frac{73}{12}$, $I'_2(0) = \frac{3}{4}$, and $I'_3(0) = \frac{16}{3}$.

(a) By eliminating I_1 and I_3 from the system, show that I_2 satisfies

$$9^2(64)^2 I_2^{(4)} + (82)(64)I''_2 + I_2 = 0.$$

(b) Find a general solution for the equation in part (a). (This gives I_2 with four arbitrary constants.)

(c) Substitute I_2 into the first equation of the system to determine a general expression for I_1. Then use the third equation of the system to find a general expression for I_3.

(d) Use the initial conditions to determine I_1, I_2, and I_3.

6.5 *Method of Variation of Parameters*

In the previous section we discussed the annihilator method and the method of undetermined coefficients. These methods work only for linear equations with constant coefficients *and* when the nonhomogeneous term is a solution to some homogeneous linear equation with constant coefficients. In this section we show how the method of **variation of parameters** discussed in Section 4.9 generalizes to higher order linear equations with variable coefficients.

Our goal is to find a particular solution to

(1) $\qquad L[y](x) = g(x),$

where $L[y] := y^{(n)} + p_1 y^{(n-1)} + \cdots + p_n y$ and the coefficient functions $p_1, \ldots, p_n$, as well as g, are continuous on (a, b). The method to be described requires that we already know a fundamental solution set $\{y_1, \ldots, y_n\}$ for the corresponding homogeneous equation

(2) $\qquad L[y](x) = 0.$

A general solution to (2) is then

(3) $\qquad y_h(x) = C_1 y_1(x) + \cdots + C_n y_n(x),$

where $C_1, \ldots, C_n$ are arbitrary constants. In the method of variation of parameters, we assume that there exists a particular solution to (1) of the form

(4) $\qquad y_p(x) = v_1(x)y_1(x) + \cdots + v_n(x)y_n(x)$

any try to determine the functions $v_1, \ldots, v_n$.

Since there are n unknown functions, we will need n conditions (equations) to determine them. These conditions are obtained as follows. Differentiating y_p in (4) gives

(5) $\qquad y_p' = (v_1 y_1' + \cdots + v_n y_n') + (v_1' y_1 + \cdots + v_n' y_n).$

To prevent second and higher order derivatives of the unknowns $v_1, \ldots, v_n$ from entering our later computations, we impose the condition

$$v_1' y_1 + \cdots + v_n' y_n = 0.$$

In a like manner, on computing $y_p'', y_p''', \ldots, y_p^{(n-1)}$, we impose $(n-2)$ additional conditions involving $v_1', \ldots, v_n'$; namely

$$v_1' y_1' + \cdots + v_n' y_n' = 0, \ldots, v_1' y_1^{(n-2)} + \cdots + v_n' y_n^{(n-2)} = 0.$$

Finally, the nth condition that we impose is that y_p satisfy the given equation (1). Using the previous conditions and the fact that $y_1, \ldots, y_n$ are solutions to the homogeneous equation, then $L[y_p] = g$ reduces to

(6) $\qquad v_1' y_1^{(n-1)} + \cdots + v_n' y_n^{(n-1)} = g,$

(see Problem 12). We therefore seek n functions $v_1', \ldots, v_n'$ that satisfy the system

(7)
$$\begin{aligned}
y_1 v_1' + \cdots + y_n v_n' &= 0, \\
&\vdots \\
y_1^{(n-2)} v_1' + \cdots + y_n^{(n-2)} v_n' &= 0, \\
y_1^{(n-1)} v_1' + \cdots + y_n^{(n-1)} v_n' &= g.
\end{aligned}$$

A sufficient condition for the existence of a solution to system (7) for x in (a, b) is that the determinant of the matrix made up of the coefficients of $v_1', \ldots, v_n'$ be different from zero for all x in (a, b). But this determinant is just the Wronskian:

(8)
$$\begin{vmatrix} y_1 & \cdots & y_n \\ & & \\ & & \\ y_1^{(n-2)} & \cdots & y_n^{(n-2)} \\ y_1^{(n-1)} & \cdots & y_n^{(n-1)} \end{vmatrix} = W[y_1, \ldots, y_n](x),$$

which is never zero on (a, b), because $\{y_1, \ldots, y_n\}$ is a fundamental solution set. Solving (7) via Cramer's rule, we find

$$
(9) \qquad v_k'(x) = \frac{g(x)W_k(x)}{W[y_1, \ldots, y_n](x)}, \qquad k = 1, \ldots, n,
$$

where $W_k(x)$ is the determinant of the matrix obtained from the Wronskian $W[y_1, \ldots, y_n](x)$ by replacing the kth column by $\mathrm{col}[0, \ldots, 0, 1]$. Using a cofactor expansion about this column, we can express $W_k(x)$ in terms of an $(n-1)$st order Wronskian:

$$
(10) \qquad W_k(x) = (-1)^{n-k}W[y_1, \ldots, y_{k-1}, y_{k+1}, \ldots, y_n](x), \qquad k = 1, \ldots, n.
$$

Integrating $v_k'(x)$ in (9) gives

$$
(11) \qquad v_k(x) = \int \frac{g(x)W_k(x)}{W[y_1, \ldots, y_n](x)}\, dx, \qquad k = 1, \ldots, n.
$$

Finally, substituting the v_k's back into (4), we obtain the particular solution

$$
(12) \qquad y_p(x) = \sum_{k=1}^{n} y_k(x) \int \frac{g(x)W_k(x)}{W[y_1, \ldots, y_n](x)}\, dx.
$$

Although equation (12) gives a neat formula for a particular solution to (1), its implementation requires one to evaluate $n+1$ determinants and then perform n integrations. This may entail several tedious computations. However, the method works even in cases when the technique of undetermined coefficients does not apply, provided, of course, that we know a fundamental solution set.

▶ *Example 1*   Find a general solution to the Cauchy-Euler equation

$$
(13) \qquad x^3 y''' + x^2 y'' - 2xy' + 2y = x^3 \sin x, \qquad x > 0,
$$

given that $\{x, x^{-1}, x^2\}$ is a fundamental solution set to the corresponding homogeneous equation.

Solution   An important first step is to divide (13) by x^3 to obtain the standard form

$$
(14) \qquad y''' + \frac{1}{x}y'' - \frac{2}{x^2}y' + \frac{2}{x^3}y = \sin x, \qquad x > 0,
$$

from which we see that $g(x) = \sin x$. Since $\{x, x^{-1}, x^2\}$ is a fundamental solution set, we can obtain a particular solution of the form

(15) $y_p(x) = v_1(x)x + v_2(x)x^{-1} + v_3(x)x^2.$

To use formula (12), we must first evaluate the four determinants

$$W[x, x^{-1}, x^2](x) = \begin{vmatrix} x & x^{-1} & x^2 \\ 1 & -x^{-2} & 2x \\ 0 & 2x^{-3} & 2 \end{vmatrix} = -6x^{-1},$$

$$W_1(x) = (-1)^{(3-1)}W[x^{-1}, x^2](x) = (-1)^2 \begin{vmatrix} x^{-1} & x^2 \\ -x^{-2} & 2x \end{vmatrix} = 3,$$

$$W_2(x) = (-1)^{(3-2)} \begin{vmatrix} x & x^2 \\ 1 & 2x \end{vmatrix} = -x^2,$$

$$W_3(x) = (-1)^{(3-3)} \begin{vmatrix} x & x^{-1} \\ 1 & -x^{-2} \end{vmatrix} = -2x^{-1}.$$

Substituting the above expressions into (12), we find

$$y_p(x) = x \int \frac{(\sin x)3}{-6x^{-1}} \, dx + x^{-1} \int \frac{(\sin x)(-x^2)}{-6x^{-1}} \, dx + x^2 \int \frac{(\sin x)(-2x^{-1})}{-6x^{-1}} \, dx$$

$$= x \int -\tfrac{1}{2}x \sin x \, dx + x^{-1} \int \tfrac{1}{6}x^3 \sin x \, dx + x^2 \int \tfrac{1}{3} \sin x \, dx,$$

which simplifies to

(16) $y_p(x) = \cos x - x^{-1} \sin x + C_1 x + C_2 x^{-1} + C_3 x^2,$

where C_1, C_2, and C_3 denote the constants of integration. Since $\{x, x^{-1}, x^2\}$ is a fundamental solution set for the homogeneous equation, we can take C_1, C_2, and C_3 to be arbitrary constants; the right-hand side of (16) then gives the desired general solution. ◀

In the preceding example the fundamental solution set $\{x, x^{-1}, x^2\}$ can be derived by substituting $y = x^r$ into the homogeneous equation corresponding to (13) (see Problem 27, Exercises 6.3). However, in dealing with other equations that have variable coefficients, the determination of a fundamental set may be extremely difficult. In Chapter 8 we tackle this problem using power series methods.

EXERCISES 6.5

In Problems 1 through 6 use the method of variation of parameters to determine a particular solution to the given equation.

1. $y''' - 2y'' + y' = x.$

2. $y''' - 3y'' + 4y = e^{2x}.$

3. $y''' + 3y'' - 4y = e^{2x}$.

4. $y''' - 3y'' + 3y' - y = e^x$.

5. $y''' + y' = \tan x$, $0 < x < \pi/2$.

6. $y''' + y' = \sec x \tan x$, $0 < x < \pi/2$.

7. Find a general solution to the Cauchy-Euler equation

$$x^3 y''' - 3x^2 y'' + 6xy' - 6y = x^{-1}, \qquad x > 0,$$

given that $\{x, x^2, x^3\}$ is a fundamental solution set for the corresponding homogeneous equation.

8. Find a general solution to the Cauchy-Euler equation

$$x^3 y''' - 2x^2 y'' + 3xy' - 3y = x^2, \qquad x > 0,$$

given that $\{x, x \ln x, x^3\}$ is a fundamental solution set for the corresponding homogeneous equation.

9. Given that $\{e^x, e^{-x}, e^{2x}\}$ is a fundamental solution set for the homogeneous equation corresponding to the equation

$$y''' - 2y'' - y' + 2y = g(x),$$

determine a formula involving integrals for a particular solution.

10. Given that $\{x, x^{-1}, x^4\}$ is a fundamental solution set for the homogeneous equation corresponding to the equation

$$x^3 y''' - x^2 y'' - 4xy' + 4y = g(x), \qquad x > 0,$$

determine a formula involving integrals for a particular solution.

11. Find a general solution to the Cauchy-Euler equation

$$x^3 y''' - 3xy' + 3y = x^4 \cos x, \qquad x > 0.$$

12. Derive the system (7) in the special case when $n = 3$. [Hint: To determine the last equation, require that $L[y_p] = g$ and use the fact that y_1, y_2, and y_3 satisfy the corresponding homogeneous equation.]

13. Show that

$$W_k(x) = (-1)^{(n-k)} W[y_1, \ldots, y_{k-1}, y_{k+1}, \ldots, y_n](x).$$

Chapter Summary

The theory and techniques for solving an nth order linear differential equation

(1) $y^{(n)} + p_1(x)y^{(n-1)} + \cdots + p_n(x)y = g(x)$

are natural extensions of the development for second order equations given in Chapter 4. Assuming that $p_1, \ldots, p_n$, and g are continuous functions on an open interval I, there is a unique solution to (1) on I that satisfies the n initial conditions: $y(x_0) = y_0$, $y'(x_0) = y_1, \ldots, y^{(n-1)}(x_0) = y_{n-1}$, where $x_0 \in I$.

For the corresponding homogeneous equation

$$(2) \qquad y^{(n)} + p_1(x)y^{(n-1)} + \cdots + p_n(x)y = 0,$$

there exists a set of n **linearly independent** solutions $\{y_1, \ldots, y_n\}$ on I. Such functions are said to form a **fundamental solution set,** and every solution to (2) can be written as a linear combination of these functions:

$$y(x) = C_1 y_1(x) + C_2 y_2(x) + \cdots + C_n y_n(x).$$

The linear independence of solutions to (2) is equivalent to the nonvanishing on I of the **Wronskian**

$$W[y_1, \ldots, y_n](x) := \det \begin{bmatrix} y_1(x) & \cdots & y_n(x) \\ y_1'(x) & \cdots & y_n'(x) \\ \vdots & & \vdots \\ y_1^{(n-1)}(x) & \cdots & y_n^{(n-1)}(x) \end{bmatrix}.$$

When equation (2) has (real) constant coefficients, so that it is of the form

$$(3) \qquad a_n y^{(n)} + a_{n-1} y^{(n-1)} + \cdots + a_0 y = 0, \qquad a_n \neq 0,$$

then the problem of determining a fundamental solution set can be reduced to the algebraic problem of solving the **auxiliary equation**

$$(4) \qquad a_n r^n + a_{n-1} r^{n-1} + \cdots + a_0 = 0.$$

If the n roots of (4), say $r_1, r_2, \ldots, r_n$, are all distinct, then

$$(5) \qquad \{e^{r_1 x}, e^{r_2 x}, \ldots, e^{r_n x}\}$$

is a fundamental solution set for (3). If some real root, say r_1, occurs with multiplicity m (e.g., $r_1 = r_2 = \cdots = r_m$), then m of the functions in (5) are replaced by

$$e^{r_1 x}, xe^{r_1 x}, \ldots, x^{m-1} e^{r_1 x}.$$

When a complex root $\alpha + i\beta$ to (4) occurs with multiplicity m, then so does its conjugate, and $2m$ members of the set (5) are replaced by the real-valued functions

$$e^{\alpha x} \sin \beta x, \, xe^{\alpha x} \sin \beta x, \ldots, \, x^{m-1} e^{\alpha x} \sin \beta x,$$

$$e^{\alpha x} \cos \beta x, \, xe^{\alpha x} \cos \beta x, \ldots, \, x^{m-1} e^{\alpha x} \cos \beta x.$$

A general solution to the nonhomogeneous equation (1) can be written as

$$y(x) = y_p(x) + y_h(x),$$

where y_p is some particular solution to (1) and y_h is a general solution to the corresponding homogeneous equation. Two useful techniques for finding particular solutions are the **annihilator method** (undetermined coefficients) and the method of **variation of parameters.**
The annihilator method applies to equations of the form

(6) $$L[y] = g(x),$$

where L is a linear differential operator with constant coefficients and the forcing term $g(x)$ is a polynomial, exponential, sine, or cosine, or a linear combination of products of these. Such a function $g(x)$ is annihilated (mapped to zero) by a linear differential operator A that also has constant coefficients. Every solution to the nonhomogeneous equation (6) is then a solution to the homogeneous equation $AL[y] = 0$, and, by comparing the solutions of the latter equation with a general solution to $L[y] = 0$, we can obtain the *form* of a particular solution to (6). These forms have previously been compiled in Table 4.1, page 204, for the method of undetermined coefficients.
The method of variation of parameters is more general in that it applies to arbitrary equations of the form (1). The idea is: Starting with a fundamental solution set $\{y_1, \ldots, y_n\}$ for (2), determine functions $v_1, \ldots, v_n$ such that

(7) $$y_p(x) = v_1(x)y_1(x) + \cdots + v_n(x)y_n(x)$$

satisfies (1). This method leads to the formula

(8) $$y_p(x) = \sum_{k=1}^{n} y_k(x) \int \frac{g(x)W_k(x)}{W[y_1, \ldots, y_n](x)} \, dx,$$

where

$$W_k(x) = (-1)^{n-k} W[y_1, \ldots, y_{k-1}, y_{k+1}, \ldots, y_n](x), \qquad k = 1, \ldots, n.$$

REVIEW PROBLEMS

1. Determine the intervals for which Theorem 1 on page 289 guarantees the existence of a solution in that interval.
   (a) $y^{(4)} - (\ln x)y'' + xy' + 2y = \cos 3x.$
   (b) $(x^2 - 1)y''' + (\sin x)y'' + \sqrt{x + 4}\, y' + e^x y = x^2 + 3.$

2. Determine whether the given functions are linearly dependent or linearly independent on the interval $(0, \infty)$.

   (a) $\{e^{2x}, x^2 e^{2x}, e^{-x}\}$.

   (b) $\{e^x \sin 2x, xe^x \sin 2x, e^x, xe^x\}$.

   (c) $\{2e^{2x} - e^x, e^{2x} + 1, e^{2x} - 3, e^x + 1\}$.

3. Show that the set of functions $\{\sin x, x \sin x, x^2 \sin x, x^3 \sin x\}$ is linearly independent on $(-\infty, \infty)$.

4. Find a general solution for the given differential equation.

   (a) $y^{(4)} + 2y''' - 4y'' - 2y' + 3y = 0$.

   (b) $y''' + 3y'' - 5y' + y = 0$.

   (c) $y^{(5)} - y^{(4)} + 2y''' - 2y'' + y' - y = 0$.

   (d) $y''' - 2y'' - y' + 2y = e^x + x$.

5. Find a general solution for the homogeneous linear differential equation with constant coefficients whose auxiliary equation is

   (a) $(r + 5)^2 (r - 2)^3 (r^2 + 1)^2 = 0$.

   (b) $r^4 (r - 1)^2 (r^2 + 2r + 4)^2 = 0$.

6. Given that $y_p = \sin(x^2)$ is a particular solution to

   $$y^{(4)} + y = (16x^4 - 11) \sin(x^2) - 48x^2 \cos(x^2)$$

   on $(0, \infty)$, find a general solution.

7. Find a differential operator that annihilates the given function.

   (a) $x^2 - 2x + 5$.

   (b) $e^{3x} + x - 1$.

   (c) $x \sin 2x$.

   (d) $x^2 e^{-2x} \cos 3x$.

   (e) $x^2 - 2x + xe^{-x} + \sin 2x - \cos 3x$.

8. Use the annihilator method to determine the form of a particular solution for the given equation.

   (a) $y'' + 6y' + 5y = e^{-x} + x^2 - 1$.

   (b) $y''' + 2y'' - 19y' - 20y = xe^{-x}$.

   (c) $y^{(4)} + 6y'' + 9y = x^2 - \sin 3x$.

   (d) $y''' - y'' + 2y = x \sin x$.

9. Find a general solution to the Cauchy-Euler equation

   $$x^3 y''' - 2x^2 y'' - 5xy' + 5y = x^{-2}, \qquad x > 0,$$

   given that $\{x, x^5, x^{-1}\}$ is a fundamental solution set to the corresponding homogeneous equation.

10. Find a general solution to the given Cauchy-Euler equation.

    (a) $4x^3 y''' + 8x^2 y'' - xy' + y = 0, \qquad x > 0$.

    (b) $x^3 y''' + 2x^2 y'' + 2xy' + 4y = 0, \qquad x > 0$.

Projects for Chapter 6

A. JUSTIFYING THE METHOD OF UNDETERMINED COEFFICIENTS

The annihilator method discussed in Section 6.4 can be used to derive the entries in Table 4.1, page 204 for the method of undetermined coefficients. To show this, it suffices to work with type VII functions—that is, functions of the form

(1) $$g(x) = p_n(x)e^{\alpha x} \cos \beta x + q_m(x)e^{\alpha x} \sin \beta x,$$

where p_n and q_m are polynomials of degrees n and m, respectively—since the other types listed in Table 4.1 are just special cases of (1).

Consider the nonhomogeneous equation

(2) $$L[y](x) = g(x),$$

where L is the linear operator

(3) $$L[y] := a_n y^{(n)} + a_{n-1} y^{(n-1)} + \cdots + a_0 y,$$

with $a_n, a_{n-1}, \ldots, a_0$ constants, and $g(x)$ as given in equation (1). Let $N := \max(n, m)$.

(a) Show that

$$A := [(D - \alpha)^2 + \beta^2]^{N+1}$$

is an annihilator for g.

(b) Show that the auxiliary equation associated with $AL[y] = 0$ is of the form

(4) $$a_n[(r - \alpha)^2 + \beta^2]^{s+N+1}(r - r_{2s+1}) \cdots (r - r_n) = 0,$$

where s (≥ 0) is the multiplicity of $\alpha \pm i\beta$ as roots of the auxiliary equation associated with $L[y] = 0$, and $r_{2s+1}, \ldots, r_n$ are the remaining roots of this equation.

(c) Find a general solution for $AL[y] = 0$ and compare it with a general solution for $L[y] = 0$ to verify that equation (2) has a particular solution of the form

$$y_p(x) = x^s e^{\alpha x}\{P_N(x) \cos \beta x + Q_N(x) \sin \beta x\},$$

where P_N and Q_N are polynomials of degree N.

B. PHASOR METHOD

The algebra of complex numbers can be used to find quickly a particular solution $y_p(x)$ to an equation of the form

(5) $$a_n y^{(n)} + a_{n-1} y^{(n-1)} + \cdots + a_1 y' + a_0 y = K \cos(\omega x + \phi),$$

where $a_n, a_{n-1}, \ldots, a_0, K, \omega$, and ϕ are given real constants. To describe this method we first note that, by Euler's formula,

$$e^{i(\omega x + \phi)} = \cos(\omega x + \phi) + i\sin(\omega x + \phi),$$

and so

$$\cos(\omega x + \phi) = \mathrm{Re}(e^{i(\omega x + \phi)}).$$

Thus, if we can find a particular solution $Y_p(x)$ to

(6) $$a_n Y^{(n)} + a_{n-1} Y^{(n-1)} + \cdots + a_1 Y' + a_0 Y = K e^{i(\omega x + \phi)},$$

then the desired solution to (5) is just

$$y_p(x) = \mathrm{Re}\, Y_p(x).$$

The method of undetermined coefficients suggests we try a solution to (6) of the form

(7) $$Y_p(x) = C e^{i\omega x},$$

where C is a *complex* constant to be determined. It will be useful to express C in complex polar form:

$$C = R e^{i\phi_f},$$

which we call the **phasor** associated with Y_p.

(a) With $Y_p(x)$ given by (7), show that

$$Y_p^{(k)}(x) = C(i\omega)^k e^{i\omega x}, \qquad k = 0, 1, \ldots.$$

(b) Substitute $Y_p(x)$ given by (7) into equation (6) and derive the algebraic equation

(8) $$[a_n(i\omega)^n + a_{n-1}(i\omega)^{n-1} + \cdots + a_1 i\omega + a_0] C = K e^{i\phi}.$$

Notice that the quantity in brackets on the left-hand side of (8) is just a complex number and so it can be written in standard form as $\alpha + i\beta$ or in polar form as $r e^{i\theta}$, where $r = \sqrt{\alpha^2 + \beta^2}$ and $\tan\theta = \beta/\alpha$.

(c) Using the polar form $r e^{i\theta}$ for the bracketed quantity in (8), show that the phasor $C = R e^{i\phi_f}$ is given by

$$R = \frac{K}{r} \quad \text{and} \quad \phi_f = \phi - \theta,$$

provided $r \neq 0$.

(d) Assuming $r \neq 0$, show that the desired solution $y_p(x)$ to (5) is

$$y_p(x) = R\cos(\omega x + \phi_f) = \frac{K}{r}\cos(\omega x + \phi - \theta).$$

To summarize, the phasor method for finding a particular solution to (5) consists of solving equation (8) for the polar form of the constant $C = Re^{i\phi_f}$ and setting $y_p(x) = R\cos(\omega x + \phi_f)$. We caution the reader that this method will fail when the modification rules for the method of undetermined coefficients apply (this is the situation when $r = 0$).

(e) Use the phasor method to determine a particular solution to each of the following.

(i) $y''' - 2y'' - y = 4\cos(x + 3)$.

(ii) $y^{(4)} + 3y^{(3)} - 2y'' - 6y = \cos(\sqrt{3}x + 1)$.

(iii) $y^{(4)} + 3y^{(3)} - 2y'' - 6y = \sin(\sqrt{3}x + 1)$.

7 Laplace Transforms

7.1 Introduction: A Simple Example

Use the method of Laplace transforms to solve the initial value problem

$$(1) \qquad y'(t) - y(t) = 1, \qquad y(0) = 0.$$

This problem is, of course, easily solved using the techniques of earlier chapters. Our purpose here is to illustrate a new approach—one that involves the use of Laplace transforms. As we shall see, this method offers some advantages over the previous techniques.

The idea behind Laplace transforms is to "simplify the problem" in much the same spirit as the substitution of $y = e^{rt}$ helped to simplify the problem of solving a linear differential equation with constant coefficients. The **Laplace transform** of a function $f(t)$ defined on $[0, \infty)$ is given by[†]

$$(2) \qquad \mathcal{L}\{f\}(s) := \int_0^\infty e^{-st} f(t)\, dt.$$

[†] *Historical Footnote:* The Laplace transform was first introduced by Pierre Laplace in 1779 in his research on probability. G. Doetsch helped develop the use of Laplace transforms to solve differential equations. His work in the 1930s served to justify the operational calculus procedures earlier used by Oliver Heaviside.

Thus the transform takes a function of t and produces a function of s. This is done by multiplying $f(t)$ by e^{-st} and then integrating with respect to t from 0 to ∞.

Because of the properties of the exponential function, there is a simple algebraic relation between the Laplace transform of a function $f(t)$ and that of its derivative $f'(t)$; namely,

(3) $\mathscr{L}\{f'\}(s) = s\mathscr{L}\{f\}(s) - f(0).$

This formula can be verified using integration by parts:

$$\mathscr{L}\{f'\}(s) = \int_0^\infty e^{-st} f'(t)\, dt = f(t)e^{-st}\Big|_{t=0}^{t=\infty} + s\int_0^\infty e^{-st} f(t)\, dt$$

$$= -f(0) + s\mathscr{L}\{f\}(s),$$

assuming that $f(t)e^{-st} \to 0$ as $t \to \infty$.

Thanks to formula (3) (and its extension to higher order derivatives), the Laplace transform can be used to reduce certain differential equations to algebraic equations. Let's now use it to solve the initial value problem given in (1).

If we take the Laplace transform of both sides of the differential equation in (1)—that is, if we multiply equation (1) by e^{-st} and integrate with respect to t—we get

(4) $\mathscr{L}\{y'\}(s) - \mathscr{L}\{y\}(s) = \mathscr{L}\{1\}(s).$

Next, from formula (3) and the condition $y(0) = 0$, we see that $\mathscr{L}\{y'\}(s) = s\mathscr{L}\{y\}(s)$. Furthermore, from definition (2) or a table of Laplace transforms, we can verify that $\mathscr{L}\{1\}(s) = 1/s$. Therefore, equation (4) can be written as

$$s\mathscr{L}\{y\}(s) - \mathscr{L}\{y\}(s) = \frac{1}{s},$$

which is an algebraic equation in $\mathscr{L}\{y\}(s)$. Solving for $\mathscr{L}\{y\}(s)$ gives

(5) $\mathscr{L}\{y\}(s) = \dfrac{1}{(s-1)s} = \dfrac{1}{s-1} - \dfrac{1}{s}.$

We previously mentioned that $\mathscr{L}\{1\}(s) = 1/s$, and from the table on the inside back cover we also find that $\mathscr{L}\{e^t\}(s) = 1/(s-1)$. It then follows from the linearity of the Laplace transform that $y(t) = e^t - 1$ satisfies equation (5); thus this function is the desired solution to (1).

The above example illustrates a nice feature of the Laplace transform method: It reduces certain initial value problems to algebraic problems with the initial conditions automatically included in the computations. Moreover, as we shall see in Section 7.6, the method of Laplace transforms often gives a nice form of the solution when a *discontinuous* forcing function is involved. In fact, the method works for *impulse* functions; that is, for functions that are zero except on a very short interval, where they are quite large.

In the next three sections we discuss in detail the definition and properties of the Laplace transform. Section 7.5 explains how Laplace transforms are used to solve initial value problems. The remaining sections describe additional properties of the transform that are useful in applications.

7.2 Definition of the Laplace Transform

In earlier chapters we studied differential operators. These operators took a function and mapped or transformed it (via differentiation) into another function. We now present an important transformation, denoted by $\mathscr{L}$, which is an integral operator.

LAPLACE TRANSFORM

Definition 1.   Let $f(t)$ be a function on $[0, \infty)$. The **Laplace transform** of $f(t)$ is the function $F(s)$ defined by the integral

(1) $$F(s) := \int_0^\infty e^{-st} f(t)\, dt.$$

The domain of $F(s)$ is all the values of s for which the integral in (1) exists.[†] The Laplace transform of $f(t)$ is denoted by both $F(s)$ and $\mathscr{L}\{f\}(s)$.

Notice that the integral in (1) is an **improper** integral that is defined by

$$\int_0^\infty e^{-st} f(t)\, dt := \lim_{N \to \infty} \int_0^N e^{-st} f(t)\, dt$$

whenever the limit exists.

▶ *Example 1*   Determine the Laplace transform of the constant function $f(t) = 1$, $t \geq 0$.

Solution   Using the definition of the transform, we compute

$$F(s) = \int_0^\infty e^{-st} \cdot 1\, dt = \lim_{N \to \infty} \int_0^N e^{-st}\, dt$$

$$= \lim_{N \to \infty} \left. \frac{-e^{-st}}{s} \right|_{t=0}^{t=N} = \lim_{N \to \infty} \left[\frac{1}{s} - \frac{e^{-sN}}{s} \right]$$

[†] We treat s as real valued, but in certain application s may be a complex variable. For a detailed treatment of complex-valued Laplace transforms see *Complex Variables and the Laplace Transforms for Engineers,* by Wilbur R. LePage, Dover Publications, New York, 1980, or *Basic Complex Analysis,* by J. E. Marsden, W. H. Freeman and Company, San Francisco, 1973.

$$F(s) = \frac{1}{s} \quad \text{for} \quad s > 0.$$

When $s \leq 0$, the integral $\int_0^\infty e^{-st}\, dt$ diverges (Why?). Hence $F(s) = 1/s$, with the domain of $F(s)$ being all $s > 0$. ◀

▶ **Example 2**   Determine the Laplace transform of $f(t) = e^{at}$, where a is a constant.

Solution   Using the definition of the transform,

$$F(s) = \int_0^\infty e^{-st} e^{at}\, dt = \int_0^\infty e^{-(s-a)t}\, dt$$

$$= \lim_{N \to \infty} \int_0^N e^{-(s-a)t}\, dt = \lim_{N \to \infty} \frac{-e^{-(s-a)t}}{s-a}\Bigg|_0^N$$

$$= \lim_{N \to \infty} \left[\frac{1}{s-a} - \frac{e^{-(s-a)N}}{s-a} \right]$$

$$= \frac{1}{s-a} \quad \text{for} \quad s > a.$$

Again, if $s \leq a$ the integral diverges, and hence the domain of $F(s)$ is all $s > a$. ◀

It is comforting to note from Example 2 that the transform of the constant function $f(t) = 1 = e^{0t}$ is $1/(s-0) = 1/s$, which agrees with the solution in Example 1.

▶ **Example 3**   Find $\mathcal{L}\{\sin bt\}$, where b is a nonzero constant.

Solution   We need to compute

$$\mathcal{L}\{\sin bt\}(s) = \int_0^\infty e^{-st} \sin bt\, dt = \lim_{N \to \infty} \int_0^N e^{-st} \sin bt\, dt.$$

Using integration by parts twice, we ultimately find

$$\mathcal{L}\{\sin bt\}(s) = \lim_{N \to \infty} \left[-\frac{e^{-st}}{s^2 + b^2} (s \sin bt + b \cos bt) \Bigg|_0^N \right]$$

$$= \lim_{N \to \infty} \left[\frac{b}{s^2 + b^2} - \frac{e^{-sN}}{s^2 + b^2} (s \sin bN + b \cos bN) \right]$$

$$= \frac{b}{s^2 + b^2} \quad \text{for} \quad s > 0. ◀$$

▶ *Example 4*   Determine the Laplace transform of

$$f(t) = \begin{cases} 2, & 0 < t < 5, \\ 0, & 5 < t < 10, \\ e^{4t}, & 10 < t. \end{cases}$$

Solution   Since $f(t)$ is defined by a different formula on different intervals, we begin by breaking up the integral in (1) into three separate parts.[†] Thus

$$F(s) = \int_0^\infty e^{-st} f(t)\, dt$$

$$= \int_0^5 e^{-st} \cdot 2\, dt + \int_5^{10} e^{-st} \cdot 0\, dt + \int_{10}^\infty e^{-st} e^{4t}\, dt$$

$$= 2 \int_0^5 e^{-st}\, dt + \lim_{N \to \infty} \int_{10}^N e^{-(s-4)t}\, dt$$

$$= \frac{2}{s} - \frac{2e^{-5s}}{s} + \lim_{N \to \infty} \left[\frac{e^{-10(s-4)}}{s-4} - \frac{e^{-(s-4)N}}{s-4} \right]$$

$$= \frac{2}{s} - \frac{2e^{-5s}}{s} + \frac{e^{-10(s-4)}}{s-4} \quad \text{for} \quad s > 4. \blacktriangleleft$$

Notice that the function $f(t)$ of Example 4 has jump discontinuities at $t = 5$ and $t = 10$. These values are reflected in the exponential terms e^{-5s} and e^{-10s} that appear in the formula for $F(s)$. We shall make this connection more precise when we discuss the unit step function in Section 7.6.

An important property of the Laplace transform is its **linearity.** That is, the Laplace transform $\mathscr{L}$ is a linear operator.

LINEARITY OF THE TRANSFORM

Theorem 1.   Let f_1 and f_2 be functions whose Laplace transforms exist for $s > \alpha$, and let c be a constant. Then

(2) $$\mathscr{L}\{f_1 + f_2\} = \mathscr{L}\{f_1\} + \mathscr{L}\{f_2\},$$

(3) $$\mathscr{L}\{cf_1\} = c\mathscr{L}\{f_1\}.$$

[†] Notice that $f(t)$ is not defined at the points $t = 0$, 5, and 10. Nevertheless, the integral in (1) is still meaningful and is unaffected by function values at finitely many points.

Proof   Using the linearity properties of integration, we have for $s > \alpha$

$$\mathscr{L}\{f_1 + f_2\}(s) = \int_0^\infty e^{-st}[f_1(t) + f_2(t)]\,dt$$

$$= \int_0^\infty e^{-st}f_1(t)\,dt + \int_0^\infty e^{-st}f_2(t)\,dt$$

$$= \mathscr{L}\{f_1\}(s) + \mathscr{L}\{f_2\}(s).$$

Hence equation (2) is satisfied. In a similar fashion we see that

$$\mathscr{L}\{cf_1\}(s) = \int_0^\infty e^{-st}[cf_1(t)]\,dt = c\int_0^\infty e^{-st}f_1(t)\,dt$$

$$= c\mathscr{L}\{f_1\}(s). \ \blacksquare\ \blacksquare$$

▶ **Example 5**   Determine $\mathscr{L}\{11 + 5e^{4t} - 6\sin 2t\}.$[†]

Solution   From the linearity property, we know that the Laplace transform of the sum of any finite number of functions is the sum of their Laplace transforms. Thus

$$\mathscr{L}\{11 + 5e^{4t} - 6\sin 2t\} = \mathscr{L}\{11\} + \mathscr{L}\{5e^{4t}\} + \mathscr{L}\{-6\sin 2t\}$$

$$= 11\mathscr{L}\{1\} + 5\mathscr{L}\{e^{4t}\} - 6\mathscr{L}\{\sin 2t\}.$$

In Examples 1, 2, and 3 we determined that

$$\mathscr{L}\{1\}(s) = \frac{1}{s}, \qquad \mathscr{L}\{e^{4t}\}(s) = \frac{1}{s-4}, \qquad \mathscr{L}\{\sin 2t\}(s) = \frac{2}{s^2 + 2^2}.$$

Using these results, we find

$$\mathscr{L}\{11 + 5e^{4t} - 6\sin 2t\}(s) = 11\left(\frac{1}{s}\right) + 5\left(\frac{1}{s-4}\right) - 6\left(\frac{2}{s^2+4}\right)$$

$$= \frac{11}{s} + \frac{5}{s-4} - \frac{12}{s^2+4}.$$

Since $\mathscr{L}\{1\}$, $\mathscr{L}\{e^{4t}\}$, and $\mathscr{L}\{\sin 2t\}$ are all defined for $s > 4$, so is $\mathscr{L}\{11 + 5e^{4t} - 6\sin 2t\}$. ◀

There are functions for which the improper integral in (1) fails to converge for any value of s. For example, this is the case for the function $f(t) = 1/t$, which grows too fast near zero. Likewise, no Laplace transform exists for the function $f(t) = e^{t^2}$, which increases

---

[†] When convenient, we suppress the dependence on the variable s and write $\mathscr{L}\{f\}$ instead of $\mathscr{L}\{f\}(s)$.

332 **Chapter 7 | Laplace Transforms**

too rapidly as $t \to \infty$. Fortunately, the set of functions for which the Laplace transform *is* defined includes many of the functions that arise in applications involving linear differential equations. We now discuss some properties that will (collectively) ensure the existence of the Laplace transform.

A function $f(t)$ defined on (a, b) is said to have a **jump discontinuity** at $t_0 \in (a, b)$ if $f(t)$ is discontinuous at t_0 and the one-sided limits

$$\lim_{t \to t_0^-} f(t) \quad \text{and} \quad \lim_{t \to t_0^+} f(t)$$

exist as finite numbers. If $t_0 = a$ (or b), a jump discontinuity occurs if the one-sided limit of $f(t)$ as $t \to a^+$ $(t \to b^-)$ exists as a finite number. We can now define:

PIECEWISE CONTINUITY

Definition 2. A function $f(t)$ is said to be **piecewise continuous on a finite interval** $[a, b]$ if $f(t)$ is continuous at every point in $[a, b]$ except possibly for a finite number of points at which $f(t)$ has a jump discontinuity.

A function $f(t)$ is said to be **piecewise continuous on $[0, \infty)$** if $f(t)$ is piecewise continuous on $[0, N]$ for all $N > 0$.

▶ **Example 6** Show that

$$f(t) = \begin{cases} t, & 0 < t < 1, \\ 2, & 1 < t < 2, \\ (t-2)^2, & 2 \le t \le 3 \end{cases}$$

is piecewise continuous on $[0, 3]$.

Solution From the graph of $f(t)$ sketched in Figure 7.1, we see that $f(t)$ is continuous on the intervals $(0, 1)$, $(1, 2)$, and $(2, 3]$. Moreover, at the points of discontinuity, $t = 0, 1$, and 2, the function has jump discontinuities since the one-sided limits exist as finite numbers. In particular, at $x = 1$, the left-hand limit is 1 and the right-hand limit is 2. Therefore, $f(t)$ is piecewise continuous on $[0, 3]$. ◀

The reader should observe that the function $f(t)$ of Example 4 is piecewise continuous on $[0, \infty)$ because it is piecewise continuous on every finite interval of the form $[0, N]$, with $N > 0$. In contrast, the function $f(t) = 1/t$ is not piecewise continuous on any interval containing the origin since it has an "infinite jump" at the origin:

$$\lim_{t \to 0^+} \frac{1}{t} = +\infty, \qquad \lim_{t \to 0^-} \frac{1}{t} = -\infty.$$

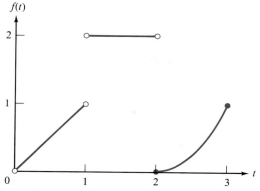

Figure 7.1 Graph of $f(t)$ in Example 6

A function that is piecewise continuous on a *finite* interval is necessarily integrable over that interval. However, piecewise continuity on $[0, \infty)$ is not enough to guarantee the existence (as a finite number) of the improper integral over $[0, \infty)$; we also need to consider the growth of the integrand for large t. Roughly speaking, we shall show that the Laplace transform of a piecewise continuous function will exist, provided that the function does not grow "faster than an exponential."

EXPONENTIAL ORDER α

Definition 3. A function $f(t)$ is said to be of **exponential order** α if there exist positive constants T and M such that

(4) $\qquad |f(t)| \leq Me^{\alpha t}, \quad$ for all $t \geq T.$

For example, $f(t) = e^{5t} \sin 2t$ is of exponential order $\alpha = 5$ since

$$|e^{5t} \sin 2t| \leq e^{5t},$$

and hence (4) holds with $M = 1$ and T any positive constant.

We use the phrase $f(t)$ *is of exponential order* to mean that for *some* value of α, the function $f(t)$ satisfies the conditions of Definition 3; that is, $f(t)$ grows no faster than a function of the form $Me^{\alpha t}$. The function e^{t^2} is *not* of exponential order. To see this, observe that

$$\lim_{t \to \infty} \frac{e^{t^2}}{e^{\alpha t}} = \lim_{t \to \infty} e^{t(t - \alpha)} = +\infty$$

for any α. Consequently, e^{t^2} grows faster than $e^{\alpha t}$ for every choice of α.

The usual functions encountered in solving linear differential equations with constant coefficients (polynomials, exponentials, sines, and cosines) are both piecewise continuous and of exponential order. As we now show, the Laplace transforms of such functions exist for large enough values of s.

CONDITIONS FOR EXISTENCE OF THE TRANSFORM

Theorem 2. If $f(t)$ is piecewise continuous on $[0, \infty)$ and of exponential order α, then $\mathscr{L}\{f\}(s)$ exists for $s > \alpha$.

Proof We need to show that the integral

$$(5) \qquad \int_0^\infty e^{-st}f(t)\,dt$$

converges for $s > \alpha$. We begin by breaking up the integral in (5) into two separate integrals:

$$(6) \qquad \int_0^T e^{-st}f(t)\,dt + \int_T^\infty e^{-st}f(t)\,dt,$$

where T is chosen so that inequality (4) holds. The first integral in (6) exists because $f(t)$ and hence $e^{-st}f(t)$ are piecewise continuous on the interval $[0, T]$ for any fixed s. To see that the second integral in (6) converges, we use the **comparison test for improper integrals.**

Since $f(t)$ is of exponential order α, we have for $t \geq T$

$$|f(t)| \leq Me^{\alpha t},$$

and hence

$$|e^{-st}f(t)| = e^{-st}\,|f(t)| \leq Me^{-(s-\alpha)t},$$

for all $t \geq T$. Now for $s > \alpha$,

$$(7) \qquad \int_T^\infty Me^{-(s-\alpha)t}\,dt = M\int_T^\infty e^{-(s-\alpha)t}\,dt = \frac{Me^{-(s-\alpha)T}}{s-\alpha} < \infty.$$

Since $|e^{-st}f(t)| \leq Me^{-(s-\alpha)t}$ for $t \geq T$ and, as seen in (7), the improper integral of the larger function converges for $s > \alpha$, then, by the comparison test, the integral

$$\int_T^\infty e^{-st}f(t)\,dt$$

converges for $s > \alpha$. Finally, since the two integrals in (6) exist, the Laplace transform $\mathscr{L}\{f\}(s)$ exists for $s > \alpha$. ∎

In Table 7.1 we have listed the Laplace transforms of some of the elementary functions. The reader should become familiar with these since they are frequently encountered in solving linear differential equations with constant coefficients. The entries in Table 7.1 can be derived from the definition of the Laplace transform. A more elaborate table of transforms is given on the inside back cover.

TABLE 7.1 BRIEF TABLE OF LAPLACE TRANSFORMS

$f(t)$	$F(s) = \mathscr{L}\{f\}(s)$
1	$\dfrac{1}{s}, \quad s > 0$
e^{at}	$\dfrac{1}{s-a}, \quad s > a$
$t^n, \quad n = 1, 2, \ldots$	$\dfrac{n!}{s^{n+1}}, \quad s > 0$
$e^{at}t^n, \quad n = 1, 2, \ldots$	$\dfrac{n!}{(s-a)^{n+1}}, \quad s > a$
$\sin bt$	$\dfrac{b}{s^2 + b^2}, \quad s > 0$
$\cos bt$	$\dfrac{s}{s^2 + b^2}, \quad s > 0$
$e^{at} \sin bt$	$\dfrac{b}{(s-a)^2 + b^2}, \quad s > a$
$e^{at} \cos bt$	$\dfrac{s-a}{(s-a)^2 + b^2}, \quad s > a$

EXERCISES 7.2

In Problems 1 through 12 use Definition 1 to determine the Laplace transform of the given function.

1. t.

2. t^2.

3. e^{6t}.

4. te^{3t}.

5. $\cos 2t$.

6. $\cos bt$, b a constant.

7. $e^{-t} \sin 2t$.

8. $e^{2t} \cos 3t$.

9. $f(t) = \begin{cases} 0, & 0 < t < 2, \\ t, & 2 < t. \end{cases}$

10. $f(t) = \begin{cases} \sin t, & 0 < t < \pi, \\ 0, & \pi < t. \end{cases}$

11. $f(t) = \begin{cases} e^{2t}, & 0 < t < 3, \\ 1, & 3 < t. \end{cases}$

12. $f(t) = \begin{cases} 1 - t, & 0 < t < 1, \\ 0, & 1 < t. \end{cases}$

In Problems 13 through 20 use the Laplace transform table and the linearity of the Laplace transform to determine the following transforms.

13. $\mathscr{L}\{5 - e^{2t} + 6t^2\}$.

14. $\mathscr{L}\{6e^{-3t} - t^2 + 2t - 8\}$.

15. $\mathscr{L}\{t^2 - 3t - 2e^{-t} \sin 3t\}$.

16. $\mathscr{L}\{t^3 - te^t + e^{4t} \cos t\}$.

17. $\mathscr{L}\{e^{3t} \sin 6t - t^3 + e^t\}$.

18. $\mathscr{L}\{t^4 - t^2 - t + \sin \sqrt{2}t\}$.

19. $\mathscr{L}\{e^{-2t} \cos \sqrt{3}t - t^2 e^{-2t}\}$.

20. $\mathscr{L}\{t^4 e^{5t} - e^t \cos \sqrt{7}t\}$.

In Problems 21 through 28 determine whether $f(t)$ is continuous, piecewise continuous, or neither on $[0, 10]$ and sketch the graph of $f(t)$.

21. $f(t) = \begin{cases} 0, & 0 \le t < 2, \\ t, & 2 \le t \le 10. \end{cases}$

22. $f(t) = \begin{cases} 1, & 0 \le t \le 1, \\ (t-2)^2, & 1 < t \le 10. \end{cases}$

23. $f(t) = \begin{cases} 1, & 0 \le t < 1, \\ t-1, & 1 < t < 3, \\ t^2 - 4, & 3 < t \le 10. \end{cases}$

24. $f(t) = \dfrac{t^2 - 3t + 2}{t^2 - 4}$.

25. $f(t) = \dfrac{t^2 - t - 20}{t^2 + 7t + 10}$.

26. $f(t) = \dfrac{t}{t^2 - 1}$.

27. $f(t) = \begin{cases} 1/t, & 0 < t < 1, \\ 1, & 1 \le t \le 2, \\ 1-t, & 2 < t \le 10. \end{cases}$

28. $f(t) = \begin{cases} \dfrac{\sin t}{t}, & t \ne 0, \\ 1, & t = 0. \end{cases}$

29. Which of the following functions are of exponential order?

(a) $t^3 \sin t$.

(b) $100e^{49t}$.

(c) e^{t^3}.

(d) $t \ln t$.

(e) $\cosh(t^2)$.

(f) $\dfrac{1}{t^2 + 1}$.

(g) $\sin(t^2) + t^4 e^{6t}$.

(h) $3 - e^{t^2} + \cos 4t$.

(i) $\exp\{t^2/(t+1)\}$.

(j) $\sin(e^{t^2}) + e^{\sin t}$.

30. For the transforms $F(s)$ in Table 7.1, what can be said about $\lim_{s \to \infty} F(s)$?

7.3 Properties of the Laplace Transform

In the previous section we defined the Laplace transform of a function $f(t)$ as

(1) $$\mathscr{L}\{f\}(s) := \int_0^\infty e^{-st} f(t)\, dt.$$

Using this definition to get an explicit expression for $\mathscr{L}\{f\}$ requires the evaluation of the improper integral in (1)—frequently a tedious task! We have already seen how the linearity property of the transform can help relieve this burden. In this section we discuss some further properties of the Laplace transform that simplify its computation. These new properties will also enable us to use the Laplace transform to solve initial value problems.

TRANSLATION PROPERTY OF TRANSFORM

Theorem 3. If the Laplace transform $\mathscr{L}\{f\}(s) = F(s)$ exists for $s > \alpha$, then

(2) $\qquad \mathscr{L}\{e^{at}f(t)\}(s) = F(s - a)$

for $s > \alpha + a$.

Handwritten annotations in right margin:

(9.) $f(t) = \begin{cases} 0, & 0 < t < 2 \\ t, & 2 < t \end{cases}$

$\mathscr{L}\{0\} = \int_0^2 e^{-st}(0)\cdot dt = 0$

because $\int_a^b 0\, dx = c\big|_a^b = c - c = 0$

$\mathscr{L}\{t\} = \int_2^t e^{-st}(t)\, dt = t e^{-st} dt$ $\qquad t e^{-st}$

$\begin{array}{c|c} t & e^{-st} \\ 0 & t - \frac{1}{s}e^{-st} \\ 1 & -\frac{1}{s^2}e^{-st} \end{array}$

$= -\frac{1}{s}t e^{-st} - \frac{1}{s^2}e^{-st}\big|_2^t$

$= \left[-\frac{1}{s}t e^{-st} - \frac{1}{s^2}e^{-st}\right] - \left[-\frac{1}{s}2e^{-2s} - \frac{1}{s^2}e^{-2s}\right]$

$= \frac{1}{s}2e^{-2s} + \frac{1}{s^2}e^{-2s}$

Proof We simply compute

$$\mathscr{L}\{e^{at}f(t)\}(s) = \int_0^\infty e^{-st}e^{at}f(t)\, dt$$

$$= \int_0^\infty e^{-(s-a)t}f(t)\, dt$$

$$= F(s - a). \quad \blacksquare\blacksquare\blacksquare$$

Theorem 3 illustrates the effect that multiplying a function $f(t)$ by e^{at} has on the Laplace transform.

$e^{-2s}\left(\dfrac{2s+1}{s^2}\right), \quad s > 0$

▶ **Example 1** Determine the Laplace transform of $e^{at}\sin bt$.

Handwritten: (11) $f(t) = \begin{cases} e^{2t}, & 0 < t < 3 \\ 1, & 3 < t \end{cases}$

Solution In Example 3 in Section 7.2 we found that

Handwritten:
$F(s) = \int_0^\infty e^{-st} f(t)\, dt$

$= \int_0^3 e^{-st}(e^{2t})\, dt + \int_3^\infty e^{-st}\cdot 1\, dt$

$= \lim_{N\to\infty}\int_0^\infty e^{-(s-2)t}\, dt + 1\int_3^\infty e^{-st}\, dt$

$= \dfrac{e^{-3(s-2)}}{s-2} - \dfrac{e^{-(s-2)N}}{s-2} + \dfrac{1}{s} - \dfrac{e^{-3s}}{s}$

$$\mathscr{L}\{\sin bt\}(s) = F(s) = \frac{b}{s^2 + b^2}.$$

Handwritten: $= \dfrac{1}{s} - \dfrac{e^{-3s}}{s} + \dfrac{e^{-3(s-2)}}{s-2}$

Thus, by the translation property of $F(s)$, we have

$$\mathscr{L}\{e^{at}\sin bt\}(s) = F(s - a) = \frac{b}{(s-a)^2 + b^2}. \quad ◀$$

Handwritten: $= \dfrac{1}{s} - \dfrac{e^{-3s}}{s} + \dfrac{e^{-3s+6}}{s-2}$ for $s > 2$

LAPLACE TRANSFORM OF THE DERIVATIVE

Theorem 4. Let $f(t)$ be continuous on $[0, \infty)$ and $f'(t)$ be piecewise continuous on $[0, \infty)$, with both of exponential order α. Then, for $s > \alpha$,

(3) $\qquad \mathscr{L}\{f'\}(s) = s\mathscr{L}\{f\}(s) - f(0).$

Proof Since $\mathscr{L}\{f'\}$ exists, we can use integration by parts (with $u = e^{-st}$ and $dv = f'(t)\,dt$) to obtain

(4)
$$\mathscr{L}\{f'\}(s) = \int_0^\infty e^{-st}f'(t)\,dt = \lim_{N \to \infty} \int_0^N e^{-st}f'(t)\,dt$$

$$= \lim_{N \to \infty} \left[e^{-st}f(t) \Big|_0^N + s \int_0^N e^{-st}f(t)\,dt \right]$$

$$= \lim_{N \to \infty} e^{-sN}f(N) - f(0) + s \lim_{N \to \infty} \int_0^N e^{-st}f(t)\,dt$$

$$= \lim_{N \to \infty} e^{-sN}f(N) - f(0) + s\mathscr{L}\{f\}(s).$$

To evaluate $\lim_{N \to \infty} e^{-sN}f(N)$, we observe that since $f(t)$ is of exponential order α, there exists a constant M such that for N large,

$$\left| e^{-sN}f(N) \right| \le e^{-sN}Me^{\alpha N} = Me^{-(s-\alpha)N}$$

Hence, for $s > \alpha$,

$$\lim_{N \to \infty} \left| e^{-sN}f(N) \right| \le \lim_{N \to \infty} Me^{-(s-\alpha)N} = 0,$$

and so

$$\lim_{N \to \infty} e^{-sN}f(N) = 0$$

for $s > \alpha$. Equation (4) now reduces to

$$\mathscr{L}\{f'\}(s) = s\mathscr{L}\{f\}(s) - f(0). \quad \blacksquare\blacksquare\blacksquare$$

Using induction, we can extend the last theorem to higher order derivatives of $f(t)$. For example,

$$\mathscr{L}\{f''\}(s) = s\mathscr{L}\{f'\}(s) - f'(0)$$
$$= s\{ s\mathscr{L}\{f\}(s) - f(0) \} - f'(0),$$

which simplifies to

(5)
$$\mathscr{L}\{f''\}(s) = s^2\mathscr{L}\{f\}(s) - sf(0) - f'(0).$$

In general we obtain the following result.

LAPLACE TRANSFORM OF HIGHER ORDER DERIVATIVES

Theorem 5. Let $f(t)$, $f'(t)$, ..., $f^{(n-1)}(t)$ be continuous on $[0, \infty)$ and $f^{(n)}(t)$ be piecewise continuous on $[0, \infty)$, with all these functions of exponential order α. Then, for $s > \alpha$,

(6) $\qquad \mathcal{L}\{f^{(n)}\}(s) = s^n \mathcal{L}\{f\}(s) - s^{n-1}f(0) - s^{n-2}f'(0) - \cdots - f^{(n-1)}(0).$

The last two theorems shed light on the reason why the Laplace transform is such a useful tool in solving initial value problems. Roughly speaking, they tell us that by using the Laplace transform we can replace "differentiation with respect to t" with "multiplication by s," thereby converting a differential equation into an algebraic one. This idea is explored in Section 7.5. For now, we show how Theorem 4 can be helpful in computing a Laplace transform.

▶ **Example 2** Using the fact that

$$\mathcal{L}\{\sin bt\}(s) = \frac{b}{s^2 + b^2},$$

determine $\mathcal{L}\{\cos bt\}$.

Solution Let $f(t) = \cos bt$. Then $f(0) = 1$ and $f'(t) = -b \sin bt$. Substituting into equation (3), we have

$$\mathcal{L}\{f'\}(s) = s\mathcal{L}\{f\}(s) - f(0),$$
$$\mathcal{L}\{-b \sin bt\}(s) = s\mathcal{L}\{\cos bt\}(s) - 1,$$
$$(-b)\frac{b}{s^2 + b^2} = s\mathcal{L}\{\cos bt\}(s) - 1.$$

Solving the last equation for $\mathcal{L}\{\cos bt\}(s)$ yields

$$\mathcal{L}\{\cos bt\}(s) = \frac{1}{s}\left[1 - \frac{b^2}{s^2 + b^2}\right] = \frac{s}{s^2 + b^2}. \quad ◀$$

Another question arises concerning the Laplace transform: If $F(s)$ is the Laplace transform of $f(t)$, is $F'(s)$ also a Laplace transform of some function of t? The answer is yes:

$$F'(s) = \mathcal{L}\{-tf(t)\}(s).$$

In fact, the following more general assertion holds.

DERIVATIVES OF THE LAPLACE TRANSFORM

Theorem 6.   Let $F(s) = \mathscr{L}\{f\}(s)$ and assume that $f(t)$ is piecewise continuous on $[0, \infty)$ and of exponential order α. Then, for $s > \alpha$,

$$(7) \qquad \mathscr{L}\{t^n f(t)\}(s) = (-1)^n \frac{d^n F}{ds^n}(s).$$

Proof   Consider the identity

$$\frac{dF}{ds}(s) = \frac{d}{ds} \int_0^\infty e^{-st} f(t)\, dt.$$

Because of the assumptions on $f(t)$, we can apply a theorem from advanced calculus (sometimes called **Leibniz's rule**) to interchange the order of integration and differentiation:

$$\frac{dF}{ds}(s) = \int_0^\infty \frac{d}{ds}(e^{-st}) f(t)\, dt$$

$$= -\int_0^\infty e^{-st} t f(t)\, dt = -\mathscr{L}\{t f(t)\}(s).$$

Thus

$$\mathscr{L}\{t f(t)\}(s) = (-1)\frac{dF}{ds}(s).$$

The general result (7) now follows by induction on n. ∎

A consequence of the above theorem is that if $f(t)$ is piecewise continuous and of exponential order, then its transform $F(s)$ has derivatives of all orders.

▶ *Example 3*   Determine $\mathscr{L}\{t \sin bt\}$.

Solution   We already know that

$$\mathscr{L}\{\sin bt\}(s) = F(s) = \frac{b}{s^2 + b^2}.$$

Differentiating $F(s)$, we obtain

$$\frac{dF}{ds}(s) = \frac{-2bs}{(s^2 + b^2)^2}.$$

Hence, using formula (7), we have

$$\mathscr{L}\{t \sin bt\}(s) = -\frac{dF}{ds}(s) = \frac{2bs}{(s^2 + b^2)^2}. \quad \blacktriangleleft$$

For easy reference, we have listed in Table 7.2 some of the basic properties of the Laplace transform.

TABLE 7.2 PROPERTIES OF LAPLACE TRANSFORMS

1. $\mathscr{L}\{f + g\} = \mathscr{L}\{f\} + \mathscr{L}\{g\}$.
2. $\mathscr{L}\{cf\} = c\mathscr{L}\{f\}$ for any constant c.
3. $\mathscr{L}\{e^{at}f(t)\}(s) = \mathscr{L}\{f\}(s - a)$.
4. $\mathscr{L}\{f'\}(s) = s\mathscr{L}\{f\}(s) - f(0)$.
5. $\mathscr{L}\{f''\}(s) = s^2\mathscr{L}\{f\}(s) - sf(0) - f'(0)$.
6. $\mathscr{L}\{f^{(n)}\}(s) = s^n\mathscr{L}\{f\}(s) - s^{n-1}f(0) - s^{n-2}f'(0) - \cdots - f^{(n-1)}(0)$.

7. $\mathscr{L}\{t^n f(t)\}(s) = (-1)^n \dfrac{d^n}{ds^n}(\mathscr{L}\{f\}(s))$.

EXERCISES 7.3

In Problems 1 through 20 determine the Laplace transform of the given function using Table 7.1, page 335, and the properties of the transform given in Table 7.2. [Hint: In Problems 12 through 20 use an appropriate trigonometric identity.]

1. $3t^2 - e^{2t}$.

2. $t^2 + e^t \sin 2t$.

3. $e^{-t}\cos 3t + e^{6t} - 1$.

4. $3t^4 - 2t^2 + 1$.

5. $e^{-2t}\sin 2t + e^{3t}t^2$.

6. $2t^2 e^{-t} - t + \cos 4t$.

7. $(t - 1)^4$.

8. $(1 + e^{-t})^2$.

9. $te^{2t}\cos 5t$.

10. $e^{-t}t \sin 2t$.

11. $\sinh bt$.

12. $\sin 3t \cos 3t$.

13. $\sin^2 t$.

14. $e^{7t}\sin^2 t$.

15. $\cos^3 t$.

16. $t \sin^2 t$.

17. $\sin 2t \sin 5t$.

18. $t \sin 2t \sin 5t$.

19. $\cos nt \sin mt$, $m \neq n$.

20. $\cos nt \cos mt$, $m \neq n$.

21. Given that $\mathscr{L}\{\cos bt\}(s) = s/(s^2 + b^2)$, use the translation property to compute $\mathscr{L}\{e^{at}\cos bt\}$.

22. Starting with the transform $\mathscr{L}\{1\}(s) = 1/s$, use formula (7) for the derivatives of the Laplace transform to show that $\mathscr{L}\{t^n\}(s) = n!/s^{n+1}$.

23. Use Theorem 4 on the Laplace transform of the derivative of $f(t)$ to determine $\mathscr{L}\{\cos^2 t\}$. Verify your answer by using the half-angle formula to derive $\mathscr{L}\{\cos^2 t\}$.

24. Show that $\mathscr{L}\{e^{at}t^n\}(s) = n!/(s-a)^{n+1}$ in two ways:

    (a) using the translation property for $F(s)$ and (b) using formula (7) for the derivatives of the Laplace transform.

25. Use formula (7) to help determine:

    (a) $\mathscr{L}\{t \cos bt\}$.   (b) $\mathscr{L}\{t^2 \cos bt\}$.

26. Let $f(t)$ be piecewise continuous on $[0, \infty)$ and of exponential order.

    (a) Show that there exist constants K and α such that

    $$|f(t)| \le Ke^{\alpha t} \quad \text{for all } t \ge 0.$$

    (b) By using the definition of the transform and estimating the integral with the help of part (a), prove that

    $$\lim_{s \to \infty} \mathscr{L}\{f\}(s) = 0.$$

27. Let $f(t)$ be piecewise continuous on $[0, \infty)$ and of exponential order α and assume that $\lim_{t \to 0^+} \dfrac{f(t)}{t}$ exists. Show that

    $$\mathscr{L}\left\{\frac{f(t)}{t}\right\}(s) = \int_s^\infty F(u)\,du,$$

    where $F(s) = \mathscr{L}\{f\}(s)$. [Hint: Use formula (7) for the derivative of the Laplace transform and the result of Problem 26.]

28. The **initial-value theorem** for Laplace transforms states that if $f(t)$ is continuous on $[0, \infty)$, $f'(t)$ is piecewise continuous on $[0, \infty)$, and both are of exponential order α, then

    $$\lim_{s \to \infty} sF(s) = f(0),$$

    where $F(s) = \mathscr{L}\{f\}(s)$. Verify this formula for $f(t) = e^{at}\sin bt$ and $f(t) = e^{at}\cos bt$.

29. The **transfer function** of a linear system is defined as the ratio of the Laplace transform of the output function $y(t)$ to the Laplace transform of the input function $g(t)$, assuming that all initial conditions are zero. If a linear system is governed by the differential equation

    $$y''(t) + 6y'(t) + 10y(t) = g(t), \qquad t > 0,$$

use the linearity property of the Laplace transform and Theorem 5 on the Laplace transform of higher order derivatives to determine the transfer function $H(s) = Y(s)/G(s)$ for this system.

30. Find the transfer function, as defined in Problem 29, for the linear system governed by

$$y''(t) + 5y'(t) + 6y(t) = g(t), \qquad t > 0.$$

7.4 Inverse Laplace Transform

In Section 7.2 we defined the Laplace transform as an integral operator that maps a function $f(t)$ into a function $F(s)$. In this section we consider the problem of finding the function $f(t)$ when we are given the transform $F(s)$. That is, we seek an **inverse mapping** for the Laplace transform.

To see the usefulness of such an inverse, let's consider the simple initial value problem

(1) $\qquad y'' - y = -t; \qquad y(0) = 0, \qquad y'(0) = 1.$

If we take the transform of both sides of equation (1) and use the linearity property of the transform, we find

(2) $\qquad \mathscr{L}\{y''\}(s) - Y(s) = -\dfrac{1}{s^2},$

where $Y(s) := \mathscr{L}\{y\}(s)$. Since we know the initial values of the solution $y(t)$, we can use Theorem 5 on the Laplace transform of higher order derivatives to express

(3) $\qquad \mathscr{L}\{y''\}(s) = s^2 Y(s) - sy(0) - y'(0) = s^2 Y(s) - 1.$

Substituting this expression into (2) yields

(4) $\qquad s^2 Y(s) - 1 - Y(s) = -\dfrac{1}{s^2}.$

Solving the algebraic equation (4) for $Y(s)$ gives

(5) $\qquad Y(s) = \dfrac{1 - \left(\dfrac{1}{s^2}\right)}{s^2 - 1} = \dfrac{s^2 - 1}{s^2(s^2 - 1)} = \dfrac{1}{s^2}.$

We now recall that $\mathscr{L}\{t\}(s) = 1/s^2$, and since $Y(s) = \mathscr{L}\{y\}(s)$, we have

$$\mathscr{L}\{y\}(s) = 1/s^2 = \mathscr{L}\{t\}(s).$$

It therefore seems reasonable to conclude that $y(t) = t$ is the solution to the initial value problem (1). A quick check confirms this!

Notice that, in the above procedure, a crucial step is to determine $y(t)$ from its Laplace transform $Y(s) = 1/s^2$. As we noted, $y(t) = t$ is such a function, but it is *not* the only function whose Laplace function is $1/s^2$. For example, the transform of

$$g(t) := \begin{cases} t, & t \neq 6, \\ 0, & t = 6 \end{cases}$$

is also $1/s^2$. This is because the transform is an integral, and integrals are not affected by changing a function's values at isolated points. The significant difference between $y(t)$ and $g(t)$ as far as we are concerned is that $y(t)$ is continuous on $[0, \infty)$ while $g(t)$ is not. Naturally, we prefer to work with continuous functions since solutions to differential equations are continuous. Fortunately, it can be shown that if two different functions have the same Laplace transform, only one of them can be continuous.[†] With this in mind we give the following definition.

INVERSE LAPLACE TRANSFORM

Definition 4.   By the **inverse Laplace transform** of $F(s)$ we mean the unique function $f(t)$ that is continuous on $[0, \infty)$ and satisfies

(6) $\mathscr{L}\{f\}(s) = F(s).$

We denote f by $\mathscr{L}^{-1}\{F\}$. In case all functions that satisfy (6) are discontinuous on $[0, \infty)$, we select a piecewise continuous function that satisfies (6) to be $\mathscr{L}^{-1}\{F\}$.

Naturally the Laplace transform tables will be a great help in determining the inverse Laplace transform of a given function $F(s)$.

▶ *Example 1*   Determine $\mathscr{L}^{-1}\{F\}$, where

(a) $F(s) = \dfrac{2}{s^3}.$ (b) $F(s) = \dfrac{3}{s^2 + 9}.$ (c) $F(s) = \dfrac{s - 1}{s^2 - 2s + 5}.$

Solution   To compute $\mathscr{L}^{-1}\{F\}$, we refer to the Laplace transform table on page 335.

(a) $\mathscr{L}^{-1}\left\{\dfrac{2}{s^3}\right\}(t) = \mathscr{L}^{-1}\left\{\dfrac{2!}{s^3}\right\}(t) = t^2.$

[†] For this result and further properties of the Laplace transform and its inverse we refer the reader to *Operational Mathematics*, Third Edition, by R. V. Churchill, McGraw-Hill, New York, 1972.

(b) $\mathscr{L}^{-1}\left\{\dfrac{3}{s^2+9}\right\}(t) = \mathscr{L}^{-1}\left\{\dfrac{3}{s^2+3^2}\right\}(t) = \sin 3t.$

(c) $\mathscr{L}^{-1}\left\{\dfrac{s-1}{s^2-2s+5}\right\}(t) = \mathscr{L}^{-1}\left\{\dfrac{s-1}{(s-1)^2+2^2}\right\}(t) = e^t \cos 2t.$

In part (c) we used the technique of completing the square to rewrite the denominator in a form that we could find in the table. ◄

In practice, we do not always encounter a transform $F(s)$ that exactly corresponds to an entry in the second column of the Laplace transform table. To handle more complicated functions $F(s)$, we use properties of $\mathscr{L}^{-1}$, just as we used properties of $\mathscr{L}$. One such tool is the linearity of the inverse Laplace transform—a property that is inherited from the linearity of the operator $\mathscr{L}$.

LINEARITY OF THE INVERSE TRANSFORM

Theorem 7. Assume that $\mathscr{L}^{-1}\{F_1\}$ and $\mathscr{L}^{-1}\{F_2\}$ exist and are continuous on $[0, \infty)$, and let c be any constant. Then

(7) $\mathscr{L}^{-1}\{F_1 + F_2\} = \mathscr{L}^{-1}\{F_1\} + \mathscr{L}^{-1}\{F_2\},$

(8) $\mathscr{L}^{-1}\{cF_1\} = c\mathscr{L}^{-1}\{F_1\}.$

The proof of Theorem 7 is outlined in Problem 37. We illustrate the usefulness of this theorem in the next example.

► **Example 2** Determine $\mathscr{L}^{-1}\left\{\dfrac{5}{s-6} - \dfrac{6s}{s^2+9} + \dfrac{3}{2s^2+8s+10}\right\}.$

Solution We begin by using the linearity property. Thus

$$\mathscr{L}^{-1}\left\{\dfrac{5}{s-6} - \dfrac{6s}{s^2+9} + \dfrac{3}{2(s^2+4s+5)}\right\}$$

$$= 5\mathscr{L}^{-1}\left\{\dfrac{1}{s-6}\right\} - 6\mathscr{L}^{-1}\left\{\dfrac{s}{s^2+9}\right\} + \dfrac{3}{2}\mathscr{L}^{-1}\left\{\dfrac{1}{s^2+4s+5}\right\}.$$

Referring to the Laplace transform tables, we see that

$$\mathscr{L}^{-1}\left\{\dfrac{1}{s-6}\right\}(t) = e^{6t} \quad \text{and} \quad \mathscr{L}^{-1}\left\{\dfrac{s}{s^2+3^2}\right\}(t) = \cos 3t.$$

This gives us the first two terms. To determine $\mathscr{L}^{-1}\{1/(s^2 + 4s + 5)\}$, we complete the square of the denominator to obtain $s^2 + 4s + 5 = (s + 2)^2 + 1$. We now recognize from the tables that

$$\mathscr{L}^{-1}\left\{\frac{1}{(s + 2)^2 + 1^2}\right\}(t) = e^{-2t} \sin t.$$

Hence

$$\mathscr{L}^{-1}\left\{\frac{5}{s - 6} - \frac{6s}{s^2 + 9} + \frac{3}{2s^2 + 8s + 10}\right\}(t) = 5e^{6t} - 6 \cos 3t + \frac{3e^{-2t}}{2} \sin t. \quad \blacktriangleleft$$

▶ **Example 3**   Determine $\mathscr{L}^{-1}\left\{\dfrac{5}{(s + 2)^4}\right\}$.

Solution   The $(s + 2)^4$ in the denominator suggests that we work with the formula

$$\mathscr{L}^{-1}\left\{\frac{n!}{(s - a)^{n+1}}\right\}(t) = e^{at}t^n.$$

Here we have $a = -2$ and $n = 3$, and so $\mathscr{L}^{-1}\{6/(s + 2)^4\}(t) = e^{-2t}t^3$. Using the linearity property, we find

$$\mathscr{L}^{-1}\left\{\frac{5}{(s + 2)^4}\right\}(t) = \frac{5}{6}\mathscr{L}^{-1}\left\{\frac{3!}{(s + 2)^4}\right\}(t) = \frac{5}{6}e^{-2t}t^3. \quad \blacktriangleleft$$

▶ **Example 4**   Determine $\mathscr{L}^{-1}\left\{\dfrac{3s + 2}{s^2 + 2s + 10}\right\}$.

Solution   By completing the square, the quadratic term in the denominator can be written

$$s^2 + 2s + 10 = s^2 + 2s + 1 + 9 = (s + 1)^2 + 3^2.$$

The form of $F(s)$ now suggests that we use one or both of the formulas

$$\mathscr{L}^{-1}\left\{\frac{s - a}{(s - a)^2 + b^2}\right\}(t) = e^{at} \cos bt,$$

$$\mathscr{L}^{-1}\left\{\frac{b}{(s - a)^2 + b^2}\right\}(t) = e^{at} \sin bt.$$

In this case, $a = -1$ and $b = 3$. The next step is to express

(9) $$\frac{3s + 2}{s^2 + 2s + 10} = A\frac{s + 1}{(s + 1)^2 + 3^2} + B\frac{3}{(s + 1)^2 + 3^2},$$

where A, B are constants to be determined. Multiplying both sides of (9) by $s^2 + 2s + 10$ leaves

$$3s + 2 = A(s + 1) + 3B = As + (A + 3B),$$

which is an identity between two polynomials in s. Equating the coefficients of like terms gives

$$A = 3, \qquad A + 3B = 2,$$

and so $A = 3$ and $B = -\frac{1}{3}$. Finally, from (9) and the linearity property, we find

$$\mathscr{L}^{-1}\left\{\frac{3s + 2}{s^2 + 2s + 10}\right\}(t) = 3\mathscr{L}^{-1}\left\{\frac{s + 1}{(s + 1)^2 + 3^2}\right\}(t) - \frac{1}{3}\mathscr{L}^{-1}\left\{\frac{3}{(s + 1)^2 + 3^2}\right\}(t)$$

$$= 3e^{-t}\cos 3t - \frac{1}{3}e^{-t}\sin 3t. \quad \blacktriangleleft$$

Given the choice of finding the inverse Laplace transform of

$$F_1(s) = \frac{7s^2 + 10s - 1}{s^3 + 3s^2 - s - 3}$$

or of

$$F_2(s) = \frac{2}{s - 1} + \frac{1}{s + 1} + \frac{4}{s + 3},$$

which would you select? No doubt $F_2(s)$ is the easier one. Actually, the two functions $F_1(s)$ and $F_2(s)$ are identical. This can be checked by combining the simple fractions that form $F_2(s)$. Thus, if we are faced with the problem of computing $\mathscr{L}^{-1}$ of a rational function such as $F_1(s)$, we will first express it, as we did $F_2(s)$, as a sum of simple rational functions. This is accomplished by the **method of partial fractions.**

We briefly review this method. Recall from calculus that a rational function of the form $P(s)/Q(s)$, where $P(s)$ and $Q(s)$ are polynomials with the degree of P less than 'the degree of Q, has a partial fraction expansion whose form is based on the linear and quadratic factors of $Q(s)$. (We assume the coefficients of the polynomials to be real numbers.) There are three cases to consider:

1. Nonrepeated linear factors.
2. Repeated linear factors.
3. Quadratic factors.

1. *Nonrepeated Linear Factors*
   If $Q(s)$ can be factored into a product of distinct linear factors,

$$Q(s) = (s - r_1)(s - r_2) \cdots (s - r_n),$$

where the r_i's are all distinct real numbers, then the partial fraction expansion has the form

$$\frac{P(s)}{Q(s)} = \frac{A_1}{s - r_1} + \frac{A_2}{s - r_2} + \cdots + \frac{A_n}{s - r_n},$$

where the A_i's are real numbers. There are various ways of determining the constants $A_1, \ldots, A_n$. In the next example we demonstrate two such methods.

▶ **Example 5**   Determine $\mathscr{L}^{-1}\{F\}$, where

$$F(s) = \frac{7s - 1}{(s + 1)(s + 2)(s - 3)}.$$

Solution   We begin by finding the partial fraction expansion for $F(s)$. Since the denominator consists of three distinct linear factors, the expansion has the form

(10)
$$\frac{7s - 1}{(s + 1)(s + 2)(s - 3)} = \frac{A}{s + 1} + \frac{B}{s + 2} + \frac{C}{s - 3},$$

where A, B, and C are real numbers to be determined.

One procedure that works for all partial fraction expansions is to first multiply the expansion equation by the denominator of the given rational function. This leaves us with two identical polynomials. Equating the coefficients of s^k leads to a system of linear equations that we can solve to determine the unknown constants. In this example we multiply (10) by $(s + 1)(s + 2)(s - 3)$ and find

(11) $7s - 1 = A(s + 2)(s - 3) + B(s + 1)(s - 3) + C(s + 1)(s + 2),$

which reduces to

(12) $7s - 1 = (A + B + C)s^2 + (-A - 2B + 3C)s + (-6A - 3B + 2C).$

Equating the coefficients of s^2, s, and 1 gives the system of linear equations

$$A + B + C = 0,$$

(13) $$-A - 2B + 3C = 7,$$

$$-6A - 3B + 2C = -1.$$

Solving this system yields $A = 2$, $B = -3$, and $C = 1$. Hence

(14)
$$\frac{7s - 1}{(s + 1)(s + 2)(s - 3)} = \frac{2}{s + 1} - \frac{3}{s + 2} + \frac{1}{s - 3}.$$

An alternative method for finding the constants A, B, and C from (11) is to choose three values for s and substitute them into (11) to obtain three linear equations in the three unknowns. If we are careful in our choice of the values for s, the system is easy to solve. In this case, let's take $s = -1$, -2, and 3, the roots of $Q(s)$. Putting $s = -1$ in (11) gives

$$-7 - 1 = A(1)(-4) + B(0) + C(0),$$
$$-8 = -4A.$$

Hence $A = 2$. Next, setting $s = -2$ gives

$$-14 - 1 = A(0) + B(-1)(-5) + C(0),$$
$$-15 = 5B,$$

and so $B = -3$. Finally, letting $s = 3$, we similarly find that $C = 1$. In the case of nonrepeated linear factors the alternative method is easier to use.

Now that we have obtained the partial fraction expansion (14), we use linearity to compute

$$\mathscr{L}^{-1}\left\{\frac{7s - 1}{(s + 1)(s + 2)(s - 3)}\right\}(t) = \mathscr{L}^{-1}\left\{\frac{2}{s + 1} - \frac{3}{s + 2} + \frac{1}{s - 3}\right\}(t)$$
$$= 2\mathscr{L}^{-1}\left\{\frac{1}{s + 1}\right\}(t) - 3\mathscr{L}^{-1}\left\{\frac{1}{s + 2}\right\}(t)$$
$$+ \mathscr{L}^{-1}\left\{\frac{1}{s - 3}\right\}(t)$$
$$= 2e^{-t} - 3e^{-2t} + e^{3t}. \blacktriangleleft$$

2. Repeated Linear Factors

Let $s - r$ be a factor of $Q(s)$ and suppose $(s - r)^m$ is the highest power of $s - r$ that divides $Q(s)$. Then the portion of the partial fraction expansion of $P(s)/Q(s)$ that corresponds to the term $(s - r)^m$ is

(15)
$$\frac{P(s)}{Q(s)} = \frac{A_1}{s - r} + \frac{A_2}{(s - r)^2} + \cdots + \frac{A_m}{(s - r)^m} + \cdots,$$

where the A_i's are real numbers.

▶ ***Example 6***   Determine $\mathscr{L}^{-1}\left\{\dfrac{s^2 + 9s + 2}{(s - 1)^2(s + 3)}\right\}$.

Solution   Since $s - 1$ is a repeated linear factor with multiplicity two and $s + 3$ is a nonrepeated linear factor, the partial fraction expansion has the form

(16)
$$\frac{s^2 + 9s + 2}{(s - 1)^2(s + 3)} = \frac{A}{s - 1} + \frac{B}{(s - 1)^2} + \frac{C}{s + 3}.$$

We begin by multiplying both sides of (16) by $(s - 1)^2(s + 3)$ to obtain

(17)
$$s^2 + 9s + 2 = A(s - 1)(s + 3) + B(s + 3) + C(s - 1)^2.$$

Now observe that when we set $s = 1$ (or $s = -3$), two terms on the right-hand side of (17) vanish, leaving a linear equation that we can solve for B (or C). Setting $s = 1$ in (17) gives

$$1 + 9 + 2 = A(0) + 4B + C(0),$$
$$12 = 4B,$$

and hence $B = 3$. Similarly, setting $s = -3$ in (17) gives

$$9 - 27 + 2 = A(0) + B(0) + 16C,$$
$$-16 = 16C.$$

Thus $C = -1$. Finally, to find A, we pick a different value for s, say $s = 0$. Then, since $B = 3$ and $C = -1$, plugging $s = 0$ into (17) yields

$$2 = -3A + 3B + C = -3A + 9 - 1,$$

so that $A = 2$. Hence

(18)
$$\frac{s^2 + 9s + 2}{(s - 1)^2(s + 3)} = \frac{2}{s - 1} + \frac{3}{(s - 1)^2} - \frac{1}{s + 3}.$$

We could also have determined the constants A, B, and C by first rewriting equation (17) in the form

(19)
$$s^2 + 9s + 2 = (A + C)s^2 + (2A + B - 2C)s + (-3A + 3B + C).$$

Then, equating the corresponding coefficients of s^2, s, and 1 in (19) and solving the resulting system, we again find $A = 2$, $B = 3$, and $C = -1$.

Now that we have derived the partial fraction expansion (18) for the given rational function, we can determine its inverse Laplace transform:

$$\mathcal{L}^{-1}\left\{\frac{s^2 + 9s + 2}{(s-1)^2(s+3)}\right\}(t) = \mathcal{L}^{-1}\left\{\frac{2}{s-1} + \frac{3}{(s-1)^2} - \frac{1}{s+3}\right\}(t)$$

$$= 2\mathcal{L}^{-1}\left\{\frac{1}{s-1}\right\}(t) + 3\mathcal{L}^{-1}\left\{\frac{1}{(s-1)^2}\right\}(t)$$

$$- \mathcal{L}^{-1}\left\{\frac{1}{s+3}\right\}(t)$$

$$= 2e^t + 3te^t - e^{-3t}. \quad \blacktriangleleft$$

3. *Quadratic Factors*

Let $(s - \alpha)^2 + \beta^2$ be a quadratic factor of $Q(s)$ that cannot be reduced to linear factors with real coefficients. Suppose that m is the highest power of $(s - \alpha)^2 + \beta^2$ that divides $Q(s)$. Then the portion of the partial fraction expansion that corresponds to $(s - \alpha)^2 + \beta^2$ is

$$\frac{P(s)}{Q(s)} = \frac{C_1 s + D_1}{(s-\alpha)^2 + \beta^2} + \frac{C_2 s + D_2}{[(s-\alpha)^2 + \beta^2]^2} + \cdots + \frac{C_m s + D_m}{[(s-\alpha)^2 + \beta^2]^m} + \cdots.$$

As we saw in Example 4, it is more convenient to express $C_i s + D_i$ in the form $A_i(s - \alpha) + \beta B_i$ when we look up the inverse Laplace transforms. So let's write the partial fraction expansion in the equivalent form

(20) $$\frac{P(s)}{Q(s)} = \frac{A_1(s - \alpha) + \beta B_1}{(s-\alpha)^2 + \beta^2} + \cdots + \frac{A_m(s - \alpha) + \beta B_m}{[(s-\alpha)^2 + \beta^2]^m} + \cdots.$$

▶ **Example 7** Determine $\mathcal{L}^{-1}\left\{\dfrac{2s^2 + 10s}{(s^2 - 2s + 5)(s + 1)}\right\}$. ✳ DON'T DO THIS WAY

Solution We first observe that the quadratic factor $s^2 - 2s + 5$ is irreducible (check the sign of the discriminant in the quadratic formula). Next we write the quadratic in the form $(s - \alpha)^2 + \beta^2$ by completing the square:

$$s^2 - 2s + 5 = (s - 1)^2 + 2^2.$$

Since $s^2 - 2s + 5$ and $s + 1$ are nonrepeated factors, the partial fraction expansion has the form

(21) $$\frac{2s^2 + 10s}{(s^2 - 2s + 5)(s + 1)} = \frac{A(s - 1) + 2B}{(s - 1)^2 + 2^2} + \frac{C}{s + 1}.$$

When we multiply both sides of (21) by the common denominator, we obtain

(22) $2s^2 + 10s = [A(s - 1) + 2B](s + 1) + C(s^2 - 2s + 5)$.

In equation (22), let's put $s = -1$, 1, and 0. With $s = -1$ we find

$$2 - 10 = [A(-2) + 2B](0) + C(8),$$
$$-8 = 8C,$$

and hence $C = -1$. With $s = 1$ in (22), we obtain

$$2 + 10 = [A(0) + 2B](2) + C(4),$$

and since $C = -1$, the last equation becomes $12 = 4B - 4$. Thus $B = 4$. Finally, setting $s = 0$ in (22) and using $C = -1$ and $B = 4$ gives

$$0 = [A(-1) + 2B](1) + C(5),$$
$$0 = -A + 8 - 5,$$
$$A = 3.$$

Hence $A = 3$, $B = 4$, and $C = -1$, so that

(23) $$\frac{2s^2 + 10s}{(s^2 - 2s + 5)(s + 1)} = \frac{3(s - 1) + 2(4)}{(s - 1)^2 + 2^2} - \frac{1}{s + 1}.$$

With this partial fraction expansion in hand, we can immediately determine the inverse Laplace transform:

$$\mathscr{L}^{-1}\left\{\frac{2s^2 + 10s}{(s^2 - 2s + 5)(s + 1)}\right\}(t) = \mathscr{L}^{-1}\left\{\frac{3(s - 1) + 2(4)}{(s - 1)^2 + 2^2} - \frac{1}{s + 1}\right\}(t)$$

$$= 3\mathscr{L}^{-1}\left\{\frac{s - 1}{(s - 1)^2 + 2^2}\right\}(t)$$

$$+ 4\mathscr{L}^{-1}\left\{\frac{2}{(s - 1)^2 + 2^2}\right\}(t) - \mathscr{L}^{-1}\left\{\frac{1}{s + 1}\right\}(t)$$

$$= 3e^t \cos 2t + 4e^t \sin 2t - e^{-t}. \quad \blacktriangleleft$$

In Section 7.7 we discuss a different method (involving convolutions) for computing inverse transforms, which does not require partial fraction decompositions. Moreover, the convolution method is convenient in the case of a rational function with a repeated quadratic factor in the denominator. Other helpful tools are described in Problems 33–36 and 38–40.

EXERCISES 7.4

In Problems 1 through 10 determine the inverse Laplace transform of the given function.

1. $\dfrac{2}{s^2 + 4}$.

2. $\dfrac{6}{(s-1)^4}$.

3. $\dfrac{s+1}{s^2 + 2s + 10}$.

4. $\dfrac{4}{s^2 + 9}$.

5. $\dfrac{3}{(2s+5)^3}$.

6. $\dfrac{1}{s^2 + 4s + 8}$.

7. $\dfrac{2s + 16}{s^2 + 4s + 13}$.

8. $\dfrac{1}{s^5}$.

9. $\dfrac{s-1}{2s^2 + s + 6}$.

10. $\dfrac{3s - 15}{2s^2 - 4s + 10}$.

In Problems 11 through 20 determine the partial fraction expansion for the given rational function.

11. $\dfrac{-s - 7}{(s+1)(s-2)}$.

12. $\dfrac{s^2 - 26s - 47}{(s-1)(s+2)(s+5)}$.

13. $\dfrac{-2s^2 - 3s - 2}{s(s+1)^2}$.

14. $\dfrac{-8s^2 - 5s + 9}{(s+1)(s-1)(s-2)}$.

15. $\dfrac{-2s^2 + 8s - 14}{(s+1)(s^2 - 2s + 5)}$.

16. $\dfrac{-5s - 36}{(s+2)(s^2 + 9)}$.

17. $\dfrac{3s + 5}{s(s-2)(s+3)}$.

18. $\dfrac{3s^2 + 5s + 3}{s^3(s+1)}$.

19. $\dfrac{1}{(s-3)(s^2 + 2s + 2)}$.

20. $\dfrac{s}{(s-1)(s^2 - 1)}$.

$$(s+1)^2 + 1$$
$$s^2 + 2s + 1 + 1$$
$$s^2 + 2s + 2$$

In Problems 21 through 30 determine $\mathscr{L}^{-1}\{F\}$.

21. $F(s) = \dfrac{s + 11}{(s-1)(s+3)}$.

22. $F(s) = \dfrac{6s^2 - 13s + 2}{s(s-1)(s-6)}$.

23. $F(s) = \dfrac{5s^2 + 34s + 53}{(s+3)^2(s+1)}$.

24. $F(s) = \dfrac{7s^2 - 41s + 84}{(s-1)(s^2 - 4s + 13)}$.

25. $F(s) = \dfrac{7s^2 + 23s + 30}{(s-2)(s^2 + 2s + 5)}$.

26. $F(s) = \dfrac{7s^3 - 2s^2 - 3s + 6}{s^3(s-2)}$.

27. $s^2 F(s) + sF(s) - 6F(s) = \dfrac{s^2 + 4}{s^2 + s}$.

28. $sF(s) + 2F(s) = \dfrac{10s^2 + 12s + 14}{s^2 - 2s + 2}$.

29. $sF(s) - F(s) = \dfrac{2s + 5}{s^2 + 2s + 1}$.

30. $s^2 F(s) - 4F(s) = \dfrac{5}{s+1}$.

31. Compute the Laplace transform of each of the following functions.

(a) $f_1(t) = \begin{cases} 0, & t = 2, \\ t, & t \neq 2. \end{cases}$

(b) $f_2(t) = \begin{cases} 5, & t = 1, \\ 2, & t = 6, \\ t, & t \neq 1, 6. \end{cases}$

(c) $f_3(t) = t$.

Which of the preceding functions is the inverse Laplace transform of $1/s^2$?

32. Compute the Laplace transform of each of the following functions.

(a) $f_1(t) = \begin{cases} t, & t = 1, 2, 3, \ldots, \\ e^t, & t \neq 1, 2, 3, \ldots. \end{cases}$
    (b) $f_2(t) = \begin{cases} e^t, & t \neq 5, 8, \\ 6, & t = 5, \\ 0, & t = 8. \end{cases}$

(c) $f_3(t) = e^t.$

Which of the preceding functions is the inverse Laplace transform of $1/(s-1)$?

Theorem 6 in Section 7.3 can be expressed in terms of the inverse Laplace transform as

$$\mathcal{L}^{-1}\left\{\frac{d^n F}{ds^n}\right\}(t) = (-t)^n f(t),$$

where $f = \mathcal{L}^{-1}\{F\}$. Use this equation in Problems 33 through 36 to compute $\mathcal{L}^{-1}\{F\}$.

33. $F(s) = \ln\left(\dfrac{s+2}{s-5}\right).$
    34. $F(s) = \ln\left(\dfrac{s-4}{s-3}\right).$

35. $F(s) = \ln\left(\dfrac{s^2+9}{s^2+1}\right).$
    36. $F(s) = \arctan(1/s).$

37. Prove Theorem 7 on the linearity of the inverse transform. [Hint: Show that the right-hand side of equation (7) is a continuous function on $[0, \infty)$ whose Laplace transform is $F_1(s) + F_2(s)$.]

38. Residue Computation. Let $P(s)/Q(s)$ be a rational function with deg $P <$ deg Q and suppose that $s - r$ is a nonrepeated linear factor of $Q(s)$. Prove that the portion of the partial fraction expansion of $P(s)/Q(s)$ corresponding to $s - r$ is

$$\frac{P(s)}{Q(s)} = \frac{A}{s-r} + \cdots,$$

where A (called the **residue**) is given by the formula

$$A = \lim_{s \to r} \frac{(s-r)P(s)}{Q(s)}.$$

39. Use the residue computation formula derived in Problem 38 to determine quickly the partial fraction expansion for

$$F(s) = \frac{2s+1}{s(s-1)(s+2)}.$$

40. Heaviside's Expansion Formula.[†]   Let $P(s)$ and $Q(s)$ be polynomials with the degree of $P(s)$ less than the degree of $Q(s)$. Let

$$Q(s) = (s - r_1)(s - r_2) \cdots (s - r_n),$$

where the r_i's are distinct real numbers. Show that

$$\mathscr{L}^{-1}\left\{\frac{P}{Q}\right\}(t) = \sum_{i=1}^{n} \frac{P(r_i)}{Q'(r_i)} e^{r_i t}.$$

41. Use Heaviside's expansion formula derived in Problem 40 to determine the inverse Laplace transform of

$$F(s) = \frac{3s^2 - 16s + 5}{(s + 1)(s - 3)(s - 2)}.$$

7.5 *Solving Initial Value Problems*

Our goal is to show how Laplace transforms can be used to solve initial value problems for linear differential equations. Recall that we have already studied ways of solving such initial value problems in Chapter 4. These previous methods required that we first find a *general solution* of the differential equation and then use the initial conditions to determine the desired solution. As we shall see, the method of Laplace transforms leads to the solution of the initial value problem *without* first finding a general solution.

Other advantages to the transform method are worth noting. For example, the technique can easily handle equations involving discontinuous forcing functions (see Section 7.6). Furthermore, the method can be used for certain linear differential equations with variable coefficients, a special class of integral equations, systems of differential equations, and partial differential equations.

METHOD OF LAPLACE TRANSFORMS

To solve an initial value problem:

(a) Take the Laplace transform of both sides of the equation.

(b) Use the properties of the Laplace transform and the initial conditions to obtain an equation for the Laplace transform of the solution and then solve this equation for the transform.

(c) Determine the inverse Laplace transform of the solution by looking it up in a table or by using a suitable method (such as partial fractions) in combination with the table.

[†] *Historical Footnote:* This formula played an important role in the "operational solution" to ordinary differential equations developed by Oliver Heaviside in the 1890s.

In step (a) we are tacitly assuming that the solution is piecewise continuous on $[0, \infty)$ and of exponential order. Once we have obtained the inverse Laplace transform in step (c), we can verify that these tacit assumptions are satisfied.

▶ **Example 1**   Solve the initial value problem

(1) $y'' - 2y' + 5y = -8e^{-t};$ $y(0) = 2,$ $y'(0) = 12.$

Solution   The differential equation in (1) is an identity between two functions of t. Hence equality holds for the Laplace transforms of these functions:

(2) $\mathcal{L}\{y'' - 2y' + 5y\} = \mathcal{L}\{-8e^{-t}\}.$

Using the linearity property of $\mathcal{L}$ and the previously computed transform of the exponential function, we can write

(3) $\mathcal{L}\{y''\}(s) - 2\mathcal{L}\{y'\}(s) + 5\mathcal{L}\{y\}(s) = \dfrac{-8}{s+1}.$

Now let $Y(s) := \mathcal{L}\{y\}(s)$. From the formulas for the Laplace transform of higher order derivatives (see Section 7.3) and the initial conditions in (1), we find

$$\mathcal{L}\{y'\}(s) = sY(s) - y(0) = sY(s) - 2,$$
$$\mathcal{L}\{y''\}(s) = s^2 Y(s) - sy(0) - y'(0) = s^2 Y(s) - 2s - 12.$$

Substituting these expressions into (3) and solving for $Y(s)$ yields

$$[s^2 Y(s) - 2s - 12] - 2[sY(s) - 2] + 5Y(s) = \frac{-8}{s+1},$$

$$(s^2 - 2s + 5)Y(s) = 2s + 8 - \frac{8}{s+1},$$

$$(s^2 - 2s + 5)Y(s) = \frac{2s^2 + 10s}{s+1},$$

(4) $Y(s) = \dfrac{2s^2 + 10s}{(s^2 - 2s + 5)(s + 1)}.$

Our remaining task is to compute the inverse transform of the rational function $Y(s)$. This was done in Example 7 of Section 7.4, where, using a partial fraction expansion, we found

(5) $y(t) = 3e^t \cos 2t + 4e^t \sin 2t - e^{-t},$

which is the solution to the initial value problem (1). ◀

As a quick check on the accuracy of our computations, the reader is advised to verify that the computed solution satisfies the given initial conditions.

▶ *Example 2*   Solve the initial value problem

(6) $y'' + 4y' - 5y = te^t;$ $y(0) = 1,$ $y'(0) = 0.$

Solution   Let $Y(s) = \mathscr{L}\{y\}(s)$. Taking the Laplace transform of both sides of the differential equation in (6) gives

(7) $\mathscr{L}\{y''\}(s) + 4\mathscr{L}\{y'\}(s) - 5Y(s) = \dfrac{1}{(s-1)^2}.$

Using the initial conditions, we can express $\mathscr{L}\{y'\}(s)$ and $\mathscr{L}\{y''\}(s)$ in terms of $Y(s)$. That is,

$$\mathscr{L}\{y'\}(s) = sY(s) - y(0) = sY(s) - 1,$$
$$\mathscr{L}\{y''\}(s) = s^2 Y(s) - sy(0) - y'(0) = s^2 Y(s) - s.$$

Substituting back into (7) and solving for $Y(s)$ gives

$$[s^2 Y(s) - s] + 4[sY(s) - 1] - 5Y(s) = \frac{1}{(s-1)^2},$$

$$(s^2 + 4s - 5)Y(s) = s + 4 + \frac{1}{(s-1)^2},$$

$$(s+5)(s-1)Y(s) = \frac{s^3 + 2s^2 - 7s + 5}{(s-1)^2},$$

(8) $Y(s) = \dfrac{s^3 + 2s^2 - 7s + 5}{(s+5)(s-1)^3}.$

The partial fraction expansion for $Y(s)$ has the form

(9) $\dfrac{s^3 + 2s^2 - 7s + 5}{(s+5)(s-1)^3} = \dfrac{A}{s+5} + \dfrac{B}{s-1} + \dfrac{C}{(s-1)^2} + \dfrac{D}{(s-1)^3}.$

Solving for the numerators, we ultimately obtain $A = \frac{35}{216}$, $B = \frac{181}{216}$, $C = -\frac{1}{36}$, and $D = \frac{1}{6}$. Substituting these values into (9) gives

(10) $Y(s) = \dfrac{35}{216}\left(\dfrac{1}{s+5}\right) + \dfrac{181}{216}\left(\dfrac{1}{s-1}\right) - \dfrac{1}{36}\left(\dfrac{1}{(s-1)^2}\right) + \dfrac{1}{12}\left(\dfrac{2}{(s-1)^3}\right),$

where we have written $D = \frac{1}{6} = (\frac{1}{12})2$ to facilitate the final step of taking the inverse transform. From the tables, we now obtain

(11) $y(t) = \dfrac{35}{216} e^{-5t} + \dfrac{181}{216} e^t - \dfrac{1}{36} te^t + \dfrac{1}{12} t^2 e^t$

as the solution to the initial value problem (6). ◄

► **Example 3**   Solve the initial value problem

(12) $w''(t) - 2w'(t) + 5w(t) = -8e^{\pi - t}; \qquad w(\pi) = 2, \qquad w'(\pi) = 12.$

Solution   To use the method of Laplace transforms, we first move the initial conditions to $t = 0$. This can be done by setting $y(t) := w(t + \pi)$. Then

(13) $y'(t) = w'(t + \pi), \qquad y''(t) = w''(t + \pi).$

Replacing t by $t + \pi$ in the differential equation in (12), we have

(14) $w''(t + \pi) - 2w'(t + \pi) + 5w(t + \pi) = -8e^{\pi - (t + \pi)} = -8e^{-t}.$

Substituting $y(t) = w(t + \pi)$ in (14), the initial value problem in (12) becomes

(15) $y''(t) - 2y'(t) + 5y(t) = -8e^{-t}; \qquad y(0) = 2, \qquad y'(0) = 12.$

Since the initial conditions in (15) are given at the origin, the Laplace transform method is now applicable. In fact, we carried out the procedure in Example 1, where we found

(16) $y(t) = 3e^t \cos 2t + 4e^t \sin 2t - e^{-t}.$

Since $w(t + \pi) = y(t)$, then $w(t) = y(t - \pi)$. Hence, replacing t by $t - \pi$ in (16) gives

(17) $w(t) = y(t - \pi) = 3e^{t - \pi} \cos 2(t - \pi) + 4e^{t - \pi} \sin 2(t - \pi) - e^{-(t - \pi)}$

$= 3e^{t - \pi} \cos 2t + 4e^{t - \pi} \sin 2t - e^{\pi - t}.$ ◄

Several important equations in mathematical physics involve linear differential equations with *variable* coefficients (see Section 8.9 for examples). Some of these equations can be solved with the help of Theorem 6, in which we proved that

(18) $\mathcal{L}\{t^n f(t)\}(s) = (-1)^n \dfrac{d^n F}{ds^n}(s).$

If we let $n = 1$ and $f(t) = y'(t)$, we find

$$\mathscr{L}\{ty'(t)\}(s) = -\frac{d}{ds}\mathscr{L}\{y'\}(s)$$

$$= -\frac{d}{ds}\left[sY(s) - y(0)\right] = -sY'(s) - Y(s).$$

Similarly, with $n = 1$ and $f(t) = y''(t)$, we obtain from (18)

$$\mathscr{L}\{ty''(t)\}(s) = -\frac{d}{ds}\mathscr{L}\{y''\}(s)$$

$$= -\frac{d}{ds}\left[s^2Y(s) - sy(0) - y'(0)\right]$$

$$= -s^2Y'(s) - 2sY(s) + y(0).$$

In fact, if we are given a linear differential equation in $y(t)$ whose coefficients are *polynomials* in t, then the method of Laplace transforms will convert the given equation into a linear differential equation in $Y(s)$ whose coefficients are polynomials in s. Moreover, if the co-efficients of the given equation are linear polynomials in t, then (regardless of the order of the given equation) the differential equation for $Y(s)$ is just a linear *first order* equation. Since we know how to solve this first order equation, the only serious obstacle we may encounter is obtaining the inverse Laplace transform of $Y(s)$. This problem may be insurmountable since the solution $y(t)$ may *not* have a Laplace transform.

In illustrating the technique, we make use of the following fact. *If $f(t)$ is piecewise continuous on* $[0, \infty)$ *and of exponential order, then*

(19) $$\lim_{s \to \infty} \mathscr{L}\{f\}(s) = 0.$$

(The reader may have already guessed this from the entries in Table 7.1, page 335.) An outline of the proof of (19) is given in Exercise 7.3, Problem 26.

▶ **Example 4** Solve the initial value problem

(20) $$y'' + 2ty' - 4y = 1, \qquad y(0) = y'(0) = 0.$$

Solution Let $Y(s) = \mathscr{L}\{y\}(s)$ and take the Laplace transform of both sides of the equation in (20):

(21) $$\mathscr{L}\{y''\}(s) + 2\mathscr{L}\{ty'(t)\}(s) - 4Y(s) = \frac{1}{s}.$$

Using the initial conditions, we find

$$\mathscr{L}\{y''\}(s) = s^2Y(s) - sy(0) - y'(0) = s^2Y(s)$$

and

$$\mathcal{L}\{ty'(t)\}(s) = -\frac{d}{ds}\mathcal{L}\{y'\}(s)$$

$$= -\frac{d}{ds}[sY(s) - y(0)] = -sY'(s) - Y(s).$$

Substituting these expressions into (21) gives

$$s^2Y(s) + 2[-sY'(s) - Y(s)] - 4Y(s) = \frac{1}{s},$$

$$-2sY'(s) + (s^2 - 6)Y(s) = \frac{1}{s},$$

(22) $$Y'(s) + \left(\frac{3}{s} - \frac{s}{2}\right)Y(s) = \frac{-1}{2s^2}.$$

Equation (22) is a linear first order equation and has the integrating factor

$$\mu(s) = e^{\int(3/s - s/2)\,ds} = e^{\ln s^3 - s^2/4} = s^3 e^{-s^2/4}$$

(see Section 2.4). Multiplying (22) by $\mu(s)$, we obtain

$$\frac{d}{ds}\{\mu(s)Y(s)\} = \frac{d}{ds}\{s^3 e^{-s^2/4}Y(s)\} = -\frac{s}{2}e^{-s^2/4}.$$

Integrating and solving for $Y(s)$ yields

$$s^3 e^{-s^2/4}Y(s) = -\int \frac{s}{2}e^{-s^2/4}\,ds = e^{-s^2/4} + C,$$

(23) $$Y(s) = \frac{1}{s^3} + C\frac{e^{s^2/4}}{s^3}.$$

Now if $Y(s)$ is the Laplace transform of a piecewise continuous function of exponential order, then it follows from equation (19) that

$$\lim_{s\to\infty} Y(s) = 0.$$

For this to occur, the constant C in equation (23) must be zero. Hence $Y(s) = 1/s^3$, and taking the inverse transform gives $y(t) = t^2/2$. We can easily verify that $y(t) = t^2/2$ is the solution to the given initial value problem by substituting it into (20). ◀

We end this section with an application from **control theory**. Let's consider a servo-mechanism that models an automatic pilot. Such a mechanism applies a torque to the steering control shaft so that a plane or boat will follow a prescribed course. If we let $y(t)$ be the true direction (angle) of the craft at time t and $g(t)$ be the desired direction at time t, then

$$e(t) := y(t) - g(t)$$

denotes the **error** or **deviation** between the desired direction and the true direction.

Let's assume that the servomechanism can measure the error $e(t)$ and feed back to the steering shaft a component of torque that is proportional to $e(t)$ but opposite in sign. Newton's second law, expressed in terms of torques, states that

(moment of inertia) × (angular acceleration) = total torque.

For the servomechanism described, this becomes

(24) $\qquad I y''(t) = -k e(t),$

where I is the moment of inertia of the steering shaft and k is a positive proportionality constant.

▶ **Example 5** Determine the error $e(t)$ fot the automatic pilot if the steering shaft is initially at rest in the zero direction and the desired direction is given by $g(t) = at$, where a is a constant.

Solution Based on the discussion leading to equation (24), a model for the mechanism is given by the initial value problem

(25) $\qquad I y''(t) = -k e(t); \qquad y(0) = 0, \qquad y'(0) = 0,$

where $e(t) = y(t) - g(t) = y(t) - at$. We begin by taking the Laplace transform of both sides of (25):

$$I \mathscr{L}\{y''\}(s) = -k \mathscr{L}\{e\}(s),$$
$$I[s^2 Y(s) - s y(0) - y'(0)] = -k E(s),$$

(26) $\qquad\qquad s^2 I Y(s) = -k E(s),$

where $Y(s) = \mathscr{L}\{y\}(s)$ and $E(s) = \mathscr{L}\{e\}(s)$. Since

$$E(s) = \mathscr{L}\{y(t) - at\}(s) = Y(s) - \mathscr{L}\{at\}(s) = Y(s) - as^{-2},$$

we find from (26) that

$$s^2 I E(s) + aI = -k E(s).$$

Solving this equation for $E(s)$ gives

$$E(s) = -\frac{aI}{s^2 I + k} = \frac{-a}{\sqrt{k/I}} \frac{\sqrt{k/I}}{s^2 + k/I}.$$

Hence, on taking the inverse Laplace transform, we obtain the error

(27) $\qquad e(t) = -\frac{a}{\sqrt{k/I}} \sin \sqrt{k/I}\, t. \blacktriangleleft$

As we can see from equation (27), the automatic pilot will oscillate back and forth about the desired course, always "oversteering" by the factor $a/\sqrt{k/I}$. Clearly we can make the error small by making k large relative to I, but then the term $\sqrt{k/I}$ becomes large, causing the error to oscillate more rapidly. As with vibrations, the oscillations or oversteering can be controlled by introducing a damping torque proportional to $e'(t)$ but opposite in sign (see Problem 40).

EXERCISES 7.5

In Problems 1 through 14 solve the given initial value problem for $y(t)$ using the method of Laplace transforms.

1. $y'' - y' - 2y = 0;$ $\qquad y(0) = -2,$ $\qquad y'(0) = 5.$

2. $y'' - 2y' + 5y = 0;$ $\qquad y(0) = 2,$ $\qquad y'(0) = 4.$

3. $y'' + 6y' + 9y = 0;$ $\qquad y(0) = -1,$ $\qquad y'(0) = 6.$

4. $y'' + 6y' + 5y = 12e^t;$ $\qquad y(0) = -1,$ $\qquad y'(0) = 7.$

5. $y'' + y = t^2 + 2;$ $\qquad y(0) = 1,$ $\qquad y'(0) = -1.$

6. $y'' - 7y' + 10y = 9 \cos t + 7 \sin t;$ $\qquad y(0) = 5,$ $\qquad y'(0) = -4.$

7. $y'' - 4y' + 5y = 4e^{3t};$ $\qquad y(0) = 2,$ $\qquad y'(0) = 7.$

8. $y'' + 4y = 4t^2 - 4t + 10;$ $\qquad y(0) = 0,$ $\qquad y'(0) = 3.$

9. $y'' + 5y' - 6y = 21e^t;$ $\qquad y(0) = -1,$ $\qquad y'(0) = 9.$

10. $y'' - 4y = 4t - 8e^{-2t};$ $\qquad y(0) = 0,$ $\qquad y'(0) = 5.$

11. $y'' - y = t - 2;$ $\qquad y(2) = 3,$ $\qquad y'(2) = 0.$

12. $y'' - 2y' + y = 6t - 2;$ $\qquad y(-1) = 3,$ $\qquad y'(-1) = 7.$

13. $y'' + y = t;$ $\qquad y(\pi) = 0,$ $\qquad y'(\pi) = 0.$

14. $y'' - y' - 2y = -8 \cos t - 2 \sin t;$ $\qquad y(\pi/2) = 1,$ $\qquad y'(\pi/2) = 0.$

In Problems 15 through 24 solve for $Y(s)$, the Laplace transform of the solution $y(t)$ to the given initial value problem.

15. $y'' - 3y' + 2y = \cos t;$ $\qquad y(0) = 0,$ $\qquad y'(0) = -1.$

16. $y'' + y' - y = t^3;$ $\qquad y(0) = 1,$ $\qquad y'(0) = 0.$

17. $y'' + 6y = t^2 - 1;$ $\qquad y(0) = 0,$ $\qquad y'(0) = -1.$

18. $y'' - 2y' - y = e^{2t} - e^t;$ $\qquad y(0) = 1,$ $\qquad y'(0) = 3.$

19. $y'' - 6y' + 5y = te^t$; $y(0) = 2$, $y'(0) = -1$.

20. $y'' + 3y' = t^3$; $y(0) = 0$, $y'(0) = 0$.

21. $y'' - 2y' + y = \cos t - \sin t$; $y(0) = 1$, $y'(0) = 3$.

22. $y'' + 5y' - y = e^t - 1$; $y(0) = 1$, $y'(0) = 1$.

23. $y'' - y = g(t)$; $y(0) = 1$, $y'(0) = 2$,   where $g(t) = \begin{cases} 1, & t < 3, \\ t, & t > 3. \end{cases}$

24. $y'' + 4y = g(t)$; $y(0) = -1$, $y'(0) = 0$,   where $g(t) = \begin{cases} t, & t < 2, \\ 5, & t > 2. \end{cases}$

In Problems 25 through 28 solve the given third order initial value problem for $y(t)$ using the method of Laplace transforms.

25. $y''' - y'' + y' - y = 0$; $y(0) = 1$, $y'(0) = 1$, $y''(0) = 3$.

26. $y''' + 3y'' + 3y' + y = 0$; $y(0) = -4$, $y'(0) = 4$, $y''(0) = -2$.

27. $y''' + 4y'' + y' - 6y = -12$; $y(0) = 1$, $y'(0) = 4$, $y''(0) = -2$.

28. $y''' + y'' + 3y' - 5y = 16e^{-t}$; $y(0) = 0$, $y'(0) = 2$, $y''(0) = -4$.

In Problems 29 through 32 use the method of Laplace transforms to find a general solution to the given differential equation by assuming $y(0) = a$ and $y'(0) = b$, where a and b are arbitrary constants.

29. $y'' - 4y' + 3y = 0$.

30. $y'' + 6y' + 5y = t$.

31. $y'' - 5y' + 6y = -6te^{2t}$.

32. $y'' + 2y' + 2y = 5$.

33. Use Theorem 6 in Section 7.3 to show that

$$\mathcal{L}\{t^2 y'(t)\}(s) = sY''(s) + 2Y'(s),$$

where $Y(s) = \mathcal{L}\{y\}(s)$.

34. Use Theorem 6 in Section 7.3 to show that

$$\mathcal{L}\{t^2 y''(t)\}(s) = s^2 Y''(s) + 4sY'(s) + 2Y(s),$$

where $Y(s) = \mathcal{L}\{y\}(s)$.

In Problems 35 through 38 find solutions to the given initial value problem.

35. $y'' + 3ty' - 6y = 1$; $y(0) = 0$, $y'(0) = 0$.

36. $ty'' - 2y' + ty = 0$; $y(0) = 1$, $y'(0) = 0$.
  [Hint: $\mathcal{L}^{-1}\{1/(s^2 + 1)^2\}(t) = (\sin t - t \cos t)/2$.]

37. $ty'' - ty' + y = 2$; $y(0) = 2$, $y'(0) = -1$.

38. $y'' + ty' - y = 0$; $y(0) = 0$, $y'(0) = 3$.

39. Determine the error $e(t)$ for the automatic pilot in Example 5 if the shaft is initially at rest in the zero direction and the desired direction is $g(t) = a$, where a is a constant.

40. In Example 5, assume that in order to control oscillations, a component of torque proportional to $e'(t)$, but opposite in sign, is also fed back to the steering shaft. Show that equation (24) is now replaced by

$$Iy''(t) = -ke(t) - \mu e'(t),$$

where μ is a positive constant. Determine the error $e(t)$ for the automatic pilot with mild damping (i.e., $\mu < 2\sqrt{Ik}$) if the steering shaft is initially at rest in the zero direction and the desired direction is given by $g(t) = a$, where a is a constant.

41. In Problem 40, determine the error $e(t)$ when the desired direction is given by $g(t) = at$, where a is a constant.

7.6 Laplace Transforms and Special Functions

In this section we study special functions that often arise when the method of Laplace transforms is applied to physical problems. Of particular interest are methods for handling functions with jump discontinuities. Jump discontinuities occur naturally in physical problems such as electric circuits with on/off switches. To handle such behavior, O. Heaviside introduced the following step function.

UNIT STEP FUNCTION

Definition 5.   The **unit step function** $u(t)$ is defined by

$$(1) \qquad u(t) := \begin{cases} 0, & t < 0, \\ 1, & 0 < t. \end{cases}$$

By shifting the argument of $u(t)$, the jump can be moved to a different location. That is,

$$(2) \qquad u(t - a) = \begin{cases} 0, & t - a < 0, \\ 1, & 0 < t - a \end{cases} = \begin{cases} 0, & t < a, \\ 1, & a < t \end{cases}$$

has its jump at $t = a$. By multiplying by a constant M, the height of the jump can also be modified (see Figure 7.2):

$$Mu(t - a) = \begin{cases} 0, & t < a, \\ M, & a < t. \end{cases}$$

Many discontinuous functions can be expressed in terms of unit step functions. For example,

$$(3) \qquad f(t) := \begin{cases} \sin t, & t < \pi, \\ t, & \pi < t \end{cases}$$

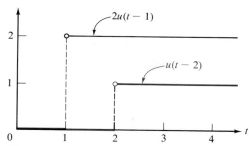

Figure 7.2 Two step functions expressed using the unit step function

can be expressed as

$$f(t) = \sin t + \begin{cases} 0, & t < \pi, \\ t - \sin t, & \pi < t \end{cases}$$

$$= \sin t + (t - \sin t)u(t - \pi).$$

The Laplace transform of $u(t - a)$ with $a \geq 0$ is

(4) $$\mathscr{L}\{u(t - a)\}(s) = \frac{e^{-as}}{s},$$

since, for $s > 0$,

$$\mathscr{L}\{u(t - a)\}(s) = \int_0^\infty e^{-st}u(t - a)\,dt = \int_a^\infty e^{-st}\,dt$$

$$= \lim_{N \to \infty} \frac{-e^{-st}}{s}\bigg|_a^N = \frac{e^{-as}}{s}.$$

Observe that $\mathscr{L}\{u(t)\} = \mathscr{L}\{1\}$ since $u(t) = 1$ for $t > 0$.

▶ **Example 1** Find the Laplace transform of

(5) $$f(t) := \begin{cases} 3, & t < 2, \\ -1, & 2 < t < 5, \\ 7, & 5 < t. \end{cases}$$

Solution We could use the definition of the Laplace transform to compute $\mathscr{L}\{f\}$, but instead let's express $f(t)$ in terms of unit step functions and then use formula (4).

The function $f(t)$ equals 3 until t reaches 2, at which point $f(t)$ jumps to -1. We can express this jump by $3 - 4u(t - 2)$ since $u(t - 2)$ is zero until t reaches 2, after which it has the value 1. At $t = 5$ the function $f(t)$ jumps from -1 to 7. This can be expressed by adding on the term $8u(t - 5)$. Hence

(6) $f(t) = 3 - 4u(t - 2) + 8u(t - 5)$.

Finally, taking the Laplace transform of (6) and using formula (4), we find

$$\mathscr{L}\{f\}(s) = 3\mathscr{L}\{1\}(s) - 4\mathscr{L}\{u(t - 2)\}(s) + 8\mathscr{L}\{u(t - 5)\}(s)$$

$$= \frac{3}{s} - \frac{4e^{-2s}}{s} + \frac{8e^{-5s}}{s}. \blacktriangleleft$$

The translation property of $F(s)$ discussed in Section 7.3 described the effect on the Laplace transform of multiplying a function by e^{at}. The next theorem illustrates an analogous effect of multiplying the Laplace transform of a function by e^{-as}.

SHIFTING PROPERTY

Theorem 8.   Let $F(s) = \mathscr{L}\{f\}(s)$ exist for $s > \alpha \geq 0$. If a is a positive constant, then

(7) $\mathscr{L}\{f(t - a)u(t - a)\}(s) = e^{-as}F(s),$

and, if $f(t)$ is continuous on $[0, \infty)$, then[†]

(8) $\mathscr{L}^{-1}\{e^{-as}F(s)\}(t) = f(t - a)u(t - a).$

Proof   By the definition of the Laplace transform, we have

(9) $$\mathscr{L}\{f(t - a)u(t - a)\}(s) = \int_0^\infty e^{-st}f(t - a)u(t - a)\,dt$$

$$= \int_a^\infty e^{-st}f(t - a)\,dt,$$

where, in the last equation, we used the fact that $u(t - a)$ is zero for $t < a$ and equals 1 for $t > a$. Now let $v = t - a$. Then we have $dv = dt$, and equation (9) becomes

$$\mathscr{L}\{f(t - a)u(t - a)\}(s) = \int_0^\infty e^{-as}e^{-sv}f(v)\,dv$$

$$= e^{-as}\int_0^\infty e^{-sv}f(v)\,dv = e^{-as}F(s). \; \blacksquare\blacksquare\blacksquare$$

[†] Although $f(t)$ is continuous on $[0, \infty)$, the function $f(t - a)u(t - a)$ may have a discontinuity at $t = a$. In such cases, it can be shown that there is no continuous function on $[0, \infty)$ whose Laplace transform is $e^{-as}F(s)$.

Notice that formula (7) includes as a special case the formula for $\mathscr{L}\{u(t - a)\}$; indeed, if we take $f(t) \equiv 1$, then $F(s) = 1/s$, and (7) becomes $\mathscr{L}\{u(t - a)\}(s) = e^{-as}/s$.

In practice it is more common to be faced with the problem of computing the transform of a function expressed as $g(t)u(t - a)$ rather than $f(t - a)u(t - a)$. To compute $\mathscr{L}\{g(t)u(t - a)\}$, we simply identify $g(t)$ with $f(t - a)$, so that $f(t) = g(t + a)$. Equation (7) then gives

(10)　　　$\mathscr{L}\{g(t)u(t - a)\}(s) = e^{-as}\mathscr{L}\{g(t + a)\}(s)$.

▶ **Example 2**　Determine the Laplace transform of $t^2 u(t - 1)$.

Solution　To apply the shifting property in equation (10), we observe that $g(t) = t^2$ and $a = 1$. Hence

$$g(t + a) = g(t + 1) = (t + 1)^2 = t^2 + 2t + 1.$$

Now the Laplace transform of $g(t + a)$

$$\mathscr{L}\{g(t + a)\}(s) = \frac{2}{s^3} + \frac{2}{s^2} + \frac{1}{s}.$$

Hence, by formula (10), we have

$$\mathscr{L}\{t^2 u(t - 1)\}(s) = e^{-s}\left\{\frac{2}{s^3} + \frac{2}{s^2} + \frac{1}{s}\right\}. \quad ◀$$

▶ **Example 3**　Determine $\mathscr{L}\{(\cos t)u(t - \pi)\}$.

Solution　Here $g(t) = \cos t$ and $a = \pi$. Hence

$$g(t + a) = g(t + \pi) = \cos(t + \pi) = -\cos t,$$

and so the Laplace transform of $g(t + a)$ is

$$\mathscr{L}\{g(t + a)\}(s) = -\mathscr{L}\{\cos t\}(s) = -\frac{s}{s^2 + 1}.$$

Thus, from formula (10), we get

$$\mathscr{L}\{(\cos t)u(t - \pi)\}(s) = -e^{-\pi s}\frac{s}{s^2 + 1}. \quad ◀$$

In Examples 2 and 3 we could also have computed the Laplace transform directly from the definition. In dealing with inverse transforms, however, we do not have a simple alternative formula[†] upon which to rely, and so formula (8) is especially useful whenever the transform has e^{-as} as a factor.

▶ **Example 4**   Determine $\mathscr{L}^{-1}\left\{\dfrac{e^{-2s}}{s^2}\right\}$.

Solution   To use shifting property (8), we first express e^{-2s}/s^2 as the product $e^{-as}F(s)$. For this purpose, we put $e^{-as} = e^{-2s}$ and $F(s) = 1/s^2$. Thus $a = 2$ and

$$f(t) = \mathscr{L}^{-1}\left\{\frac{1}{s^2}\right\}(t) = t.$$

It now follows from the shifting property that

$$\mathscr{L}^{-1}\left\{\frac{e^{-2s}}{s^2}\right\}(t) = f(t-2)u(t-2) = (t-2)u(t-2). \quad ◀$$

As illustrated by the next example, step functions arise in the modeling of on/off switches, changes in polarity, etc.

▶ **Example 5**   The current I in an RLC series circuit is governed by the initial value problem

(11) $I''(t) + 4I(t) = g(t); \qquad I(0) = 0, \qquad I'(0) = 0,$

where

$$g(t) := \begin{cases} 1, & 0 < t < 1, \\ -1, & 1 < t < 2, \\ 0, & 2 < t. \end{cases}$$

Determine the current as a function of time t.

Solution   Let $J(s) := \mathscr{L}\{I\}(s)$. Then we have $\mathscr{L}\{I''\}(s) = s^2 J(s)$. Expressing

$$g(t) = u(t) - 2u(t-1) + u(t-2),$$

[†] Under certain conditions the inverse transform is given by the contour integral

$$\mathscr{L}^{-1}\{F\}(t) = \frac{1}{2\pi i}\int_{\alpha - i\infty}^{\alpha + i\infty} e^{st} F(s)\, ds.$$

See, for example, *Complex Variables and the Laplace Transform for Engineers*, by Wilbur R. LePage, Dover Publications, New York, 1980.

we find that

$$\mathcal{L}\{g\}(s) = \frac{1}{s} - \frac{2e^{-s}}{s} + \frac{e^{-2s}}{s}.$$

Thus, when we take the Laplace transform of both sides of (11), we obtain

$$\mathcal{L}\{I''\}(s) + 4\mathcal{L}\{I\}(s) = \mathcal{L}\{g\}(s),$$

$$s^2 J(s) + 4J(s) = \frac{1}{s} - \frac{2e^{-s}}{s} + \frac{e^{-2s}}{s},$$

(12) $$J(s) = \frac{1}{s(s^2 + 4)} - \frac{2e^{-s}}{s(s^2 + 4)} + \frac{e^{-2s}}{s(s^2 + 4)}.$$

To find $I = \mathcal{L}^{-1}\{J\}$, we first observe that

$$J(s) = F(s) - 2e^{-s}F(s) + e^{-2s}F(s),$$

where

$$F(s) := \frac{1}{s(s^2 + 4)} = \frac{1}{4}\left(\frac{1}{s}\right) - \frac{1}{4}\left(\frac{s}{s^2 + 4}\right).$$

Computing the inverse transform of $F(s)$ gives

$$f(t) := \mathcal{L}^{-1}\{F\}(t) = \tfrac{1}{4} - \tfrac{1}{4}\cos 2t.$$

Hence, via the shifting property (8), we find

$$I(t) = \mathcal{L}^{-1}\{F(s) - 2e^{-s}F(s) + e^{-2s}F(s)\}(t)$$
$$= f(t) - 2f(t - 1)u(t - 1) + f(t - 2)u(t - 2)$$
$$= (\tfrac{1}{4} - \tfrac{1}{4}\cos 2t) - [\tfrac{1}{2} - \tfrac{1}{2}\cos 2(t - 1)]u(t - 1)$$
$$+ [\tfrac{1}{4} - \tfrac{1}{4}\cos 2(t - 2)]u(t - 2). \ \blacktriangleleft$$

Periodic functions are another class of functions that occur frequently in applications.

PERIODIC FUNCTION

Definition 6. A function $f(t)$ is said to be **periodic of period T** if

$$f(t + T) = f(t)$$

for all t in the domain of f.

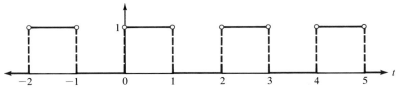

Figure 7.3 Graph of square wave function $f(t)$

As we know, the sine and cosine functions are periodic with period 2π, and the tangent function is periodic with period π.[†] To specify a periodic function, it is sufficient to give its values over one period. For example, the square wave function in Figure 7.3 can be expressed as

(13) $\qquad f(t) := \begin{cases} 1, & 0 < t < 1, \\ 0, & 1 < t < 2 \end{cases}$ and $f(t)$ has period 2.

▶ **Example 6**   Determine $\mathscr{L}\{f\}$, where $f(t)$ is the square wave function in (13).

Solution   Since $f(t)$ has period 2, it will prove convenient to write

$$\mathscr{L}\{f\}(s) = \int_0^\infty e^{-st} f(t)\, dt$$

(14) $\qquad = \int_0^2 e^{-st} f(t)\, dt + \int_2^4 e^{-st} f(t)\, dt + \int_4^6 e^{-st} f(t)\, dt + \cdots .$

In (14), we put $v = t$ in the first integral, $v = t - 2$ in the second integral, $v = t - 4$ in the third integral, and so on. This gives

$$\mathscr{L}\{f\}(s) = \int_0^2 e^{-sv} f(v)\, dv + \int_0^2 e^{-s(v+2)} f(v+2)\, dv$$
$$+ \int_0^2 e^{-s(v+4)} f(v+4)\, dv + \cdots ,$$

and since $f(v) = f(v + 2) = f(v + 4) = \cdots$, we find

$$\mathscr{L}\{f\}(s) = \int_0^2 e^{-sv} f(v)\, dv + e^{-2s} \int_0^2 e^{-sv} f(v)\, dv + e^{-4s} \int_0^2 e^{-sv} f(v)\, dv + \cdots$$
$$= \{1 + e^{-2s} + e^{-4s} + \cdots\} \int_0^2 e^{-sv} f(v)\, dv .$$

Now the series in braces is a **geometric series** with ratio $r = e^{-2s}$, which sums to $1/(1 - r)$

[†] A function that has period T will also have period $2T$, $3T$, etc. For example, the sine function has periods 2π, 4π, 6π, etc. Some authors refer to the smallest period as the **fundamental period** or just the period of the function.

or $1/(1 - e^{-2s})$ for $s > 0$. Hence

(15) $$\mathcal{L}\{f\}(s) = \frac{\int_0^2 e^{-sv}f(v)\,dv}{1 - e^{-2s}}.$$

Evaluating the integral in equation (15), we obtain (see (13))

$$\int_0^2 e^{-sv}f(v)\,dv = \int_0^1 e^{-sv}\,dv = \frac{1}{s} - \frac{e^{-s}}{s} = \frac{1 - e^{-s}}{s}.$$

Thus,

(16) $$\mathcal{L}\{f\}(s) = \frac{1 - e^{-s}}{s(1 - e^{-2s})} = \frac{1}{s(1 + e^{-s})}. \quad \blacktriangleleft$$

With minor modifications the derivation of formula (15) gives the following more general result.

TRANSFORM OF PERIODIC FUNCTION

Theorem 9. If $f(t)$ has period T and is piecewise continuous on $[0, T]$, then

(17) $$\mathcal{L}\{f\}(s) = \frac{\int_0^T e^{-st}f(t)\,dt}{1 - e^{-sT}}.$$

Returning to Example 6, we could have chosen to express the square wave in terms of unit step functions and then computed its Laplace transform. That is, $f(t)$ in (13) can be written in the form

(18) $$f(t) = u(t) - u(t - 1) + u(t - 2) - u(t - 3) + \cdots,$$

for $t > 0$. Using the linearity of the Laplace transform, we find

$$\mathcal{L}\{f\}(s) = \mathcal{L}\{u(t)\}(s) - \mathcal{L}\{u(t - 1)\}(s) + \mathcal{L}\{u(t - 2)\}(s) + \cdots$$

$$= \frac{1}{s} - \frac{e^{-s}}{s} + \frac{e^{-2s}}{s} - \frac{e^{-3s}}{s} + \cdots$$

$$= \frac{1}{s}\{1 - e^{-s} + (e^{-s})^2 - (e^{-s})^3 + \cdots\}$$

$$= \frac{1}{s}\left\{\frac{1}{1 + e^{-s}}\right\} = \frac{1}{s(1 + e^{-s})}.$$

This agrees with equation (16).

In the preceding computation we determined the Laplace transform of $f(t)$ by writing $f(t)$ as a series of functions with known Laplace transforms. This approach can also be used for functions that have a power series expansion since we know that

$$\mathscr{L}\{t^n\}(s) = \frac{n!}{s^{n+1}}, \qquad n = 0, 1, 2, \ldots.$$

▶ **Example 7**   Determine $\mathscr{L}\{f\}$, where

$$f(t) := \begin{cases} \dfrac{\sin t}{t}, & t \neq 0, \\ 1, & t = 0. \end{cases}$$

Solution   We begin by expressing $f(t)$ in a Taylor series about $t = 0$. Since

$$\sin t = t - \frac{t^3}{3!} + \frac{t^5}{5!} - \frac{t^7}{7!} + \cdots,$$

then dividing by t we obtain

$$f(t) = \frac{\sin t}{t} = 1 - \frac{t^2}{3!} + \frac{t^4}{5!} - \frac{t^6}{7!} + \cdots$$

for $t > 0$. This representation also holds at $t = 0$ since

$$\lim_{t \to 0} f(t) = \lim_{t \to 0} \frac{\sin t}{t} = 1.$$

Observe that $f(t)$ is continuous on $[0, \infty)$ and of exponential order, and hence its Laplace transform exists for all s large. Using the linearity of the transform, we find

$$\mathscr{L}\{f\}(s) = \mathscr{L}\{1\}(s) - \frac{1}{3!}\mathscr{L}\{t^2\}(s) + \frac{1}{5!}\mathscr{L}\{t^4\}(s) + \cdots$$

$$= \frac{1}{s} - \frac{2!}{3!s^3} + \frac{4!}{5!s^5} - \frac{6!}{7!s^7} + \cdots$$

$$= \frac{1}{s} - \frac{1}{3s^3} + \frac{1}{5s^5} - \frac{1}{7s^7} + \cdots.$$

While it may not be obvious, it can be verified (see Problem 50) that for $s > 1$ the above series converges to the function arctan$(1/s)$. Thus

(19) $$\mathscr{L}\left\{\frac{\sin t}{t}\right\}(s) = \arctan\frac{1}{s}.\ \blacktriangleleft$$

A similar procedure involving the series expansion for $F(s)$ in powers of $1/s$ can be used to compute $f(t) = \mathscr{L}^{-1}\{F\}(t)$ (see Problems 51–53).

We have previously shown, for every nonnegative integer n, that $\mathscr{L}\{t^n\}(s) = n!/s^{n+1}$. But what if the power of t is *not* an integer—is this formula still valid? To answer this question we need to extend the idea of "factorial." This is accomplished by the gamma function.[†]

GAMMA FUNCTION

Definition 7. The **gamma function** $\Gamma(t)$ is defined by

(20) $$\Gamma(t) := \int_0^\infty e^{-u}u^{t-1}\,du, \qquad t > 0.$$

It can be shown that the integral in (20) converges for $t > 0$. A useful property of the gamma function is the recursive relation

(21) $$\Gamma(t + 1) = t\Gamma(t).$$

This identity follows from the definition (20) after performing an integration by parts:

$$\Gamma(t + 1) = \int_0^\infty e^{-u}u^t\,du = \lim_{N\to\infty}\int_0^N e^{-u}u^t\,du$$

$$= \lim_{N\to\infty}\left\{-e^{-u}u^t\Big|_0^N + \int_0^N te^{-u}u^{t-1}\,du\right\}$$

$$= \lim_{N\to\infty} -e^{-N}N^t + t\lim_{N\to\infty}\int_0^N e^{-u}u^{t-1}\,du$$

$$= 0 + t\Gamma(t) = t\Gamma(t).$$

When t is a positive integer, say $t = n$, then the recursive relation (21) can be repeatedly applied to obtain

$$\Gamma(n + 1) = n\Gamma(n) = n(n - 1)\Gamma(n - 1) = \cdots$$
$$= n(n - 1)(n - 2)\cdots 2\Gamma(1).$$

[†] *Historical Footnote:* This definition of the gamma function is credited to Leonhard Euler.

It follows from the definition (20) that $\Gamma(1) = 1$, and so we find

(22) $\Gamma(n + 1) = n!$.

Thus the gamma function extends the notion of factorial!
    As an application of the gamma function, let's return to the problem of determining the Laplace transform of an arbitrary power of t. We now verify that the formula

(23) $\mathscr{L}\{t^r\}(s) = \dfrac{\Gamma(r + 1)}{s^{r+1}}$

holds for every constant $r > -1$.
    By definition,

$$\mathscr{L}\{t^r\}(s) = \int_0^\infty e^{-st}t^r \, dt.$$

Let's make the substitution $u = st$. Then $du = s \, dt$, and we find

$$\mathscr{L}\{t^r\}(s) = \int_0^\infty e^{-u}\left(\frac{u}{s}\right)^r\left(\frac{1}{s}\right) du$$

$$= \frac{1}{s^{r+1}} \int_0^\infty e^{-u}u^r \, du = \frac{\Gamma(r + 1)}{s^{r+1}}.$$

Notice that when $r = n$ is a nonnegative integer, then $\Gamma(n + 1) = n!$, and so formula (23) reduces to the familiar formula for $\mathscr{L}\{t^n\}$.

EXERCISES 7.6

In Problems 1 through 8 determine the Laplace transform of the given function.

1. $u(t - 1) - u(t - 4)$.

2. $2u(t - 1) - u(t - 2) + 2u(t - 3)$.

3. $(t - 1)^2 u(t - 1)$.

4. $(t - 2)u(t - 2)$.

5. $tu(t - 1)$.

6. $(t + 1)u(t - 2)$.

7. $e^t u(t - 3)$.

8. $(\sin t)u\left(t - \dfrac{\pi}{2}\right)$.

In Problems 9 through 16 determine the inverse Laplace transform of the given function.

9. $\dfrac{e^{-3s}}{s^2}$.

10. $\dfrac{e^{-2s}}{s - 1}$.

11. $\dfrac{e^{-s}}{s^2 + 4}$.

12. $\dfrac{e^{-3s}}{s^2 + 9}$.

13. $\dfrac{se^{-3s}}{s^2 + 4s + 5}$.

14. $\dfrac{e^{-2s} - 3e^{-4s}}{s + 2}$.

15. $\dfrac{e^{-3s}(s-5)}{(s+1)(s+2)}.$

16. $\dfrac{e^{-s}(3s^2-s+2)}{(s-1)(s^2+1)}.$

17. The current $I(t)$ in an *RLC* series circuit is governed by the initial value problem

$$I''(t) + 4I(t) = g(t); \qquad I(0) = 1, \qquad I'(0) = 3,$$

where

$$g(t) := \begin{cases} 3\sin t, & 0 \le t \le 2\pi, \\ 0, & 2\pi < t. \end{cases}$$

Determine the current as a function of time t.

18. The current $I(t)$ in an *RLC* series circuit is governed by the initial value problem

$$I''(t) + 2I'(t) + 2I(t) = g(t); \qquad I(0) = 10, \qquad I'(0) = 0,$$

where

$$g(t) := \begin{cases} 20, & 0 < t < 3\pi, \\ 0, & 3\pi < t < 4\pi, \\ 20, & 4\pi < t. \end{cases}$$

Determine the current as a function of time t.

In Problems 19 through 22 determine $\mathscr{L}\{f\}$; where $f(t)$ is periodic with given period. Also graph $f(t)$.

19. $f(t) = t, \quad 0 < t < 2,$ and $f(t)$ has period 2.

20. $f(t) = e^t, \quad 0 < t < 1,$ and $f(t)$ has period 1.

21. $f(t) = \begin{cases} e^{-t}, & 0 < t < 1, \\ 1, & 1 < t < 2, \end{cases}$ and $f(t)$ has period 2.

22. $f(t) = \begin{cases} t, & 0 < t < 1, \\ 1 - t, & 1 < t < 2, \end{cases}$ and $f(t)$ has period 2.

In Problems 23 through 26 determine $\mathscr{L}\{f\}$; where the periodic function is described by its graph.

23. $f(t)$

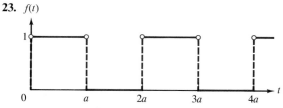

Figure 7.4 Square wave

24. $f(t)$

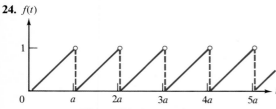

Figure 7.5 Sawtooth wave

25. $f(t)$

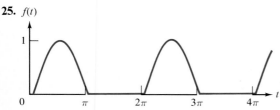

Figure 7.6 Half-rectified sine wave

26. $f(t)$

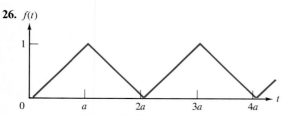

Figure 7.7 Triangular wave

In Problems 27 through 30 solve the given initial value problem using the method of Laplace transforms. Sketch the graph of the solution.

27. $y'' + y = u(t - 3)$; $y(0) = 0$, $y'(0) = 1$.

28. $y'' + y = u(t - 2) - u(t - 4)$; $y(0) = 1$, $y'(0) = 0$.

29. $y'' + y = t - tu(t - 2)$; $y(0) = 0$, $y'(0) = 1$.

30. $y'' + y = 3 \sin 2t - 3(\sin 2t)u(t - 2\pi)$; $y(0) = 1$, $y'(0) = -2$.

In Problems 31 through 36 solve the given initial value problem using the method of Laplace transforms.

31. $y'' + 2y' + 2y = u(t - 2\pi) - u(t - 4\pi)$; $y(0) = 1$, $y'(0) = 1$.

32. $y'' + 4y' + 4y = u(t - \pi) - u(t - 2\pi)$; $y(0) = 0$, $y'(0) = 0$.

33. $y'' + 3y' + 2y = e^{-3t}u(t - 2)$; $y(0) = 2$, $y'(0) = -3$.

34. $y'' + 5y' + 6y = tu(t - 2)$; $y(0) = 0$, $y'(0) = 1$.

35. $y'' - y = u(t - 1) - u(t - 2) + u(t - 3) - u(t - 4)$; $y(0) = 2$, $y'(0) = 0$.

36. $y'' - y = 3u(t - 1) - 2u(t - 2)$; $y(0) = 0$, $y'(0) = 2$.

37. Show that if $\mathscr{L}\{g\}(s) = [(s + \alpha)(1 - e^{-Ts})]^{-1}$, where $T > 0$ is fixed, then

(24)
$$g(t) = e^{-\alpha t} + e^{-\alpha(t-T)}u(t - T) + e^{-\alpha(t-2T)}u(t - 2T)$$
$$+ e^{-\alpha(t-3T)}u(t - 3T) + \cdots .$$

[Hint: Use the fact that $1 + x + x^2 + \cdots = 1/(1 - x)$.]

38. The function $g(t)$ in (24) can be expressed in a more convenient form as follows:

(a) Show that for each $n = 0, 1, 2, \ldots$,

$$g(t) = e^{-\alpha t}\left[\frac{e^{(n+1)\alpha T} - 1}{e^{\alpha T} - 1}\right] \quad \text{for} \quad nT < t < (n + 1)T.$$

[Hint: Use the fact that $1 + x + x^2 + \cdots + x^n = (x^{n+1} - 1)/(x - 1)$.]

(b) Let $v = t - (n + 1)T$. Show that when $nT < t < (n+1)T$, then $-T < v < 0$ and

(25)
$$g(t) = \frac{e^{-\alpha v}}{e^{\alpha T} - 1} - \frac{e^{-\alpha t}}{e^{\alpha T} - 1}.$$

(c) Use the facts that the first term in (25) is periodic with period T and the second term is independent of n to sketch the graph of $g(t)$ in (25) for $\alpha = 1$ and $T = 2$.

39. Show that if $\mathscr{L}\{g\}(s) = \beta[(s^2 + \beta^2)(1 - e^{-Ts})]^{-1}$, then

(26)
$$g(t) = \sin \beta t + [\sin \beta(t - T)]u(t - T)$$
$$+ [\sin \beta(t - 2T)]u(t - 2T)$$
$$+ [\sin \beta(t - 3T)]u(t - 3T) + \cdots .$$

40. Use the result of Problem 39 to show that

$$\mathscr{L}^{-1}\left\{\frac{1}{(s^2 + 1)(1 - e^{-\pi s})}\right\}(t) = g(t),$$

where $g(t)$ is periodic with period 2π and

$$g(t) := \begin{cases} \sin t, & 0 \le t \le \pi, \\ 0, & \pi \le t \le 2\pi. \end{cases}$$

In Problems 41 and 42 use the method of Laplace transforms and the results of Problems 37 and 38 to solve the initial value problem

$$y'' + 3y' + 2y = f(t); \qquad y(0) = 0, \qquad y'(0) = 0,$$

where $f(t)$ is the periodic function defined in the stated problem.

41. Problem 20.

42. Problem 23 with $a = 1$.

In Problems 43 through 46 find a Taylor series for $f(t)$ about $t = 0$. Assuming that the Laplace transform of $f(t)$ can be computed term by term, find an expansion for $\mathcal{L}\{f\}(s)$ in powers of $1/s$. If possible, sum the series.

43. $f(t) = e^t$.

44. $f(t) = \sin t$.

45. $f(t) = \dfrac{1 - \cos t}{t}$.

46. $f(t) = e^{-t^2}$.

47. Using the recursive relation (21) and the fact that $\Gamma(\tfrac{1}{2}) = \sqrt{\pi}$, determine

  (a) $\mathcal{L}\{t^{-1/2}\}$.

  (b) $\mathcal{L}\{t^{7/2}\}$.

48. Use the recursive relation (21) and the fact that $\Gamma(\tfrac{1}{2}) = \sqrt{\pi}$ to show that

$$\mathcal{L}^{-1}\{s^{-(n+1/2)}\}(t) = \frac{2^n t^{n-1/2}}{1 \cdot 3 \cdot 5 \cdots (2n-1)\sqrt{\pi}},$$

  where n is a positive integer.

49. Use the method discussed in Example 6 to show that if $f(t)$ has period T and is piecewise continuous on $[0, T)$, then equation (17) holds.

50. By replacing s by $1/s$ in the Maclaurin series expansion for arctan s, show that

$$\arctan \frac{1}{s} = \frac{1}{s} - \frac{1}{3s^3} + \frac{1}{5s^5} - \frac{1}{7s^7} + \cdots.$$

51. Find an expansion for $e^{-1/s}$ in powers of $1/s$. Use the expansion for $e^{-1/s}$ to obtain an expansion for $s^{-1/2} e^{-1/s}$ in terms of $1/s^{n+1/2}$. Assuming that the inverse Laplace transform can be computed term by term, show that

$$\mathcal{L}^{-1}\{s^{-1/2}e^{-1/s}\}(t) = \frac{1}{\sqrt{\pi t}} \cos 2\sqrt{t}.$$

  [Hint: Use the result of Problem 48.]

52. Use the procedure discussed in Problem 51 to show that

$$\mathcal{L}^{-1}\{s^{-3/2}e^{-1/s}\}(t) = \frac{1}{\sqrt{\pi}} \sin 2\sqrt{t}.$$

53. Find an expansion for $\ln[1 + (1/s^2)]$ in powers of $1/s$. Assuming that the inverse Laplace transform can be computed term by term, show that

$$\mathcal{L}^{-1}\left\{\ln\left(1 + \frac{1}{s^2}\right)\right\}(t) = \frac{2}{t}(1 - \cos t).$$

54. The **unit gate function** $G_a(t)$ is defined by

$$G_a(t) := \begin{cases} 0, & t < 0, \\ 1, & 0 < t < a, \\ 0, & a < t. \end{cases}$$

(a) Show that $G_a(t) = u(t) - u(t - a)$.
(b) Verify that $\mathscr{L}\{G_a\}(s) = (1/s)(1 - e^{-as})$.
(c) Show that $\mathscr{L}\{G_a(t - b)\}(s) = (1/s)(e^{-bs} - e^{-(a+b)s})$.

In Problems 55 and 56 use the results of Problem 54 and the method of Laplace transforms to solve the given initial value problem.

55. $y'' - y = G_3(t - 1); \qquad y(0) = 0, \qquad y'(0) = 2.$

56. $y'' - y = G_4(t - 3); \qquad y(0) = 1, \qquad y'(0) = -1.$

★ 7.7 Convolution

Consider the initial value problem

(1) $\qquad y'' + y = g(t); \qquad y(0) = 0, \qquad y'(0) = 0.$

If we let $Y(s) = \mathscr{L}\{y\}(s)$ and $G(s) = \mathscr{L}\{g\}(s)$, then taking the Laplace transform of both sides of (1) yields

$$s^2 Y(s) + Y(s) = G(s),$$

and hence

(2) $\qquad Y(s) = \left(\dfrac{1}{s^2 + 1} \right) G(s).$

That is, the Laplace transform of the solution to (1) is the product of the Laplace transform of sin t and the Laplace transform of the forcing term $g(t)$. What we would now like to have is a simple formula for $y(t)$ in terms of sin t and $g(t)$. Just as the integral of a product is not the product of the integrals, $y(t)$ is not the product of sin t and $g(t)$. However, we can express $y(t)$ as the convolution of sin t and $g(t)$.

CONVOLUTION

Definition 8. Let $f(t)$ and $g(t)$ be piecewise continuous on $[0, \infty)$. The **convolution** of $f(t)$ and $g(t)$, denoted $f * g$, is defined by

(3) $\qquad (f * g)(t) := \displaystyle\int_0^t f(t - v)g(v)\, dv.$

For example, the convolution of t and t^2 is

$$t * t^2 = \int_0^t (t - v)v^2 \, dv = \int_0^t (tv^2 - v^3)\, dv$$

$$= \left(\frac{tv^3}{3} - \frac{v^4}{4} \right)\Bigg|_0^t = \frac{t^4}{3} - \frac{t^4}{4} = \frac{t^4}{12}.$$

Although convolution is different from ordinary multiplication of functions, it does satisfy some of the same properties as multiplication.

PROPERTIES OF CONVOLUTION

Theorem 10.   Let $f(t)$, $g(t)$, and $h(t)$ be piecewise continuous on $[0, \infty)$. Then

(4) $$f * g = g * f,$$

(5) $$f * (g + h) = (f * g) + (f * h),$$

(6) $$(f * g) * h = f * (g * h),$$

(7) $$f * 0 = 0.$$

Proof   To prove equation (4), we begin with the definition

$$(f * g)(t) := \int_0^t f(t - v)g(v)\, dv.$$

Using the change of variables $w = t - v$, we have

$$(f * g)(t) = \int_t^0 f(w)g(t - w)(-dw) = \int_0^t g(t - w)f(w)\, dw = (g * f)(t),$$

which proves (4). The proofs of equations (5) and (6) are left to the exercises (see Problems 31 and 32). Equation (7) is obvious since $f(t - v) \cdot 0 \equiv 0$. ∎

Returning to our original goal, we now prove that if $Y(s)$ is the product of the Laplace transforms $F(s)$ and $G(s)$, then $y(t)$ is the convolution $(f * g)(t)$.

CONVOLUTION THEOREM

Theorem 11.   Let $f(t)$ and $g(t)$ be piecewise continuous on $[0, \infty)$ and of exponential order α, and set $F(s) = \mathscr{L}\{f\}(s)$ and $G(s) = \mathscr{L}\{g\}(s)$. Then

(8) $$\mathscr{L}\{f * g\}(s) = F(s)G(s),$$

or, equivalently,

(9) $$\mathscr{L}^{-1}\{F(s)G(s)\}(t) = (f * g)(t).$$

Proof   Starting with the left-hand side of (8), we use the definition of convolution to write for $s > \alpha$

$$\mathscr{L}\{f * g\}(s) = \int_0^\infty e^{-st}\left(\int_0^t f(t - v)g(v)\, dv \right) dt.$$

To simplify the evaluation of this iterated integral, we introduce the unit step function $u(t - v)$ and write

$$\mathscr{L}\{f * g\}(s) = \int_0^\infty e^{-st}\left(\int_0^\infty u(t - v)f(t - v)g(v)\, dv \right) dt,$$

where we have used the fact that $u(t - v) = 0$ if $v > t$. Reversing the order of integration[†] gives

(10) $$\mathscr{L}\{f * g\}(s) = \int_0^\infty g(v)\left(\int_0^\infty e^{-st}u(t - v)f(t - v)\, dt \right) dv.$$

Recall from the shifting property in Section 7.6 that the integral in parentheses in equation (10) equals $e^{-sv}F(s)$. Hence

(11) $$\mathscr{L}\{f * g\}(s) = \int_0^\infty g(v)e^{-sv}F(s)\, dv = F(s) \int_0^\infty e^{-sv}g(v)\, dv = F(s)G(s).$$

This proves formula (8). ∎∎∎

For the initial value problem (1), recall that we found

$$Y(s) = \left(\frac{1}{s^2 + 1} \right) G(s) = \mathscr{L}\{\sin t\}(s)\mathscr{L}\{g\}(s).$$

It now follows from the convolution theorem that

(12) $$y(t) = \sin t * g(t) = \int_0^t \sin(t - v)g(v)\, dv.$$

Thus we have obtained an integral representation for the solution to the initial value problem (1) for any forcing function $g(t)$ that is piecewise continuous on $[0, \infty)$ and of exponential order.

▶ *Example 1*   Use the convolution theorem to solve the initial value problem

(13) $$y'' - y = g(t); \qquad y(0) = 1, \qquad y'(0) = 1,$$

where $g(t)$ is piecewise continuous on $[0, \infty)$ and of exponential order.

[†] This is permitted since, for each $s > \alpha$, the absolute value of the integrand is integrable on $(0, \infty) \times (0, \infty)$.

Solution Let $Y(s) = \mathscr{L}\{y\}(s)$ and $G(s) = \mathscr{L}\{g\}(s)$. Taking the Laplace transform of both sides of the differential equation in (13) and using the initial conditions gives

$$s^2 Y(s) - s - 1 - Y(s) = G(s).$$

Solving for $Y(s)$, we have

$$Y(s) = \frac{s+1}{s^2 - 1} + \left(\frac{1}{s^2 - 1}\right) G(s) = \frac{1}{s-1} + \left(\frac{1}{s^2 - 1}\right) G(s).$$

Hence

$$y(t) = \mathscr{L}^{-1}\left\{\frac{1}{s-1}\right\}(t) + \mathscr{L}^{-1}\left\{\frac{1}{s^2 - 1}\, G(s)\right\}(t)$$

$$= e^t + \mathscr{L}^{-1}\left\{\frac{1}{s^2 - 1}\, G(s)\right\}(t).$$

Referring to the table of Laplace transforms on the inside back cover, we find

$$\mathscr{L}\{\sinh t\}(s) = \frac{1}{s^2 - 1},$$

so we can now express

$$\mathscr{L}^{-1}\left\{\frac{1}{s^2 - 1}\, G(s)\right\}(t) = \sinh t * g(t).$$

Thus

(14)
$$y(t) = e^t + \int_0^t \sinh(t - v)g(v)\, dv$$

is the solution to the initial value problem (13). ◄

► **Example 2**   Use the convolution theorem to find $\mathscr{L}^{-1}\{1/(s^2 + 1)^2\}$.

Solution   Write

$$\frac{1}{(s^2 + 1)^2} = \left(\frac{1}{s^2 + 1}\right)\left(\frac{1}{s^2 + 1}\right).$$

Since $\mathcal{L}\{\sin t\}(s) = 1/(s^2 + 1)$, it follows from the convolution theorem that

$$\mathcal{L}^{-1}\left\{\frac{1}{(s^2+1)^2}\right\}(t) = \sin t * \sin t = \int_0^t \sin(t-v)\sin v \, dv$$

$$= \frac{1}{2}\int_0^t [\cos(2v - t) - \cos t] \, dv^\dagger$$

$$= \frac{1}{2}\left[\frac{\sin(2v - t)}{2}\right]_0^t - \frac{1}{2}t\cos t$$

$$= \frac{1}{2}\left[\frac{\sin t}{2} - \frac{\sin(-t)}{2}\right] - \frac{1}{2}t\cos t$$

$$= \frac{\sin t - t\cos t}{2}. \quad \blacktriangleleft$$

As the preceding example attests, the convolution theorem is useful in determining the inverse transforms of rational functions of s. In fact, it provides an alternative to the method of partial fractions. For example,

$$\mathcal{L}^{-1}\left\{\frac{1}{(s-a)(s-b)}\right\}(t) = \mathcal{L}^{-1}\left\{\left(\frac{1}{s-a}\right)\left(\frac{1}{s-b}\right)\right\}(t) = e^{at} * e^{bt},$$

and all that remains in finding the inverse is to compute the convolution $e^{at} * e^{bt}$.

In the early 1900s, V. Volterra introduced **integro-differential** equations in his study of population growth. These equations enabled him to take into account "hereditary influences." In certain cases, these equations involved a convolution. As the next example shows, the convolution theorem helps to solve such integro-differential equations.

▶ *Example 3* Solve the integro-differential equation

(15) $\qquad y'(t) = 1 - \int_0^t y(t-v)e^{-2v} \, dv, \qquad y(0) = 1.$

Solution Equation (15) can be written as

(16) $\qquad y'(t) = 1 - y(t) * e^{-2t}.$

---

† Here we used the identity $\sin\alpha \sin\beta = \frac{1}{2}[\cos(\beta - \alpha) - \cos(\beta + \alpha)].$

Let $Y(s) = \mathcal{L}\{y\}(s)$. Taking the Laplace transform of (16) (with the help of the convolution theorem) and solving for $Y(s)$, we obtain

$$sY(s) - 1 = \frac{1}{s} - Y(s)\left(\frac{1}{s+2}\right)$$

$$sY(s) + \left(\frac{1}{s+2}\right)Y(s) = 1 + \frac{1}{s}$$

$$\left(\frac{s^2 + 2s + 1}{s+2}\right)Y(s) = \frac{s+1}{s}$$

$$Y(s) = \frac{(s+1)(s+2)}{s(s+1)^2} = \frac{s+2}{s(s+1)}$$

$$Y(s) = \frac{2}{s} - \frac{1}{s+1}.$$

Hence $y(t) = 2 - e^{-t}$. ◀

The **transfer function** $H(s)$ of a linear system is defined as the ratio of the Laplace transform of the output function $y(t)$ to the Laplace transform of the input function $g(t)$, assuming that all initial conditions are zero. That is, $H(s) = Y(s)/G(s)$. If the linear system is governed by the differential equation

(17) $\qquad ay'' + by' + cy = g(t), \qquad t > 0,$

where a, b, and c are constants, we can compute the transfer function as follows. Take the Laplace transform of both sides of (17) to get

(18) $\qquad as^2 Y(s) - asy(0) - ay'(0) + bsY(s) - by(0) + cY(s) = G(s).$

Since the initial conditions are assumed to be zero, equation (18) reduces to

$$(as^2 + bs + c)Y(s) = G(s).$$

Thus the transfer function for equation (17) is

(19) $\qquad H(s) = \dfrac{Y(s)}{G(s)} = \dfrac{1}{as^2 + bs + c}.$

The function $h(t) := \mathcal{L}^{-1}\{H\}(t)$ is called the **impulse response function** for the system. A physical justification for this terminology is given in Section 7.8.

▶ *Example 4*   A linear system is governed by the differential equation

(20) $y'' + 2y' + 5y = g(t).$

Find the transfer function for the system, the impulse response function, and give a formula for the solution to (20), assuming that $y(0) = y'(0) = 0$.

Solution   Taking the Laplace transform of (20) and assuming the initial conditions on $y(t)$ to be zero, we find

$$s^2 Y(s) + 2s Y(s) + 5 Y(s) = G(s).$$

Thus the transfer function is

(21) $H(s) = \dfrac{Y(s)}{G(s)} = \dfrac{1}{s^2 + 2s + 5} = \dfrac{1}{(s+1)^2 + 2^2}.$

The inverse Laplace transform of $H(s)$ is the impulse response function

(22) $h(t) = \mathscr{L}^{-1}\{H\}(t) = \dfrac{1}{2}\mathscr{L}^{-1}\left\{\dfrac{2}{(s+1)^2 + 2^2}\right\}(t)$

$$= \dfrac{1}{2}e^{-t}\sin 2t.$$

To obtain a formula for $y(t)$, observe from (21) that

$$Y(s) = G(s)H(s).$$

Thus, by the convolution theorem, we have

(23) $y(t) = (g * h)(t) = \dfrac{1}{2}\displaystyle\int_0^t g(t - v)e^{-v}\sin 2v\, dv.$ ◀

EXERCISES 7.7

In Problems 1 through 4 use the convolution theorem to obtain a formula for the solution to the given initial value problem, where g(t) is piecewise continuous on [0, ∞) *and of exponential order.*

1. $y'' + y = g(t);$ $y(0) = 0,$ $y'(0) = 1.$

2. $y'' + 9y = g(t);$ $y(0) = 1,$ $y'(0) = 0.$

3. $y'' + 4y' + 5y = g(t);$ $y(0) = 1,$ $y'(0) = 1.$

4. $y'' - 2y' + y = g(t);$ $y(0) = -1,$ $y'(0) = 1.$

In Problems 5 through 12 use the convolution theorem to find the inverse Laplace transform of the given function.

5. $\dfrac{1}{(s + 1)(s + 2)}$.

6. $\dfrac{1}{s(s^2 + 1)}$.

7. $\dfrac{1}{(s^2 + 4)^2}$.

8. $\dfrac{s}{(s^2 + 1)^2}$.

9. $\dfrac{1}{s^2(s^2 + 1)}$.

10. $\dfrac{1}{s^3(s^2 + 1)}$.

11. $\dfrac{s}{(s - 1)(s + 2)}$. $\left[\text{Hint: } \dfrac{s}{s - 1} = 1 + \dfrac{1}{s - 1}.\right]$

12. $\dfrac{s + 1}{(s^2 + 1)^2}$.

13. Find the Laplace transform of

$$f(t) := \int_0^t \sin(t - v)e^v \, dv.$$

14. Find the Laplace transform of

$$f(t) := \int_0^t (t - v)e^{3v} \, dv.$$

In Problems 15 through 22 solve the given integral equation or integro-differential equation for y(t).

15. $y(t) + \int_0^t (t - v)y(v) \, dv = t^2$.

16. $y(t) + \int_0^t (t - v)y(v) \, dv = 1$.

17. $y(t) + \int_0^t e^{t - v}y(v) \, dv = \sin t$.

18. $y(t) + 3 \int_0^t y(v) \sin(t - v) \, dv = t$.

19. $y(t) + \int_0^t (t - v)^2 y(v) \, dv = t^3 + 3$.

20. $y'(t) + \int_0^t (t - v)y(v) \, dv = t$, $\quad y(0) = 0$.

21. $y'(t) + y(t) - \int_0^t y(v) \sin(t - v) \, dv = -\sin t$, $\quad y(0) = 1$.

22. $y'(t) - 2 \int_0^t e^{t - v}y(v) \, dv = t$, $\quad y(0) = 2$.

In Problems 23 through 28 a linear system is governed by the given differential equation. Find the transfer function H(s) for the system and the impulse response function h(t).

23. $y'' + 9y = g(t)$.

24. $y'' - 9y = g(t)$.

25. $y'' - y' - 6y = g(t)$.

26. $y'' + 2y' - 15y = g(t)$.

27. $y'' + 2y' + 5y = g(t)$.

28. $y'' - 4y' + 5y = g(t)$.

29. Use the convolution theorem and Laplace transforms to compute $1 * 1 * 1$.

30. Use the convolution theorem and Laplace transforms to compute $1 * t * t^2$.

31. Prove property (5) in Theorem 10.

32. Prove property (6) in Theorem 10.

33. Use the convolution theorem to show that

$$\mathscr{L}^{-1}\left\{\dfrac{F(s)}{s}\right\}(t) = \int_0^t f(v) \, dv,$$

where $F(s) = \mathscr{L}\{f\}(s)$.

34. Using Theorem 5 in Section 7.3 and the convolution theorem, show that

$$\int_0^t \int_0^v f(z) \, dz \, dv = \mathcal{L}^{-1} \left\{ \frac{F(s)}{s^2} \right\}(t) = t \int_0^t f(v) \, dv - \int_0^t v f(v) \, dv,$$

where $F(s) = \mathcal{L}\{f\}(s)$.

★ 7.8 *Impulses and the Dirac Delta Function*

In mechanical systems, electric circuits, bending of beams, and other applications, one encounters functions that have a very large value over a very short interval. For example, the strike of a hammer exerts a relatively large force over a relatively short time, and a heavy weight concentrated at a spot on a suspended beam exerts a large force over a very small section of the beam. In order to deal with violent forces of short duration, physicists and engineers use the delta function introduced by Paul A. M. Dirac.

DIRAC DELTA FUNCTION

Definition 9. The **Dirac delta function** $\delta(t)$ is characterized by the following two properties:

$$(1) \qquad \delta(t) = \begin{cases} 0, & t \neq 0, \\ \text{"infinite,"} & t = 0 \end{cases}$$

and

$$(2) \qquad \int_{-\infty}^{\infty} f(t)\delta(t) \, dt = f(0)$$

for any function $f(t)$ that is continuous on an open interval containing $t = 0$.

By shifting the argument of $\delta(t)$, we have $\delta(t - a) = 0$, $t \neq a$, and

$$(3) \qquad \int_{-\infty}^{\infty} f(t)\delta(t - a) \, dt = f(a)$$

for any function $f(t)$ that is continuous on an interval containing $t = a$.

It is obvious that $\delta(t - a)$ is not a function in the usual sense; instead it is an example of what is called a **generalized function** or a **distribution.** In spite of this shortcoming, the Dirac delta function was successfully used for several years to solve various physics and engineering problems before Laurent Schwartz mathematically justified its use!

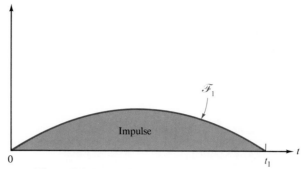

Figure 7.8 Force due to a blow from a hammer

A heuristic argument for the existence of the Dirac delta function can be made by considering the impulse of a force over a short interval. If a force $\mathscr{F}(t)$ is applied from time t_0 to time t_1, then the **impulse** due to $\mathscr{F}$ is the integral

$$\text{Impulse} := \int_{t_0}^{t_1} \mathscr{F}(t)\, dt.$$

By Newton's second law we see that

(4) $$\int_{t_0}^{t_1} \mathscr{F}(t)\, dt = \int_{t_0}^{t_1} m\, \frac{dv}{dt}\, dt = mv(t_1) - mv(t_0),$$

where m denotes mass and v denotes velocity. Since mv represents the momentum, we can interpret equation (4) as saying: **the impulse equals the change in momentum.**

When a hammer strikes an object, it transfers momentum to the object. This change in momentum takes place over a very short period of time, say $[0, t_1]$. If we let $\mathscr{F}_1(t)$ represent the force due to the hammer, then the *area* under the curve $\mathscr{F}_1(t)$ is the impulse or change in momentum (see Figure 7.8). If, as is illustrated in Figure 7.9, the same change in momentum takes place over shorter and shorter time intervals, say $[0, t_2]$ or $[0, t_3]$, then the average

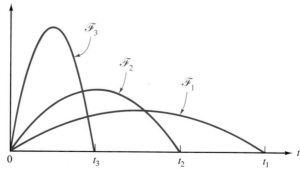

Figure 7.9 Forces with the same impulse

force must get greater and greater in order for the impulses (the areas under the curves $\mathscr{F}_n$) to remain the same. In fact, if the forces $\mathscr{F}_n$ having the same impulse act, respectively, over the intervals $[0, t_n]$, where $t_n \to 0$ as $n \to \infty$, then $\mathscr{F}_n$ approaches a function that is zero for $t \neq 0$ but has an infinite value for $t = 0$. Moreover, the areas under the $\mathscr{F}_n$'s have a common value. Normalizing this value to be 1 gives

$$\int_{-\infty}^{\infty} \mathscr{F}_n(t)\, dt = 1 \qquad \text{for all } n.$$

From these limiting properties of the $\mathscr{F}_n$'s, we derive a "function" δ that satisfies property (1) and the integral condition

(5) $$\int_{-\infty}^{\infty} \delta(t)\, dt = 1.$$

Notice that (5) is a special case of property (2) that is obtained by taking $f(t) \equiv 1$. It is interesting to note that (5) actually implies the general property (2) (see Problem 33).

The Laplace transform of the Dirac delta function can be quickly derived from property (3). Since $\delta(t - a) = 0$ for $t \neq a$, setting $f(t) = e^{-st}$ in (3), we find for $a \geq 0$

$$\int_{0}^{\infty} e^{-st}\delta(t - a)\, dt = \int_{-\infty}^{\infty} e^{-st}\delta(t - a)\, dt = e^{-as}.$$

Thus, for $a \geq 0$,

(6) $$\mathscr{L}\{\delta(t - a)\}(s) = e^{-as}.$$

An interesting connection exists between the unit step function and the Dirac delta function. Observe that as a consequence of equation (5) and the fact that $\delta(x - a)$ is zero for $x < a$ and for $x > a$, we have

(7) $$\int_{-\infty}^{t} \delta(x - a)\, dx = \begin{cases} 0, & t < a, \\ 1, & t > a \end{cases}$$
$$= u(t - a).$$

If we formally differentiate both sides of (7) with respect to t (in the spirit of the fundamental theorem of calculus), we find

$$\delta(t - a) = u'(t - a).$$

Thus it appears that the Dirac delta function is the derivative of the unit step function. That is, in fact, the case if we consider "differentiation" in a more general sense.[†]

[†] See *Distributions, Complex Variables, and Fourier Transforms*, by H. J. Bremermann, Addison-Wesley, Reading, Massachusetts, 1966.

The next example uses the Dirac delta function to solve a mechanical vibration problem. Such a problem can be modeled by a *sequence* of differential equations involving impulse-type forcing functions $\mathscr{F}_n(t)$, where the impulse takes place over time intervals that tend to zero as $n \to \infty$ (see Figure 7.9). With this approach the corresponding sequence of solutions $y_n(t)$ tends to a function $y(t)$ that is the solution to the problem with a Dirac delta forcing function. Instead of using this sequential approach, it is easier to work directly with the delta function and its properties.

▶ **Example 1**   A mass attached to a spring is released from rest 1 m below the equilibrium position for the spring-mass system and begins to vibrate. After π seconds the mass is struck by a hammer exerting an impulse on the mass. The system is governed by the initial value problem

(8)
$$\frac{d^2x}{dt^2} + 9x = 3\delta(t - \pi); \qquad x(0) = 1, \qquad \frac{dx}{dt}(0) = 0,$$

where $x(t)$ denotes the displacement from equilibrium at time t. Determine $x(t)$.

Solution   Let $X(s) = \mathscr{L}\{x\}(s)$. Since

$$\mathscr{L}\{x''\}(s) = s^2 X(s) - s \quad \text{and} \quad \mathscr{L}\{\delta(t - \pi)\}(s) = e^{-\pi s},$$

taking the Laplace transform of both sides of (8) and solving for $X(s)$ yields

$$s^2 X(s) - s + 9X(s) = 3e^{-\pi s}$$

$$X(s) = \frac{s}{s^2 + 9} + e^{-\pi s}\frac{3}{s^2 + 9}$$

$$= \mathscr{L}\{\cos 3t\}(s) + e^{-\pi s}\mathscr{L}\{\sin 3t\}(s).$$

Using the shifting property (cf. Section 7.6) to determine the inverse Laplace transform of $X(s)$, we find

$$x(t) = \cos 3t + \sin 3(t - \pi)u(t - \pi)$$

$$= \begin{cases} \cos 3t, & t < \pi, \\ \cos 3t - \sin 3t, & \pi < t \end{cases}$$

$$= \begin{cases} \cos 3t, & t < \pi, \\ \sqrt{2}\cos\left(3t + \frac{\pi}{4}\right), & \pi < t. \end{cases}$$

The graph of $x(t)$ is given in color in Figure 7.10. For comparison, the dashed curve depicts the displacement of an undisturbed vibrating spring. ◀

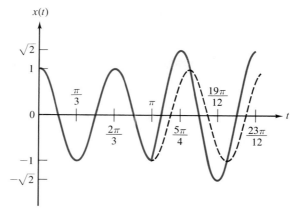

Figure 7.10 Displacement of a
vibrating spring that is struck by
a hammer at $t = \pi$

In Section 7.7 we defined the **impulse response function** for

(9) $ay'' + by' + cy = g(t),$

as the function $h(t) := \mathscr{L}^{-1}\{H\}(t)$, where $H(s)$ is the **transfer function.** Recall that $H(s)$ is
the ratio

$$H(s) := \frac{Y(s)}{G(s)},$$

where $Y(s)$ is the Laplace transform of the solution to (9) with zero initial conditions and
$G(s)$ is the Laplace transform of $g(t)$. It is important to note that $H(s)$, and hence $h(t)$, does
not depend on the choice of the function $g(t)$ in (9) (see equation (19) in Section 7.7). In
fact, if we take $g(t) = \delta(t)$, it turns out that *the impulse response function can be obtained
by solving the initial value problem*

(10) $ay'' + by'' + cy = \delta(t);$ $y(0) = 0,$ $y'(0) = 0.$

Indeed, with $g(t) = \delta(t)$, we have $G(s) = 1$, and hence $H(s) = Y(s)$. Consequently $h(t) = y(t)$.

▶ **Example 2**   A linear system is governed by

(11) $y'' + 4y' + 5y = g(t).$

Determine the impulse response function.

Solution   The desired function $h(t)$ is obtained by solving the initial value problem

(12) $y'' + 4y' + 5y = \delta(t);$ $y(0) = 0,$ $y'(0) = 0.$

Let $Y(s) = \mathcal{L}\{y\}(s)$. Using the method of Laplace transforms, we find

$$s^2 Y(s) + 4s Y(s) + 5Y(s) = 1,$$

$$Y(s) = \frac{1}{s^2 + 4s + 5} = \frac{1}{(s + 2)^2 + 1}.$$

Hence

(13) $h(t) = y(t) = \mathcal{L}^{-1}\{Y\}(t) = e^{-2t}\sin t.$ ◀

A peculiarity of using the Dirac delta function is that the "solution" to (12) does not satisfy both initial conditions. This may be disturbing, but since $\delta(t)$ is infinite at $t = 0$, we might expect something unusual to occur. Nevertheless, the function $h(t)$ obtained by the above procedure can be used along with the convolution theorem to express the solution to any initial value problem of the form

(14) $y'' + 4y' + 5y = g(t);$ $y(0) = 0,$ $y'(0) = 0,$

where $g(t)$ is continuous on $[0, \infty)$ and of exponential order. Indeed, since $Y(s) = G(s)H(s)$, it follows from (13) and the convolution theorem that

$$y(t) = (g * h)(t) = \int_0^t g(t - v)e^{-2v}\sin v \, dv.$$

EXERCISES 7.8

In Problems 1 through 6 evaluate the given integral.

1. $\int_{-\infty}^{\infty} e^{3t}\,\delta(t)\,dt.$

2. $\int_{-\infty}^{\infty} (t^2 - 1)\delta(t)\,dt.$

3. $\int_{-\infty}^{\infty} (\sin 3t)\delta\left(t - \frac{\pi}{2}\right)dt.$

4. $\int_{-\infty}^{\infty} e^{-2t}\,\delta(t + 1)\,dt.$

5. $\int_{-1}^{1} (\cos 2t)\delta(t)\,dt.$

6. $\int_0^{\infty} e^{-2t}\,\delta(t - 1)\,dt.$

In Problems 7 through 12 determine the Laplace transform of the given function.

7. $3\delta(t - 1).$

8. $\delta(t - 1) - \delta(t - 3).$

9. $t\delta(t - 1).$

10. $t^3\delta(t - 3).$

11. $e^t\delta(t - 3).$

12. $\delta(t - \pi)\sin t.$

In Problems 13 through 20 solve the given initial value problem.

13. $y'' + y = \delta(t - \pi);$ $y(0) = 0,$ $y'(0) = 0.$

14. $y'' + 2y' + 2y = \delta(t - \pi);$ $y(0) = 1,$ $y'(0) = 1.$

15. $y'' + 2y' - 3y = \delta(t - 1) - \delta(t - 2);$ $y(0) = 2,$ $y'(0) = -2.$

16. $y'' - 2y' - 3y = 2\delta(t-1) - \delta(t-3);$ $\qquad y(0) = 2,$ $\qquad y'(0) = 2.$

17. $y'' - y' - 2y = 3\delta(t-1) + e^t;$ $\qquad y(0) = 0,$ $\qquad y'(0) = 3.$

18. $y'' - y = 4\delta(t-2) + t^2;$ $\qquad y(0) = 0,$ $\qquad y'(0) = 2.$

19. $y'' + 6y' + 5y = e^t\delta(t-1);$ $\qquad y(0) = 0,$ $\qquad y'(0) = 4.$

20. $y'' + 5y' + 6y = e^{-t}\delta(t-2);$ $\qquad y(0) = 2,$ $\qquad y'(0) = -5.$

In Problems 21 through 24 solve the given initial value problem and sketch a graph of the solution.

21. $y'' + y = \delta(t - 2\pi);$ $\qquad y(0) = 0,$ $\qquad y'(0) = 1.$

22. $y'' + y = \delta(t - \pi/2);$ $\qquad y(0) = 0,$ $\qquad y'(0) = 1.$

23. $y'' + y = -\delta(t - \pi) + \delta(t - 2\pi);$ $\qquad y(0) = 0,$ $\qquad y'(0) = 1.$

24. $y'' + y = \delta(t - \pi) - \delta(t - 2\pi);$ $\qquad y(0) = 0,$ $\qquad y'(0) = 1.$

In Problems 25 through 28 find the impulse response function h(t) by using the fact that h(t) is the solution to the initial value problem with g(t) = δ(t) and zero initial conditions.

25. $y'' + 4y' + 8y = g(t).$ $\qquad\qquad\qquad$ **26.** $y'' - 2y' + 5y = g(t).$

27. $y'' - 6y' + 13y = g(t).$ $\qquad\qquad\qquad$ **28.** $y'' - y = g(t).$

29. A mass attached to a spring is released from rest 1 m below the equilibrium position for the spring-mass system and begins to vibrate. After $\pi/2$ seconds, the mass is struck by a hammer exerting an impulse on the mass. The system is governed by the initial value problem

$$\frac{d^2x}{dt^2} + 9x = -3\delta\left(t - \frac{\pi}{2}\right); \qquad x(0) = 1, \qquad \frac{dx}{dt}(0) = 0,$$

where $x(t)$ denotes the displacement from equilibrium at time t. What happens to the mass after it is struck?

30. You have probably heard that soldiers are told not to march in cadence when crossing a bridge. By solving the initial value problem

$$y'' + y = \sum_{k=1}^{\infty} \delta(t - 2k\pi); \qquad y(0) = 0, \qquad y'(0) = 0,$$

explain why soldiers are so instructed. [Hint: See Section 5.3.]

31. A linear system is said to be **stable** if its impulse response function $h(t)$ remains bounded as $t \to \infty$. If the linear system is governed by

$$ay'' + by' + cy = g(t),$$

where b and c are not both zero, show that the system is stable if and only if the real parts of the roots to

$$ar^2 + br + c = 0$$

are less than or equal to zero.

32. A linear system is said to be **asymptotically stable** if its impulse response function satisfies $h(t) \to 0$ as $t \to \infty$. If the linear system is governed by

$$ay'' + by' + cy = g(t),$$

show that the system is asymptotically stable if and only if the real parts of the roots to

$$ar^2 + br + c = 0$$

are strictly less than zero.

33. The Dirac delta function may also be characterized by the properties

$$\delta(t) = \begin{cases} 0, & t \neq 0, \\ \text{``infinite,''} & t = 0 \end{cases} \quad \text{and} \quad \int_{-\infty}^{\infty} \delta(t)\,dt = 1.$$

Formally using the mean value theorem for definite integrals, verify that if $f(t)$ is continuous, then the above properties imply

$$\int_{-\infty}^{\infty} f(t)\delta(t)\,dt = f(0).$$

34. Formally using integration by parts, show that

$$\int_{-\infty}^{\infty} f(t)\delta'(t)\,dt = -f'(0).$$

Also show that, in general,

$$\int_{-\infty}^{\infty} f(t)\delta^{(n)}(t)\,dt = (-1)^n f^{(n)}(0).$$

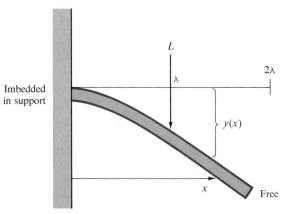

Figure 7.11 Beam imbedded in a support under a concentrated load at $x = \lambda$

35. Figure 7.11 shows a beam of length 2λ that is imbedded in a support on the left and free on the right. The vertical deflection of the beam a distance x from the support is denoted by $y(x)$. If the beam has a concentrated load L acting on it in the center of the beam, then the deflection must satisfy the boundary value problem

$$EIy^{(4)}(x) = L\delta(x - \lambda); \qquad y(0) = y'(0) = y''(2\lambda) = y'''(2\lambda) = 0,$$

where E, the modulus of elasticity, and I, a moment of inertia, are constants. Find a formula for the displacement $y(x)$ in terms of the constants λ, L, E, and I. [Hint: Let $y''(0) = A$ and $y'''(0) = B$. First solve the fourth order initial value problem and then use the conditions $y''(2\lambda) = y'''(2\lambda) = 0$ to determine A and B.]

Chapter Summary

The use of the Laplace transform helps to simplify the process of solving initial value problems for certain differential and integral equations, especially when a discontinuous forcing function is involved. The Laplace transform $\mathscr{L}\{f\}$ of a function $f(t)$ is defined by

$$\mathscr{L}\{f\}(s) := \int_0^\infty e^{-st}f(t)\,dt,$$

for all values of s for which the improper integral exists. If $f(t)$ is piecewise continuous on $[0, \infty)$ and of exponential order α (that is, $|f(t)|$ grows no faster than a constant times $e^{\alpha t}$ as $t \to \infty$), then $\mathscr{L}\{f\}(s)$ exists for all $s > \alpha$.

The Laplace transform can be interpreted as an integral operator that maps a function $f(t)$ to a function $F(s)$. The transforms of commonly occurring functions appear in Table 7.1, page 335, and on the inside back cover. The use of these tables is enhanced by several important properties of the operator $\mathscr{L}$.

Linearity: $\mathscr{L}\{af + bg\} = a\mathscr{L}\{f\} + b\mathscr{L}\{g\}$.

Translation Property: $\mathscr{L}\{e^{at}f(t)\}(s) = F(s - a)$, where $F = \mathscr{L}\{f\}$.

Shifting Property: $\mathscr{L}\{g(t)u(t - a)\}(s) = e^{-as}\mathscr{L}\{g(t + a)\}(s)$, where $u(t - a)$ is the step function that equals 1 for $t > a$ and 0 for $t < a$. If $f(t)$ is continuous, then

$$\mathscr{L}^{-1}\{e^{-as}F(s)\}(t) = f(t - a)u(t - a),$$

where $f = \mathscr{L}^{-1}\{F\}$.

Convolution Property: $\mathscr{L}\{f * g\} = \mathscr{L}\{f\}\mathscr{L}\{g\}$, where $f * g$ denotes the convolution function

$$(f * g)(t) := \int_0^t f(t - v)g(v)\,dv.$$

One reason for the usefulness of the Laplace transform lies in the simple formula for the transform of the derivative f':

(1) $\mathcal{L}\{f'\}(s) = sF(s) - f(0)$,   where $F = \mathcal{L}\{f\}$.

This formula shows that, by using the Laplace transform, "differentiation with respect to t" can be replaced by the simple operation of "multiplication by s." The extension of (1) to higher order derivatives is

(2) $\mathcal{L}\{f^{(n)}\}(s) = s^n F(s) - s^{n-1}f(0) - s^{n-2}f'(0) - \cdots - f^{(n-1)}(0)$.

To solve an initial value problem of the form

(3) $ay'' + by' + cy = f(t)$; $y(0) = \alpha$, $y'(0) = \beta$

via the Laplace transform method, one takes the transform of both sides of the differential equation in (3). Using the linearity of $\mathcal{L}$ and formula (2) leads to an equation involving the Laplace transform $Y(s)$ of the (unknown) solution $y(t)$. The next step is to solve this simpler equation for $Y(s)$. Finally, one computes the *inverse* Laplace transform of $Y(s)$ to obtain the desired solution. This last step of finding $\mathcal{L}^{-1}\{Y\}$ is often the most difficult—sometimes requiring a partial fractions decomposition, a judicious use of the properties of the transform, and/or an excursion through the Laplace transform tables.

For the special problem in (3), where a, b, and c are constants, the differential equation is transformed to a simple *algebraic* equation for $Y(s)$. Another nice feature of this latter equation is that it incorporates the initial conditions. When the coefficients of the equation in (3) depend on t, the following formula may be helpful in taking the transform:

$$\mathcal{L}\{t^n f(t)\}(s) = (-1)^n \frac{d^n F}{ds^n}(s), \quad \text{where} \quad F = \mathcal{L}\{f\}.$$

If the forcing function $f(t)$ in equation (3) has jump discontinuities, it is often convenient to write $f(t)$ in terms of unit step functions $u(t-a)$ before proceeding with the Laplace transform method. The transform of a periodic forcing function $f(t)$ with period T is given by

$$\mathcal{L}\{f\}(s) = \frac{\int_0^T e^{-st} f(t)\, dt}{1 - e^{-sT}}.$$

The Dirac delta function $\delta(t)$ is useful in modeling a system that is excited by a large force applied over a short time interval. It is not a function in the usual sense, but can be roughly interpreted as the derivative of a unit step function. The transform of $\delta(t-a)$ is

$$\mathcal{L}\{\delta(t-a)\}(s) = e^{-as}, \quad a \geq 0.$$

REVIEW PROBLEMS

In Problems 1 and 2 use the definition of the Laplace transform to determine $\mathscr{L}\{f\}$.

1. $f(t) = \begin{cases} 3, & 0 \le t \le 2, \\ 6 - t, & 2 < t. \end{cases}$

2. $f(t) = \begin{cases} e^{-t}, & 0 \le t \le 5, \\ -1, & 5 < t. \end{cases}$

In Problems 3 through 10 determine the Laplace transform of the given function.

3. $t^2 e^{-9t}$.

4. $e^{3t} \sin 4t$.

5. $e^{2t} - t^3 + t^2 - \sin 5t$.

6. $7e^{2t} \cos 3t - 2e^{7t} \sin 5t$.

7. $t \cos 6t$.

8. $(t + 3)^2 - (e^t + 3)^2$.

9. $t^2 u(t - 4)$.

10. $f(t) = \cos t, \quad -\pi/2 \le t \le \pi/2$, and $f(t)$ has period π.

In Problems 11 through 17 determine the inverse Laplace transform of the given function.

11. $\dfrac{7}{(s + 3)^3}$.

12. $\dfrac{2s - 1}{s^2 - 4s + 6}$.

13. $\dfrac{4s^2 + 13s + 19}{(s - 1)(s^2 + 4s + 13)}$.

14. $\dfrac{s^2 + 16s + 9}{(s + 1)(s + 3)(s - 2)}$.

15. $\dfrac{2s^2 + 3s - 1}{(s + 1)^2(s + 2)}$.

16. $\dfrac{1}{(s^2 + 9)^2}$.

17. $\dfrac{e^{-2s}(4s + 2)}{(s - 1)(s + 2)}$.

18. Find the Taylor series for $f(t) = e^{-t^2}$ about $t = 0$, and, assuming that the Laplace transform of $f(t)$ can be computed term by term, find an expansion for $\mathscr{L}\{f\}(s)$ in powers of $1/s$.

In Problems 19 through 24 solve the given initial value problem for y(t) using the method of Laplace transforms.

19. $y'' - 7y' + 10y = 0; \quad y(0) = 0, \quad y'(0) = -3$.

20. $y'' + 6y' + 9y = 0; \quad y(0) = -3, \quad y'(0) = 10$.

21. $y'' + 2y' + 2y = t^2 + 4t; \quad y(0) = 0, \quad y'(0) = -1$.

22. $y'' + 9y = 10e^{2t}; \quad y(0) = -1, \quad y'(0) = 5$.

23. $y'' + 3y' + 4y = u(t - 1); \quad y(0) = 0, \quad y'(0) = 1$.

24. $y'' - 4y' + 4y = t^2 e^t; \quad y(0) = 0, \quad y'(0) = 0$.

In Problems 25 and 26 find solutions to the given initial value problem.

25. $ty'' + 2(t - 1)y' - 2y = 0; \quad y(0) = 0, \quad y'(0) = 0$.

26. $ty'' + 2(t - 1)y' + (t - 2)y = 0; \quad y(0) = 1, \quad y'(0) = -1$.

In Problems 27 and 28 solve the given equation for y(t).

27. $y(t) + \displaystyle\int_0^t (t - v)y(v)\, dv = e^{-3t}$.

28. $y'(t) - 2\displaystyle\int_0^t y(v)\sin(t - v)\, dv = 1; \quad y(0) = -1$.

29. A linear system is governed by

$$y'' - 5y' + 6y = g(t).$$

Find the transfer function and the impulse response function.

30. Solve the initial value problem

$$y'' + 4y = \delta\left(t - \frac{\pi}{2}\right); \qquad y(0) = 0, \qquad y'(0) = 1.$$

Projects for Chapter 7

A. DUHAMEL'S FORMULAS

For a linear system governed by the equation

(1) $\qquad ay'' + by' + cy = g(t),$

where a, b, and c are real constants, the function

(2) $\qquad H(s) := \dfrac{\mathcal{L}\{y\}(s)}{\mathcal{L}\{g\}(s)} = \dfrac{\mathcal{L}\{\text{output}\}}{\mathcal{L}\{\text{input}\}},$

where all initial conditions are taken to be zero, is called the **transfer function** for the system. (As mentioned in Section 7.7, the transfer function $H(s)$ depends only on the constants a, b, c of the system; it is not affected by the choice of g.) If the input function $g(t)$ is the unit step function $u(t)$, then equation (2) yields

$$\mathcal{L}\{y\}(s) = \mathcal{L}\{u\}(s)H(s) = \frac{H(s)}{s}.$$

The solution (output function) in this special case is called the **indicial admittance** and is denoted by $A(t)$. Hence $\mathcal{L}\{A\}(s) = H(s)/s$.

It is possible to express the response $y(t)$ of the system to a general input function $g(t)$ in terms of $g(t)$ and the indicial admittance $A(t)$. To derive these relations, proceed as follows:

(a) Show that

(3) $\qquad \mathcal{L}\{y\}(s) = s\mathcal{L}\{A\}(s)\mathcal{L}\{g\}(s).$

(b) Now apply the convolution theorem to (3) and show that

(4) $\qquad y(t) = \dfrac{d}{dt}\left[\int_0^t A(t - v)g(v)\,dv\right] = \dfrac{d}{dt}\left[\int_0^t A(v)g(t - v)\,dv\right].$

(c) To perform the differentiation indicated in (4), one can use **Leibniz's rule:**

$$\frac{d}{dt}\left[\int_{a(t)}^{b(t)} f(v,t)\,dv\right] = \int_{a(t)}^{b(t)} \frac{\partial f}{\partial t}(v,t)\,dv + f(b(t),t)\frac{db}{dt}(t) - f(a(t),t)\frac{da}{dt}(t),$$

where f and $\partial f/\partial t$ are assumed continuous in v and t, and $a(t)$, $b(t)$ are differentiable functions of t. Applying this rule to (4), derive the formulas

(5) $$y(t) = \int_0^t A'(t-v)g(v)\,dv,$$

(6) $$y(t) = \int_0^t A(v)g'(t-v)\,dv + A(t)g(0).$$

[Hint: Recall that the initial conditions on A are $A(0) = A'(0) = 0$.]

(d) In equations (5) and (6), make the change of variables $w = t - v$ and show that

(7) $$y(t) = \int_0^t A'(w)g(t-w)\,dw,$$

(8) $$y(t) = \int_0^t A(t-w)g'(w)\,dw + A(t)g(0).$$

Equations (5)–(8) are referred to as **Duhamel's formulas,** in honor of the French mathematician J. M. C. Duhamel. These formulas are helpful in determining the response of the system to a general input $g(t)$, since the indicial admittance of the system can be determined experimentally by measuring the response of the system to a unit step function.

(e) The impulse response function $h(t)$ is defined as $h(t) := \mathcal{L}^{-1}\{H\}(t)$, where $H(s)$ is the transfer function. Show that $h(t) = A'(t)$, so that equations (5) and (7) can be written in the form

(9) $$y(t) = \int_0^t h(t-v)g(v)\,dv = \int_0^t h(v)g(t-v)\,dv.$$

We remark that the indicial admittance is the response of the system to a unit step function, and the impulse response function is the response to the unit impulse or delta function (see Section 7.8). But, the delta function is the derivative (in a generalized sense) of the unit step function. Therefore, the fact that $h(t) = A'(t)$ is not really surprising.

B. FREQUENCY RESPONSE MODELING

Frequency response modeling of a linear system is based on the premise that the dynamics of a linear system can be recovered from a knowledge of how the system responds to sinusoidal inputs. (This will be made mathematically precise in Theorem 12.) In other words, to determine (or identify) a linear system, all one has to do is observe how the system reacts to sinusoidal inputs.

Let's assume that we have a linear system governed by

(10) $$y'' + py' + qy = g(t),$$

where p and q are real constants. The function $g(t)$ is called the **forcing function** or **input function.** When $g(t)$ is a sinusoid, the particular solution to (10) obtained by the method of undetermined coefficients is the **steady-state solution** or **output function** $y_{ss}(t)$ corresponding to $g(t)$. We can think of a linear system

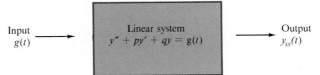

Figure 7.12 Block diagram depicting a linear system

as a compartment or block into which goes an input function g and out of which comes the output function y_{ss} (see Figure 7.12). To **identify** a linear system means to determine the coefficients p and q in equation (10).

It will be convenient for us to work with complex variables. A complex number z is usually expressed in the form $z = \alpha + i\beta$, with α, β real numbers and i denoting $\sqrt{-1}$. We can also express z in polar form, $z = re^{i\theta}$, where $r^2 = \alpha^2 + \beta^2$ and $\tan\theta = \beta/\alpha$. Here r (≥ 0) is called the **magnitude** and θ the **phase angle** of z.

The following theorem gives the relationship between the linear system and its response to sinusoidal inputs in terms of the **transfer function** $H(s)$ (see Project A, equation (2)).

STEADY-STATE SOLUTIONS TO SINUSOIDAL INPUTS

Theorem 12.   Let $H(s)$ be the transfer function for equation (10). If $H(s)$ is finite at $s = i\omega$, with ω real, then the steady-state solution to (10) for $g(t) = e^{i\omega t}$ is

(11) $$y_{ss}(t) = H(i\omega)e^{i\omega t} = H(i\omega)\{\cos\omega t + i\sin\omega t\}.$$

(a) Prove Theorem 12. [Hint: Guess $y_{ss}(t) = Ae^{i\omega t}$ and show that $A = H(i\omega)$.]

(b) Use Theorem 12 to show that if $g(t) = \sin\omega t$, then the steady-state solution to (10) is $M(\omega)\sin(\omega t + N(\omega))$, where $H(i\omega) = M(\omega)e^{iN(\omega)}$ is the polar form for $H(i\omega)$.

(c) Solve for $M(\omega)$ and $N(\omega)$ in terms of p and q.

(d) Experimental results for modeling done by frequency response methods are usually presented in **frequency response**[†] or **Bode plots.** There are two types of Bode plots. The first is of the log of the magnitude $M(\omega)$ of $H(i\omega)$ versus the angular frequency ω using a log scale for ω. The second is a plot of the phase angle or argument $N(\omega)$ of $H(i\omega)$ versus the angular frequency using a log scale for ω. The Bode plots for the transfer function $H(s) = (1 + 0.2s + s^2)^{-1}$ are given in Figure 7.13.

Sketch the Bode plots of the linear system governed by equation (10) with $p = 0.5$ and $q = 1.0$. Use $\omega = 0.3, 0.6, 0.9, 1.2$, and 1.5 for the plot of $M(\omega)$ and $\omega = 0.5, 0.8, 1, 2$, and 5 for the plot of $N(\omega)$.

(e) Assume we know that $q = 1$. When we input a sine wave with $\omega = 2$, the system settles into a steady-state sinusoidal output with magnitude $M(2) = 0.325$. Find p and thus identify the linear system.

[†] Frequency response curves are also discussed in Section 5.3.

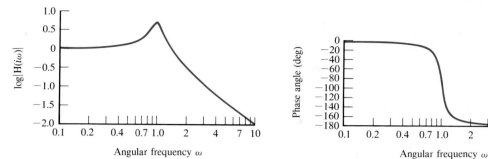

Figure 7.13 Bode plots for
$$H(i\omega) = \left[1 + 0.2(i\omega) + (i\omega)^2\right]^{-1}$$

(f) Suppose that a sine wave input with $\omega = 2$ produces a steady-state sinusoidal output with magnitude $M(2) = 0.447$ and that when $\omega = 4$, then $M(4) = 0.085$. Find p and q and thus identify the system.

We remark that in most applications there are some inaccuracies in the measurement of the magnitudes and frequencies. To compensate for these errors, sinusoids with several different frequencies are used as input. A least squares approximation for p and q is then found. For a discussion of frequency response modeling as a mathematical modeling tool see the chapter by W. F. Powers, "Modeling Linear Systems by Frequency Response Methods," in *Differential Equations Models,* by M. Braun, C. Coleman, and D. Drew (eds.), Springer-Verlag, New York, 1983, Chapter 9. Additional examples may be found in *Schaum's Outline on Feedback and Control Systems,* by J. J. DiStefano, A. R. Stubberud, and I. J. Williams, McGraw-Hill, New York, 1967, Chapter 15.

Series Solution of Linear Differential Equations

8.1 Introduction: A Problem in Astrophysics

In the early 1900s a German astrophysicist, Robert Emden, encountered the following problem in his study of the thermal behavior of a spherical gaseous cloud.

> Determine the first point on the positive x-axis where the solution to the initial value problem
>
> **(1)** $\qquad xy''(x) + 2y'(x) + xy(x) = 0;\qquad y(0) = 1,\qquad y'(0) = 0$
>
> is zero.

The variables x and y in (1) are proportional to, respectively, the distance to the center of the cloud and the gravitational potential of the gas. The initial conditions correspond to the fact that $y(x)$, the potential, has been normalized to be 1 at the center of the cloud and that, at the center of the cloud, the gravitational forces cancel and the net force is zero.

Astrophysicists and astronomers use equation (1) to approximate the density and internal temperatures of certain stars and nebula.[†]

The differential equation in (1) appears nice enough since it is a linear second order equation; however, there are two difficulties. First, while (1) is linear, it has variable coefficients, and hence the methods discussed in Chapter 4 do not apply. Second, we are given initial conditions at $x = 0$, which is precisely where the coefficient of $y''(x)$ is zero. Consequently, even the theoretical results of Chapter 4 do not apply to this problem. While the prospects for finding an explicit solution to the initial value problem appear dim, the physical situation that is modeled suggests that the problem *has* a solution and the solution should be "nice" (analytic). Having faith in the model, let's assume that the solution has a power series expansion denoted by

(2) $$y(x) = a_0 + a_1 x + a_2 x^2 + \cdots = \sum_{n=0}^{\infty} a_n x^n.$$

If we differentiate $y(x)$ as given in (2), term by term, we obtain

(3) $$y'(x) = a_1 + 2a_2 x + 3a_3 x^2 + \cdots = \sum_{n=1}^{\infty} na_n x^{n-1},$$

(4) $$y''(x) = 2a_2 + 6a_3 x + 12a_4 x^2 + \cdots = \sum_{n=2}^{\infty} n(n-1)a_n x^{n-2}.$$

Substituting these series representations for y, y', and y'' in equation (1), we get

$$x(2a_2 + 6a_3 x + 12a_4 x^2 + \cdots + (n+1)na_{n+1}x^{n-1} + \cdots)$$
$$+ 2(a_1 + 2a_2 x + 3a_3 x^2 + 4a_4 x^3 + \cdots + (n+1)a_{n+1}x^n + \cdots)$$
$$+ x(a_0 + a_1 x + a_2 x^2 + \cdots + a_{n-1}x^{n-1} + \cdots) = 0.$$

Grouping like terms gives

(5) $$2a_1 + (6a_2 + a_0)x + (12a_3 + a_1)x^2 + (20a_4 + a_2)x^3$$
$$+ \cdots + ([(n+1)n + 2(n+1)]a_{n+1} + a_{n-1})x^n + \cdots = 0.$$

Now, in order for the power series to sum identically to zero, each of the coefficients must be zero. This means

$$2a_1 = 0, \qquad 6a_2 + a_0 = 0, \qquad 12a_3 + a_1 = 0,$$

[†] Equation (1) is called the **Lane-Emden equation of index $n = 1$** and is discussed in detail in *An Introduction to the Study of Stellar Structure*, by S. Chandrasekhar, Dover Publications, Inc., New York, 1958, Chapter IV.

and, in general,

(6) $(n + 2)(n + 1)a_{n+1} + a_{n-1} = 0.$

Solving, we find

$$a_1 = 0, \qquad a_2 = -\tfrac{1}{6}a_0, \qquad a_3 = -\tfrac{1}{12}a_1 = 0,$$

and, in general,

(7) $a_{n+1} = \dfrac{-a_{n-1}}{(n+2)(n+1)}.$

Since $a_1 = 0$, it follows from (7) that a_3, a_5, a_7, etc., are zero. For the even coefficients, a_2, a_4, etc., we see from repeated applications of (7) that

(8) $a_{2k} = \dfrac{-a_{2k-2}}{(2k+1)(2k)} = \dfrac{-1}{(2k+1)(2k)} \cdot \dfrac{-a_{2k-4}}{(2k-1)(2k-2)} = \cdots$

$$= \frac{(-1)^k a_0}{(2k+1)(2k)\cdots(3)(2)} = \frac{(-1)^k a_0}{(2k+1)!}.$$

Knowing the coefficients of $y(x)$, we insert them into expansion (2) and obtain

(9) $y(x) = a_0\left(1 - \dfrac{1}{6}x^2 + \dfrac{1}{120}x^4 + \cdots + \dfrac{(-1)^k x^{2k}}{(2k+1)!} + \cdots\right)$

as a solution to the differential equation.

Next, we substitute in the initial conditions $y(0) = 1$, $y'(0) = 0$. From (9) we see that $y(0) = a_0$ and $y'(0) = 0$. Hence $a_0 = 1$. (Notice our good fortune: Equation (9) has only one parameter, a_0, yet we are able to satisfy *both* initial conditions.) Letting $a_0 = 1$ in (9), we find that the solution to the initial value problem (1) is

(10) $y(x) = 1 - \dfrac{1}{6}x^2 + \dfrac{1}{120}x^4 - \dfrac{1}{5040}x^6 + \cdots + \dfrac{(-1)^k x^{2k}}{(2k+1)!} + \cdots.$

Now recall that we are interested in the first (positive) zero of $y(x)$. To locate this zero, it would be desirable to have a closed-form expression for $y(x)$. Again good fortune is with us: The expansion in (10) is a recognizable one. It is the Taylor series for $(\sin x)/x$. Hence $y(x) = (\sin x)/x$, and the first positive zero of $y(x)$ occurs when $\sin x = 0$; that is, when $x = \pi$.

In this chapter we study methods for determining series expansions for solutions to differential equations with variable coefficients. In particular, we determine the form of the series expansion, a recurrence relation for determining the coefficients a_n, and the interval of convergence of the expansion.

8.2 Power Series, Analytic Functions, and the Taylor Series Method[†]

The differential equations studied in earlier chapters often possessed solutions expressible in terms of elementary functions such as polynomials, exponentials, sines, and cosines. However, many important equations arise that do not have solutions that can be so conveniently expressed. In previous chapters, when we encountered such an equation we either expressed the solution as an integral (see Problem 27 in Exercises 2.2) or tried to approximate it numerically (see Sections 3.6 and 3.7). In this chapter, our goal is to obtain a representation for the solution as a power series. We begin with a brief review of the basic definitions and properties of power series and real analytic functions.

POWER SERIES

A **power series** about the point x_0 is an expression of the form

(1)
$$\sum_{n=0}^{\infty} a_n(x - x_0)^n = a_0 + a_1(x - x_0) + a_2(x - x_0)^2 + \cdots,$$

where x is a variable and the a_n's are constants. We say that (1) **converges** at the point $x = r$ if the infinite series (of real numbers) $\sum_{n=0}^{\infty} a_n(r - x_0)^n$ converges; that is, the limit of the partial sums,

(2)
$$\lim_{N \to \infty} \sum_{n=0}^{N} a_n(r - x_0)^n,$$

exists (as a finite number). If this limit does not exist, the power series is said to **diverge** at $x = r$. Observe that (1) converges at $x = x_0$ since

(3)
$$\sum_{n=0}^{\infty} a_n(x_0 - x_0)^n = a_0 + 0 + 0 + \cdots = a_0.$$

But what about convergence for other values of x? As stated in Theorem 1, a power series of the form (1) converges for all values of x in some "interval" centered at x_0 and diverges for x outside this interval. Moreover, at the interior points of this interval, the power series converges **absolutely** in the sense that $\sum_{n=0}^{\infty} |a_n(x - x_0)^n|$ converges. (Recall that absolute convergence of a series implies (ordinary) convergence of the series.)

[†] This section contains review material from calculus and a discussion of the Taylor series method briefly introduced in Project A in Chapter 1.

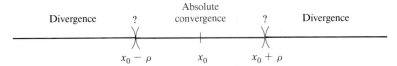

Figure 8.1 Interval of convergence

RADIUS OF CONVERGENCE

Theorem 1. For each power series of the form (1), there is a number ρ $(0 \le \rho \le \infty)$, called the **radius of convergence** of the power series, such that (1) converges absolutely for $|x - x_0| < \rho$ and diverges for $|x - x_0| > \rho$. (See Figure 8.1.)

If the series (1) converges for all values of x, then $\rho = \infty$. When the series (1) converges only at x_0, then $\rho = 0$.

Notice that Theorem 1 settles the question of convergence except at the endpoints $x_0 \pm \rho$. Thus these two points require separate analysis. To determine the radius of convergence ρ, one method that is often easy to apply is the ratio test.

RATIO TEST

Theorem 2. If

$$(4) \qquad \lim_{n \to \infty} \left| \frac{a_{n+1}}{a_n} \right| = L,$$

where $0 \le L \le \infty$, then the radius of convergence of the power series $\sum_{n=0}^{\infty} a_n(x - x_0)^n$ is $\rho = 1/L$, with $\rho = \infty$ if $L = 0$ and $\rho = 0$ if $L = \infty$.

Remark We caution the reader that if the limit of the ratio $|a_{n+1}/a_n|$ does not exist, then methods other than the ratio test (e.g., root test) must be used to determine ρ.

▶ **Example 1** Determine the convergence set of

$$(5) \qquad \sum_{n=0}^{\infty} \frac{(-2)^n}{n+1} (x - 3)^n.$$

Solution Since $a_n = (-2)^n/(n + 1)$, we have

$$\lim_{n \to \infty} \left| \frac{a_{n+1}}{a_n} \right| = \lim_{n \to \infty} \left| \frac{(-2)^{n+1}(n + 1)}{(-2)^n(n + 2)} \right|$$

$$= \lim_{n \to \infty} \frac{2(n + 1)}{(n + 2)} = 2 = L.$$

By the ratio test, the radius of convergence is $\rho = \frac{1}{2}$. Hence the series (5) converges absolutely for $|x - 3| < \frac{1}{2}$ and diverges when $|x - 3| > \frac{1}{2}$. It remains only to determine what happens when $|x - 3| = \frac{1}{2}$, that is, when $x = \frac{5}{2}$ and $x = \frac{7}{2}$.

Setting $x = \frac{5}{2}$, the series (5) becomes the harmonic series $\sum_{n=0}^{\infty} (n + 1)^{-1}$, which is known to diverge. When $x = \frac{7}{2}$ the series (5) becomes an **alternating** harmonic series, which is known to converge. Thus the power series converges for each x in the half-open interval $(\frac{5}{2}, \frac{7}{2}]$; outside this interval it diverges. ◄

For each value of x for which the power series $\sum_{n=0}^{\infty} a_n(x - x_0)^n$ converges, we get a number that is the sum of the series. It is appropriate to denote this sum by $f(x)$ since its value depends on the choice of x. Thus we write

$$f(x) = \sum_{n=0}^{\infty} a_n(x - x_0)^n,$$

for all numbers x in the convergence interval. For example, the **geometric series** $\sum_{n=0}^{\infty} x^n$ has the radius of convergence $\rho = 1$ and the sum function $f(x) = 1/(1 - x)$; that is,

(6) $$\frac{1}{1 - x} = 1 + x + x^2 + \cdots = \sum_{n=0}^{\infty} x^n \quad \text{for} \quad -1 < x < 1.$$

Given two power series

(7) $$f(x) = \sum_{n=0}^{\infty} a_n(x - x_0)^n, \qquad g(x) = \sum_{n=0}^{\infty} b_n(x - x_0)^n,$$

with nonzero radii of convergence, we wish to find power series representations for the sum, product, and quotient of the functions $f(x)$ and $g(x)$. The sum is simply obtained by termwise addition:

(8) $$f(x) + g(x) = \sum_{n=0}^{\infty} (a_n + b_n)(x - x_0)^n$$

for all x in the common interval of convergence of the power series in (7). The power series representation for the product $f(x)g(x)$ is a bit more complicated. To provide motivation for the formula, we treat the power series for $f(x)$ and $g(x)$ as "long polynomials," apply the distributive law, and group the terms in powers of $(x - x_0)$:

$$[a_0 + a_1(x - x_0) + a_2(x - x_0)^2 + \cdots] \cdot [b_0 + b_1(x - x_0) + b_2(x - x_0)^2 + \cdots]$$
$$= a_0 b_0 + (a_0 b_1 + a_1 b_0)(x - x_0) + (a_0 b_2 + a_1 b_1 + a_2 b_0)(x - x_0)^2 + \cdots.$$

The general formula for the product is

(9) $$f(x)g(x) = \sum_{n=0}^{\infty} c_n (x - x_0)^n,$$

where

(10) $$c_n := \sum_{k=0}^{n} a_k b_{n-k}.$$

The power series in (9) is called the **Cauchy product,** and it will converge for all x in the common *open* interval of convergence for the power series in (7).[†]
   The quotient $f(x)/g(x)$ will also have a power series expansion about x_0 provided that $g(x_0) \neq 0$. However, the radius of convergence for this quotient series may be smaller than that for $f(x)$ or $g(x)$. Unfortunately, there is no nice formula for obtaining the coefficients in the power series for $f(x)/g(x)$. However, we can use the Cauchy product to divide power series indirectly (see Problem 13). The quotient series can also be obtained by formally carrying out polynomial long division (see Problem 14).
   The next theorem explains, in part, why power series are so useful.

DIFFERENTIATION AND INTEGRATION OF POWER SERIES

Theorem 3.   If the series $f(x) = \sum_{n=0}^{\infty} a_n(x - x_0)^n$ has a positive radius of convergence ρ, then termwise differentiation gives the power series for the derivative of f:

$$f'(x) = \sum_{n=1}^{\infty} n a_n (x - x_0)^{n-1} \quad \text{for} \quad |x - x_0| < \rho,$$

and termwise integration gives the power series for the integral of f:

$$\int f(x)\,dx = \sum_{n=0}^{\infty} \frac{a_n}{n+1} (x - x_0)^{n+1} + C \quad \text{for} \quad |x - x_0| < \rho.$$

[†] Actually, it may happen that the radius of convergence of the power series in (9) (or (8)) is larger than that for $\sum a_n(x - x_0)^n$ and for $\sum b_n(x - x_0)^n$.

▶ *Example 2* Starting with the geometric series (6) for $1/(1 - x)$, find a power series for each of the following functions:

$$(a) \quad \frac{1}{1 + x^2}, \qquad (b) \quad \frac{1}{(1 - x)^2}, \qquad (c) \quad \arctan x.$$

Solution (a) Replacing x by $-x^2$ in (6) immediately gives

$$(11) \qquad \frac{1}{1 + x^2} = 1 - x^2 + x^4 - x^6 + \cdots + (-1)^n x^{2n} + \cdots.$$

(b) Notice that $1/(1 - x)^2$ is the derivative of the function $f(x) = 1/(1 - x)$. Hence on differentiating (6) term by term, we obtain

$$(12) \qquad f'(x) = \frac{1}{(1 - x)^2} = 1 + 2x + 3x^2 + 4x^3 + \cdots + nx^{n-1} + \cdots.$$

(c) Since

$$\arctan x = \int_0^x \frac{1}{1 + t^2}\, dt,$$

we can integrate the series in (11) termwise to obtain the series for $\arctan x$. Thus

$$\int_0^x \frac{1}{1 + t^2}\, dt = \int_0^x \{1 - t^2 + t^4 - t^6 + \cdots + (-1)^n t^{2n} + \cdots\}\, dt$$

$$(13) \qquad \arctan x = x - \frac{1}{3}x^3 + \frac{1}{5}x^5 - \frac{1}{7}x^7 + \cdots + \frac{(-1)^n x^{2n+1}}{2n + 1} + \cdots. \quad ◀$$

It is important to keep in mind that since the geometric series (6) has the (open) interval of convergence $(-1, 1)$, the representations (11), (12), and (13) are at least valid in this interval. (Actually, the series (13) for $\arctan x$ converges for all $|x| \le 1$.)

The index of summation in a power series is a dummy index just like the variable of integration in a definite integral. Hence

$$\sum_{n=0}^{\infty} a_n(x - x_0)^n = \sum_{k=0}^{\infty} a_k(x - x_0)^k = \sum_{i=0}^{\infty} a_i(x - x_0)^i.$$

Just as there are times when we want to change the variable of integration, there are situations (and we will encounter many in this chapter) when it is desirable to change or shift the index of summation.

▶ *Example 3*   Express the series

(14) $$\sum_{n=2}^{\infty} n(n-1)a_n x^{n-2},$$

using the index k, where $k = n - 2$.

Solution   Since $k = n - 2$, we have $n = k + 2$. When $n = 2$, then $k = 0$. Hence, substituting into (14) we find

$$\sum_{n=2}^{\infty} n(n-1)a_n x^{n-2} = \sum_{k=0}^{\infty} (k+2)(k+1)a_{k+2} x^k. \quad ◀$$

ANALYTIC FUNCTIONS

Not all functions are expressible as power series. Those distinguished functions that can be so represented are called **analytic.**

ANALYTIC FUNCTION

Definition 1.   A function f is said to be **analytic at** x_0 if, in an open interval about x_0, this function is the sum of a power series $\sum_{n=0}^{\infty} a_n(x - x_0)^n$ that has a positive radius of convergence.

For example, a polynomial function $b_0 + b_1 x + \cdots + b_n x^n$ is analytic at every x_0 since we can always rewrite it in the form $a_0 + a_1(x - x_0) + \cdots + a_n(x - x_0)^n$. A rational function $P(x)/Q(x)$, where $P(x)$ and $Q(x)$ are polynomials without a common factor, is an analytic function except at those x_0 for which $Q(x_0) = 0$. As the reader may recall from calculus, the elementary functions e^x, $\sin x$, and $\cos x$ are analytic for all x, while $\ln x$ is analytic for $x > 0$. Indeed, we have the familiar representations

(15) $$e^x = 1 + x + \frac{x^2}{2!} + \frac{x^3}{3!} + \cdots = \sum_{n=0}^{\infty} \frac{x^n}{n!},$$

(16) $$\sin x = x - \frac{x^3}{3!} + \frac{x^5}{5!} - \cdots = \sum_{n=0}^{\infty} \frac{(-1)^n}{(2n+1)!} x^{2n+1},$$

(17) $$\cos x = 1 - \frac{x^2}{2!} + \frac{x^4}{4!} - \cdots = \sum_{n=0}^{\infty} \frac{(-1)^n}{(2n)!} x^{2n},$$

(18) $$\ln x = (x-1) - \frac{1}{2}(x-1)^2 + \frac{1}{3}(x-1)^3 - \cdots = \sum_{n=1}^{\infty} \frac{(-1)^{n-1}}{n}(x-1)^n.$$

where (15), (16), and (17) are valid for all x, whereas (18) is valid for x in the half-open interval (0, 2]. In (18) the expansion is about $x_0 = 1$. However, a power series representation for ln x can be derived about any $x_0 > 0$.

From Theorem 3 on the differentiation of power series, we see that a function f analytic at x_0 is differentiable in a neighborhood of x_0. Moreover, because f' has a power series representation in this neighborhood, it too is analytic at x_0. Repeating this argument, we see that f'', $f^{(3)}$, etc., exist and are analytic at x_0.

A formula for the coefficients in the power series of an analytic function is given in the next theorem.

TAYLOR AND MACLAURIN SERIES

Theorem 4. If f is analytic at x_0, then the representation

(19)
$$f(x) = \sum_{n=0}^{\infty} \frac{f^{(n)}(x_0)}{n!} (x - x_0)^n$$

$$= f(x_0) + f'(x_0)(x - x_0) + \frac{f''(x_0)}{2!} (x - x_0)^2 + \cdots,$$

holds in some open interval centered at x_0.

The series (19) is called the **Taylor series** for f about x_0. When $x_0 = 0$, it is also referred to as the **Maclaurin series** for f.

To determine the Taylor series for an analytic function f, a direct but sometimes tedious approach is to compute the successive derivatives of f and evaluate them at x_0. For example, the series in (15), (16), (17), and (18) can be derived in this manner.

Power series expansions also have a uniqueness property; namely, if the equation

$$\sum_{n=0}^{\infty} a_n(x - x_0)^n = \sum_{n=0}^{\infty} b_n(x - x_0)^n$$

holds in some *open* interval about x_0, then $a_n = b_n$ for $n = 0, 1, 2, \ldots$. Hence, if "by hook or by crook" we can produce a power series expansion for an analytic function, then this power series must be its Taylor series. For example, the expansion for arctan x given in (13) of Example 2 must be its Maclaurin expansion.

The reader will also find it helpful to keep in mind that if f and g are analytic at x_0, then so are $f + g$, cf, fg, and f/g, provided $g(x_0) \neq 0$. These facts follow from the algebraic properties of power series discussed earlier.

TAYLOR SERIES METHOD

We can use the Taylor series representation to obtain a series solution to an initial value problem. Assuming that we know the problem has an analytic solution, say by some existence theorem, then we can use the initial conditions and the differential equation itself to compute the successive derivatives of the solution at the initial point. Substituting these values into formula (19) for the Taylor series, we then obtain a representation of the solution as a power series about the initial point x_0. This procedure, called the **Taylor series method,** is illustrated in the next example.

▶ **Example 4**   Determine the first few terms of a power series solution for the initial value problem

$$(20) \qquad y' = \frac{1}{x + y + 1}, \qquad y(0) = 0.$$

Solution   Let's assume that the solution to this initial value problem is analytic at $x = 0$. Then we can write

$$(21) \qquad y(x) = \sum_{n=0}^{\infty} \frac{y^{(n)}(0)}{n!} x^n.$$

We already know that $y(0) = 0$, and substituting $x = 0$ and $y = 0$ into equation (20) we find that $y'(0) = 1$. To determine $y''(0)$ we differentiate both sides of the equation in (20) with respect to x, getting an expression for $y''(x)$ in terms of x, $y(x)$, and $y'(x)$. That is,

$$(22) \qquad y''(x) = (-1)[x + y(x) + 1]^{-2}[1 + y'(x)].$$

Substituting $x = 0$, $y(0) = 0$, and $y'(0) = 1$ in (22), we obtain

$$y''(0) = (-1)(1)^{-2}(1 + 1) = -2.$$

Similarly, differentiating (22) and substituting, we obtain

$$y^{(3)}(x) = 2[x + y(x) + 1]^{-3}[1 + y'(x)]^2 - (x + y(x) + 1)^{-2}y''(x),$$
$$y^{(3)}(0) = 2(1)^{-3}(1 + 1)^2 - (1)^{-2}(-2) = 10.$$

Repeating this procedure, we can determine $y^{(n)}(0)$ for any value of n, although the amount of work needed to compute $y^{(n)}(0)$ increases as n increases. Finally, substituting into (21), we find that the first few terms of the Maclaurin series of the solution to (20) are

$$y(x) = x - x^2 + \tfrac{5}{3}x^3 + \cdots. \quad \blacktriangleleft$$

The Taylor series method applies to nonlinear as well as linear equations. This is in contrast to the methods in the remainder of this chapter, which are restricted to linear equations.

One disadvantage of the Taylor series method is that by computing finitely many terms of the Taylor expansion, there is no way of knowing the radius of convergence of the series. Fortunately, when the differential equation is linear, there are existence theorems that give a minimum value for this radius (see Theorem 5 in Section 8.4).

EXERCISES 8.2 _____

In Problems 1 through 6 determine the convergence set of the given power series.

1. $\displaystyle\sum_{n=0}^{\infty} \frac{3^n}{n!} x^n.$

2. $\displaystyle\sum_{n=0}^{\infty} \frac{2^{-n}}{n+1} (x-1)^n.$

3. $\displaystyle\sum_{n=0}^{\infty} \frac{n^2}{2^n} (x+2)^n.$

4. $\displaystyle\sum_{n=1}^{\infty} \frac{4}{n^2+2n} (x-3)^n.$

5. $\displaystyle\sum_{n=0}^{\infty} \frac{(n+2)!}{n!} (x+2)^n.$

6. $\displaystyle\sum_{n=1}^{\infty} \frac{3}{n^3} (x-2)^n.$

In Problems 7 and 8 find the power series expansion for $f(x) + g(x)$, given the expansions for $f(x)$ and $g(x)$.

7. $\displaystyle f(x) = \sum_{n=0}^{\infty} \frac{1}{n+1} x^n, \qquad g(x) = \sum_{n=1}^{\infty} 2^{-n} x^{n-1}.$

8. $\displaystyle f(x) = \sum_{n=3}^{\infty} \frac{2^n}{n!} (x-1)^{n-3}, \qquad g(x) = \sum_{n=1}^{\infty} \frac{n^2}{2^n} (x-1)^{n-1}.$

In Problems 9 through 12 find the first three nonzero terms in the power series expansion for the product $f(x)g(x)$.

9. $\displaystyle f(x) = e^x = \sum_{n=0}^{\infty} \frac{1}{n!} x^n, \qquad g(x) = \sin x = \sum_{k=0}^{\infty} \frac{(-1)^k}{(2k+1)!} x^{2k+1}.$

10. $\displaystyle f(x) = e^{-x} = \sum_{n=0}^{\infty} \frac{(-1)^n}{n!} x^n, \qquad g(x) = (1+x)^{-1} = \sum_{n=0}^{\infty} (-1)^n x^n.$

11. $\displaystyle f(x) = \sin x = \sum_{k=0}^{\infty} \frac{(-1)^k}{(2k+1)!} x^{2k+1}, \qquad g(x) = \cos x = \sum_{k=0}^{\infty} \frac{(-1)^k}{(2k)!} x^{2k}.$

12. $\displaystyle f(x) = e^x = \sum_{n=0}^{\infty} \frac{1}{n!} x^n, \qquad g(x) = e^{-x} = \sum_{n=0}^{\infty} \frac{(-1)^n}{n!} x^n.$

13. Find the first few terms of the power series for the quotient

(23) $$q(x) = \left(\sum_{n=0}^{\infty} \frac{1}{2^n} x^n \right) \bigg/ \left(\sum_{n=0}^{\infty} \frac{1}{n!} x^n \right)$$

by completing the following:

(a) Let $q(x) = \sum_{n=0}^{\infty} a_n x^n$, where the coefficients a_n are to be determined. Show that $\sum_{n=0}^{\infty} x^n/2^n$ is the Cauchy product of $q(x)$ and $\sum_{n=0}^{\infty} x^n/n!$.

(b) Use formula (10) of the Cauchy product to deduce the equations

$$\frac{1}{2^0} = a_0, \qquad \frac{1}{2} = a_0 + a_1, \qquad \frac{1}{2^2} = \frac{a_0}{2} + a_1 + a_2,$$

$$\frac{1}{2^3} = \frac{a_0}{6} + \frac{a_1}{2} + a_2 + a_3, \ldots$$

(c) Solve the equations in part (b) to determine the constants a_0, a_1, a_2, a_3.

14. To find the first few terms in the power series for the quotient in (23) treat the power series in the numerator and denominator as "long polynomials" and carry out long division. That is, perform

$$1 + x + \tfrac{1}{2}x^2 + \cdots \overline{\big)\, 1 + \tfrac{1}{2}x + \tfrac{1}{4}x^2 + \cdots}.$$

In Problems 15 through 18 find a power series expansion for $f'(x)$, given the expansion for $f(x)$.

15. $f(x) = (1 + x)^{-1} = \displaystyle\sum_{n=0}^{\infty} (-1)^n x^n.$

16. $f(x) = \sin x = \displaystyle\sum_{k=0}^{\infty} \frac{(-1)^k}{(2k + 1)!} x^{2k+1}.$

17. $f(x) = \displaystyle\sum_{n=0}^{\infty} a_n x^n.$

18. $f(x) = \displaystyle\sum_{n=1}^{\infty} n a_n x^{n-1}.$

In Problems 19 and 20 find a power series expansion for $g(x) := \int_0^x f(t)\,dt$ given the expansion for $f(x)$.

19. $f(x) = (1 + x)^{-1} = \displaystyle\sum_{n=0}^{\infty} (-1)^n x^n.$

20. $f(x) = \dfrac{\sin x}{x} = \displaystyle\sum_{k=0}^{\infty} \frac{(-1)^k}{(2k + 1)!} x^{2k}.$

In Problems 21 through 26 express the given power series using the new index k, where the relationship between k and n is given.

21. $\displaystyle\sum_{n=1}^{\infty} n a_n x^{n-1}, \qquad k = n - 1.$

22. $\displaystyle\sum_{n=2}^{\infty} n(n - 1) a_n x^{n+2}, \qquad k = n + 2.$

23. $\displaystyle\sum_{n=0}^{\infty} a_n x^{n+1}, \qquad k = n + 1.$

24. $\displaystyle\sum_{n=1}^{\infty} a_n x^n, \qquad k = n - 1.$

25. $\displaystyle\sum_{n=2}^{\infty} n(n - 1) a_n x^{n+1}, \qquad k = n + 1.$

26. $\displaystyle\sum_{n=1}^{\infty} n a_n x^{n+1}, \qquad k = n + 1.$

In Problems 27 through 32 determine the Taylor series about the point x_0 for the given functions and values of x_0.

27. $f(x) = \cos x, \qquad x_0 = \pi.$

28. $f(x) = x^{-1}, \qquad x_0 = 1.$

29. $f(x) = \ln(1 + x), \qquad x_0 = 0.$

30. $f(x) = \dfrac{1 + x}{1 - x}, \qquad x_0 = 0.$

31. $f(x) = x^3 + 3x - 4, \qquad x_0 = 1.$

32. $f(x) = \sqrt{x}, \qquad x_0 = 1.$

33. The Taylor series for $f(x) = \ln x$ about $x_0 = 1$ given in equation (18) can also be obtained as follows.

(a) Starting with the expansion $1/(1 - s) = \sum_{n=0}^{\infty} s^n$ and observing that

$$\frac{1}{x} = \frac{1}{1 + (x - 1)},$$

obtain the Taylor series for $1/x$ about $x_0 = 1$.

(b) Since $\ln x = \int_1^x 1/t \, dt$, use the result of part (a) and termwise integration to obtain the Taylor series for $f(x) = \ln x$ about $x_0 = 1$.

34. Let $f(x)$ and $g(x)$ be analytic at x_0. Determine whether the following statements are always true or sometimes false.

(a) $3f(x) + g(x)$ is analytic at x_0.

(b) $f(x)/g(x)$ is analytic at x_0.

(c) $f'(x)$ is analytic at x_0.

(d) $[f(x)]^3 - \int_{x_0}^x g(t) \, dt$ is analytic at x_0.

(e) $\sin[f(x)]$ is analytic at x_0.

In Problems 35 through 42 use the Taylor series method to determine the first three nonzero terms of a series solution for the given initial value problem.

35. $y' = y^2;$ $\quad y(0) = 1.$

36. $y' = x^2 + y^2;$ $\quad y(0) = 1.$

37. $y' = \sin y + e^x;$ $\quad y(0) = 0.$

38. $y' = \sin(x + y);$ $\quad y(0) = 0.$

39. $y'' + y = 0;$ $\quad y(0) = 0,$ $\quad y'(0) = 1.$

40. $y'' + xy = 0;$ $\quad y(0) = 1,$ $\quad y'(0) = 0.$

41. $y'' + \sin y = 0;$ $\quad y(0) = 1,$ $\quad y'(0) = 0.$

42. $y'' + y^3 = \sin x;$ $\quad y(0) = 0,$ $\quad y'(0) = 0.$

43. Let

$$f(x) = \begin{cases} e^{-1/x^2}, & x \neq 0, \\ 0, & x = 0. \end{cases}$$

Show that $f^{(n)}(0) = 0$ for $n = 0, 1, 2, \ldots$, and hence that the Maclaurin series for $f(x)$ is $0 + 0 + 0 + \cdots$, which converges for all x, but is equal to $f(x)$ only when $x = 0$.

44. Van der Pol Equation. In the study of the vacuum tube, the following equation is encountered:

$$y'' + (0.1)(y^2 - 1)y' + y = 0.$$

Use the Taylor series method to find the first three nonzero terms of the series solution for the initial values $y(0) = 1$, $y'(0) = 0$.

45. Duffing's Equation. In the study of a nonlinear spring with periodic forcing the following equation arises

$$y'' + ky + ry^3 = A \cos \omega t.$$

Let $k = r = A = 1$ and $\omega = 10$. Use the Taylor series method to find the first three nonzero terms of the series solution for the initial values $y(0) = 0$, $y'(0) = 1$.

8.3 *Power Series Solutions to Linear Differential Equations*

In this section we demonstrate a method for obtaining a power series solution to a linear differential equation with polynomial coefficients. This method is easier to use than the Taylor series method discussed in Section 8.2 and sometimes gives a nice expression for the general term in the power series expansion. Knowing the form of the general term also allows us to test for the radius of convergence of the power series.

We begin by writing the linear differential equation

(1) $$a_2(x)y'' + a_1(x)y' + a_0(x)y = 0$$

in the standard form

(2) $$y'' + p(x)y' + q(x)y = 0,$$

where $p(x) := a_1(x)/a_2(x)$ and $q(x) := a_0(x)/a_2(x)$.

ORDINARY AND SINGULAR POINTS

Definition 2. A point x_0 is called an **ordinary point** of equation (1) if both $p = a_1/a_2$ and $q = a_0/a_2$ are analytic at x_0. If x_0 is not an ordinary point, it is called a **singular point** of the equation.

▶ *Example 1* Determine all the singular points of

(3) $$xy'' + x(1 - x)^{-1}y' + (\sin x)y = 0.$$

Solution Dividing equation (3) by x, we find that

$$p(x) = \frac{x}{x(1 - x)}, \qquad q(x) = \frac{\sin x}{x}.$$

The singular points of (3) are those points where $p(x)$ *or* $q(x)$ fails to be analytic. Observe that $p(x)$ and $q(x)$ are the ratios of functions that are everywhere analytic. Hence $p(x)$ and $q(x)$ are analytic except, *perhaps,* when their denominators are zero. For $p(x)$ this occurs at $x = 0$ and $x = 1$. But since we can cancel an x in the numerator and denominator of $p(x)$, that is

$$p(x) = \frac{x}{x(1 - x)} = \frac{1}{1 - x},$$

we see that $p(x)$ is actually analytic at $x = 0$.[†] Therefore $p(x)$ is analytic except at $x = 1$. For $q(x)$, the denominator is zero at $x = 0$. Just as with $p(x)$, this zero is removable, since $q(x)$ has the power series expansion

(4) $$q(x) = \frac{\sin x}{x} = \frac{x - \frac{x^3}{3!} + \frac{x^5}{5!} - \cdots}{x} = 1 - \frac{x^2}{3!} + \frac{x^4}{5!} - \cdots.$$

Thus $q(x)$ is everywhere analytic. Consequently the only singular point of equation (3) is $x = 1$. ◄

At an ordinary point x_0 of equation (1) (or (2)), the coefficient functions $p(x)$ and $q(x)$ are analytic, and hence we might expect that the solutions to these equations inherit this property. From the discussion in Section 4.3 on linear second order equations, the continuity of p and q in a neighborhood of x_0 is sufficient to imply that equation (2) has two linearly independent solutions defined in that neighborhood. But analytic functions are not merely continuous—they possess derivatives of all orders in a neighborhood of x_0. Thus we can differentiate equation (2) to show that $y^{(3)}$ exists and, by a "bootstrap" argument, prove that solutions to (2) must likewise possess derivatives of all orders. Although we cannot conclude by this reasoning that the solutions enjoy the stronger property of analyticity, this is nonetheless the case (see Theorem 5 in Section 8.4). Hence, in a neighborhood of an ordinary point x_0, the solutions to (1) (or (2)) can be expressed as a power series about x_0.

To illustrate the power series method about an ordinary point, let's look at a simple *first order* linear differential equation.

► **Example 2**   Find a power series solution about $x = 0$ to

(5) $$y' + 2xy = 0.$$

Solution   The coefficient of y is the polynomial $2x$ which is analytic everywhere, and so $x = 0$ is an ordinary point[††] of equation (5). Thus we expect to find a power series solution of the form

(6) $$y(x) = a_0 + a_1 x + a_2 x^2 + \cdots = \sum_{n=0}^{\infty} a_n x^n.$$

Our task is to determine the coefficients a_n.

[†] Such points are called **removable singularities.** In this chapter we assume in such cases that the function has been defined (or redefined) so that it is analytic at the point.

[††] By an ordinary point of a first order equation $y' + q(x)y = 0$ we mean a point where $q(x)$ is analytic.

For this purpose we need the expansion for $y'(x)$ that is given by termwise differentiation of (6):

$$(7) \qquad y'(x) = 0 + a_1 + 2a_2x + 3a_3x^2 + \cdots = \sum_{n=1}^{\infty} na_nx^{n-1}.$$

We now substitute the series expansions for y and y' into (5) and obtain

$$\sum_{n=1}^{\infty} na_nx^{n-1} + 2x \sum_{n=0}^{\infty} a_nx^n = 0,$$

which simplifies to

$$(8) \qquad \sum_{n=1}^{\infty} na_nx^{n-1} + \sum_{n=0}^{\infty} 2a_nx^{n+1} = 0.$$

To add the two power series in (8), we add the coefficients of like powers of x. If we write out the first few terms of these summations and add, we get

$$(a_1 + 2a_2x + 3a_3x^2 + 4a_4x^3 + \cdots) + (2a_0x + 2a_1x^2 + 2a_2x^3 + \cdots) = 0,$$

$$(9) \qquad a_1 + (2a_2 + 2a_0)x + (3a_3 + 2a_1)x^2 + (4a_4 + 2a_2)x^3 + \cdots = 0.$$

In order for the power series on the left-hand side of equation (9) to be identically zero, we must have all the coefficients equal to zero. Thus

$$a_1 = 0, \qquad 2a_2 + 2a_0 = 0,$$

$$3a_3 + 2a_1 = 0, \qquad 4a_4 + 2a_2 = 0, \qquad \text{etc.}$$

Solving the preceding system, we find

$$a_1 = 0, \qquad a_2 = -a_0, \qquad a_3 = -\tfrac{2}{3}a_1 = 0,$$

$$a_4 = -\tfrac{1}{2}a_2 = -\tfrac{1}{2}(-a_0) = \tfrac{1}{2}a_0.$$

Hence the power series for the solution takes the form

$$(10) \qquad y(x) = a_0 - a_0x^2 + \tfrac{1}{2}a_0x^4 + \cdots.$$

While the first few terms displayed in (10) are useful, we would much prefer to have a formula for the *general term* in the power series expansion for the solution. To achieve this goal, let's return to equation (8). This time, instead of just writing out a few terms, let's shift the indices in the two power series so that they sum over the same powers of x, say x^k. To do this, we shift the index in the first summation in (8) by setting $k = n - 1$. Then $n = k + 1$ and $k = 0$ when $n = 1$. Hence the first summation in (8) becomes

(11) $$\sum_{n=1}^{\infty} na_n x^{n-1} = \sum_{k=0}^{\infty} (k + 1)a_{k+1}x^k.$$

In the second summation of (8) we put $k = n + 1$ so that $n = k - 1$ and $k = 1$ when $n = 0$. This gives

(12) $$\sum_{n=0}^{\infty} 2a_n x^{n+1} = \sum_{k=1}^{\infty} 2a_{k-1}x^k.$$

Substituting (11) and (12) into (8) yields

(13) $$\sum_{k=0}^{\infty} (k + 1)a_{k+1}x^k + \sum_{k=1}^{\infty} 2a_{k-1}x^k = 0.$$

Since the first summation in (13) begins at $k = 0$ and the second at $k = 1$, we break up the first into

$$\sum_{k=0}^{\infty} (k + 1)a_{k+1}x^k = a_1 + \sum_{k=1}^{\infty} (k + 1)a_{k+1}x^k.$$

Then (13) becomes

(14) $$a_1 + \sum_{k=1}^{\infty} [(k + 1)a_{k+1} + 2a_{k-1}]x^k = 0.$$

When we now set all the coefficients in (14) equal to zero, we find

$$a_1 = 0,$$

and, for all $k \geq 1$,

(15) $$(k + 1)a_{k+1} + 2a_{k-1} = 0.$$

Equation (15) is a **recurrence relation** that we can use to determine the coefficient a_{k+1} in terms of a_{k-1}, that is,

$$a_{k+1} = -\frac{2}{k + 1} a_{k-1}.$$

Setting $k = 1, 2, \ldots, 8$, and using the fact that $a_1 = 0$, we find

$$a_2 = -\frac{2}{2} a_0 = -a_0 \quad (k = 1), \qquad a_3 = -\frac{2}{3} a_1 = 0 \quad (k = 2),$$

$$a_4 = -\frac{2}{4} a_2 = \frac{1}{2} a_0 \quad (k = 3), \qquad a_5 = -\frac{2}{5} a_3 = 0 \quad (k = 4),$$

$$a_6 = -\frac{2}{6} a_4 = -\frac{1}{3!} a_0 \quad (k = 5), \qquad a_7 = -\frac{2}{7} a_5 = 0 \quad (k = 6),$$

$$a_8 = -\frac{2}{8} a_6 = \frac{1}{4!} a_0 \quad (k = 7), \qquad a_9 = -\frac{2}{9} a_7 = 0 \quad (k = 8).$$

After a moment's reflection, we realize that

(16) $\qquad a_{2n} = \frac{(-1)^n}{n!} a_0, \qquad n = 1, 2, \ldots,$

(17) $\qquad a_{2n+1} = 0, \qquad n = 0, 1, 2, \ldots.$

Substituting back into the expression (6), we obtain the power series solution

(18) $\qquad y(x) = a_0 - a_0 x^2 + \frac{1}{2!} a_0 x^4 + \cdots = a_0 \sum_{n=0}^{\infty} \frac{(-1)^n}{n!} x^{2n}.$

Since a_0 is left undetermined, it serves as an arbitrary constant, and hence (18) gives a general solution to equation (5). ◄

Using the ratio test, it can be verified that the power series in (18) has radius of convergence $\rho = \infty$. Moreover, (18) is reminiscent of the expansion for the exponential function; the reader should check that it converges to

$$y(x) = a_0 e^{-x^2}.$$

This general solution to the simple equation (5) can also be obtained by the method of separation of variables.

In the next example we use the power series method to obtain a general solution to a linear second order differential equation.

► **Example 3** Find a general solution to

(19) $\qquad 2y'' + xy' + y = 0$

in the form of a power series about the ordinary point $x = 0$.

Solution   Writing

(20) $$y(x) = a_0 + a_1 x + a_2 x^2 + \cdots = \sum_{n=0}^{\infty} a_n x^n,$$

we differentiate termwise to obtain

$$y'(x) = a_1 + 2a_2 x + 3a_3 x^2 + \cdots = \sum_{n=1}^{\infty} n a_n x^{n-1},$$

$$y''(x) = 2a_2 + 6a_3 x + 12a_4 x^2 + \cdots = \sum_{n=2}^{\infty} n(n-1) a_n x^{n-2}.$$

Substituting these power series into equation (19), we find

(21) $$\sum_{n=2}^{\infty} 2n(n-1) a_n x^{n-2} + \sum_{n=1}^{\infty} n a_n x^n + \sum_{n=0}^{\infty} a_n x^n = 0.$$

To simplify the addition of the three summations in (21), let's shift the indices so that the general term in each is a constant times x^k. For the first summation we substitute $k = n - 2$ and get

$$\sum_{n=2}^{\infty} 2n(n-1) a_n x^{n-2} = \sum_{k=0}^{\infty} 2(k+2)(k+1) a_{k+2} x^k.$$

In the second and third summations we can take $k = n$. With these changes of indices equation (21) becomes

$$\sum_{k=0}^{\infty} 2(k+2)(k+1) a_{k+2} x^k + \sum_{k=1}^{\infty} k a_k x^k + \sum_{k=0}^{\infty} a_k x^k = 0.$$

Next, we separate the x^0 terms from the others and then combine the like powers of x in the three summations to get

(22) $$4a_2 + a_0 + \sum_{k=1}^{\infty} [2(k+2)(k+1) a_{k+2} + k a_k + a_k] x^k = 0.$$

Setting the coefficients of the power series on the left-hand side of (22) equal to zero yields

(23) $$4a_2 + a_0 = 0$$

and the recurrence relation

(24) $$2(k+2)(k+1) a_{k+2} + (k+1) a_k = 0, \qquad k \geq 1.$$

We can now use (23) and (24) to determine all the coefficients a_k of the solution in terms of a_0 and a_1. Solving (24) for a_{k+2} gives

(25) $\qquad a_{k+2} = \dfrac{-1}{2(k+2)} a_k, \qquad k \geq 1.$

Thus

$$a_2 = \dfrac{-1}{2^2} a_0$$

$$a_3 = \dfrac{-1}{2 \cdot 3} a_1 \qquad\qquad (k=1)$$

$$a_4 = \dfrac{-1}{2 \cdot 4} a_2 = \dfrac{1}{2^2 \cdot 2 \cdot 4} a_0 \qquad (k=2)$$

$$a_5 = \dfrac{-1}{2 \cdot 5} a_3 = \dfrac{1}{2^2 \cdot 3 \cdot 5} a_1 \qquad (k=3)$$

$$a_6 = \dfrac{-1}{2 \cdot 6} a_4 = \dfrac{-1}{2^3 \cdot 2 \cdot 4 \cdot 6} a_0 = \dfrac{-1}{2^6 \cdot 3!} a_0 \qquad (k=4)$$

$$a_7 = \dfrac{-1}{2 \cdot 7} a_5 = \dfrac{-1}{2^3 \cdot 3 \cdot 5 \cdot 7} a_1 \qquad (k=5)$$

$$a_8 = \dfrac{-1}{2 \cdot 8} a_6 = \dfrac{1}{2^4 \cdot 2 \cdot 4 \cdot 6 \cdot 8} a_0 = \dfrac{1}{2^8 \cdot 4!} a_0 \qquad (k=6).$$

The pattern for the coefficients is now apparent. With a_0 and a_1 taken as arbitrary constants, we find

$$a_{2n} = \dfrac{(-1)^n}{2^{2n}n!} a_0, \qquad n \geq 1,$$

and

$$a_{2n+1} = \dfrac{(-1)^n}{2^n[1 \cdot 3 \cdot 5 \cdots (2n+1)]} a_1, \qquad n \geq 1.$$

From this, two linearly independent solutions emerge; namely

(26) $\qquad y_1(x) = \displaystyle\sum_{n=0}^{\infty} \dfrac{(-1)^n}{2^{2n}n!} x^{2n},$

(27) $\qquad y_2(x) = \displaystyle\sum_{n=0}^{\infty} \dfrac{(-1)^n}{2^n[1 \cdot 3 \cdot 5 \cdots (2n+1)]} x^{2n+1}.$

Hence a general solution to (19) is $a_0 y_1(x) + a_1 y_2(x)$. ◄

The method illustrated in Example 3 can also be used to solve initial value problems. Suppose that we are given the values of $y(0)$ and $y'(0)$; then, from equation (20) we see that $a_0 = y(0)$ and $a_1 = y'(0)$. Knowing these two coefficients leads to a unique power series solution for the initial value problem.

The recurrence relation (24) in Example 3 involved just two of the coefficients, a_{k+2} and a_k, and we were fortunate in being able to deduce from this relation the general form for the coefficient a_n. However, many cases arise that lead to more complicated two-term or even to many-term recurrence relations. When this occurs, it may be impossible to determine the general form for the coefficients a_n. In the next example we consider an equation that gives rise to a three-term recurrence relation.

▶ **Example 4** Find the first few terms in a power series expansion about $x = 0$ for a general solution to

(28) $$(1 + x^2)y'' - y' + y = 0.$$

Solution Since $p(x) = -(1 + x^2)^{-1}$ and $q(x) = (1 + x^2)^{-1}$ are analytic at $x = 0$, then $x = 0$ is an ordinary point for equation (28). Hence we can express a general solution to (28) in the form

(29) $$y(x) = \sum_{n=0}^{\infty} a_n x^n.$$

Substituting this expansion into (28) yields

$$(1 + x^2) \sum_{n=2}^{\infty} n(n-1)a_n x^{n-2} - \sum_{n=1}^{\infty} na_n x^{n-1} + \sum_{n=0}^{\infty} a_n x^n = 0,$$

(30) $$\sum_{n=2}^{\infty} n(n-1)a_n x^{n-2} + \sum_{n=2}^{\infty} n(n-1)a_n x^n - \sum_{n=1}^{\infty} na_n x^{n-1} + \sum_{n=0}^{\infty} a_n x^n = 0.$$

To sum over like powers x^k, we put $k = n - 2$ in the first summation, $k = n - 1$ in the third, and $k = n$ in the second and fourth summations of (30). This gives

$$\sum_{k=0}^{\infty} (k+2)(k+1)a_{k+2}x^k + \sum_{k=2}^{\infty} k(k-1)a_k x^k - \sum_{k=0}^{\infty} (k+1)a_{k+1}x^k + \sum_{k=0}^{\infty} a_k x^k = 0.$$

Separating the terms corresponding to $k = 0$ and $k = 1$ and combining the rest under one summation, we have

(31) $$(2a_2 - a_1 + a_0) + (6a_3 - 2a_2 + a_1)x$$
$$+ \sum_{k=2}^{\infty} [(k+2)(k+1)a_{k+2} - (k+1)a_{k+1} + (k(k-1)+1)a_k]x^k = 0.$$

Setting the coefficients equal to zero gives

(32) $\qquad 2a_2 - a_1 + a_0 = 0,$

(33) $\qquad 6a_3 - 2a_2 + a_1 = 0,$

and the recurrence relation

(34) $\qquad (k + 2)(k + 1)a_{k+2} - (k + 1)a_{k+1} + (k^2 - k + 1)a_k = 0, \qquad k \geq 2.$

We can solve (32) for a_2 in terms of a_0 and a_1:

$$a_2 = \frac{a_1 - a_0}{2}.$$

Now that we have a_2, we can use (33) to express a_3 in terms of a_0 and a_1:

$$a_3 = \frac{2a_2 - a_1}{6} = \frac{(a_1 - a_0) - a_1}{6} = \frac{-a_0}{6}.$$

Solving the recurrence relation (34) for a_{k+2}, we obtain

(35) $\qquad a_{k+2} = \dfrac{(k + 1)a_{k+1} - (k^2 - k + 1)a_k}{(k + 2)(k + 1)}, \qquad k \geq 2.$

For $k = 2$, 3, and 4 this gives

$$a_4 = \frac{3a_3 - 3a_2}{4 \cdot 3} = \frac{a_3 - a_2}{4}$$

$$= \frac{\dfrac{-a_0}{6} - \left(\dfrac{a_1 - a_0}{2}\right)}{4} = \frac{2a_0 - 3a_1}{24} \qquad (k = 2),$$

$$a_5 = \frac{4a_4 - 7a_3}{5 \cdot 4} = \frac{3a_0 - a_1}{40} \qquad (k = 3),$$

$$a_6 = \frac{5a_5 - 13a_4}{6 \cdot 5} = \frac{36a_1 - 17a_0}{720} \qquad (k = 4).$$

We can now express a general solution in terms up to order 6, using a_0 and a_1 as the arbitrary constants. Thus

(36)
$$y(x) = a_0 + a_1 x + \left(\frac{a_1 - a_0}{2}\right)x^2 - \frac{a_0}{6}x^3$$

$$+ \left(\frac{2a_0 - 3a_1}{24}\right)x^4 + \left(\frac{3a_0 - a_1}{40}\right)x^5 + \left(\frac{36a_1 - 17a_0}{720}\right)x^6 + \cdots$$

$$= a_0(1 - \tfrac{1}{2}x^2 - \tfrac{1}{6}x^3 + \tfrac{1}{12}x^4 + \tfrac{3}{40}x^5 - \tfrac{17}{720}x^6 + \cdots)$$

$$+ a_1(x + \tfrac{1}{2}x^2 - \tfrac{1}{8}x^4 - \tfrac{1}{40}x^5 + \tfrac{1}{20}x^6 + \cdots). \blacktriangleleft$$

Given specific values for a_0 and a_1, will the partial sums of the power series representation (36) yield useful approximations to the solution when $x = 0.5$? What about when $x = 2.3$ or $x = 7.8$? The answers to these questions certainly depend on the radius of convergence of the power series in (36). But since we were not able to determine a general form for the coefficients a_n in this example, we cannot use the ratio test (or other methods such as the root test, integral test, or comparison test) to compute the radius ρ. In the next section we remedy this situation by giving a simple procedure that determines a lower bound for the radius of convergence of power series solutions.

EXERCISES 8.3

In Problems 1 through 10 determine all the singular points of the given differential equation.

1. $x^2 y'' + 3y' - xy = 0.$

2. $(x + 1)y'' - x^2 y' + 3y = 0.$

3. $(x^2 - 2)y'' + 2y' + (\sin x)y = 0.$

4. $(x^2 + x)y'' + 3y' - 6xy = 0.$

5. $(x^2 - 1)y'' + (1 - x)y' + (x^2 - 2x + 1)y = 0.$

6. $(x^2 - x - 2)y'' + (x + 1)y' - (x - 2)y = 0.$

7. $(\sin x)y'' + (\cos x)y = 0.$

8. $e^x y'' - (x^2 - 1)y' + 2xy = 0.$

9. $(\sin x)y'' - (\ln x)y = 0.$

10. $[\ln(x - 1)]y'' + (\sin 2x)y' - e^x y = 0.$

In Problems 11 through 18 find at least the first four nonzero terms in a power series expansion about $x = 0$ for a general solution to the given differential equation.

11. $y' + (x + 2)y = 0.$

12. $y' - y = 0.$

13. $y'' - x^2 y = 0.$

14. $(x^2 + 1)y'' + y = 0.$

15. $y'' + (x - 1)y' + y = 0.$

16. $y'' - 2y' + y = 0.$

17. $y'' - x^2 y' + y = 0.$

18. $(2x - 3)y'' - xy' + y = 0.$

In Problems 19 through 24 find a power series expansion about $x = 0$ for a general solution to the given differential equation. Your answer should include a general formula for the coefficients.

19. $y' - 2xy = 0.$

20. $y'' + y = 0.$

21. $y'' - xy' + 4y = 0.$

22. $y'' - x^2 y' - xy = 0.$

23. $y'' - xy = 0.$

24. $(x^2 + 1)y'' - xy' + y = 0.$

In Problems 25 through 32 find at least the first four nonzero terms in a power series expansion about $x = 0$ for the solution to the given initial value problem.

25. $y'' + 3xy' - y = 0;$ $y(0) = 2,$ $y'(0) = 0.$

26. $y'' - 2xy' - 2y = 0$; $y(0) = -1$, $y'(0) = 2$.

27. $y'' + y' - xy = 0$; $y(0) = 1$, $y'(0) = -2$.

28. $(x^2 + 2)y'' + 2xy' + 3y = 0$; $y(0) = 1$, $y'(0) = 2$.

29. $(x^2 - x + 1)y'' - y' - y = 0$; $y(0) = 0$, $y'(0) = 1$.

30. $y'' - 4xy' + 5y = 0$; $y(0) = -1$, $y'(0) = 1$.

31. $y'' + (x - 2)y' - y = 0$; $y(0) = -1$, $y'(0) = 0$.

32. $(x + 1)y'' - y = 0$; $y(0) = 0$, $y'(0) = 1$.

33. Use the ratio test to show that the radius of convergence of the series in equation (18) is infinite. [Hint: First consider the series $\sum_{n=0}^{\infty} (-1)^n x^n / n!$.]

34. **Emden's Equation.** A classical nonlinear equation that occurs in the study of the thermal behavior of a spherical cloud is **Emden's equation**

$$y'' + \frac{2}{x} y' + y^n = 0,$$

with initial conditions $y(0) = 1$, $y'(0) = 0$. (See Section 8.1 for the case when $n = 1$.) Assuming n is a positive integer, show that the first few terms in a power series solution are

$$y = 1 - \frac{x^2}{3!} + n\frac{x^4}{5!} + \cdots.$$

[Hint: Substitute $y = 1 + c_2 x^2 + c_3 x^3 + c_4 x^4 + c_5 x^5 + \cdots$ into the equation and carefully compute the first few terms in y^n.]

35. **Airy's Equation.** In aerodynamics one encounters the following initial value problem for **Airy's equation:**

$$y'' + xy = 0;   y(0) = 1,   y'(0) = 0.$$

(a) Find the first ten terms in a power series expansion about $x = 0$ for the solution, and graph this polynomial for $-10 \le x \le 10$.

(b) Using the Runge-Kutta method (see Section 5.6) with $h = 0.05$, approximate the solution on the interval $[0, 10]$, i.e., at the points 0.05, 0.1, 0.15, etc.

(c) Using the Runge-Kutta method with $h = 0.05$, approximate the solution on the interval $[-10, 0]$. [Hint: With the change of variables $z = -x$, it suffices to approximate the solution to $y'' - zy = 0$; $y(0) = 1$, $y'(0) = 0$, on the interval $[0, 10]$.]

(d) Using your knowledge of constant coefficient equations as a basis for guessing the behavior of the solutions to Airy's equation, decide whether the power series approximation obtained in part (a) or the numerical approximation obtained in parts (b) and (c) better describe the true behavior of the solution on the interval $[-10, 10]$.

★ *8.4 Equations with Analytic Coefficients*

In Section 8.3 we introduced a method for obtaining a power series solution about an ordinary point. In this section we continue the discussion of this procedure. We begin by stating a basic existence theorem for the equation

(1) $$y''(x) + p(x)y'(x) + q(x)y(x) = 0,$$

which justifies the power series method.

EXISTENCE OF ANALYTIC SOLUTIONS

Theorem 5.   Suppose that x_0 is an ordinary point for equation (1). Then (1) has two linearly independent analytic solutions of the form

(2) $$y(x) = \sum_{n=0}^{\infty} a_n(x - x_0)^n.$$

Moreover, the radius of convergence of any power series solution of the form given by (2) is at least as large as the distance from x_0 to the nearest singular point (real or complex-valued) of equation (1).

The key element in the proof of Theorem 5 is the construction of a convergent geometric series that dominates the series expansion (2) of a solution to equation (1). The convergence of the series in (2) then follows by the comparison test. The details of the proof can be found in more advanced books on differential equations.[†]

As we saw in Section 8.3, the power series method gives us a general solution in the same form as (2), with a_0 and a_1 as arbitrary constants. The two linearly independent solutions referred to in Theorem 5 can be obtained by taking $a_0 = 1$, $a_1 = 0$ for the first and $a_0 = 0$, $a_1 = 1$ for the second. Thus we can extend Theorem 5 by saying that *equation (1) has a general solution of the form (2), with a_0 and a_1 as the arbitrary constants.*

The second part of Theorem 5 gives a simple way of determining a minimum value for the radius of convergence of the power series. We need only find the singular points of equation (1), then determine the distance between the ordinary point x_0 and the nearest singular point.

[†] See, for example, *Intermediate Differential Equations*, Second Edition, by Earl D. Rainville, Macmillan, New York, 1964, Chapter 3, Section 22.

Solution   Here $p(x) = e^x$ and $q(x) = 1 + x^2$, both of which are analytic for all x. Thus by Theorem 5, the initial value problem (10) has a power series solution

(11) $$y(x) = \sum_{n=0}^{\infty} a_n x^n$$

that converges for all x ($\rho = \infty$). To find the first few terms of this series, we first expand $p(x) = e^x$ in its Maclaurin series:

$$e^x = 1 + x + \frac{x^2}{2!} + \frac{x^3}{3!} + \cdots .$$

Substituting the expansions for $y(x)$, $y'(x)$, $y''(x)$, and e^x into (10) gives

(12) $$\sum_{n=2}^{\infty} n(n-1)a_n x^{n-2} + \left(1 + x + \frac{x^2}{2} + \frac{x^3}{6} + \frac{x^4}{24} + \cdots\right) \sum_{n=1}^{\infty} na_n x^{n-1}$$

$$+ (1 + x^2) \sum_{n=0}^{\infty} a_n x^n = 0.$$

Because of the computational difficulties due to the appearance of the product of the power series for e^x and $y'(x)$, we concern ourselves with just those terms up to order 4. Writing out (12) and keeping track of all such terms, we find

(13) $(2a_2 + 6a_3 x + 12a_4 x^2 + 20a_5 x^3 + 30a_6 x^4 + \cdots)$

$+ (a_1 + 2a_2 x + 3a_3 x^2 + 4a_4 x^3 + 5a_5 x^4 + \cdots)$ $1 \cdot \sum na_n x^{n-1}$

$+ (a_1 x + 2a_2 x^2 + 3a_3 x^3 + 4a_4 x^4 + \cdots)$ $x \cdot \sum na_n x^{n-1}$

$+ (\tfrac{1}{2}a_1 x^2 + a_2 x^3 + \tfrac{3}{2}a_3 x^4 + \cdots)$ $\tfrac{1}{2}x^2 \cdot \sum na_n x^{n-1}$

$+ (\tfrac{1}{6}a_1 x^3 + \tfrac{1}{3}a_2 x^4 + \cdots)$ $\cdot$

$+ (\tfrac{1}{24}a_1 x^4 + \cdots)$ $\cdot$

$+ (a_0 + a_1 x + a_2 x^2 + a_3 x^3 + a_4 x^4 + \cdots)$ $1 \cdot \sum a_n x^n$

$+ (a_0 x^2 + a_1 x^3 + a_2 x^4 + \cdots) = 0.$ $x^2 \cdot \sum a_n x^n$

Grouping the like powers of x in equation (13) (the x^2 terms are shown in color) and then setting the coefficients equal to zero yields the system of equations

$$2a_2 + a_1 + a_0 = 0,$$

$$6a_3 + 2a_2 + 2a_1 = 0,$$

$$12a_4 + 3a_3 + 3a_2 + \tfrac{1}{2}a_1 + a_0 = 0,$$

$$20a_5 + 4a_4 + 4a_3 + a_2 + \tfrac{7}{6}a_1 = 0,$$

$$30a_6 + 5a_5 + 5a_4 + \tfrac{3}{2}a_3 + \tfrac{4}{3}a_2 + \tfrac{1}{24}a_1 = 0.$$

The initial conditions in (10) imply that $y(0) = a_0 = 1$ and $y'(0) = a_1 = 0$. Using these values for a_0 and a_1, we can solve the above system first for a_2, then a_3, and so on:

$$2a_2 + 0 + 1 = 0 \Rightarrow a_2 = -\tfrac{1}{2},$$
$$6a_3 - 1 + 0 = 0 \Rightarrow a_3 = \tfrac{1}{6},$$
$$12a_4 + \tfrac{1}{2} - \tfrac{3}{2} + 0 + 1 = 0 \Rightarrow a_4 = 0,$$
$$20a_5 + 0 + \tfrac{2}{3} - \tfrac{1}{2} + 0 = 0 \Rightarrow a_5 = -\tfrac{1}{120},$$
$$30a_6 - \tfrac{1}{24} + 0 + \tfrac{1}{4} - \tfrac{2}{3} + 0 = 0 \Rightarrow a_6 = \tfrac{11}{720}.$$

Thus the solution to the initial value problem in (10) is

(14) $\qquad y(x) = 1 - \tfrac{1}{2}x^2 + \tfrac{1}{6}x^3 - \tfrac{1}{120}x^5 + \tfrac{11}{720}x^6 + \cdots.$ ◀

Thus far we have used the power series method only for homogeneous equations. But the same method applies, with obvious modifications, to nonhomogeneous equations of the form

(15) $\qquad y''(x) + p(x)y'(x) + q(x)y(x) = g(x),$

provided the forcing term $g(x)$ and the coefficient functions are analytic at x_0. For example, to find a power series about $x = 0$ for a general solution to

(16) $\qquad y''(x) - xy'(x) - y(x) = \sin x,$

we use the substitution $y(x) = \sum a_n x^n$ to obtain a power series expansion for the left-hand side of (16). We then equate the coefficients of this series with the corresponding coefficients of the Maclaurin expansion for $\sin x$:

$$\sin x = \sum_{n=0}^{\infty} \frac{(-1)^n}{(2n+1)!} x^{2n+1}.$$

Carrying out the details (see Problem 20), we ultimately find that an expansion for a general solution to (16) is

(17) $\qquad y(x) = a_0 y_1(x) + a_1 y_2(x) + y_p(x),$

where

(18) $\qquad y_1(x) = 1 + \tfrac{1}{2}x^2 + \tfrac{1}{8}x^4 + \tfrac{1}{48}x^6 + \cdots,$

(19) $\qquad y_2(x) = x + \tfrac{1}{3}x^3 + \tfrac{1}{15}x^5 + \tfrac{1}{105}x^7 + \cdots,$

are the solutions to the homogeneous equation associated with equation (16), and

(20) $\qquad y_p(x) = \tfrac{1}{6}x^3 + \tfrac{1}{40}x^5 + \tfrac{19}{5040}x^7 + \cdots$

is a particular solution to equation (16).

EXERCISES 8.4 _____

In Problems 1 through 6 find a minimum value for the radius of convergence of a power series solution about x_0.

1. $y'' - xy' - 3y = 0$, $x_0 = 2$.

2. $(x + 1)y'' - 3xy' + 2y = 0$, $x_0 = 1$.

3. $(1 + x^2)y'' - 3y = 0$, $x_0 = 1$.

4. $(x^2 - 5x + 6)y'' - 3xy' - y = 0$, $x_0 = 0$.

5. $y'' - (\tan x)y' + y = 0$, $x_0 = 0$.

6. $(1 + x^3)y'' - xy' + 3x^2y = 0$, $x_0 = 1$.

In Problems 7 through 12 find at least the first four nonzero terms in a power series expansion about x_0 *for a general solution to the given differential equation with the given value for* x_0.

7. $y' - 2xy = 0$, $x_0 = -1$.

8. $y' + 2(x - 1)y = 0$, $x_0 = 1$.

9. $(x^2 - 2x)y'' + 2y = 0$, $x_0 = 1$.

10. $x^2y'' - xy' + 2y = 0$, $x_0 = 2$.

11. $y'' + (3x - 1)y' - y = 0$, $x_0 = -1$.

12. $x^2y'' - y' + y = 0$, $x_0 = 2$.

In Problems 13 through 19 find at least the first four nonzero terms in a power series expansion of the solution to the given initial value problem.

13. $y' + (\sin x)y = 0$, $y(0) = 1$.

14. $y' - e^x y = 0$, $y(0) = 1$.

15. $y'' + xy' + e^x y = 0$, $y(0) = 0$, $y'(0) = -1$.

16. $(x^2 + 1)y'' - e^x y' + y = 0$, $y(0) = 1$, $y'(0) = 1$.

17. $y'' - (\sin x)y = 0$, $y(\pi) = 1$, $y'(\pi) = 0$.

18. $y'' - (\cos x)y' - y = 0$, $y(\pi/2) = 1$, $y'(\pi/2) = 1$.

19. $y'' - e^{2x}y' + (\cos x)y = 0$, $y(0) = -1$, $y'(0) = 1$.

20. To derive the general solution given by equations (17)–(20) for the non-homogeneous equation (16), complete the following steps:

  (a) Substitute $y(x) = \sum_{n=0}^{\infty} a_n x^n$ and the Maclaurin series for $\sin x$ into equation (16) to obtain

  (21) $$(2a_2 - a_0) + \sum_{k=1}^{\infty} [(k + 2)(k + 1)a_{k+2} - (k + 1)a_k]x^k$$

  $$= \sum_{n=0}^{\infty} \frac{(-1)^n}{(2n + 1)!} x^{2n+1}.$$

  (b) Equate the coefficients of like powers of x on both sides of equation (21) and thereby deduce the equations

  $$a_2 = \frac{a_0}{2}, \quad a_3 = \frac{1}{6} + \frac{a_1}{3}, \quad a_4 = \frac{a_0}{8},$$

  $$a_5 = \frac{1}{40} + \frac{a_1}{15}, \quad a_6 = \frac{a_0}{48}, \quad a_7 = \frac{19}{5040} + \frac{a_1}{105}.$$

  (c) Show that the relations in part (b) yield the general solution to (16) given in equations (17)–(20).

In Problems 21 through 28 use the procedure illustrated in Problem 20 to find at least the first four nonzero terms in a power series expansion about $x = 0$ of a general solution to the given differential equation.

21. $y' - xy = \sin x.$ **22.** $y' + xy = e^x.$

23. $y'' + xy' + y = x^2 + 2x + 1.$ **24.** $y'' - 2xy' + 3y = x^2.$

25. $y'' - xy' + 2y = \cos x.$ **26.** $(1 + x^2)y'' - xy' + y = e^{-x}.$

27. $(1 - x^2)y'' - y' + y = \tan x.$ **28.** $y'' - (\sin x)y = \cos x.$

29. The equation

$$(1 - x^2)y'' - 2xy' + n(n + 1)y = 0,$$

where n is a nonnegative integer, is called **Legendre's equation.** This equation occurs in applications of differential equations to physics and engineering.

(a) Find a power series expansion about $x = 0$ for a solution to Legendre's equation.

(b) Show that for n a nonnegative integer, there exists an nth degree polynomial that is a solution to Legendre's equation. These polynomials, up to a constant multiple, are called **Legendre polynomials.**

(c) Determine the first three Legendre polynomials, up to a constant multiple.

★ 8.5 *Cauchy-Euler Equations Revisited*

In the previous sections we considered methods for obtaining power series solutions about an ordinary point for a linear second order equation. However, in certain instances we may want a series expansion about a *singular point* of the equation. (This was the case for the Lane-Emden equation discussed in Section 8.1.) To motivate a procedure for finding such expansions, we return to the class of **Cauchy-Euler equations.** In Section 4.10 we solved these equations by making the change of variables $x = e^t$, which transforms a Cauchy-Euler equation into an equation with constant coefficients. However, it is more instructive for our study of series expansions about singular points to work directly in the variable x.

Recall that a second order homogeneous Cauchy-Euler equation has the form

(1) $\qquad ax^2 y''(x) + bxy'(x) + cy(x) = 0, \qquad x > 0,$

where $a\, (\neq 0)$, b, and c are (real) constants. Since here $p(x) = b/ax$ and $q(x) = c/ax^2$, it follows that $x = 0$ is a singular point for (1).

As we found in Section 4.10, equation (1) has solutions of the form $y = x^r$. To determine the values for r, we can proceed as follows. Let L be the differential operator defined by the left-hand side of equation (1), that is,

(2) $\qquad L[y](x) := ax^2 y''(x) + bxy'(x) + cy(x),$

and set

(3) $w(r, x) := x^r.$

When we substitute $w(r, x)$ for $y(x)$ in (2), we find

(4) $L[w](x) = ax^2 r(r - 1)x^{r-2} + bxrx^{r-1} + cx^r$
             $= \{ar^2 + (b - a)r + c\}x^r.$

From (4) we see that $w = x^r$ is a solution to (1) if and only if r satisfies

(5) $ar^2 + (b - a)r + c = 0.$

Equation (5) is referred to as the **auxiliary** or **indicial equation** for (1).
    When the indicial equation has two distinct roots, we have

(6) $L[w](x) = a(r - r_1)(r - r_2)x^r,$

from which it follows that equation (1) has the two linearly independent solutions

(7) $y_1(x) = w(r_1, x) = x^{r_1}, \qquad x > 0,$
(8) $y_2(x) = w(r_2, x) = x^{r_2}, \qquad x > 0.$

    When r_1 and r_2 are complex conjugates, $\alpha \pm i\beta$, we can use Euler's formula to express

$$x^{\alpha + i\beta} = e^{(\alpha + i\beta)\ln x} = e^{\alpha \ln x}\cos(\beta \ln x) + ie^{\alpha \ln x}\sin(\beta \ln x)$$
$$= x^\alpha \cos(\beta \ln x) + ix^\alpha \sin(\beta \ln x).$$

Since the real and imaginary parts of $x^{\alpha + i\beta}$ must also be solutions to (1), we can replace
(7) and (8) by the two linearly independent real-valued solutions

(9) $y_1(x) = x^\alpha \cos(\beta \ln x), \qquad y_2(x) = x^\alpha \sin(\beta \ln x).$

    If the indicial equation (5) has a repeated real root r_0, then

(10) $L[w](x) = a(r - r_0)^2 x^r.$

Setting $r = r_0$ gives the solution

(11) $y_1(x) = w(r_0, x) = x^{r_0}, \qquad x > 0.$

To find a second linearly independent solution, we make the following observation. Since
the right-hand side of (10) has the factor $(r - r_0)^2$, then taking the partial derivative of (10)
with respect to r and setting $r = r_0$, we get *zero*. That is,

(12) $\dfrac{\partial}{\partial r}\{L[w](x)\}\Big|_{r=r_0} = \{a(r - r_0)^2 x^r \ln x + 2a(r - r_0)x^r\}\Big|_{r=r_0} = 0.$

While it may not appear that we have made any progress toward finding a second solution, a closer look at the expression on the left-hand side of (12) will soon vindicate our efforts.

First note that $w(r, x) = x^r$ has continuous partial derivatives of all orders with respect to both r and x. Hence the mixed partial derivatives are equal:

$$\frac{\partial^3 w}{\partial r \partial x^2} = \frac{\partial^3 w}{\partial x^2 \partial r}, \qquad \frac{\partial^2 w}{\partial r \partial x} = \frac{\partial^2 w}{\partial x \partial r}.$$

Consequently, for the differential operator L, we have

$$
\begin{aligned}
\textbf{(13)} \qquad \frac{\partial}{\partial r} L[w](x) &= \frac{\partial}{\partial r} \left\{ ax^2 \frac{\partial^2 w}{\partial x^2} + bx \frac{\partial w}{\partial x} + cw \right\} \\
&= ax^2 \frac{\partial^3 w}{\partial r \partial x^2} + bx \frac{\partial^2 w}{\partial r \partial x} + c \frac{\partial w}{\partial r} \\
&= ax^2 \frac{\partial^3 w}{\partial x^2 \partial r} + bx \frac{\partial^2 w}{\partial x \partial r} + c \frac{\partial w}{\partial r} \\
&= L\left[\frac{\partial w}{\partial r} \right](x).
\end{aligned}
$$

With this fact, (12) can be written as

$$\textbf{(14)} \qquad L\left[\frac{\partial w}{\partial r} \right]\bigg|_{r = r_0} = 0.$$

Thus for the case of a repeated root r_0, a second linearly independent solution to (1) is

$$\textbf{(15)} \qquad y_2(x) = \frac{\partial w}{\partial r}(r_0, x) = \frac{\partial}{\partial r}(x^r)\bigg|_{r = r_0} = x^{r_0} \ln x, \qquad x > 0.$$

▶ *Example 1* Find a general solution to

$$\textbf{(16)} \qquad 4x^2 y''(x) + y(x) = 0, \qquad x > 0.$$

Solution Let $w(r, x) = x^r$ and let L denote the left-hand side of (16). A short calculation (or equation (4)) gives

$$L[w](x) = (4r^2 - 4r + 1)x^r.$$

Solving the indicial equation

$$4r^2 - 4r + 1 = (2r - 1)^2 = 4(r - \tfrac{1}{2})^2 = 0$$

yields the repeated root $r_0 = \frac{1}{2}$. Thus a general solution to (16) is obtained from equations (11) and (15) by setting $r_0 = \frac{1}{2}$. That is,

(17) $y(x) = C_1\sqrt{x} + C_2\sqrt{x}\, \ln x,$ $x > 0.$ ◄

In Section 8.7 we discuss the problem of finding a second linearly independent series solution to certain differential equations. As we shall see, operator methods similar to those described in this section will lead to the desired second solution.

EXERCISES 8.5

In Problems 1 through 12 use the substitution $y = x^r$ to find a general solution to the given equation for $x > 0$.

1. $2x^2y''(x) + 13xy'(x) + 15y(x) = 0.$

2. $x^2y''(x) + 6xy'(x) + 6y(x) = 0.$

3. $x^2y''(x) + 2xy'(x) - 3y(x) = 0.$

4. $x^2y''(x) - xy'(x) + 17y(x) = 0.$

5. $\dfrac{d^2y}{dx^2} = \dfrac{5}{x}\dfrac{dy}{dx} - \dfrac{13}{x^2}y.$

6. $\dfrac{d^2y}{dx^2} = \dfrac{1}{x}\dfrac{dy}{dx} - \dfrac{4}{x^2}y.$

7. $2x^2y''(x) + 5xy'(x) - 2y(x) = 0.$

8. $4x^2y''(x) + 5y(x) = 0.$

9. $x^3y'''(x) + 4x^2y''(x) + 10xy'(x) - 10y(x) = 0.$

10. $x^3y'''(x) + 4x^2y''(x) + xy'(x) = 0.$

11. $x^3y'''(x) + 9x^2y''(x) + 19xy'(x) + 8y(x) = 0.$

12. $x^3y'''(x) + 3x^2y''(x) + 5xy'(x) - 5y(x) = 0.$

In Problems 13 and 14 use variation of parameters to find a general solution to the given equation for $x > 0$.

13. $x^2y''(x) - 2xy'(x) + 2y(x) = x^{-1/2}.$

14. $x^2y''(x) + 2xy'(x) - 2y(x) = 6x^{-2} + 3x.$

In Problems 15 through 17 solve the given initial value problem.

15. $x^2y''(x) - 12y(x) = 0;$ $y(1) = 3,$ $y'(1) = 5.$

16. $x^2y''(x) + 5xy'(x) + 4y(x) = 0;$ $y(1) = 3,$ $y'(1) = 7.$

17. $x^3y'''(x) + 6x^2y''(x) + 29xy'(x) - 29y(x) = 0;$ $y(1) = 2,$ $y'(1) = -3,$ $y''(1) = 19.$

18. When r_0 is a repeated root of the auxiliary equation $ar^2 + br + c = 0$, then $y_1(t) = e^{r_0 t}$ is a solution to the equation $ay'' + by' + cy = 0$, where a, b, and c are constants. Use a derivation similar to the one given in this section for the case when the indicial equation has a repeated root to show that a second linearly independent solution is $y_2(t) = te^{r_0 t}$.

19. Let $L[y](x) := x^3y'''(x) + xy'(x) - y(x)$.

   (a) Show that $L[x^r](x) = (r - 1)^3x^r$.

   (b) Using an extension of the argument given in this section for the case when the indicial equation has a double root, show that $L[y] = 0$ has the general solution

$$y(x) = C_1x + C_2x\, \ln x + C_3x(\ln x)^2.$$

8.6 *Method of Frobenius*

In the previous section we showed that a homogeneous Cauchy-Euler equation has a solution of the form $y(x) = x^r$, $x > 0$, where r is a certain constant. Cauchy-Euler equations have, of course, a very special form with only one singular point (at $x = 0$). In this section we show how the theory for Cauchy-Euler equations generalizes to other equations that have a special type of singularity.

To motivate the procedure, let's rewrite the Cauchy-Euler equation,

(1) $\qquad ax^2 y''(x) + bxy'(x) + cy(x) = 0, \qquad x > 0,$

in the standard form

(2) $\qquad y''(x) + p(x)y'(x) + q(x)y(x) = 0, \qquad x > 0,$

where

$$p(x) = \frac{p_0}{x}, \qquad q(x) = \frac{q_0}{x^2},$$

and p_0, q_0 are the constants b/a and c/a, respectively. When we substitute $w(r, x) = x^r$ into equation (2), we get

$$[r(r - 1) + p_0 r + q_0]x^{r-2} = 0,$$

which yields the indicial equation

(3) $\qquad r(r - 1) + p_0 r + q_0 = 0.$

Thus, if r_1 is a root of (3), then $w(r_1, x) = x^{r_1}$ is a solution to equations (1) and (2).

Let's now assume, more generally, that (2) is an equation for which $xp(x)$ and $x^2 q(x)$, instead of being constants, are *analytic functions*. That is, in some open interval about $x = 0$,

(4) $\qquad xp(x) = p_0 + p_1 x + p_2 x^2 + \cdots = \sum_{n=0}^{\infty} p_n x^n,$

(5) $\qquad x^2 q(x) = q_0 + q_1 x + q_2 x^2 + \cdots = \sum_{n=0}^{\infty} q_n x^n.$

It follows from (4) and (5) that

(6) $\qquad \lim_{x \to 0} xp(x) = p_0 \quad \text{and} \quad \lim_{x \to 0} x^2 q(x) = q_0,$

and hence, for x near 0 we have $xp(x) \approx p_0$ and $x^2 q(x) \approx q_0$. Therefore, it is reasonable to expect that the solutions to (2) will behave (for x near 0) like the solutions to the Cauchy-Euler equation

$$x^2 y'' + p_0 x y' + q_0 y = 0.$$

When $p(x)$ and $q(x)$ satisfy (4) and (5), we say that the singular point at $x = 0$ is regular. More generally we state:

REGULAR SINGULAR POINT

Definition 3.   A singular point x_0 of

(7) $y''(x) + p(x)y'(x) + q(x)y(x) = 0$

is said to be a **regular singular point** if both $(x - x_0)p(x)$ and $(x - x_0)^2 q(x)$ are analytic at x_0.[†] Otherwise x_0 is called an **irregular singular point.**

▶ *Example 1*   Classify the singular points of the equation

(8) $(x^2 - 1)^2 y''(x) + (x + 1)y'(x) - y(x) = 0.$

Solution   Here

$$p(x) = \frac{x + 1}{(x^2 - 1)^2} = \frac{1}{(x + 1)(x - 1)^2},$$

$$q(x) = \frac{-1}{(x^2 - 1)^2} = \frac{-1}{(x + 1)^2(x - 1)^2},$$

from which we see that ± 1 are the singular points of (8). For the singularity at 1, we have

$$(x - 1)p(x) = \frac{1}{(x + 1)(x - 1)},$$

which is not analytic at $x = 1$. Therefore $x = 1$ is an irregular singular point.
    For the singularity at -1, we have

$$(x + 1)p(x) = \frac{1}{(x - 1)^2}, \qquad (x + 1)^2 q(x) = \frac{-1}{(x - 1)^2},$$

both of which are analytic at $x = -1$. Hence $x = -1$ is a regular singular point. ◀

[†] In the terminology of complex variables, p has a pole of order at most 1, and q has a pole of order at most 2 at x_0.

Let's assume that $x = 0$ is a regular singular point for equation (7), so that $p(x)$ and $q(x)$ satisfy (4) and (5); that is,

(9) $$p(x) = \sum_{n=0}^{\infty} p_n x^{n-1}, \qquad q(x) = \sum_{n=0}^{\infty} q_n x^{n-2}.$$

The idea of the mathematician Frobenius was that, since Cauchy-Euler equations have solutions of the form x^r, then for the regular singular point $x = 0$ there should be solutions to (7) of the form x^r *times an analytic function.*[†] Hence we seek solutions to (7) of the form

(10) $$w(r, x) = x^r \sum_{n=0}^{\infty} a_n x^n = \sum_{n=0}^{\infty} a_n x^{n+r}, \qquad x > 0.$$

Without loss of generality, we assume that a_0 is an arbitrary nonzero constant, and so we are left with determining r and the coefficients a_n, $n \geq 1$. Differentiating $w(r, x)$ with respect to x, we have

(11) $$w'(r, x) = \sum_{n=0}^{\infty} (n + r)a_n x^{n+r-1},$$

(12) $$w''(r, x) = \sum_{n=0}^{\infty} (n + r)(n + r - 1)a_n x^{n+r-2}.$$

If we substitute the above expansions for $w(r, x)$, $w'(r, x)$, $w''(r, x)$, $p(x)$, and $q(x)$ into (7), we obtain

(13) $$\sum_{n=0}^{\infty} (n + r)(n + r - 1)a_n x^{n+r-2} + \left(\sum_{n=0}^{\infty} p_n x^{n-1} \right)\left(\sum_{n=0}^{\infty} (n + r)a_n x^{n+r-1} \right)$$
$$+ \left(\sum_{n=0}^{\infty} q_n x^{n-2} \right)\left(\sum_{n=0}^{\infty} a_n x^{n+r} \right) = 0.$$

Now we use the Cauchy product to perform the series multiplications and then group like powers of x, starting with the lowest power, x^{r-2}. This gives

(14) $$[r(r - 1) + p_0 r + q_0]a_0 x^{r-2}$$
$$+ [(r + 1)ra_1 + (r + 1)p_0 a_1 + p_1 r a_0 + q_0 a_1 + q_1 a_0]x^{r-1} + \cdots = 0.$$

In order for the expansion on the left-hand side of equation (14) to sum to zero, each coefficient must be zero. Considering the first term, x^{r-2}, we find

(15) $$[r(r - 1) + p_0 r + q_0]a_0 = 0.$$

[†] *Historical Footnote:* George Frobenius (1848–1917) developed this method in 1873. He is also known for his research on group theory.

Since we have assumed that $a_0 \neq 0$, the quantity in brackets must be zero. This gives the indicial equation that is the same as the one we derived for Cauchy-Euler equations.

INDICIAL EQUATION

Definition 4.   If x_0 is a regular singular point of $y'' + py' + qy = 0$, then the **indicial equation** for this point is

(16) $r(r - 1) + p_0 r + q_0 = 0,$

where

$$p_0 := \lim_{x \to x_0} (x - x_0)p(x), \qquad q_0 := \lim_{x \to x_0} (x - x_0)^2 q(x).$$

The roots of the indicial equation are called the **exponents (indices)** of the singularity x_0.

▶ **Example 2**   Find the indicial equation and the exponents at the singularity $x = -1$ of

(17) $(x^2 - 1)^2 y''(x) + (x + 1)y'(x) - y(x) = 0.$

Solution   In Example 1 we showed that $x = -1$ is a regular singular point. Since $p(x) = (x + 1)^{-1}(x - 1)^{-2}$ and $q(x) = -(x + 1)^{-2}(x - 1)^{-2}$, we find

$$p_0 = \lim_{x \to -1} (x + 1)p(x) = \lim_{x \to -1} (x - 1)^{-2} = \tfrac{1}{4},$$

$$q_0 = \lim_{x \to -1} (x + 1)^2 q(x) = \lim_{x \to -1} \left[-(x - 1)^{-2} \right] = -\tfrac{1}{4}.$$

Substituting these values for p_0 and q_0 into (16), we obtain the indicial equation

(18) $r(r - 1) + \tfrac{1}{4}r - \tfrac{1}{4} = 0.$

Multiplying by 4 and factoring gives $(4r + 1)(r - 1) = 0$. Hence $r = 1$, $-\tfrac{1}{4}$ are the exponents. ◀

As we have seen, we can use the indicial equation to determine those values of r for which the coefficient of x^{r-2} in (14) is zero. If we set the coefficient of x^{r-1} in (14) equal to zero, we have

(19) $[(r + 1)r + (r + 1)p_0 + q_0]a_1 + (p_1 r + q_1)a_0 = 0.$

Since a_0 is arbitrary and we know the p_i's, q_i's, and r, we can solve equation (19) for a_1 provided that the coefficient of a_1 in (19) is not zero. This will be the case if we take r to be the larger of the two roots of the indicial equation (see Problem 43). Similarly, when we set the coefficient of x^r equal to zero, we can solve for a_2 in terms of the p_i's, q_i's, r, a_0, and a_1. Continuing in this manner, we can recursively solve for the a_n's. The procedure is illustrated in the following example.

▶ **Example 3** Find a series expansion about the regular singular point $x = 0$ for a solution to

(20) $(x + 2)x^2 y'' - xy' + (1 + x)y = 0,\qquad x > 0.$

Solution Here $p(x) = -x^{-1}(x + 2)^{-1}$ and $q(x) = x^{-2}(x + 2)^{-1}(1 + x)$, and so

$$p_0 = \lim_{x\to 0} xp(x) = \lim_{x\to 0}\left[-(x + 2)^{-1}\right] = -\tfrac{1}{2},$$

$$q_0 = \lim_{x\to 0} x^2 q(x) = \lim_{x\to 0} (x + 2)^{-1}(1 + x) = \tfrac{1}{2}.$$

Since $x = 0$ is a regular singular point, we seek a solution to (20) of the form

(21) $w(r, x) = x^r \sum_{n=0}^{\infty} a_n x^n = \sum_{n=0}^{\infty} a_n x^{n+r}.$

By the previous discussion, r must satisfy the indicial equation (16). Substituting for p_0 and q_0 in (16), we obtain

$$r(r - 1) - \tfrac{1}{2}r + \tfrac{1}{2} = 0,$$

which simplifies to $2r^2 - 3r + 1 = (2r - 1)(r - 1) = 0$. Thus $r = 1$ and $r = \tfrac{1}{2}$ are the roots of the indicial equation associated with $x = 0$.

Let's use the larger root $r = 1$ and solve for a_1, a_2, etc., to obtain the solution $w(1, x)$. We can simplify the computations by substituting $w(r, x)$ directly into equation (20), where the coefficients are polynomials in x, rather than dividing by $(x + 2)x^2$ and having to work with the rational functions $p(x)$ and $q(x)$. Inserting $w(r, x)$ in (20) and recalling the formulas for $w'(r, x)$ and $w''(r, x)$ in (11) and (12) gives (with $r = 1$)

(22) $(x + 2)x^2 \sum_{n=0}^{\infty} (n + 1)na_n x^{n-1} - x\sum_{n=0}^{\infty} (n + 1)a_n x^n$

$+ (1 + x)\sum_{n=0}^{\infty} a_n x^{n+1} = 0,$

which we can write as

(23) $\sum_{n=0}^{\infty} (n + 1)na_n x^{n+2} + \sum_{n=0}^{\infty} 2(n + 1)na_n x^{n+1} - \sum_{n=0}^{\infty} (n + 1)a_n x^{n+1}$

$+ \sum_{n=0}^{\infty} a_n x^{n+1} + \sum_{n=0}^{\infty} a_n x^{n+2} = 0.$

Next we shift the indices so that each summation in (23) is over x^k. With $k = n + 2$ in the first and last summations and $k = n + 1$ in the rest, (23) becomes

(24) $$\sum_{k=2}^{\infty} [(k-1)(k-2)+1]a_{k-2}x^k + \sum_{k=1}^{\infty} [2k(k-1)-k+1]a_{k-1}x^k = 0.$$

Separating off the $k = 1$ term and combining the rest under one summation yields

(25) $$[2(1)(0)-1+1]a_0 x + \sum_{k=2}^{\infty} [(k^2-3k+3)a_{k-2} + (2k-1)(k-1)a_{k-1}]x^k = 0.$$

Notice that the coefficient of x in (25) is zero. This is because $r = 1$ is a root of the indicial equation, which is the equation we obtained by setting the coefficient of the lowest power of x equal to zero.

We can now determine the a_k's in terms of a_0 by setting the coefficients of x^k in equation (25) equal to zero for $k = 2$, 3, etc. This gives the recurrence relation

(26) $$(k^2-3k+3)a_{k-2} + (2k-1)(k-1)a_{k-1} = 0,$$

or, equivalently,

(27) $$a_{k-1} = -\frac{k^2-3k+3}{(2k-1)(k-1)}a_{k-2}, \qquad k \geq 2.$$

Setting $k = 2$, 3, and 4 in (27), we find

$$a_1 = -\tfrac{1}{3}a_0 \qquad\qquad (k = 2),$$
$$a_2 = -\tfrac{3}{10}a_1 = \tfrac{1}{10}a_0 \qquad (k = 3),$$
$$a_3 = -\tfrac{1}{3}a_2 = -\tfrac{1}{30}a_0 \qquad (k = 4).$$

Substituting these values for r, a_1, a_2, and a_3 into (21) gives

(28) $$w(1, x) = a_0 x^1 (1 - \tfrac{1}{3}x + \tfrac{1}{10}x^2 - \tfrac{1}{30}x^3 + \cdots),$$

where a_0 is arbitrary. In particular, for $a_0 = 1$, we get the solution

$$y_1(x) = x - \tfrac{1}{3}x^2 + \tfrac{1}{10}x^3 - \tfrac{1}{30}x^4 + \cdots, \qquad x > 0. \ \blacktriangleleft$$

To find a second linearly independent solution to equation (20), we could try setting $r = \tfrac{1}{2}$ and solving for $a_1, a_2, \ldots,$ to obtain a solution $w(\tfrac{1}{2}, x)$ (see Problem 44). In this particular case, the approach would work. However, if we encounter an indicial equation that has a repeated root, then the method of Frobenius would yield just one solution (apart from constant multiples). To find the desired second solution we must use another technique, such as the reduction of order procedure discussed in Section 4.4. We tackle the problem of finding a second linearly independent solution in the next section.

The method of Frobenius can be summarized as follows:

METHOD OF FROBENIUS

To derive a series solution about the singular point x_0 of

$$(29) \qquad a_2(x)y''(x) + a_1(x)y'(x) + a_0(x)y(x) = 0, \qquad x > x_0:$$

(a) Set $p(x) := a_1(x)/a_2(x)$, $q(x) := a_0(x)/a_2(x)$. If both $(x - x_0)p(x)$ and $(x - x_0)^2 q(x)$ are analytic at x_0, then x_0 is a regular singular point and the remaining steps apply.

(b) Solve the indicial equation $r(r-1) + p_0 r + q_0 = 0$, where $p_0 := \lim_{x \to x_0} (x - x_0)p(x)$ and $q_0 := \lim_{x \to x_0} (x - x_0)^2 q(x)$. Label the roots r_1, r_2 with $r_1 \geq r_2$ (or $\operatorname{Re} r_1 \geq \operatorname{Re} r_2$).

(c) Let

$$(30) \qquad w(r, x) = (x - x_0)^r \sum_{n=0}^{\infty} a_n(x - x_0)^n = \sum_{n=0}^{\infty} a_n(x - x_0)^{n+r},$$

and, using termwise differentiation, substitute $w(r, x)$ into equation (29) to obtain an equation of the form

$$A_0(x - x_0)^{r+J} + A_1(x - x_0)^{r+J+1} + \cdots = 0.$$

(d) Set the coefficients $A_0, A_1, A_2, \ldots$ equal to zero. (Notice that the equation $A_0 = 0$ is just a constant multiple of the indicial equation.)

(e) Use the system of equations

$$A_0 = 0, \qquad A_1 = 0, \ldots, \qquad A_k = 0,$$

to find a recurrence relation involving a_k and $a_0, a_1, \ldots, a_{k-1}$.

(f) Take $r = r_1$, the larger root, and use the relation obtained in step (e) to recursively determine $a_1, a_2, \ldots$ in terms of a_0 and r_1.

(g) A series expansion of a solution to (29) is

$$(31) \qquad w(r_1, x) = (x - x_0)^{r_1} \sum_{n=0}^{\infty} a_n(x - x_0)^n, \qquad x > x_0,$$

where a_0 is arbitrary and the a_n's are defined in terms of a_0 and r_1.

One important question that remains concerns the radius of convergence of the power series that appears in (31). The following theorem contains an answer.[†]

FROBENIUS'S THEOREM

Theorem 6. If x_0 is a regular singular point of equation (29), then there exists at least one series solution of the form (30), where $r = r_1$ is the larger root of the associated indicial equation. Moreover, this series converges for all x such that $0 < x - x_0 < R$, where R is the distance from x_0 to the nearest other singular point (real or complex) of (29).

For simplicity, in the examples that follow we consider only series expansions about the regular singular point $x = 0$, and only those equations for which the associated indicial equation has real roots.

The following three examples not only illustrate the method of Frobenius, but are important examples to which we refer in later sections.

▶ **Example 4**   Find a series solution about the regular singular point $x = 0$ of

(32) $$x^2 y''(x) - xy'(x) + (1 - x)y(x) = 0, \qquad x > 0.$$

Solution   Here $p(x) = -x^{-1}$ and $q(x) = (1 - x)x^{-2}$. It is easy to check that $x = 0$ is a regular singular point of (32), so we compute

$$p_0 = \lim_{x \to 0} xp(x) = \lim_{x \to 0} -1 = -1,$$

$$q_0 = \lim_{x \to 0} x^2 q(x) = \lim_{x \to 0} (1 - x) = 1.$$

Then the indicial equation is

$$r(r - 1) - r + 1 = r^2 - 2r + 1 = (r - 1)^2 = 0,$$

which has the roots $r_1 = r_2 = 1$.

Next we substitute

(33) $$w(r, x) = x^r \sum_{n=0}^{\infty} a_n x^n = \sum_{n=0}^{\infty} a_n x^{n+r}$$

[†] For a proof of this theorem see *Ordinary Differential Equations*, by E. L. Ince, Dover Publications, Inc., New York, 1956, Chapter XVI.

into (32) and obtain

(34)
$$x^2 \sum_{n=0}^{\infty} (n+r)(n+r-1)a_n x^{n+r-2} - x \sum_{n=0}^{\infty} (n+r)a_n x^{n+r-1}$$
$$+ (1-x) \sum_{n=0}^{\infty} a_n x^{n+r} = 0,$$

which we write as

(35)
$$\sum_{n=0}^{\infty} (n+r)(n+r-1)a_n x^{n+r} - \sum_{n=0}^{\infty} (n+r)a_n x^{n+r}$$
$$+ \sum_{n=0}^{\infty} a_n x^{n+r} - \sum_{n=0}^{\infty} a_n x^{n+r+1} = 0.$$

Shifting the indices so that each summation in (35) is over x^{k+r}, we take $k = n + 1$ in the last summation and $k = n$ in the rest. This gives

(36)
$$\sum_{k=0}^{\infty} [(k+r)(k+r-1) - (k+r) + 1]a_k x^{k+r} - \sum_{k=1}^{\infty} a_{k-1} x^{k+r} = 0.$$

Singling out the term corresponding to $k = 0$ and combining the rest under one summation yields

(37)
$$[r(r-1) - r + 1]a_0 x^r$$
$$+ \sum_{k=1}^{\infty} \{[(k+r)(k+r-1) - (k+r) + 1]a_k - a_{k-1}\}x^{k+r} = 0.$$

When we set the coefficients equal to zero, we obtain

(38)
$$[r(r-1) - r + 1]a_0 = 0,$$

and, for $k \geq 1$, the recurrence relation

(39)
$$[(k+r)^2 - 2(k+r) + 1]a_k - a_{k-1} = 0,$$

which reduces to

(40)
$$(k+r-1)^2 a_k - a_{k-1} = 0.$$

Relation (40) can be used to solve for a_k in terms of a_{k-1}:

(41)
$$a_k = \frac{1}{(k+r-1)^2} a_{k-1}, \qquad k \geq 1.$$

Setting $r = r_1 = 1$ in (38) gives (as expected) $0 \cdot a_0 = 0$, and in (41) gives

(42) $\qquad a_k = \dfrac{1}{k^2} a_{k-1}, \qquad k \geq 1.$

For $k = 1$, 2, and 3, we now find

$$a_1 = \frac{1}{1^2} a_0 = a_0 \qquad\qquad\qquad (k = 1),$$

$$a_2 = \frac{1}{2^2} a_1 = \frac{1}{(2 \cdot 1)^2} a_0 = \frac{1}{4} a_0 \qquad (k = 2),$$

$$a_3 = \frac{1}{3^2} a_2 = \frac{1}{(3 \cdot 2 \cdot 1)^2} a_0 = \frac{1}{36} a_0 \quad (k = 3).$$

In general, we have

(43) $\qquad a_k = \dfrac{1}{(k!)^2} a_0.$

Hence equation (32) has a series solution given by

(44) $\qquad w(1, x) = a_0 x \{ 1 + x + \frac{1}{4} x^2 + \frac{1}{36} x^3 + \cdots \}$

$$= a_0 x \sum_{k=0}^{\infty} \frac{1}{(k!)^2} x^k, \qquad x > 0. \blacktriangleleft$$

Since $x = 0$ is the only singular point for equation (32), it follows from Frobenius's theorem or directly by the ratio test that the series solution (44) converges for all $x > 0$.

In the next two examples, we only outline the method; the reader is invited to furnish the intermediate steps.

▶ **Example 5**   Find a series solution about the regular singular point $x = 0$ of

(45) $\qquad xy''(x) + 4y'(x) - xy(x) = 0, \qquad x > 0.$

Solution   Since $p(x) = 4/x$ and $q(x) = -1$, we see that $x = 0$ is indeed a regular singular point and

$$p_0 = \lim_{x \to 0} xp(x) = 4, \qquad q_0 = \lim_{x \to 0} x^2 q(x) = 0.$$

The indicial equation is

$$r(r-1) + 4r = r^2 + 3r = r(r+3) = 0,$$

with roots $r_1 = 0$ and $r_2 = -3$.
Now substitute

(46) $$w(r, x) = x^r \sum_{n=0}^{\infty} a_n x^n = \sum_{n=0}^{\infty} a_n x^{n+r}$$

into (45). After a little algebra and a shift in indices, we get

(47) $$[r(r-1) + 4r]a_0 x^{r-1} + [(r+1)r + 4(r+1)]a_1 x^r$$

$$+ \sum_{k=1}^{\infty} [(k+r+1)(k+r+4)a_{k+1} - a_{k-1}]x^{k+r} = 0.$$

Next we set the coefficients equal to zero and find

(48) $$[r(r-1) + 4r]a_0 = 0,$$

(49) $$[(r+1)r + 4(r+1)]a_1 = 0,$$

and, for $k \geq 1$, the recurrence relation

(50) $$(k+r+1)(k+r+4)a_{k+1} - a_{k-1} = 0.$$

For $r = r_1 = 0$, equation (48) becomes $0 \cdot a_0 = 0$ and (49) becomes $4 \cdot a_1 = 0$. Hence, while a_0 is arbitrary, a_1 must be zero. Setting $r = r_1 = 0$ in (50), we find

(51) $$a_{k+1} = \frac{1}{(k+1)(k+4)} a_{k-1}, \qquad k \geq 1,$$

from which it follows (after a few experimental computations) that $a_{2k+1} = 0$ for $k = 0, 1, \ldots$, and

(52) $$a_{2k} = \frac{1}{[2 \cdot 4 \cdots (2k)][5 \cdot 7 \cdots (2k+3)]} a_0$$

$$= \frac{1}{2^k k! [5 \cdot 7 \cdots (2k+3)]} a_0, \qquad k \geq 1.$$

Hence equation (45) has a series solution

(53) $$w(0, x) = a_0 \left\{ 1 + \sum_{k=1}^{\infty} \frac{1}{2^k k! [5 \cdot 7 \cdots (2k+3)]} x^{2k} \right\}, \qquad x > 0. \blacktriangleleft$$

If in Example 5 we had worked with the root $r = r_2 = -3$, then we would actually have obtained *two* linearly independent solutions (see Problem 45).

▶ **Example 6**   Find a series solution about the regular singular point $x = 0$ of

(54) $$xy''(x) + 3y'(x) - xy(x) = 0, \qquad x > 0.$$

Solution   Since $p(x) = 3/x$ and $q(x) = -1$, we see that $x = 0$ is a regular singular point. Moreover,

$$p_0 = \lim_{x \to 0} xp(x) = 3, \qquad q_0 = \lim_{x \to 0} x^2 q(x) = 0,$$

and so the indicial equation is

(55) $$r(r - 1) + 3r = r^2 + 2r = r(r + 2) = 0,$$

with roots $r_1 = 0$ and $r_2 = -2$.
   Substituting

(56) $$w(r, x) = x^r \sum_{n=0}^{\infty} a_n x^n = \sum_{n=0}^{\infty} a_n x^{n+r}$$

into (54) ultimately gives

(57) $$[r(r - 1) + 3r]a_0 x^{r-1} + [(r + 1)r + 3(r + 1)]a_1 x^r$$

$$+ \sum_{k=1}^{\infty} [(k + r + 1)(k + r + 3)a_{k+1} - a_{k-1}]x^{k+r} = 0.$$

Setting the coefficients equal to zero, we have

(58) $$[r(r - 1) + 3r]a_0 = 0,$$
(59) $$[(r + 1)r + 3(r + 1)]a_1 = 0,$$

and, for $k \geq 1$, the recurrence relation

(60) $$(k + r + 1)(k + r + 3)a_{k+1} - a_{k-1} = 0.$$

With $r = r_1 = 0$, these equations lead to the following formulas: $a_{2k+1} = 0, k = 0, 1, \ldots,$ and

(61) $$a_{2k} = \frac{1}{[2 \cdot 4 \cdots (2k)][4 \cdot 6 \cdots (2k + 2)]} a_0 = \frac{1}{2^{2k} k!(k + 1)!} a_0, \qquad k \geq 0.$$

Hence equation (54) has a series solution

$$(62) \qquad w(0, x) = a_0 \sum_{k=0}^{\infty} \frac{1}{2^{2k} k! (k+1)!} x^{2k}, \qquad x > 0. \blacktriangleleft$$

Unlike Example 5, if we work with the second root $r = r_2 = -2$ in Example 6, then we do *not* obtain a second linearly independent solution (see Problem 46).

In the preceding examples we were able to use the method of Frobenius to find a series solution valid to the right $(x > 0)$ of the regular singular point $x = 0$. For $x < 0$, we can use the change of variables $x = -t$ and then solve the resulting equation for $t > 0$.

The method of Frobenius also applies to higher order linear equations (see Problems 35–38).

EXERCISES 8.6

In Problems 1 through 10 classify each singular point (real or complex) of the given equation as regular or irregular.

1. $x^2 y'' - 5xy' + 7y = 0.$

2. $x^2 y'' + 8xy' - 3xy = 0.$

3. $(x^2 - 4)y'' + (x + 2)y' + 3y = 0.$

4. $(x^2 - 1)y'' + xy' + 3y = 0.$

5. $(x^2 - 1)^2 y'' - (x - 1)y' + 3y = 0.$

6. $(x^2 + 1)y'' + 7x^2 y' - 3xy = 0.$

7. $(x^2 - x - 2)^2 y'' + (x^2 - 4)y' - xy = 0.$

8. $(x^2 - x)y'' + xy' + 7y = 0.$

9. $x^3 (x - 1)y'' + (x^2 - 3x)(\sin x)y' - xy = 0.$

10. $(x^2 + 2x - 8)^2 y'' + (3x + 12)y' - x^2 y = 0.$

In Problems 11 through 18 find the indicial equation and the exponents for the specified singularity of the given differential equation.

11. $x^2 y'' + 4xy' + 2y = 0,$ at $x = 0.$

12. $x^2 y'' - 2xy' - 10y = 0,$ at $x = 0.$

13. $(x^2 - x - 2)^2 y'' + (x^2 - 4)y' - 6xy = 0,$ at $x = 2.$

14. $(x^2 - 4)y'' + (x + 2)y' + 3y = 0,$ at $x = -2.$

15. $(x^2 - 1)^2 y'' - (x - 1)y' - 3y = 0,$ at $x = 1.$

16. $(x - 1)^2 y'' + (x^2 - 1)y' - 12y = 0,$ at $x = 1.$

17. $x^3 y'' + x(\sin x)y' - (\tan x)y = 0,$ at $x = 0.$

18. $4x(\sin x)y'' - 3y = 0,$ at $x = 0.$

In Problems 19 through 24 use the method of Frobenius to find at least the first four nonzero terms in the series expansion about $x = 0$ for a solution to the given equation for $x > 0$.

19. $2x(x - 1)y'' + 3(x - 1)y' - y = 0.$

20. $9x^2 y'' + 9x^2 y' + 2y = 0.$

21. $x^2 y'' + xy' + x^2 y = 0.$

22. $xy'' + y' - 4y = 0.$

23. $x^2 y'' + (x^2 + x)y' - y = 0.$

24. $3xy'' + (2 - x)y' - y = 0.$

In Problems 25 through 34 use the method of Frobenius to find a general formula for the coefficient a_n in a series expansion about $x = 0$ for a solution to the given equation for $x > 0$.

25. $4x^2 y'' + 2x^2 y' - (x + 3)y = 0.$

26. $x^2 y'' + (x^2 - x)y' + y = 0.$

27. $xy'' - y' - xy = 0.$

28. $x^2 y'' - x(1 + x)y' + y = 0.$

29. $3xy'' + 2(1 - x)y' - 4y = 0$.

30. $xy'' + (x - 1)y' - 2y = 0$.

31. $xy'' + (1 - x)y' - y = 0$.

32. $3x^2y'' + 8xy' + (x - 2)y = 0$.

33. $x(x + 1)y'' + (x + 5)y' - 4y = 0$.

34. $xy'' + (x + 2)y' - y = 0$.

In Problems 35 through 38 use the method of Frobenius to find at least the first four nonzero terms in the series expansion about $x = 0$ for a solution to the given linear third order equation for $x > 0$.

35. $6x^3y''' + 13x^2y'' + (x + x^2)y' + xy = 0$.

36. $6x^3y''' + 13x^2y'' - (x^2 + 3x)y' - xy = 0$.

37. $6x^3y''' + 11x^2y'' - 2xy' - (x - 2)y = 0$.

38. $6x^3y''' + (13x^2 - x^3)y'' + xy' - xy = 0$.

In Problems 39 and 40 try to use the method of Frobenius to find a series expansion about the irregular singular point $x = 0$ for a solution to the given differential equation. If the method works, give at least the first four nonzero terms in the expansion. If the method does not work, explain what went wrong.

39. $x^2y'' + (3x - 1)y' + y = 0$.

40. $x^2y'' + y' - 2y = 0$.

In certain applications it is desirable to have an expansion about the point at infinity. To obtain such an expansion, we use the change of variables $z = 1/x$ and expand about $z = 0$. In Problems 41 and 42 show that infinity is a regular singular point of the given differential equation by showing that $z = 0$ is a regular singular point for the transformed equation in z. Also find at least the first four nonzero terms in the series expansion about infinity of a solution to the original equation in x.

41. $x^3y'' - x^2y' - y = 0$.

42. $18(x - 4)^2(x - 6)y'' + 9x(x - 4)y' - 32y = 0$.

43. Show that if r_1 and r_2 are roots of the indicial equation (16), with r_1 the larger root (Re $r_1 \geq$ Re r_2), then the coefficient of a_1 in equation (19) is not zero when $r = r_1$.

44. To obtain a second linearly independent solution to equation (20):

(a) Substitute $w(r, x)$ given in (21) into (20) and conclude that the coefficients a_k, $k \geq 1$ must satisfy the recurrence relation

$$(k + r - 1)(2k + 2r - 1)a_k$$
$$+ \left[(k + r - 1)(k + r - 2) + 1\right]a_{k-1} = 0.$$

(b) Use the recurrence relation with $r = \frac{1}{2}$ to derive the second series solution

$$w(\tfrac{1}{2}, x) = a_0(x^{1/2} - \tfrac{3}{4}x^{3/2} + \tfrac{7}{32}x^{7/2} - \tfrac{133}{1920}x^{9/2} + \cdots).$$

(c) Use the recurrence relation with $r = 1$ to obtain $w(1, x)$ in (28).

45. In Example 5, show that if we choose $r = r_2 = -3$, then we obtain *two* linearly independent solutions to equation (45). [Hint: a_0 and a_3 are arbitrary constants.]

46. In Example 6, show that if we choose $r = r_2 = -2$, then we obtain a solution that is a constant multiple of the solution given in (62). [Hint: $a_0 = a_1 = 0$ and a_2 is arbitrary.]

8.7 Finding a Second Linearly Independent Solution

In the previous section we showed that if $x = 0$ is a regular singular point of

$$(1) \qquad y''(x) + p(x)y'(x) + q(x)y(x) = 0, \qquad x > 0,$$

then the method of Frobenius can be used to find a series solution valid for x near zero. The first step in the method is to find the roots r_1 and r_2 (Re $r_1 \geq$ Re r_2) of the associated indicial equation

$$(2) \qquad r(r - 1) + p_0 r + q_0 = 0.$$

Then, utilizing the larger root r_1, equation (1) has a series solution of the form

$$(3) \qquad w(r_1, x) = x^{r_1} \sum_{n=0}^{\infty} a_n x^n = \sum_{n=0}^{\infty} a_n x^{n+r_1},$$

where $a_0 \neq 0$. In order to find a second linearly independent solution, our first inclination is to set $r = r_2$ and seek a solution of the form

$$(4) \qquad w(r_2, x) = x^{r_2} \sum_{n=0}^{\infty} a_n x^n = \sum_{n=0}^{\infty} a_n x^{n+r_2}.$$

This procedure will work *provided that $r_1 - r_2$ is not an integer.* However, when $r_1 - r_2$ is an integer, the Frobenius method with $r = r_2$ may just lead to the same solution that we obtained using the root r_1. (This is obviously true when $r_1 = r_2$.)

▶ **Example 1** Find the first few terms in the series expansion about the regular singular point $x = 0$ for a general solution to

$$(5) \qquad (x + 2)x^2 y''(x) - xy'(x) + (1 + x)y(x) = 0, \qquad x > 0.$$

Solution In Example 3 of Section 8.6 we used the method of Frobenius to find a series solution for (5). In the process we determined that $p_0 = -\frac{1}{2}$, $q_0 = \frac{1}{2}$, and that the indicial equation has roots $r_1 = 1$, $r_2 = \frac{1}{2}$. Since these roots do not differ by an integer ($r_1 - r_2 = \frac{1}{2}$), the method of Frobenius will give two linearly independent solutions of the form

$$(6) \qquad w(r, x) := x^r \sum_{n=0}^{\infty} a_n x^n = \sum_{n=0}^{\infty} a_n x^{n+r}.$$

In Problem 44 of Exercises 8.6 the reader was requested to show that substituting $w(r, x)$ into (5) leads to the recurrence relation

(7) $$(k + r - 1)(2k + 2r - 1)a_k + [(k + r - 1)(k + r - 2) + 1]a_{k-1} = 0, \qquad k \geq 1.$$

With $r = r_1 = 1$ and $a_0 = 1$ we find

(8) $$y_1(x) = x - \tfrac{1}{3}x^2 + \tfrac{1}{10}x^3 - \tfrac{1}{30}x^4 + \cdots$$

as obtained in the previous section. Moreover, taking $r = r_2 = \tfrac{1}{2}$ and $a_0 = 1$ in (7) leads to the second solution,

(9) $$y_2(x) = x^{1/2} - \tfrac{3}{4}x^{3/2} + \tfrac{7}{32}x^{7/2} - \tfrac{133}{1920}x^{9/2} + \cdots.$$

Consequently, a general solution to equation (5) is

(10) $$y(x) = c_1 y_1(x) + c_2 y_2(x), \qquad x > 0,$$

where $y_1(x)$ and $y_2(x)$ are the series solutions given in equations (8) and (9). ◀

When the indicial equation has repeated roots, $r_1 = r_2$, substituting $r = r_2$ just gives us back the first solution and gets us nowhere. However, in such a case, we can use the reduction of order formula discussed in Section 4.4 to obtain a second linearly independent solution.

Recall that if $f(x)$ is a nontrivial solution to equation (1), then a second linearly independent solution is given by the reduction of order formula

(11) $$y(x) = f(x) \int \frac{e^{-\int p(x)\,dx}}{[f(x)]^2}\,dx.$$

In the next example we use this formula to hunt for a second series solution.

▶ **Example 2** Find the first few terms in the series expansion about the regular singular point $x = 0$ for a general solution to

(12) $$x^2 y''(x) - xy'(x) + (1 - x)y(x) = 0, \qquad x > 0.$$

Solution In Example 4 of Section 8.6 we used the method of Frobenius to obtain a series solution to equation (12). In the process we found the indicial equation to be $r^2 - 2r + 1 = 0$, which has roots $r_1 = r_2 = 1$. Working with $r_1 = 1$, we derived the series solution

(13) $$y_1(x) = x + x^2 + \tfrac{1}{4}x^3 + \tfrac{1}{36}x^4 + \tfrac{1}{576}x^5 + \cdots = \sum_{k=0}^{\infty} \frac{1}{(k!)^2} x^{k+1},$$

(see equation (44) in Section 8.6 with $a_0 = 1$).

Since $p(x) = -x^{-1}$ for equation (12), we can substitute $f(x) = y_1(x)$ and $p(x) = -x^{-1}$ into the reduction of order formula (11) to obtain

(14) $$y_2(x) = y_1(x) \int \frac{e^{\int x^{-1} dx}}{[y_1(x)]^2}\, dx = y_1(x) \int \frac{e^{\ln x}}{[y_1(x)]^2}\, dx$$

$$= y_1(x) \int \frac{x}{\left[x + x^2 + \frac{1}{4}x^3 + \frac{1}{36}x^4 + \frac{1}{576}x^5 + \cdots\right]^2}\, dx.$$

Using the Cauchy product to square the series in the denominator and canceling out an x gives

(15) $$y_2(x) = y_1(x) \int \frac{x}{\left[x^2 + 2x^3 + \frac{3}{2}x^4 + \frac{5}{9}x^5 + \frac{35}{288}x^6 + \cdots\right]}\, dx$$

$$= y_1(x) \int \left\{\frac{1}{x + 2x^2 + \frac{3}{2}x^3 + \frac{5}{9}x^4 + \frac{35}{288}x^5 + \cdots}\right\} dx.$$

Next, we can use long division to compute the power series for the quotient in the curly brackets, obtaining

(16) $$y_2(x) = y_1(x) \int \left\{\frac{1}{x} - 2 + \frac{5}{2}x - \frac{23}{9}x^2 + \cdots\right\} dx.$$

Integrating term by term, we then find

(17) $$y_2(x) = y_1(x)\{\ln x - 2x + \tfrac{5}{4}x^2 - \tfrac{23}{27}x^3 + \cdots\}$$

$$= y_1(x) \ln x + y_1(x)(-2x + \tfrac{5}{4}x^2 - \tfrac{23}{27}x^3 + \cdots).$$

Now we substitute the series for $y_1(x)$ given in (13) and use the Cauchy product to obtain

(18) $$y_2(x) = y_1(x) \ln x + (x + x^2 + \tfrac{1}{4}x^3 + \cdots)(-2x + \tfrac{5}{4}x^2 - \tfrac{23}{27}x^3 + \cdots)$$

$$= y_1(x) \ln x + (-2x^2 - \tfrac{3}{4}x^3 - \tfrac{11}{108}x^4 + \cdots).$$

Hence a general solution to equation (12) is

(19) $$y(x) = c_1 y_1(x) + c_2 y_2(x), \qquad x > 0,$$

where c_1 and c_2 are arbitrary constants and $y_1(x)$ and $y_2(x)$ are given by (13) and (18). ◄

The previous example illustrates the drawback to using the reduction of order formula to find a second linearly independent solution: We must square a series and then compute its reciprocal. As a result, it is very difficult to determine the general term in the series expansion for $y_2(x)$.

In Example 2 the roots of the indicial equation are equal, and we found a second linearly independent solution (18) that involves the first solution $y_1(x)$ multiplied by ln x. This should not be too surprising if we recall the analogous situation for a Cauchy-Euler equation having an indicial equation with repeated roots. As we shall soon see, if an indicial equation has roots that differ by an integer, then the expansion of the second solution may also involve the term $y_1(x)$ ln x. In the following theorem we give the *form* of two linearly independent solutions for the three cases where the roots of the indicial equation (a) do not differ by an integer, (b) are equal, or (c) differ by a nonzero integer.

FORM OF SECOND LINEARLY INDEPENDENT SOLUTION

Theorem 7. Let x_0 be a regular singular point for $y'' + py' + qy = 0$ and let r_1 and r_2 be the roots of the associated indicial equation, where $r_1 \geq r_2$ (Re $r_1 \geq$ Re r_2).

   (a) If $r_1 - r_2$ is not an integer, then there exist two linearly independent solutions of the form

$$(20) \qquad y_1(x) = \sum_{n=0}^{\infty} a_n(x - x_0)^{n+r_1}, \qquad a_0 \neq 0,$$

$$(21) \qquad y_2(x) = \sum_{n=0}^{\infty} b_n(x - x_0)^{n+r_2}, \qquad b_0 \neq 0.$$

   (b) If $r_1 = r_2$, then there exist two linearly independent solutions of the form

$$(22) \qquad y_1(x) = \sum_{n=0}^{\infty} a_n(x - x_0)^{n+r_1}, \qquad a_0 \neq 0,$$

$$(23) \qquad y_2(x) = y_1(x) \ln(x - x_0) + \sum_{n=1}^{\infty} b_n(x - x_0)^{n+r_1}.$$

   (c) If $r_1 - r_2$ is a positive integer, then there exist two linearly independent solutions of the form

$$(24) \qquad y_1(x) = \sum_{n=0}^{\infty} a_n(x - x_0)^{n+r_1}, \qquad a_0 \neq 0,$$

$$(25) \qquad y_2(x) = Cy_1(x) \ln(x - x_0) + \sum_{n=0}^{\infty} b_n(x - x_0)^{n+r_2}, \qquad b_0 \neq 0,$$

where C is a constant that could be zero.

In each case of the theorem, $y_1(x)$ is just the series solution obtained by the method of Frobenius, with $r = r_1$. When $r_1 - r_2$ is not an integer, the method of Frobenius yields a second linearly independent solution by taking $r = r_2$. In Section 8.8 we derive the formulas stated in Theorem 7 for cases (b) and (c). For now, let's see how knowing the form of the second solution enables us to obtain it. Again, for simplicity, we consider only indicial equations having real roots.

▶ **Example 3** Find the first few terms in the series expansion about the regular singular point $x = 0$ for two linearly independent solutions to

(26) $$x^2 y''(x) - xy'(x) + (1 - x)y(x) = 0, \qquad x > 0.$$

Solution This is the same equation we considered in Example 2, where we used the reduction of order formula to find a second linearly independent solution. This time let's try to find a second solution using Theorem 7. Recall that $r_1 = r_2 = 1$ and so $y_2(x)$ has the form given in (23) (with $x_0 = 0$); that is,

(27) $$y_2(x) = y_1(x) \ln x + \sum_{n=1}^{\infty} b_n x^{n+1},$$

where (cf. (13))

(28) $$y_1(x) = \sum_{k=0}^{\infty} \frac{1}{(k!)^2} x^{k+1}.$$

Our goal is to determine the coefficients b_n by substituting $y_2(x)$ directly into equation (26). We begin by differentiating $y_2(x)$ in (27) to obtain

$$y_2'(x) = y_1'(x) \ln x + x^{-1} y_1(x) + \sum_{n=1}^{\infty} (n+1)b_n x^n,$$

$$y_2''(x) = y_1''(x) \ln x - x^{-2} y_1(x) + 2x^{-1} y_1'(x) + \sum_{n=1}^{\infty} n(n+1)b_n x^{n-1}.$$

Substituting $y_2(x)$ into (26) yields

(29) $$x^2 \left\{ y_1''(x) \ln x - x^{-2} y_1(x) + 2x^{-1} y_1'(x) + \sum_{n=1}^{\infty} n(n+1)b_n x^{n-1} \right\}$$

$$- x \left\{ y_1'(x) \ln x + x^{-1} y_1(x) + \sum_{n=1}^{\infty} (n+1)b_n x^n \right\}$$

$$+ (1 - x) \left\{ y_1(x) \ln x + \sum_{n=1}^{\infty} b_n x^{n+1} \right\} = 0,$$

which simplifies to

(30) $\quad \{x^2y_1''(x) - xy_1'(x) + (1-x)y_1(x)\} \ln x - 2y_1(x) + 2xy_1'(x)$

$$+ \sum_{n=1}^{\infty} n(n+1)b_n x^{n+1} - \sum_{n=1}^{\infty} (n+1)b_n x^{n+1} + \sum_{n=1}^{\infty} b_n x^{n+1} - \sum_{n=1}^{\infty} b_n x^{n+2} = 0.$$

Notice that the factor in front of $\ln x$ is just the left-hand side of equation (26) with $y = y_1$. Since y_1 is a solution to (26), this factor is zero. With this observation and a shift in the indices of summation, equation (30) can be rewritten as

(31) $\quad 2xy_1'(x) - 2y_1(x) + b_1 x^2 + \sum_{k=2}^{\infty} (k^2 b_k - b_{k-1})x^{k+1} = 0.$

Before we can set the coefficients equal to zero, we must substitute back in the series expansions for $y_1(x)$ and $y_1'(x)$. From (28), we see that $y_1'(x) = \sum_{k=0}^{\infty} (k+1)x^k/(k!)^2$, and inserting this series together with (28) into (31) we find

(32) $\quad \sum_{k=0}^{\infty} \frac{2(k+1) - 2}{(k!)^2} x^{k+1} + b_1 x^2 + \sum_{k=2}^{\infty} (k^2 b_k - b_{k-1})x^{k+1} = 0.$

Listing separately the $k = 0$ and $k = 1$ terms and combining the remaining terms gives

(33) $\quad (2 + b_1)x^2 + \sum_{k=2}^{\infty} \left[\frac{2k}{(k!)^2} + k^2 b_k - b_{k-1} \right]x^{k+1} = 0.$

Next, we set the coefficients in (33) equal to zero. From the x^2 term we have $2 + b_1 = 0$, and so $b_1 = -2$. From the x^{k+1} term we obtain

$$\frac{2k}{(k!)^2} + k^2 b_k - b_{k-1} = 0,$$

or

(34) $\quad b_k = \frac{1}{k^2}\left[b_{k-1} - \frac{2k}{(k!)^2} \right], \quad k \geq 2.$

Taking $k = 2$ and 3, we compute

(35) $\quad b_2 = \frac{1}{2^2}\left[b_1 - 1 \right] = \frac{-3}{4}, \qquad b_3 = \frac{1}{9}\left[-\frac{3}{4} - \frac{6}{36} \right] = \frac{-11}{108}.$

Hence, a second linearly independent solution to (26) is

(36) $\quad y_2(x) = y_1(x) \ln x - 2x^2 - \frac{3}{4}x^3 - \frac{11}{108}x^4 + \cdots. \quad \blacktriangleleft$

If we compare the different methods used in Examples 2 and 3 for obtaining a second linearly independent solution, we find that the technique of Example 3 has an advantage: It yields a recurrence relation, equation (34), that can be used to solve recursively for the coefficients b_k.

In the next two examples we consider the case when the difference between the roots of the indicial equation is a positive integer. In Example 4, it turns out that the constant C in formula (25) must be taken to be zero (i.e., no ln x term is present), while in Example 5, this constant is nonzero (i.e., a ln x term is present). Since the solutions to these examples require several intermediate computations, we do not display all the details. Rather, we encourage the reader to take an active part by bridging the gaps.

▶ *Example 4*   Find the first few terms in the series expansion about the regular singular point $x = 0$ for a general solution to

(37) $xy''(x) + 4y'(x) - xy(x) = 0, \qquad x > 0.$

Solution   In Example 5 of Section 8.6 we used the method of Frobenius to find a series expansion about $x = 0$ for a solution to equation (37). There we found the indicial equation to be $r^2 + 3r = 0$, which has roots $r_1 = 0$ and $r_2 = -3$. Working with $r_1 = 0$, we obtained the series solution

(38) $y_1(x) = 1 + \frac{1}{10}x^2 + \frac{1}{280}x^4 + \cdots,$

(see equation (53) in Section 8.6, with $a_0 = 1$).

Since $r_1 - r_2 = 3$ is a positive integer, it follows from Theorem 7 that equation (37) has a second linearly independent solution of the form

(39) $y_2(x) = Cy_1(x) \ln x + \sum_{n=0}^{\infty} b_n x^{n-3}.$

When we substitute this expression for y_2 into equation (37), we obtain

(40) $x \left\{ Cy_1''(x) \ln x + 2Cx^{-1}y_1'(x) - Cx^{-2}y_1(x) + \sum_{n=0}^{\infty} (n-3)(n-4)b_n x^{n-5} \right\}$

$+ 4 \left\{ Cy_1'(x) \ln x + Cx^{-1}y_1(x) + \sum_{n=0}^{\infty} (n-3)b_n x^{n-4} \right\}$

$- x \left\{ Cy_1(x) \ln x + \sum_{n=0}^{\infty} b_n x^{n-3} \right\} = 0,$

which simplifies to

(41) $\{xy_1''(x) + 4y_1'(x) - xy_1(x)\}C \ln x + 3Cx^{-1}y_1(x) + 2Cy_1'(x)$

$+ \sum_{n=0}^{\infty} (n-3)(n-4)b_n x^{n-4} + \sum_{n=0}^{\infty} 4(n-3)b_n x^{n-4} - \sum_{n=0}^{\infty} b_n x^{n-2} = 0.$

The factor in braces is zero because $y_1(x)$ satisfies equation (37). Combining the summations and simplifying, equation (41) becomes

$$\text{(42)} \qquad 3Cx^{-1}y_1(x) + 2Cy_1'(x) - 2b_1x^{-3} + \sum_{k=2}^{\infty}\left[k(k-3)b_k - b_{k-2}\right]x^{k-4} = 0.$$

Substituting in the series for $y_1(x)$ and writing out the first few terms of the summation in (42), we obtain

$$\text{(43)} \qquad -2b_1x^{-3} + (-2b_2 - b_0)x^{-2} + (3C - b_1)x^{-1} + (4b_4 - b_2)$$
$$+ (\tfrac{7}{10}C + 10b_5 - b_3)x + (18b_6 - b_4)x^2 + (\tfrac{11}{280}C + 28b_7 - b_5)x^3$$
$$+ \cdots = 0.$$

Next, we set the coefficients equal to zero:

$$-2b_1 = 0 \Rightarrow b_1 = 0, \qquad\qquad -2b_2 - b_0 = 0 \Rightarrow b_2 = -\tfrac{1}{2}b_0,$$
$$3C - b_1 = 0 \Rightarrow C = \tfrac{1}{3}b_1 = 0, \qquad 4b_4 - b_2 = 0 \Rightarrow b_4 = \tfrac{1}{4}b_2 = -\tfrac{1}{8}b_0,$$
$$\tfrac{7}{10}C + 10b_5 - b_3 = 0 \Rightarrow b_5 = \frac{b_3 - \tfrac{7}{10}C}{10} = \tfrac{1}{10}b_3,$$
$$18b_6 - b_4 = 0 \Rightarrow b_6 = \tfrac{1}{18}b_4 = -\tfrac{1}{144}b_0,$$
$$\tfrac{11}{280}C + 28b_7 - b_5 = 0 \Rightarrow b_7 = \frac{b_5 - \tfrac{11}{280}C}{28} = \tfrac{1}{280}b_3.$$

Substituting the above values for C and the b_n's back into equation (39) gives

$$\text{(44)} \qquad y_2(x) = b_0\{x^{-3} - \tfrac{1}{2}x^{-1} - \tfrac{1}{8}x - \tfrac{1}{144}x^3 + \cdots\}$$
$$+ b_3\{1 + \tfrac{1}{10}x^2 + \tfrac{1}{280}x^4 + \cdots\},$$

where b_0 and b_3 are arbitrary constants. Observe that the expression in braces following b_3 is just the series expansion for $y_1(x)$ given in equation (38). Hence, in order to obtain a second linearly independent solution, we must choose b_0 to be nonzero. Taking $b_0 = 1$ and $b_3 = 0$ gives

$$\text{(45)} \qquad y_2(x) = x^{-3} - \tfrac{1}{2}x^{-1} - \tfrac{1}{8}x - \tfrac{1}{144}x^3 + \cdots.$$

Therefore, a general solution to equation (37) is

$$y(x) = c_1y_1(x) + c_2y_2(x), \qquad x > 0,$$

where $y_1(x)$ and $y_2(x)$ are given in (38) and (45). (Notice that the right-hand side of (44) is also a general solution to (37), with b_0 and b_3 as the two arbitrary constants.) ◄

▶ *Example 5* Find the first few terms in the series expansion about the regular singular point $x = 0$ for two linearly independent solutions to

(46) $$xy''(x) + 3y'(x) - xy(x) = 0, \qquad x > 0.$$

Solution In Example 6 of Section 8.6 we used the method of Frobenius to find a series expansion about $x = 0$ for a solution to equation (46). The indicial equation turned out to be $r^2 + 2r = 0$, which has roots $r_1 = 0$ and $r_2 = -2$. Using $r_1 = 0$, we obtained the series solution

(47) $$y_1(x) = 1 + \tfrac{1}{8}x^2 + \tfrac{1}{192}x^4 + \tfrac{1}{9216}x^6 + \cdots,$$

(see equation (62) in Section 8.6 and put $a_0 = 1$).

Since $r_1 - r_2 = 2$ is a positive integer, it follows from Theorem 7 that equation (46) has a second linearly independent solution of the form

(48) $$y_2(x) = Cy_1(x) \ln x + \sum_{n=0}^{\infty} b_n x^{n-2}.$$

Plugging the expansion for $y_2(x)$ into equation (46) and simplifying yields

(49) $$\{xy_1''(x) + 3y_1'(x) - xy_1(x)\}C \ln x + 2Cx^{-1}y_1(x) + 2Cy_1'(x)$$
$$+ \sum_{n=0}^{\infty} (n-2)(n-3)b_n x^{n-3} + \sum_{n=0}^{\infty} 3(n-2)b_n x^{n-3} - \sum_{n=0}^{\infty} b_n x^{n-1} = 0.$$

Again the factor in braces is zero, because $y_1(x)$ is a solution to equation (46). If we combine the summations and simplify, equation (49) becomes

(50) $$2Cx^{-1}y_1(x) + 2Cy_1'(x) - b_1 x^{-2} + \sum_{k=2}^{\infty} [k(k-2)b_k - b_{k-2}]x^{k-3} = 0.$$

Substituting in the series expansions for $y_1(x)$ and $y_1'(x)$ and writing out the first few terms of the summation in (50) leads to

(51) $$-b_1 x^{-2} + (2C - b_0)x^{-1} + (3b_3 - b_1) + (\tfrac{3}{4}C + 8b_4 - b_2)x$$
$$+ (15b_5 - b_3)x^2 + (\tfrac{5}{96}C + 24b_6 - b_4)x^3 + \cdots = 0.$$

When we set the coefficients in (51) equal to zero it turns out that we are free to choose C and b_2 as arbitrary constants:

$$-b_1 = 0 \qquad \Rightarrow b_1 = 0,$$

$$2C - b_0 = 0 \qquad \Rightarrow b_0 = 2C \qquad (C \text{ arbitrary}),$$

$$3b_3 - b_1 = 0 \qquad \Rightarrow b_3 = \tfrac{1}{3}b_1 = 0,$$

$$8b_4 - b_2 + \tfrac{3}{4}C = 0 \quad \Rightarrow b_4 = \frac{b_2 - \tfrac{3}{4}C}{8} = \tfrac{1}{8}b_2 - \tfrac{3}{32}C \qquad (b_2 \text{ arbitrary}),$$

$$15b_5 - b_3 = 0 \qquad \Rightarrow b_5 = \tfrac{1}{15}b_3 = 0,$$

$$24b_6 - b_4 + \tfrac{5}{96}C = 0 \Rightarrow b_6 = \frac{b_4 - \tfrac{5}{96}C}{24} = \tfrac{1}{192}b_2 - \tfrac{7}{1152}C.$$

Substituting these values for C and the b_n's back into (48), we obtain the solution

(52)
$$y_2(x) = C\{y_1(x) \ln x + 2x^{-2} - \tfrac{3}{32}x^2 - \tfrac{7}{1152}x^4 + \cdots\}$$
$$+ b_2\{1 + \tfrac{1}{8}x^2 + \tfrac{1}{192}x^4 + \cdots\},$$

where C and b_2 are arbitrary constants. Since the second series is b_2 times the series expansion for $y_1(x)$, we obtain a second linearly independent solution by choosing $C = 1$ and $b_2 = 0$. Thus a second linearly independent solution is

(53)
$$y_2(x) = y_1(x) \ln x + 2x^{-2} - \tfrac{3}{32}x^2 - \tfrac{7}{1152}x^4 + \cdots. \quad \blacktriangleleft$$

EXERCISES 8.7 ——————————————————————————

In Problems 1 through 16 find at least the first three nonzero terms in the series expansion about $x = 0$ for a general solution to the given equation for $x > 0$. (These are the same equations as in Problems 19 through 34 of Exercises 8.6.)

1. $2x(x - 1)y'' + 3(x - 1)y' - y = 0$.

2. $9x^2y'' + 9x^2y' + 2y = 0$.

3. $x^2y'' + xy' + x^2y = 0$.

4. $xy'' + y' - 4y = 0$.

5. $x^2y'' + (x^2 + x)y' - y = 0$.

6. $3xy'' + (2 - x)y' - y = 0$.

7. $4x^2y'' + 2x^2y' - (x + 3)y = 0$.

8. $x^2y'' + (x^2 - x)y' + y = 0$.

9. $xy'' - y' - xy = 0$.

10. $x^2y'' - x(1 + x)y' + y = 0$.

11. $3xy'' + 2(1 - x)y' - 4y = 0$.

12. $xy'' + (x - 1)y' - 2y = 0$.

13. $xy'' + (1 - x)y' - y = 0$.

14. $3x^2y'' + 8xy' + (x - 2)y = 0$.

15. $x(x + 1)y'' + (x + 5)y' - 4y = 0$.

16. $xy'' + (x + 2)y' - y = 0$.

In Problems 17 through 20 find at least the first three nonzero terms in the series expansion about $x = 0$ for a general solution to the given linear third order equation for $x > 0$. (These are the same equations as in Problems 35 through 38 in Exercises 8.6.)

17. $6x^3y''' + 13x^2y'' + (x + x^2)y' + xy = 0.$

18. $6x^3y''' + 13x^2y'' - (x^2 + 3x)y' - xy = 0.$

19. $6x^3y''' + 11x^2y'' - 2xy' - (x - 2)y = 0.$

20. $6x^3y''' + (13x^2 - x^3)y'' + xy' - xy = 0.$

21. Use the method of Frobenius and the reduction of order formula, equation (11), to find at least the first three nonzero terms in the series expansion about the irregular singular point $x = 0$ for a general solution to the differential equation

$$x^2y'' + y' - 2y = 0.$$

22. The equation

$$xy''(x) + (1 - x)y'(x) + ny(x) = 0,$$

where n is a nonnegative integer, is called **Laguerre's differential equation.** Show that for each n this equation has a polynomial solution of degree n. These polynomials are denoted by $L_n(x)$ and are called **Laguerre polynomials.** The first few Laguerre polynomials are

$$L_0(x) = 1, \qquad L_1(x) = -x + 1, \qquad L_2(x) = x^2 - 4x + 2.$$

23. Use the results of Problem 22 and the reduction of order formula, equation (11), to obtain the first few terms in a series expansion about $x = 0$ for a general solution for $x > 0$ to Laguerre's differential equation for $n = 0$ and 1.

★ 8.8 More on the Cases When Roots Differ by an Integer

In this section we discuss another procedure for obtaining a second linearly independent solution when the indicial equation has equal roots or the roots differ by a positive integer. As a consequence of the approach, we will verify the formulas given in parts (b) and (c) of Theorem 7 in the previous section.

Suppose that $x = 0$ is a regular singular point for

(1) $$y''(x) + p(x)y'(x) + q(x)y(x) = 0$$

and that the indicial equation has equal roots, $r_1 = r_2$. As usual, let's try to find a solution to equation (1) of the form

(2) $$w(r, x) = x^r \sum_{n=0}^{\infty} a_n x^n = \sum_{n=0}^{\infty} a_n x^{n+r},$$

where a_0 is an arbitrary nonzero constant. Proceeding as in the method of Frobenius, we substitute the series $p(x) = \sum_{n=0}^{\infty} p_n x^{n-1}$, $q(x) = \sum_{n=0}^{\infty} q_n x^{n-2}$ and the expansions for $w(r, x)$, $w'(r, x)$, and $w''(r, x)$ into equation (1). After some algebra we arrive at the expansion

$$(3) \qquad [r(r-1) + p_0 r + q_0]a_0 x^{r-2}$$
$$+ [(r+1)ra_1 + p_0(r+1)a_1 + p_1 r a_0 + q_0 a_1 + q_1 a_0]x^{r-1} + \cdots = 0$$

(see equations (9)–(14) in Section 8.6). Until now our next step has been to set the coefficient of x^{r-2} equal to zero, which has the effect of forcing r to be a specific number, namely a root of the indicial equation. As we shall see, there is an advantage to treating r as a *variable,* and so, for the moment, we ignore the x^{r-2} term and set the remaining coefficients in (3) equal to zero. From the x^{r-1} term we get

$$(4) \qquad (r+1)ra_1 + p_0(r+1)a_1 + p_1 r a_0 + q_0 a_1 + q_1 a_0 = 0.$$

To simplify the computations, we take $a_0 = 1$ and then solve for a_1 in (4):

$$(5) \qquad a_1 = -\frac{p_1 r + q_1}{(r+1)r + p_0(r+1) + q_0}.$$

For a given differential equation, the quantities p_0, p_1, q_0, and q_1 are known, so (5) can be regarded as a formula for a_1 in terms of the variable r. That is, a_1 is a function of r, and we will denote it by $a_1(r)$. In a similar fashion, we set the successive coefficients in (3) equal to zero and obtain a_n in terms of r. Again we denote this functional dependence by $a_n(r)$.

Since we have chosen the $a_n(r)$'s so that all the coefficients in (3) are equal to zero except for the coefficient of x^{r-2}, substituting $w(r, x)$ into the left-hand side of equation (1) yields

$$(6) \qquad w''(r, x) + p(x)w'(r, x) + q(x)w(r, x) = [r(r-1) + p_0 r + q_0]x^{r-2}.$$

If we let L denote the differential operator defined by the left-hand side of (1), then we can rewrite (6) as

$$(7) \qquad L[w(r, x)](x) = [r(r-1) + p_0 r + q_0]x^{r-2}.$$

Now since we are assuming that the indicial equation has roots $r_1 = r_2$, then $r(r-1) + p_0 r + q_0 = (r - r_1)^2$. Hence equation (7) has the form

$$(8) \qquad L[w(r, x)](x) = (r - r_1)^2 x^{r-2}.$$

Setting $r = r_1$ gives $L[w(r_1, x)](x) = 0$, and therefore, as we know from the method of Frobenius, $w(r_1, x)$ is a solution to equation (1).

To find a second linearly independent solution, let's revive the procedure that effectively dealt with repeated roots associated with a Cauchy-Euler equation (see Section 8.5). Namely, we take the partial derivative with respect to r of both sides of equation (8). This gives

(9) $\qquad \dfrac{\partial}{\partial r} L[w(r, x)](x) = 2(r - r_1)x^{r-2} + (r - r_1)^2 x^{r-2} \ln x.$

Setting $r = r_1$, we find

(10) $\qquad \dfrac{\partial}{\partial r} L[w(r_1, x)](x) = 0.$

Assuming that $w(r, x)$ has continuous third order partial derivatives with respect to both r and x, we can then interchange the order of differentiation and obtain

(11) $\qquad L\left[\dfrac{\partial w}{\partial r} (r_1, x) \right](x) = 0.$

Hence $\partial w / \partial r$ evaluated at $r = r_1$ is a second solution to equation (1). Let's now find its series expansion.

Since

(12) $\qquad w(r, x) = x^r \displaystyle\sum_{n=0}^{\infty} a_n(r)x^n,$

then

(13) $\qquad \dfrac{\partial w}{\partial r} (r, x) = x^r \ln x \displaystyle\sum_{n=0}^{\infty} a_n(r)x^n + x^r \sum_{n=0}^{\infty} a_n'(r)x^n.$

Here $a_n'(r)$ is the derivative of $a_n(r)$ with respect to r. Moreover, since we have taken $a_0(r) \equiv 1$, then $a_0'(r) \equiv 0$. Putting $r = r_1$ in (13), we then get

$$\dfrac{\partial w}{\partial r} (r_1, x) = \left\{ x^{r_1} \sum_{n=0}^{\infty} a_n(r_1)x^n \right\} \ln x + x^{r_1} \sum_{n=1}^{\infty} a_n'(r_1)x^n,$$

which simplifies to

(14) $\qquad \dfrac{\partial w}{\partial r} (r_1, x) = w(r_1, x) \ln x + \displaystyle\sum_{n=1}^{\infty} a_n'(r_1)x^{n+r_1}.$

Notice that with $y_1(x) = w(r_1, x)$ and $b_n = a_n'(r_1)$, the right-hand side of (14) is the same as the formula for the second linearly independent solution claimed in Theorem 7, equation (23).

▶ *Example 1*   Find series expansions about the regular singular point $x = 0$ for two linearly independent solutions to

(15) $x^2 y''(x) - xy'(x) + (1 - x)y(x) = 0,$ $x > 0.$

Solution   We considered this same equation in Example 4 of Section 8.6 and in Examples 2 and 3 of Section 8.7. The indicial equation is $r^2 - 2r + 1 = 0$, which has roots $r_1 = r_2 = 1$. We now use our new procedure to find two linearly independent solutions.

Let

(16) $w(r, x) = x^r \sum_{n=0}^{\infty} a_n x^n = \sum_{n=0}^{\infty} a_n x^{n+r}.$

Taking the derivatives of $w(r, x)$ with respect to x, substituting them into (15), and setting the coefficients equal to zero yields the recurrence relation

(17) $a_k = \dfrac{1}{(r + k - 1)^2} a_{k-1},$ $k \geq 1,$

(see equation (41) in Section 8.6). Taking $a_0 = 1$ and solving equation (17) recursively for the a_k's in terms of r, we find

$$a_1 = \frac{1}{r^2} a_0 = \frac{1}{r^2}, \qquad a_2 = \frac{1}{(r + 1)^2} a_1 = \frac{1}{[(r + 1)(r)]^2},$$

$$a_3 = \frac{1}{(r + 2)^2} a_2 = \frac{1}{[(r + 2)(r + 1)r]^2},$$

and, in general,

(18) $a_k(r) = \dfrac{1}{[(r + k - 1)(r + k - 2) \cdots r]^2},$ $k \geq 1.$

Setting $r = r_1 = 1$ in equation (18) gives

(19) $a_k(1) = \dfrac{1}{[k(k - 1) \cdots 2 \cdot 1]^2} = \dfrac{1}{(k!)^2},$ $k \geq 1.$

Hence one solution is

(20) $y_1(x) = w(1, x) = \sum_{n=0}^{\infty} a_n(1)x^{n+1} = \sum_{n=0}^{\infty} \frac{1}{(n!)^2} x^{n+1}.$

Here we used the fact that $a_0 = 1 = (0!)^{-2}.$

To get a second linearly independent solution to (15), we must differentiate $a_k(r)$ in equation (18) with respect to r. This is easily done using logarithmic differentiation. We begin by taking the logarithm of both sides of (18), then implicitly differentiate with respect to r. That is,

$$
(21) \qquad \ln a_k(r) = \ln[(r + k - 1)(r + k - 2)\cdots r]^{-2}
$$
$$
= -2 \ln(r + k - 1) - 2 \ln(r + k - 2) - \cdots - 2 \ln r,
$$

and, differentiating with respect to r, we get

$$
\frac{a_k'(r)}{a_k(r)} = -\frac{2}{r + k - 1} - \frac{2}{r + k - 2} - \cdots - \frac{2}{r},
$$

which yields

$$
a_k'(r) = -2a_k(r)\left\{\frac{1}{r + k - 1} + \frac{1}{r + k - 2} + \cdots + \frac{1}{r}\right\}.
$$

Setting $r = 1$ and using formula (19) for $a_k(1)$, we obtain

$$
(22) \qquad a_k'(1) = \frac{-2}{(k!)^2}\left\{\frac{1}{k} + \frac{1}{k - 1} + \cdots + \frac{1}{1}\right\}, \qquad k \geq 1.
$$

We now insert these values into formula (14), which we have shown gives a second linearly independent solution:

$$
(23) \qquad y_2(x) = \frac{\partial w}{\partial r}(1, x) = w(1, x) \ln x + \sum_{n=1}^{\infty} a_n'(1)x^{n+1}
$$
$$
= w(1, x) \ln x + \sum_{n=1}^{\infty} \frac{-2}{(n!)^2}\left\{\frac{1}{n} + \frac{1}{n - 1} + \cdots + \frac{1}{1}\right\}x^{n+1}.
$$

Thus two linearly independent solutions to equation (15) are given by the series for $y_1(x)$ in (20) and the series for $y_2(x)$ in (23). ◄

The previous procedure can be modified to accommodate the case when the roots of the indicial equation differ by a positive integer. For this purpose, the new ingredient is to treat a_0 also as a function of r. Proceeding as in the case of a repeated root, we must now include a_0 in equation (7):

$$
(24) \qquad L[w(r, x)](x) = [r(r - 1) + p_0 r + q_0]a_0 x^{r-2}
$$
$$
= (r - r_1)(r - r_2)a_0 x^{r-2},
$$

where r_1, r_2 are the roots of the indicial equation. As we shall soon see, it is convenient to put

(25) $a_0 = r - r_2$,

so that equation (24) becomes

(26) $L[w(r, x)](x) = (r - r_1)(r - r_2)^2 x^{r-2}$.

We now exploit the fact that the right-hand side of (26) has the repeated factor $(r - r_2)^2$. Taking the partial derivative with respect to r of both sides of equation (26) gives

(27) $\dfrac{\partial}{\partial r} L[w(r, x)](x) = (r - r_2)^2 x^{r-2} + 2(r - r_1)(r - r_2)x^{r-2}$

$+ (r - r_1)(r - r_2)^2 x^{r-2} \ln x$.

Assuming, as before, that $w(r, x)$ has continuous third order partial derivatives with respect to r and x, then

(28) $\dfrac{\partial}{\partial r} L[w(r, x)](x) = L\left[\dfrac{\partial w}{\partial r}(r, x)\right](x)$.

Hence on setting $r = r_2$ in (27), we see that

(29) $L\left[\dfrac{\partial w}{\partial r}(r_2, x)\right](x) = 0$.

Thus the partial derivative $\partial w/\partial r$ evaluated at $r = r_2$ is a solution to equation (1). To write out the series expansion for this solution, we first express $w(r, x)$ in the form

$$w(r, x) = x^r \sum_{n=0}^{\infty} a_n(r)x^n,$$

where we have indicated the fact that all the coefficients a_n (including a_0) are functions of r. Then

(30) $\dfrac{\partial w}{\partial r}(r, x) = x^r \ln x \sum_{n=0}^{\infty} a_n(r)x^n + x^r \sum_{n=0}^{\infty} a_n'(r)x^n$

$= w(r, x) \ln x + x^r \sum_{n=0}^{\infty} a_n'(r)x^n$,

where $a'_n(r)$ is the derivative of $a_n(r)$ with respect to r. Setting $r = r_2$, we obtain the solution

(31) $$\frac{\partial w}{\partial r}(r_2, x) = w(r_2, x) \ln x + \sum_{n=0}^{\infty} a'_n(r_2)x^{n+r_2},$$

where $a_0 = r - r_2$.

The preceding analysis suggests the following procedure when the roots of the indicial equation for (1) differ by a positive integer J. First determine $w(r, x)$, where the coefficients $a_n(r)$ depend on r. If substituting $r = r_2$ leaves a_0 *and* a_J arbitrary, then $w(r_2, x)$ is a general solution, with a_0 and a_J the arbitrary constants (see Problem 9). If this substitution leaves a_J arbitrary but $a_i \equiv 0$ for $i = 0, 1, \ldots, J - 1$, then $w(r_2, x) = w(r_1, x)$ is one solution and the second solution is given by $(\partial w/\partial r)(r_2, x)$ (see Problem 10).[†]

The preceding methods are particularly useful in determining the form of the general term in the series expansion of a second linearly independent solution when the recurrence relation is a two-term relation. With suitable modifications these methods can also be used for higher order equations.

EXERCISES 8.8

In Problems 1 through 8 use the method discussed in this section to obtain the series expansion about the regular singular point $x = 0$ for two linearly independent solutions to the given equation whose indicial equation has repeated roots.

1. $xy'' + y' - 4y = 0.$
2. $xy'' + (1 - x)y' - y = 0.$
3. $x^2y'' + (x^2 - x)y' + y = 0.$

4. $x^2y'' + xy' + x^2y = 0.$
5. $x^2y'' + 3x(1 + x)y' + y = 0.$
6. $x^2y'' - xy' + (1 - x^3)y = 0.$

7. $xy'' + y' - 3y = 0.$
8. $x^2y'' + (3x - x^2)y' + y = 0.$

9. To find a series expansion for a general solution to

$$xy''(x) + 4y'(x) - xy(x) = 0, \qquad x > 0:$$

(a) Show that the coefficients of $w(r, x)$ satisfy the recurrence relation

$$(k + r + 1)(k + r + 4)a_{k+1} - a_{k-1} = 0, \qquad k \geq 1.$$

(b) Setting $r = r_2$, show that not only is a_0 arbitrary, but the recurrence relation gives $0 \cdot a_3 = 0$, and hence a_3 is also arbitrary.

(c) Use the recurrence relation to obtain a series expansion for a general solution with a_0 and a_3 as the arbitrary constants. Compare your answer with Example 4 in Section 8.7.

10. To find a series expansion for a general solution to

$$xy''(x) + 3y'(x) - xy(x) = 0, \qquad x > 0:$$

_____

[†] Further details are given in *Intermediate Differential Equations*, Second Edition, by Earl D. Rainville, Macmillan, New York, 1964, Sections 30–32.

(a) Show that the coefficients of $w(r, x)$ satisfy the recurrence relation

$$(k + r + 1)(k + r + 3)a_{k+1} - a_{k-1} = 0, \qquad k \geq 1.$$

(b) Show that $a_1 \equiv 0$ and hence

$$a_{2n+1}(r) \equiv 0, \qquad n = 0, 1, 2, \ldots.$$

(c) Set $r = -2$ and use the recurrence relation to show that $a_0(-2)$ must be zero.

(d) Let $a_0(r) = r + 2$ so that $a_0(-2) = 0$. Show that $a_2(r) = (r + 4)^{-1}$ and, for $n \geq 2$,

$$a_{2n}(r) = \frac{1}{(r + 2n + 2)[(r + 2n)^2 \cdots (r + 6)^2(r + 4)^2]}.$$

(e) Find the series solution $w(-2, x)$.

(f) Let $a_0(r) = r + 2$ and show that $a_0'(r) = 1$, $a_2'(r) = -(r + 4)^{-2}$, and, for $n \geq 2$,

$$a_{2n}'(r) = \frac{(-1)}{(r + 2n + 2)[(r + 2n)^2 \cdots (r + 4)^2]}$$

$$\times \left\{ \frac{1}{r + 2n + 2} + \frac{2}{r + 2n} + \cdots + \frac{2}{r + 4} \right\}.$$

[Hint: Use logarithmic differentiation.]

(g) Find the series solution $(\partial w/\partial r)(-2, x)$. Compare your answers with Example 5 in Section 8.7.

In Problems 11 through 16 use the methods discussed in this section to obtain the series expansion about the regular singular point $x = 0$ for two linearly independent solutions for $x > 0$ to the given equation whose roots of the indicial equation differ by a positive integer.

11. $x(1 - x)y'' - 3y' + 2y = 0.$ **12.** $4x^2y'' + 2x^2y' - (x + 3)y = 0.$ **13.** $xy'' + (x + 2)y' - y = 0.$

14. $xy'' - y' - xy = 0.$ **15.** $xy'' + (x - 1)y' - 2y = 0.$ **16.** $xy'' + xy' + y = 0.$

In Problems 17 through 20 use the method discussed in this section to obtain the series expansion about the regular singular point $x = 0$ for three linearly independent solutions to the given linear third order equation for $x > 0$. [Hint: If the indicial equation has a root of multiplicity three, it is helpful to consider $\partial^2 w/\partial r^2$.]

17. $2x^3y''' + (5x^2 - x^3)y'' + xy' - xy = 0.$ **18.** $3x^3y''' + 5x^2y'' + (x^2 - x)y' + xy = 0.$

19. $x^2y''' + 3xy'' + y' - y = 0.$ **20.** $x^3y''' + (x^3 + 6x^2)y'' - (x^2 - 7x)y' + (x + 1)y = 0.$

21. In Problem 10, let $a_0 = r - r_1 = r$ (instead of $r - r_2$), then solve for $a_n(r)$. Show that if you now set $r = r_1 = 0$, then you obtain $y_3(x) = w(0, x) \equiv 0$, and

$$y_4(x) = \frac{\partial w}{\partial r}(0, x) = 0 \cdot \ln x + \sum_{n=0}^{\infty} b_n x^n.$$

Hence you get only one linearly independent solution.

★ *8.9* *Special Functions*

In advanced work in applied mathematics, engineering, and physics a few special second order equations arise with amazing frequency. These equations have been extensively studied, and volumes have been written on the properties of their solutions. Three of these equations are the hypergeometric equation, Bessel's equation, and Legendre's equation. The solutions to these and other equations that occur in applications are often referred to as **special functions.** We shall briefly consider the three equations mentioned above. For a more detailed study of special functions we refer the reader to *Mathematical Methods in the Physical Sciences,* by M. L. Boas, John Wiley and Sons, New York, 1983; *Special Functions,* by E. D. Rainville, Macmillan, New York, 1960; and *Higher Transcendental Functions,* by A. Erdelyi (ed.), McGraw-Hill, New York, 1953, 3 volumes.

HYPERGEOMETRIC EQUATION

The linear second order differential equation

(1) $$x(1 - x)y'' + [\gamma - (\alpha + \beta + 1)x]y' - \alpha\beta y = 0,$$

where α, β, and γ are fixed parameters, is called the **hypergeometric equation.** This equation has singular points at $x = 0$ and 1, both of which are regular. Thus a series expansion about $x = 0$ for a solution to (1) obtained by the method of Frobenius will converge at least for $0 < x < 1$ (see Theorem 6, page 444). To find this expansion, observe that the indicial equation associated with $x = 0$ is

$$r(r - 1) + \gamma r = r(r - (1 - \gamma)) = 0,$$

which has roots 0 and $1 - \gamma$. If γ is not an integer, then we can use the root $r = 0$ to obtain a solution to (1) of the form

(2) $$y_1(x) = \sum_{n=0}^{\infty} a_n x^n.$$

Substituting $y_1(x)$ given in (2) into (1), shifting indices, and simplifying ultimately leads to the equation

(3) $$\sum_{n=1}^{\infty} [n(n + \gamma - 1)a_n - (n + \alpha - 1)(n + \beta - 1)a_{n-1}]x^{n-1} = 0.$$

Setting the series coefficients equal to zero yields the recurrence relation

(4) $$n(n + \gamma - 1)a_n - (n + \alpha - 1)(n + \beta - 1)a_{n-1} = 0, \qquad n \geq 1.$$

Since $n \geq 1$ and γ is not an integer, there is no fear of dividing by zero when we rewrite (4) as

(5) $$a_n = \frac{(n + \alpha - 1)(n + \beta - 1)}{n(n + \gamma - 1)} a_{n-1}.$$

Solving recursively for a_n, we obtain

(6) $$a_n = \frac{\alpha(\alpha + 1) \cdots (\alpha + n - 1)\beta(\beta + 1) \cdots (\beta + n - 1)}{n!\gamma(\gamma + 1) \cdots (\gamma + n - 1)} a_0, \qquad n \geq 1.$$

If we employ the **factorial function** $(t)_n$, which is defined for nonnegative integers n by

(7)
$$(t)_n := t(t + 1)(t + 2) \cdots (t + n - 1), \qquad n \geq 1,$$
$$(t)_0 := 1, \qquad t \neq 0,$$

then we can express a_n more compactly as

(8) $$a_n = \frac{(\alpha)_n(\beta)_n}{n!(\gamma)_n} a_0, \qquad n \geq 1.$$

If we take $a_0 = 1$ and then substitute the expression for a_n in (8) into (2), we obtain the following solution to the hypergeometric equation:

(9) $$y_1(x) = 1 + \sum_{n=1}^{\infty} \frac{(\alpha)_n(\beta)_n}{n!(\gamma)_n} x^n.$$

The solution given in (9) is called a **Gaussian hypergeometric function** and is denoted by the symbol $F(\alpha, \beta; \gamma; x)$.[†] That is,

(10) $$F(\alpha, \beta; \gamma; x) := 1 + \sum_{n=1}^{\infty} \frac{(\alpha)_n(\beta)_n}{n!(\gamma)_n} x^n.$$

Hypergeometric functions are generalizations of the geometric series. To see this, observe that for any constant β that is not zero or a negative integer,

$$F(1, \beta; \beta; x) = 1 + x + x^2 + x^3 + \cdots.$$

[†] *Historical Footnote:* A detailed study of this function was done by Carl Friedrich Gauss in 1813. The mathematical historian E. T. Bell refers to Gauss as the Prince of Mathematicians.

It is interesting to note that many other familiar functions can be expressed in terms of the hypergeometric function. For example,

(11) $$F(\alpha, \beta; \beta; x) = (1 - x)^{-\alpha},$$

(12) $$F(1, 1; 2; x) = -x^{-1} \ln(1 - x),$$

(13) $$F\left(\frac{1}{2}, 1; \frac{3}{2}; x^2\right) = \frac{1}{2} x^{-1} \ln\left(\frac{1 + x}{1 - x}\right),$$

(14) $$F\left(\frac{1}{2}, 1; \frac{3}{2}; -x^2\right) = x^{-1} \arctan x.$$

We leave the verification of these formulas for the reader.

To obtain a second linearly independent solution to (1) when γ is not an integer, we use the other root, $1 - \gamma$, of the indicial equation, and seek a solution of the form

(15) $$y_2(x) = \sum_{n=0}^{\infty} b_n x^{n+1-\gamma}.$$

Substituting $y_2(x)$ into equation (1) and solving for b_n, we eventually arrive at

(16) $$y_2(x) = x^{1-\gamma} + \sum_{n=1}^{\infty} \frac{(\alpha + 1 - \gamma)_n (\beta + 1 - \gamma)_n}{n!(2 - \gamma)_n} x^{n+1-\gamma}.$$

Factoring out $x^{1-\gamma}$, we see that the second solution $y_2(x)$ can be expressed in terms of a hypergeometric function. That is,

(17) $$y_2(x) = x^{1-\gamma} F(\alpha + 1 - \gamma, \beta + 1 - \gamma; 2 - \gamma; x).$$

When γ is an integer, one of the formulas given in (9) or (16) (corresponding to the larger root, 0 or $1 - \gamma$) still gives a solution. We then use the techniques of this chapter to obtain a second linearly independent solution, which may or may not involve a logarithmic term. We omit a discussion of these solutions.

In many books the hypergeometric function is expressed in terms of the gamma function $\Gamma(x)$ instead of the factorial function. Recall that in Section 7.6 we defined

(18) $$\Gamma(x) := \int_0^{\infty} e^{-u} u^{x-1} \, du, \qquad x > 0$$

and showed that

(19) $$\Gamma(x + 1) = x\Gamma(x), \qquad x > 0.$$

It follows from repeated use of relation (19) that

(20) $(t)_n = \dfrac{\Gamma(t + n)}{\Gamma(t)}$

for $t > 0$ and n any nonnegative integer. Using relation (20), we can express the hypergeometric function as

(21) $F(\alpha, \beta; \gamma; x) = \dfrac{\Gamma(\gamma)}{\Gamma(\alpha)\Gamma(\beta)} \displaystyle\sum_{n=0}^{\infty} \dfrac{\Gamma(\alpha + n)\Gamma(\beta + n)}{n!\,\Gamma(\gamma + n)}\, x^n.$

BESSEL'S EQUATION

The linear second order differential equation

(22) $x^2 y'' + xy' + (x^2 - v^2)y = 0,$

where $v \geq 0$ is a fixed parameter, is called **Bessel's equation of order v.** This equation has a regular singular point at $x = 0$ and no other singular points in the complex plane. Hence a series solution for (22) obtained by the method of Frobenius will converge for $0 < x < \infty$.

The indicial equation for (22) is

$$r(r - 1) + r - v^2 = (r - v)(r + v) = 0,$$

which has roots $r_1 = v$ and $r_2 = -v$. If v is not an integer, then the method of Frobenius yields two linearly independent solutions, given by

(23) $y_1(x) = a_0 \displaystyle\sum_{n=0}^{\infty} \dfrac{(-1)^n}{2^{2n} n! (1 + v)_n}\, x^{2n+v},$

(24) $y_2(x) = b_0 \displaystyle\sum_{n=0}^{\infty} \dfrac{(-1)^n}{2^{2n} n! (1 - v)_n}\, x^{2n-v}.$

If in (23) we take

$$a_0 = \dfrac{1}{2^v \Gamma(1 + v)},$$

then it follows from relation (20) that the function

(25) $J_v(x) := \displaystyle\sum_{n=0}^{\infty} \dfrac{(-1)^n}{n!\,\Gamma(1 + v + n)}\left(\dfrac{x}{2}\right)^{2n+v}.$

is a solution to (22). We call $J_\nu(x)$ the **Bessel function of the first kind of order ν.**[†] Similarly, taking

$$b_0 = \frac{1}{2^{-\nu}\Gamma(1-\nu)}$$

in equation (24) gives the solution

(26) $$J_{-\nu}(x) := \sum_{n=0}^{\infty} \frac{(-1)^n}{n!\Gamma(1-\nu+n)}\left(\frac{x}{2}\right)^{2n-\nu},$$

which is the Bessel function of the first kind of order $-\nu$. When $r_1 - r_2 = 2\nu$ is not an integer, we know by Theorem 7 of Section 8.7 that $J_\nu(x)$ and $J_{-\nu}(x)$ are linearly independent. Moreover, it can be shown that if ν is not an integer, even though 2ν is, then $J_\nu(x)$ and $J_{-\nu}(x)$ are still linearly independent.

What happens in the remaining case when ν is a nonnegative integer, say $\nu = m$? While $J_m(x)$ is still a solution, the function $J_{-m}(x)$ is not even properly defined, because formula (26) will involve the gamma function evaluated at a nonpositive integer. From a more in-depth study of the gamma function, it turns out that $1/\Gamma(k) = 0$, for $k = 0, -1, -2, \ldots$. Hence (26) becomes

(27) $$J_{-m}(x) = \sum_{n=0}^{\infty} \frac{(-1)^n}{n!\Gamma(1-m+n)}\left(\frac{x}{2}\right)^{2n-m} = \sum_{n=m}^{\infty} \frac{(-1)^n}{n!\Gamma(1-m+n)}\left(\frac{x}{2}\right)^{2n-m}.$$

Comparing (27) with the formula (25) for $J_m(x)$, we see (after a shift in index) that

(28) $$J_{-m}(x) = (-1)^m J_m(x),$$

which means that $J_{-m}(x)$ and $J_m(x)$ are linearly *dependent*. To resolve the problem of finding a second linearly independent solution in the case when ν is a nonnegative integer, we can use the method discussed in Section 8.8 (see Problem 27). There is, however, another approach to this problem, which we now describe.

For ν not an integer, we can take linear combinations of $J_\nu(x)$ and $J_{-\nu}(x)$ to obtain other solutions to (22). In particular, let

(29) $$Y_\nu(x) := \frac{\cos(\nu\pi)J_\nu(x) - J_{-\nu}(x)}{\sin(\nu\pi)}, \qquad \nu \text{ not an integer,}$$

for $x > 0$. The function $Y_\nu(x)$ is called the **Bessel function of the second kind of order ν,** and, as can be verified, $J_\nu(x)$ and $Y_\nu(x)$ are linearly independent. Notice that when ν is an integer, the denominator in (29) is zero; but, by formula (28), so is the numerator! Hence it is reasonable to hope that, in a limiting sense, formula (29) is still meaningful. In fact, using

---

[†] *Historical Footnote:* Frederic Wilhelm Bessel (1784–1846) started his career in commercial navigation and later became an astronomer. In 1817, Bessel introduced the functions $J_\nu(x)$ in his study of planetary orbits.

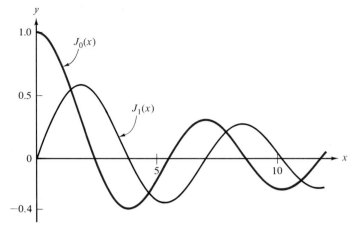

Figure 8.2 Graphs of the Bessel
functions $J_0(x)$ and $J_1(x)$

l'Hôpital's rule, it is possible to show that, for m a nonnegative integer, the function defined
by

$$(30) \qquad Y_m(x) := \lim_{v \to m} \frac{\cos(v\pi)J_v(x) - J_{-v}(x)}{\sin(v\pi)}$$

for $x > 0$, is a solution to (22) with $v = m$. Furthermore, $J_m(x)$ and $Y_m(x)$ are linearly independent. We again call $Y_m(x)$ the Bessel function of the second kind of order m. In the literature the function $Y_m(x)$ is also denoted by $N_m(x)$ and referred to as the **Neumann function**
or **Weber function.**

Figure 8.2 shows the graphs of $J_0(x)$ and $J_1(x)$, and Figure 8.3 the graphs of $Y_0(x)$ and
$Y_1(x)$. Notice that the curves for $J_0(x)$ and $J_1(x)$ behave like damped sine waves and have
zeros that interlace (see Problem 28).

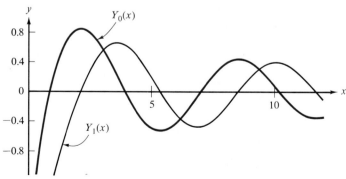

Figure 8.3 Graphs of the Bessel
functions $Y_0(x)$ and $Y_1(x)$

There are several useful recurrence relations involving Bessel functions. For example,

(31) $\dfrac{d}{dx}\left[x^{v}J_{v}(x)\right] = x^{v}J_{v-1}(x),$

(32) $\dfrac{d}{dx}\left[x^{-v}J_{v}(x)\right] = -x^{-v}J_{v+1}(x),$

(33) $J_{v+1}(x) = \dfrac{2v}{x}J_{v}(x) - J_{v-1}(x),$

(34) $J_{v+1}(x) = J_{v-1}(x) - 2J'_{v}(x).$

Furthermore, analogous equations hold for Bessel functions of the second kind.

To illustrate the techniques involved in proving the recurrence relations, let's verify relation (31). We begin by substituting series (25) for $J_{v}(x)$ into the left-hand side of (31). Differentiating, we get

(35) $\dfrac{d}{dx}\left[x^{v}J_{v}(x)\right] = \dfrac{d}{dx}\left\{x^{v}\displaystyle\sum_{n=0}^{\infty}\dfrac{(-1)^{n}}{n!\Gamma(1+v+n)}\left(\dfrac{x}{2}\right)^{2n+v}\right\}$

$= \dfrac{d}{dx}\left\{\displaystyle\sum_{n=0}^{\infty}\dfrac{(-1)^{n}x^{2n+2v}}{n!\Gamma(1+v+n)2^{2n+v}}\right\}$

$= \displaystyle\sum_{n=0}^{\infty}\dfrac{(-1)^{n}(2n+2v)x^{2n+2v-1}}{n!\Gamma(1+v+n)2^{2n+v}}.$

Since $\Gamma(1+v+n) = (v+n)\Gamma(v+n)$, we have from (35)

$\dfrac{d}{dx}\left[x^{v}J_{v}(x)\right] = \displaystyle\sum_{n=0}^{\infty}\dfrac{(-1)^{n}2x^{2n+2v-1}}{n!\Gamma(v+n)2^{2n+v}},$

and factoring out an x^{v} gives

$\dfrac{d}{dx}\left[x^{v}J_{v}(x)\right] = x^{v}\displaystyle\sum_{n=0}^{\infty}\dfrac{(-1)^{n}}{n!\Gamma(1+(v-1)+n)}\left(\dfrac{x}{2}\right)^{2n+v-1} = x^{v}J_{v-1}(x),$

as claimed in equation (31). We leave the verifications of the remaining relations as exercises (see Problems 22–24).

LEGENDRE'S EQUATION

The linear second order differential equation

(36) $(1-x^{2})y'' - 2xy' + n(n+1)y = 0,$

where n is a fixed nonnegative integer, is called **Legendre's equation.**[†] This equation has a regular singular point at 1, and hence a series solution for (36) about $x = 1$ may be obtained by the method of Frobenius. By setting $z = x - 1$, equation (36) is transformed into

$$(37) \qquad z(z + 2)\frac{d^2y}{dz^2} + 2(z + 1)\frac{dy}{dz} - n(n + 1)y = 0.$$

The indicial equation for (37) at $z = 0$ is

$$r(r - 1) + r = r^2 = 0,$$

which has roots $r_1 = r_2 = 0$. Upon substituting

$$y(z) = \sum_{k=0}^{\infty} a_k z^k$$

into (37) and proceeding as usual, we arrive at the solution

$$(38) \qquad y_1(x) = 1 + \sum_{k=1}^{\infty} \frac{(-n)_k(n + 1)_k}{k!(1)_k}\left(\frac{1 - x}{2}\right)^k,$$

where we have expressed y_1 in terms of the original variable x and have taken $a_0 = 1$. We have written the solution in the above form because it is now obvious from (38) that

$$(39) \qquad y_1(x) = F\left(-n, n + 1; 1; \frac{1 - x}{2}\right),$$

where F is the Gaussian hypergeometric function defined in (10).

For n a nonnegative integer, the factor

$$(-n)_k = (-n)(-n + 1)(-n + 2)\cdots(-n + k - 1)$$

will be zero for $k \geq n + 1$. Hence the solution given in (38) and (39) is a *polynomial* of degree n. Moreover, $y_1(1) = 1$. These polynomial solutions of equation (36) are called the **Legendre polynomials** or **spherical polynomials** and are traditionally denoted by $P_n(x)$. That is,

$$(40) \qquad P_n(x) := 1 + \sum_{k=1}^{n} \frac{(-n)_k(n + 1)_k}{k!(1)_k}\left(\frac{1 - x}{2}\right)^k.$$

[†] *Historical Footnote:* Solutions to this equation were obtained by Adrien Marie Legendre (1752–1833) in 1785 and are referred to as Legendre functions.

If we expand about $x = 0$, then $P_n(x)$ takes the form

(41)
$$P_n(x) = 2^{-n} \sum_{m=0}^{[n/2]} \frac{(-1)^m (2n - 2m)!}{(n - m)! m! (n - 2m)!} x^{n-2m},$$

where $[n/2]$ is the greatest integer less than or equal to $n/2$ (see Problem 34). The first three Legendre polynomials are

$$P_0(x) = 1, \qquad P_1(x) = x, \qquad P_2(x) = \tfrac{3}{2}x^2 - \tfrac{1}{2}.$$

The Legendre polynomials satisfy the **orthogonality condition**

(42)
$$\int_{-1}^{1} P_m(x) P_n(x) \, dx = 0 \quad \text{for} \quad n \neq m.$$

To see this we first rewrite equation (36) in what is called the **selfadjoint form:**

(43)
$$[(1 - x^2) y']' + n(n + 1)y = 0.$$

Since $P_n(x)$ and $P_m(x)$ satisfy (43) with parameters n and m respectively, we have

(44)
$$[(1 - x^2) P_n'(x)]' + n(n + 1) P_n(x) = 0,$$

(45)
$$[(1 - x^2) P_m'(x)]' + m(m + 1) P_m(x) = 0.$$

Multiplying (44) by $P_m(x)$ and (45) by $P_n(x)$ and then subtracting, we find

$$P_m(x)[(1 - x^2) P_n'(x)]' - P_n(x)[(1 - x^2) P_m'(x)]'$$
$$+ [n(n + 1) - m(m + 1)] P_m(x) P_n(x) = 0,$$

which can be rewritten in the form

(46)
$$(n^2 - m^2 + n - m) P_m(x) P_n(x) = P_n(x)[(1 - x^2) P_m'(x)]'$$
$$- P_m(x)[(1 - x^2) P_n'(x)]'.$$

It is a straightforward calculation to show that the right-hand side of (46) is just

$$\{(1 - x^2)[P_n(x) P_m'(x) - P_n'(x) P_m(x)]\}'.$$

Using this fact and the identity $n^2 - m^2 + n - m = (n - m)(n + m + 1)$, equation (46) becomes

(47)
$$(n - m)(n + m + 1) P_m(x) P_n(x) = \{(1 - x^2)[P_n(x) P_m'(x) - P_n'(x) P_m(x)]\}'.$$

Integrating both sides of (47) from $x = -1$ to $x = 1$ yields

(48)
$$(n - m)(n + m + 1) \int_{-1}^{1} P_m(x)P_n(x)\,dx$$

$$= \int_{-1}^{1} \{(1 - x^2)[P_n(x)P_m'(x) - P_n'(x)P_m(x)]\}'\,dx$$

$$= \{(1 - x^2)[P_n(x)P_m'(x) - P_n'(x)P_m(x)]\}\Big|_{-1}^{1}$$

$$= 0,$$

because $1 - x^2 = 0$ for $x = \pm 1$. Since n and m are nonnegative integers with $n \neq m$, then $(n - m)(n + m + 1) \neq 0$, and so equation (42) follows from (48).

Legendre polynomials also satisfy the **recurrence formula**

(49)
$$(n + 1)P_{n+1}(x) = (2n + 1)xP_n(x) - nP_{n-1}(x)$$

and **Rodrigues's formula**

(50)
$$P_n(x) = \frac{1}{2^n n!} \frac{d^n}{dx^n}\{(x^2 - 1)^n\}$$

(see Problems 32 and 33).

The Legendre polynomials are generated by the function $(1 - 2xz + z^2)^{-1/2}$ in the sense that

(51)
$$(1 - 2xz + z^2)^{-1/2} = \sum_{n=0}^{\infty} P_n(x)z^n, \qquad |z| < 1, \qquad |x| < 1.$$

That is, if we expand $(1 - 2xz + z^2)^{-1/2}$ in a Taylor series about $z = 0$, treating x as a fixed parameter, then the coefficients of z^n are the Legendre polynomials $P_n(x)$. The function $(1 - 2xz + z^2)^{-1/2}$ is called a **generating function** for $P_n(x)$ and can be derived from the recurrence formula (49) (see Problem 35).

The Legendre polynomials are an example of a class of special functions called **classical orthogonal polynomials.**[†] The latter includes, for example, the **Jacobi polynomials,** $P_n^{(\alpha,\,\beta)}(x)$; the **Gegenbauer** or **ultraspherical polynomials,** $C_n^{\lambda}(x)$; **Chebyshev** (Tchebichef) **polynomials,** $T_n(x)$ and $U_n(x)$; **Laguerre polynomials,** $L_n^{\alpha}(x)$; and the **Hermite polynomials,** $H_n(x)$. The properties of the classical orthogonal polynomials can be found in the books mentioned earlier in this section or in the *Handbook of Mathematical Functions with Formulas, Graphs, and Mathematical Tables,* by M. Abramowitz and I. A. Stegum (eds.), National Bureau of Standards, Applied Mathematics Series 55, U.S. Government Printing Office, Washington, D.C., 1964, Chapter 22.

[†] Here orthogonality is used in the more general sense that $\int_a^b p_n(x)p_m(x)w(x)\,dx = 0$ for $n \neq m$, where $w(x)$ is a weight function on the interval (a, b).

EXERCISES 8.9

In Problems 1 through 4 express a general solution to the given equation using Gaussian hypergeometric functions.

1. $x(1 - x)y'' + (\frac{1}{2} - 4x)y' - 2y = 0$.

2. $2x(1 - x)y'' + (1 - 6x)y' - 2y = 0$.

3. $3x(1 - x)y'' + (1 - 27x)y' - 45y = 0$.

4. $2x(1 - x)y'' + (3 - 10x)y' - 6y = 0$.

In Problems 5 through 8 verify the following formulas by expanding each function in a power series about $x = 0$.

5. $F(\alpha, \beta; \beta; x) = (1 - x)^{-\alpha}$.

6. $F(1, 1; 2; x) = -x^{-1}\ln(1 - x)$.

7. $F(\frac{1}{2}, 1; \frac{3}{2}; x^2) = \frac{1}{2}x^{-1}\ln\left(\dfrac{1 + x}{1 - x}\right)$.

8. $F(\frac{1}{2}, 1; \frac{3}{2}; -x^2) = x^{-1}\arctan x$.

In Problems 9 and 10 use one of the methods discussed in Section 8.7 to obtain two linearly independent solutions to the given hypergeometric equation.

9. $x(1 - x)y'' + (1 - 3x)y' - y = 0$.

10. $x(1 - x)y'' + (2 - 2x)y' - \frac{1}{4}y = 0$.

11. Show that the **confluent hypergeometric equation**

$$xy'' + (\gamma - x)y' - \alpha y = 0,$$

where α and γ are fixed parameters and γ is not an integer, has two linearly independent solutions

$$y_1(x) = {}_1F_1(\alpha; \gamma; x) := 1 + \sum_{n=1}^{\infty} \frac{(\alpha)_n}{n!(\gamma)_n} x^n$$

and

$$y_2(x) = x^{1-\gamma}{}_1F_1(\alpha + 1 - \gamma; 2 - \gamma; x).$$

12. Use the property of the gamma function given in (19) to derive relation (20).

In Problems 13 through 18 express a general solution to the given equation using Bessel functions of either the first or second kind.

13. $4x^2y'' + 4xy' + (4x^2 - 1)y = 0$.

14. $9x^2y'' + 9xy' + (9x^2 - 4)y = 0$.

15. $x^2y'' + xy' + (x^2 - 1)y = 0$.

16. $x^2y'' + xy' + x^2y = 0$.

17. $9x^2y'' + 9xy' + (9x^2 - 16)y = 0$.

18. $x^2y'' + xy' + (x^2 - 16)y = 0$.

In Problems 19 and 20 a Bessel equation is given. For the appropriate choice of ν, the Bessel function $J_\nu(x)$ is one solution. Use one of the methods discussed in Section 8.7 to obtain a second linearly independent solution.

19. $x^2y'' + xy' + (x^2 - 1)y = 0$.

20. $x^2y'' + xy' + (x^2 - 4)y = 0$.

21. Show that $x^\nu J_\nu(x)$ satisfies the equation

$$xy'' + (1 - 2\nu)y' + xy = 0, \qquad x > 0,$$

and use this result to find a solution for the equation

$$xy'' - 2y' + xy = 0, \qquad x > 0.$$

In Problems 22 through 24 derive the indicated recurrence formulas.

22. Formula (32).   **23.** Formula (33).   **24.** Formula (34).

25. Show that $J_{1/2}(x) = (2/\pi x)^{1/2} \sin x$ and

$$J_{-1/2}(x) = (2/\pi x)^{1/2} \cos x.$$

26. The Bessel functions of order $\nu = n + \frac{1}{2}$, n any integer, are called the **spherical Bessel functions.** Use relation (33) and the results of Problem 25 to show that the spherical Bessel functions can be represented in terms of $\sin x$, $\cos x$, and powers of x. Demonstrate this by determining a closed form for $J_{-3/2}(x)$ and $J_{5/2}(x)$.

27. Use the method discussed in Section 8.8 to determine a second linearly independent solution to Bessel's equation of order zero in terms of the Bessel function $J_0(x)$.

28. Show that between two consecutive positive roots (zeros) of $J_1(x)$ there is a root of $J_0(x)$. This interlacing property of the roots of Bessel functions is illustrated in Figure 8.2. [Hint: Use relation (31) and Rolle's theorem from calculus.]

29. Use formula (41) to determine the first five Legendre polynomials.

30. Show that the Legendre polynomials of even degree are even functions of x, while those of odd degree are odd functions.

31. (a) Show that the orthogonality condition (42) for Legendre polynomials implies that

$$\int_{-1}^{1} P_n(x)q(x)\,dx = 0$$

for *any* polynomial $q(x)$ of degree at most $n - 1$. [Hint: The polynomials $P_0, P_1, \ldots, P_{n-1}$ are linearly independent and hence span the space of all polynomials of degree at most $n - 1$. Thus $q(x) = a_0 P_0(x) + a_1 P_1(x) + \cdots + a_{n-1}P_{n-1}(x)$ for suitable constants a_k.]

(b) Prove that if $Q_n(x)$ is a polynomial of degree n such that

$$\int_{-1}^{1} Q_n(x)P_k(x)\,dx = 0 \quad \text{for} \quad k = 0, 1, \ldots, n - 1,$$

then $Q_n(x) = cP_n(x)$ for some constant c. [Hint: Select c so that the co-efficient of x^n for $Q_n(x) - cP_n(x)$ is zero. Then, since $P_0, \ldots, P_{n-1}$ is a basis,

$$Q_n(x) - cP_n(x) = a_0P_0(x) + \cdots + a_{n-1}P_{n-1}(x).$$

Multiply the last equation by $P_k(x)$ $(0 \le k \le n-1)$ and integrate from $x = -1$ to $x = 1$ to show that each a_k is zero.]

32. Deduce the recurrence formula (49) for Legendre polynomials by completing the following steps.

(a) Show that the function $Q_{n-1}(x) := (n+1)P_{n+1}(x) - (2n+1)xP_n(x)$ is a polynomial of degree $n-1$. [Hint: Compute the coefficient of the x^{n+1} term using the representation (40). The coefficient of x^n is also zero because $P_{n+1}(x)$ and $xP_n(x)$ are both odd or both even functions, a consequence of Problem 30.]

(b) Using the result of Problem 31(a), show that

$$\int_{-1}^{1} Q_{n-1}(x)P_k(x)\,dx = 0 \quad \text{for} \quad k = 0, 1, \ldots, n-2.$$

(c) From Problem 31(b) conclude that $Q_{n-1}(x) = cP_{n-1}(x)$ and, by taking $x = 1$, show that $c = -n$. [Hint: Recall that $P_m(1) = 1$ for all m.] From the definition of $Q_{n-1}(x)$ in part (a), the recurrence formula now follows.

33. To prove Rodrigues's formula (50) for Legendre polynomials, complete the following steps.

(a) Let $v_n(x) := \dfrac{d^n}{dx^n}\{(x^2-1)^n\}$ and show that $v_n(x)$ is a polynomial of degree n with the coefficient of x^n equal to $(2n)!/n!$.

(b) Use integration by parts n times to show that, for any polynomial $q(x)$ of degree less than n,

$$\int_{-1}^{1} v_n(x)q(x)\,dx = 0.$$

[Hint: For example, when $n = 2$,

$$\int_{-1}^{1} \frac{d^2}{dx^2}\{(x^2-1)^2\}q(x)\,dx$$

$$= q(x)\frac{d}{dx}\{(x^2-1)^2\}\Big|_{-1}^{1} - \{q'(x)(x^2-1)\}\Big|_{-1}^{1}$$

$$+ \int_{-1}^{1} q''(x)(x^2-1)^2\,dx.$$

Since $n = 2$, the degree of $q(x)$ is at most 1, and so $q''(x) \equiv 0$. Thus

$$\int_{-1}^{1} \frac{d^2}{dx^2}\{(x^2-1)^2\}q(x)\,dx = 0.]$$

(c) Use the result of Problem 31(b) to conclude that $P_n(x) = cv_n(x)$ and show that $c = 1/2^n n!$ by comparing the coefficients of x^n in $P_n(x)$ and $v_n(x)$.

34. Use Rodrigues's formula (50) to obtain the representation (41) for the Legendre polynomials $P_n(x)$. [Hint: From the binomial formula,

$$P_n(x) = \frac{1}{2^n n!} \frac{d^n}{dx^n} \{(x^2 - 1)^n\}$$

$$= \frac{1}{2^n n!} \frac{d^n}{dx^n} \left\{ \sum_{m=0}^{n} \frac{n!(-1)^m}{(n-m)!m!} x^{2n-2m} \right\}.\Big]$$

35. The generating function in (51) for Legendre polynomials can be derived from the recurrence formula (49) as follows. Let x be fixed and set $f(z) := \sum_{n=0}^{\infty} P_n(x)z^n$. The goal is to determine an explicit formula for $f(z)$.

(a) Show that multiplying each term in the recurrence formula (49) by z^n and summing the terms from $n = 1$ to ∞ leads to the differential equation

$$\frac{df}{dz} = \frac{x - z}{1 - 2xz + z^2} f.$$

$$\left[\text{Hint:} \right.$$

$$\sum_{n=1}^{\infty} (n+1)P_{n+1}(x)z^n = \sum_{n=0}^{\infty} (n+1)P_{n+1}(x)z^n - P_1(x)$$

$$= \frac{df}{dz} - x. \Big]$$

(b) Solve the differential equation derived in part (a) and use the initial condition $f(0) = P_0(x) \equiv 1$ to obtain $f(z) = (1 - 2xz + z^2)^{-1/2}$.

36. Find a series solution about $x = 0$ for the equation

$$(1 - x^2)y'' - 2xy' + 2y = 0$$

by first finding a polynomial solution and then using the reduction of order formula given in equation (11) in Section 8.7.

37. The **Hermite polynomials** $H_n(x)$ are polynomial solutions to Hermite's equation

$$y'' - 2xy' + 2ny = 0.$$

The Hermite polynomials are generated by

$$e^{2tx - t^2} = \sum_{n=0}^{\infty} \frac{H_n(x)}{n!} t^n.$$

Use this equation to determine the first four Hermite polynomials.

38. The **Chebyshev** (Tchebichef) **polynomials** $T_n(x)$ are polynomial solutions to Chebyshev's equation

$$(1 - x^2)y'' - xy' + n^2 y = 0.$$

The Chebyshev polynomials satisfy the recurrence relation

$$T_{n+1}(x) = 2xT_n(x) - T_{n-1}(x),$$

with $T_0(x) = 1$ and $T_1(x) = x$. Use this recurrence relation to determine the next three Chebyshev polynomials.

39. The **Laguerre polynomials** $L_n(x)$ are polynomial solutions to Laguerre's equation

$$xy'' + (1 - x)y' + ny = 0.$$

The Laguerre polynomials satisfy Rodrigues's formula,

$$L_n(x) = \frac{e^x}{n!} \frac{d^n}{dx^n} (x^n e^{-x}).$$

Use this formula to determine the first four Laguerre polynomials.

Chapter Summary

Power series solutions to differential equations are useful alternatives when explicit solutions involving elementary functions cannot be found.

POWER SERIES

Every power series $\sum_{n=0}^{\infty} a_n(x - x_0)^n$ has a **radius of convergence** ρ, $0 \le \rho \le \infty$, such that the series converges absolutely for $|x - x_0| < \rho$ and diverges when $|x - x_0| > \rho$. By the ratio test,

$$\frac{1}{\rho} = \lim_{n \to \infty} \frac{|a_{n+1}|}{|a_n|},$$

provided that this limit exists as an extended real number. A function $f(x)$ that is the sum of a power series in some open interval about x_0 is said to be **analytic at x_0**. If f is analytic at x_0, its power series representation about x_0 is the **Taylor series**

$$f(x) = \sum_{n=0}^{\infty} \frac{f^{(n)}(x_0)}{n!} (x - x_0)^n.$$

TAYLOR SERIES METHOD

If it is known that the solution $y(x)$ to the initial value problem

$$y' = F(x, y), \qquad y(x_0) = y_0$$

is analytic at the initial point x_0, then the first few terms of its Taylor expansion about x_0 can be computed by successively differentiating the equation:

$$y(x_0) = y_0, \qquad y'(x_0) = F(x_0, y_0),$$

$$y''(x_0) = \frac{\partial F}{\partial x}(x_0, y_0) + \frac{\partial F}{\partial y}(x_0, y_0)F(x_0, y_0), \qquad \text{etc.}$$

However, this Taylor series method involves increasingly tedious computations.

POWER SERIES METHOD FOR AN ORDINARY POINT

In the case of a linear equation of the form

(1) $\qquad y'' + p(x)y' + q(x)y = 0,$

where p and q are analytic at x_0, the point x_0 is called an **ordinary point,** and the equation has a pair of linearly independent solutions expressible as power series about x_0. The radii of convergence of these series solutions are at least as large as the distance from x_0 to the nearest singularity (real or complex) of the equation. To find power series solutions to (1), we substitute $y(x) = \sum_{n=0}^{\infty} a_n(x - x_0)^n$ into (1), group like terms, and set the coefficients of the resulting power series equal to zero. This leads to a recurrence relation for the coefficients a_n, which, in some cases, may even yield a general formula for the a_n. The same method applies to the nonhomogeneous version of (1), provided that the forcing function is also analytic at x_0.

REGULAR SINGULAR POINTS

If, in equation (1), either p or q fails to be analytic at x_0, then x_0 is a **singular point** of (1). If x_0 is a singular point for which $(x - x_0)p(x)$ and $(x - x_0)^2 q(x)$ are both analytic at x_0, then x_0 is a **regular singular point.** The Cauchy-Euler equation,

(2) $\qquad ax^2 \dfrac{d^2 y}{dx^2} + bx \dfrac{dy}{dx} + cy = 0, \qquad x > 0,$

has a regular singular point at $x = 0$, and a general solution to (2) can be obtained by substituting $y = x^r$ and examining the roots of the resulting indicial equation $ar^2 + (b - a)r + c = 0$.

METHOD OF FROBENIUS

For an equation of the form (1) with a regular singular point at x_0, a series solution can be found by the **method of Frobenius.** This is obtained by substituting

$$w(r, x) = (x - x_0)^r \sum_{n=0}^{\infty} a_n(x - x_0)^n$$

into (1), finding a recurrence relation for the coefficients, and choosing $r = r_1$, the larger root of the **indicial equation**

(3) $\qquad r(r - 1) + p_0 r + q_0 = 0,$

where $p_0 := \lim_{x \to x_0} (x - x_0)p(x)$, $q_0 := \lim_{x \to x_0} (x - x_0)^2 q(x)$.

FINDING A SECOND LINEARLY INDEPENDENT SOLUTION

If the two roots r_1, r_2 of the indicial equation (3) do not differ by an integer, then a second linearly independent solution to (1) can be found by taking $r = r_2$ in the method of Frobenius. However, if $r_1 = r_2$ or $r_1 - r_2$ is a positive integer, then discovering a second solution requires a different approach. This may be a reduction of order procedure, the utilization of Theorem 7 which gives the *forms* of the solutions, or an operator approach in which, in the method of Frobenius, the coefficients a_n are treated as functions of r.

SPECIAL FUNCTIONS

Some special functions in physics and engineering that arise from series solutions to linear second order equations with polynomial coefficients are Gaussian hypergeometric functions, $F(\alpha, \beta; \gamma; x)$; Bessel functions $J_\nu(x)$; and orthogonal polynomials such as those of Legendre, Chebyshev, Laguerre, and Hermite.

REVIEW PROBLEMS

1. Use the Taylor series method to determine the first four nonzero terms of a series solution for the given initial value problem.
   (a) $y' = xy - y^2$; $\quad y(0) = 1.$
   (b) $y'' - x^3 y' + xy^2 = 0$; $\quad y(0) = -1,$ $\quad y'(0) = 1.$

2. Determine all the singular points of the given equation and classify them as regular or irregular.
   (a) $(x^2 - 4)^2 y'' + (x - 4)y' + xy = 0.$ $\qquad$ (b) $(\sin x)y'' + y = 0.$

3. Find at least the first four nonzero terms in a power series expansion about $x = 0$ for a general solution to the given equation.
   (a) $y'' + x^2 y' - 2y = 0.$ $\qquad$ (b) $y'' + e^{-x}y' - y = 0.$

4. Find a general formula for the coefficient a_n in a power series expansion about $x = 0$ for a general solution to the given equation.

   (a) $(1 - x^2)y'' + xy' + 3y = 0$.   (b) $(x^2 - 2)y'' + 3y = 0$.

5. Find at least the first four nonzero terms in a power series expansion about $x = 2$ for a general solution to

$$y'' + (x - 2)y' - y = 0.$$

6. Use the substitution $y = x^r$ to find a general solution to the given equation for $x > 0$.

   (a) $2x^2 y''(x) + 5xy'(x) - 12y(x) = 0$.
   (b) $x^3 y'''(x) + 3x^2 y''(x) - 2xy'(x) - 2y(x) = 0$.

7. Use the method of Frobenius to find at least the first four nonzero terms in the series expansion about $x = 0$ for a solution to the given equation for $x > 0$.

   (a) $x^2 y'' - 5xy' + (9 - x)y = 0$.
   (b) $x^2 y'' + (x^2 + 2x)y' - 2y = 0$.

8. Find the indicial equation and its roots and state (but do not compute) the form of the series expansion about $x = 0$ (as in Theorem 7 on page 454) for two linearly independent solutions of the given equation for $x > 0$.

   (a) $x^2 y'' + (\sin x)y' - 4y = 0$.   (b) $2xy'' + 5y' + xy = 0$.
   (c) $(x \sin x)y'' + xy' + (\tan x)y = 0$.

9. Find at least the first three nonzero terms in the series expansion about $x = 0$ for a general solution to the given equation for $x > 0$.

   (a) $x^2 y'' - x(1 + x)y' + y = 0$.   (b) $xy'' + y' - 2y = 0$.
   (c) $2xy'' + 6y' + y = 0$.   (d) $x^2 y'' + (x - 2)y = 0$.

10. Express a general solution to the given equation using Gaussian hypergeometric functions or Bessel functions.

   (a) $x(1 - x)y'' + (\frac{1}{2} - 6x)y' - 6y = 0$.
   (b) $9x^2 y'' + 9xy' + (9x^2 - 1)y = 0$.

Projects for Chapter 8

A. SPHERICALLY SYMMETRIC SOLUTIONS TO SCHRÖDINGER'S EQUATION FOR THE HYDROGEN ATOM

In quantum mechanics one is interested in determining the wave function and energy states of an atom. These are determined from Schrödinger's equation. In the case of the hydrogen atom, it is possible to find wave functions ψ that are functions only of r, the distance from the proton to the electron. Such functions are called **spherically symmetric** and satisfy the simpler equation

(1) $$\frac{1}{r}\frac{d^2}{dr^2}(r\psi) = \frac{-8m\pi^2}{h^2}\left(E + \frac{e_0^2}{r}\right)\psi,$$

where e_0^2, m, and h are constants, and E, also a constant, represents the energy of the atom, which we assume here to be negative.

(a) Show that with the substitutions

$$r = \frac{h^2}{4\pi^2 m e_0^2}\, \rho, \qquad E = \frac{2\pi^2 m e_0^4}{h^2}\, \varepsilon$$

equation (1) reduces to

$$\frac{d^2(\rho\psi)}{d\rho^2} = -\left(\varepsilon + \frac{2}{\rho}\right)\rho\psi.$$

(b) If $f := \rho\psi$, then the preceding equation becomes

(2) $$\frac{d^2 f}{d\rho^2} = -\left(\varepsilon + \frac{2}{\rho}\right) f.$$

Show that the substitution $f(\rho) = e^{-\alpha\rho} g(\rho)$, where α is a positive constant, transforms (2) into

(3) $$\frac{d^2 g}{d\rho^2} - 2\alpha\frac{dg}{d\rho} + \left(\frac{2}{\rho} + \varepsilon + \alpha^2\right) g = 0.$$

(c) If we choose $\alpha^2 = -\varepsilon$ (ε negative), then (3) becomes

(4) $$\frac{d^2 g}{d\rho^2} - 2\alpha\frac{dg}{d\rho} + \frac{2}{\rho} g = 0.$$

Show that a power series solution $g(\rho) = \sum_{k=1}^{\infty} a_k \rho^k$ (starting with $k = 1$) for (4) must have coefficients a_k that satisfy the recurrence relation

(5) $$a_{k+1} = \frac{2(\alpha k - 1)}{k(k+1)} a_k, \qquad k \geq 1.$$

(d) Now for $a_1 = 1$ and k very large, $a_{k+1} \approx (2\alpha/k)a_k$ and so $a_{k+1} \approx (2\alpha)^k/k!$, which are the coefficients for $e^{2\alpha\rho}$. Hence g acts like $e^{2\alpha\rho}$, and so $f(\rho) = e^{-\alpha\rho}g(\rho)$ is like $e^{\alpha\rho}$. Going back further we then see that $\psi \approx e^{\alpha\rho}/\rho$. Therefore, when $r = h^2\rho/4\pi^2 m e_0^2$ is large, so is ψ. Roughly speaking, $\psi^2(r)$ is proportional to the probability of finding an electron a distance r from the proton. Thus the above argument would imply that the electron in a hydrogen atom is more likely to be found at a very large distance from the proton! Since this makes no sense physically, we ask: Do there exist positive values for α for which ψ remains bounded as r becomes large?

Show that when $\alpha = 1/n$, $n = 1, 2, 3, \ldots$, then $g(\rho)$ is a polynomial of degree n, and argue that ψ is therefore bounded.

(e) Let E_n and $\psi_n(\rho)$ denote, respectively, the energy state and wave function corresponding to $\alpha = 1/n$. Find E_n (in terms of the constants e_0^2, m, and h) and $\psi_n(\rho)$ for $n = 1, 2$, and 3.

B. DEFORMATION OF CIRCULAR PLATES

In the analysis of a deformation due to a uniform load on a certain circular plate there arises the equation

(6)
$$x^2[1 - (\varepsilon x)^k]\frac{d^2\phi}{dx^2} + x[1 - (\varepsilon x)^k - 3k(\varepsilon x)^k]\frac{d\phi}{dx} - [1 - (\varepsilon x)^k + 3kv(\varepsilon x)^k]\phi = 0,$$

where ε, k, and v are constants. Here x is proportional to the distance from the center of the plate and ϕ is the angle between the normal to the deformed surface of the plate and the normal to that surface at the center of the plate.

(a) Show that the substitution $z = \varepsilon x$ transforms (6) into

(7)
$$z^2(1 - z^k)\frac{d^2\phi}{dz^2} + (1 - z^k - 3kz^k)\, z\, \frac{d\phi}{dz} - (1 - z^k + 3kvz^k)\phi = 0.$$

(b) Now let $\phi = z\psi$. Show that (7) becomes

(8)
$$z^2(1 - z^k)\frac{d^2\psi}{dz^2} + 3(1 - z^k - kz^k)\, z\, \frac{d\psi}{dz} - 3k(v + 1)z^k\psi = 0.$$

(c) Set $z^k = \sigma$. Show that (8) reduces to

(9)
$$\sigma(1 - \sigma)\frac{d^2\psi}{d\sigma^2} + \left[\frac{k + 2}{k} - \left(1 + \frac{2 + 3k}{k}\right)\sigma\right]\frac{d\psi}{d\sigma} - \frac{3(v + 1)}{k}\,\psi = 0.$$

(d) Observe that (9) is a hypergeometric equation (see Section 8.9) with

$$\gamma = \frac{k + 2}{k}, \qquad \alpha + \beta = \frac{2 + 3k}{k}, \qquad \alpha\beta = \frac{3(v + 1)}{k}.$$

Show that if α_1 and α_2 are the two roots of

$$kr^2 - (2 + 3k)r + 3(v + 1) = 0,$$

then a solution to equation (6) is

$$\phi(x) = \varepsilon x F\left(\alpha_1, \alpha_2; \frac{k + 2}{k}; \varepsilon^k x^k\right),$$

where F is the Gaussian hypergeometric function.

Systems of Differential Equations and Their Applications

9.1 Introduction: Analysis of an Electric Network

At time $t = 0$ the charge on the capacitor in the electric network shown in Figure 9.1 is 2 coulombs, while the current through the capacitor is zero. Determine the charge on the capacitor and the currents in the various branches of the network at any time $t > 0$.

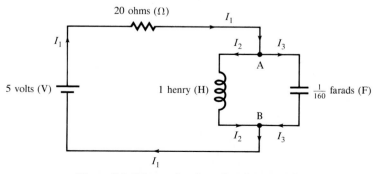

20 ohms (Ω)

I_1

I_1

I_2 I_3

A

5 volts (V)

1 henry (H)

$\frac{1}{160}$ farads (F)

B

I_2 I_3

I_1

Figure 9.1 Schematic of an electric network

In Section 5.4 we derived a mathematical model for a simple RLC series circuit. There we used the following fundamental conservation laws, referred to as **Kirchhoff's laws:**

1. In a given branch of a network the current I passing through each of the elements must be the same.

2. The algebraic sum of the instantaneous changes in potential (voltage drops) around a closed circuit (loop) must be zero.

For electric networks consisting of more than one circuit, an additional conservation law, also due to Kirchhoff, is required:

3. In an electric network, the algebraic sum of the currents flowing to a junction point must be zero.

To determine the charge and currents in the electric network in Figure 9.1, we begin by observing that the network consists of three closed circuits: loop 1 through the battery, resistor, and inductor; loop 2 through the battery, resistor, and capacitor; and loop 3 containing the capacitor and inductor. Taking advantage of the first conservation law, we denote the current passing through the battery and the resistor by I_1, the current through the inductor by I_2, and the current through the capacitor by I_3. For consistency of notation, we denote the charge on the capacitor by q_3; hence, $I_3 = dq_3/dt$.

As discussed in Section 5.4, the voltage drop at a resistor is RI, at an inductor $L\,dI/dt$, and at a capacitor q/C. So, applying Kirchhoff's second law to the electric network in Figure 9.1, we find for loop 1,

(1)
$$\frac{dI_2}{dt} + 20I_1 = 5;$$

(inductor)   (resistor)   (battery)

for loop 2,

(2)
$$20I_1 + 160q_3 = 5;$$

(resistor)   (capacitor)   (battery)

and for loop 3,

(3)
$$-\frac{dI_2}{dt} + 160q_3 = 0.$$

(inductor)   **(capacitor)**

(The minus sign in (3) arises from taking a clockwise path around loop 3, so that the current passing through the inductor is $-I_2$.) Notice that these three equations are not independent: we can obtain equation (3) by subtracting (1) from (2). Hence, we have only two equations from which to determine the three unknowns I_1, I_2, and q_3. If we now apply the third conservation law to the two junction points in the network, we find at point A that $I_1 - I_2 - I_3 = 0$, and at point B that $I_2 + I_3 - I_1 = 0$. In both cases we get $I_1 = I_2 + I_3$, where $I_3 = dq_3/dt$. Substituting for I_1 in (2) now gives

(4) $$20I_2 + 20\frac{dq_3}{dt} + 160q_3 = 5.$$

From equations (3) and (4), we can eliminate the function I_2 and its derivatives and obtain a single second order equation for q_3. This can be accomplished if we multiply equation (3) by 20, differentiate equation (4) with respect to t, and then add the resulting equations. This yields

(5) $$20\frac{d^2q_3}{dt^2} + 160\frac{dq_3}{dt} + 3200q_3 = 0.$$

To obtain the initial conditions for (5), recall that at time $t = 0$ the charge on the capacitor is 2 coulombs and the current is zero. Hence

(6) $$q_3(0) = 2, \quad \frac{dq_3}{dt}(0) = 0.$$

We can now solve the initial value problem (5)–(6) using the techniques of Chapter 4 or 7. Ultimately we find

$$q_3(t) = 2e^{-4t}\cos 12t + \frac{2}{3}e^{-4t}\sin 12t,$$

$$I_3(t) = \frac{dq_3}{dt}(t) = -\frac{80}{3}e^{-4t}\sin 12t.$$

Next, to determine I_2, we substitute these expressions into (4) and obtain

$$I_2(t) = \frac{1}{4} - \frac{dq_3}{dt}(t) - 8q_3(t)$$

$$= \frac{1}{4} - 16e^{-4t}\cos 12t + \frac{64}{3}e^{-4t}\sin 12t.$$

Finally, from $I_1 = I_2 + I_3$, we obtain

$$I_1(t) = \frac{1}{4} - 16e^{-4t}\cos 12t - \frac{16}{3}e^{-4t}\sin 12t.$$

In retrospect, we see that applying Kirchhoff's laws to the network of Figure 9.1 leads to the system consisting of equations (3) and (4). In this chapter we describe two techniques for solving similar systems. The first, which we successfully used to solve the network problem, is called the **elimination method** and involves transforming a system into a single higher order equation (as in (5)). The second method involves the use of Laplace transforms to convert the linear system of differential equations with initial conditions into a linear system of algebraic equations. A third technique, involving matrix algebra, is developed in Chapter 10.

In Section 9.4 we study the applications to multiple compartment systems and to mechanical systems with multiple degrees of freedom. In Section 9.5 we present a numerical method for approximating the solution to a system of first order differential equations with initial conditions. Finally, in Section 9.6, we introduce a qualitative method called **phase plane analysis,** which applies to a class of nonlinear systems.

9.2 Elimination Method for Linear Systems

Until now we have concentrated on solving differential equations that involve a single dependent variable. In this chapter we are interested in finding a solution to a *system* of differential equations that involve two or more dependent variables. Here we restrict our study to a system of linear differential equations, or what is called a **linear system.**

The general form for a linear system of two first order differential equations is

(1)
$$a_1(t)x'(t) + a_2(t)x(t) + b_1(t)y'(t) + b_2(t)y(t) = f_1(t),$$
$$c_1(t)x'(t) + c_2(t)x(t) + d_1(t)y'(t) + d_2(t)y(t) = f_2(t),$$

where the coefficients a_1, a_2, b_1, b_2, c_1, c_2, d_1, d_2, and the nonhomogeneous terms f_1 and f_2 are given functions of t. A **solution** to system (1) is a pair of functions $x(t)$, $y(t)$ that satisfy (1) on some interval I.

A fundamental procedure for solving linear systems with constant coefficients is based on the technique of elimination that is used to solve a system of algebraic equations. This method is performed more easily if we express the linear system in operator notation, where $D := d/dt$ (see Section 4.2). We demonstrate the **elimination method** in the following example.

▶ *Example 1*   Solve the system

(2)
$$x'(t) = 3x(t) - 4y(t),$$
$$y'(t) = 4x(t) - 7y(t).$$

Solution   First we write the system using the operator notation:

(3)
$$4 \quad (D - 3)[x] + 4y = 0,$$
$$ -4x + (D + 7)[y] = 0.$$

$4x - 12x + 4\cos$

$D-3(-4x + (D+7)[y] = 0.)$ $-4x + 12x \quad (D-3)(D+7)[y]$

$(D^2 + 4D - 2)[y] = 0$

We can eliminate x from this system by adding 4 times the first equation to $(D - 3)$ applied to the second equation; this gives

$$(16 + (D - 3)(D + 7))[y] = 4 \cdot 0 + (D - 3)[0] = 0,$$

$$D^2 + 4D - 21 + 16$$

which simplifies to

(4) $(D^2 + 4D - 5)[y] = 0.$

Now equation (4) is just a second order linear equation in y with constant coefficients that has the general solution

(5) $y(t) = C_1 e^{-5t} + C_2 e^t.$

To find $x(t)$, we have two options. One is to return to system (3) and eliminate y. This is accomplished by "multiplying" the first equation in (3) by $(D + 7)$ and the second equation by -4 and then adding to obtain

(6) $(D^2 + 4D - 5)[x] = 0.$

Coincidentally, equation (6) is the same as equation (4) except that here the unknown function is $x(t)$. Hence

(7) $x(t) = K_1 e^{-5t} + K_2 e^t,$

where we have taken K_1 and K_2 to be the arbitrary constants, which are not necessarily the same as C_1 and C_2 used in equation (5).

It is reasonable to expect that system (2) will involve only two arbitrary constants since it consists of two first order equations. To determine the relationships among the four constants C_1, C_2, K_1, and K_2, we substitute the expressions for $x(t)$ and $y(t)$ given in (5) and (7) into one of the equations in (2), say the first. This yields

$$-5K_1 e^{-5t} + K_2 e^t = 3K_1 e^{-5t} + 3K_2 e^t - 4C_1 e^{-5t} - 4C_2 e^t,$$

which simplifies to

(8) $(4C_1 - 8K_1)e^{-5t} + (4C_2 - 2K_2)e^t = 0.$

Since e^t and e^{-5t} are linearly independent functions on any interval, equation (8) holds for all t only if

$$4C_1 - 8K_1 = 0 \quad \text{and} \quad 4C_2 - 2K_2 = 0.$$

$$-8K_1 = -4C_1$$
$$K_1 = \frac{C_1}{2}$$

Therefore, $K_1 = C_1/2$ and $K_2 = 2C_2.$

A solution to system (2) is then given by the pair

(9) $x(t) = \frac{1}{2}C_1 e^{-5t} + 2C_2 e^t$, $y(t) = C_1 e^{-5t} + C_2 e^t$.

As you might expect, the pair in (9) is a **general solution** to (2) in the sense that *any* solution to (2) can be expressed in this fashion (see Section 10.3).

A simpler method for determining $x(t)$ once $y(t)$ is known is to use the system to obtain an equation for $x(t)$ in terms of $y(t)$ and $y'(t)$. In this example, solving the second equation in (2) for $x(t)$ gives

$$x(t) = \frac{1}{4}y'(t) + \frac{7}{4}y(t).$$

Substituting $y(t)$ as given in (5) yields

$$x(t) = \frac{1}{4}\left[-5C_1 e^{-5t} + C_2 e^t\right] + \frac{7}{4}\left[C_1 e^{-5t} + C_2 e^t\right]$$
$$= \frac{1}{2}C_1 e^{-5t} + 2C_2 e^t,$$

which agrees with (9). ◄

The above procedure works, more generally, for any linear system with *constant coefficients* regardless of the order of the equations. For example, if we let L_1, L_2, L_3, and L_4 denote linear differential operators with constant coefficients (i.e., polynomials in D), then the method can be applied to the linear system

(10) $L_1[x] + L_2[y] = f_1$,
$$L_3[x] + L_4[y] = f_2.$$

Since the system has constant coefficients, the operators commute (e.g., $L_2 L_4 = L_4 L_2$), and we can eliminate variables in the usual algebraic fashion. Eliminating the variable y in (10) gives

(11) $(L_1 L_4 - L_2 L_3)[x] = g_1$,

where $g_1 := L_4[f_1] - L_2[f_2]$. Similarly, eliminating the variable x in (10) yields

(12) $(L_1 L_4 - L_2 L_3)[y] = g_2$,

where $g_2 := L_1[f_2] - L_3[f_1]$. Now if $L_1 L_4 - L_2 L_3$ is a differential operator of order n, then a general solution for (11) contains n arbitrary constants, and a general solution for (12) also contains n arbitrary constants; thus a total of $2n$ constants arise. However, as we saw in Example 1, there are only n of these that are independent for the system; the remaining constants can be expressed in terms of these.[†] The pair of general solutions to

---

[†] For a proof of this fact see *Ordinary Differential Equations*, by M. Tenebaum and H. Pollard, Harper and Row Publishers, Inc., New York, 1963. Chapter 7.

(11) and (12) written in terms of the n independent constants is called a **general solution for the system.**

If it turns out that $L_1 L_4 - L_2 L_3$ is the zero operator, the system is said to be **degenerate.** As with the anomalous problem of solving for the points of intersection of two parallel or coincident lines, a degenerate system may have no solutions, or if it does possess solutions, they may involve any number of arbitrary constants (see Problems 21 and 22).

ELIMINATION PROCEDURE FOR SYSTEMS

To find a general solution for the system

$$L_1[x] + L_2[y] = f_1,$$
$$L_3[x] + L_4[y] = f_2,$$

where L_1, L_2, L_3, and L_4 are polynomials in $D = d/dt$:

(a) Make sure that the system is written in operator form.

(b) Eliminate one of the variables, say y, to obtain equation (11) for $x(t)$. CAUTION: If $L_1 L_4 - L_2 L_3$ is the zero operator, the remaining steps do not apply; the system is degenerate, and a separate analysis is required to determine whether there are no solutions or infinitely many linearly independent ones.

(c) Solve equation (11) for $x(t)$. The expression for $x(t)$ will contain n arbitrary constants, where n is the order of the differential operator $L_1 L_4 - L_2 L_3$.

(d) (Short cut) If possible, use the system to derive an equation that involves $y(t)$ but not its derivatives. (Otherwise, go to step e.) Substitute the expression for $x(t)$ into this equation to get a formula for $y(t)$. The expressions for $x(t)$, $y(t)$ give the desired general solution.

(e) Eliminate x from the system to obtain equation (12) for $y(t)$. Solve this equation to get an expression for $y(t)$ involving n new arbitrary constants.

(f) Reduce the $2n$ arbitrary constants to n by substituting the expressions for $x(t)$ and $y(t)$ into one or both of the equations in the system. Write the expressions for $x(t)$ and $y(t)$ in terms of these n constants to get a general solution.

▶ **Example 2** Find a general solution for

(13)
$$x''(t) + y'(t) - x(t) + y(t) = -1,$$
$$x'(t) + y'(t) - x(t) = t^2.$$

Solution   We begin by expressing the system in operator notation:

(14)
$$(D^2 - 1)[x] + (D + 1)[y] = -1,$$
$$(D - 1)[x] + D[y] = t^2.$$

Here $L_1 := D^2 - 1$, $L_2 := D + 1$, $L_3 := D - 1$, and $L_4 := D$.
Eliminating y from (14) gives (cf. (11)):

$$((D^2 - 1)D - (D + 1)(D - 1))[x] = D[-1] - (D + 1)[t^2],$$

which reduces to

(15)
$$(D - 1)((D + 1)D - (D + 1))[x] = -2t - t^2,$$
$$(D - 1)^2(D + 1)[x] = -2t - t^2.$$

Since we have found that $L_1 L_4 - L_2 L_3 = (D - 1)^2(D + 1)$, which has order three, there will be three arbitrary constants in a general solution to system (13).

The homogeneous equation associated with (15) has the auxiliary equation $(r - 1)^2(r + 1) = 0$ with roots $r = 1, 1, -1$. Hence a general solution for this homogeneous equation is

(16) $x_h(t) = C_1 e^t + C_2 t e^t + C_3 e^{-t}.$

To find a particular solution to (15) we use the method of undetermined coefficients with $x_p(t) = At^2 + Bt + C$. Substituting into (15) and solving for A, B, and C yields (after a little algebra)

(17) $x_p(t) = -t^2 - 4t - 6.$

Thus a general solution to equation (15) is

(18) $x(t) = x_h(t) + x_p(t) = C_1 e^t + C_2 t e^t + C_3 e^{-t} - t^2 - 4t - 6.$

To find $y(t)$, we take the short cut described in step (d) of the elimination procedure box. Subtracting the second equation in (14) from the first, we find

$$(D^2 - D)[x] + y = -1 - t^2,$$

so that

(19) $y = (D - D^2)[x] - 1 - t^2.$

Inserting in (19) the expression for $x(t)$ given in (18), we obtain

$$y(t) = C_1 e^t + C_2(te^t + e^t) - C_3 e^{-t} - 2t - 4$$
$$- [C_1 e^t + C_2(te^t + 2e^t) + C_3 e^{-t} - 2] - 1 - t^2,$$

(20) $\qquad y(t) = -C_2 e^t - 2C_3 e^{-t} - t^2 - 2t - 3.$

The formulas for $x(t)$ in (18) and $y(t)$ in (20) give the desired general solution to (13). ◀

The elimination method also applies to linear systems with three or more equations and unknowns; however, the process becomes more cumbersome as the number of equations and unknowns increases. One alternative is to use the matrix approach described in Chapter 10; another is to approximate the solution numerically using techniques like those discussed in Section 9.5.

CONVERSION OF HIGHER ORDER EQUATIONS TO FIRST ORDER SYSTEMS

In carrying out the elimination method, we derived from the system a higher order differential equation (involving one dependent variable). In the *converse* direction, it is possible (and often useful) to rewrite an mth order differential equation as a system of m **first order** equations. For instance, most numerical procedures for approximating the solution to an initial value problem for a higher order differential equation require that the problem first be restated as a system of first order equations (see Section 9.5). Furthermore, as we will see in Chapter 10, the powerful machinery of linear algebra can be easily applied in such a setting.

When an mth order system is written as

$$x_1'(t) = f_1(t, x_1, x_2, \ldots, x_m),$$
$$x_2'(t) = f_2(t, x_1, x_2, \ldots, x_m),$$

(21)
$$\vdots$$

$$x_m'(t) = f_m(t, x_1, x_2, \ldots, x_m),$$

we say it is in **normal form.** Any mth order differential equation

(22) $\qquad y^{(m)}(t) = f(t, y, y', \ldots, y^{(m-1)})$

can be converted into a first order system in normal form by setting

(23) $\qquad x_1(t) := y(t), \quad x_2(t) := y'(t), \quad \ldots, \quad x_m(t) := y^{(m-1)}(t).$

With this substitution, we obtain

$$x_1'(t) = y'(t) = x_2(t),$$
$$x_2'(t) = y''(t) = x_3(t),$$

(24)

.
.
.

$$x_{m-1}'(t) = y^{(m-1)}(t) = x_m(t),$$
$$x_m'(t) = y^{(m)}(t) = f(t, x_1, x_2, \ldots, x_m).$$

If equation (22) has initial conditions $y(t_0) = a_1$, $y'(t_0) = a_2, \ldots, y^{(m-1)}(t_0) = a_m$, then system (24) has initial conditions $x_1(t_0) = a_1$, $x_2(t_0) = a_2, \ldots, x_m(t_0) = a_m$.

▶ *Example 3*   Convert the initial value problem

(25) $y''(t) + 3y'(t) + 2y(t) = 0;$ $y(0) = 1,$ $y'(0) = 3$

into an initial value problem for a system in normal form.

Solution   We first express the differential equation in (25) as

$$y''(t) = -3y'(t) - 2y(t).$$

Setting $x_1(t) := y(t)$ and $x_2(t) := y'(t)$, we obtain

$$x_1'(t) = x_2(t),$$
$$x_2'(t) = -3x_2(t) - 2x_1(t).$$

The initial conditions in (25) transform to $x_1(0) = 1$, $x_2(0) = 3$. ◀

EXERCISES 9.2

In Problems 1 through 20 use the elimination method to find a general solution for the given linear system, where x', y', z' denote differentiation with respect to t.

1. $x' = 3y,$
$y' = 2x - y.$

2. $x' + y' = -2y,$
$y' = x - 2y.$

3. $x' = x - y,$
$y' = y - 4x.$

4. $x' + 2y = 0,$
$x' - y' = 0.$

5. $x' + y' - x = 5,$
$x' + y' + y = 1.$

6. $x' = 3x - 2y + \sin t,$
$y' = 4x - y - \cos t.$

7. $(D + 1)[x] - (D + 1)[y] = e^t,$
$(D - 1)[x] + (2D + 1)[y] = 5.$

8. $(D - 3)[x] + (D - 1)[y] = t,$
$(D + 1)[x] + (D + 4)[y] = 1.$

9. $x' + y' + 2x \quad = 0,$
$\quad x' + y' - x - y = \sin t.$

10. $2x' + y' - x - y = e^{-t},$
$\quad x' + y' + 2x + y = e^{t}.$

11. $D^2[x] + D[y] = 2,$
$\quad 4x + D[y] = 6.$

12. $(D^2 - 1)[x] + 5y = e^{t},$
$\quad 2x + (D^2 + 2)[y] = 0.$

13. $\dfrac{dx}{dt} + y = t^2,$

$\quad -x + \dfrac{dy}{dt} = 1.$

14. $\dfrac{dx}{dt} = x - 4y,$

$\quad \dfrac{dy}{dt} = x + y.$

15. $\dfrac{dx}{dt} = 5x + 2y + 5t,$

$\quad \dfrac{dy}{dt} = 3x + 4y + 17t.$

16. $\dfrac{dx}{dt} + x + \dfrac{dy}{dt} = e^{4t},$

$\quad 2x + \dfrac{d^2 y}{dt^2} = 0.$

17. $y'' + x' + x = \sin t,$
$\quad y' - y + x = 0.$

18. $x'' + 5x - 4y = 0,$
$\quad -x + y'' + 2y = 0.$

19. $x' = 3x + y - z,$
$\quad y' = x + 2y - z,$
$\quad z' = 3x + 3y - z.$

20. $x' = y + z,$
$\quad y' = x + z,$
$\quad z' = x + y.$

In Problems 21 and 22 show that the given linear system is degenerate. By attempting to solve the system, determine whether it has no solutions or infinitely many linearly independent solutions.

21. $(D - 1)[x] + (D - 1)[y] = -3e^{-2t},$
$\quad (D + 2)[x] + (D + 2)[y] = 3e^{t}.$

22. $D[x] + (D + 1)[y] = e^{t},$
$\quad D[x] + (D + 1)[y] = 0.$

In Problems 23 through 26 convert the given initial value problem into an initial value problem for a system in normal form.

23. $y''(t) = \cos(t - y) + y^2(t); \quad y(0) = 1, \quad y'(0) = 0.$

24. $y''(t) + ty'(t) - 3y(t) = t^2; \quad y(0) = 3, \quad y'(0) = -6.$

25. $y^{(4)}(t) - y^{(3)}(t) + 7y(t) = \cos t; \quad y(0) = y'(0) = 1, \quad y''(0) = 0, \quad y^{(3)}(0) = 2.$

26. $y^{(6)}(t) = [y'(t)]^3 - \sin(y(t)) + e^{2t}; \quad y(0) = \cdots = y^{(5)}(0) = 0.$

In Problems 27 through 30 find a system of differential equations and initial conditions for the currents in the networks given in the schematic diagram, assuming that all initial currents are zero. Solve for the currents in each branch of the network (see Section 9.1 for a discussion of electric networks).

27.

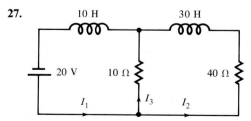

Figure 9.2 *RL* network for Problem 27

28.

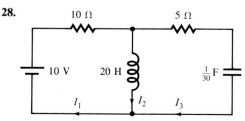

Figure 9.3 *RLC* network for Problem 28

29.

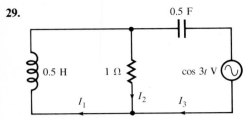

Figure 9.4 *RLC* network for Problem 29

30.

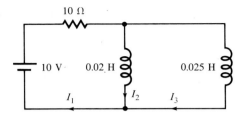

Figure 9.5 *RL* network for Problem 30

★ 9.3 Solving Linear Systems with Laplace Transforms

In Chapter 7 we used the Laplace transform to reduce an initial value problem for a linear differential equation with constant coefficients to a linear algebraic equation, where the unknown was the transform of the solution. We then solved for the transform, took the inverse Laplace transform, and obtained the solution to the initial value problem. In a similar manner we can use the Laplace transform to reduce certain systems of linear differential equations with initial conditions to a system of linear algebraic equations, where again the unknowns are the transforms of the functions that make up the solution. Solving for these unknowns and taking their inverse Laplace transforms, we can then obtain the solution to the initial value problem for the system.

▶ **Example 1**   Solve the initial value problem

(1)
$$x'(t) - 2y(t) = 4t, \qquad x(0) = 4,$$
$$y'(t) + 2y(t) - 4x(t) = -4t - 2, \qquad y(0) = -5.$$

Solution   Let $X(s) := \mathscr{L}\{x\}(s)$ and $Y(s) := \mathscr{L}\{y\}(s)$. Taking the Laplace transform of both sides of the differential equations in (1) gives (see the Laplace transform table on the inside back cover)

(2)
$$\mathscr{L}\{x'\}(s) - 2Y(s) = \frac{4}{s^2},$$
$$\mathscr{L}\{y'\}(s) + 2Y(s) - 4X(s) = -\frac{4}{s^2} - \frac{2}{s}.$$

Using the initial conditions in (1), we can express $\mathscr{L}\{x'\}(s)$ in terms of $X(s)$, and $\mathscr{L}\{y'\}(s)$ in terms of $Y(s)$. Namely,

(3)
$$\mathscr{L}\{x'\}(s) = sX(s) - x(0) = sX(s) - 4,$$
$$\mathscr{L}\{y'\}(s) = sY(s) - y(0) = sY(s) + 5.$$

Substituting these expressions into system (2) and simplifying, we find

(4)
$$sX(s) - 2Y(s) = \frac{4s^2 + 4}{s^2},$$

$$-4X(s) + (s + 2)Y(s) = -\frac{5s^2 + 2s + 4}{s^2}.$$

To eliminate $Y(s)$ from (4), we multiply the first equation by $(s + 2)$ and the second by 2 and then add to obtain

$$[s(s + 2) - 8]X(s) = \frac{(s + 2)(4s^2 + 4)}{s^2} - \frac{10s^2 + 4s + 8}{s^2}.$$

This simplifies to

(5) $\qquad X(s) = \dfrac{4s - 2}{(s + 4)(s - 2)}.$

To compute the inverse transform, we first write $X(s)$ in the partial fraction form

(6) $\qquad X(s) = \dfrac{3}{s + 4} + \dfrac{1}{s - 2}.$

Hence, from the Laplace transform table on the inside back cover, we find that

(7) $\qquad x(t) = 3e^{-4t} + e^{2t}.$

To determine $y(t)$ we could solve system (4) for $Y(s)$ and then compute its inverse Laplace transform. However, it is easier just to solve the first equation in system (1) for $y(t)$ in terms of $x(t)$. Thus

$$y(t) = \tfrac{1}{2}x'(t) - 2t.$$

Substituting $x(t)$ from equation (7), we find that

(8) $\qquad y(t) = -6e^{-4t} + e^{2t} - 2t.$

The solution to the initial value problem (1) consists of the pair of functions $x(t)$, $y(t)$ given by equations (7) and (8). ◀

EXERCISES 9.3

In Problems 1 through 12 use the method of Laplace transforms to solve the given initial value problem. Here x′, y′, etc., denotes differentiation with respect to t, and so does the symbol D.

1. $x' = x - y;$ $\qquad x(0) = -1,$
$\quad\;\; y' = 2x + 4y;$ $\qquad y(0) = 0.$

2. $x' = 3x - 2y;$ $\qquad x(0) = 1,$
$\quad\;\; y' = 3y - 2x;$ $\qquad y(0) = 1.$

3. $x' + 2y = 0;$ $x(0) = -1,$
    $x' - y' = 0;$ $y(0) = 2.$

4. $x' = y + \sin t;$ $x(0) = 2,$
    $y' = x + 2\cos t;$ $y(0) = 0.$

5. $x' - 3x + 2y = \sin t;$ $x(0) = 0,$
    $4x - y' - y = \cos t;$ $y(0) = 0.$

6. $x' - x - y = 1;$ $x(0) = 0,$
    $-x + y' - y = 0;$ $y(0) = -\frac{5}{2}.$

7. $(D - 4)[x] + 6y = 9e^{-3t};$ $x(0) = -9,$
    $x - (D - 1)[y] = 5e^{-3t};$ $y(0) = 4.$

8. $D[x] + y = 0;$ $x(0) = \frac{7}{4},$
    $4x + D[y] = 3;$ $y(0) = 4.$

9. $x'' + 2y' = -x;$ $x(0) = 2,$ $x'(0) = -7,$
   $-3x'' + 2y'' = 3x - 4y;$ $y(0) = 4,$ $y'(0) = -9.$

10. $x'' + y = 1;$ $x(0) = 1,$ $x'(0) = 1,$
   $x + y'' = -1;$ $y(0) = 1,$ $y'(0) = -1.$

11. $D^2[x] - y = t^2;$ $x(0) = 3, x'(0) = (2 + \sqrt{3})/2,$
    $x + D[y] = 2;$ $y(0) = (2 + \sqrt{3})/2.$

12. $(D - 1)[x] + y = t;$ $x(0) = 0,$
    $D[x] + D^2[y] = 1;$ $y(0) = 1,$ $y'(0) = -1.$

13. Use the method of Laplace transforms to solve

$$x' = 3x + y - 2z; \quad x(0) = -6,$$
$$y' = -x + 2y + z; \quad y(0) = 2,$$
$$z' = 4x + y - 3z; \quad z(0) = -12.$$

14. Use the method of Laplace transforms to solve

$$x'' + y' = 2; \quad x(0) = 3, \quad x'(0) = 0,$$
$$4x + y' = 6; \quad y(1) = 4. \qquad \text{[Hint: Let } y(0) = c \text{ and then solve for } c.]$$

In Problems 15 and 16 find a system of differential equations and initial conditions for the currents in the networks given by the schematic diagrams, assuming that the initial currents are all zero. Solve for the currents in each branch of the network (see Section 9.1 for a discussion of electric networks).

15.

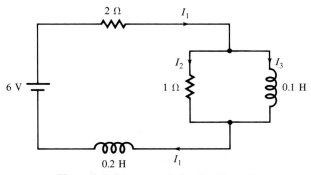

Figure 9.6 *RL* network for Problem 15

16.

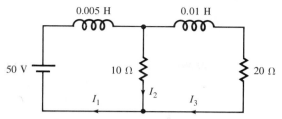

Figure 9.7 *RL* network for Problem 16

9.4 Some Applications of Linear Systems

In Section 9.1 we saw how linear systems arise in a mathematical model for an electric network. Such systems also occur in the study of mechanical systems when there is more than one degree of freedom (see Section 6.1) and in compartmental analysis models involving two or more compartments. In this section we demonstrate three applications of linear systems. The first involves a coupled spring-mass system (see Sections 5.1–5.3 for a discussion of single spring-mass systems).

▶ *Example 1*   Three springs, with spring constants k_1, k_2, k_3, and two masses m_1, m_2 are attached in a straight line on a horizontal frictionless surface with the ends of the outside springs fixed (see Figure 9.8). The system is set in motion by holding the mass m_1 at its equilibrium position and pulling the mass m_2 to the right of its equilibrium position a distance α and then releasing both masses. Determine the equations of motion for the two masses in the special case where $m_1 = m_2 = m$ and $k_1 = k_2 = k_3 = k$.

Solution   Let x_1 and x_2 represent the displacements of the masses m_1 and m_2 to the right of their respective equilibrium positions. Since we can neglect friction and there are no other external forces acting on the masses, the only forces we need consider are those due to the springs.

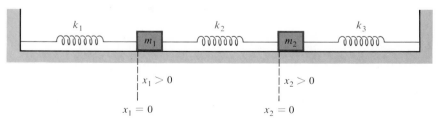

Figure 9.8 Coupled spring-mass system with fixed ends

The mass m_1 has a force F_1 acting on its left side due to the left spring and a force F_2 acting on its right side due to the middle spring. Applying Hooke's law, we see that

(1) $F_1 = -k_1 x_1$ and $F_2 = +k_2(x_2 - x_1)$,

where $(x_2 - x_1)$ is the net displacement of the middle spring from its initial or equilibrium length. The mass m_2 has a force F_3 acting on its left side due to the middle spring and a force F_4 acting on its right side due to the right spring. Again, using Hooke's law, we have

(2) $F_3 = -k_2(x_2 - x_1)$ and $F_4 = -k_3 x_2$.

Applying Newton's second law to each of the masses gives

$$m_1 x_1'' = F_1 + F_2 = -k_1 x_1 + k_2(x_2 - x_1),$$
$$m_2 x_2'' = F_3 + F_4 = -k_2(x_2 - x_1) - k_3 x_2,$$

or

(3) $(m_1 D^2 + k_1 + k_2)[x_1] - k_2 x_2 = 0,$

(4) $-k_2 x_1 + (m_2 D^2 + k_2 + k_3)[x_2] = 0.$

The initial conditions are

(5) $x_1(0) = 0,$ $x_1'(0) = 0,$ $x_2(0) = \alpha,$ $x_2'(0) = 0.$

To solve the initial value problem (3)–(5), we use the elimination method of Section 9.2 on the system (3)–(4). Eliminating x_2 gives

(6) $((m_2 D^2 + k_2 + k_3)(m_1 D^2 + k_1 + k_2) - k_2^2)[x_1] = 0.$

For $m_1 = m_2 = m$ and $k_1 = k_2 = k_3 = k$, equation (6) reduces to

(7) $((mD^2 + 2k)^2 - k^2)[x_1] = 0.$

This has the auxiliary equation

(8) $(mr^2 + 2k)^2 - k^2 = (mr^2 + k)(mr^2 + 3k) = 0,$

with roots $\pm i\sqrt{k/m}$, $\pm i\sqrt{3k/m}$. Setting $\omega := \sqrt{k/m}$, we get a general solution to (7):

(9) $x_1(t) = C_1 \cos \omega t + C_2 \sin \omega t + C_3 \cos \sqrt{3}\,\omega t + C_4 \sin \sqrt{3}\,\omega t.$

To obtain $x_2(t)$, we solve for $x_2(t)$ in (3) and substitute $x_1(t)$ as given in (9). Upon simplifying, we get

(10) $\qquad x_2(t) = C_1 \cos \omega t + C_2 \sin \omega t - C_3 \cos \sqrt{3}\,\omega t - C_4 \sin \sqrt{3}\,\omega t.$

Using the initial conditions in (5) to determine the constants, we find (after a little algebra)

$$C_1 = \frac{\alpha}{2}, \qquad C_2 = 0, \qquad C_3 = -\frac{\alpha}{2}, \qquad C_4 = 0.$$

Thus the equations of motion for the two masses are

(11)
$$x_1(t) = \frac{\alpha}{2}\,(\cos \omega t - \cos \sqrt{3}\,\omega t),$$

$$x_2(t) = \frac{\alpha}{2}\,(\cos \omega t + \cos \sqrt{3}\,\omega t). \ \blacktriangleleft$$

As in the case of a single spring-mass system (see Section 5.1), the frequencies obtained by solving the auxiliary equation (8),

(12) $\qquad f_1 := \dfrac{\omega}{2\pi} = \dfrac{1}{2\pi}\sqrt{\dfrac{k}{m}} \quad \text{and} \quad f_2 := \dfrac{\sqrt{3}\,\omega}{2\pi} = \dfrac{1}{2\pi}\sqrt{\dfrac{3k}{m}},$

are called the **normal** or **natural frequencies** of the system (ω and $\sqrt{3}\,\omega$ are the **angular frequencies** of the system). It is evident from equation (6) that for most choices of the constants m_1, m_2, k_1, k_2, and k_3, the system would have had two normal frequencies. For more complex systems involving more springs and degrees of freedom, there are many normal frequencies. These frequencies are of great interest to mechanical and civil engineers involved in the stress analysis of such structures as buildings and bridges.

Corresponding to the two normal frequencies for the coupled system discussed in Example 1, there are two normal or natural modes of vibration. These modes correspond to the special cases when the system is vibrating at only one frequency. For example, when $C_1 = C_2 = 0$ in (9) and (10), both x_1 and x_2 are oscillating, with a normal frequency $\sqrt{3}\,\omega/2\pi$. In this case the normal mode is $x_1(t) = -x_2(t)$, so that the masses vibrate as mirror images of each other. When $C_3 = C_4 = 0$, we get the normal frequency $\omega/2\pi$. Here the normal mode is $x_1(t) = x_2(t)$, and the masses move with the same relative positions.

The next example is a mixing problem involving two interconnected tanks. (See Section 3.2 for a discussion of mixing problems with one tank.)

▶ *Example 2*   Two large tanks, each holding 100 gal of liquid, are interconnected by pipes, with the liquid flowing from tank A into tank B at a rate of 3 gal/min and from B into A at a rate of 1 gal/min (see Figure 9.9). The liquid inside each tank is kept well stirred. A brine

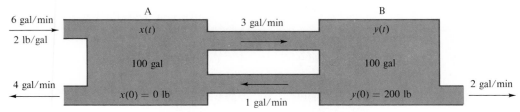

Figure 9.9 Mixing problem for interconnected tanks

solution with a concentration of 2 lb/gal of salt flows into tank A at a rate of 6 gal/min. The (diluted) solution flows out of the system from tank A at 4 gal/min and from tank B at 2 gal/min. If, initially, tank A contains only water and tank B contains 200 lb of salt, determine the amount of salt in each tank at time $t \geq 0$.

Solution We approach this interconnected tank problem as a compartmental analysis problem involving two compartments.

Let $x(t)$ denote the amount of salt in tank A at time t and $y(t)$ the amount of salt in tank B. Since liquid flows into tank A at 7 gal/min and flows out at the same rate, the volume of liquid in tank A remains constant. Similarly, the volume of liquid in tank B remains constant. Let's now determine the rate of change in the amount of salt in tank A. Salt enters tank A from the outside at a rate of $(6)(2) = 12$ lb/min and from tank B at a rate of $y/100$ lb/min. Salt leaves tank A to enter tank B at $3x/100$ lb/min and leaves the system at $4x/100$ lb/min. Using the compartmental analysis model,

$$\frac{dx}{dt} = \text{INPUT RATE} - \text{OUTPUT RATE},$$

the rate of change in the amount of salt in tank A is

(13) $\qquad \dfrac{dx}{dt} = 12 + \dfrac{1}{100} y - \dfrac{3}{100} x - \dfrac{4}{100} x.$

In a similar fashion, we can show that the rate of change in the amount of salt in tank B satisfies

(14) $\qquad \dfrac{dy}{dt} = \dfrac{3}{100} x - \dfrac{3}{100} y.$

We can rewrite (13) and (14) as the system

(15) $\qquad (D + 0.07)[x] - 0.01y = 12,$

(16) $\qquad -0.03x + (D + 0.03)[y] = 0.$

Eliminating x from this system gives

$$(-0.0003 + (D + 0.07)(D + 0.03))[y] = 0.36,$$

which simplifies to

(17) $(D^2 + 0.1D + 0.0018)[y] = 0.36.$

The auxiliary equation for the homogeneous equation associated with (17) is $r^2 + 0.1r + 0.0018 = 0$, which has roots

(18) $r_1 = \dfrac{-5 - \sqrt{7}}{100} \approx -0.0765, \qquad r_2 = \dfrac{-5 + \sqrt{7}}{100} \approx -0.0235.$

To determine a particular solution to (17), we just substitute $y_p = a$ into (17) and solve for the constant a. This gives $y_p = 200$. Therefore, a general solution to (17) is

(19) $y(t) = C_1 e^{r_1 t} + C_2 e^{r_2 t} + 200,$

where r_1 and r_2 are given in (18).

To determine $x(t)$, we solve for x in (16) to obtain

$$x = \tfrac{100}{3}(D + 0.03)[y],$$

and then insert the expression for $y(t)$ given in (19). This yields

(20) $x(t) = \dfrac{-2 - \sqrt{7}}{3} C_1 e^{r_1 t} + \dfrac{-2 + \sqrt{7}}{3} C_2 e^{r_2 t} + 200.$

Finally, to determine the constants C_1 and C_2, we use the initial conditions $x(0) = 0$ and $y(0) = 200$. Substituting x and y given in (19) and (20) into these initial conditions and solving yields $C_1 = -C_2 = 300/\sqrt{7} \approx 113$. Hence the amounts of salt at time t in tanks A and B are, respectively,

(21) $x(t) = -\left(100 + \dfrac{200}{\sqrt{7}}\right) e^{r_1 t} - \left(100 - \dfrac{200}{\sqrt{7}}\right) e^{r_2 t} + 200 \text{ lb},$

(22) $y(t) = \dfrac{300}{\sqrt{7}} e^{r_1 t} - \dfrac{300}{\sqrt{7}} e^{r_2 t} + 200 \text{ lb}.$ ◀

An important observation that we can make here is that since r_1 and r_2 are negative, the amount of salt in each tank approaches 200 lb as $t \to \infty$. Hence the concentration of salt in each tank approaches 2 lb/gal, which is the concentration of salt in the brine entering tank A.

The next example concerns a heating problem for a building with two zones (rooms) that utilizes the analysis of Section 3.3.

▶ *Example 3*   A building consists of two zones A and B (see Figure 9.10). Only zone A is heated by a furnace, which generates 80,000 Btu per hour. The heat capacity of zone A is $\frac{1}{4}$°F per thousand Btu. The time constants for heat transfer are: between zone A and the outside, 4 hr; between the unheated zone B and the outside, 5 hr; and between the two zones, 2 hr. If the outside temperature stays at 0°F, how cold can it get in the unheated zone B?

Solution   To answer the question we use a two-compartment model along with Newton's law of cooling (see Section 3.3).

Let $x(t)$ and $y(t)$ denote the temperatures in zones A and B, respectively. The rate at which the temperature in zone A changes depends on the addition of heat from the furnace and any temperature loss (or gain) from the outside or the other zone. The rate at which the furnace affects temperature is just the number of thousands of Btu per hour times the heat capacity; that is, $(80)(\frac{1}{4})$°F or 20°F per hour.

Recall that Newton's law of cooling states that the rate of change in temperature due to a difference in temperature between two regions is proportional to that difference. Between zone A and the outside this is $k_1(0 - x) = -k_1 x$, and between zones A and B it is $k_2(y - x)$. Hence, for room A, the rate of change in temperature is

(23) $x'(t) = 20 - k_1 x(t) + k_2(y(t) - x(t)).$

Recall from the discussion in Section 3.3 that the time constant associated with Newton's law of cooling is just $1/K$, where K is the proportionality constant for heat transfer. Therefore, $1/k_1 = 4$ and $1/k_2 = 2$. Solving for k_1 and k_2 and substituting into (23) gives

(24) $x'(t) = 20 - \frac{1}{4}x(t) + \frac{1}{2}(y(t) - x(t)).$

A similar argument for zone B yields

(25) $y'(t) = \frac{1}{2}(x(t) - y(t)) - \frac{1}{5}y(t).$

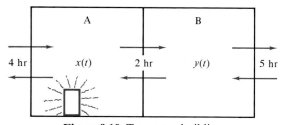

Figure 9.10 Two-zone building with one zone heated

We can rewrite (24) and (25) as the system

(26) $\qquad (D + \frac{3}{4})[x] - \frac{1}{2}y = 20,$

(27) $\qquad -\frac{1}{2}x + (D + \frac{7}{10})[y] = 0.$

Since we are only interested in the temperature in zone B, we eliminate x from the above system and obtain

$$(-\frac{1}{4} + (D + \frac{3}{4})(D + \frac{7}{10}))[y] = 10,$$

which simplifies to

(28) $\qquad (D^2 + \frac{58}{40}D + \frac{11}{40})[y] = 10.$

From standard methods we find that a general solution to (28) is

(29) $\qquad y(t) = c_1 e^{r_1 t} + c_2 e^{r_2 t} + \frac{400}{11},$

where

$$r_1 = \frac{-58 - \sqrt{1604}}{80} \approx -1.23, \qquad r_2 = \frac{-58 + \sqrt{1604}}{80} \approx -0.22.$$

We assume that the initial temperatures of the zones are sufficiently high that the temperature in zone B steadily decreases. (For example, assume $x(0) = y(0) = 70°F$.) Since r_1 and r_2 are negative, the two exponential terms in (29) go to zero as $t \to \infty$, and hence $y(t)$ decreases to $\frac{400}{11} \approx 36.4°F$. Consequently, the temperature in zone B can never get below $36.4°F$. ◀

EXERCISES 9.4

1. Two springs and two masses are attached in a straight line on a horizontal frictionless surface as illustrated in Figure 9.11. The system is set in motion by holding the mass m_1 at its equilibrium position and pulling the mass

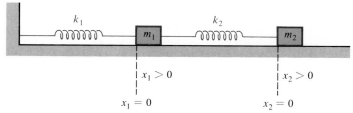

Figure 9.11 Coupled spring-mass system with one end free

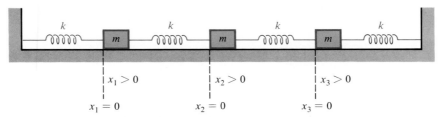

Figure 9.12 Coupled spring-mass system with three degrees of freedom

m_2 to the right of its equilibrium position a distance 1 m and then releasing both masses. Determine the equations of motion for the two masses if $m_1 = m_2 = 1$ kg, $k_1 = 3$ N/m, and $k_2 = 2$ N/m.

2. Determine the equations of motion for the two masses described in Problem 1 if $m_1 = 2$ kg, $m_2 = 1$ kg, $k_1 = 2$ N/m, and $k_2 = 4$ N/m.

3. Four springs with the same spring constant and three equal masses are attached in a straight line on a horizontal frictionless surface as illustrated in Figure 9.12. Determine the normal frequencies for the system and describe the three normal modes of vibration.

4. Two springs, two masses, and a dashpot are attached in a straight line on a horizontal frictionless surface as shown in Figure 9.13. Derive the system of differential equations for the displacements x_1 and x_2.

5. Two springs, two masses, and a dashpot are attached in a straight line on a horizontal frictionless surface as shown in Figure 9.14. The system is set

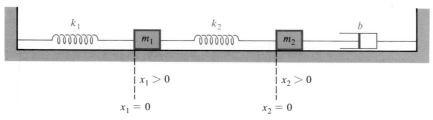

Figure 9.13 Coupled spring-mass system with one end damped

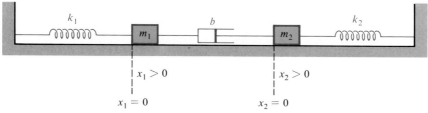

Figure 9.14 Coupled spring-mass system with damping between the masses

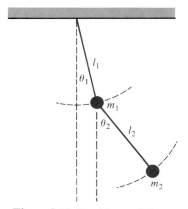

Figure 9.15 Double pendulum

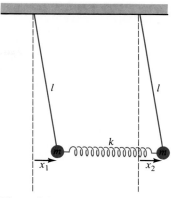

Figure 9.16 Coupled pendulums

in motion by holding the mass m_2 at its equilibrium position and pushing the mass m_1 to the left of its equilibrium position a distance 2 ft and then releasing both masses. Determine the equations of motion for the two masses if $m_1 = m_2 = 1$ slug, $k_1 = k_2 = 1$ lb/ft, and $b = 1$ lb-sec/ft.

6. A double pendulum swinging in a vertical plane under the influence of gravity (see Figure 9.15) satisfies the system

$$(m_1 + m_2)l_1^2 \theta_1'' + m_2 l_1 l_2 \theta_2'' + (m_1 + m_2)l_1 g \theta_1 = 0,$$

$$m_2 l_2^2 \theta_2'' + m_2 l_1 l_2 \theta_1'' + m_2 l_2 g \theta_2 = 0,$$

where θ_1 and θ_2 are small angles. Solve the system when $m_1 = 3$ slugs, $m_2 = 2$ slugs, $l_1 = l_2 = 5$ ft, $\theta_1(0) = \pi/6$, $\theta_2(0) = \theta_1'(0) = \theta_2'(0) = 0$.

7. The motion of a pair of identical pendulums coupled by a spring is modeled by the system

$$mx_1'' = -\frac{mg}{l}x_1 - k(x_1 - x_2),$$

$$mx_2'' = -\frac{mg}{l}x_2 + k(x_1 - x_2),$$

for small displacements (see Figure 9.16). Determine the two normal frequencies for the system.

8. In Example 2, 3 gal/min of liquid flowed from tank A into tank B and 1 gal/min from B into A. Determine the amount of salt in each tank at time $t \geq 0$ if, instead, 5 gal/min flows from A into B and 3 gal/min flows from B into A, with all other data the same.

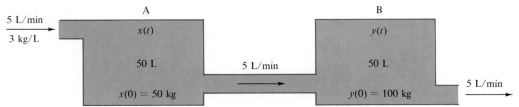

Figure 9.17 Mixing problem for the flow through two tanks

9. Two large tanks, each holding 50 L of liquid, are interconnected by a pipe with liquid flowing from tank A into tank B at a rate of 5 L/min (see Figure 9.17). The liquid inside each tank is kept well stirred. A salt brine with concentration 3 kg/L of salt flows into tank A at a rate of 5 L/min. The solution flows out of the system from tank B at 5 L/min. If, initially, tank A contains 50 kg of salt and tank B contains 100 kg, determine the amount of salt in each tank at time $t \geq 0$.

10. In Example 2, assume now that no solution flows out of the system from tank B, only 1 gal/min flows from A into B, and only 4 gal/min of brine flows into the system at tank A; other data being the same. Determine the amounts of salt in each tank at time $t \geq 0$.

11. In Example 3, if the insulation between zones A and B were better—say if the time constant for heat transfer between zones A and B were 3 hr— then how cold could it get in the unheated zone B?

12. In Example 3, if a small furnace that generates 1000 Btu/hr is placed in zone B, determine the coldest it could get in zone B if zone B has a heat capacity of $2°$F per thousand Btu.

13. A house, for cooling purposes, consists of two zones; the attic area zone A and the living area zone B (see Figure 9.18). The living area is cooled by a 2-ton air conditioning unit that removes 24,000 Btu/hr. The heat capacity of zone B is $\frac{1}{2}°$F per thousand Btu. The time constant for heat transfer between zone A and the outside is 2 hr, between zone B and the outside is 4 hr, and between the two zones is 4 hr. If the outside temperature stays at $100°$F, how warm can it get in the attic zone A?

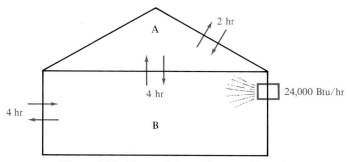

Figure 9.18 Air-conditioned house with attic

9.5 Numerical Methods for Higher Order Equations and Systems

In Section 5.6 we obtained a numerical method for approximating the solution to an initial value problem for a second order differential equation by converting the second order equation to a system of first order equations. A similar approach works for higher order equations. Using the reduction procedure discussed at the end of Section 9.2, a higher order equation can always be converted to a system of first order equations in normal form. We must now extend the numerical technique for solving an initial value problem for a single first order equation to a technique for a system of equations in normal form. To see how these extensions are done, let's recall the classical Runge-Kutta method of order four, which we discussed in Section 3.6.

For the initial value problem

(1) $$x' = f(t, x), \qquad x(t_0) = x_0,$$

the recursive formulas for the fourth order Runge-Kutta method are

$$t_{n+1} = t_n + h, \qquad n = 0, 1, \ldots,$$

(2) $$x_{n+1} = x_n + \frac{1}{6}(k_1 + 2k_2 + 2k_3 + k_4),$$

where h is the step size and

(3)
$$k_1 = hf(t_n, x_n), \qquad k_2 = hf\left(t_n + \frac{h}{2}, x_n + \frac{1}{2}k\right),$$

$$k_3 = hf\left(t_n + \frac{h}{2}, x_n + \frac{1}{2}k_2\right), \qquad k_4 = hf(t_n + h, x_n + k_3).$$

Let $x_1(t), \ldots, x_m(t)$ be the components of the solution to the system of m first order equations

(4)
$$x_1'(t) = f_1(t, x_1, x_2, \ldots, x_m),$$
$$x_2'(t) = f_2(t, x_1, x_2, \ldots, x_m),$$

$$\cdot$$
$$\cdot$$
$$\cdot$$

$$x_m'(t) = f_m(t, x_1, x_2, \ldots, x_m)$$

that satisfy the initial conditions

(5) $x_1(t_0) = a_1, \quad x_2(t_0) = a_2, \quad \dots, \quad x_m(t_0) = a_m.$

Let $x_{n,i}$ denote an approximation to $x_i(t_n)$ for $i = 1, 2, \dots, m$ and $t_n = t_0 + nh$ for $n = 0$, $1, \dots$. The recursive formulas for the fourth order Runge-Kutta method for systems are obtained from the formulas for a single equation given in (2)–(3) by treating the quantities x_n, k_1, k_2, k_3, and k_4 as vectors; that is, $\mathbf{x}_n = (x_{n,1}, \dots, x_{n,m})$, $\mathbf{k}_1 = (k_{1,1}, \dots, k_{1,m})$, $\mathbf{k}_2 = (k_{2,1}, \dots, k_{2,m})$, and so on. With this approach, the equations in (2)–(3) become vector equations. Writing these equations in component form gives the following recursive formulas for the fourth order Runge-Kutta method for systems:

(6) $t_{n-1} := t_n + h, \qquad n = 0, 1, 2, \dots$

(7) $x_{n+1,i} := x_{n,i} + \dfrac{1}{6}(k_{1,i} + 2k_{2,i} + 2k_{3,i} + k_{4,i}),$

$$i = 1, 2, \dots, m,$$

where h is the step size and

$$k_{1,i} := hf_i(t_n, x_{n,1}, x_{n,2}, \dots, x_{n,m}),$$
$$i = 1, 2, \dots, m;$$

$$k_{2,i} := hf_i\left(t_n + \frac{h}{2}, x_{n,1} + \frac{1}{2}k_{1,1}, x_{n,2} + \frac{1}{2}k_{1,2}, \dots, x_{n,m} + \frac{1}{2}k_{1,m}\right),$$
$$i = 1, 2, \dots, m;$$

$$k_{3,i} := hf_i\left(t_n + \frac{h}{2}, x_{n,1} + \frac{1}{2}k_{2,1}, x_{n,2} + \frac{1}{2}k_{2,2}, \dots, x_{n,m} + \frac{1}{2}k_{2,m}\right),$$
$$i = 1, 2, \dots, m;$$

$$k_{4,i} := hf_i(t_n + h, x_{n,1} + k_{3,1}, x_{n,2} + k_{3,2}, \dots, x_{n,m} + k_{3,m}),$$
$$i = 1, 2, \dots, m.$$

It is important to note that each $k_{2,i}$ depends on all the $k_{1,i}$'s and hence all the $k_{1,i}$'s must be computed before any of the $k_{2,i}$'s. Similarly, each $k_{2,i}$ must be computed before the $k_{3,i}$'s and each $k_{3,i}$ before any $k_{4,i}$.

The Runge-Kutta algorithm of Chapter 3 for a single first order equation can be easily modified to handle systems (see page 515). For systems the procedure stops when each component of two successive approximations differs by less than a prescribed tolerance ε, or it stops after a prescribed maximum number of iterations.

FOURTH ORDER RUNGE-KUTTA ALGORITHM FOR SYSTEMS

Purpose   To approximate the solution to the initial value problem

$$x_i' = f_i(t, x_1, \ldots, x_m);$$

$$x_i(t_0) = a_i, \qquad i = 1, 2, \ldots, m$$

at $t = c$.

INPUT $m, t_0, a_1, \ldots, a_m, c$
          ε (tolerance)
          M (maximum number of iterations)

Step 1   Set $z_i = a_i, \qquad i = 1, 2, \ldots, m$

Step 2   For $n = 0$ to M do Steps 3–9

Step 3   Set $h = (c - t_0)2^{-n}, \quad t = t_0, \quad x_1 = a_1, \quad \ldots, \quad x_m = a_m$

Step 4   For $j = 1$ to 2^n do Steps 5 and 6

Step 5   Set $k_{1,i} = hf_i(t, x_1, \ldots, x_m),$
$$i = 1, \ldots, m;$$

$$k_{2,i} = hf_i\left(t + \frac{h}{2}, x_1 + \frac{1}{2}k_{1,1}, \ldots, x_m + \frac{1}{2}k_{1,m}\right),$$

$$i = 1, \ldots, m;$$

$$k_{3,i} = hf_i\left(t + \frac{h}{2}, x_1 + \frac{1}{2}k_{2,1}, \ldots, x_m + \frac{1}{2}k_{2,m}\right),$$

$$i = 1, \ldots, m;$$

$$k_{4,i} = hf_i(t + h, x_1 + k_{3,1}, \ldots, x_m + k_{3,m}),$$

$$i = 1, \ldots, m$$

Step 6   Set $t = t + h$;

$$x_i = x_i + \frac{1}{6}(k_{1,i} + 2k_{2,i} + 2k_{3,i} + k_{4,i}),$$

$$i = 1, \ldots, m$$

Step 7   Print $t, x_1, x_2, \ldots, x_m$

Step 8   If $|z_i - x_i| < \varepsilon$ for $i = 1, \ldots, m$, go to Step 12

Step 9   Set $z_i = x_i, \qquad i = 1, \ldots, m$

Step 10   Print "$x_i(c)$ is approximately,"; x_i (for $i = 1, \ldots, m$);
           "but may not be within the tolerance"; ε

Step 11   Go to Step 13

Step 12   Print "$x_i(c)$ is approximately,"; x_i (for $i = 1, \ldots, m$);
           "with tolerance"; ε

Step 13   Stop

OUTPUT   Approximations of the solution to the initial value problem at $t = c$, using 2^n steps.

AN APPLICATION TO POPULATION DYNAMICS

A mathematical model for the population dynamics of competing species, one a predator with population $x_2(t)$ and the other its prey with population $x_1(t)$, was developed independently in the early 1900s by A. J. Lotka and V. Volterra. They assume that there is plenty of food available for the prey to eat, so the birth rate of the prey should follow the Malthusian or exponential law (see Section 3.2); that is, the birth rate of the prey is Ax_1, where A is a positive constant. The death rate of the prey depends on the number of interactions between the predators and the prey. This is modeled by the expression Bx_1x_2, where B is a positive constant. Therefore, the rate of change in the population of the prey per unit time is $dx_1/dt = Ax_1 - Bx_1x_2$. Assuming that the predators depend entirely on the prey for their food, it is argued that the birth rate of the predators depends on the number of interactions with the prey; that is, the birth rate of predators is Dx_1x_2, where D is a positive constant. The death rate of the predators is assumed to be Cx_2, because without food the population would die off at a rate proportional to the population present. Hence the rate of change in the population of predators per unit time is $dx_2/dt = -Cx_2 + Dx_1x_2$. Combining these two equations, we obtain the Volterra-Lotka system for the population dynamics of two competing species:

(8)
$$x_1' = Ax_1 - Bx_1x_2,$$
$$x_2' = -Cx_2 + Dx_1x_2.$$

Such systems are in general not explicitly solvable. In the following example, we obtain an approximate solution for such a system.

▶ **Example 1** Use the fourth order Runge-Kutta algorithm for systems to approximate the solution of the initial value problem

(9)
$$x_1' = 2x_1 - 2x_1x_2; \qquad x_1(0) = 1,$$
$$x_2' = -x_2 + x_1x_2; \qquad x_2(0) = 3,$$

at $t = 1$ with a tolerance of 0.0001.

Solution Here $f_1(t, x_1, x_2) = 2x_1 - 2x_1x_2$ and $f_2(t, x_1, x_2) = x_1x_2 - x_2$. With the starting values $t_0 = 0$, $x_{0,1} = 1$, and $x_{0,2} = 3$, we proceed with the algorithm to compute $x_1(1; 1)$ and $x_2(1; 1)$, the approximations to $x_1(1)$, $x_2(1)$ using $h = 1$. We find

$$k_{1,1} = hf_1(t_0, x_{0,1}, x_{0,2}) = h(2x_{0,1} - 2x_{0,1}x_{0,2}) = 2(1) - 2(1)(3) = -4,$$
$$k_{1,2} = hf_2(t_0, x_{0,1}, x_{0,2}) = h(x_{0,1}x_{0,2} - x_{0,2}) = (1)(3) - 3 = 0,$$

$$k_{2,1} = hf_1\left(t_0 + \frac{h}{2}, x_{0,1} + \frac{1}{2}k_{1,1}, x_{0,2} + \frac{1}{2}k_{1,2}\right)$$

$$= h\left[2\left(x_{0,1} + \frac{1}{2}k_{1,1}\right) - 2\left(x_{0,1} + \frac{1}{2}k_{1,1}\right)\left(x_{0,2} + \frac{1}{2}k_{1,2}\right)\right]$$

$$= 2\left(1 + \frac{1}{2}(-4)\right) - 2\left(1 + \frac{1}{2}(-4)\right)\left(3 + \frac{1}{2}(0)\right)$$

$$= -2 + 2(3) = 4.$$

$$k_{2,2} = hf_2\left(t_0 + \frac{h}{2}, x_{0,1} + \frac{1}{2}k_{1,1}, x_{0,2} + \frac{1}{2}k_{1,2}\right)$$

$$= h\left[\left(x_{0,1} + \frac{1}{2}k_{1,1}\right)\left(x_{0,2} + \frac{1}{2}k_{1,2}\right) - \left(x_{0,2} + \frac{1}{2}k_{1,2}\right)\right]$$

$$= \left[1 + \frac{1}{2}(-4)\right]\left[3 + \frac{1}{2}(0)\right] - \left[3 + \frac{1}{2}(0)\right]$$

$$= (-1)(3) - 3 = -6.$$

Similarly, we find

$$k_{3,1} = hf_1\left(t_0 + \frac{h}{2}, x_{0,1} + \frac{1}{2}k_{2,1}, x_{0,2} + \frac{1}{2}k_{2,2}\right) = 6,$$

$$k_{3,2} = hf_2\left(t_0 + \frac{h}{2}, x_{0,1} + \frac{1}{2}k_{2,1}, x_{0,2} + \frac{1}{2}k_{2,2}\right) = 0,$$

$$k_{4,1} = hf_1(t_0 + h, x_{0,1} + k_{3,1}, x_{0,2} + k_{3,2}) = -28,$$

$$k_{4,2} = hf_2(t_0 + h, x_{0,1} + k_{3,1}, x_{0,2} + k_{3,2}) = 18.$$

Hence from (7) we compute

$$x_{1,1} = x_{0,1} + \frac{1}{6}(k_{1,1} + 2k_{2,1} + 2k_{3,1} + k_{4,1})$$

$$= 1 + \frac{1}{6}[-4 + 8 + 12 - 28] = -1,$$

$$x_{1,2} = x_{0,2} + \frac{1}{6}(k_{1,2} + 2k_{2,2} + 2k_{3,2} + k_{4,2})$$

$$= 3 + \frac{1}{6}(0 - 12 + 0 + 18) = 4.$$

Repeating the algorithm with $h = \frac{1}{2}$, we obtain the approximations $x_1(1; 2^{-1})$ and $x_2(1; 2^{-1})$ for $x_1(1)$ and $x_2(1)$. In Table 9.1 we list the approximations $x_1(1; 2^{-n})$ and

n	h	$x_1(1; 2^{-n})$	$x_2(1; 2^{-n})$
	TABLE 9.1 APPROXIMATIONS OF THE SOLUTION TO SYSTEM (9) IN EXAMPLE 1		
0	1.0	−1.0	4.0
1	0.5	0.14662	1.47356
2	0.25	0.07885	1.46469
3	0.125	0.07741	1.46446
4	0.0625	0.07735	1.46445

$x_2(1; 2^{-n})$ for $x_1(1)$ and $x_2(1)$, using step size $h = 2^{-n}$ for $n = 0, 1, 2, 3,$ and 4. We stopped at $n = 4$ since both

$$|x_1(1; 2^{-3}) - x_1(1; 2^{-4})| = 0.00006 < 0.0001$$

and

$$|x_2(1; 2^{-3}) - x_2(1; 2^{-4})| = 0.00001 < 0.0001.$$

Hence $x_1(1) \approx 0.07735$ and $x_2(1) \approx 1.46445$, with tolerance 0.0001. ◄

To get a better feel for the solution to system (9), we have graphed in Figure 9.19 an approximation of the solution, using linear interpolation to connect the points. This approximation was obtained using step size $h = 0.125$ and the fourth order Runge-Kutta method for systems. From the graph it appears that the components x_1 and x_2 are periodic in the variable t. In the next section we study the qualitative behavior of a system of two first order equations using a technique called **phase plane analysis.** This technique is also used in Project C to study general Volterra-Lotka equations and, in particular, to show that these equations have periodic solutions.

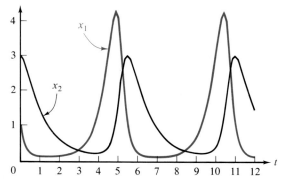

Figure 9.19 Graphs of the components of an approximate solution to the Volterra-Lotka system (9)

EXERCISES 9.5

The reader will find it helpful to have a microcomputer available or access to a mainframe.

In Problems 1 through 8 use fourth order Runge-Kutta for systems with $h = 0.25$ to find an approximation for the solution to the given initial value problem at the times $t = 0.25$, $t = 0.5$, $t = 0.75$, and $t = 1.0$.

1. $x' = 3x - y$, $x(0) = 0$,
   $y' = x - 2y$, $y(0) = 2$.

2. $x' = -x^2 + y^2 + 1$, $x(0) = 0$,
   $y' = -y$, $y(0) = 1$.

3. $x' = \cos(x + y)$, $x(0) = 1$,
   $y' = (x^2 + t)^{-1} + t$, $y(0) = 0.5$.

4. $x' = e^{-x^2} + y$, $x(0) = 1$.
   $y' = x^2 - y + t$, $y(0) = 1$.

5. $y''' - ty'' + ty' - 3y = 0$; $y(0) = 1$, $y'(0) = -1$, $y''(0) = 0$.

6. $y^{(4)} + 3y''' - 2y' + (\sin t)y = 0$; $y(0) = 0$, $y'(0) = 1$, $y''(0) = 0$, $y'''(0) = 0$.

7. $y^{(4)} - t^2 y' + e^t y = t + 1$; $y(0) = -1$, $y'(0) = 1$, $y''(0) = 1$, $y'''(0) = -1$.

8. $y''' - \sin y = t$; $y(0) = 1$, $y'(0) = 0$, $y''(0) = 0$.

9. Using fourth order Runge-Kutta for systems with $h = 0.125$, approximate the solution to the initial value problem

$$x' = 2x - y,   \quad x(0) = 0,$$
$$y' = 3x + 6y,   \quad y(0) = -2$$

at $t = 1$. Compare this approximation to the actual solution
$x(t) = e^{5t} - e^{3t}$, $y(t) = e^{3t} - 3e^{5t}$.

10. Using the Runge-Kutta algorithm for systems with the stopping procedure based on the relative error and a tolerance of $\varepsilon = 0.02$, approximate the solution to the initial value problem

$$x' = 6x - 3y,   \quad x(0) = -1,$$
$$y' = 2x + y,   \quad y(0) = 0$$

at $t = 1$.

11. Using the Runge-Kutta algorithm for systems with the stopping procedure based on the absolute error and a tolerance of $\varepsilon = 0.001$, approximate the solution to the initial value problem

$$x' = 3x - 4y,   \quad x(0) = 1,$$
$$y' = 2x - 3y,   \quad y(0) = 1$$

at $t = 1$.

12. Using the Runge-Kutta algorithm for systems with the stopping procedure based on the absolute error and a tolerance of $\varepsilon = 0.0001$, approximate the solution to the initial value problem

$$y''' - y'' - y = t^2; \qquad y(0) = 0, \qquad y'(0) = 1, \qquad y''(0) = 0,$$

at $t = 1$.

13. Using the Runge-Kutta algorithm for systems with the stopping procedure based on the relative error and a tolerance of $\varepsilon = 0.01$, approximate the solution to the initial value problem

$$y''' + y'' + y^2 = t; \qquad y(0) = 1, \qquad y'(0) = 0, \qquad y''(0) = 1,$$

at $t = 1$.

14. In Section 3.5 we discussed the improved Euler's method for approximating the solution to a first order equation. Extend the improved Euler's method to systems and give the recursive formulas in component form.

15. Use fourth order Runge-Kutta for systems with $h = 0.1$ to approximate the solution to the initial value problem

$$x' = yz, \qquad x(0) = 0,$$

$$y' = -xz, \qquad y(0) = 1,$$

$$z' = -xy/2, \qquad z(0) = 1$$

at $t = 1$.

16. Combat Model. A mathematical model for conventional versus guerrilla combat is given by the system

$$x_1' = -(0.1)x_1 x_2, \qquad x_1(0) = 10,$$

$$x_2' = -x_1, \qquad x_2(0) = 15,$$

where x_1 and x_2 are the strengths of guerrilla and conventional troops, respectively, and 0.1 and 1 are the *combat effectiveness coefficients*. Who will win the conflict, the conventional troops or the guerrillas? [Hint: Use the Runge-Kutta method for systems with $h = 0.1$ to approximate the solutions.]

17. Generalized Blasius Equation. H. Blasius, in his study of laminar flow of a fluid, encountered an equation of the form

$$y''' + yy'' = (y')^2 - 1.$$

Use the Runge-Kutta method for systems with $h = 0.1$ to approximate the solution that satisfies the initial conditions $y(0) = 0$, $y'(0) = 0$, and $y''(0) = 1.32824$. Sketch this solution on the interval $[0, 2]$.

18. Lunar Orbit. The motion of a moon moving in a planar orbit about a planet is governed by the equations

$$x'' = -G\frac{mx}{r^3}, \qquad y'' = -G\frac{my}{r^3},$$

where $r := (x^2 + y^2)^{1/2}$, G is the gravitational constant, and m is the mass of the moon. Assume that $Gm = 1$. When $x(0) = 1$, $x'(0) = y(0) = 0$, and $y'(0) = 1$, the motion is a circular orbit of radius 1 and period 2π.

(a) Setting $x_1 = x$, $x_2 = x'$, $x_3 = y$, $x_4 = y'$, express the governing equations as a first order system in normal form.

(b) Using $h = 2\pi/100 \approx 0.0628318$, compute one orbit of this moon (i.e., let $n = 100$). Do your approximations agree with the fact that the orbit is a circle of radius 1?

19. Predator-Prey Model. The Volterra-Lotka predator-prey model predicts some rather interesting behavior that is evident in certain biological systems. For example, if you fix the initial population of prey but increase the initial population of predators, then the population cycle for the prey becomes more severe in the sense that there is a long period of time with a reduced population of prey followed by a short period when the population of prey is very large. To demonstrate this behavior, use the fourth order Runge-Kutta method for systems with $h = 0.5$ to approximate the populations of prey x and of predators y over the period $[0, 5]$ that satisfy the Volterra-Lotka system

$$x' = x(3 - y),$$

$$y' = y(x - 3)$$

under each of the following initial conditions:

(a) $x(0) = 2$, $y(0) = 4$. **(b)** $x(0) = 2$, $y(0) = 5$. **(c)** $x(0) = 2$, $y(0) = 7$.

20. Spring Pendulum. Let a mass be attached to one end of a spring with spring constant k and the other end attached to the ceiling. Let l_0 be the natural length of the spring and let $l(t)$ be its length at time t. If $\theta(t)$ is the angle between the pendulum and the vertical, then the motion of the spring pendulum is governed by the system

$$l''(t) - l(t)\theta'(t) - g \cos \theta(t) + \frac{k}{m}(l - l_0) = 0,$$

$$l^2(t)\theta''(t) + 2l(t)l'(t)\theta'(t) + gl(t) \sin \theta(t) = 0.$$

Assume $g = 1$, $k = m = 1$, and $l_0 = 4$. When the system is at rest, $l = l_0 + mg/k = 5$.

(a) Describe the motion of the pendulum when $l(0) = 5.5$, $l'(0) = 0$, $\theta(0) = 0$, and $\theta'(0) = 0$. [Hint: Use fourth order Runge-Kutta for systems with $h = 0.1$ to approximate the solution on the interval $[0, 10]$.]

(b) When the pendulum is both stretched and given an angular displacement, the motion of the pendulum is more complicated. Using Runge-Kutta for systems with $h = 0.1$ to approximate the solution, sketch the graph of the length l and the angular displacement θ on the interval $[0, 10]$ if $l(0) = 5.5$, $l'(0) = 0$, $\theta(0) = 0.5$, and $\theta'(0) = 0$.

9.6 *Nonlinear Autonomous Systems*

In this section we study systems of two first order equations of the form

(1)

$$\frac{dx}{dt} = f(x, y),$$

$$\frac{dy}{dt} = g(x, y),$$

where f and g are real-valued functions that do not depend explicitly on t. Such systems are called **autonomous.** An example of an autonomous system is the Volterra-Lotka system

$$\frac{dx}{dt} = Ax - Bxy,$$

$$\frac{dy}{dt} = -Cy + Dxy$$

discussed in Section 9.5. As with all autonomous systems, the parameters involved (here, A, B, C, and D) are *time independent.*

A **solution** to (1) on an interval I is a pair of functions $x(t)$, $y(t)$ that satisfy (1) for all t in I. The set of points $\{(x(t), y(t)); t \in I\}$ in the xy-plane is called a **trajectory,**[†] and the xy-plane is referred to as the **phase plane.**

If the pair $x(t)$, $y(t)$ is a solution to (1), then so is the pair $x(t + c)$, $y(t + c)$, for any constant c, because (thinking of t as time) the system (1) is not time dependent. To be more precise, let $X(t) := x(t + c)$ and $Y(t) := y(t + c)$. Then, by the chain rule,

$$\frac{dX}{dt}(t) = \frac{dx}{dt}(t + c) = f(x(t + c), y(t + c)) = f(X(t), Y(t)),$$

$$\frac{dY}{dt}(t) = \frac{dy}{dt}(t + c) = g(x(t + c), y(t + c)) = g(X(t), Y(t)),$$

which proves that $X(t)$, $Y(t)$ is also a solution to (1).

For nonlinear autonomous systems, obtaining explicit solutions $x(t)$, $y(t)$ may be an extraordinarily difficult task. However, in certain cases, it is possible to obtain the trajectories for the system that give us valuable qualitative information about the solution. Here we give a brief introduction to the study of the qualitative behavior of autonomous systems.[††]

[†] Trajectories are also called **solution curves, paths,** or **orbits.**

[††] *Historical Footnote:* The study of the qualitative behavior of autonomous systems was begun by the great French mathematician **J. Henri Poincaré** (1854–1912) in 1881 in his work in celestial mechanics. His work was continued by **I. Bendixson** in 1901 in his study of closed trajectories.

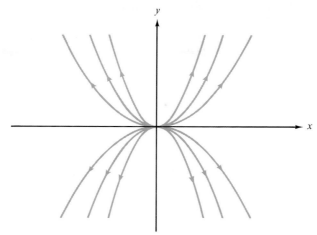

Figure 9.20 Phase plane diagram
for $x' = x$, $y' = 2y$

A more thorough discussion can be found in *Ordinary Differential Equations,* Third Edition, by G. Birkhoff and G. C. Rota, John Wiley and Sons, Inc., New York, 1978, Chapter 5.

To illustrate the idea of trajectories, we start with a simple example of two uncoupled linear equations.

▶ *Example 1*   Find solutions to the autonomous system

(2)
$$\frac{dx}{dt} = x, \qquad \frac{dy}{dt} = 2y$$

and sketch their trajectories.

Solution   Solving separately each equation in (2), we quickly find that $x(t) = c_1 e^t$, $y(t) = c_2 e^{2t}$ are solutions. Expressing y in terms of x, we obtain the trajectories

(3) $y = c_2(e^t)^2 = c_2(x/c_1)^2 = kx^2,$

where $k = c_2/c_1^2$ is an arbitrary constant. These parabolic trajectories are sketched in the phase plane diagram, Figure 9.20.

The arrows on the trajectories in Figure 9.20 indicate the direction or **flow** of a particle as it travels along the trajectory. In equation (3) we see that as x moves away from zero, y increases if k is positive (this is the case for the trajectories above the x-axis) and decreases if k is negative (the trajectories below the x-axis). Hence, the flow is away from the origin. ◀

In the preceding example, the origin is the trajectory of the constant solution $x \equiv 0$, $y \equiv 0$. Such points and solutions play an important role in the study of autonomous systems.

CRITICAL POINTS AND EQUILIBRIUM SOLUTIONS

Definition 1. A point (x_0, y_0), where $f(x_0, y_0) = 0$ and $g(x_0, y_0) = 0$, is called a **critical point** of the system $dx/dt = f(x, y)$, $dy/dt = g(x, y)$, and the corresponding constant solution $x(t) \equiv x_0$, $y(t) \equiv y_0$ is called an **equilibrium solution.** The set of all critical points is called the **critical point set.**

▶ **Example 2** Find the critical points and corresponding equilibrium solutions of

(4)
$$\frac{dx}{dt} = -y(y - 2),$$

$$\frac{dy}{dt} = (x - 2)(y - 2).$$

Solution To find the critical points we solve the system

$$-y(y - 2) = 0, \qquad (x - 2)(y - 2) = 0.$$

One family of solutions to this system is given by $y = 2$ with x arbitrary; that is, the line $y = 2$. If $y \neq 2$, then the system simplifies to $-y = 0$, and $x - 2 = 0$, which has the solution $x = 2$, $y = 0$. Hence the critical point set consists of the isolated point $(2, 0)$ and the horizontal line $y = 2$. The corresponding equilibrium solutions are $x(t) \equiv 2$, $y(t) \equiv 0$, and the family $x(t) \equiv c$, $y(t) \equiv 2$, where c is an arbitrary constant. ◀

Although we succeeded in finding the equilibrium solutions to the nonlinear system (4) of Example 2, determining other explicit solutions to this system is beyond our present capabilities. However, we can determine the trajectories for the system using techniques for solving first order equations discussed in Chapter 2.

▶ **Example 3** Determine the trajectories of system (4).

Solution Unlike Example 1, we are not able to determine the trajectories by first computing the solutions. But we do know that when $dx/dt \neq 0$, the chain rule yields

(5)
$$\frac{dy}{dx} = \frac{dy/dt}{dx/dt} = \frac{(x - 2)(y - 2)}{-y(y - 2)} = -\frac{x - 2}{y}.$$

In (5) we have a first order differential equation whose solutions in x and y contain the trajectories of system (4). Solving (5) by separation of variables, we obtain

$$\frac{y^2}{2} = \int y\,dy = -\int (x-2)\,dx = -\frac{(x-2)^2}{2} + c,$$

which is just the family of concentric circles

(6) $y^2 + (x-2)^2 = k,$

with centers located at $(2, 0)$. Thus each trajectory of (4) lies on a circle given in (6). In Figure 9.21 we have sketched these circles and the critical points of (4).

Now that we know that the trajectories lie on the circles in (6), what remains is to analyze the flow along each trajectory. For this purpose we use the given equation $dx/dt = -y(y-2)$. If $y > 2$, we see that $dx/dt < 0$. Hence x is decreasing when $y > 2$. This means that the flow is from right to left along the arc of a circle that lies above the line $y = 2$. For $0 < y < 2$, we have $dx/dt > 0$, and so in this region the flow is from left to right. Furthermore, for $y < 0$, we have $dx/dt < 0$, and again the flow is from right to left.

We now observe in Figure 9.21 that there are four types of trajectories associated with system (4): (a) those that begin above the line $y = 2$ and follow the arc of a circle counter-clockwise back to that line; (b) those that begin below the line $y = 2$ and follow the arc of a circle clockwise back to that line; (c) those that continually move clockwise around a circle centered at $(2, 0)$ with radius less than 2 (i.e., do not intersect the line $y = 2$); and finally, (d) the critical points $(2, 0)$ and $y = 2$, x arbitrary. ◄

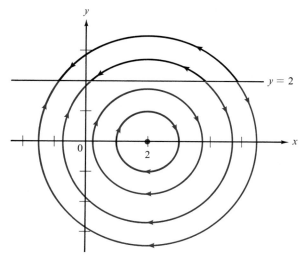

Figure 9.21 Phase plane diagram for $x' = -y(y-2)$, $y' = (x-2)(y-2)$

The curves given in equation (6) are called the **integral curves** of (4). They are the level curves of the function $V(x, y) := (x - 2)^2 + y^2$, which is called a **first integral of** (4).[†] As we observed earlier, a trajectory must lie on an integral curve.

In Example 3 we observed that the nonperiodic trajectories (a) and (b) begin and end at a critical point, namely at a point on the line $y = 2$. This fact is a consequence of the following theorem:

LIMIT POINTS ARE CRITICAL POINTS

Theorem 1. Let the pair $x(t)$, $y(t)$ be a solution on $[0, \infty)$ to the autonomous system $dx/dt = f(x, y)$, $dy/dt = g(x, y)$, where f and g are continuous in the plane. If the limits

$$x_\omega := \lim_{t \to \infty} x(t) \quad \text{and} \quad y_\omega := \lim_{t \to \infty} y(t)$$

exist and are finite, then the limit point (x_ω, y_ω) is a critical point for the system.

Proof To show that (x_ω, y_ω) is a critical point, we must prove that $f(x_\omega, y_\omega) = g(x_\omega, y_\omega) = 0$. First observe that, by the continuity of f,

$$\lim_{t \to \infty} x'(t) = \lim_{t \to \infty} f(x(t), y(t)) = f(x_\omega, y_\omega).$$

Let's suppose to the contrary that $f(x_\omega, y_\omega) \neq 0$; say, $w := f(x_\omega, y_\omega) > 0$ (a similar argument will handle the case when $w < 0$). For any $\varepsilon > 0$, we can choose N sufficiently large so that

$$\left| f(x_\omega, y_\omega) - f(x(t), y(t)) \right| < \varepsilon \quad \text{for all } t \geq N.$$

Taking $\varepsilon = w/2$, we have $|w - f(x(t), y(t))| < w/2$ and so $x'(t) = f(x(t), y(t)) > w/2$. But if $x'(t) > w/2$ for all $t \geq N$, then $x(t)$ must lie above some line with positive slope $w/2$. Hence $\lim_{t \to \infty} x(t) = +\infty$, which contradicts the assumption that this limit is finite. Therefore, $f(x_\omega, y_\omega) = 0$. A similar argument also shows that $g(x_\omega, y_\omega) = 0$. Hence the limit point (x_ω, y_ω) is a critical point. ∎

The proof of Theorem 1 can be easily modified to show that a limit point (x_α, y_α), where

$$x_\alpha := \lim_{t \to -\infty} x(t), \qquad y_\alpha := \lim_{t \to -\infty} y(t),$$

[†] In classical mechanics the first integral V is associated with the total energy of the system, and hence a level curve is a curve along which the energy is constant. In fluid mechanics V is called the **stream function.**

is also a critical point. As a consequence of Theorem 1, we observe that *the only points in the phase plane where a nonperiodic trajectory can begin* $(t \to -\infty)$ *or end* $(t \to +\infty)$ *are the critical points.* For example, in Figure 9.21, the trajectories that lie above the line $y = 2$ begin at a critical point on the line $y = 2$ and end at a critical point on the line.

A sketch of the critical point set for a system, along with representative integral curves and their trajectories with arrows indicating the flow, is called a **phase plane diagram.** The use of these diagrams to obtain qualitative information about the solutions of the system is referred to as **phase plane analysis.** In many cases the integral curves must be obtained using numerical techniques (see Project D).

PHASE PLANE ANALYSIS

To sketch a phase plane diagram for the system $dx/dt = f(x, y)$, $dy/dt = g(x, y)$:

(a) Find the critical point set consisting of the solutions to the system $f(x, y) = 0$, $g(x, y) = 0$. Sketch this set in the xy-plane.

(b) Solve the first order equation $dy/dx = g(x, y)/f(x, y)$. Use the solution to sketch some representative integral curves for the system.

(c) Determine the direction of the flow along the integral curves using either of the equations $dx/dt = f(x, y)$ or $dy/dt = g(x, y)$. This gives the trajectories.

It can be shown that system (1) has a unique solution satisfying $x(t_0) = x_0$, $y(t_0) = y_0$, provided that f and g have continuous partial derivatives in the xy-plane. This is helpful in sketching the trajectories of a system because it means that two trajectories cannot intersect (in finite time).

Autonomous systems arise in the study of the motion of a particle governed by Newton's second law, $md^2x/dt^2 = F(x, dx/dt)$, when the forcing function F does not depend explicitly on t.

▶ **Example 4**   A mass is attached to a spring and encounters friction as it moves along a surface (see Figure 9.22 on page 528). The motion is governed by

(7) $$m \frac{d^2x}{dt^2} + \mu \, \mathrm{sign}\left(\frac{dx}{dt}\right) + kx = 0,$$

where m is the mass, μ a positive constant depending on the mass of the object and the coefficient of friction between the mass and the surface, k is the spring constant, and $\mathrm{sign}(x')$ is the function that is $+1$ when $x' > 0$ and -1 when $x' < 0$. Describe the motion of the mass for the case where $m = \mu = k = 1$.

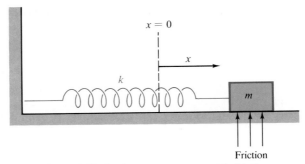

x = 0

x

k

m

Friction

Figure 9.22 Spring-mass system with friction

Solution   To study the motion governed by (7), we convert equation (7) into a system by introducing the velocity $v := x'$ as the second dependent variable. [†] Then we get

(8)
$$x' = v,$$
$$v' = x'' = -x \mp 1, \qquad x' \gtrless 0,$$

where we take $\mp$ to be *minus* for $x' > 0$ and plus for $x' < 0$.

The critical points of (8) in the xv-plane are $(1, 0)$, $(-1, 0)$. (Technically, we have not defined the system for $v = x' = 0$ since sign(x') is defined only for $x' \neq 0$. We shall return to this problem later.)

To find the integral curves of (8), we solve

(9)
$$\frac{dv}{dx} = \frac{dv/dt}{dx/dt} = \frac{-x \mp 1}{v}, \qquad v \gtrless 0.$$

Separating variables and integrating gives

$$v^2 + (x \pm 1)^2 = c, \qquad v \gtrless 0.$$

Therefore, the integral curves in the xv-plane are concentric semicircles in the upper half plane with centers are $(-1, 0)$ and concentric semicircles in the lower half plane with centers at $(1, 0)$ (see Figure 9.23). Since $x' = v$, the flow is left to right for $v > 0$ and right to left for $v < 0$.

To understand the motion of the mass, let's consider the case when the mass is released (with zero velocity) at $x = 7.5$. In the phase plane the mass begins at the point $(7.5, 0)$ and

---

†*Historical Footnote:* The resulting xv-plane is referred to as the **Poincaré phase plane** in honor of **J. Henri Poincaré** (1854–1912), who did fundamental work in celestial mechanics, differential equations, and topology.

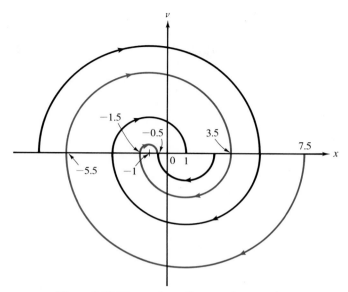

Figure 9.23 Phase plane diagram for a spring-mass system with friction

follows the flow along the semicircular trajectory in the lower half plane until it reaches the point $(-5.5, 0)$ (see the colored curve in Figure 9.23). (This corresponds to the mass moving from $x = 7.5$ to $x = -5.5$.) The flow now takes the mass from $(-5.5, 0)$ along the semicircular trajectory in the upper half plane to the point $(3.5, 0)$. (The mass has moved from $x = -5.5$ to $x = 3.5$.) The mass now follows the trajectory in the lower half plane to $(-1.5, 0)$ and then the trajectory in the upper half plane to $(-0.5, 0)$. (The mass is now at $x = -0.5$.) At the point $(-0.5, 0)$ we have a problem! The trajectory in the lower half plane that touches the point $(-0.5, 0)$ flows *into* that point. In other words, $(-0.5, 0)$ sits at the endpoint of the two trajectories connecting it.[†] Hence the mass is trapped or stopped at $x = -0.5$. To understand what is happening, let's look at the physical situation. When $x = -0.5$, the force on the mass due to the spring is just $kx = -0.5$. But friction can apply a force up to 1. Therefore, friction cancels out the force due to the spring and prevents the mass from moving away from the spot $x = -0.5$. Consequently, the motion is stopped at $x = -0.5$. ◄

For other applications of phase plane analysis, we refer the reader to *Differential Equations and Their Applications*, by Martin Braun, Springer-Verlag, New York, 1975, Chapter 4 and *Linear and Nonlinear Differential Equations*, by I. D. Huntley and R. M. Johnson, Ellis Horwood Ltd., Chichester, England, 1983, Chapter 7.

[†] Note that these trajectories do not end in a critical point. This does not violate Theorem 1 because system (8) fails to satisfy the continuity assumptions in that theorem.

EXERCISES 9.6 _____

In Problems 1 and 2 verify that the pair $x(t)$, $y(t)$, is a solution to the given system. Find the trajectory of the given solution and sketch its graph in the phase plane.

1. $\dfrac{dx}{dt} = 3y^3$, $\quad \dfrac{dy}{dt} = y$; $\quad x(t) = e^{3t}$, $\quad y(t) = e^t$.

2. $\dfrac{dx}{dt} = 1$, $\quad \dfrac{dy}{dt} = 3x^2$; $\quad x(t) = t + 1$, $\quad y(t) = t^3 + 3t^2 + 3t$.

In Problems 3 through 8 find the critical point set for the given system.

3. $\dfrac{dx}{dt} = x - y$,

   $\dfrac{dy}{dt} = x^2 + y^2 - 1$.

4. $\dfrac{dx}{dt} = y - 1$,

   $\dfrac{dy}{dt} = x + y + 5$.

5. $\dfrac{dx}{dt} = x^2 - 2xy$,

   $\dfrac{dy}{dt} = 3xy - y^2$.

6. $\dfrac{dx}{dt} = 3x^2 - xy$,

   $\dfrac{dy}{dt} = 4xy - 3y^2$.

7. $\dfrac{dx}{dt} = y^2 - 3y + 2$,

   $\dfrac{dy}{dt} = (x - 1)(y - 2)$.

8. $\dfrac{dx}{dt} = (x + 1)(y - 2)$,

   $\dfrac{dy}{dt} = x^2 - x - 2$.

In Problems 9 through 14 determine the integral curves for the given system.

9. $\dfrac{dx}{dt} = y - 1$,

   $\dfrac{dy}{dt} = e^{x+y}$.

10. $\dfrac{dx}{dt} = x^2$,

    $\dfrac{dy}{dt} = x^2 + y^2 + xy$.

11. $\dfrac{dx}{dt} = \dfrac{x^2}{y}$,

    $\dfrac{dy}{dt} = x - y$.

12. $\dfrac{dx}{dt} = x^2 - 2y^{-3}$,

    $\dfrac{dy}{dt} = 3x^2 - 2xy$.

13. $\dfrac{dx}{dt} = 2y - x$,

    $\dfrac{dy}{dt} = e^x + y$.

14. $\dfrac{dx}{dt} = x + y + 6$,

    $\dfrac{dy}{dt} = 3x - y - 6$.

In Problems 15 through 20 determine the integral curves and sketch a phase plane diagram for the given system.

15. $\dfrac{dx}{dt} = 2y$,

    $\dfrac{dy}{dt} = 2x$.

16. $\dfrac{dx}{dt} = -8y$,

    $\dfrac{dy}{dt} = 18x$.

17. $\dfrac{dx}{dt} = (y - x)(y - 1)$,

    $\dfrac{dy}{dt} = (x - y)(x - 1)$.

18. $\dfrac{dx}{dt} = (x - 4)(1 - y)$,

    $\dfrac{dy}{dt} = (x + 1)(x - 4)$.

19. $\dfrac{dx}{dt} = \dfrac{3}{y}$,

    $\dfrac{dy}{dt} = \dfrac{2}{x}$.

20. $\dfrac{dx}{dt} = xy^2 - x$,

    $\dfrac{dy}{dt} = 2y^3 - 4y$.

In Problems 21 through 24 determine the integral curves and sketch an xv-phase plane diagram for the given equation.

21. $\dfrac{d^2x}{dt^2} - x = 0.$

22. $\dfrac{d^2x}{dt^2} + x = 0.$

23. $\dfrac{d^2x}{dt^2} + x + x^5 = 0.$

24. $\dfrac{d^2x}{dt^2} + x^3 = 0.$

25. A model for the spread of a disease through a population or an **epidemic model,** is given by the system

$$\frac{dS}{dt} = -aSI,$$

$$\frac{dI}{dt} = aSI - bI,$$

where a and b are positive constants. Here $S(t)$ represents the susceptible population and $I(t)$ the infected population. Give a phase plane analysis for this system. (Only the first quadrant is of any interest; why?) Explain why an epidemic occurs (the number of infected persons increases) when $S(0) > b/a$.

26. The motion of a simple pendulum is governed by the equation

$$\frac{d^2\theta}{dt^2} + \sin\theta = 0,$$

where θ represents the angular displacement from the vertical of the pendulum. Give a phase plane analysis for the equation and interpret the results physically.

27. The motion of a spring-mass system in which the spring is "hard" and does not satisfy Hooke's law is governed by the equation

$$\frac{d^2x}{dt^2} + x + x^3 = 0,$$

where x represents the displacement from equilibrium. Give a phase plane analysis for the equation and interpret the results physically.

28. The motion of an object falling through the air is governed by the equation

$$\frac{d^2x}{dt^2} = g - \frac{g}{V^2}\frac{dx}{dt}\left|\frac{dx}{dt}\right|,$$

where x is the distance fallen and V is a constant called the terminal velocity. Give a phase plane analysis for the equation and interpret the results physically.

Chapter Summary

Systems of differential equations arise in a variety of areas, such as electric networks, coupled spring-mass systems, multiple compartmental analysis models, and predator-prey models. There are two elementary methods for solving a **linear system with constant coefficients.** The first is the **elimination method.** For this method, we begin by expressing the system in operator form. For example, a linear system of two equations and two unknowns has the form

(1) $\qquad L_1[x] + L_2[y] = f_1,$

(2) $\qquad L_3[x] + L_4[y] = f_2.$

If we formally eliminate y from the above system, we obtain the single equation

(3) $\qquad (L_1 L_4 - L_2 L_3)[x] = g_1,$

where $g_1 := L_4[f_1] - L_2[f_2]$. We can solve this linear equation with constant coefficients for x by using the techniques discussed in Chapters 4 and 6. This solution will involve n arbitrary constants where n is the order of the operator $L_1 L_4 - L_2 L_3$. We then solve for y in terms of these same constants.

The second technique is the method of **Laplace transforms** and is applicable to initial value problems. As is the case for a single differential equation, taking the Laplace transform of each of the equations transforms the system of differential equations with initial conditions into a system of algebraic equations in which the unknowns are the Laplace transforms $X_i(s)$ of the unknown solutions $x_i(t)$. Solving for the transforms and then calculating their inverse transforms gives the solution to the original problem. Properties of the Laplace transform are discussed in Chapter 7.

In certain instances it is helpful to express a higher order differential equation as a system of first order equations in **normal form.** This is the case when one wants to use a numerical method such as a fourth order Runge-Kutta algorithm to obtain an approximation for the solution to an initial value problem for a higher order equation, or when one wants to use phase plane analysis on a second order nonlinear differential equation. To reduce the mth order equation $y^{(m)}(t) = f(t, y, y', \ldots, y^{(m-1)})$ to a normal system, set $x_1 = y$, $x_2 = y', \ldots,$ and $x_m = y^{(m-1)}$. This leads to

(4) $\qquad x_1' = x_2, \quad x_2' = x_3, \ldots, \quad x_{m-1}' = x_m, \quad x_m' = f(t, x_1, \ldots, x_m).$

The numerical techniques for first order equations discussed in Sections 3.5 and 3.6 each have extensions to first order systems in normal form. These techniques also apply to higher order equations once they have been reduced to a system in normal form. In Section 9.5 we discussed the extension of the fourth order Runge-Kutta algorithm to systems.

A technique for studying the qualitative behavior of solutions to the nonlinear **autonomous system**

(5) $\qquad \dfrac{dx}{dt} = f(x, y), \qquad \dfrac{dy}{dt} = g(x, y)$

is the method of **phase plane analysis.** To sketch a phase plane diagram for (5), we begin by finding the **critical points,** which are solutions to the system

$$f(x, y) = 0, \qquad g(x, y) = 0.$$

Next we solve (either analytically or numerically) the first order equation $dy/dx = g(x, y)/f(x, y)$ and use the solutions to sketch some integral curves for (5). Returning to the original equations in (5), we can determine the **flow** along each integral curve and hence sketch the **trajectories** of the system. This information can be used to describe the behavior of the solutions to the system even though the solutions themselves cannot be found.

REVIEW PROBLEMS

In Problems 1 through 6 use the elimination method to find a general solution for the given linear system, where x', y', *and D denote differentiation with respect to t.*

1. $x' = y$,
$\quad y' = 3x$.

2. $x' + y' = 2y$,
$\quad y' = x - y$.

3. $(D + 2)[x] + (D - 1)[y] = t$,
$\quad (D - 1)[x] + (D + 1)[y] = 0$.

4. $(D - 3)[x] + D[y] = 0$,
$\quad (D + 1)[x] - y = 0$.

5. $x'' + y' + y = 0$,
$\quad x' - x + y = 0$.

6. $x'' - x + 5y = 2$,
$\quad 2x + y'' + 2y = 0$.

In Problems 7 through 10 use the method of Laplace transforms to solve the given initial value problem.

7. $x' + y' = x - y$, $\quad x(0) = 1$,
$\quad x' - y' = x - y$, $\quad y(0) = 0$.

8. $x' = x - 2y$, $\quad x(0) = 0$,
$\quad y' = 3x + y$, $\quad y(0) = 1$.

9. $x'' = y$, $\quad x(0) = 1$, $\quad x'(0) = 0$,
$\quad y' = x$, $\quad y(0) = 0$.

10. $x' = 2x + y$, $\quad x(0) = 1$,
$\quad y' = x + y$, $\quad y(0) = 2$.

In Problems 11 and 12 convert the given initial value problem into an initial value problem for a system in normal form.

11. $y'''(t) + ty''(t) + 3y'(t) + 2y(t) = 2e^{-t}$; $\quad y(0) = 2$, $\quad y'(0) = 3$, $\quad y''(0) = 2$.

12. $y''(t) + y'(t) - \tan y(t) = \cos t$; $\quad y(3) = 4$, $\quad y'(3) = -6$.

In Problems 13 through 18 sketch a phase plane diagram for the given system.

13. $\dfrac{dx}{dt} = 2x$,

$\dfrac{dy}{dt} = y$.

14. $\dfrac{dx}{dt} = \dfrac{1}{y}$,

$\dfrac{dy}{dt} = \dfrac{3}{x}$.

15. $\dfrac{dx}{dt} = y$,

$\dfrac{dy}{dt} = 4x$.

16. $\dfrac{dx}{dt} = -y$,

$\dfrac{dy}{dt} = 9x$.

17. $\dfrac{dx}{dt} = y$,

$\dfrac{dy}{dt} = -y^2 \tan x$.

18. $\dfrac{dx}{dt} = 1 - y$,

$\dfrac{dy}{dt} = x + 3$.

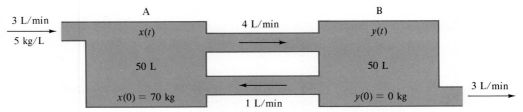

Figure 9.24 Mixing problem for interconnected tanks

19. **Arms Race.** A mathematical model for an arms race between two countries whose expenditures for defense are expressed by the variables $x(t)$ and $y(t)$ is given by the linear system

$$\frac{dx}{dt} = 2y - x + a, \qquad x(0) = 1,$$

$$\frac{dy}{dt} = 4x - 3y + b, \qquad y(0) = 4,$$

where a and b are constants that measure the trust (or distrust) each country has for the other. Determine whether there is going to be disarmament (x and y approach 0 as t increases), a stabilized arms race (x and y approach a constant as $t \to \infty$), or a runaway arms race (x and y approach ∞ as $t \to \infty$).

20. Two large tanks, each holding 50 L of liquid, are interconnected by pipes, with the liquid flowing from tank A into tank B at a rate of 4 L/min and from B into A at a rate of 1 L/min (see Figure 9.24). The liquid inside each tank is kept well stirred. A brine solution with a concentration of 5 kg/L of salt flows into tank A at a rate of 3 L/min. The (diluted) solution flows out of the system from tank B at 3 L/min. If, initially, tank A contains 70 kg of salt and tank B contains only water, determine the amount of salt in each tank at time $t \geq 0$.

Projects for Chapter 9

A. CLEANING UP THE GREAT LAKES

A simple mathematical model that can be used to determine the time it would take to clean up the Great Lakes can be developed using a multiple compartmental analysis approach. In particular, we can view each Great Lake as a tank that contains a liquid in which is dissolved a particular pollutant (DDT, phosphorus, mercury). Schematically, we view the Great Lakes as consisting of five tanks connected as indicated in Figure 9.25.

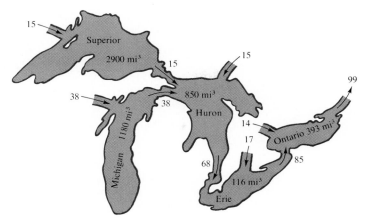

Figure 9.25 Compartmental model of the Great Lakes with flow rates (mi³/year) and volumes (mi³)

For our model we make the following assumptions:

1. The volume of each lake remains constant.
2. The flow rates are constant throughout the year.
3. When a liquid enters the lake, perfect mixing occurs and the pollutants are uniformly distributed.
4. Pollutants are dissolved in the water and enter or leave by inflow or outflow of solution.

Before using this model to obtain estimates on the cleanup times for the lakes, we consider some simpler models.

(a) Use the outflow rates given in Figure 9.25 to determine the time it would take to "drain" each lake. This gives a lower bound on how long it would take to remove all the pollutants.

(b) A better estimate is obtained by assuming that each lake is a separate tank with *only* clean water flowing in. Use this approach to determine how long it would take for the pollution level in each lake to be reduced to 50% of its original level. How long would it take to reduce the pollution to 5% of its original level?

(c) Finally, to take into account the fact that pollution from one lake flows into the next lake in the chain, use the entire multiple compartment model given in Figure 9.25 to determine when the pollution level in each lake has been reduced to 50% of its original level, assuming that pollution has ceased (that is, inflows not from a lake are clean water). Assume that all the lakes initially have the same pollution concentration p. How long would it take for the pollution to be reduced to 5% of its original level?

For a detailed discussion of this model see *An Introduction to Mathematical Modeling,* by Edward A. Bender, John Wiley and Sons, Inc., New York, 1978, Chapter 8.

B. EFFECTS OF HUNTING ON PREDATOR-PREY SYSTEMS

Cyclic variations in the populations of predators and their prey have been studied using the Volterra-Lotka predator-prey model given by the system

(1) $$\frac{dx}{dt} = Ax - Bxy,$$

(2) $$\frac{dy}{dt} = -Cy + Dxy,$$

where A, B, C, and D are positive constants, $x(t)$ is the population of prey at time t, and $y(t)$ is the population of predators. It can be shown that such a system has a periodic solution (see Project C). That is, there exists some constant T such that $x(t) = x(t + T)$ and $y(t) = y(t + T)$ for all t. This periodic or cyclic variation in the populations has been observed in various systems such as sharks–food fish, lynx–rabbits, and ladybird beetles–cottony cushion scale. Because of this periodic behavior, it is useful to consider the average populations $\bar{x}$ and $\bar{y}$ defined by

$$\bar{x} := \frac{1}{T}\int_0^T x(t)\,dt, \qquad \bar{y} := \frac{1}{T}\int_0^T y(t)\,dt.$$

(a) Show that $\bar{x} = C/D$ and $\bar{y} = A/B$. [Hint: Use equation (1) and the fact that $x(0) = x(T)$ to show that

$$\int_0^T (A - By(t))\,dt = \int_0^T \frac{x'(t)}{x(t)}\,dt = 0.]$$

(b) To determine the effect of indiscriminate hunting on the populations, assume that hunting reduces the rate of change in a population by a constant times the population. Then, the predator-prey system satisfies the new set of equations

(3) $$\frac{dx}{dt} = Ax - Bxy - \varepsilon x = (A - \varepsilon)x - Bxy,$$

(4) $$\frac{dy}{dt} = -Cy + Dxy - \delta y = -(C + \delta)y + Dxy,$$

where ε and δ are positive constants with $\varepsilon < A$. What effect does this have on the average population of prey? On the average population of predators?

(c) Assume that the hunting is done selectively, as in shooting only rabbits (or shooting only lynx). Then we have $\varepsilon > 0$ and $\delta = 0$ (or $\varepsilon = 0$ and $\delta > 0$) in (3)–(4). What effect does this have on the average populations of predator and prey?

(d) In a rural county, foxes prey mainly on rabbits but occasionally include a chicken in their diet. The farmers decide to put a stop to the chicken killing by hunting the foxes. What do you predict will happen? What happens to the farmers' gardens?

For a discussion of other differential equation models in population biology, see *Differential Equation Models,* by Martin Braun, Courtney S. Coleman, and Donald A. Drew (eds.), Springer-Verlag, New York, 1983, Part V.

C. PERIODIC SOLUTIONS TO VOLTERRA-LOTKA SYSTEMS

As stated in Project B, the Volterra-Lotka predator-prey model is given by the system (1)–(2), where $x(t)$ and $y(t)$ are the populations of the prey and the predators, respectively, and A, B, C, and D are positive constants. For autonomous systems such as (1)–(2), the existence of a closed integral curve that does not contain a critical point implies the existence of a periodic solution (see Section 9.6). To show that (1)–(2) has such an integral curve, proceed as follows:

(a) Determine the critical points of system (1)–(2).

(b) Show that the integral curves of (1)–(2) can be expressed in the form $w(x)z(y) = k$, where $w(x) := x^C e^{-Dx}$ and $z(y) := y^A e^{-By}$.

(c) Show that $w(x) = x^C e^{-Dx}$ has the properties $w(0) = 0$, $\lim_{x \to \infty} w(x) = 0$, and $w(x)$ attains a maximum value of $M_w := (C/D)^C e^{-C}$ for $x > 0$ at $x = C/D$. Sketch the graph of $w(x)$. Similarly, show that $z(y) = y^A e^{-By}$ has the properties $z(0) = 0$, $\lim_{y \to \infty} z(y) = 0$, and $z(y)$ attains a maximum value of $M_z := (A/B)^A e^{-A}$ for $y > 0$ at $y = A/B$. Sketch the graph of $z(y)$.

(d) Show that the product $w(x)z(y)$ is bounded by $M_w M_z$ for x, $y > 0$, and hence there is no solution with x, $y > 0$ for $w(x)z(y) = k$ when $k > M_w M_z$. Moreover, show that the only solution when $k = M_w M_z$ is $x = C/D$, $y = A/B$.

(e) Assume that $0 < k < M_w M_z$. Show that when $y = A/B$, there are two solutions to $w(x)z(y) = k$, one being $x_{\min} < C/D$ and the other $x_{\max} > C/D$.

(f) Again, assume that $0 < k < M_w M_z$. Show that for x fixed, the equation $w(x)z(y) = k$ has (i) no solution when $x < x_{\min}$ or $x > x_{\max}$, (ii) one solution $y = A/B$ when $x = x_{\min}$ or $x_{\max}$, and (iii) two solutions $y_1(x) < A/B < y_2(x)$ when $x_{\min} < x < x_{\max}$ (see Figure 9.26).

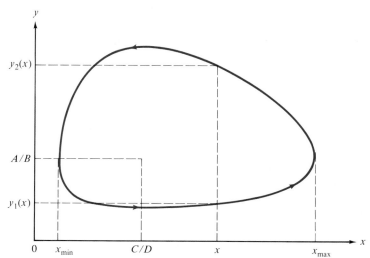

Figure 9.26 Integral curve for a Volterra-Lotka system

(g) Using the results of parts (e) and (f), argue that system (1)–(2) has a family of closed integral curves in the first quadrant that surround the critical point $(C/D, A/B)$. Hence the system has a periodic solution.

D. LIMIT CYCLES AND THE VAN DER POL EQUATION

In the study of triode vacuum tubes one encounters the **van der Pol equation:**[†]

(5) $$x''(t) - \mu(1 - x^2(t))x'(t) + x(t) = 0, \qquad \mu > 0.$$

To study this equation, we let $y(t) = x'(t)$ and then express (5) as an equivalent system in normal form.

(a) Show that van der Pol's equation is equivalent to the system

(6)
$$\frac{dx}{dt} = y,$$

$$\frac{dy}{dt} = \mu(1 - x^2)y - x,$$

and the integral curves of (6) satisfy the first order equation

(7) $$y\frac{dy}{dx} = \mu(1 - x^2)y - x.$$

(b) For $\mu = 0.1$, sketch some integral curves for van der Pol's equation either by numerically solving system (6) using the methods discussed in Section 9.5 or by numerically solving equation (7) using the methods discussed in Section 3.7. Do this for the initial conditions $x(0) = 0.5$, $x'(0) = 0$ and for $x(0) = 4$, $x'(0) = 0$.

Notice that one of the integral curves in part (b) spirals in while the other spirals out. If you continued the approximation long enough in time, then you would find that both curves approach a closed curve that is approximately a circle of radius 2 centered at the origin. This closed curve is called a **limit cycle** for the van der Pol equation, and is the trajectory of a periodic solution to system (6) and hence to van der Pol's equation.

(c) If the two integral curves are typical of the integral curves for van der Pol's equation, describe the behavior of arbitrary solutions to van der Pol's equation.

(d) For $\mu = 1$, numerically obtain a phase plane diagram for van der Pol's equation. Is there a limit cycle when $\mu = 1$ and hence a periodic solution?

[†] *Historical Footnote:* Experimental research by **E. V. Appleton** and **B. van der Pol** in 1921 on the oscillations of an electric circuit containing a triode generator (vacuum tube) led to the nonlinear equation now called **van der Pol's equation.** Methods of solution were developed by van der Pol in 1926–1927. **Mary L. Cartwright** continued research into nonlinear oscillation theory and together with **J. E. Littlewood** obtained existence results for forced oscillations in nonlinear systems in 1945.

Matrix Methods for Linear Systems

10.1 Introduction

In Chapter 9 we presented two elementary techniques for solving linear systems of differential equations and discussed their application to electric networks, mechanical systems with more than one degree of freedom, and multiple compartment systems. These techniques work quite well when the number of variables is small. However, for large electric networks or mechanical systems with many degrees of freedom, these methods are cumbersome and disguise the underlying theory. One way out of the maze is to use matrix methods.

Recall that a system of n linear first order differential equations is in **normal form** when it is expressed as

$$x_1'(t) = a_{11}(t)x_1(t) + \cdots + a_{1n}(t)x_n(t) + f_1(t),$$
$$x_2'(t) = a_{21}(t)x_1(t) + \cdots + a_{2n}(t)x_n(t) + f_2(t),$$

(1)

$$\cdot \qquad \cdot \qquad \qquad \cdot \qquad \cdot$$
$$\cdot \qquad \cdot \qquad \qquad \cdot \qquad \cdot$$
$$\cdot \qquad \cdot \qquad \qquad \cdot \qquad \cdot$$

$$x_n'(t) = a_{n1}(t)x_1(t) + \cdots + a_{nn}(t)x_n(t) + f_n(t).$$

The structure of such a system suggests that there might be a more convenient way of expressing it. This is in fact the case. Using matrices and vectors, system (1) can be written in the compact form

(2) $\qquad \mathbf{x}'(t) = \mathbf{A}(t)\mathbf{x}(t) + \mathbf{f}(t),$

where $\mathbf{x}(t) = \text{col}(x_1(t), \ldots, x_n(t))$ and $\mathbf{f}(t) = \text{col}(f_1(t), \ldots, f_n(t))$ are vectors and $\mathbf{A}(t) = [a_{ij}(t)]$ is a matrix. Not only is (2) easier to write and remember, but it also serves as a reminder that first order linear systems behave much like linear first order differential equations.

In this chapter we use matrix methods to study systems of first order differential equations in normal form. We assume that the reader is acquainted with the computational aspects of linear algebra usually taught in a basic linear algebra course[†]—in particular, matrix addition and multiplication, solving systems of linear equations, evaluating determinants, and computing the inverse of a matrix. For the reader's convenience, we give a brief review of matrices in the next section. There we also introduce vector and matrix functions and discuss their calculus.

The advantages of the matrix approach become evident in Section 10.3, where we develop the theory for linear systems in normal form. This development parallels very closely the discussion of linear second order equations in Section 4.3 and the theory of linear higher order equations in Section 6.2. In particular, we discuss linear dependence of vector functions, fundamental solution sets, and the Wronskian of a set of solutions.

In Sections 10.4 and 10.5 we give a procedure for determining a fundamental solution set for a homogeneous normal system with constant coefficients. The approach is analogous to that used for scalar equations. For example, the role previously played by the auxiliary equation and its roots is now taken by the characteristic equation for the matrix and its eigenvalues and eigenvectors. In Section 10.6 we give extensions of the methods of undetermined coefficients and variation of parameters.

The connection between first order normal systems and first order linear equations alluded to earlier is discussed in Section 10.7. There the concept of a matrix exponential function $e^{\mathbf{A}t}$ is discussed. Moreover, we demonstrate how to use the matrix exponential function to obtain a general solution for a homogeneous system.

★ 10.2 A Brief Review of Matrices and Vectors

A **matrix** is a rectangular array of numbers arranged in rows and columns. An $m \times n$ matrix—that is, a matrix with m rows and n columns—is usually denoted by

$$
(1) \qquad \mathbf{A} := \begin{bmatrix} a_{11} & a_{12} & \cdots & a_{1n} \\ a_{21} & a_{22} & \cdots & a_{2n} \\ \cdot & \cdot & & \cdot \\ \cdot & \cdot & & \cdot \\ \cdot & \cdot & & \cdot \\ a_{m1} & a_{m2} & \cdots & a_{mn} \end{bmatrix},
$$

where the element in the ith row and jth column is a_{ij}. The notation $[a_{ij}]$ is also used to designate $\mathbf{A}$. The matrices we will work with usually consist of real numbers, but in certain instances we allow complex number entries.

[†] A suitable reference is *Elementary Linear Algebra*, by A. Wayne Roberts, Benjamin/Cummings Publishing Co., Menlo Park, California, 1982, or almost any other introductory linear algebra text.

The matrix obtained from **A** by interchanging its rows and columns is called the **transpose** of **A** and is denoted by $\mathbf{A}^T$. For example, if

$$\mathbf{A} = \begin{bmatrix} 1 & 2 & 6 \\ -1 & 2 & -1 \end{bmatrix}, \quad \text{then} \quad \mathbf{A}^T = \begin{bmatrix} 1 & -1 \\ 2 & 2 \\ 6 & -1 \end{bmatrix}.$$

Some matrices of special interest are **square matrices,** which have the same number of rows and columns; **diagonal matrices,** which are square matrices with only zero entries off the main diagonal (that is, $a_{ij} = 0$ if $i \neq j$); and (column) **vectors,** which are $n \times 1$ matrices. For example, if

$$(2) \qquad \mathbf{A} = \begin{bmatrix} 3 & 4 & -1 \\ 2 & 6 & 5 \\ 0 & 1 & 4 \end{bmatrix}, \qquad \mathbf{B} = \begin{bmatrix} 3 & 0 & 0 \\ 0 & 0 & 0 \\ 0 & 0 & 7 \end{bmatrix}, \qquad \mathbf{x} = \begin{bmatrix} 4 \\ 2 \\ 1 \end{bmatrix},$$

then **A** is a square matrix, **B** is a diagonal matrix, and **x** is a vector. An $m \times n$ matrix whose entries are all zero is called a **zero matrix** and is denoted by **0**. The $n \times n$ diagonal matrix with ones down the main diagonal is called the **identity matrix** and is denoted by **I**, or by $\mathbf{I}_n$ when the size of the matrix is important.

For consistency, we denote matrices by boldfaced capitals **A, B, C, I, X, Y,** etc., and reserve boldfaced lowercase letters such as **c, x, y,** and **z** for vectors. We also write $\mathbf{x} = \mathrm{col}(x_1, \ldots, x_n)$ to mean the vector whose transpose is $\mathbf{x}^T = [x_1 \; x_2 \ldots x_n]$.

ALGEBRA OF MATRICES

We need the following properties of matrices:

Matrix Addition. Addition is performed by adding corresponding elements; that is, the *sum* of two $m \times n$ matrices is

$$\mathbf{A} + \mathbf{B} = [a_{ij}] + [b_{ij}] = [a_{ij} + b_{ij}].$$

Scalar Multiplication. If **A** is an $m \times n$ matrix and r is a number (scalar), then the **scalar multiple** of **A** by r is the matrix $r\mathbf{A}$ obtained from **A** by multiplying each element in **A** by the number r. That is, $r\mathbf{A} = r[a_{ij}] = [ra_{ij}]$. The special case of $(-1)\mathbf{A}$ is written $-\mathbf{A}$.

Properties of Matrix Addition and Scalar Multiplication. If **A, B,** and **C** are $m \times n$ matrices and r, s are scalars, then

$$\mathbf{A} + (\mathbf{B} + \mathbf{C}) = (\mathbf{A} + \mathbf{B}) + \mathbf{C}, \qquad \mathbf{A} + \mathbf{B} = \mathbf{B} + \mathbf{A},$$

$$\mathbf{A} + \mathbf{0} = \mathbf{A}, \qquad \mathbf{A} + (-\mathbf{A}) = \mathbf{0},$$

$$r(\mathbf{A} + \mathbf{B}) = r\mathbf{A} + r\mathbf{B}, \qquad (r + s)\mathbf{A} = r\mathbf{A} + s\mathbf{A},$$

$$r(s\mathbf{A}) = (rs)\mathbf{A} = s(r\mathbf{A}).$$

Matrix Multiplication. If **A** is an $m \times n$ matrix and **B** is an $n \times p$ matrix, then the **product** of **A** and **B** is the $m \times p$ matrix **AB** defined by

(3) $$\mathbf{AB} := [c_{ij}], \quad \text{where} \quad c_{ij} := \sum_{k=1}^{n} a_{ik}b_{kj}$$

for $i = 1, \ldots, m$ and $j = 1, \ldots, p$. Observe that the ijth entry in **AB** is the dot product of the ith row of **A** and the jth column of **B**. For example,

$$\begin{bmatrix} 1 & 0 & 1 \\ 3 & -1 & 2 \end{bmatrix} \begin{bmatrix} 1 & 2 \\ -1 & -1 \\ 4 & 1 \end{bmatrix} = \begin{bmatrix} 1+0+4 & 2+0+1 \\ 3+1+8 & 6+1+2 \end{bmatrix} = \begin{bmatrix} 5 & 3 \\ 12 & 9 \end{bmatrix}.$$

It is important to keep in mind that matrix multiplication does not commute; that is, **AB** may not equal **BA**. This is certainly true if **A** is 2×3 and **B** is 3×2, since then **AB** is 2×2 while **BA** is 3×3. In some cases **AB** may be defined while **BA** is not. Even for square matrices, **AB** is not necessarily equal to **BA** (see Problem 8).

Properties of Matrix Multiplication.

(4) $(\mathbf{AB})\mathbf{C} = \mathbf{A}(\mathbf{BC}).$ (Associativity)

(5) $(\mathbf{A} + \mathbf{B})\mathbf{C} = \mathbf{AC} + \mathbf{BC}.$ (Distributivity)

(6) $\mathbf{A}(\mathbf{B} + \mathbf{C}) = \mathbf{AB} + \mathbf{AC}.$ (Distributivity)

(7) $(r\mathbf{A})\mathbf{B} = r(\mathbf{AB}) = \mathbf{A}(r\mathbf{B}).$ (Associativity)

Let **A** be an $m \times n$ matrix and let **x** and **y** be $n \times 1$ vectors. Then **Ax** is an $m \times 1$ vector, and so we can think of multiplication by **A** as defining an operator that maps $n \times 1$ vectors into $m \times 1$ vectors. A consequence of properties (6) and (7) is that multiplication by **A** defines a **linear operator,** since $\mathbf{A}(\mathbf{x} + \mathbf{y}) = \mathbf{Ax} + \mathbf{Ay}$ and $\mathbf{A}(r\mathbf{x}) = r\mathbf{Ax}$. Moreover, if **A** is an $m \times n$ matrix and **B** is an $n \times p$ matrix, then the $m \times p$ matrix **AB** defines a linear operator that is the composition of the linear operator defined by **B** with the linear operator defined by **A**. That is, $(\mathbf{AB})\mathbf{x} = \mathbf{A}(\mathbf{Bx})$, where **x** is a $p \times 1$ vector.

Inverse of a Matrix. For square matrices we say that **B** is the **inverse** of **A**, denoted $\mathbf{B} = \mathbf{A}^{-1}$, if $\mathbf{AB} = \mathbf{BA} = \mathbf{I}$. Obviously, if **B** is the inverse of **A**, then **A** is the inverse of **B**. A matrix that has an inverse is called **invertible** or **nonsingular.** If no inverse exists, the matrix is said to be **singular.** For example, the identity matrix is invertible $(\mathbf{I}^{-1} = \mathbf{I})$, but the zero matrix is singular.

Finding the Inverse of a Matrix. By a **row operation** we mean any one of the following:

(a) Interchanging two rows of the matrix.

(b) Multiplying a row of the matrix by a nonzero scalar.

(c) Adding a scalar multiple of one row of the matrix to another row.

If the $n \times n$ matrix $\mathbf{A}$ has an inverse, then $\mathbf{A}^{-1}$ can be determined by performing row operations on the $n \times 2n$ matrix $[\mathbf{A} \mid \mathbf{I}]$ obtained by writing $\mathbf{A}$ and $\mathbf{I}$ side by side. In particular, we perform row operations on the matrix $[\mathbf{A} \mid \mathbf{I}]$ until the first n rows and columns form the identity matrix; that is, the new matrix is $[\mathbf{I} \mid \mathbf{B}]$. Then $\mathbf{A}^{-1} = \mathbf{B}$. We remark that if this procedure fails to produce a matrix of the form $[\mathbf{I} \mid \mathbf{B}]$, then $\mathbf{A}$ has no inverse.

▶ **Example 1**   Find the inverse of $\mathbf{A} = \begin{bmatrix} 1 & 2 & 1 \\ 1 & 3 & 2 \\ 1 & 0 & 1 \end{bmatrix}$.

Solution   We first form the matrix $[\mathbf{A} \mid \mathbf{I}]$ and row-reduce the matrix to $[\mathbf{I} \mid \mathbf{A}^{-1}]$. Computing, we find

The matrix $[\mathbf{A} \mid \mathbf{I}]$ $\qquad \begin{bmatrix} 1 & 2 & 1 & \vdots & 1 & 0 & 0 \\ 1 & 3 & 2 & \vdots & 0 & 1 & 0 \\ 1 & 0 & 1 & \vdots & 0 & 0 & 1 \end{bmatrix}.$

Subtract the first row from the second and third to obtain $\qquad \begin{bmatrix} 1 & 2 & 1 & \vdots & 1 & 0 & 0 \\ 0 & 1 & 1 & \vdots & -1 & 1 & 0 \\ 0 & -2 & 0 & \vdots & -1 & 0 & 1 \end{bmatrix}.$

Add 2 times the second row to the third row to obtain $\qquad \begin{bmatrix} 1 & 2 & 1 & \vdots & 1 & 0 & 0 \\ 0 & 1 & 1 & \vdots & -1 & 1 & 0 \\ 0 & 0 & 2 & \vdots & -3 & 2 & 1 \end{bmatrix}.$

Subtract 2 times the second row from the first to obtain $\qquad \begin{bmatrix} 1 & 0 & -1 & \vdots & 3 & -2 & 0 \\ 0 & 1 & 1 & \vdots & -1 & 1 & 0 \\ 0 & 0 & 2 & \vdots & -3 & 2 & 1 \end{bmatrix}.$

Multiply the third row by $\frac{1}{2}$ to obtain $\qquad \begin{bmatrix} 1 & 0 & -1 & \vdots & 3 & -2 & 0 \\ 0 & 1 & 1 & \vdots & -1 & 1 & 0 \\ 0 & 0 & 1 & \vdots & -\frac{3}{2} & 1 & \frac{1}{2} \end{bmatrix}.$

Add the third row to the first, then subtract the third row from the second to obtain $\qquad \begin{bmatrix} 1 & 0 & 0 & \vdots & \frac{3}{2} & -1 & \frac{1}{2} \\ 0 & 1 & 0 & \vdots & \frac{1}{2} & 0 & -\frac{1}{2} \\ 0 & 0 & 1 & \vdots & -\frac{3}{2} & 1 & \frac{1}{2} \end{bmatrix}.$

The matrix shown in color is $\mathbf{A}^{-1}$.   ◀

Determinants.   For a 2×2 matrix $\mathbf{A}$, the **determinant of A**, denoted det $\mathbf{A}$ or $|\mathbf{A}|$, is defined by

$$\det \mathbf{A} := \begin{vmatrix} a_{11} & a_{12} \\ a_{21} & a_{22} \end{vmatrix} = a_{11}a_{22} - a_{12}a_{21}.$$

We can define the determinant of a 3×3 matrix **A** in terms of its cofactor expansion about the first row; that is,

$$\det \mathbf{A} := \begin{vmatrix} a_{11} & a_{12} & a_{13} \\ a_{21} & a_{22} & a_{23} \\ a_{31} & a_{32} & a_{33} \end{vmatrix} = a_{11} \begin{vmatrix} a_{22} & a_{23} \\ a_{32} & a_{33} \end{vmatrix} - a_{12} \begin{vmatrix} a_{21} & a_{23} \\ a_{31} & a_{33} \end{vmatrix} + a_{13} \begin{vmatrix} a_{21} & a_{22} \\ a_{31} & a_{32} \end{vmatrix}.$$

For example,

$$\begin{vmatrix} 1 & 2 & 1 \\ 0 & 3 & 5 \\ 2 & 1 & -1 \end{vmatrix} = 1 \begin{vmatrix} 3 & 5 \\ 1 & -1 \end{vmatrix} - 2 \begin{vmatrix} 0 & 5 \\ 2 & -1 \end{vmatrix} + 1 \begin{vmatrix} 0 & 3 \\ 2 & 1 \end{vmatrix}$$

$$= 1(-3 - 5) - 2(0 - 10) + 1(0 - 6) = 6.$$

The determinant of an $n \times n$ matrix can be similarly defined by a cofactor expansion involving $(n - 1)$st order determinants; however, a more practical way to evaluate the determinant when n is large is to row-reduce the matrix to upper triangular form. Since here we deal mainly with 2×2 and 3×3 matrices, we refer the reader to an elementary linear algebra text for a further discussion of evaluating determinants.[†]

The next theorem summarizes many of the results from elementary linear algebra that we need.

MATRICES AND SYSTEMS OF EQUATIONS

Theorem 1.   Let **A** be an $n \times n$ matrix. The following statements are equivalent:

(a) $\mathbf{Ax} = \mathbf{0}$ has nontrivial solutions $(\mathbf{x} \neq \mathbf{0})$.

(b) **A** is singular.

(c) The determinant of **A** is zero.

(d) The columns (rows) of **A** form a linearly dependent set.

In part (d) the statement that the n columns of **A** are linearly dependent means that there exist scalars $c_1, \ldots, c_n$ *not all zero* such that

$$c_1 \mathbf{a}_1 + c_2 \mathbf{a}_2 + \cdots + c_n \mathbf{a}_n = \mathbf{0},$$

where $\mathbf{a}_j$ is the vector forming the jth column of **A**.

[†] See *Elementary Linear Algebra*, by A. Wayne Roberts, Benjamin/Cummings Publishing Co., Menlo Park, California, 1982.

CALCULUS OF MATRICES

If we allow the entries $a_{ij}(t)$ in a matrix $\mathbf{A}(t)$ to be functions of the variable t, then $\mathbf{A}(t)$ is a **matrix function of** t. Similarly, if the entries $x_i(t)$ of a vector $\mathbf{x}(t)$ are functions of t, then $\mathbf{x}(t)$ is a **vector function of** t.

These matrix and vector functions have a calculus much like that of real-valued functions. A matrix $\mathbf{A}(t)$ is said to be **continuous at** t_0 if each entry $a_{ij}(t)$ is continuous at t_0. Moreover, $\mathbf{A}(t)$ is **differentiable at** t_0 if each entry $a_{ij}(t)$ is differentiable at t_0, and we write

(8) $$\frac{d\mathbf{A}}{dt}(t_0) = \mathbf{A}'(t_0) := [a'_{ij}(t_0)].$$

Similarly, we define

(9) $$\int_a^b \mathbf{A}(t)\, dt := \left[\int_a^b a_{ij}(t)\, dt \right].$$

▶ **Example 2** Let $\mathbf{A}(t) = \begin{bmatrix} t^2 + 1 & \cos t \\ e^t & 1 \end{bmatrix}$.

Find: (a) $\mathbf{A}'(t)$. (b) $\int_0^1 \mathbf{A}(t)\, dt$.

Solution Using formulas (8) and (9), we compute

(a) $\mathbf{A}'(t) = \begin{bmatrix} 2t & -\sin t \\ e^t & 0 \end{bmatrix}$. (b) $\int_0^1 \mathbf{A}(t)\, dt = \begin{bmatrix} \frac{4}{3} & \sin 1 \\ e - 1 & 1 \end{bmatrix}$. ◀

The basic properties of differentiation are valid for matrix functions.

Differentiation Formulas for Matrix Functions.

(10) $$\frac{d}{dt}(\mathbf{CA}) = \mathbf{C}\frac{d\mathbf{A}}{dt}, \quad \mathbf{C} \text{ a constant matrix.}$$

(11) $$\frac{d}{dt}(\mathbf{A} + \mathbf{B}) = \frac{d\mathbf{A}}{dt} + \frac{d\mathbf{B}}{dt}.$$

(12) $$\frac{d}{dt}(\mathbf{AB}) = \mathbf{A}\frac{d\mathbf{B}}{dt} + \frac{d\mathbf{A}}{dt}\mathbf{B}.$$

In formula (12) the order in which the matrices are written is very important, because matrix multiplication does not always commute.

EXERCISES 10.2

1. Let $\mathbf{A} := \begin{bmatrix} 2 & 1 \\ 3 & 5 \end{bmatrix}$ and $\mathbf{B} := \begin{bmatrix} -1 & 0 \\ 2 & -3 \end{bmatrix}$.

   Find: (a) $\mathbf{A}^T$. (b) $\mathbf{A} + \mathbf{B}$. (c) $3\mathbf{A} - \mathbf{B}$.

2. Let $\mathbf{A} := \begin{bmatrix} 2 & 0 & 5 \\ 2 & 1 & 1 \end{bmatrix}$ and $\mathbf{B} := \begin{bmatrix} 1 & -1 & 2 \\ 0 & 3 & -2 \end{bmatrix}$.

   Find: (a) $\mathbf{B}^T$. (b) $\mathbf{A} + \mathbf{B}$. (c) $7\mathbf{A} - 4\mathbf{B}$.

3. Let $\mathbf{A} := \begin{bmatrix} 2 & 4 \\ 1 & 1 \end{bmatrix}$ and $\mathbf{B} := \begin{bmatrix} -1 & 3 \\ 5 & 1 \end{bmatrix}$.

   Find: (a) $\mathbf{AB}$. (b) $\mathbf{A}^2 = \mathbf{AA}$. (c) $\mathbf{B}^2 = \mathbf{BB}$.

4. Let $\mathbf{A} := \begin{bmatrix} 2 & 1 \\ 0 & 4 \\ -1 & 3 \end{bmatrix}$ and $\mathbf{B} := \begin{bmatrix} 1 & 1 & -1 \\ 0 & 3 & 1 \end{bmatrix}$.

   Find: (a) $\mathbf{AB}$. (b) $\mathbf{BA}$. (c) $\mathbf{A}^T\mathbf{A}$.

5. Let $\mathbf{A} := \begin{bmatrix} 1 & -2 \\ 2 & -3 \end{bmatrix}$, $\mathbf{B} := \begin{bmatrix} 1 & 0 \\ 1 & 1 \end{bmatrix}$, and $\mathbf{C} := \begin{bmatrix} -1 & 1 \\ 2 & 1 \end{bmatrix}$.

   Find: (a) $\mathbf{AB}$. (b) $\mathbf{AC}$. (c) $\mathbf{A(B + C)}$.

6. Let $\mathbf{A} := \begin{bmatrix} 1 & 2 \\ 1 & 1 \end{bmatrix}$, $\mathbf{B} := \begin{bmatrix} 0 & 3 \\ 1 & 2 \end{bmatrix}$, and $\mathbf{C} := \begin{bmatrix} 1 & -4 \\ 1 & 1 \end{bmatrix}$.

   Find: (a) $\mathbf{AB}$. (b) $\mathbf{(AB)C}$. (c) $\mathbf{(A + B)C}$.

7. Let $\mathbf{x} := \begin{bmatrix} 1 \\ 2 \\ 4 \end{bmatrix}$ and $\mathbf{y} := \begin{bmatrix} 2 \\ 4 \\ -1 \end{bmatrix}$. Find: (a) $\mathbf{x}^T\mathbf{x}$. (b) $\mathbf{y}^T\mathbf{y}$. (c) $\mathbf{x}^T\mathbf{y}$. (d) $\mathbf{y}^T\mathbf{x}$.

8. Let $\mathbf{A} := \begin{bmatrix} 2 & -1 \\ -3 & 4 \end{bmatrix}$ and $\mathbf{B} := \begin{bmatrix} 1 & 2 \\ 3 & 2 \end{bmatrix}$.

   Verify that $\mathbf{AB} \neq \mathbf{BA}$.

In Problems 9 through 14 compute the inverse of the given matrix, if it exists.

9. $\begin{bmatrix} 2 & 1 \\ -1 & 4 \end{bmatrix}$.

10. $\begin{bmatrix} 4 & 1 \\ 5 & 9 \end{bmatrix}$.

11. $\begin{bmatrix} 1 & 1 & 1 \\ 1 & 2 & 1 \\ 2 & 3 & 2 \end{bmatrix}$.

12. $\begin{bmatrix} 1 & 1 & 1 \\ 1 & 2 & 3 \\ 0 & 1 & 1 \end{bmatrix}$.

13. $\begin{bmatrix} -2 & -1 & 1 \\ 2 & 1 & 0 \\ 3 & 1 & -1 \end{bmatrix}$.

14. $\begin{bmatrix} 1 & 1 & 1 \\ 1 & -1 & 2 \\ 1 & 1 & 4 \end{bmatrix}$.

In Problems 15 through 18 find the matrix function $\mathbf{X}^{-1}(t)$ whose value at t is the inverse of the given matrix $\mathbf{X}(t)$.

15. $\mathbf{X}(t) = \begin{bmatrix} e^t & e^{4t} \\ e^t & 4e^{4t} \end{bmatrix}$.

16. $\mathbf{X}(t) = \begin{bmatrix} \sin 2t & \cos 2t \\ 2\cos 2t & -2\sin 2t \end{bmatrix}$.

17. $\mathbf{X}(t) = \begin{bmatrix} e^t & e^{-t} & e^{2t} \\ e^t & -e^{-t} & 2e^{2t} \\ e^t & e^{-t} & 4e^{2t} \end{bmatrix}$.

18. $\mathbf{X}(t) = \begin{bmatrix} e^{3t} & 1 & t \\ 3e^{3t} & 0 & 1 \\ 9e^{3t} & 0 & 0 \end{bmatrix}$.

In Problems 19 through 24 evaluate the given determinant.

19. $\begin{vmatrix} 4 & 3 \\ -1 & 2 \end{vmatrix}$.

20. $\begin{vmatrix} 12 & 8 \\ 3 & 2 \end{vmatrix}$.

21. $\begin{vmatrix} 1 & 0 & 0 \\ 3 & 1 & 2 \\ 1 & 5 & -2 \end{vmatrix}$.

22. $\begin{vmatrix} 1 & 0 & 2 \\ 0 & 3 & -1 \\ -1 & 2 & 1 \end{vmatrix}$.

23. $\begin{vmatrix} 1 & 4 & 3 \\ -1 & -1 & 2 \\ 4 & 5 & 2 \end{vmatrix}$.

24. $\begin{vmatrix} 1 & 4 & 4 \\ 3 & 0 & -3 \\ 1 & 6 & 2 \end{vmatrix}$.

In Problems 25 through 27 determine the values of r for which $\det(\mathbf{A} - r\mathbf{I}) = 0$.

25. $\mathbf{A} = \begin{bmatrix} 1 & 1 \\ -2 & 4 \end{bmatrix}$.

26. $\mathbf{A} = \begin{bmatrix} 3 & 3 \\ 2 & 4 \end{bmatrix}$.

27. $\mathbf{A} = \begin{bmatrix} 0 & 0 & 0 \\ 0 & 1 & 0 \\ 1 & 0 & 1 \end{bmatrix}$.

28. Illustrate the equivalence of the assertions (a)–(d) in Theorem 1 for the matrix

$$\mathbf{A} = \begin{bmatrix} 4 & -2 & 2 \\ -2 & 4 & 2 \\ 2 & 2 & 4 \end{bmatrix}$$

as follows.

(a) Determine a nontrivial solution $\mathbf{x}$ to $\mathbf{Ax} = \mathbf{0}$.
(b) Show that the row reduction procedure applied to $[\mathbf{A} \ \vdots \ \mathbf{I}]$ fails to produce the inverse of $\mathbf{A}$.
(c) Calculate $\det \mathbf{A}$.
(d) Find scalars c_1, c_2, and c_3, *not all zero* so that $c_1\mathbf{a}_1 + c_2\mathbf{a}_2 + c_3\mathbf{a}_3 = \mathbf{0}$, where $\mathbf{a}_1$, $\mathbf{a}_2$, and $\mathbf{a}_3$ are the columns of $\mathbf{A}$.

In Problems 29 and 30 find $d\mathbf{x}/dt$ for the given vector functions.

29. $\mathbf{x}(t) = \begin{bmatrix} e^{3t} \\ 2e^{3t} \\ -e^{3t} \end{bmatrix}$.

30. $\mathbf{x}(t) = \begin{bmatrix} e^{-t} \sin 3t \\ 0 \\ -e^{-t} \sin 3t \end{bmatrix}$.

In Problems 31 and 32 find $d\mathbf{X}/dt$ for the given matrix functions.

31. $\mathbf{X}(t) = \begin{bmatrix} e^{5t} & 3e^{2t} \\ -2e^{5t} & -e^{2t} \end{bmatrix}$.

32. $\mathbf{X}(t) = \begin{bmatrix} \sin 2t & \cos 2t & e^{-2t} \\ -\sin 2t & 2\cos 2t & 3e^{-2t} \\ 3\sin 2t & \cos 2t & e^{-2t} \end{bmatrix}$.

In Problems 33 and 34 verify that the given vector satisfies the given system.

33. $\mathbf{x}' = \begin{bmatrix} 1 & 1 \\ -2 & 4 \end{bmatrix} \mathbf{x}, \quad \mathbf{x} = \begin{bmatrix} e^{3t} \\ 2e^{3t} \end{bmatrix}.$

34. $\mathbf{x}' = \begin{bmatrix} 0 & 0 & 0 \\ 0 & 1 & 0 \\ 1 & 0 & 1 \end{bmatrix} \mathbf{x}, \quad \mathbf{x} = \begin{bmatrix} 0 \\ e^t \\ -3e^t \end{bmatrix}.$

In Problems 35 and 36 verify that the given matrix satisfies the given matrix differential equation.

35. $\mathbf{X}' = \begin{bmatrix} 1 & -1 \\ 2 & 4 \end{bmatrix} \mathbf{X}, \quad \mathbf{X} = \begin{bmatrix} e^{2t} & e^{3t} \\ -e^{2t} & -2e^{3t} \end{bmatrix}.$

36. $\mathbf{X}' = \begin{bmatrix} 1 & 0 & 0 \\ 0 & 3 & -2 \\ 0 & -2 & 3 \end{bmatrix} \mathbf{X}, \quad \mathbf{X} = \begin{bmatrix} e^t & 0 & 0 \\ 0 & e^t & e^{5t} \\ 0 & e^t & -e^{5t} \end{bmatrix}.$

In Problems 37 and 38 the matrices $\mathbf{A}(t)$ and $\mathbf{B}(t)$ are given. Find:

(a) $\int \mathbf{A}(t)\,dt.$ **(b)** $\int_0^1 \mathbf{B}(t)\,dt.$ **(c)** $\dfrac{d}{dt}\left[\mathbf{A}(t)\mathbf{B}(t)\right].$

37. $\mathbf{A}(t) = \begin{bmatrix} t & e^t \\ 1 & e^t \end{bmatrix}, \quad \mathbf{B}(t) = \begin{bmatrix} \cos t & -\sin t \\ \sin t & \cos t \end{bmatrix}.$

38. $\mathbf{A}(t) = \begin{bmatrix} 1 & e^{-2t} \\ 3 & e^{-2t} \end{bmatrix}, \quad \mathbf{B}(t) = \begin{bmatrix} e^{-t} & e^{-t} \\ -e^{-t} & 3e^{-t} \end{bmatrix}.$

39. An $n \times n$ matrix $\mathbf{A}$ is called **symmetric** if $\mathbf{A}^T = \mathbf{A}$; that is, if $a_{ij} = a_{ji}$, for all $i, j = 1, \ldots, n$. Show that if $\mathbf{A}$ is an $n \times n$ matrix, then $\mathbf{A} + \mathbf{A}^T$ is a symmetric matrix.

40. Let $\mathbf{A}$ be an $m \times n$ matrix. Show that $\mathbf{A}^T\mathbf{A}$ is a symmetric $n \times n$ matrix and $\mathbf{A}\mathbf{A}^T$ is a symmetric $m \times m$ matrix (see Problem 39).

10.3 Linear Systems in Normal Form

Using matrix notation, a system of n linear differential equations in normal form can be written as

(1) $\mathbf{x}'(t) = \mathbf{A}(t)\mathbf{x}(t) + \mathbf{f}(t),$

where $\mathbf{x}(t) = \text{col}(x_1(t), \ldots, x_n(t))$, $\mathbf{f}(t) = \text{col}(f_1(t), \ldots, f_n(t))$, and $\mathbf{A}(t) = [a_{ij}(t)]$ is an $n \times n$ matrix. As with a scalar linear differential equation, a system is called **homogeneous** when $\mathbf{f}(t) \equiv \mathbf{0}$; otherwise, it is called **nonhomogeneous.** When the elements of $\mathbf{A}$ are all constants, the system is said to have **constant coefficients.**

In Section 9.2 we observed that a linear differential equation

(2) $y^{(n)}(t) + p_1(t)y^{(n-1)}(t) + \cdots + p_n(t)y(t) = g(t)$

can be rewritten as a first order system in normal form using the substitution $x_1(t) = y(t)$, $x_2(t) = y'(t), \ldots, x_n(t) = y^{(n-1)}(t)$. In particular, equation (2) becomes $\mathbf{x}'(t) = \mathbf{A}(t)\mathbf{x}(t) + \mathbf{f}(t)$, where $\mathbf{x}(t) = \text{col}(x_1(t), \ldots, x_n(t))$, $\mathbf{f}(t) = \text{col}(0, \ldots, 0, g(t))$, and

$$\mathbf{A}(t) = \begin{bmatrix} 0 & 1 & 0 & \cdots & 0 & 0 \\ 0 & 0 & 1 & & 0 & 0 \\ \vdots & \vdots & \vdots & & \vdots & \vdots \\ 0 & 0 & 0 & \cdots & 0 & 1 \\ -p_n(t) & -p_{n-1}(t) & -p_{n-2}(t) & \cdots & -p_2(t) & -p_1(t) \end{bmatrix}.$$

The theory for systems in normal form parallels very closely the theory of linear differential equations presented in Chapters 4 and 6. In many cases the proofs for scalar linear differential equations carry over to normal systems with appropriate modifications. Conversely, results for normal systems apply to scalar linear equations since, as we showed, any scalar linear equation can be expressed as a normal system. This is the case with the existence and uniqueness theorems for linear differential equations.

The **initial value problem** for the normal system (1) is the problem of finding a differentiable vector function $\mathbf{x}(t)$ that satisfies the system on an interval I and also satisfies the **initial condition** $\mathbf{x}(t_0) = \mathbf{x}_0$, where t_0 is a given point of I and $\mathbf{x}_0 = \text{col}(x_{1,0}, \ldots, x_{n,0})$ is a given vector.

EXISTENCE AND UNIQUENESS

Theorem 2. Suppose that $\mathbf{A}(t)$ and $\mathbf{f}(t)$ are continuous on an open interval I that contains the point t_0. Then, for any choice of the initial vector $\mathbf{x}_0 = \text{col}(x_{1,0}, \ldots, x_{n,0})$, there exists a unique solution $\mathbf{x}(t)$ on the whole interval I to the initial value problem

(3) $\mathbf{x}'(t) = \mathbf{A}(t)\mathbf{x}(t) + \mathbf{f}(t), \qquad \mathbf{x}(t_0) = \mathbf{x}_0.$

We discuss this result in Chapter 11 of the extended version of the text, entitled *Fundamentals of Differential Equations and Boundary Value Problems*, and obtain as corollaries the existence and uniqueness theorems for second order equations (Theorem 2, Section 4.2) and higher order linear equations (Theorem 1, Section 6.2).

If we rewrite system (1) as $\mathbf{x}' - \mathbf{Ax} = \mathbf{f}$ and define the operator $L[\mathbf{x}] := \mathbf{x}' - \mathbf{Ax}$, then we can express system (1) in the operator form $L[\mathbf{x}] = \mathbf{f}$. Here the operator L maps vector functions into vector functions. Moreover, L is a *linear* operator in the sense that for any scalars a, b and vector functions $\mathbf{x}, \mathbf{y}$ we have

$$L[a\mathbf{x} + b\mathbf{y}] = aL[\mathbf{x}] + bL[\mathbf{y}].$$

The proof of this linearity follows from the properties of matrix multiplication (see Problem 25).

As a consequence of the linearity of L, if $\mathbf{x}_1, \ldots, \mathbf{x}_n$ are solutions to the homogeneous system $\mathbf{x}' = \mathbf{Ax}$, or $L[\mathbf{x}] = \mathbf{0}$ in operator notation, then any linear combination of these vectors, $c_1\mathbf{x}_1 + \cdots + c_n\mathbf{x}_n$, is also a solution. Moreover, we will see that if the solutions $\mathbf{x}_1, \ldots, \mathbf{x}_n$ are linearly independent, then *every* solution to $L[\mathbf{x}] = \mathbf{0}$ can be expressed as $c_1\mathbf{x}_1 + \cdots + c_n\mathbf{x}_n$ for an appropriate choice of the constants $c_1, \ldots, c_n$.

LINEAR DEPENDENCE OF VECTOR FUNCTIONS

Definition 1. The m vector functions $\mathbf{x}_1, \ldots, \mathbf{x}_m$ are said to be **linearly dependent** on an **interval** I if there exist constants $c_1, \ldots, c_m$, not all zero, such that

(4) $$c_1\mathbf{x}_1(t) + \cdots + c_m\mathbf{x}_m(t) = \mathbf{0},$$

for all t in I. If the vectors are not linearly dependent, they are said to be **linearly independent on** I.

▶ **Example 1** Show that the vector functions $\mathbf{x}_1(t) = \text{col}(e^t, 0, e^t)$, $\mathbf{x}_2(t) = \text{col}(3e^t, 0, 3e^t)$, and $\mathbf{x}_3(t) = \text{col}(t, 1, 0)$ are linearly dependent on $(-\infty, \infty)$.

Solution Notice that $\mathbf{x}_2$ is just 3 times $\mathbf{x}_1$ and therefore $3\mathbf{x}_1(t) - \mathbf{x}_2(t) + 0 \cdot \mathbf{x}_3(t) = \mathbf{0}$ for all t. Hence, $\mathbf{x}_1, \mathbf{x}_2$, and $\mathbf{x}_3$ are linearly dependent on $(-\infty, \infty)$. ◀

▶ **Example 2** Show that the vector functions $\mathbf{x}_1(t) = \text{col}(e^{2t}, 0, e^{2t})$, $\mathbf{x}_2(t) = \text{col}(e^{2t}, e^{2t}, -e^{2t})$, and $\mathbf{x}_3(t) = \text{col}(e^t, 2e^t, e^t)$ are linearly independent on $(-\infty, \infty)$.

Solution To prove independence, we assume that c_1, c_2, and c_3 are constants for which

(5) $$c_1\mathbf{x}_1(t) + c_2\mathbf{x}_2(t) + c_3\mathbf{x}_3(t) = \mathbf{0}$$

holds at every t in $(-\infty, \infty)$ and show that $c_1 = c_2 = c_3 = 0$. Since equation (5) must hold for $t = 0$, we have

$$c_1\begin{bmatrix} 1 \\ 0 \\ 1 \end{bmatrix} + c_2\begin{bmatrix} 1 \\ 1 \\ -1 \end{bmatrix} + c_3\begin{bmatrix} 1 \\ 2 \\ 1 \end{bmatrix} = \mathbf{0},$$

which is equivalent to the system of linear equations

(6)
$$
\begin{aligned}
c_1 + c_2 + c_3 &= 0, \\
c_2 + 2c_3 &= 0, \\
c_1 - c_2 + c_3 &= 0.
\end{aligned}
$$

Either by solving (6) or by checking that the determinant of its coefficients is nonzero, we see that (6) has only the trivial solution $c_1 = c_2 = c_3 = 0$. Therefore, the vector functions $\mathbf{x}_1$, $\mathbf{x}_2$, and $\mathbf{x}_3$ are linearly independent on $(-\infty, \infty)$ (in fact, on any interval containing $t = 0$). ◀

As the previous example illustrates, if $\mathbf{x}_1(t), \ldots, \mathbf{x}_n(t)$ are n vector functions having n components, then these vectors will be linearly independent on an interval I if the determinant

$$\det[\mathbf{x}_1(t) \quad \cdots \quad \mathbf{x}_n(t)]$$

is not zero at some point t in I. Because of the analogy with scalar equations, we call this determinant the **Wronskian.**

WRONSKIAN

Definition 2. The **Wronskian** of n vector functions $\mathbf{x}_1(t) = \text{col}(x_{1,1}, \ldots, x_{n,1}), \ldots,$ $\mathbf{x}_n(t) = \text{col}(x_{1,n}, \ldots, x_{n,n})$ is defined to be the real-valued function

$$(7) \qquad W[\mathbf{x}_1, \ldots, \mathbf{x}_n](t) := \begin{vmatrix} x_{1,1}(t) & x_{1,2}(t) & \cdots & x_{1,n}(t) \\ x_{2,1}(t) & x_{2,2}(t) & \cdots & x_{2,n}(t) \\ \cdot & \cdot & & \cdot \\ \cdot & \cdot & & \cdot \\ \cdot & \cdot & & \cdot \\ x_{n,1}(t) & x_{n,2}(t) & \cdots & x_{n,n}(t) \end{vmatrix}.$$

If $\mathbf{x}_1, \ldots, \mathbf{x}_n$ are *linearly independent solutions* on I to the same $n \times n$ homogeneous system, then we can use the existence and uniqueness theorem to prove that the Wronskian $W(t) := W[\mathbf{x}_1, \ldots, \mathbf{x}_n](t)$ is never zero on I. Suppose to the contrary that the determinant $W(t_0) = 0$ at some t_0 in I; then from part (d) of Theorem 1, page 544, there exist scalars $c_1, \ldots, c_n$ *not all zero* such that

$$c_1\mathbf{x}_1(t_0) + \cdots + c_n\mathbf{x}_n(t_0) = \mathbf{0}.$$

But since $c_1\mathbf{x}_1(t) + \cdots + c_n\mathbf{x}_n(t)$ and the zero vector are both solutions to $\mathbf{x}' = \mathbf{A}\mathbf{x}$ on I, and they agree at point t_0, these solutions must be identical on I according to Theorem 2. That is,

$$c_1\mathbf{x}_1(t) + \cdots + c_n\mathbf{x}_n(t) = \mathbf{0}$$

for all t in I. But, this contradicts the given information that $\mathbf{x}_1, \ldots, \mathbf{x}_n$ are linearly independent on I. We have shown that $W(t_0) \neq 0$ and since t_0 is an arbitrary point, it follows that $W(t) \neq 0$ for all $t \in I$.

The preceding argument has two important implications that parallel the scalar case. First, *the Wronskian of solutions to* $\mathbf{x}' = \mathbf{Ax}$ *is either identically zero or never zero on I* (see also Problem 31). Second, *a set of n solutions* $\mathbf{x}_1, \ldots, \mathbf{x}_n$ *to* $\mathbf{x}' = \mathbf{Ax}$ *on I is linearly independent on I if and only if their Wronskian is never zero on I.* With these facts in hand, we can imitate the proof given for the scalar case in Section 6.2 (Theorem 2) to obtain the following representation theorem for the solutions to $\mathbf{x}' = \mathbf{Ax}$.

REPRESENTATION OF SOLUTIONS (HOMOGENEOUS CASE)

Theorem 3.   Let $\mathbf{x}_1, \ldots, \mathbf{x}_n$ be n linearly independent solutions to the homogeneous system

(8) $\mathbf{x}'(t) = \mathbf{A}(t)\mathbf{x}(t)$

on the interval I, where $\mathbf{A}(t)$ is an $n \times n$ matrix function continuous on I. Then every solution to (8) on I can be expressed in the form

(9) $\mathbf{x}(t) = c_1\mathbf{x}_1(t) + \cdots + c_n\mathbf{x}_n(t),$

where $c_1, \ldots, c_n$ are constants.

A set of solutions $\{\mathbf{x}_1, \ldots, \mathbf{x}_n\}$ that are linearly independent on I or, equivalently, whose Wronskian does not vanish on I, is called a **fundamental solution set** for (8) on I. The linear combination in (9), written with arbitrary constants, is referred to as a **general solution** to (8).

If we take the vectors in a fundamental solution set and let them form the columns of a matrix $\mathbf{X}(t)$, that is,

(10) $\mathbf{X}(t) := \begin{bmatrix} x_{1,1}(t) & x_{1,2}(t) & \cdots & x_{1,n}(t) \\ x_{2,1}(t) & x_{2,2}(t) & \cdots & x_{2,n}(t) \\ \cdot & \cdot & & \cdot \\ \cdot & \cdot & & \cdot \\ \cdot & \cdot & & \cdot \\ x_{n,1}(t) & x_{n,2}(t) & \cdots & x_{n,n}(t) \end{bmatrix},$

then $\det \mathbf{X}(t) = W[\mathbf{x}_1, \ldots, \mathbf{x}_n](t)$. The matrix in (10) is called a **fundamental matrix** for (8), and we can use it to express the general solution (9) as

$\mathbf{x}(t) = \mathbf{X}(t)\mathbf{c},$

where $\mathbf{c} = \text{col}(c_1, \ldots, c_n)$ is an arbitrary constant vector. Since $\det \mathbf{X} = W[\mathbf{x}_1, \ldots, \mathbf{x}_n]$ is never zero on I, it follows from Theorem 1 in Section 10.2 that $\mathbf{X}(t)$ is invertible for every t in I.

▶ **Example 3**   Verify that the set

$$
S = \left\{ \begin{bmatrix} e^{2t} \\ e^{2t} \\ e^{2t} \end{bmatrix}, \begin{bmatrix} -e^{-t} \\ 0 \\ e^{-t} \end{bmatrix}, \begin{bmatrix} 0 \\ e^{-t} \\ -e^{-t} \end{bmatrix} \right\}
$$

is a fundamental solution set for the system

(11) $\mathbf{x}'(t) = \begin{bmatrix} 0 & 1 & 1 \\ 1 & 0 & 1 \\ 1 & 1 & 0 \end{bmatrix} \mathbf{x}(t)$

on the interval $(-\infty, \infty)$ and find a fundamental matrix for (11). Also determine a general solution for (11).

Solution   Substituting the first vector in the set S into the right-hand side of (11) gives

$$
\mathbf{Ax} = \begin{bmatrix} 0 & 1 & 1 \\ 1 & 0 & 1 \\ 1 & 1 & 0 \end{bmatrix} \begin{bmatrix} e^{2t} \\ e^{2t} \\ e^{2t} \end{bmatrix} = \begin{bmatrix} 2e^{2t} \\ 2e^{2t} \\ 2e^{2t} \end{bmatrix} = \mathbf{x}'(t);
$$

hence this vector satisfies system (11) for all t. Similar computations verify that the remaining vectors in S are also solutions to (11) on $(-\infty, \infty)$. To show that S is a fundamental solution set, it is enough to observe that the Wronskian

$$
W(t) = \begin{vmatrix} e^{2t} & -e^{-t} & 0 \\ e^{2t} & 0 & e^{-t} \\ e^{2t} & e^{-t} & -e^{-t} \end{vmatrix} = e^{2t} \begin{vmatrix} 0 & e^{-t} \\ e^{-t} & -e^{-t} \end{vmatrix} + e^{-t} \begin{vmatrix} e^{2t} & e^{-t} \\ e^{2t} & -e^{-t} \end{vmatrix} = -3
$$

is never zero.

A fundamental matrix $\mathbf{X}(t)$ for (11) is just the matrix we used to compute the Wronskian; that is,

(12) $\mathbf{X}(t) := \begin{bmatrix} e^{2t} & -e^{-t} & 0 \\ e^{2t} & 0 & e^{-t} \\ e^{2t} & e^{-t} & -e^{-t} \end{bmatrix}.$

A general solution to (11) can now be expressed as

$$
\mathbf{x}(t) = \mathbf{X}(t)\mathbf{c} = c_1 \begin{bmatrix} e^{2t} \\ e^{2t} \\ e^{2t} \end{bmatrix} + c_2 \begin{bmatrix} -e^{-t} \\ 0 \\ e^{-t} \end{bmatrix} + c_3 \begin{bmatrix} 0 \\ e^{-t} \\ -e^{-t} \end{bmatrix}. \quad ◀
$$

It is easy to check that the fundamental matrix in (12) satisfies the equation

$$(13) \qquad \mathbf{X}'(t) = \begin{bmatrix} 0 & 1 & 1 \\ 1 & 0 & 1 \\ 1 & 1 & 0 \end{bmatrix} \mathbf{X}(t).$$

In general, a fundamental matrix for a system $\mathbf{x}' = \mathbf{A}\mathbf{x}$ satisfies the corresponding **matrix differential equation** $\mathbf{X}' = \mathbf{A}\mathbf{X}$.

Another consequence of the linearity of the operator L defined by $L[\mathbf{x}] := \mathbf{x}' - \mathbf{A}\mathbf{x}$ is the **superposition principle** for linear systems. It states that if $\mathbf{x}_1$ and $\mathbf{x}_2$ are solutions, respectively, to the nonhomogeneous systems

$$L[\mathbf{x}] = \mathbf{g}_1 \quad \text{and} \quad L[\mathbf{x}] = \mathbf{g}_2,$$

then $c_1\mathbf{x}_1 + c_2\mathbf{x}_2$ is a solution to

$$L[\mathbf{x}] = c_1\mathbf{g}_1 + c_2\mathbf{g}_2.$$

Using this superposition principle and the representation theorem for homogeneous systems, we can prove the following theorem.

REPRESENTATION OF SOLUTIONS (NONHOMOGENEOUS CASE)

Theorem 4. Let $\mathbf{x}_p$ be a particular solution to the nonhomogeneous system

$$(14) \qquad \mathbf{x}'(t) = \mathbf{A}(t)\mathbf{x}(t) + \mathbf{f}(t)$$

on the interval I, and let $\{\mathbf{x}_1, \ldots, \mathbf{x}_n\}$ be a fundamental solution set on I for the corresponding homogeneous system $\mathbf{x}'(t) = \mathbf{A}(t)\mathbf{x}(t)$. Then every solution to (14) on I can be expressed in the form

$$(15) \qquad \mathbf{x}(t) = \mathbf{x}_p(t) + c_1\mathbf{x}_1(t) + \cdots + c_n\mathbf{x}_n(t),$$

where $c_1, \ldots, c_n$ are constants.

The proof of this theorem is almost identical to the proofs of Theorem 7 in Section 4.7 and Theorem 4 in Section 6.2. We leave it as an exercise.

The linear combination of $\mathbf{x}_p, \mathbf{x}_1, \ldots, \mathbf{x}_n$ in (15) written with arbitrary constants $c_1, \ldots, c_n$ is called a **general solution** of (14). This general solution can also be expressed as $\mathbf{x} = \mathbf{x}_p + \mathbf{X}\mathbf{c}$, where $\mathbf{X}$ is a fundamental matrix for the homogeneous system and $\mathbf{c}$ is an arbitrary constant vector.

Below we summarize the results of this section as they apply to the problem of finding a general solution to a system of n linear first order differential equations in normal form.

APPROACH TO SOLVING NORMAL SYSTEMS

1. To obtain a general solution to the $n \times n$ homogeneous system $\mathbf{x}' = \mathbf{A}\mathbf{x}$:

    (a) Find a fundamental solution set $\{\mathbf{x}_1, \ldots, \mathbf{x}_n\}$ that consists of n linearly independent solutions to the homogeneous system.

    (b) A general solution is

    $$\mathbf{x} = \mathbf{X}\mathbf{c} = c_1\mathbf{x}_1 + \cdots + c_n\mathbf{x}_n,$$

    where $\mathbf{c} = \operatorname{col}(c_1, \ldots, c_n)$ is a constant vector and $\mathbf{X} = [\mathbf{x}_1, \ldots, \mathbf{x}_n]$ is the fundamental matrix whose columns are the vectors in the fundamental solution set.

2. To obtain a general solution to the nonhomogeneous system $\mathbf{x}' = \mathbf{A}\mathbf{x} + \mathbf{f}$:

    (a) Find a particular solution $\mathbf{x}_p$ to the nonhomogeneous system.

    (b) A general solution to the nonhomogeneous system is

    $$\mathbf{x} = \mathbf{x}_p + \mathbf{X}\mathbf{c} = \mathbf{x}_p + c_1\mathbf{x}_1 + \cdots + c_n\mathbf{x}_n,$$

    where $\mathbf{X}\mathbf{c} = c_1\mathbf{x}_1 + \cdots + c_n\mathbf{x}_n$ is the general solution to the homogeneous system obtained in Part 1.

The remainder of this chapter is devoted to methods for finding fundamental solution sets in the homogeneous case and particular solutions for nonhomogeneous systems.

EXERCISES 10.3

In Problems 1 through 4 write the given system in the matrix form $\mathbf{x}' = \mathbf{A}\mathbf{x} + \mathbf{f}$.

1. $x'(t) = 3x(t) - y(t) + t^2,$
$y'(t) = -x(t) + 2y(t) + e^t.$

2. $r'(t) = 2r(t) + \sin t,$
$\theta'(t) = r(t) - \theta(t) + 1.$

3. $\dfrac{dx}{dt} = x + y + z,$

$\dfrac{dy}{dt} = 2x - y + 3z,$

$\dfrac{dz}{dt} = x + 5z.$

4. $\dfrac{dx}{dt} = t^2 x - y - z + t,$

$\dfrac{dy}{dt} = e^t z + 5,$

$\dfrac{dz}{dt} = tx - y + 3z - e^t.$

In Problems 5 through 8 rewrite the given scalar equation as a first order system in normal form. Express the system in the matrix form $\mathbf{x}' = \mathbf{A}\mathbf{x} + \mathbf{f}$.

5. $y''(t) - 3y'(t) - 10y(t) = \sin t$.

6. $y''(t) + y(t) = t^2$.

7. $\dfrac{d^4 y}{dt^4} + y = t^2$.

8. $\dfrac{d^3 y}{dt^3} - \dfrac{dy}{dt} + y = \cos t$.

In Problems 9 through 12 write the given system as a set of scalar equations.

9. $\mathbf{x}' = \begin{bmatrix} 2 & 1 \\ -1 & 3 \end{bmatrix} \mathbf{x} + e^t \begin{bmatrix} t \\ 1 \end{bmatrix}$.

10. $\mathbf{x}' = \begin{bmatrix} 5 & 0 \\ -2 & 4 \end{bmatrix} \mathbf{x} + e^{-2t} \begin{bmatrix} 2 \\ -3 \end{bmatrix}$.

11. $\mathbf{x}' = \begin{bmatrix} 1 & 0 & 1 \\ -1 & 2 & 5 \\ 0 & 5 & 1 \end{bmatrix} \mathbf{x} + e^t \begin{bmatrix} 1 \\ 0 \\ 0 \end{bmatrix} + t \begin{bmatrix} 0 \\ 1 \\ 0 \end{bmatrix}$.

12. $\mathbf{x}' = \begin{bmatrix} 0 & 1 & 0 \\ 0 & 0 & 1 \\ -1 & 1 & 2 \end{bmatrix} \mathbf{x} + t \begin{bmatrix} 1 \\ -1 \\ 2 \end{bmatrix} + \begin{bmatrix} 3 \\ 1 \\ 0 \end{bmatrix}$.

In Problems 13 through 18 determine whether the given vector functions are linearly dependent (LD) or linearly independent (LI) on the interval $(-\infty, \infty)$.

13. $\begin{bmatrix} t \\ 3 \end{bmatrix}$, $\begin{bmatrix} 4 \\ 1 \end{bmatrix}$.

14. $\begin{bmatrix} \sin t \\ \cos t \end{bmatrix}$, $\begin{bmatrix} \sin 2t \\ \cos 2t \end{bmatrix}$.

15. $\begin{bmatrix} te^{-t} \\ e^{-t} \end{bmatrix}$, $\begin{bmatrix} e^{-t} \\ e^{-t} \end{bmatrix}$.

16. $e^t \begin{bmatrix} 1 \\ 5 \end{bmatrix}$, $e^t \begin{bmatrix} -3 \\ -15 \end{bmatrix}$.

17. $e^{2t} \begin{bmatrix} 1 \\ 0 \\ 5 \end{bmatrix}$, $e^{2t} \begin{bmatrix} 1 \\ 1 \\ -1 \end{bmatrix}$, $e^{3t} \begin{bmatrix} 0 \\ 1 \\ 0 \end{bmatrix}$.

18. $\begin{bmatrix} 1 \\ 0 \\ 1 \end{bmatrix}$, $\begin{bmatrix} t \\ 0 \\ t \end{bmatrix}$, $\begin{bmatrix} t^2 \\ 0 \\ t^2 \end{bmatrix}$.

In Problems 19 through 22 the given vector functions are solutions to the system $\mathbf{x}'(t) = \mathbf{A}\mathbf{x}(t)$. *Determine whether they form a fundamental solution set. If they do, find a fundamental matrix for the system and give a general solution.*

19. $\mathbf{x}_1 = e^{-t} \begin{bmatrix} 3 \\ 2 \end{bmatrix}$, $\mathbf{x}_2 = e^{4t} \begin{bmatrix} 1 \\ -1 \end{bmatrix}$.

20. $\mathbf{x}_1 = e^{2t} \begin{bmatrix} 1 \\ -2 \end{bmatrix}$, $\mathbf{x}_2 = e^{2t} \begin{bmatrix} -2 \\ 4 \end{bmatrix}$.

21. $\mathbf{x}_1 = \begin{bmatrix} e^{-t} \\ 2e^{-t} \\ e^{-t} \end{bmatrix}$, $\mathbf{x}_2 = \begin{bmatrix} e^t \\ 0 \\ e^t \end{bmatrix}$, $\mathbf{x}_3 = \begin{bmatrix} e^{3t} \\ -e^{3t} \\ 2e^{3t} \end{bmatrix}$.

22. $\mathbf{x}_1 = \begin{bmatrix} e^t \\ e^t \\ e^t \end{bmatrix}$, $\mathbf{x}_2 = \begin{bmatrix} \sin t \\ \cos t \\ -\sin t \end{bmatrix}$, $\mathbf{x}_3 = \begin{bmatrix} -\cos t \\ \sin t \\ \cos t \end{bmatrix}$.

23. Verify that the vector functions

$$\mathbf{x}_1 = \begin{bmatrix} e^t \\ e^t \end{bmatrix} \quad \text{and} \quad \mathbf{x}_2 = \begin{bmatrix} e^{-t} \\ 3e^{-t} \end{bmatrix}$$

are solutions to the homogeneous system

$$\mathbf{x}' = \mathbf{A}\mathbf{x} = \begin{bmatrix} 2 & -1 \\ 3 & -2 \end{bmatrix} \mathbf{x},$$

on $(-\infty, \infty)$, and that

$$\mathbf{x}_p = \frac{3}{2}\begin{bmatrix} te^t \\ te^t \end{bmatrix} - \frac{1}{4}\begin{bmatrix} e^t \\ 3e^t \end{bmatrix} + \begin{bmatrix} t \\ 2t \end{bmatrix} - \begin{bmatrix} 0 \\ 1 \end{bmatrix}$$

is a particular solution to the nonhomogeneous system $\mathbf{x}' = \mathbf{A}\mathbf{x} + \mathbf{f}(t)$, where $\mathbf{f}(t) = \text{col}(e^t, t)$. Find a general solution to $\mathbf{x}' = \mathbf{A}\mathbf{x} + \mathbf{f}(t)$.

24. Verify that the vector functions

$$\mathbf{x}_1 = \begin{bmatrix} e^{3t} \\ 0 \\ e^{3t} \end{bmatrix}, \qquad \mathbf{x}_2 = \begin{bmatrix} -e^{3t} \\ e^{3t} \\ 0 \end{bmatrix}, \qquad \mathbf{x}_3 = \begin{bmatrix} -e^{-3t} \\ -e^{-3t} \\ e^{-3t} \end{bmatrix}$$

are solutions to the homogeneous system

$$\mathbf{x}' = \mathbf{A}\mathbf{x} = \begin{bmatrix} 1 & -2 & 2 \\ -2 & 1 & 2 \\ 2 & 2 & 1 \end{bmatrix} \mathbf{x},$$

on $(-\infty, \infty)$, and that

$$\mathbf{x}_p = \begin{bmatrix} 5t + 1 \\ 2t \\ 4t + 2 \end{bmatrix}$$

is a particular solution to $\mathbf{x}' = \mathbf{A}\mathbf{x} + \mathbf{f}(t)$, where $\mathbf{f}(t) = \text{col}(-9, 0, -18)$. Find a general solution to $\mathbf{x}' = \mathbf{A}\mathbf{x} + \mathbf{f}(t)$.

25. Prove that the operator defined by $L[\mathbf{x}] := \mathbf{x}' - \mathbf{A}\mathbf{x}$, where $\mathbf{A}$ is an $n \times n$ matrix function and $\mathbf{x}$ is an $n \times 1$ vector function, is a linear operator.

26. Let $\mathbf{X}(t)$ be a fundamental matrix for the system $\mathbf{x}' = \mathbf{A}\mathbf{x}$. Show that $\mathbf{x}(t) = \mathbf{X}(t)\mathbf{X}^{-1}(t_0)\mathbf{x}_0$ is the solution to the initial value problem $\mathbf{x}' = \mathbf{A}\mathbf{x}$, $\mathbf{x}(t_0) = \mathbf{x}_0$.

In Problems 27 and 28 verify that $\mathbf{X}(t)$ is a fundamental matrix for the given system and compute $\mathbf{X}^{-1}(t)$. Use the result of Problem 26 to find the solution to the given initial value problem.

27. $\mathbf{x}' = \begin{bmatrix} 0 & 6 & 0 \\ 1 & 0 & 1 \\ 1 & 1 & 0 \end{bmatrix} \mathbf{x}$, $\quad \mathbf{x}(0) = \begin{bmatrix} -1 \\ 0 \\ 1 \end{bmatrix}$; $\quad \mathbf{X}(t) = \begin{bmatrix} 6e^{-t} & -3e^{-2t} & 2e^{3t} \\ -e^{-t} & e^{-2t} & e^{3t} \\ -5e^{-t} & e^{-2t} & e^{3t} \end{bmatrix}$.

28. $\mathbf{x}' = \begin{bmatrix} 2 & 3 \\ 3 & 2 \end{bmatrix}\mathbf{x}, \qquad \mathbf{x}(0) = \begin{bmatrix} 3 \\ -1 \end{bmatrix}; \qquad \mathbf{X}(t) = \begin{bmatrix} e^{-t} & e^{5t} \\ -e^{-t} & e^{5t} \end{bmatrix}.$

29. Show that

$$\begin{vmatrix} t^2 & t|t| \\ 2t & 2|t| \end{vmatrix} \equiv 0$$

on $(-\infty, \infty)$, but that the two column vectors

$$\begin{bmatrix} t^2 \\ 2t \end{bmatrix}, \qquad \begin{bmatrix} t|t| \\ 2|t| \end{bmatrix}$$

are linearly independent on $(-\infty, \infty)$.

30. Abel's formula. If $\mathbf{x}_1, \ldots, \mathbf{x}_n$ are any n solutions to the $n \times n$ system $\mathbf{x}'(t) = \mathbf{A}(t)\mathbf{x}(t)$, then Abel's formula gives a representation for the Wronskian $W(t) := W[\mathbf{x}_1, \ldots, \mathbf{x}_n](t)$. Namely,

$$W(t) = W(t_0) \exp\left(\int_{t_0}^{t} \{a_{11}(s) + \cdots + a_{nn}(s)\}\, ds \right),$$

where $a_{11}(s), \ldots, a_{nn}(s)$ are the main diagonal elements of $\mathbf{A}(s)$. Prove this formula in the special case when $n = 3$. [Hint: Follow the outline in Problem 31 of Exercises 6.2.]

31. Using Abel's formula, prove that the Wronskian of n solutions to $\mathbf{x}' = \mathbf{A}\mathbf{x}$ on the interval I is either identically zero on I or never zero on I.

32. Prove that a fundamental solution set for the homogeneous system $\mathbf{x}'(t) = \mathbf{A}(t)\mathbf{x}(t)$ always exists on an interval I, provided that $\mathbf{A}(t)$ is continuous on I. [Hint: Use the existence and uniqueness theorem (Theorem 2) and make judicious choices for $\mathbf{x}_0$.]

33. Prove Theorem 3 on the representation of solutions of the homogeneous system.

34. Prove Theorem 4 on the representation of solutions of the nonhomogeneous system.

10.4 Homogeneous Linear Systems with Constant Coefficients

In this section we discuss a procedure for obtaining a general solution for the homogeneous system

(1) $\qquad \mathbf{x}'(t) = \mathbf{A}\mathbf{x}(t),$

where $\mathbf{A}$ is a (real) *constant* $n \times n$ matrix. The general solution we seek will be defined for all t because the elements of $\mathbf{A}$ are just constant functions, which are continuous on $(-\infty, \infty)$ (recall Theorem 2, page 549). In Section 10.3 we showed that a general solution to (1) can be constructed from a fundamental solution set consisting of n linearly independent solutions to (1). Thus our goal is to find n such vector solutions.

In Chapter 4 we were successful in solving homogeneous linear equations with constant coefficients by guessing that the equation had a solution of the form e^{rt}. Since any scalar linear equation can be expressed as a system, it is reasonable to expect system (1) to have solutions of the form

(2) $\mathbf{x}(t) = e^{rt}\mathbf{u},$

where r is a constant and $\mathbf{u}$ is a constant vector, both of which must be determined. Substituting $e^{rt}\mathbf{u}$ for $\mathbf{x}(t)$ in (1) gives

$$re^{rt}\mathbf{u} = \mathbf{A}e^{rt}\mathbf{u} = e^{rt}\mathbf{A}\mathbf{u}.$$

Canceling the factor e^{rt} and rearranging terms, we find that

(3) $(\mathbf{A} - r\mathbf{I})\mathbf{u} = \mathbf{0},$

where $r\mathbf{I}$ denotes the diagonal matrix with r's along its main diagonal.

The preceding calculation shows that $\mathbf{x}(t) = e^{rt}\mathbf{u}$ is a solution to (1) if and only if r and $\mathbf{u}$ satisfy equation (3). Since the trivial case, $\mathbf{u} = \mathbf{0}$, is of no help in finding linearly independent solutions to (1), we require that $\mathbf{u} \neq \mathbf{0}$. Such vectors are given a special name.

EIGENVALUES AND EIGENVECTORS

Definition 3.   Let $\mathbf{A} = [a_{ij}]$ be an $n \times n$ constant matrix. The **eigenvalues** of $\mathbf{A}$ are those (real or complex) numbers r for which $(\mathbf{A} - r\mathbf{I})\mathbf{u} = \mathbf{0}$ has at least one nontrivial solution[†] $\mathbf{u}$. The corresponding nontrivial solutions $\mathbf{u}$ are called the **eigenvectors** of $\mathbf{A}$ associated with r.

As stated in Theorem 1 of Section 10.2, a linear homogeneous system of n algebraic equations in n unknowns has a nontrivial solution if and only if the determinant of its coefficients is zero. Hence a necessary and sufficient condition for (3) to have a nontrivial solution is that

(4) $|\mathbf{A} - r\mathbf{I}| = 0.$

[†] We will allow $\mathbf{u}$ to have complex-number entries.

Expanding the determinant in (4), we find that it is an *n*th degree polynomial in *r*; that is,

(5) $|\mathbf{A} - r\mathbf{I}| = p(r).$

Therefore, *finding the eigenvalues of a matrix* **A** *is equivalent to finding the zeros of the polynomial p(r)*. Equation (4) is called the **characteristic equation** of **A**, and *p(r)* in (5) is the **characteristic polynomial** of **A**. The characteristic equation plays a role for systems similar to the role played by the auxiliary equation for scalar linear equations.

▶ *Example 1*   Find the eigenvalues and eigenvectors of the matrix

$$\mathbf{A} := \begin{bmatrix} 2 & -3 \\ 1 & -2 \end{bmatrix}.$$

Solution   The characteristic equation for **A** is

(6) $|\mathbf{A} - r\mathbf{I}| = \begin{vmatrix} 2-r & -3 \\ 1 & -2-r \end{vmatrix} = (2-r)(-2-r) + 3 = r^2 - 1 = 0.$

Hence the eigenvalues of **A** are $r_1 = 1$, $r_2 = -1$. To find the eigenvectors corresponding to $r_1 = 1$, we must solve $(\mathbf{A} - r_1\mathbf{I})\mathbf{u} = \mathbf{0}$. Substituting for **A** and r_1 gives

(7) $\begin{bmatrix} 1 & -3 \\ 1 & -3 \end{bmatrix} \begin{bmatrix} u_1 \\ u_2 \end{bmatrix} = \begin{bmatrix} 0 \\ 0 \end{bmatrix}.$

Notice that this matrix equation is equivalent to the single scalar equation $u_1 - 3u_2 = 0$. Therefore the solutions to (7) are obtained by assigning an arbitrary value for u_2, say $u_2 = s$, and setting $u_1 = 3u_2 = 3s$. Consequently, the eigenvectors associated with $r_1 = 1$ can be expressed as

(8) $\mathbf{u}_1 = s\begin{bmatrix} 3 \\ 1 \end{bmatrix}.$

For $r_2 = -1$, the equation $(\mathbf{A} - r_2\mathbf{I})\mathbf{u} = \mathbf{0}$ becomes

(9) $\begin{bmatrix} 3 & -3 \\ 1 & -1 \end{bmatrix} \begin{bmatrix} u_1 \\ u_2 \end{bmatrix} = \begin{bmatrix} 0 \\ 0 \end{bmatrix}.$

Solving (9), we obtain $u_1 = s$ and $u_2 = s$. Therefore, the eigenvectors associated with the eigenvalue $r_2 = -1$ are

(10) $\mathbf{u}_2 = s\begin{bmatrix} 1 \\ 1 \end{bmatrix}.$ ◀

We remark that in the above example the collection (8) of all eigenvectors associated with $r_1 = 1$ forms a one-dimensional subspace when the zero vector is adjoined. The same is true for $r_2 = -1$. These subspaces are called **eigenspaces.**

▶ *Example 2* Find the eigenvalues and eigenvectors of the matrix

$$\mathbf{A} := \begin{bmatrix} 1 & 2 & -1 \\ 1 & 0 & 1 \\ 4 & -4 & 5 \end{bmatrix}.$$

Solution The characteristic equation for **A** is

$$(11) \qquad |\mathbf{A} - r\mathbf{I}| = \begin{vmatrix} 1-r & 2 & -1 \\ 1 & -r & 1 \\ 4 & -4 & 5-r \end{vmatrix} = 0,$$

which simplifies to $(r-1)(r-2)(r-3) = 0$. Hence the eigenvalues of **A** are $r_1 = 1$, $r_2 = 2$, and $r_3 = 3$. To find the eigenvectors corresponding to $r_1 = 1$, we set $r = 1$ in $(\mathbf{A} - r\mathbf{I})\mathbf{u} = \mathbf{0}$. This gives

$$(12) \qquad \begin{bmatrix} 0 & 2 & -1 \\ 1 & -1 & 1 \\ 4 & -4 & 4 \end{bmatrix} \begin{bmatrix} u_1 \\ u_2 \\ u_3 \end{bmatrix} = \begin{bmatrix} 0 \\ 0 \\ 0 \end{bmatrix}.$$

Using elementary row operations (Gaussian elimination), we see that (12) is equivalent to the two equations

$$(13) \qquad \begin{aligned} u_1 - u_2 + u_3 &= 0, \\ 2u_2 - u_3 &= 0. \end{aligned}$$

Thus we can obtain the solutions to (12) by assigning an arbitrary value to u_2, say $u_2 = s$, solving $2u_2 - u_3 = 0$ for u_3 to get $u_3 = 2s$, and then solving $u_1 - u_2 + u_3 = 0$ for u_1 to get $u_1 = -s$. Hence the eigenvectors associated with $r_1 = 1$ are

$$(14) \qquad \mathbf{u}_1 = s \begin{bmatrix} -1 \\ 1 \\ 2 \end{bmatrix}.$$

For $r_2 = 2$, we solve

$$(15) \qquad \begin{bmatrix} -1 & 2 & -1 \\ 1 & -2 & 1 \\ 4 & -4 & 3 \end{bmatrix} \begin{bmatrix} u_1 \\ u_2 \\ u_3 \end{bmatrix} = \begin{bmatrix} 0 \\ 0 \\ 0 \end{bmatrix}$$

in a similar fashion to obtain the eigenvectors

(16) $\qquad \mathbf{u}_2 = s \begin{bmatrix} -2 \\ 1 \\ 4 \end{bmatrix}.$

Finally, for $r_3 = 3$, we solve

(17) $\qquad \begin{bmatrix} -2 & 2 & -1 \\ 1 & -3 & 1 \\ 4 & -4 & 2 \end{bmatrix} \begin{bmatrix} u_1 \\ u_2 \\ u_3 \end{bmatrix} = \begin{bmatrix} 0 \\ 0 \\ 0 \end{bmatrix}$

and get the eigenvectors

(18) $\qquad \mathbf{u}_3 = s \begin{bmatrix} -1 \\ 1 \\ 4 \end{bmatrix}.$ ◄

Let's return to the problem of finding a general solution to a homogeneous system of differential equations. We have already shown that $e^{rt}\mathbf{u}$ is a solution to (1) if r is an eigenvalue and $\mathbf{u}$ a corresponding eigenvector. The question is: Can we obtain n linearly independent solutions to the homogeneous system by finding all the eigenvalues and eigenvectors of $\mathbf{A}$?

---

n LINEARLY INDEPENDENT EIGENVECTORS

Theorem 5. Suppose that the $n \times n$ constant matrix $\mathbf{A}$ has n linearly independent eigenvectors $\mathbf{u}_1, \mathbf{u}_2, \ldots, \mathbf{u}_n$. Let r_i be the eigenvalue[†] corresponding to $\mathbf{u}_i$. Then

(19) $\qquad \{e^{r_1 t}\mathbf{u}_1, e^{r_2 t}\mathbf{u}_2, \ldots, e^{r_n t}\mathbf{u}_n\}$

is a fundamental solution set on $(-\infty, \infty)$ for the homogeneous system $\mathbf{x}' = \mathbf{A}\mathbf{x}$. Consequently, a general solution of $\mathbf{x}' = \mathbf{A}\mathbf{x}$ is

(20) $\qquad \mathbf{x}(t) = c_1 e^{r_1 t}\mathbf{u}_1 + c_2 e^{r_2 t}\mathbf{u}_2 + \cdots + c_n e^{r_n t}\mathbf{u}_n,$

where $c_1, \ldots, c_n$ are arbitrary constants.

[†] The eigenvalues $r_1, \ldots, r_n$ may be real or complex and need not be distinct. In this section the cases we discuss have real eigenvalues. We discuss complex eigenvalues in Section 10.5.

Proof As we have seen, the vector functions listed in (19) are solutions to the homogeneous system. Moreover, their Wronskian is

$$W(t) = \det[e^{r_1 t}\mathbf{u}_1, \quad \ldots, \quad e^{r_n t}\mathbf{u}_n] = e^{(r_1 + \cdots + r_n)t}\det[\mathbf{u}_1, \quad \ldots, \quad \mathbf{u}_n].$$

Since the eigenvectors are assumed to be linearly independent, it follows from Theorem 1 in Section 10.2 that $\det[\mathbf{u}_1, \ldots, \mathbf{u}_n]$ is not zero. Hence the Wronskian $W(t)$ is never zero. This shows that (19) is a fundamental solution set, and consequently a general solution is given by (20). ∎

An application of Theorem 5 is given in the next example.

▶ ***Example 3*** Find a general solution of

(21) $$\mathbf{x}'(t) = \mathbf{A}\mathbf{x}(t), \quad \text{where} \quad \mathbf{A} = \begin{bmatrix} 2 & -3 \\ 1 & -2 \end{bmatrix}.$$

Solution In Example 1 we showed that the matrix $\mathbf{A}$ has eigenvalues $r_1 = 1$ and $r_2 = -1$. Taking $s = 1$ in equations (8) and (10), we get the corresponding eigenvectors

$$\mathbf{u}_1 = \begin{bmatrix} 3 \\ 1 \end{bmatrix} \quad \text{and} \quad \mathbf{u}_2 = \begin{bmatrix} 1 \\ 1 \end{bmatrix}.$$

Since $\mathbf{u}_1$ and $\mathbf{u}_2$ are linearly independent, it follows from Theorem 5 that a general solution to (21) is

(22) $$\mathbf{x}(t) = c_1 e^t \begin{bmatrix} 3 \\ 1 \end{bmatrix} + c_2 e^{-t} \begin{bmatrix} 1 \\ 1 \end{bmatrix}. \quad ◀$$

If we sum the vectors on the right-hand side of equation (22) and then write out the expressions for the components of $\mathbf{x}(t) = \text{col}(x_1(t), x_2(t))$, we get

(23)
$$x_1(t) = 3c_1 e^t + c_2 e^{-t},$$
$$x_2(t) = c_1 e^t + c_2 e^{-t}.$$

This is the familiar form of a general solution for a system, as discussed in Chapter 9.

A useful property of eigenvectors that concerns their linear independence is stated in the next theorem.

LINEAR INDEPENDENCE OF EIGENVECTORS

Theorem 6. If $r_1, \ldots, r_m$ are *distinct* eigenvalues for the matrix $\mathbf{A}$ and $\mathbf{u}_i$ is an eigenvector associated with r_i, then $\mathbf{u}_1, \ldots, \mathbf{u}_m$ are linearly independent.

Proof   Let's first treat the case $m = 2$. Suppose, to the contrary, that $\mathbf{u}_1$ and $\mathbf{u}_2$ are linearly dependent, so that

(24) $\mathbf{u}_1 = c\mathbf{u}_2$

for some constant c. Multiplying both sides of (24) by $\mathbf{A}$ and using the fact that $\mathbf{u}_1$ and $\mathbf{u}_2$ are eigenvectors with corresponding eigenvalues r_1 and r_2, we obtain

(25) $r_1\mathbf{u}_1 = cr_2\mathbf{u}_2.$

Next we multiply (24) by r_2 and then subtract from (25) to get

(26) $(r_1 - r_2)\mathbf{u}_1 = \mathbf{0}.$

Since $\mathbf{u}_1$ is not the zero vector, (26) implies that $r_1 = r_2$. But this violates the assumption that the eigenvalues are distinct! Hence $\mathbf{u}_1$ and $\mathbf{u}_2$ are linearly independent.

The cases $2 < m \leq n$ follow by induction. The details of the proof are left as an exercise. ∎

Combining Theorems 5 and 6, we get the following corollary.

---

n DISTINCT EIGENVALUES

Corollary 1.   If the $n \times n$ constant matrix $\mathbf{A}$ has n distinct eigenvalues $r_1, \ldots, r_n$ and $\mathbf{u}_i$ is an eigenvector associated with r_i, then

$$\{e^{r_1 t}\mathbf{u}_1, \ldots, e^{r_n t}\mathbf{u}_n\}$$

is a fundamental solution set for the homogeneous system $\mathbf{x}' = \mathbf{A}\mathbf{x}$.

▶ **_Example 4_**   Solve the initial value problem

(27) $\mathbf{x}'(t) = \begin{bmatrix} 1 & 2 & -1 \\ 1 & 0 & 1 \\ 4 & -4 & 5 \end{bmatrix} \mathbf{x}(t), \qquad \mathbf{x}(0) = \begin{bmatrix} -1 \\ 0 \\ 0 \end{bmatrix}.$

Solution   In Example 2 we showed that the 3×3 coefficient matrix $\mathbf{A}$ has the three distinct eigenvalues $r_1 = 1$, $r_2 = 2$, and $r_3 = 3$. If we set $s = 1$ in equations (14), (16), and (18), we obtain the corresponding eigenvectors

$$\mathbf{u}_1 = \begin{bmatrix} -1 \\ 1 \\ 2 \end{bmatrix}, \qquad \mathbf{u}_2 = \begin{bmatrix} -2 \\ 1 \\ 4 \end{bmatrix}, \qquad \mathbf{u}_3 = \begin{bmatrix} -1 \\ 1 \\ 4 \end{bmatrix},$$

whose linear independence is guaranteed by Corollary 1. Hence a general solution to (27) is

$$(28) \qquad \mathbf{x}(t) = c_1 e^t \begin{bmatrix} -1 \\ 1 \\ 2 \end{bmatrix} + c_2 e^{2t} \begin{bmatrix} -2 \\ 1 \\ 4 \end{bmatrix} + c_3 e^{3t} \begin{bmatrix} -1 \\ 1 \\ 4 \end{bmatrix}$$

$$= \begin{bmatrix} -e^t & -2e^{2t} & -e^{3t} \\ e^t & e^{2t} & e^{3t} \\ 2e^t & 4e^{2t} & 4e^{3t} \end{bmatrix} \begin{bmatrix} c_1 \\ c_2 \\ c_3 \end{bmatrix}.$$

To satisfy the initial condition in (27), we solve

$$\mathbf{x}(0) = \begin{bmatrix} -1 & -2 & -1 \\ 1 & 1 & 1 \\ 2 & 4 & 4 \end{bmatrix} \begin{bmatrix} c_1 \\ c_2 \\ c_3 \end{bmatrix} = \begin{bmatrix} -1 \\ 0 \\ 0 \end{bmatrix}$$

and find that $c_1 = 0$, $c_2 = 1$, and $c_3 = -1$. Inserting these values into (28) gives the desired solution. ◄

There is a special class of $n \times n$ matrices that *always* have real eigenvalues and *always* have n linearly independent eigenvectors. These are the real symmetric matrices.

REAL SYMMETRIC MATRICES

Definition 4. A **real symmetric matrix A** is a matrix with real entries that satisfies $\mathbf{A}^T = \mathbf{A}$.

Taking the transpose of a matrix interchanges its rows and columns, which is equivalent to "flipping" the matrix about its main diagonal. Consequently $\mathbf{A}^T = \mathbf{A}$ if and only if $\mathbf{A}$ is symmetric about its main diagonal.

If $\mathbf{A}$ is an $n \times n$ real symmetric matrix, it is known[†] that there always exist n linearly independent eigenvectors. Thus, Theorem 5 applies, and a general solution to $\mathbf{x}' = \mathbf{A}\mathbf{x}$ is given by (20).

[†] See *Elementary Linear Algebra,* by A. Wayne Roberts, Benjamin/Cummings Publishing Co., Menlo Park, California, 1982, Chapter 6.

▶ *Example 5* Find a general solution of

(29) $$\mathbf{x}'(t) = \mathbf{A}\mathbf{x}(t), \quad \text{where} \quad \mathbf{A} = \begin{bmatrix} 1 & -2 & 2 \\ -2 & 1 & 2 \\ 2 & 2 & 1 \end{bmatrix}.$$

Solution Since $\mathbf{A}$ is symmetric, we are assured that $\mathbf{A}$ has three linearly independent eigenvectors. To find them, we first compute the characteristic equation for $\mathbf{A}$:

(30) $$|\mathbf{A} - r\mathbf{I}| = \begin{vmatrix} 1 - r & -2 & 2 \\ -2 & 1 - r & 2 \\ 2 & 2 & 1 - r \end{vmatrix} = -(r - 3)^2(r + 3) = 0.$$

Thus the eigenvalues of $\mathbf{A}$ are $r_1 = r_2 = 3$ and $r_3 = -3$.

Notice that the eigenvalue $r = 3$ has multiplicity 2 when considered as a root of the characteristic equation. Therefore, we must find *two* linearly independent eigenvectors associated with $r = 3$. Substituting $r = 3$ in $(\mathbf{A} - r\mathbf{I})\mathbf{u} = \mathbf{0}$ gives

(31) $$\begin{bmatrix} -2 & -2 & 2 \\ -2 & -2 & 2 \\ 2 & 2 & -2 \end{bmatrix} \begin{bmatrix} u_1 \\ u_2 \\ u_3 \end{bmatrix} = \begin{bmatrix} 0 \\ 0 \\ 0 \end{bmatrix}.$$

Since the system (31) is equivalent to the single equation $-u_1 - u_2 + u_3 = 0$, we can obtain its solutions by assigning an arbitrary value to u_2, say $u_2 = v$, and an arbitrary value to u_3, say $u_3 = s$. Solving for u_1, we find $u_1 = u_3 - u_2 = s - v$. Therefore, the eigenvectors associated with $r_1 = r_2 = 3$ can be expressed as

(32) $$\mathbf{u} = \begin{bmatrix} s - v \\ v \\ s \end{bmatrix} = s \begin{bmatrix} 1 \\ 0 \\ 1 \end{bmatrix} + v \begin{bmatrix} -1 \\ 1 \\ 0 \end{bmatrix}.$$

By first taking $s = 1$, $v = 0$ and then taking $s = 0$, $v = 1$, we get the two linearly independent eigenvectors

(33) $$\mathbf{u}_1 = \begin{bmatrix} 1 \\ 0 \\ 1 \end{bmatrix}, \quad \mathbf{u}_2 = \begin{bmatrix} -1 \\ 1 \\ 0 \end{bmatrix}.$$

For $r_3 = -3$, we solve

(34) $$(\mathbf{A} + 3\mathbf{I})\mathbf{u} = \begin{bmatrix} 4 & -2 & 2 \\ -2 & 4 & 2 \\ 2 & 2 & 4 \end{bmatrix} \begin{bmatrix} u_1 \\ u_2 \\ u_3 \end{bmatrix} = \begin{bmatrix} 0 \\ 0 \\ 0 \end{bmatrix},$$

to obtain the eigenvectors $\text{col}(-s, -s, s)$. Taking $s = 1$ gives

(35)
$$\mathbf{u}_3 = \begin{bmatrix} -1 \\ -1 \\ 1 \end{bmatrix}.$$

Since the eigenvectors $\mathbf{u}_1$, $\mathbf{u}_2$, and $\mathbf{u}_3$ are linearly independent, a general solution to (29) is

$$\mathbf{x}(t) = c_1 e^{3t} \begin{bmatrix} 1 \\ 0 \\ 1 \end{bmatrix} + c_2 e^{3t} \begin{bmatrix} -1 \\ 1 \\ 0 \end{bmatrix} + c_3 e^{-3t} \begin{bmatrix} -1 \\ -1 \\ 1 \end{bmatrix}. \quad \blacktriangleleft$$

It is possible for a matrix to have a repeated eigenvalue but not have two linearly independent corresponding eigenvectors. In particular, the matrix

(36)
$$\mathbf{A} = \begin{bmatrix} 1 & -1 \\ 4 & -3 \end{bmatrix}$$

has the repeated eigenvalue $r_1 = r_2 = -1$, but all the eigenvectors associated with $r = -1$ are of the form $\mathbf{u} = s \, \text{col}(1, 2)$. Consequently, no two eigenvectors are linearly independent.

Analogous to the situation for a scalar equation, the system $\mathbf{x}' = \mathbf{Ax}$, where $\mathbf{A}$ is given in (36), has two linearly independent solutions of the form

(37)
$$\mathbf{x}_1(t) = e^{-t}\mathbf{u}_1, \qquad \mathbf{x}_2(t) = te^{-t}\mathbf{u}_1 + e^{-t}\mathbf{u}_2.$$

Here $\mathbf{u}_1$ is an eigenvector of $\mathbf{A}$, say $\mathbf{u}_1 = \text{col}(1, 2)$, and $\mathbf{u}_2$ is determined by substituting $\mathbf{x}_2(t)$ into $\mathbf{x}' = \mathbf{Ax}$ and solving (see Problem 25).

When a matrix $\mathbf{A}$ has an eigenvalue r of multiplicity 3, then it can be shown that there exist three linearly independent solutions to $\mathbf{x}' = \mathbf{Ax}$ of the form

$$\mathbf{x}_1(t) = e^{rt}\mathbf{k}_1, \qquad \mathbf{x}_2(t) = te^{rt}\mathbf{k}_2 + e^{rt}\mathbf{k}_3,$$

(38)
$$\mathbf{x}_3(t) = \frac{t^2}{2} e^{rt}\mathbf{k}_4 + te^{rt}\mathbf{k}_5 + e^{rt}\mathbf{k}_6.$$

The vectors $\mathbf{k}_2$, $\mathbf{k}_4$, or $\mathbf{k}_5$ may be zero, depending on the number of linearly independent eigenvectors associated with the eigenvalue r (see Problems 27–30).

Another approach to handling repeated eigenvalues that involves using the concept of the exponential of a matrix is discussed in Section 10.7.

EXERCISES 10.4

In Problems 1 through 8 find the eigenvalues and eigenvectors of the given matrix.

1. $\begin{bmatrix} -4 & 2 \\ 2 & -1 \end{bmatrix}$.

2. $\begin{bmatrix} 6 & -3 \\ 2 & 1 \end{bmatrix}$.

3. $\begin{bmatrix} 1 & -1 \\ 2 & 4 \end{bmatrix}$.

4. $\begin{bmatrix} 1 & 5 \\ 1 & -3 \end{bmatrix}$.

5. $\begin{bmatrix} 1 & 0 & 0 \\ 0 & 0 & 2 \\ 0 & 2 & 0 \end{bmatrix}$.

6. $\begin{bmatrix} 0 & 1 & 1 \\ 1 & 0 & 1 \\ 1 & 1 & 0 \end{bmatrix}$.

7. $\begin{bmatrix} 1 & 0 & 0 \\ 2 & 3 & 1 \\ 0 & 2 & 4 \end{bmatrix}$.

8. $\begin{bmatrix} -3 & 1 & 0 \\ 0 & -3 & 1 \\ 4 & -8 & 2 \end{bmatrix}$.

In Problems 9 through 14 find a general solution of the system $\mathbf{x}'(t) = \mathbf{A}\mathbf{x}(t)$ *for the given matrix* $\mathbf{A}$.

9. $\mathbf{A} = \begin{bmatrix} 1 & 3 \\ 12 & 1 \end{bmatrix}$.

10. $\mathbf{A} = \begin{bmatrix} -1 & \frac{3}{4} \\ -5 & 3 \end{bmatrix}$.

11. $\mathbf{A} = \begin{bmatrix} 1 & 2 & 2 \\ 2 & 0 & 3 \\ 2 & 3 & 0 \end{bmatrix}$.

12. $\mathbf{A} = \begin{bmatrix} 1 & 2 & 3 \\ 0 & 1 & 0 \\ 2 & 1 & 2 \end{bmatrix}$.

13. $\mathbf{A} = \begin{bmatrix} -1 & 1 & 0 \\ 1 & 2 & 1 \\ 0 & 3 & -1 \end{bmatrix}$.

14. $\mathbf{A} = \begin{bmatrix} -7 & 0 & 6 \\ 0 & 5 & 0 \\ 6 & 0 & 2 \end{bmatrix}$.

In Problems 15 through 20 find a fundamental matrix for the system $\mathbf{x}'(t) = \mathbf{A}\mathbf{x}(t)$ *for the given matrix* $\mathbf{A}$.

15. $\mathbf{A} = \begin{bmatrix} 5 & 4 \\ -1 & 0 \end{bmatrix}$.

16. $\mathbf{A} = \begin{bmatrix} -1 & 1 \\ 8 & 1 \end{bmatrix}$.

17. $\mathbf{A} = \begin{bmatrix} 0 & 1 & 0 \\ 0 & 0 & 1 \\ 8 & -14 & 7 \end{bmatrix}$.

18. $\mathbf{A} = \begin{bmatrix} 1 & 1 & 1 \\ 0 & 3 & 2 \\ 0 & 0 & 5 \end{bmatrix}$.

19. $\mathbf{A} = \begin{bmatrix} 1 & 2 & -1 \\ 1 & 0 & 1 \\ 4 & -4 & 5 \end{bmatrix}$.

20. $\mathbf{A} = \begin{bmatrix} 3 & 1 & -1 \\ 1 & 3 & -1 \\ 3 & 3 & -1 \end{bmatrix}$.

In Problems 21 through 24 solve the given initial value problem.

21. $\mathbf{x}'(t) = \begin{bmatrix} 6 & -3 \\ 2 & 1 \end{bmatrix} \mathbf{x}(t)$, $\mathbf{x}(0) = \begin{bmatrix} -10 \\ -6 \end{bmatrix}$.

22. $\mathbf{x}'(t) = \begin{bmatrix} 1 & 3 \\ 3 & 1 \end{bmatrix} \mathbf{x}(t)$, $\mathbf{x}(0) = \begin{bmatrix} 3 \\ 1 \end{bmatrix}$.

23. $\mathbf{x}'(t) = \begin{bmatrix} 1 & -2 & 2 \\ -2 & 1 & -2 \\ 2 & -2 & 1 \end{bmatrix} \mathbf{x}(t)$, $\mathbf{x}(0) = \begin{bmatrix} -2 \\ -3 \\ 2 \end{bmatrix}$.

24. $\mathbf{x}'(t) = \begin{bmatrix} 0 & 1 & 1 \\ 1 & 0 & 1 \\ 1 & 1 & 0 \end{bmatrix} \mathbf{x}(t)$, $\mathbf{x}(0) = \begin{bmatrix} -1 \\ 4 \\ 0 \end{bmatrix}$.

25. (a) Show that the matrix

$$\mathbf{A} = \begin{bmatrix} 1 & -1 \\ 4 & -3 \end{bmatrix}$$

has the repeated eigenvalue $r = -1$, and all the eigenvectors are of the form $\mathbf{u} = s \, \mathrm{col}(1, 2)$.

(b) Use the result of part (a) to obtain a nontrivial solution $\mathbf{x}_1(t)$ to the system $\mathbf{x}' = \mathbf{A}\mathbf{x}$.

(c) To obtain a second linearly independent solution to $\mathbf{x}' = \mathbf{A}\mathbf{x}$, try $\mathbf{x}_2(t) = te^{-t}\mathbf{u}_1 + e^{-t}\mathbf{u}_2$. [Hint: Substitute $\mathbf{x}_2$ into the system $\mathbf{x}' = \mathbf{A}\mathbf{x}$

and derive the relations

$$(A + I)u_1 = 0, \qquad (A + I)u_2 = u_1.$$

Since u_1 must be an eigenvector, set $u_1 = \text{col}(1, 2)$ and solve for u_2.]

26. Use the method discussed in Problem 25 to find a general solution to the system

$$x'(t) = \begin{bmatrix} 5 & -3 \\ 3 & -1 \end{bmatrix} x(t).$$

27. (a) Show that the matrix

$$A = \begin{bmatrix} 2 & 1 & 6 \\ 0 & 2 & 5 \\ 0 & 0 & 2 \end{bmatrix}$$

has the repeated eigenvalue $r = 2$ with multiplicity 3, and that all the eigenvectors of A are of the form $u = s \, \text{col}(1, 0, 0)$.

(b) Use the result of part (a) to obtain a solution to the system $x' = Ax$ of the form $x_1(t) = e^{2t}u_1$.

(c) To obtain a second linearly independent solution to $x' = Ax$, try $x_2(t) = te^{2t}u_1 + e^{2t}u_2$. [Hint: Show that u_1 and u_2 must satisfy

$$(A - 2I)u_1 = 0, \qquad (A - 2I)u_2 = u_1.]$$

(d) To obtain a third linearly independent solution to $x' = Ax$, try

$$x_3(t) = \frac{t^2}{2} e^{2t}u_1 + te^{2t}u_2 + e^{2t}u_3.$$

[Hint: Show that u_1, u_2, and u_3 must satisfy

$$(A - 2I)u_1 = 0, \qquad (A - 2I)u_2 = u_1, \qquad (A - 2I)u_3 = u_2.]$$

28. Use the method discussed in Problem 27 to find a general solution to the system

$$x'(t) = \begin{bmatrix} 3 & -2 & 1 \\ 2 & -1 & 1 \\ -4 & 4 & 1 \end{bmatrix} x(t).$$

29. (a) Show that the matrix

$$A = \begin{bmatrix} 2 & 1 & 1 \\ 1 & 2 & 1 \\ -2 & -2 & -1 \end{bmatrix}$$

has the repeated eigenvalue $r = 1$ of multiplicity 3 and that all the eigenvectors of **A** are of the form $\mathbf{u} = s \operatorname{col}(-1, 1, 0) + v \operatorname{col}(-1, 0, 1)$.

(b) Use the result of part (a) to obtain two linearly independent solutions to the system $\mathbf{x}' = \mathbf{Ax}$ of the form

$$\mathbf{x}_1(t) = e^t \mathbf{u}_1 \quad \text{and} \quad \mathbf{x}_2(t) = e^t \mathbf{u}_2.$$

(c) To obtain a third linearly independent solution to $\mathbf{x}' = \mathbf{Ax}$, try

$$\mathbf{x}_3(t) = t e^t \mathbf{u}_3 + e^t \mathbf{u}_4.$$

[Hint: Show that $\mathbf{u}_3$ and $\mathbf{u}_4$ must satisfy

$$(\mathbf{A} - \mathbf{I})\mathbf{u}_3 = \mathbf{0}, \qquad (\mathbf{A} - \mathbf{I})\mathbf{u}_4 = \mathbf{u}_3.$$

Choose $\mathbf{u}_3$, an eigenvector of **A**, so that you can solve for $\mathbf{u}_4$.]

30. Use the method discussed in Problem 29 to find a general solution to the system

$$\mathbf{x}'(t) = \begin{bmatrix} 1 & 3 & -2 \\ 0 & 7 & -4 \\ 0 & 9 & -5 \end{bmatrix} \mathbf{x}(t).$$

31. Use the substitution $x_1 = y$, $x_2 = y'$ to convert the linear equation $ay'' + by' + cy = 0$, where a, b, and c are constants, into a normal system. Show that the characteristic equation for this system is the same as the auxiliary equation for the original equation.

32. Show that the **Cauchy-Euler system**

$$t\mathbf{x}'(t) = \mathbf{Ax}(t),$$

where **A** is a constant matrix, has nontrivial solutions of the form $\mathbf{x}(t) = t^r \mathbf{u}$ if and only if r is an eigenvalue of **A** and **u** is a corresponding eigenvector.

In Problems 33 and 34 use the result of Problem 32 to find a general solution of the given system.

33. $t\mathbf{x}'(t) = \begin{bmatrix} 1 & 3 \\ -1 & 5 \end{bmatrix} \mathbf{x}(t), \ t > 0.$

34. $t\mathbf{x}'(t) = \begin{bmatrix} -4 & 2 \\ 2 & -1 \end{bmatrix} \mathbf{x}(t), \ t > 0.$

35. Two tanks, each holding 50 quarts (qt) of liquid are interconnected by pipes, with liquid flowing from tank A into tank B at a rate of 4 qt/min and from tank B into tank A at 1 qt/min (see Figure 10.1). The liquid inside each tank is kept well stirred. Pure water flows into tank A at a rate of 3 qt/min, and the solution flows out of tank B at 3 qt/min. If, initially, tank A contains 25 lb of salt and tank B contains no salt (only water), determine the amount of salt in each tank at time $t \geq 0$.

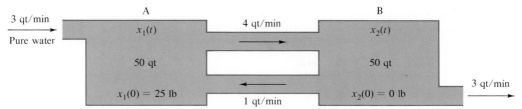

Figure 10.1 Mixing problem for interconnected tanks

36. To complete the proof of Theorem 6, assume the induction hypothesis that $\mathbf{u}_1, \ldots, \mathbf{u}_k$, $2 \le k \le n - 1$, are linearly independent.

(a) Show that if

$$c_1\mathbf{u}_1 + \cdots + c_k\mathbf{u}_k + c_{k+1}\mathbf{u}_{k+1} = \mathbf{0},$$

then

$$c_1(r_1 - r_{k+1})\mathbf{u}_1 + \cdots + c_k(r_k - r_{k+1})\mathbf{u}_k = \mathbf{0}.$$

(b) Use the result of part (a) and the induction hypothesis to conclude that $\mathbf{u}_1, \ldots, \mathbf{u}_{k+1}$ are linearly independent. The theorem follows by induction.

37. To find a general solution to the system

$$\mathbf{x}' = \mathbf{Ax} = \begin{bmatrix} 1 & 3 & -1 \\ 3 & 0 & 1 \\ -1 & 1 & 2 \end{bmatrix} \mathbf{x}$$

proceed as follows:

(a) Use a numerical procedure for finding roots to approximate the eigenvalues.

(b) If r is an eigenvalue, then let $\mathbf{u} = \text{col}(u_1, u_2, u_3)$ be an eigenvector associated with r. To solve for $\mathbf{u}$, assume $u_1 = 1$. (If not u_1, then either u_2 or u_3 may be chosen to be 1. Why?) Now solve the system

$$(\mathbf{A} - r\mathbf{I}) \begin{bmatrix} 1 \\ u_2 \\ u_3 \end{bmatrix} = \begin{bmatrix} 0 \\ 0 \\ 0 \end{bmatrix}$$

for u_2 and u_3. Use this procedure to find approximations for three linearly independent eigenvectors for $\mathbf{A}$.

(c) Use these approximations to give a general solution to the system.

10.5 Complex Eigenvalues

In the previous section we showed that the homogeneous system

(1) $\mathbf{x}'(t) = \mathbf{A}\mathbf{x}(t),$

where $\mathbf{A}$ is a constant $n \times n$ matrix, has a solution of the form $\mathbf{x}(t) = e^{rt}\mathbf{u}$ if and only if r is an eigenvalue of $\mathbf{A}$ and $\mathbf{u}$ is a corresponding eigenvector. In this section we show how to obtain two real vector solutions to system (1) when $\mathbf{A}$ is real and has a pair[†] of complex conjugate eigenvalues $\alpha + i\beta$ and $\alpha - i\beta$.

Suppose that $r_1 = \alpha + i\beta$ (α and β real numbers) is an eigenvalue of $\mathbf{A}$ with corresponding eigenvector $\mathbf{z} = \mathbf{a} + i\mathbf{b}$, where $\mathbf{a}$ and $\mathbf{b}$ are real constant vectors. We first observe that the complex conjugate of $\mathbf{z}$, namely, $\bar{\mathbf{z}} := \mathbf{a} - i\mathbf{b}$, is an eigenvector associated with the eigenvalue $r_2 = \alpha - i\beta$. To see this, note that taking the complex conjugate of $(\mathbf{A} - r_1\mathbf{I})\mathbf{z} = \mathbf{0}$ yields $(\mathbf{A} - \bar{r}_1\mathbf{I})\bar{\mathbf{z}} = \mathbf{0}$, because the conjugate of the product is the product of the conjugates and $\mathbf{A}$ and $\mathbf{I}$ have real entries ($\bar{\mathbf{A}} = \mathbf{A}, \bar{\mathbf{I}} = \mathbf{I}$). Since $r_2 = \bar{r}_1$, we see that $\bar{\mathbf{z}}$ is an eigenvector associated with r_2. Therefore, two linearly independent complex vector solutions to (1) are

(2) $\mathbf{w}_1(t) = e^{r_1 t}\mathbf{z} = e^{(\alpha + i\beta)t}(\mathbf{a} + i\mathbf{b}),$

(3) $\mathbf{w}_2(t) = e^{r_2 t}\bar{\mathbf{z}} = e^{(\alpha - i\beta)t}(\mathbf{a} - i\mathbf{b}).$

As in Section 4.5, where we handled complex roots to the auxiliary equation, let's use one of these complex solutions and Euler's formula to obtain two real vector solutions. With the aid of Euler's formula we rewrite $\mathbf{w}_1(t)$ as

$$\mathbf{w}_1(t) = e^{\alpha t}(\cos \beta t + i \sin \beta t)(\mathbf{a} + i\mathbf{b})$$
$$= e^{\alpha t}\{(\cos \beta t\, \mathbf{a} - \sin \beta t\, \mathbf{b}) + i(\sin \beta t\, \mathbf{a} + \cos \beta t\, \mathbf{b})\}.$$

We have thereby expressed $\mathbf{w}_1(t)$ in the form $\mathbf{w}_1(t) = \mathbf{x}_1(t) + i\mathbf{x}_2(t)$, where $\mathbf{x}_1(t)$ and $\mathbf{x}_2(t)$ are the two real vector functions

(4) $\mathbf{x}_1(t) := e^{\alpha t} \cos \beta t\, \mathbf{a} - e^{\alpha t} \sin \beta t\, \mathbf{b},$

(5) $\mathbf{x}_2(t) := e^{\alpha t} \sin \beta t\, \mathbf{a} + e^{\alpha t} \cos \beta t\, \mathbf{b}.$

Since $\mathbf{w}_1(t)$ is a solution to (1), then

$$\mathbf{x}_1'(t) + i\mathbf{x}_2'(t) = \mathbf{w}_1'(t) = \mathbf{A}\mathbf{w}_1(t) = \mathbf{A}\mathbf{x}_1(t) + i\mathbf{A}\mathbf{x}_2(t).$$

[†] Recall that the complex roots of a polynomial equation with real coefficients must occur in complex conjugate pairs.

Equating the real and imaginary parts yields

$$\mathbf{x}_1'(t) = \mathbf{A}\mathbf{x}_1(t) \quad \text{and} \quad \mathbf{x}_2'(t) = \mathbf{A}\mathbf{x}_2(t).$$

Hence $\mathbf{x}_1(t)$ and $\mathbf{x}_2(t)$ are real vector solutions to (1) associated with the complex conjugate eigenvalues $\alpha \pm i\beta$. Since $\mathbf{a}$ and $\mathbf{b}$ are not both the zero vector, it can be shown that $\mathbf{x}_1(t)$ and $\mathbf{x}_2(t)$ are linearly independent vector functions on $(-\infty, \infty)$ (see Problem 11).
   Let's summarize our findings.

COMPLEX EIGENVALUES

If the real matrix $\mathbf{A}$ has complex conjugate eigenvalues $\alpha \pm i\beta$ with corresponding eigenvectors $\mathbf{a} \pm i\mathbf{b}$, then two linearly independent real vector solutions to $\mathbf{x}'(t) = \mathbf{A}\mathbf{x}(t)$ are

(6) $\qquad e^{\alpha t}\cos\beta t\ \mathbf{a} - e^{\alpha t}\sin\beta t\ \mathbf{b},$

(7) $\qquad e^{\alpha t}\sin\beta t\ \mathbf{a} + e^{\alpha t}\cos\beta t\ \mathbf{b}.$

▶ **Example 1** Find a general solution of

(8) $\qquad \mathbf{x}'(t) = \begin{bmatrix} -1 & 2 \\ -1 & -3 \end{bmatrix}\mathbf{x}(t).$

Solution The characteristic equation for $\mathbf{A}$ is

(9) $\qquad |\mathbf{A} - r\mathbf{I}| = \begin{vmatrix} -1-r & 2 \\ -1 & -3-r \end{vmatrix} = r^2 + 4r + 5 = 0.$

Hence $\mathbf{A}$ has eigenvalues $r = -2 \pm i$.
   To find a general solution we need only find an eigenvector associated with the eigenvalue $r = -2 + i$. Substituting $r = -2 + i$ into $(\mathbf{A} - r\mathbf{I})\mathbf{z} = \mathbf{0}$ gives

(10) $\qquad \begin{bmatrix} 1-i & 2 \\ -1 & -1-i \end{bmatrix}\begin{bmatrix} z_1 \\ z_2 \end{bmatrix} = \begin{bmatrix} 0 \\ 0 \end{bmatrix}.$

The solutions to (10) are $z_1 = 2s$ and $z_2 = (-1+i)s$, with s arbitrary. Hence, the eigenvectors associated with $r = -2 + i$ are $\mathbf{z} = s\,\mathrm{col}(2, -1+i)$. Taking $s = 1$ gives the eigenvector

(11) $$\mathbf{z} = \begin{bmatrix} 2 \\ -1 + i \end{bmatrix} = \begin{bmatrix} 2 \\ -1 \end{bmatrix} + i \begin{bmatrix} 0 \\ 1 \end{bmatrix}.$$

We have found that $\alpha = -2$, $\beta = 1$, $\mathbf{a} = \text{col}(2, -1)$, and $\mathbf{b} = \text{col}(0, 1)$, and so a general solution to (8) is

(12) $$\mathbf{x}(t) = c_1 \left\{ e^{-2t} \cos t \begin{bmatrix} 2 \\ -1 \end{bmatrix} - e^{-2t} \sin t \begin{bmatrix} 0 \\ 1 \end{bmatrix} \right\}$$

$$+ c_2 \left\{ e^{-2t} \sin t \begin{bmatrix} 2 \\ -1 \end{bmatrix} + e^{-2t} \cos t \begin{bmatrix} 0 \\ 1 \end{bmatrix} \right\}$$

$$= c_1 \begin{bmatrix} 2e^{-2t} \cos t \\ -e^{-2t}(\cos t + \sin t) \end{bmatrix} + c_2 \begin{bmatrix} 2e^{-2t} \sin t \\ e^{-2t}(\cos t - \sin t) \end{bmatrix}. \blacktriangleleft$$

In Section 9.4 we discussed coupled spring-mass systems with fixed ends, as illustrated in Figure 9.8 on page 503. There we showed that the motion of the masses is governed by the second order system

(13) $$m_1 x_1'' = -k_1 x_1 + k_2(x_2 - x_1),$$
$$m_2 x_2'' = -k_2(x_2 - x_1) - k_3 x_2.$$

In the special case where $m_1 = m_2 = 1$ kg, $k_1 = 1$ N/m, $k_2 = 2$ N/m,   and $k_3 = 3$ N/m, system (13) becomes

(14) $$x_1'' = -x_1 + 2(x_2 - x_1),$$
$$x_2'' = -2(x_2 - x_1) - 3x_2.$$

If we introduce the new variables $y_1 := x_1$, $y_2 := x_1'$, $y_3 := x_2$, $y_4 := x_2'$, then we can rewrite system (14) in the normal form

(15) $$\mathbf{y}'(t) = \mathbf{A}\,\mathbf{y}(t) = \begin{bmatrix} 0 & 1 & 0 & 0 \\ -3 & 0 & 2 & 0 \\ 0 & 0 & 0 & 1 \\ 2 & 0 & -5 & 0 \end{bmatrix} \mathbf{y}(t).$$

You may recall from the discussion in Section 9.4 that the spring-mass system vibrates (oscillates) at **normal frequencies** that we determine from the frequencies of the sine and cosine functions present in the solutions to the system. It follows from formulas (6) and (7) that these normal frequencies are given by $\beta/2\pi$, where $\pm i\beta$ are complex conjugate eigenvalues of the coefficient matrix $\mathbf{A}$.

▶ *Example 2* Determine the normal frequencies for the coupled spring-mass system governed by the system (15).

Solution To find the eigenvalues of **A**, we must solve the characteristic equation

$$(16) \qquad |\mathbf{A} - r\mathbf{I}| = \begin{vmatrix} -r & 1 & 0 & 0 \\ -3 & -r & 2 & 0 \\ 0 & 0 & -r & 1 \\ 2 & 0 & -5 & -r \end{vmatrix} = r^4 + 8r^2 + 11 = 0.$$

From the quadratic formula we find $r^2 = -4 \pm \sqrt{5}$, and so the four eigenvalues of **A** are $\pm i\sqrt{4 - \sqrt{5}}$ and $\pm i\sqrt{4 + \sqrt{5}}$. Hence the two normal frequencies for system (15) are

$$\frac{\sqrt{4 - \sqrt{5}}}{2\pi} \approx 0.211 \quad \text{and} \quad \frac{\sqrt{4 + \sqrt{5}}}{2\pi} \approx 0.397. \quad \blacktriangleleft$$

EXERCISES 10.5

In Problems 1 through 4 find a general solution of the system $\mathbf{x}'(t) = \mathbf{A}\mathbf{x}(t)$ for the given matrix **A**.

1. $\mathbf{A} = \begin{bmatrix} -2 & -5 \\ 1 & 2 \end{bmatrix}.$

2. $\mathbf{A} = \begin{bmatrix} 2 & -4 \\ 2 & -2 \end{bmatrix}.$

3. $\mathbf{A} = \begin{bmatrix} 1 & 2 & -1 \\ 0 & 1 & 1 \\ 0 & -1 & 1 \end{bmatrix}.$

4. $\mathbf{A} = \begin{bmatrix} 5 & -5 & -5 \\ -1 & 4 & 2 \\ 3 & -5 & -3 \end{bmatrix}.$

In Problems 5 through 8 find a fundamental matrix for the system $\mathbf{x}'(t) = \mathbf{A}\mathbf{x}(t)$ for the given matrix **A**.

5. $\mathbf{A} = \begin{bmatrix} -2 & -2 \\ 4 & 2 \end{bmatrix}.$

6. $\mathbf{A} = \begin{bmatrix} -1 & -2 \\ 8 & -1 \end{bmatrix}.$

7. $\mathbf{A} = \begin{bmatrix} 0 & 0 & 1 \\ 0 & 0 & -1 \\ 0 & 1 & 0 \end{bmatrix}.$

8. $\mathbf{A} = \begin{bmatrix} 0 & 1 & 1 \\ -1 & 0 & 1 \\ -1 & -1 & 0 \end{bmatrix}.$

In Problems 9 and 10 solve the given initial value problem.

9. $\mathbf{x}'(t) = \begin{bmatrix} -3 & -1 \\ 2 & -1 \end{bmatrix} \mathbf{x}(t), \quad \mathbf{x}(0) = \begin{bmatrix} -1 \\ 0 \end{bmatrix}.$

10. $\mathbf{x}'(t) = \begin{bmatrix} 1 & 0 & -1 \\ 0 & 2 & 0 \\ 1 & 0 & 1 \end{bmatrix} \mathbf{x}(t), \quad \mathbf{x}(0) = \begin{bmatrix} -2 \\ 2 \\ -1 \end{bmatrix}.$

11. Show that $\mathbf{x}_1(t)$ and $\mathbf{x}_2(t)$ given by equations (4) and (5) are linearly independent on $(-\infty, \infty)$, provided that $\beta \neq 0$ and **a** and **b** are not both the zero vector.

12. Show that $\mathbf{x}_1(t)$ and $\mathbf{x}_2(t)$ given by equations (4) and (5) can be obtained as linear combinations of $\mathbf{w}_1(t)$ and $\mathbf{w}_2(t)$ given by equations (2) and (3). [Hint: Show that

$$\mathbf{x}_1(t) = \frac{\mathbf{w}_1(t) + \mathbf{w}_2(t)}{2}, \qquad \mathbf{x}_2(t) = \frac{\mathbf{w}_1(t) - \mathbf{w}_2(t)}{2i}.\bigg]$$

In Problems 13 and 14 use the results of Problem 32 in Exercises 10.4 to find a general solution to the given Cauchy-Euler system for t > 0.

13. $t\mathbf{x}'(t) = \begin{bmatrix} -1 & -1 & 0 \\ 2 & -1 & 1 \\ 0 & 1 & -1 \end{bmatrix} \mathbf{x}(t).$

14. $t\mathbf{x}'(t) = \begin{bmatrix} -1 & -1 \\ 9 & -1 \end{bmatrix} \mathbf{x}(t).$

15. For the coupled spring-mass system governed by system (13), assume that $m_1 = m_2 = 1$ kg, $k_1 = k_2 = 2$ N/m, and $k_3 = 3$ N/m. Determine the normal frequencies for this coupled spring-mass system.

10.6   Nonhomogeneous Linear Systems

The techniques discussed in Chapter 4 for finding a particular solution to the nonhomogeneous equation $y'' + p(x)y' + q(x)y = g(x)$ have natural extensions to nonhomogeneous linear systems.

UNDETERMINED COEFFICIENTS

The method of undetermined coefficients can be used to find a particular solution to the nonhomogeneous linear system

(1) $\mathbf{x}'(t) = \mathbf{A}\mathbf{x}(t) + \mathbf{f}(t),$

where $\mathbf{A}$ is an $n \times n$ *constant* matrix and the entries of $\mathbf{f}(t)$ are polynomials, exponential functions, sines and cosines, or finite sums and products of these functions. We can use Table 4.1 (discussed in Section 4.8 and reproduced inside the back cover) as a *guide* in choosing the form of a particular solution $\mathbf{x}_p(t)$. Some exceptions are discussed in the exercises (see Problems 15–18).

▶ **Example 1**   Find a general solution of

(2) $\mathbf{x}'(t) = \mathbf{A}\mathbf{x}(t) + t\mathbf{g},$ where $\mathbf{A} = \begin{bmatrix} 1 & -2 & 2 \\ -2 & 1 & 2 \\ 2 & 2 & 1 \end{bmatrix}$ and $\mathbf{g} = \begin{bmatrix} -9 \\ 0 \\ -18 \end{bmatrix}.$

Solution   In Example 5 in Section 10.4 we found that a general solution to the corresponding homogeneous system $\mathbf{x}' = \mathbf{Ax}$ is

$$(3) \qquad \mathbf{x}_h(t) = c_1 e^{3t} \begin{bmatrix} 1 \\ 0 \\ 1 \end{bmatrix} + c_2 e^{3t} \begin{bmatrix} -1 \\ 1 \\ 0 \end{bmatrix} + c_3 e^{-3t} \begin{bmatrix} -1 \\ -1 \\ 1 \end{bmatrix}.$$

Since the entries in $\mathbf{f}(t) := t\mathbf{g}$ are just linear functions of t, we seek a particular solution of the form[†]

$$(4) \qquad \mathbf{x}_p(t) = t\mathbf{a} + \mathbf{b} = t \begin{bmatrix} a_1 \\ a_2 \\ a_3 \end{bmatrix} + \begin{bmatrix} b_1 \\ b_2 \\ b_3 \end{bmatrix},$$

where the constant vectors $\mathbf{a}$ and $\mathbf{b}$ are to be determined. Substituting this expression for $\mathbf{x}_p(t)$ into system (2) yields

$$\mathbf{a} = \mathbf{A}(t\mathbf{a} + \mathbf{b}) + t\mathbf{g},$$

which can be written as

$$(5) \qquad t(\mathbf{Aa} + \mathbf{g}) + (\mathbf{Ab} - \mathbf{a}) = \mathbf{0}.$$

Setting the "coefficients" of the vector polynomial in (5) equal to zero yields the two systems

$$(6) \qquad \mathbf{Aa} = -\mathbf{g},$$
$$(7) \qquad \mathbf{Ab} = \mathbf{a}.$$

Using Gaussian elimination to solve (6) for $\mathbf{a}$ gives $\mathbf{a} = \text{col}(5, 2, 4)$. Next we substitute for $\mathbf{a}$ in (7) and solve for $\mathbf{b}$ to obtain $\mathbf{b} = \text{col}(1, 0, 2)$. Hence, a particular solution for (2) is

$$(8) \qquad \mathbf{x}_p(t) = t\mathbf{a} + \mathbf{b} = t \begin{bmatrix} 5 \\ 2 \\ 4 \end{bmatrix} + \begin{bmatrix} 1 \\ 0 \\ 2 \end{bmatrix} = \begin{bmatrix} 5t + 1 \\ 2t \\ 4t + 2 \end{bmatrix}.$$

A general solution for (2) is $\mathbf{x}(t) = \mathbf{x}_h(t) + \mathbf{x}_p(t)$, where $\mathbf{x}_h(t)$ is given in (3) and $\mathbf{x}_p(t)$ in (8). ◄

In the preceding example, the nonhomogeneous term $\mathbf{f}(t)$ was a vector polynomial. If, instead, $\mathbf{f}(t)$ has the form

$$\mathbf{f}(t) = \text{col}(1, t, \sin t),$$

[†] Notice that none of the terms in $\mathbf{x}_p(t)$ is a solution to the corresponding homogeneous system $\mathbf{x}' = \mathbf{Ax}$.

then, using the superposition principle, we would seek a particular solution of the form

$$\mathbf{x}_p(t) = t\mathbf{a} + \mathbf{b} + \sin t \, \mathbf{c} + \cos t \, \mathbf{d}.$$

Similarly, if

$$\mathbf{f}(t) = \text{col}(t, e^t, t^2),$$

we would take

$$\mathbf{x}_p(t) = t^2\mathbf{a} + t\mathbf{b} + \mathbf{c} + e^t\mathbf{d}.$$

Of course we must modify our guess should one of the terms be a solution to the corresponding homogeneous system.

VARIATION OF PARAMETERS

In Section 4.9 we discussed the method of variation of parameters for a second order linear equation. Simply put, the idea is that if a general solution to the homogeneous equation has the form $x_h(t) = c_1x_1(t) + c_2x_2(t)$, where $x_1(t)$ and $x_2(t)$ are linearly independent solutions to the homogeneous equation, then a particular solution to the nonhomogeneous equation would have the form $x_p(t) = v_1(t)x_1(t) + v_2(t)x_2(t)$, where $v_1(t)$ and $v_2(t)$ are certain functions of t. A similar idea can be used for systems.

Let $\mathbf{X}(t)$ be a fundamental matrix for the homogeneous system

$$(9) \qquad \mathbf{x}'(t) = \mathbf{A}(t)\mathbf{x}(t),$$

where now *the entries of* **A** *may be any continuous functions of* t. Since a general solution to (9) is given by $\mathbf{X}(t)\mathbf{c}$, where $\mathbf{c}$ is a constant $n \times 1$ vector, we seek a particular solution to the nonhomogeneous system

$$(10) \qquad \mathbf{x}'(t) = \mathbf{A}(t)\mathbf{x}(t) + \mathbf{f}(t)$$

of the form

$$(11) \qquad \mathbf{x}_p(t) = \mathbf{X}(t)\mathbf{v}(t),$$

where $\mathbf{v}(t) = \text{col}(v_1(t), \dots, v_n(t))$ is a vector function of t to be determined.

To derive a formula for $\mathbf{v}(t)$, we first differentiate (11) using the matrix version of the product rule to obtain

$$\mathbf{x}_p'(t) = \mathbf{X}(t)\mathbf{v}'(t) + \mathbf{X}'(t)\mathbf{v}(t).$$

Substituting the expressions for $\mathbf{x}_p(t)$ and $\mathbf{x}_p'(t)$ into (10) yields

$$(12) \qquad \mathbf{X}(t)\mathbf{v}'(t) + \mathbf{X}'(t)\mathbf{v}(t) = \mathbf{A}(t)\mathbf{X}(t)\mathbf{v}(t) + \mathbf{f}(t).$$

Since $\mathbf{X}(t)$ satisfies the matrix equation $\mathbf{X}'(t) = \mathbf{A}(t)\mathbf{X}(t)$, equation (12) becomes

$$\mathbf{X}v' + \mathbf{A}\mathbf{X}v = \mathbf{A}\mathbf{X}v + \mathbf{f},$$
$$\mathbf{X}v' = \mathbf{f}.$$

Multiplying both sides of the last equation by $\mathbf{X}^{-1}(t)$ (which exists since the columns of $\mathbf{X}(t)$ are linearly independent) gives

(13) $v'(t) = \mathbf{X}^{-1}(t)\mathbf{f}(t).$

Integrating equation (13), we obtain

(14) $v(t) = \displaystyle\int \mathbf{X}^{-1}(t)\mathbf{f}(t)\,dt.$

Hence a particular solution to (10) is

(15) $\mathbf{x}_p(t) = \mathbf{X}(t)v(t) = \mathbf{X}(t)\displaystyle\int \mathbf{X}^{-1}(t)\mathbf{f}(t)\,dt.$

Combining (15) with the solution $\mathbf{X}(t)\mathbf{c}$ to the homogeneous system yields the following general solution to (10):

(16) $\mathbf{x}(t) = \mathbf{X}(t)\mathbf{c} + \mathbf{X}(t)\displaystyle\int \mathbf{X}^{-1}(t)\mathbf{f}(t)\,dt.$

The elegance of the derivation of the variation of parameters formula (15) for systems becomes evident when one compares it with the more lengthy derivations for the scalar case in Sections 4.9 and 6.5.

Given an initial value problem of the form

(17) $\mathbf{x}'(t) = \mathbf{A}(t)\mathbf{x}(t) + \mathbf{f}(t), \qquad \mathbf{x}(t_0) = \mathbf{x}_0,$

we can use the initial condition $\mathbf{x}(t_0) = \mathbf{x}_0$ to solve for $\mathbf{c}$ in (16) and thereby derive the formula

(18) $\mathbf{x}(t) = \mathbf{X}(t)\mathbf{X}^{-1}(t_0)\mathbf{x}_0 + \mathbf{X}(t)\displaystyle\int_{t_0}^{t} \mathbf{X}^{-1}(s)\mathbf{f}(s)\,ds$

for the solution to (17) (see Problem 21).

To apply the variation of parameters formulas it is necessary first to determine a fundamental matrix $\mathbf{X}(t)$ for the homogeneous system. In the case when the coefficient matrix $\mathbf{A}$ is constant, we have discussed methods for finding $\mathbf{X}(t)$. However, if the entries of $\mathbf{A}$ depend on t, the determination of $\mathbf{X}(t)$ may be extremely difficult.

▶ *Example 2*   Find the solution to the initial value problem

(19) $$\mathbf{x}'(t) = \begin{bmatrix} 2 & -3 \\ 1 & -2 \end{bmatrix} \mathbf{x}(t) + \begin{bmatrix} e^{2t} \\ 1 \end{bmatrix}, \quad \mathbf{x}(0) = \begin{bmatrix} -1 \\ 0 \end{bmatrix}.$$

Solution   In Example 3 in Section 10.4 we found two linearly independent solutions to the corresponding homogeneous system; namely,

$$\mathbf{x}_1(t) = \begin{bmatrix} 3e^t \\ e^t \end{bmatrix} \quad \text{and} \quad \mathbf{x}_2(t) = \begin{bmatrix} e^{-t} \\ e^{-t} \end{bmatrix}.$$

Hence a fundamental matrix for the homogeneous system is

(20) $$\mathbf{X}(t) = \begin{bmatrix} 3e^t & e^{-t} \\ e^t & e^{-t} \end{bmatrix}.$$

Although the solution to (19) can be found via the method of undetermined coefficients, we shall find it directly from formula (18). For this purpose we need $\mathbf{X}^{-1}(t)$. One way[†] to obtain $\mathbf{X}^{-1}(t)$ is to form the augmented matrix

$$\begin{bmatrix} 3e^t & e^{-t} & \vdots & 1 & 0 \\ e^t & e^{-t} & \vdots & 0 & 1 \end{bmatrix}$$

and row-reduce this matrix to the matrix $[\mathbf{I} \quad \vdots \quad \mathbf{X}^{-1}(t)]$. This gives

(21) $$\mathbf{X}^{-1}(t) = \begin{bmatrix} \frac{1}{2}e^{-t} & -\frac{1}{2}e^{-t} \\ -\frac{1}{2}e^t & \frac{3}{2}e^t \end{bmatrix}.$$

Substituting into formula (18), we obtain the solution

$$\mathbf{x}(t) = \begin{bmatrix} 3e^t & e^{-t} \\ e^t & e^{-t} \end{bmatrix} \begin{bmatrix} \frac{1}{2} & -\frac{1}{2} \\ -\frac{1}{2} & \frac{3}{2} \end{bmatrix} \begin{bmatrix} -1 \\ 0 \end{bmatrix} + \begin{bmatrix} 3e^t & e^{-t} \\ e^t & e^{-t} \end{bmatrix} \int_0^t \begin{bmatrix} \frac{1}{2}e^{-s} & -\frac{1}{2}e^{-s} \\ -\frac{1}{2}e^s & \frac{3}{2}e^s \end{bmatrix} \begin{bmatrix} e^{2s} \\ 1 \end{bmatrix} ds$$

$$= \begin{bmatrix} -\frac{3}{2}e^t + \frac{1}{2}e^{-t} \\ -\frac{1}{2}e^t + \frac{1}{2}e^{-t} \end{bmatrix} + \begin{bmatrix} 3e^t & e^{-t} \\ e^t & e^{-t} \end{bmatrix} \int_0^t \begin{bmatrix} \frac{1}{2}e^s - \frac{1}{2}e^{-s} \\ \frac{1}{2}e^{3s} + \frac{3}{2}e^s \end{bmatrix} ds$$

$$= \begin{bmatrix} -\frac{3}{2}e^t + \frac{1}{2}e^{-t} \\ -\frac{1}{2}e^t + \frac{1}{2}e^{-t} \end{bmatrix} + \begin{bmatrix} 3e^t & e^{-t} \\ e^t & e^{-t} \end{bmatrix} \begin{bmatrix} \frac{1}{2}e^t + \frac{1}{2}e^{-t} - 1 \\ \frac{3}{2}e^t - \frac{1}{6}e^{3t} - \frac{4}{3} \end{bmatrix}$$

$$= \begin{bmatrix} -\frac{9}{2}e^t - \frac{5}{6}e^{-t} + \frac{4}{3}e^{2t} + 3 \\ -\frac{3}{2}e^t - \frac{5}{6}e^{-t} + \frac{1}{3}e^{2t} + 2 \end{bmatrix}. \quad ◀$$

---

† This procedure works for an invertible matrix of any dimension. For an arbitrary 2×2 invertible matrix $\mathbf{U}(t)$, a formula for $\mathbf{U}^{-1}(t)$ is derived in Problem 22.

EXERCISES 10.6

In Problems 1 through 4 use the method of undetermined coefficients to find a general solution to the system $\mathbf{x}'(t) = \mathbf{A}\mathbf{x}(t) + \mathbf{f}(t)$, *where* $\mathbf{A}$ *and* $\mathbf{f}(t)$ *are given.*

1. $\mathbf{A} = \begin{bmatrix} 6 & 1 \\ 4 & 3 \end{bmatrix}$, $\quad \mathbf{f}(t) = \begin{bmatrix} -11 \\ -5 \end{bmatrix}$.

2. $\mathbf{A} = \begin{bmatrix} 1 & 1 \\ 4 & 1 \end{bmatrix}$, $\quad \mathbf{f}(t) = \begin{bmatrix} -t - 1 \\ -4t - 2 \end{bmatrix}$.

3. $\mathbf{A} = \begin{bmatrix} 1 & -2 & 2 \\ -2 & 1 & 2 \\ 2 & 2 & 1 \end{bmatrix}$, $\quad \mathbf{f}(t) = \begin{bmatrix} 2e^t \\ 4e^t \\ -2e^t \end{bmatrix}$.

4. $\mathbf{A} = \begin{bmatrix} 2 & 2 \\ 2 & 2 \end{bmatrix}$, $\quad \mathbf{f}(t) = \begin{bmatrix} -4\cos t \\ -\sin t \end{bmatrix}$.

In Problems 5 through 12 use the variation of parameters formula (16) to find a general solution of the system $\mathbf{x}'(t) = \mathbf{A}\mathbf{x}(t) + \mathbf{f}(t)$, *where* $\mathbf{A}$ *and* $\mathbf{f}(t)$ *are given.*

5. $\mathbf{A} = \begin{bmatrix} 1 & 2 \\ 3 & 2 \end{bmatrix}$, $\quad \mathbf{f}(t) = \begin{bmatrix} 1 \\ -1 \end{bmatrix}$.

6. $\mathbf{A} = \begin{bmatrix} 0 & 1 \\ -1 & 0 \end{bmatrix}$, $\quad \mathbf{f}(t) = \begin{bmatrix} 1 \\ 0 \end{bmatrix}$.

7. $\mathbf{A} = \begin{bmatrix} 2 & 1 \\ -3 & -2 \end{bmatrix}$, $\quad \mathbf{f}(t) = \begin{bmatrix} 2e^t \\ 4e^t \end{bmatrix}$.

8. $\mathbf{A} = \begin{bmatrix} 0 & -1 \\ 1 & 0 \end{bmatrix}$, $\quad \mathbf{f}(t) = \begin{bmatrix} t^2 \\ 1 \end{bmatrix}$.

9. $\mathbf{A} = \begin{bmatrix} -4 & 2 \\ 2 & -1 \end{bmatrix}$, $\quad \mathbf{f}(t) = \begin{bmatrix} t^{-1} \\ 4 + 2t^{-1} \end{bmatrix}$.

10. $\mathbf{A} = \begin{bmatrix} 0 & 1 \\ -1 & 0 \end{bmatrix}$, $\quad \mathbf{f}(t) = \begin{bmatrix} 8\sin t \\ 0 \end{bmatrix}$.

11. $\mathbf{A} = \begin{bmatrix} 0 & 1 & 1 \\ 1 & 0 & 1 \\ 1 & 1 & 0 \end{bmatrix}$, $\quad \mathbf{f}(t) = \begin{bmatrix} 3e^t \\ -e^t \\ -e^t \end{bmatrix}$.

12. $\mathbf{A} = \begin{bmatrix} 1 & -1 & 1 \\ 0 & 0 & 1 \\ 0 & -1 & 2 \end{bmatrix}$, $\quad \mathbf{f}(t) = \begin{bmatrix} 0 \\ e^t \\ e^t \end{bmatrix}$.

In Problems 13 and 14 find the solution to the given initial value problem.

13. $\mathbf{x}'(t) = \begin{bmatrix} 0 & 2 \\ -1 & 3 \end{bmatrix} \mathbf{x}(t) + \begin{bmatrix} e^t \\ -e^t \end{bmatrix}$, $\quad \mathbf{x}(0) = \begin{bmatrix} 5 \\ 4 \end{bmatrix}$.

14. $\mathbf{x}'(t) = \begin{bmatrix} 0 & 2 \\ 4 & -2 \end{bmatrix} \mathbf{x}(t) + \begin{bmatrix} 4t \\ -4t - 2 \end{bmatrix}$, $\quad \mathbf{x}(0) = \begin{bmatrix} 4 \\ -5 \end{bmatrix}$.

15. To find a general solution to the system

$$(22) \qquad \mathbf{x}'(t) = \begin{bmatrix} 0 & 1 \\ -2 & 3 \end{bmatrix} \mathbf{x}(t) + \mathbf{f}(t), \quad \text{where} \quad \mathbf{f}(t) = \begin{bmatrix} e^t \\ 0 \end{bmatrix}:$$

(a) Find a fundamental solution set for the corresponding homogeneous system.

(b) The obvious choice for a particular solution would be a vector function of the form $\mathbf{x}_p(t) = e^t\mathbf{a}$; however, the homogeneous system has a solution of this form. The next choice would be $\mathbf{x}_p(t) = te^t\mathbf{a}$. Show that this choice does *not* work.

(c) For systems, multiplying by t is not always sufficient. The proper guess is

$$\mathbf{x}_p(t) = te^t\mathbf{a} + e^t\mathbf{b}.$$

Use this guess to find a particular solution of (22).

(d) Use the results of parts (a) and (c) to find a general solution of (22).

16. In Problem 15 we found that a proper guess for a particular solution to system (22) is $\mathbf{x}_p(t) = te^t\mathbf{a} + e^t\mathbf{b}$. In some cases $\mathbf{a}$ or $\mathbf{b}$ may be zero.

(a) Find a particular solution for system (22) if $\mathbf{f}(t) = \text{col}(3e^t, 6e^t)$.

(b) Find a particular solution for system (22) if $\mathbf{f}(t) = \text{col}(e^t, e^t)$.

17. Find a general solution of the system

$$\mathbf{x}'(t) = \begin{bmatrix} 0 & 1 & 1 \\ 1 & 0 & 1 \\ 1 & 1 & 0 \end{bmatrix} \mathbf{x}(t) + \begin{bmatrix} -1 \\ -1 - e^{-t} \\ -2e^{-t} \end{bmatrix}.$$

[Hint: Use superposition to determine the particular solution.]

18. Find a particular solution for the system

$$\mathbf{x}'(t) = \begin{bmatrix} 1 & -1 \\ -1 & 1 \end{bmatrix} \mathbf{x}(t) + \begin{bmatrix} -3 \\ 1 \end{bmatrix}.$$

[Hint: Try $\mathbf{x}_p(t) = t\mathbf{a} + \mathbf{b}$.]

In Problems 19 and 20 find a general solution to the given Cauchy-Euler system for $t > 0$. Remember to express the system in the form $\mathbf{x}'(t) = \mathbf{A}(t)\mathbf{x}(t) + \mathbf{f}(t)$ before using the variation of parameters formula.

19. $t\mathbf{x}'(t) = \begin{bmatrix} 2 & -1 \\ 3 & -2 \end{bmatrix} \mathbf{x}(t) + \begin{bmatrix} t^{-1} \\ 1 \end{bmatrix}.$

20. $t\mathbf{x}'(t) = \begin{bmatrix} 4 & -3 \\ 8 & -6 \end{bmatrix} \mathbf{x}(t) + \begin{bmatrix} t \\ 2t \end{bmatrix}.$

21. Derive formula (18) from (16) using the initial condition $\mathbf{x}(t_0) = \mathbf{x}_0$.

22. Let $\mathbf{U}(t)$ be the invertible 2×2 matrix

$$\mathbf{U}(t) := \begin{bmatrix} a(t) & b(t) \\ c(t) & d(t) \end{bmatrix}.$$

Show that

$$\mathbf{U}^{-1}(t) = \frac{1}{[a(t)d(t) - b(t)c(t)]} \begin{bmatrix} d(t) & -b(t) \\ -c(t) & a(t) \end{bmatrix}.$$

23. Use the variation of parameters formula (15) to derive a formula for a particular solution y_p to the scalar equation $y'' + p(t)y' + q(t)y = g(t)$ in terms of two linearly independent solutions $y_1(t)$, $y_2(t)$ of the corresponding homogeneous equation. Show that your answer agrees with the formulas derived in Section 4.9. [Hint: First write the scalar equation in system form.]

24. Conventional Combat Model. In modeling a pair of conventional forces in combat, the following system arises

$$\mathbf{x}' = \begin{bmatrix} -a & -b \\ -c & -d \end{bmatrix} \mathbf{x} + \begin{bmatrix} p \\ q \end{bmatrix},$$

where $\mathbf{x} = \text{col}(x_1, x_2)$. The variables $x_1(t)$ and $x_2(t)$ represent the strengths of opposing forces at time t. The terms $-ax_1$ and $-dx_2$ represent the *operational loss rates* and the terms $-bx_2$ and $-cx_1$ represent the *combat loss rates* for the troops x_1 and x_2, respectively. The constants p and q represent the respective rates of reinforcement. Let $a = 1$, $b = 4$, $c = 3$, $d = 2$, and $p = q = 5$. By solving the appropriate initial value problem, determine which forces will win if **(a)** $x_1(0) = 20$, $x_2(0) = 20$. **(b)** $x_1(0) = 21$, $x_2(0) = 20$. **(c)** $x_1(0) = 20$, $x_2(0) = 21$.

★ *10.7* *The Matrix Exponential Function*

In this chapter we have developed various ways to extend techniques for scalar differential equations to systems. In this section we take a substantial step further by showing that, with the right notation, the formulas for solving normal systems with constant coefficients are identical to the formulas for solving first order equations with constant coefficients. For example, we know that a general solution to the equation $x'(t) = ax(t)$, where a is a constant, is $x(t) = ce^{at}$. Analogously, we shall show that a general solution to the normal system

(1) $$\mathbf{x}'(t) = \mathbf{A}\mathbf{x}(t),$$

where $\mathbf{A}$ is a constant $n \times n$ matrix, is $\mathbf{x}(t) = e^{\mathbf{A}t}\mathbf{c}$. Our first task is to define the matrix exponential $e^{\mathbf{A}t}$.

If $\mathbf{A}$ is a constant $n \times n$ matrix, we define $e^{\mathbf{A}t}$ by taking the series expansion for e^{at} and replacing a by $\mathbf{A}$; that is,

(2) $$e^{\mathbf{A}t} := \mathbf{I} + \mathbf{A}t + \mathbf{A}^2 \frac{t^2}{2!} + \cdots + \mathbf{A}^n \frac{t^n}{n!} + \cdots .$$

By the right-hand side of (2) we mean the $n \times n$ matrix whose elements are power series with coefficients given by the corresponding entries in the matrices $\mathbf{I}$, $\mathbf{A}$, $\mathbf{A}^2/2!, \ldots$.

If $\mathbf{A}$ is a diagonal matrix, then the computation of $e^{\mathbf{A}t}$ is straightforward. For example, if

$$\mathbf{A} = \begin{bmatrix} -1 & 0 \\ 0 & 2 \end{bmatrix},$$

then

$$\mathbf{A}^2 = \mathbf{A}\mathbf{A} = \begin{bmatrix} 1 & 0 \\ 0 & 4 \end{bmatrix}, \qquad \mathbf{A}^3 = \begin{bmatrix} -1 & 0 \\ 0 & 8 \end{bmatrix}, \qquad \ldots, \qquad \mathbf{A}^n = \begin{bmatrix} (-1)^n & 0 \\ 0 & 2^n \end{bmatrix},$$

and so

$$e^{\mathbf{A}t} = \sum_{n=0}^{\infty} \mathbf{A}^n \frac{t^n}{n!} = \begin{bmatrix} \sum\limits_{n=0}^{\infty} (-1)^n \dfrac{t^n}{n!} & 0 \\[2mm] 0 & \sum\limits_{n=0}^{\infty} 2^n \dfrac{t^n}{n!} \end{bmatrix} = \begin{bmatrix} e^{-t} & 0 \\ 0 & e^{2t} \end{bmatrix}.$$

More generally, if $\mathbf{A}$ is an $n \times n$ *diagonal* matrix with $r_1, r_2, \ldots, r_n$ down its main diagonal, then $e^{\mathbf{A}t}$ is the diagonal matrix with $e^{r_1 t}, e^{r_2 t}, \ldots, e^{r_n t}$ down its main diagonal (see Problem 22). If $\mathbf{A}$ is not a diagonal matrix, the computation of $e^{\mathbf{A}t}$ is more involved. We deal with this important problem later in this section.

It can be shown that the series (2) converges for all t and has many of the same properties[†] as the scalar exponential e^{at}.

PROPERTIES OF THE MATRIX EXPONENTIAL FUNCTION

Theorem 7. Let $\mathbf{A}$ and $\mathbf{B}$ be $n \times n$ constant matrices and r, s, and t be real (or complex) numbers. Then,

(a) $e^{\mathbf{A}0} = e^{\mathbf{0}} = \mathbf{I}$.

(b) $e^{\mathbf{A}(t+s)} = e^{\mathbf{A}t}e^{\mathbf{A}s}$.

(c) $(e^{\mathbf{A}t})^{-1} = e^{-\mathbf{A}t}$.

(d) $e^{(\mathbf{A}+\mathbf{B})t} = e^{\mathbf{A}t}e^{\mathbf{B}t}$, provided that $\mathbf{AB} = \mathbf{BA}$.

(e) $e^{r\mathbf{I}t} = e^{rt}\mathbf{I}$.

Property (c) has profound implications. First, it asserts that for any matrix $\mathbf{A}$, the matrix $e^{\mathbf{A}t}$ *has* an inverse for all t. Moreover, this inverse is obtained by simply replacing t by $-t$. In applying property (d) (the law of exponents), care must be exercised because of the stipulation that the matrices $\mathbf{A}$ and $\mathbf{B}$ commute (see Problem 21).

Another important property of the matrix exponential arises from the fact that we can differentiate the series in (2) term by term. This gives

$$\frac{d}{dt}(e^{\mathbf{A}t}) = \frac{d}{dt}\left(\mathbf{I} + \mathbf{A}t + \mathbf{A}^2 \frac{t^2}{2} + \cdots + \mathbf{A}^n \frac{t^n}{n!} + \cdots \right)$$

$$= \mathbf{A} + \mathbf{A}^2 t + \mathbf{A}^3 \frac{t^2}{2} + \cdots + \mathbf{A}^n \frac{t^{n-1}}{(n-1)!} + \cdots$$

$$= \mathbf{A}\left[\mathbf{I} + \mathbf{A}t + \mathbf{A}^2 \frac{t^2}{2} + \cdots + \mathbf{A}^{n-1} \frac{t^{n-1}}{(n-1)!} + \cdots \right].$$

[†] For proofs of these and other properties of the matrix exponential function, see *Matrices and Linear Transformations*, by Charles G. Cullen, Addison-Wesley Publishing Co., Reading, Massachusetts, 1972, Chapter 8.

Hence

$$\frac{d}{dt}(e^{\mathbf{A}t}) = \mathbf{A}e^{\mathbf{A}t},$$

and so $e^{\mathbf{A}t}$ *is a solution to the matrix differential equation* $\mathbf{X}' = \mathbf{A}\mathbf{X}$. Since $e^{\mathbf{A}t}$ is invertible (property (c)), it follows that the columns of $e^{\mathbf{A}t}$ are linearly independent solutions to system (1). Combining these facts we have:

$e^{\mathbf{A}t}$ IS A FUNDAMENTAL MATRIX

Theorem 8.   If $\mathbf{A}$ is an $n \times n$ constant matrix, then the columns of the matrix exponential $e^{\mathbf{A}t}$ form a fundamental solution set for the system $\mathbf{x}'(t) = \mathbf{A}\mathbf{x}(t)$. Therefore, $e^{\mathbf{A}t}$ is a fundamental matrix for the system, and a general solution is $\mathbf{x}(t) = e^{\mathbf{A}t}\mathbf{c}$.

Knowing that $e^{\mathbf{A}t}$ is a fundamental matrix is of practical use provided we can calculate $e^{\mathbf{A}t}$. As we observed, if $\mathbf{A}$ is a diagonal matrix, then we simply exponentiate the diagonal elements (times t) to obtain $e^{\mathbf{A}t}$. Also, if $\mathbf{B}$ is a **nilpotent** matrix, that is, $\mathbf{B}^k = \mathbf{0}$ for some positive integer k, then the series for $e^{\mathbf{B}t}$ has only a finite number of terms, since $\mathbf{B}^k = \mathbf{B}^{k+1} = \cdots = \mathbf{0}$. In such cases $e^{\mathbf{B}t}$ reduces to

$$e^{\mathbf{B}t} = \mathbf{I} + \mathbf{B}t + \cdots + \mathbf{B}^{k-1}\frac{t^{k-1}}{(k-1)!}.$$

Using the law of exponents and this fact about nilpotent matrices, we can determine $e^{\mathbf{A}t}$ for a special class of matrices. Let r be a scalar. Since

$$e^{\mathbf{A}t} = e^{r\mathbf{I}t}e^{(\mathbf{A}-r\mathbf{I})t} = e^{rt}e^{(\mathbf{A}-r\mathbf{I})t},$$

we get a finite representation for $e^{\mathbf{A}t}$ if $\mathbf{B} = \mathbf{A} - r\mathbf{I}$ is nilpotent for some r. In fact, when the characteristic polynomial for $\mathbf{A}$ has the form $p(r) = (r_1 - r)^n$, that is, when $\mathbf{A}$ has one eigenvalue r_1 of multiplicity n, it is a consequence of the Cayley-Hamilton theorem[†] that $(r_1\mathbf{I} - \mathbf{A})^n = \mathbf{0}$. Hence $\mathbf{A} - r_1\mathbf{I}$ is nilpotent and

$$(3) \qquad e^{\mathbf{A}t} = e^{r_1 t}\left\{\mathbf{I} + (\mathbf{A} - r_1\mathbf{I})t + \cdots + (\mathbf{A} - r_1\mathbf{I})^{n-1}\frac{t^{n-1}}{(n-1)!}\right\}.$$

[†] The Cayley-Hamilton theorem states that a matrix satisfies its own characteristic equation. That is, $p(\mathbf{A}) = \mathbf{0}$. For a discussion of this theorem, see *Matrices and Linear Transformations,* by Charles G. Cullen, Addison-Wesley Publishing Co., Reading, Massachusetts, 1972, Chapter 5.

▶ *Example 1*   Find the fundamental matrix $e^{\mathbf{A}t}$ for the system

(4) $\mathbf{x}' = \mathbf{A}\mathbf{x}$,   where $\mathbf{A} = \begin{bmatrix} 2 & 1 & 1 \\ 1 & 2 & 1 \\ -2 & -2 & -1 \end{bmatrix}$.

Solution   We begin by computing the characteristic polynomial for $\mathbf{A}$:

(5) $p(r) = |\mathbf{A} - r\mathbf{I}| = \begin{vmatrix} 2-r & 1 & 1 \\ 1 & 2-r & 1 \\ -2 & -2 & -1-r \end{vmatrix} = -r^3 + 3r^2 - 3r + 1 = -(r-1)^3.$

Thus $r = 1$ is an eigenvalue of $\mathbf{A}$ with multiplicity 3. By the Cayley-Hamilton theorem, $(\mathbf{A} - \mathbf{I})^3 = \mathbf{0}$, and so

(6) $e^{\mathbf{A}t} = e^t e^{(\mathbf{A}-\mathbf{I})t} = e^t \left\{ \mathbf{I} + (\mathbf{A} - \mathbf{I})t + (\mathbf{A} - \mathbf{I})^2 \dfrac{t^2}{2} \right\}.$

Computing, we find

$\mathbf{A} - \mathbf{I} = \begin{bmatrix} 1 & 1 & 1 \\ 1 & 1 & 1 \\ -2 & -2 & -2 \end{bmatrix}$ and $(\mathbf{A} - \mathbf{I})^2 = \begin{bmatrix} 0 & 0 & 0 \\ 0 & 0 & 0 \\ 0 & 0 & 0 \end{bmatrix}.$

Substituting into (6) yields

(7) $e^{\mathbf{A}t} = e^t \begin{bmatrix} 1 & 0 & 0 \\ 0 & 1 & 0 \\ 0 & 0 & 1 \end{bmatrix} + te^t \begin{bmatrix} 1 & 1 & 1 \\ 1 & 1 & 1 \\ -2 & -2 & -2 \end{bmatrix} = \begin{bmatrix} e^t + te^t & te^t & te^t \\ te^t & e^t + te^t & te^t \\ -2te^t & -2te^t & e^t - 2te^t \end{bmatrix}.$ ◀

In the preceding example we used the nilpotency of the matrix $\mathbf{A} - r\mathbf{I}$ to compute $e^{\mathbf{A}t}$ directly. In general, we cannot expect nilpotency to hold, but we can take advantage of the following relationship between fundamental matrices to help compute $e^{\mathbf{A}t}$.

RELATIONSHIP BETWEEN FUNDAMENTAL MATRICES

Lemma 1.   Let $\mathbf{X}(t)$ and $\mathbf{Y}(t)$ be two fundamental matrices for the same system $\mathbf{x}' = \mathbf{A}\mathbf{x}$. Then, there exists a constant matrix $\mathbf{C}$ such that $\mathbf{X}(t) = \mathbf{Y}(t)\mathbf{C}$.

Proof Let $\mathbf{x}_1(t), \ldots, \mathbf{x}_n(t)$ be the columns of $\mathbf{X}(t)$ and let $\mathbf{y}_1(t), \ldots, \mathbf{y}_n(t)$ be the columns of $\mathbf{Y}(t)$. Since $\{\mathbf{y}_1(t), \ldots, \mathbf{y}_n(t)\}$ is a fundamental solution set and $\mathbf{x}_j(t), j = 1, \ldots, n$ are solutions to $\mathbf{x}' = \mathbf{A}\mathbf{x}$, there exist constants $c_{1j}, c_{2j}, \ldots, c_{nj}$ such that

$$\mathbf{x}_j(t) = c_{1j}\mathbf{y}_1(t) + c_{2j}\mathbf{y}_2(t) + \cdots + c_{nj}\mathbf{y}_n(t)$$

for each $j = 1, \ldots, n$. But this is equivalent to writing $\mathbf{X}(t) = \mathbf{Y}(t)\mathbf{C}$, where $\mathbf{C} = [c_{ij}]$. ∎

We now use Lemma 1 to find a formula for $e^{\mathbf{A}t}$ when a fundamental matrix $\mathbf{X}(t)$ for $\mathbf{x}' = \mathbf{A}\mathbf{x}$ is known. Since $e^{\mathbf{A}t}$ is also a fundamental matrix for the system, Lemma 1 asserts that $e^{\mathbf{A}t} = \mathbf{X}(t)\mathbf{C}$ for some constant matrix $\mathbf{C}$. Setting $t = 0$ yields $\mathbf{I} = \mathbf{X}(0)\mathbf{C}$, and solving for $\mathbf{C}$ we get $\mathbf{C} = \mathbf{X}^{-1}(0)$. Hence

$$(8) \qquad e^{\mathbf{A}t} = \mathbf{X}(t)\mathbf{X}^{-1}(0).$$

Although formula (8) is useful, it does place the burden of determining $e^{\mathbf{A}t}$ on finding a fundamental matrix $\mathbf{X}(t)$. Fortunately, we can use the *properties* of the matrix exponential $e^{\mathbf{A}t}$ to help simplify this task. Since the columns of a fundamental matrix must have the form $e^{\mathbf{A}t}\mathbf{u}$, let's try to find n vectors $\mathbf{u}$ for which the computation of $e^{\mathbf{A}t}\mathbf{u}$ is tractable.

We begin by using the relation $e^{\mathbf{A}t} = e^{rt}e^{(\mathbf{A} - r\mathbf{I})t}$ to express $e^{\mathbf{A}t}\mathbf{u}$ as

$$(9) \qquad e^{\mathbf{A}t}\mathbf{u} = e^{rt}e^{(\mathbf{A} - r\mathbf{I})t}\mathbf{u}$$

$$= e^{rt}\left\{\mathbf{u} + t(\mathbf{A} - r\mathbf{I})\mathbf{u} + \cdots + \frac{t^k}{k!}(\mathbf{A} - r\mathbf{I})^k\mathbf{u} + \cdots\right\}.$$

Now we know that if r is an eigenvalue of $\mathbf{A}$ and $\mathbf{u}$ is a corresponding eigenvector, then $e^{rt}\mathbf{u}$ is a solution to (1). Indeed, in this situation $(\mathbf{A} - r\mathbf{I})\mathbf{u} = (\mathbf{A} - r\mathbf{I})^2\mathbf{u} = \cdots = \mathbf{0}$, and so the series in (9) reduces to the first term, $e^{rt}\mathbf{u}$. While it is too much to expect $\mathbf{A} - r\mathbf{I}$ to be nilpotent, it is not too much to ask that $(\mathbf{A} - r\mathbf{I})^k\mathbf{u} = \mathbf{0}$ for some nontrivial vector $\mathbf{u}$ and some positive integer k.

GENERALIZED EIGENVECTORS

Definition 5. Let $\mathbf{A}$ be an $n \times n$ constant matrix and r be an eigenvalue of $\mathbf{A}$. A nontrivial vector $\mathbf{u}$ that satisfies

$$(10) \qquad (\mathbf{A} - r\mathbf{I})^k\mathbf{u} = \mathbf{0}$$

for some positive integer k is called a **generalized eigenvector** associated with r.

A consequence of the primary decomposition theorem in advanced linear algebra[†] is that if the characteristic polynomial for $\mathbf{A}$ is

$$p(r) = (r_1 - r)^{m_1} \cdots (r_k - r)^{m_k},$$

where the r_i's are distinct eigenvalues of $\mathbf{A}$ and m_i is the multiplicity of the eigenvalue r_i, then for each i there exist m_i linearly independent generalized eigenvectors associated with r_i, and the combined set of $n = m_1 + \cdots + m_k$ generalized eigenvectors is linearly independent. Moreover, if $\mathbf{u}$ is a generalized eigenvector associated with r_i, then $(\mathbf{A} - r_i\mathbf{I})^{m_i}\mathbf{u} = \mathbf{0}$. This leads to the following procedure for finding n linearly independent solutions to system (1).

SOLVING SYSTEMS USING GENERALIZED EIGENVECTORS

To obtain a fundamental solution set for $\mathbf{x}' = \mathbf{A}\mathbf{x}$:

(a) Compute the characteristic polynomial $p(t) = |\mathbf{A} - r\mathbf{I}|$ and find the distinct eigenvalues $r_1, \ldots, r_k$.

(b) For each eigenvalue r_i, find m_i linearly independent generalized eigenvectors, where m_i is the multiplicity of the eigenvalue r_i.

(c) Use the n linearly independent generalized eigenvectors obtained in (b) to compute the n linearly independent solutions to $\mathbf{x}' = \mathbf{A}\mathbf{x}$ of the form

(11) $$e^{\mathbf{A}t}\mathbf{u} = e^{rt}\left\{\mathbf{u} + t(\mathbf{A} - r\mathbf{I})\mathbf{u} + \frac{t^2}{2}(\mathbf{A} - r\mathbf{I})^2\mathbf{u} + \cdots\right\},$$

where r is an eigenvalue and $\mathbf{u}$ is a corresponding generalized eigenvector. If r has multiplicity m_i, then the above series reduces to the first m_i terms.

▶ **Example 2**   Find the fundamental matrix $e^{\mathbf{A}t}$ for the system

(12) $$\mathbf{x}' = \mathbf{A}\mathbf{x}, \quad \text{where} \quad \mathbf{A} = \begin{bmatrix} 1 & 0 & 0 \\ 1 & 3 & 0 \\ 0 & 1 & 1 \end{bmatrix}.$$

[†] *Matrices and Linear Transformations*, by Charles G. Cullen, Theorem 5.11, page 196.

Solution We begin by finding the characteristic polynomial for **A**:

$$p(r) = |\mathbf{A} - r\mathbf{I}| = \begin{vmatrix} 1-r & 0 & 0 \\ 1 & 3-r & 0 \\ 0 & 1 & 1-r \end{vmatrix} = -(r-1)^2(r-3).$$

Hence the eigenvalues of **A** are $r = 1$ with multiplicity 2 and $r = 3$ with multiplicity 1.

Since $r = 1$ has multiplicity 2, we must determine two linearly independent associated generalized eigenvectors. We begin by solving $(\mathbf{A} - \mathbf{I})\mathbf{u} = \mathbf{0}$; that is,

$$(13) \qquad \begin{bmatrix} 0 & 0 & 0 \\ 1 & 2 & 0 \\ 0 & 1 & 0 \end{bmatrix} \begin{bmatrix} u_1 \\ u_2 \\ u_3 \end{bmatrix} = \begin{bmatrix} 0 \\ 0 \\ 0 \end{bmatrix}.$$

Solving, we obtain $u_1 = u_2 = 0$ and $u_3 = s$, where s is arbitrary. Thus there is at most one linearly independent eigenvector corresponding to $r = 1$, and with $s = 1$ we choose $\mathbf{u}_1 = \text{col}(0, 0, 1)$. Hence one solution to (12) is

$$(14) \qquad \mathbf{x}_1(t) = e^t \mathbf{u}_1 = e^t \begin{bmatrix} 0 \\ 0 \\ 1 \end{bmatrix} = \begin{bmatrix} 0 \\ 0 \\ e^t \end{bmatrix}.$$

Next we solve $(\mathbf{A} - \mathbf{I})^2 \mathbf{u} = \mathbf{0}$. From

$$(15) \qquad (\mathbf{A} - \mathbf{I})^2 \mathbf{u} = \begin{bmatrix} 0 & 0 & 0 \\ 2 & 4 & 0 \\ 1 & 2 & 0 \end{bmatrix} \begin{bmatrix} u_1 \\ u_2 \\ u_3 \end{bmatrix} = \begin{bmatrix} 0 \\ 0 \\ 0 \end{bmatrix},$$

we find $u_2 = s$, $u_1 = -2u_2 = -2s$, and $u_3 = v$, where s and v are arbitrary. Taking $s = 1$ and $v = 0$, we obtain the generalized eigenvector $\mathbf{u}_2 = \text{col}(-2, 1, 0)$, which is linearly independent of $\mathbf{u}_1$. Now we use $\mathbf{u}_2$ to obtain a second solution to (12). Since $(\mathbf{A} - \mathbf{I})^2 \mathbf{u}_2 = \mathbf{0}$, formula (11) reduces to

$$(16) \qquad \mathbf{x}_2(t) = e^{\mathbf{A}t} \mathbf{u}_2 = e^t\{\mathbf{u}_2 + t(\mathbf{A} - \mathbf{I})\mathbf{u}_2\}$$

$$= e^t \begin{bmatrix} -2 \\ 1 \\ 0 \end{bmatrix} + te^t \begin{bmatrix} 0 & 0 & 0 \\ 1 & 2 & 0 \\ 0 & 1 & 0 \end{bmatrix} \begin{bmatrix} -2 \\ 1 \\ 0 \end{bmatrix}$$

$$= e^t \begin{bmatrix} -2 \\ 1 \\ 0 \end{bmatrix} + te^t \begin{bmatrix} 0 \\ 0 \\ 1 \end{bmatrix} = \begin{bmatrix} -2e^t \\ e^t \\ te^t \end{bmatrix}.$$

For the eigenvalue $r = 3$, we solve $(\mathbf{A} - 3\mathbf{I})\mathbf{u} = \mathbf{0}$, that is,

$$
(17) \qquad
\begin{bmatrix}
-2 & 0 & 0 \\
1 & 0 & 0 \\
0 & 1 & -2
\end{bmatrix}
\begin{bmatrix}
u_1 \\
u_2 \\
u_3
\end{bmatrix}
=
\begin{bmatrix}
0 \\
0 \\
0
\end{bmatrix},
$$

to obtain the eigenvector $\mathbf{u}_3 = \mathrm{col}(0, 2, 1)$. Hence a third linearly independent solution to (12) is

$$
(18) \qquad
\mathbf{x}_3(t) = e^{3t}\mathbf{u}_3 = e^{3t}
\begin{bmatrix}
0 \\
2 \\
1
\end{bmatrix}
=
\begin{bmatrix}
0 \\
2e^{3t} \\
e^{3t}
\end{bmatrix}.
$$

The matrix $\mathbf{X}(t)$ whose columns are the vectors $\mathbf{x}_1(t)$, $\mathbf{x}_2(t)$, and $\mathbf{x}_3(t)$ given in equations (14), (16), and (18), respectively, that is,

$$
(19) \qquad
\mathbf{X}(t) =
\begin{bmatrix}
0 & -2e^t & 0 \\
0 & e^t & 2e^{3t} \\
e^t & te^t & e^{3t}
\end{bmatrix},
$$

is a fundamental matrix for (12). Setting $t = 0$ and then computing $\mathbf{X}^{-1}(0)$, we find

$$
(20) \qquad
\mathbf{X}(0) =
\begin{bmatrix}
0 & -2 & 0 \\
0 & 1 & 2 \\
1 & 0 & 1
\end{bmatrix}
\quad \text{and} \quad
\mathbf{X}^{-1}(0) =
\begin{bmatrix}
-\frac{1}{4} & -\frac{1}{2} & 1 \\
-\frac{1}{2} & 0 & 0 \\
\frac{1}{4} & \frac{1}{2} & 0
\end{bmatrix}.
$$

It now follows from formula (8) that

$$
(21) \qquad
e^{\mathbf{A}t} = \mathbf{X}(t)\mathbf{X}^{-1}(0) =
\begin{bmatrix}
0 & -2e^t & 0 \\
0 & e^t & 2e^{3t} \\
e^t & te^t & e^{3t}
\end{bmatrix}
\begin{bmatrix}
-\frac{1}{4} & -\frac{1}{2} & 1 \\
-\frac{1}{2} & 0 & 0 \\
\frac{1}{4} & \frac{1}{2} & 0
\end{bmatrix}
$$

$$
=
\begin{bmatrix}
e^t & 0 & 0 \\
-\frac{1}{2}e^t + \frac{1}{2}e^{3t} & e^{3t} & 0 \\
-\frac{1}{4}e^t - \frac{1}{2}te^t + \frac{1}{4}e^{3t} & -\frac{1}{2}e^t + \frac{1}{2}e^{3t} & e^t
\end{bmatrix}. \quad \blacktriangleleft
$$

Use of the fundamental matrix $e^{\mathbf{A}t}$ simplifies many computations. For example, the properties $e^{\mathbf{A}t}e^{-\mathbf{A}s} = e^{\mathbf{A}(t-s)}$ and $(e^{\mathbf{A}t_0})^{-1} = e^{-\mathbf{A}t_0}$ enable us to rewrite the variation of parameters formula (18) in Section 10.6 in a simpler form; namely, the solution to the initial value problem $\mathbf{x}' = \mathbf{A}\mathbf{x} + \mathbf{f}(t)$, $\mathbf{x}(t_0) = \mathbf{x}_0$ is given by

(22) $$\mathbf{x}(t) = e^{\mathbf{A}(t-t_0)}\mathbf{x}_0 + \int_{t_0}^{t} e^{\mathbf{A}(t-s)}\mathbf{f}(s)\,ds,$$

which is a system version of the formula for the solution to the scalar initial value problem $x' = ax + f(t)$, $x(t_0) = x_0$.

EXERCISES 10.7

*In Problems 1 through 6: (a) Show that the given matrix **A** satisfies $(\mathbf{A} - r\mathbf{I})^k = \mathbf{0}$ for some number r and some positive integer k; (b) use this fact to determine the matrix $e^{\mathbf{A}t}$. [Hint: Compute the characteristic polynomial and use the Cayley-Hamilton theorem.]*

1. A $= \begin{bmatrix} 1 & -1 \\ 1 & 3 \end{bmatrix}$.

2. A $= \begin{bmatrix} 3 & -2 \\ 0 & 3 \end{bmatrix}$.

3. A $= \begin{bmatrix} 2 & 1 & -1 \\ -3 & -1 & 1 \\ 9 & 3 & -4 \end{bmatrix}$.

4. A $= \begin{bmatrix} 0 & 1 & 0 \\ 0 & 0 & 1 \\ -1 & -3 & -3 \end{bmatrix}$.

5. A $= \begin{bmatrix} -2 & 0 & 0 \\ 4 & -2 & 0 \\ 1 & 0 & -2 \end{bmatrix}$.

6. A $= \begin{bmatrix} 2 & 1 & 3 \\ 0 & 2 & -1 \\ 0 & 0 & 2 \end{bmatrix}$.

In Problems 7 through 10 determine $e^{\mathbf{A}t}$ by first finding a fundamental matrix $\mathbf{X}(t)$ for $\mathbf{x}' = \mathbf{A}\mathbf{x}$ and then using formula (8).

7. A $= \begin{bmatrix} 1 & 1 \\ 4 & 1 \end{bmatrix}$.

8. A $= \begin{bmatrix} 0 & 1 \\ -1 & 0 \end{bmatrix}$.

9. A $= \begin{bmatrix} 0 & 1 & 0 \\ 0 & 0 & 1 \\ 1 & -1 & 1 \end{bmatrix}$.

10. A $= \begin{bmatrix} 0 & 2 & 2 \\ 2 & 0 & 2 \\ 2 & 2 & 0 \end{bmatrix}$.

In Problems 11 and 12 determine $e^{\mathbf{A}t}$ by using generalized eigenvectors to find a fundamental matrix and then using formula (8).

11. A $= \begin{bmatrix} 5 & -4 & 0 \\ 1 & 0 & 2 \\ 0 & 2 & 5 \end{bmatrix}$.

12. A $= \begin{bmatrix} 1 & 1 & 1 \\ 2 & 1 & -1 \\ 0 & -1 & 1 \end{bmatrix}$.

*In Problems 13 through 16 use the generalized eigenvectors of **A** to find a general solution to the system $\mathbf{x}'(t) = \mathbf{A}\mathbf{x}(t)$, where **A** is given.*

13. A $= \begin{bmatrix} 0 & 1 & 0 \\ 0 & 0 & 1 \\ -2 & -5 & -4 \end{bmatrix}$.

14. A $= \begin{bmatrix} 0 & 0 & 1 \\ 0 & 1 & 2 \\ 0 & 0 & 1 \end{bmatrix}$.

15. A $= \begin{bmatrix} -1 & -8 & 1 \\ -1 & -3 & 2 \\ -4 & -16 & 7 \end{bmatrix}$.

16. A $= \begin{bmatrix} 1 & 0 & 1 & 2 \\ 1 & 1 & 2 & 1 \\ 0 & 0 & 2 & 0 \\ 0 & 0 & 1 & 1 \end{bmatrix}$.

17. Use the results of Problem 5 to find the solution to the initial value problem

$$\mathbf{x}'(t) = \begin{bmatrix} -2 & 0 & 0 \\ 4 & -2 & 0 \\ 1 & 0 & -2 \end{bmatrix}\mathbf{x}(t), \qquad \mathbf{x}(0) = \begin{bmatrix} 1 \\ 1 \\ -1 \end{bmatrix}.$$

18. Use your answer to Problem 12 to find the solution to the initial value problem

$$\mathbf{x}'(t) = \begin{bmatrix} 1 & 1 & 1 \\ 2 & 1 & -1 \\ 0 & -1 & 1 \end{bmatrix} \mathbf{x}(t), \qquad \mathbf{x}(0) = \begin{bmatrix} -1 \\ 0 \\ 3 \end{bmatrix}.$$

19. Use the results of Problem 3 and the variation of parameters formula (22) to find the solution to the initial value problem

$$\mathbf{x}'(t) = \begin{bmatrix} 2 & 1 & -1 \\ -3 & -1 & 1 \\ 9 & 3 & -4 \end{bmatrix} \mathbf{x}(t) + \begin{bmatrix} 0 \\ t \\ 0 \end{bmatrix}, \qquad \mathbf{x}(0) = \begin{bmatrix} 0 \\ 3 \\ 0 \end{bmatrix}.$$

20. Use your answer to Problem 9 and the variation of parameters formula (22) to find the solution to the initial value problem

$$\mathbf{x}'(t) = \begin{bmatrix} 0 & 1 & 0 \\ 0 & 0 & 1 \\ 1 & -1 & 1 \end{bmatrix} \mathbf{x}(t) + \begin{bmatrix} 0 \\ 0 \\ t \end{bmatrix}, \qquad \mathbf{x}(0) = \begin{bmatrix} 1 \\ -1 \\ 0 \end{bmatrix}.$$

21. Let

$$\mathbf{A} = \begin{bmatrix} 1 & 2 \\ -1 & 3 \end{bmatrix} \quad \text{and} \quad \mathbf{B} = \begin{bmatrix} 2 & 1 \\ 0 & 1 \end{bmatrix}.$$

(a) Show that $\mathbf{AB} \neq \mathbf{BA}$.

(b) Show that property (d) in Theorem 7 does not hold for these matrices. That is, show that $e^{(\mathbf{A}+\mathbf{B})t} \neq e^{\mathbf{A}t}e^{\mathbf{B}t}$.

22. Let $\mathbf{A}$ be a diagonal $n \times n$ matrix with entries $r_1, \ldots, r_n$ down its main diagonal. To compute $e^{\mathbf{A}t}$:

(a) Show that $\mathbf{A}^k$ is the diagonal matrix with entries $r_1^k, \ldots, r_n^k$ down its main diagonal.

(b) Use the result of part (a) to show that $e^{\mathbf{A}t}$ is the diagonal matrix with entries $e^{r_1 t}, \ldots, e^{r_n t}$ down its main diagonal.

Chapter Summary

In this chapter we discussed the theory of linear systems in normal form and presented methods for solving such systems. The theory and methods are natural extensions of the development for second order and higher order linear equations. The important properties and techniques are listed below.

HOMOGENEOUS NORMAL SYSTEMS

$$\mathbf{x}'(t) = \mathbf{A}(t)\mathbf{x}(t)$$

The $n \times n$ matrix function $\mathbf{A}(t)$ is assumed to be continuous on an interval I.

Fundamental Solution Set: $\{\mathbf{x}_1, \ldots, \mathbf{x}_n\}$

The n vector solutions $\mathbf{x}_1(t), \ldots, \mathbf{x}_n(t)$ of the homogeneous system on the interval I form a **fundamental solution set,** provided that they are linearly independent on I or, equivalently, that their **Wronskian**

$$W[\mathbf{x}_1, \ldots, \mathbf{x}_n](t) := \det[\mathbf{x}_1, \ldots, \mathbf{x}_n] = \begin{vmatrix} x_{1,1}(t) & x_{1,2}(t) & \ldots & x_{1,n}(t) \\ x_{2,1}(t) & x_{2,2}(t) & \ldots & x_{2,n}(t) \\ \cdot & \cdot & & \cdot \\ \cdot & \cdot & & \cdot \\ \cdot & \cdot & & \cdot \\ x_{n,1}(t) & x_{n,2}(t) & \ldots & x_{n,n}(t) \end{vmatrix}$$

is never zero on I.

Fundamental Matrix: $\mathbf{X}(t)$

An $n \times n$ matrix function $\mathbf{X}(t)$ whose column vectors form a fundamental solution set for the homogeneous system is called a **fundamental matrix.** The determinant of $\mathbf{X}(t)$ is the Wronskian of the fundamental solution set. Since the Wronskian is never zero on the interval I, then $\mathbf{X}^{-1}(t)$ exists for t in I.

General Solution to Homogeneous System: $\mathbf{Xc} = c_1\mathbf{x}_1 + \cdots + c_n\mathbf{x}_n$

If $\mathbf{X}(t)$ is a fundamental matrix whose column vectors are $\mathbf{x}_1, \ldots, \mathbf{x}_n$, then a general solution to the homogeneous system is

$$\mathbf{x}(t) = \mathbf{X}(t)\mathbf{c} = c_1\mathbf{x}_1(t) + c_2\mathbf{x}_2(t) + \cdots + c_n\mathbf{x}_n(t),$$

where $\mathbf{c} = \text{col}(c_1, \ldots, c_n)$ is an arbitrary constant vector.

Homogeneous Systems with Constant Coefficients

The form of a general solution for a homogeneous system with constant coefficients depends on the eigenvalues and eigenvectors of the $n \times n$ constant matrix $\mathbf{A}$. An **eigenvalue** of $\mathbf{A}$ is a number r such that the system $\mathbf{Au} = r\mathbf{u}$ has a nontrivial solution $\mathbf{u}$ called an **eigenvector** of $\mathbf{A}$ associated with the eigenvalue r. Finding the eigenvalues of $\mathbf{A}$ is equivalent to finding the roots of the **characteristic equation**

$$|\mathbf{A} - r\mathbf{I}| = 0.$$

The corresponding eigenvectors are found by solving the system $(\mathbf{A} - r\mathbf{I})\mathbf{u} = \mathbf{0}$.

If the matrix $\mathbf{A}$ has n linearly independent eigenvectors $\mathbf{u}_1, \ldots, \mathbf{u}_n$ and r_i is the eigenvalue corresponding to the eigenvector $\mathbf{u}_i$, then

$$\{e^{r_1 t}\mathbf{u}_1, e^{r_2 t}\mathbf{u}_2, \ldots, e^{r_n t}\mathbf{u}_n\}$$

is a fundamental solution set for the homogeneous system. A class of matrices that always has n linearly independent eigenvectors is the set of **symmetric** matrices—that is, matrices that satisfy $\mathbf{A} = \mathbf{A}^T$.

If $\mathbf{A}$ has complex conjugate eigenvalues $\alpha \pm i\beta$ and associated eigenvectors $\mathbf{z} = \mathbf{a} \pm i\mathbf{b}$, where $\mathbf{a}$ and $\mathbf{b}$ are real vectors, then two linearly independent real vector solutions to the homogeneous system are

$$e^{\alpha t} \cos \beta t \, \mathbf{a} - e^{\alpha t} \sin \beta t \, \mathbf{b}, \qquad e^{\alpha t} \sin \beta t \, \mathbf{a} + e^{\alpha t} \cos \beta t \, \mathbf{b}.$$

When $\mathbf{A}$ has a repeated eigenvalue r of multiplicity m, then it is possible that $\mathbf{A}$ does *not* have n linearly independent eigenvectors. However, associated with r are m linearly independent solutions to the homogeneous system of the form

$$\mathbf{x}_1(t) = e^{rt}\mathbf{k}_{1,1}, \qquad \mathbf{x}_2(t) = e^{rt}\mathbf{k}_{2,1} + te^{rt}\mathbf{k}_{2,2}, \quad \ldots,$$

$$\mathbf{x}_m(t) = e^{rt}\mathbf{k}_{m,1} + te^{rt}\mathbf{k}_{m,2} + \cdots + \frac{t^{m-1}}{(m-1)!} e^{rt}\mathbf{k}_{m,m}.$$

NONHOMOGENEOUS NORMAL SYSTEMS

$$\mathbf{x}'(t) = \mathbf{A}(t)\mathbf{x}(t) + \mathbf{f}(t)$$

The $n \times n$ matrix function $\mathbf{A}(t)$ and the vector function $\mathbf{f}(t)$ are assumed continuous on an interval I.

General Solution to Nonhomogeneous System: $\mathbf{x}_p + \mathbf{Xc}$

If $\mathbf{x}_p(t)$ is any particular solution for the nonhomogeneous system and $\mathbf{X}(t)$ is a fundamental matrix for the associated homogeneous system, then a general solution for the nonhomogeneous system is

$$\mathbf{x}(t) = \mathbf{x}_p(t) + \mathbf{X}(t)\mathbf{c} = \mathbf{x}_p(t) + c_1\mathbf{x}_1(t) + \cdots + c_n\mathbf{x}_n(t),$$

where $\mathbf{x}_1(t), \ldots, \mathbf{x}_n(t)$ are the column vectors of $\mathbf{X}(t)$ and $\mathbf{c} = \mathrm{col}(c_1, \ldots, c_n)$ is an arbitrary constant vector.

Undetermined Coefficients

If the nonhomogeneous term $\mathbf{f}(t)$ is a vector whose components are polynomials, or exponential or sinusoidal functions, and $\mathbf{A}$ is a constant matrix, then one can use an extension of the method of undetermined coefficients to decide the form of a particular solution to the nonhomogeneous system.

Variation of Parameters: $\mathbf{X}(t)v(t)$

Let $\mathbf{X}(t)$ be a fundamental matrix for the homogeneous system. A particular solution to the nonhomogeneous system is given by the **variation of parameters formula**

$$\mathbf{x}_p(t) = \mathbf{X}(t)v(t) = \mathbf{X}(t) \int \mathbf{X}^{-1}(t)\mathbf{f}(t)\, dt.$$

MATRIX EXPONENTIAL FUNCTION

If $\mathbf{A}$ is a constant $n \times n$ matrix, then the matrix exponential function

$$e^{\mathbf{A}t} := \mathbf{I} + \mathbf{A}t + \mathbf{A}^2 \frac{t^2}{2!} + \cdots + \mathbf{A}^n \frac{t^n}{n!} + \cdots$$

is a fundamental matrix for the homogeneous system $\mathbf{x}'(t) = \mathbf{A}\mathbf{x}(t)$. The matrix exponential has some of the same properties as the scalar exponential e^{at}. In particular,

$$e^{\mathbf{0}} = \mathbf{I}, \qquad e^{\mathbf{A}(t+s)} = e^{\mathbf{A}t}e^{\mathbf{A}s}, \qquad (e^{\mathbf{A}t})^{-1} = e^{-\mathbf{A}t}.$$

If $(\mathbf{A} - r\mathbf{I})^k = \mathbf{0}$ for some r and k, then the series for $e^{\mathbf{A}t}$ has only a finite number of terms:

$$e^{\mathbf{A}t} = e^{rt}\left\{\mathbf{I} + (\mathbf{A} - r\mathbf{I})t + \cdots + (\mathbf{A} - r\mathbf{I})^{k-1}\frac{t^{k-1}}{(k-1)!}\right\}.$$

The matrix exponential function $e^{\mathbf{A}t}$ can also be computed from any fundamental matrix $\mathbf{X}(t)$ via the formula

$$e^{\mathbf{A}t} = \mathbf{X}(t)\mathbf{X}^{-1}(0).$$

GENERALIZED EIGENVECTORS

If r is an eigenvalue of $\mathbf{A}$, then a **generalized eigenvector** associated with r is a nonzero vector $\mathbf{u}$ that satisfies $(\mathbf{A} - r\mathbf{I})^k\mathbf{u} = \mathbf{0}$ for some positive integer k. *Every* matrix $\mathbf{A}$ has a set of n linearly independent generalized eigenvectors that can be used to compute a fundamental solution set. In particular, associated with each generalized eigenvector $\mathbf{u}$ and corresponding eigenvalue r is a solution to the homogeneous system $\mathbf{x}'(t) = \mathbf{A}\mathbf{x}(t)$ of the form

$$e^{\mathbf{A}t}\mathbf{u} = e^{rt}\left\{\mathbf{u} + t(\mathbf{A} - r\mathbf{I})\mathbf{u} + \frac{t^2}{2!}(\mathbf{A} - r\mathbf{I})^2\mathbf{u} + \cdots\right\}.$$

If r has multiplicity m, then the above series reduces to the first m terms.

REVIEW PROBLEMS

In Problems 1 through 4 find a general solution for the system $\mathbf{x}'(t) = \mathbf{Ax}(t)$, *where* $\mathbf{A}$ *is given.*

1. $\mathbf{A} = \begin{bmatrix} 6 & -3 \\ 2 & 1 \end{bmatrix}$.

2. $\mathbf{A} = \begin{bmatrix} 3 & 2 \\ -5 & 1 \end{bmatrix}$.

3. $\mathbf{A} = \begin{bmatrix} 1 & 2 & 0 & 0 \\ 2 & 1 & 0 & 0 \\ 0 & 0 & 1 & 2 \\ 0 & 0 & 2 & 1 \end{bmatrix}$.

4. $\mathbf{A} = \begin{bmatrix} 1 & 1 & 0 \\ 0 & 1 & 0 \\ 0 & 0 & 2 \end{bmatrix}$.

In Problems 5 and 6 find a fundamental matrix for the system $\mathbf{x}'(t) = \mathbf{Ax}(t)$, *where* $\mathbf{A}$ *is given.*

5. $\mathbf{A} = \begin{bmatrix} 1 & -1 \\ 2 & 4 \end{bmatrix}$.

6. $\mathbf{A} = \begin{bmatrix} 5 & 0 & 0 \\ 0 & -4 & 3 \\ 0 & 3 & 4 \end{bmatrix}$.

In Problems 7 through 10 find a general solution for the system $\mathbf{x}'(t) = \mathbf{Ax}(t) + \mathbf{f}(t)$, *where* $\mathbf{A}$ *and* $\mathbf{f}(t)$ *are given.*

7. $\mathbf{A} = \begin{bmatrix} 1 & 1 \\ 4 & 1 \end{bmatrix}$, $\quad \mathbf{f}(t) = \begin{bmatrix} 5 \\ 6 \end{bmatrix}$.

8. $\mathbf{A} = \begin{bmatrix} -4 & 2 \\ 2 & -1 \end{bmatrix}$, $\quad \mathbf{f}(t) = \begin{bmatrix} e^{4t} \\ 3e^{4t} \end{bmatrix}$.

9. $\mathbf{A} = \begin{bmatrix} 2 & 1 & -1 \\ -3 & -1 & 1 \\ 9 & 3 & -4 \end{bmatrix}$, $\quad \mathbf{f}(t) = \begin{bmatrix} t \\ 0 \\ 1 \end{bmatrix}$.

10. $\mathbf{A} = \begin{bmatrix} 2 & -2 & 3 \\ 0 & 3 & 2 \\ 0 & -1 & 2 \end{bmatrix}$, $\quad \mathbf{f}(t) = \begin{bmatrix} e^{-t} \\ 2 \\ 1 \end{bmatrix}$.

In Problems 11 and 12 solve the given initial value problem.

11. $\mathbf{x}'(t) = \begin{bmatrix} 0 & 1 \\ -2 & 3 \end{bmatrix} \mathbf{x}(t)$, $\quad \mathbf{x}(0) = \begin{bmatrix} 1 \\ -1 \end{bmatrix}$.

12. $\mathbf{x}'(t) = \begin{bmatrix} 2 & 1 \\ -4 & 2 \end{bmatrix} \mathbf{x}(t) + \begin{bmatrix} te^{2t} \\ e^{2t} \end{bmatrix}$, $\quad \mathbf{x}(0) = \begin{bmatrix} 2 \\ 2 \end{bmatrix}$.

In Problems 13 and 14 find a general solution for the Cauchy-Euler system $t\mathbf{x}'(t) = \mathbf{Ax}(t)$, *where* $\mathbf{A}$ *is given.*

13. $\mathbf{A} = \begin{bmatrix} 0 & 3 & 1 \\ 1 & 2 & 1 \\ 1 & 3 & 0 \end{bmatrix}$.

14. $\mathbf{A} = \begin{bmatrix} 1 & 2 & -1 \\ 2 & 1 & 1 \\ -1 & 1 & 0 \end{bmatrix}$.

In Problems 15 and 16 find the fundamental matrix $e^{\mathbf{A}t}$ *for the system* $\mathbf{x}'(t) = \mathbf{Ax}(t)$, *where* $\mathbf{A}$ *is given.*

15. $\mathbf{A} = \begin{bmatrix} 4 & 2 & 3 \\ 2 & 1 & 2 \\ -1 & 2 & 0 \end{bmatrix}$.

16. $\mathbf{A} = \begin{bmatrix} 0 & 1 & 4 \\ 0 & 0 & 2 \\ 0 & 0 & 0 \end{bmatrix}$.

Projects for Chapter 10

A. UNCOUPLING NORMAL SYSTEMS

The easiest normal systems to solve are systems of the form

(1) $\mathbf{x}'(t) = \mathbf{D}\mathbf{x}(t),$

where $\mathbf{D}$ is an $n \times n$ diagonal matrix. Such a system actually consists of n uncoupled equations

(2) $x_i'(t) = d_{ii}x_i(t), \qquad i = 1, \ldots, n,$

whose solution is

$$x_i(t) = c_i e^{d_{ii}t},$$

where the c_i's are arbitrary constants. This raises the following question: When can we *uncouple* a normal system?

To answer this question, we need the following result from linear algebra. An $n \times n$ matrix $\mathbf{A}$ is diagonalizable if and only if $\mathbf{A}$ has n linearly independent eigenvectors $\mathbf{p}_1, \ldots, \mathbf{p}_n$. Moreover, if $\mathbf{P}$ is the matrix whose columns are $\mathbf{p}_1, \ldots, \mathbf{p}_n$, then

(3) $\mathbf{P}^{-1}\mathbf{A}\mathbf{P} = \mathbf{D},$

where $\mathbf{D}$ is the diagonal matrix whose entry d_{ii} is the eigenvalue associated with the vector $\mathbf{p}_i$.

  (a) Use the above result to show that the system

(4) $\mathbf{x}'(t) = \mathbf{A}\mathbf{x}(t),$

where $\mathbf{A}$ is an $n \times n$ diagonalizable matrix, is equivalent to an uncoupled system

(5) $\mathbf{y}'(t) = \mathbf{D}\mathbf{y}(t),$

where $\mathbf{y} = \mathbf{P}^{-1}\mathbf{x}$ and $\mathbf{D} = \mathbf{P}^{-1}\mathbf{A}\mathbf{P}$.

  (b) Solve system (5).

  (c) Use the results of parts (a) and (b) to show that a general solution to (4) is given by

$$\mathbf{x}(t) = c_1 e^{d_{11}t}\mathbf{p}_1 + c_2 e^{d_{22}t}\mathbf{p}_2 + \cdots + c_n e^{d_{nn}t}\mathbf{p}_n.$$

  (d) Use the procedure discussed in parts (a)–(c) to obtain a general solution for the system

$$\mathbf{x}'(t) = \begin{bmatrix} 1 & 2 & -1 \\ 1 & 0 & 1 \\ 4 & -4 & 5 \end{bmatrix}\mathbf{x}(t).$$

Specify $\mathbf{P}$, $\mathbf{D}$, $\mathbf{P}^{-1}$, and $\mathbf{y}$.

B. MATRIX LAPLACE TRANSFORM METHOD

The Laplace transform method for solving linear differential equations with constant coefficients was discussed in Chapter 7. This method can also be used for systems of differential equations as described in Section 9.3. To apply the procedure for equations given in matrix form, we first extend the definition of the Laplace operator $\mathscr{L}$ to a column vector of functions $\mathbf{x} = \text{col}(x_1(t), \dots, x_n(t))$ by taking the transform of each component:

$$\mathscr{L}\{\mathbf{x}\}(s) := \text{col}(\mathscr{L}\{x_1\}(s), \dots, \mathscr{L}\{x_n\}(s)).$$

With this notation, the vector analogue of the important property relating the Laplace transform of the derivative of a function (see Theorem 4, Chapter 7, page 337) becomes

(6) $\mathscr{L}\{\mathbf{x}'\}(s) = s\mathscr{L}\{\mathbf{x}\}(s) - \mathbf{x}(0).$

Now suppose we are given the initial value problem

(7) $\mathbf{x}' = \mathbf{A}\mathbf{x} + \mathbf{f}(t), \qquad \mathbf{x}(0) = \mathbf{x}_0,$

where $\mathbf{A}$ is a constant $n \times n$ matrix. Let $\hat{\mathbf{x}}(s)$ denote the Laplace transform of $\mathbf{x}(t)$ and $\hat{\mathbf{f}}(s)$ denote the transform of $\mathbf{f}(t)$. Then, taking the transform of the system and using the relation (6), we get

$$\mathscr{L}\{\mathbf{x}'\} = \mathscr{L}\{\mathbf{A}\mathbf{x} + \mathbf{f}\},$$
$$s\hat{\mathbf{x}} - \mathbf{x}_0 = \mathbf{A}\hat{\mathbf{x}} + \hat{\mathbf{f}}.$$

Next we collect the $\hat{\mathbf{x}}$ terms and solve for $\hat{\mathbf{x}}$ by premultiplying by $(s\mathbf{I} - \mathbf{A})^{-1}$:

$$(s\mathbf{I} - \mathbf{A})\hat{\mathbf{x}} = \hat{\mathbf{f}} + \mathbf{x}_0$$
$$\hat{\mathbf{x}} = (s\mathbf{I} - \mathbf{A})^{-1}(\hat{\mathbf{f}} + \mathbf{x}_0).$$

Finally, we obtain the solution $\mathbf{x}(t)$ by taking the inverse Laplace transform:

$$\mathbf{x} = \mathscr{L}^{-1}\{\hat{\mathbf{x}}\} = \mathscr{L}^{-1}\{(s\mathbf{I} - \mathbf{A})^{-1}(\hat{\mathbf{f}} + \mathbf{x}_0)\}.$$

In applying the matrix Laplace transform method, it is straightforward (but possibly tedious) to compute $(s\mathbf{I} - \mathbf{A})^{-1}$, but the computation of the inverse transform may require some of the special techniques (such as partial fractions) discussed in Chapter 7.

   (a) In the preceding procedure we used the property that $\mathscr{L}\{\mathbf{A}\mathbf{x}\} = \mathbf{A}\mathscr{L}\{\mathbf{x}\}$ for any constant $n \times n$ matrix $\mathbf{A}$. Show that this property follows from the linearity of the transform in the scalar case.

   (b) Use the matrix Laplace transform method to solve the following initial value problems:

(i) $\mathbf{x}'(t) = \begin{bmatrix} 0 & 2 \\ -1 & 3 \end{bmatrix} \mathbf{x}(t), \qquad \mathbf{x}(0) = \begin{bmatrix} -1 \\ 3 \end{bmatrix}.$

(ii) $\mathbf{x}'(t) = \begin{bmatrix} 3 & -2 \\ 4 & -1 \end{bmatrix} \mathbf{x}(t) + \begin{bmatrix} \sin t \\ -\cos t \end{bmatrix}, \qquad \mathbf{x}(0) = \begin{bmatrix} 0 \\ 0 \end{bmatrix}.$

C. UNDAMPED SECOND ORDER SYSTEMS

In the study of vibrations of mechanical systems, one encounters systems of the form

(8) $\qquad \mathbf{x}''(t) = \mathbf{B}\mathbf{x}(t),$

where **B** is an $n \times n$ constant matrix. Experience with studying vibrations for a simple spring-mass system (see Section 5.1) suggests that we seek a solution to (8) of the form

(9) $\qquad \mathbf{x} = \cos \omega t \ \mathbf{v} \quad \text{or} \quad \mathbf{x} = \sin \omega t \ \mathbf{v},$

where **v** is a constant vector and ω is a positive constant.

      (a) Show that system (8) has a nontrivial solution of the form given in (9) if and only if $-\omega^2$ is an eigenvalue of **B**.

      (b) If **B** is an $n \times n$ constant matrix, then system (8) can be written as a system of $2n$ first order equations in normal form. Thus, a general solution to (8) can be formed from $2n$ linearly independent solutions to (8). Use the result of part **(a)** to find a general solution to the following second order systems.

$$\textbf{(i)} \ \ \mathbf{x}'' = \begin{bmatrix} -5 & -4 \\ 1 & 0 \end{bmatrix} \mathbf{x}.$$

$$\textbf{(ii)} \ \ \mathbf{x}'' = \begin{bmatrix} -5 & 2 \\ 2 & -2 \end{bmatrix} \mathbf{x}.$$

$$\textbf{(iii)} \ \ \mathbf{x}'' = \begin{bmatrix} -1 & -2 & 1 \\ -1 & 0 & -1 \\ -4 & 4 & -5 \end{bmatrix} \mathbf{x}.$$

$$\textbf{(iv)} \ \ \mathbf{x}'' = \begin{bmatrix} 2 & -1 & 0 \\ -1 & 2 & -1 \\ 0 & -1 & 2 \end{bmatrix} \mathbf{x}.$$

Partial Differential Equations

11.1 Introduction: A Model for Heat Flow

Develop a model for the flow of heat through a thin, insulated wire whose ends are kept at a constant temperature of 0°C and whose initial temperature distribution is to be specified.

Suppose that the wire is placed along the x-axis with $x = 0$ at the left end of the wire and $x = L$ at the right end (see Figure 11.1). If we let u denote the temperature of the wire,

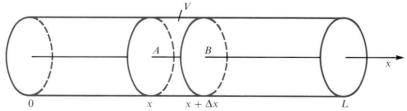

Figure 11.1 Heat flow through a thin piece of wire

600

then u depends upon the time t and upon the position x within the wire. (We will assume the wire is thin and hence u is constant throughout a cross section of the wire corresponding to a fixed value of x.) Since the wire is insulated, we assume that no heat enters or leaves through the sides of the wire.

To develop a model for heat flow through a thin wire, let's consider the small volume element V of wire between the two cross-sectional planes A and B that are perpendicular to the x-axis, with plane A located at x and plane B located at $x + \Delta x$ (see Figure 11.1).

The temperature on plane A at time t is $u(x, t)$ and on plane B is $u(x + \Delta x, t)$. We will need the following principles of physics which describe heat flow:[†]

1. **Heat Conduction:** The rate of heat flow (the amount of heat per unit time flowing through a unit of cross-sectional area at A) is proportional to $\partial u / \partial x$, the temperature gradient at A. The proportionality constant k is called the **thermal conductivity** of the material.

2. **Direction of Heat Flow:** The direction of heat flow is always from points of higher temperature to points of lower temperature.

3. **Specific Heat Capacity:** The amount of heat necessary to raise the temperature of an object of mass m by an amount Δu is $cm \, \Delta u$, where the constant c is the **specific heat capacity** of the material.

If we let H represent the amount of heat flowing from left to right through the surface A during an interval of time Δt, then the formula for heat conduction becomes

(1) $$H(x) = -ka \, \Delta t \, \frac{\partial u}{\partial x}(x, t),$$

where a is the cross-sectional area of the wire. The negative sign follows from the second principle—if $\partial u / \partial x$ is positive, then heat flows from right to left (hotter to colder).

Similarly, the amount of heat flowing from left to right across plane B during an interval of time Δt is

$$H(x + \Delta x) = -ka \, \Delta t \, \frac{\partial u}{\partial x}(x + \Delta x, t).$$

The net change in the heat ΔH in volume V is the amount entering at end A minus the amount leaving at end B. That is,

(2) $$\Delta H = H(x) - H(x + \Delta x) = ka \, \Delta t \left[\frac{\partial u}{\partial x}(x + \Delta x, t) - \frac{\partial u}{\partial x}(x, t) \right].$$

Now by the third principle, the net change in heat is given by $\Delta H = cm \, \Delta u$, where Δu is the change in temperature and c is the specific heat capacity. If we assume the change

---

[†] For a discussion of heat transfer see *University Physics*, Sixth Edition, by F. W. Sears, M. W. Zemansky, and H. D. Young, Addison-Wesley Publishing Co., Reading, Massachusetts, 1982.

in temperature in the volume V is essentially equal to the change in temperature at x, that is $\Delta u = u(x, t + \Delta t) - u(x, t)$, and that the mass of the volume V of wire is $a\delta \Delta x$, where δ is the density of the wire, a is the cross-sectional area and Δx is the length, then

(3) $\Delta H = c\delta a\, \Delta x[u(x, t + \Delta t) - u(x, t)].$

Equating the change in heat given in equations (2) and (3) yields

$$ka\,\Delta t\left[\frac{\partial u}{\partial x}(x + \Delta x, t) - \frac{\partial u}{\partial x}(x, t)\right] = c\delta a\,\Delta x[u(x, t + \Delta t) - u(x, t)].$$

Now dividing both sides by Δx and Δt and then taking the limits as Δx and Δt approach zero, we obtain

(4) $k\dfrac{\partial^2 u}{\partial x^2}(x, t) = c\delta\,\dfrac{\partial u}{\partial t}(x, t)$

or

(5) $\dfrac{\partial u}{\partial t}(x, t) = \beta\,\dfrac{\partial^2 u}{\partial x^2}(x, t),$

where the positive constant $\beta := k/\delta c$ is the **diffusivity** of the material. Equation (5) is the **one-dimensional heat flow equation.**

Equation (5) governs the flow of heat in the wire. We have two other constraints in our original problem. First, we are keeping the ends of the wire at $0°C$. Thus we require that

(6) $u(0, t) = u(L, t) = 0,$

for all t. These are called **boundary conditions.** Second, we must be given the initial temperature distribution $f(x)$. That is, we require

(7) $u(x, 0) = f(x), \qquad 0 < x < L.$

Equation (7) is referred to as the **initial condition** on u.

Combining equations (5), (6), and (7), we have the following mathematical model for the heat flow in a wire whose ends are kept at the constant temperature $0°C$:

(8) $\dfrac{\partial u}{\partial t}(x, t) = \beta\,\dfrac{\partial^2 u}{\partial x^2}(x, t), \qquad 0 < x < L, \qquad t > 0,$

(9) $u(0, t) = u(L, t) = 0, \qquad t > 0,$

(10) $u(x, 0) = f(x), \qquad 0 < x < L.$

This model is an example of an **initial-boundary value problem.**

In higher dimensions the heat flow equation (or just **heat equation**) has the form

$$\frac{\partial u}{\partial t} = \beta \, \Delta u,$$

where Δu is the **Laplacian** of u. In two and three dimensions the Laplacian is defined, respectively, as

$$\Delta u := \frac{\partial^2 u}{\partial x^2} + \frac{\partial^2 u}{\partial y^2} \quad \text{and} \quad \Delta u := \frac{\partial^2 u}{\partial x^2} + \frac{\partial^2 u}{\partial y^2} + \frac{\partial^2 u}{\partial z^2}.$$

When the temperature reaches a steady-state, that is, when u does not depend on time, then $\partial u / \partial t = 0$ and the temperature satisfies **Laplace's equation**

(11) $\Delta u = 0.$

One classical technique for solving the initial-boundary value problem for the heat equation (8)–(10) is the method of *separation of variables*, which effectively allows us to replace the partial derivatives by ordinary derivatives. This technique is discussed in the next section. In using separation of variables, one is often required to express a given function as a trigonometric series. Such series are called *Fourier series*; their properties are discussed in Sections 11.3 and 11.4. We devote the remaining three sections to the three basic partial differential equations that arise in applications: the heat equation, the wave equation, and Laplace's equation.

11.2 Method of Separation of Variables

The method of separation of variables is a classical technique that is effective in solving several types of partial differential equations. The idea is roughly the following. We think of a solution, say $u(x, t)$, to a partial differential equation as being an infinite linear combination of simple component functions $u_n(x, t)$, $n = 0, 1, 2, \ldots$, which also satisfy the equation and certain boundary conditions. (This is a reasonable assumption provided the partial differential equation and the boundary conditions are linear and homogeneous.) To determine a component solution, $u_n(x, t)$, we assume it can be written with its variables separated; that is, as

$$u_n(x, t) = X_n(x) T_n(t).$$

Substituting this form for a solution into the partial differential equation and using the boundary conditions leads to two *ordinary* differential equations for the unknown functions $X_n(x)$ and $T_n(t)$. In this way we have reduced the problem of solving a partial differential equation to the more familiar problem of solving a differential equation that involves only one variable. In this section we will illustrate this technique for the heat equation and the wave equation.

In the previous section we derived the following initial-boundary value problem as a mathematical model for the heat flow in a wire whose ends are kept at the constant temperature zero.

$$\text{(1)} \qquad \frac{\partial u}{\partial t}(x, t) = \beta \frac{\partial^2 u}{\partial x^2}(x, t), \qquad 0 < x < L, \qquad t > 0,$$

$$\text{(2)} \qquad u(0, t) = u(L, t) = 0, \qquad t > 0,$$

$$\text{(3)} \qquad u(x, 0) = f(x), \qquad 0 < x < L.$$

To solve this problem by the method of separation of variables, we begin by assuming that equation (1) has a solution of the form

$$\text{(4)} \qquad u(x, t) = X(x)T(t),$$

where X is a function of x alone and T is a function of t alone. To determine X and T, we first compute the partial derivatives of u in (4) to obtain

$$\text{(5)} \qquad \frac{\partial u}{\partial t} = X(x)T'(t) \quad \text{and} \quad \frac{\partial^2 u}{\partial x^2} = X''(x)T(t).$$

Substituting these expressions into (1) gives

$$\text{(6)} \qquad X(x)T'(t) = \beta X''(x)T(t),$$

and separating variables yields

$$\text{(7)} \qquad \frac{T'(t)}{\beta T(t)} = \frac{X''(x)}{X(x)}.$$

We now observe that the functions on the left-hand side of (7) depend only on t, while those of the right-hand side depend only on x. Since x and t are variables that are independent of one another, the two ratios in (7) must equal some *constant* K. Thus,

$$\frac{X''(x)}{X(x)} = K \quad \text{and} \quad \frac{T'(t)}{\beta T(t)} = K,$$

or

$$\text{(8)} \qquad X''(x) - KX(x) = 0 \quad \text{and} \quad T'(t) - \beta K T(t) = 0.$$

Consequently, for separable solutions, we have reduced the problem of solving the partial differential equation (1) to solving the two *ordinary* differential equations in (8).

Before proceeding, let's consider the boundary conditions in (2). Since $u(x, t) = X(x)T(t)$, these conditions are

(9) $\qquad X(0)T(t) = 0 \quad$ and $\quad X(L)T(t) = 0, \qquad t > 0.$

Hence either $T(t) = 0$ for all $t > 0$, which implies that $u(x, t) \equiv 0$, or

(10) $\qquad X(0) = X(L) = 0.$

Ignoring the trivial solution, we combine the boundary conditions in (10) with the differential equation for X in (8) and obtain the *boundary value problem*

(11) $\qquad X''(x) - KX(x) = 0, \qquad X(0) = X(L) = 0,$

where K can be any constant.

Notice that the function $X(x) \equiv 0$ is a solution for every K and, depending on the choice of K, this may be the *only* solution to the boundary value problem (11). Thus if we seek a nontrivial solution $u(x, t) = X(x)T(t)$ to (1)–(2), we must first determine those values of K for which the boundary value problem (11) has a nontrivial solution. These special values of K are called **eigenvalues,** and the corresponding nontrivial solutions to (11) are the **eigenfunctions.**

To solve (11), we begin with the auxiliary equation $r^2 - K = 0$ and consider three cases.

Case 1. $K > 0$. In this case, the roots of the auxiliary equation are $\pm\sqrt{K}$, so a general solution to the differential equation in (11) is

(12) $\qquad X(x) = C_1 e^{\sqrt{K}x} + C_2 e^{-\sqrt{K}x}.$

To determine C_1 and C_2, we appeal to the boundary conditions:

(13) $\qquad X(0) = C_1 + C_2 = 0,$

(14) $\qquad X(L) = C_1 e^{\sqrt{K}L} + C_2 e^{-\sqrt{K}L} = 0.$

From (13) we see that $C_2 = -C_1$. Hence (14) can be written as $C_1(e^{\sqrt{K}L} - e^{-\sqrt{K}L}) = 0$ or $C_1(e^{2\sqrt{K}L} - 1) = 0$. Having assumed that $K > 0$, it follows that $(e^{2\sqrt{K}L} - 1) > 0$. Therefore, C_1, and hence C_2, is zero. Consequently, there is *no* nontrivial solution to (11) for $K > 0$.

Case 2. $K = 0$. Here $r = 0$ is a repeated root to the auxiliary equation, and a general solution to the differential equation is

$$X(x) = C_1 + C_2x.$$

The boundary conditions in (11) yield $C_1 = 0$ and $C_1 + C_2L = 0$, which imply that $C_1 = C_2 = 0$. Thus, for $K = 0$, there is no nontrivial solution to (11).

Case 3. $K < 0$. In this case the roots of the auxiliary equation are $\pm i\sqrt{-K}$. (Note that $-K > 0$ since $K < 0$.) Thus, a general solution to $X'' - KX = 0$ is

(15) $X(x) = C_1 \cos \sqrt{-K}\, x + C_2 \sin \sqrt{-K}\, x.$

This time the boundary conditions $X(0) = X(L) = 0$ give the system

(16)
$$C_1 = 0,$$
$$C_1 \cos \sqrt{-K}\, L + C_2 \sin \sqrt{-K}\, L = 0.$$

Since $C_1 = 0$, the system reduces to solving $C_2 \sin \sqrt{-K}\, L = 0$. Hence, either $\sin \sqrt{-K}\, L = 0$ or $C_2 = 0$. Now $\sin \sqrt{-K}\, L = 0$ only when $\sqrt{-K}\, L = n\pi$, where n is an integer. Therefore, (11) has a nontrivial solution ($C_2 \neq 0$) when $\sqrt{-K}\, L = n\pi$ or $K = -(n\pi/L)^2$, $n = 1, 2, 3, \ldots$. Furthermore, the nontrivial solutions (eigenfunctions) X_n corresponding to the eigenvalue $K = -(n\pi/L)^2$ are given by (cf. (15))

(17) $X_n(x) = a_n \sin\left(\dfrac{n\pi x}{L}\right),$

where the a_n's are arbitrary nonzero constants.

Having determined that $K = -(n\pi/L)^2$ for some positive integer n, let's consider the second equation in (8) with $K = -(n\pi/L)^2$:

(18) $T'(t) + \beta\left(\dfrac{n\pi}{L}\right)^2 T(t) = 0.$

For each $n = 1, 2, 3, \ldots$, a general solution to the linear first order equation (18) is

(19) $T_n(t) = b_n e^{-\beta(n\pi/L)^2 t}.$

Combining this with equation (17), we obtain, for each $n = 1, 2, 3, \ldots$ the function

(20) $u_n(x, t) := X_n(x)T_n(t) = a_n \sin(n\pi x/L) b_n e^{-\beta(n\pi/L)^2 t}$
$$= c_n e^{-\beta(n\pi/L)^2 t} \sin(n\pi x/L),$$

where c_n is an arbitrary constant.

We would like to conclude that each $u_n(x, t)$ is a solution to (1)–(2). But, we have shown *only* that *if* (1)–(2) have a solution of the form $u(x, t) = X(x)T(t)$, then u must be one of the functions given in (20). We leave it for the reader to verify, by direct substitution, that the functions in (20) are indeed solutions to (1)–(2).

A simple computation also shows that if u_n and u_m are solutions to (1)–(2), then so is any linear combination $au_n + bu_m$. (This is a consequence of the fact that the operator $L := \partial/\partial t - \beta \partial^2/\partial x^2$ is a *linear* operator and the boundary conditions in (2) are *homo-*

geneous.) Furthermore, if we take an *infinite* sum of these functions, that is,

(21) $u(x, t) = \sum_{n=1}^{\infty} u_n(x, t) = \sum_{n=1}^{\infty} c_n e^{-\beta(n\pi/L)^2 t} \sin(n\pi x/L),$

then this formal series will again be a solution to (1)–(2), provided that the infinite series has the proper convergence behavior.

For a solution u of the form (21), we can determine the constants c_n by using the initial condition (3). This gives

(22) $u(x, 0) = \sum_{n=1}^{\infty} c_n \sin\left(\frac{n\pi x}{L}\right) = f(x), \qquad 0 < x < L.$

We have thus reduced the problem (1)–(3) of heat flow in a thin wire to the problem of determining an expansion for $f(x)$ of the form

(23) $f(x) = \sum_{n=1}^{\infty} c_n \sin\left(\frac{n\pi x}{L}\right).$

Such an expansion is called a **Fourier sine series** and will be discussed in the next two sections. If we choose the c_n's so that equation (23) holds, then the expansion for $u(x, t)$ in (21) is called a **formal solution** to the heat flow problem (1)–(3). If this expansion converges to a function with continuous second partial derivatives, then the formal solution is an actual (genuine) solution. Moreover, the solution is unique.

▶ *Example 1*   Find the solution to the heat flow problem

(24) $\dfrac{\partial u}{\partial t} = 7 \dfrac{\partial^2 u}{\partial x^2};$ 　　　　　 $0 < x < \pi, \qquad t > 0,$

(25) $u(0, t) = u(\pi, t) = 0,$ 　　　　 $t > 0,$

(26) $u(x, 0) = 3 \sin 2x - 6 \sin 5x, \qquad 0 < x < \pi.$

Solution   Comparing equation (24) with (1), we see that $\beta = 7$ and $L = \pi$. Hence, we need only determine the values of c_n in formula (23). That is, we must have

(27) $u(x, 0) = 3 \sin 2x - 6 \sin 5x = \sum_{n=1}^{\infty} c_n \sin nx.$

Equating the coefficients of like terms, we find that

$c_2 = 3 \quad \text{and} \quad c_5 = -6,$

and the remaining c_n's are zero. Hence, from (21), the solution to the heat flow problem (24)–(26) is

(28)
$$u(x, t) = c_2 e^{-\beta(2\pi/L)^2 t} \sin(2\pi x/L) + c_5 e^{-\beta(5\pi/L)^2 t} \sin(5\pi x/L)$$
$$= 3e^{-28t} \sin 2x - 6e^{-175t} \sin 5x. \quad \blacktriangleleft$$

The vibrating string problem concerns the transverse vibrations of a string stretched between two points, such as a guitar string or piano wire. The goal is to find a function $u(x, t)$ that gives the displacement (deflection) of the string at any point x $(0 \le x \le L)$ and any time $t \ge 0$ (see Figure 11.2). In developing the mathematical model, it is assumed that the string is perfectly flexible and has constant linear density, the tension on the string is constant, gravity is negligible, and no other forces are acting on the string. Under these conditions and the additional assumption that the displacements $u(x, t)$ are small in comparison to the length of the string, it turns out that the motion of the string is governed by the following initial-boundary value problem:[†]

(29)
$$\frac{\partial^2 u}{\partial t^2} = \alpha^2 \frac{\partial^2 u}{\partial x^2}; \qquad 0 < x < L, \qquad t > 0,$$

(30)
$$u(0, t) = u(L, t) = 0, \qquad t \ge 0,$$

(31)
$$u(x, 0) = f(x), \qquad 0 \le x \le L,$$

(32)
$$\frac{\partial u}{\partial t}(x, 0) = g(x), \qquad 0 \le x \le L.$$

The constant α^2 appearing in (29) is strictly positive and depends on the linear density and the tension of the string. The boundary conditions in (30) reflect the fact that the string is held fixed at the two endpoints $x = 0$ and $x = L$. Equations (31) and (32) specify, respectively, the initial displacement of the string and the initial velocity of each point on the string. For the initial and boundary conditions to be consistent, we assume that $f(0) = f(L) = 0$ and $g(0) = g(L) = 0$.

Let's apply the method of separation of variables to the initial-boundary value problem for the vibrating string (29)–(32). We begin by assuming that equation (29) has a solution

Figure 11.2 Displacement of string at time t

[†] For a derivation of this mathematical model, see *Applied Differential Equations*, Third Edition, by Murray R. Spiegel, Prentice-Hall, Inc., Englewood Cliffs, New Jersey, 1980.

of the form

(33) $u(x, t) = X(x)T(t),$

where X is a function of x alone and T is a function of t alone. Differentiating u in (33), we obtain

(34) $\dfrac{\partial^2 u}{\partial t^2} = X(x)T''(t), \qquad \dfrac{\partial^2 u}{\partial x^2} = X''(x)T(t).$

Substituting these expressions into (29), we have

(35) $X(x)T''(t) = \alpha^2 X''(x)T(t),$

and separating variables gives

$$\dfrac{T''(t)}{\alpha^2 T(t)} = \dfrac{X''(x)}{X(x)}.$$

Just as before, these ratios must equal some constant K:

(36) $\dfrac{X''(x)}{X(x)} = K \quad \text{and} \quad \dfrac{T''(t)}{\alpha^2 T(t)} = K.$

Furthermore, with $u(x, t) = X(x)T(t)$, the boundary conditions in (30) give

(37) $X(0)T(t) = 0, \qquad X(L)T(t) = 0, \qquad t \geq 0.$

In order for the equations in (37) to hold for all $t \geq 0$, either $T(t) \equiv 0$, which implies that $u(x, t) \equiv 0$, or

(38) $X(0) = X(L) = 0.$

Ignoring the trivial solution, we combine the boundary conditions in (38) with the differential equation for X in (36) and obtain the boundary value problem

(39) $X''(x) - KX(x) = 0, \qquad X(0) = X(L) = 0,$

where K can be any constant.

This is the same boundary value problem that we encountered earlier while solving the heat equation. There we found that the eigenvalues are

$$K = -\left(\dfrac{n\pi}{L}\right)^2, \qquad n = 1, 2, 3, \ldots,$$

with corresponding eigenfunctions (nontrivial solutions)

(40) $\qquad X_n(x) = c_n \sin\left(\dfrac{n\pi x}{L}\right),$

where the c_n's are arbitrary nonzero constants.

Having determined that $K = -(n\pi/L)^2$ for some positive integer n, let's consider the second equation in (36) for such K:

(41) $\qquad T''(t) + \dfrac{\alpha^2 n^2 \pi^2}{L^2}\, T(t) = 0.$

For each $n = 1, 2, 3, \ldots$, a general solution to (41) is

(42) $\qquad T_n(t) = c_{n,1}\cos\dfrac{n\pi\alpha}{L}\,t + c_{n,2}\sin\dfrac{n\pi\alpha}{L}\,t.$

Combining this with equation (40), we obtain, for each $n = 1, 2, 3, \ldots$, the function

$$u_n(x, t) = X_n(x)T_n(t) = \left(c_n \sin\dfrac{n\pi x}{L}\right)\left(c_{n,1}\cos\dfrac{n\pi\alpha}{L}\,t + c_{n,2}\sin\dfrac{n\pi\alpha}{L}\,t\right),$$

(43) $\qquad u_n(x, t) = \left(a_n\cos\dfrac{n\pi\alpha}{L}\,t + b_n\sin\dfrac{n\pi\alpha}{L}\,t\right)\sin\dfrac{n\pi x}{L}.$

Using the fact that linear combinations of solutions to (29)–(30) are again solutions, we consider the infinite sum of the functions in (43):

(44) $\qquad u(x, t) = \displaystyle\sum_{n=1}^{\infty}\left[a_n\cos\dfrac{n\pi\alpha}{L}\,t + b_n\sin\dfrac{n\pi\alpha}{L}\,t\right]\sin\dfrac{n\pi x}{L}.$

For a solution of the form (44), substituting it into the initial conditions (31)–(32) gives

(45) $\qquad u(x, 0) = \displaystyle\sum_{n=1}^{\infty} a_n\sin\dfrac{n\pi x}{L} = f(x), \qquad\qquad 0 \le x \le L,$

(46) $\qquad \dfrac{\partial u}{\partial t}(x, 0) = \displaystyle\sum_{n=1}^{\infty}\dfrac{n\pi\alpha}{L}\,b_n\sin\dfrac{n\pi x}{L} = g(x), \qquad 0 \le x \le L.$

We have now reduced the vibrating string problem (24)–(32) to the problem of determining the Fourier sine series expansions for $f(x)$ and $g(x)$:

(47) $\qquad f(x) = \displaystyle\sum_{n=1}^{\infty} a_n\sin\dfrac{n\pi x}{L}, \qquad g(x) = \displaystyle\sum_{n=1}^{\infty} B_n\sin\dfrac{n\pi x}{L},$

where $B_n = (n\pi\alpha/L)b_n$. If we choose the a_n's and b_n's so that the equations in (45) and (46) hold, then the expansion for $u(x, t)$ in (44) is a **formal solution** to the vibrating string problem (29)–(32). If this expansion converges to a function with continuous second partial derivatives, then the formal solution is an actual (genuine) solution.

▶ **Example 2** Find the solution to the vibrating string problem

(48)
$$\frac{\partial^2 u}{\partial t^2} = 4\frac{\partial^2 u}{\partial x^2}; \qquad\qquad 0 < x < \pi, \qquad t > 0,$$

(49)
$$u(0, t) = u(\pi, t) = 0, \qquad\qquad t \geq 0,$$

(50)
$$u(x, 0) = \sin 3x - 4\sin 10x, \qquad 0 \leq x \leq \pi,$$

(51)
$$\frac{\partial u}{\partial t}(x, 0) = 2\sin 4x + \sin 6x, \qquad 0 \leq x \leq \pi.$$

Solution Comparing equation (48) with equation (29), we see that $\alpha = 2$ and $L = \pi$. Hence we need only determine the values of the coefficients a_n and b_n in formula (44). The a_n's are chosen so that equation (45) holds; that is,

(52)
$$u(x, 0) = \sin 3x - 4\sin 10x = \sum_{n=1}^{\infty} a_n\sin nx.$$

Equating coefficients of like terms, we see that

$$a_3 = 1, \qquad a_{10} = -4,$$

and the remaining a_n's are zero. Similarly, referring to equation (46), we must choose the b_n's so that

$$\frac{\partial u}{\partial t}(x, 0) = 2\sin 4x + \sin 6x = \sum_{n=1}^{\infty} n2b_n\sin nx.$$

Comparing coefficients, we find

$$2 = (4)(2)b_4 \quad \text{or} \quad b_4 = \tfrac{1}{4},$$
$$1 = (6)(2)b_6 \quad \text{or} \quad b_6 = \tfrac{1}{12},$$

and the remaining b_n's are zero. Hence, from formula (44), the solution to the vibrating string problem (48)–(51) is

(53)
$$u(x, t) = \cos 6t \sin 3x + \tfrac{1}{4}\sin 8t \sin 4x$$
$$+ \tfrac{1}{12}\sin 12t \sin 6x - 4\cos 20t \sin 10x. \quad ◀$$

In later sections the method of separation of variables is used to study a wide variety of problems for the heat, wave, and Laplace's equations. However, to use the method effectively, one must be able to compute trigonometric series (or, more generally, eigenfunctions expansions) such as the Fourier sine series that we encountered here. These expansions are discussed in the next two sections.

EXERCISES 11.2

In Problems 1 through 8 determine all the solutions, if any, to the given boundary value problem by first finding a general solution to the differential equation.

1. $y'' - y = 0$; $0 < x < 1$, $y(0) = 0$, $y(1) = -4$.

2. $y'' - 6y' + 5y = 0$; $0 < x < 2$, $y(0) = 1$, $y(2) = 1$.

3. $y'' + 4y = 0$; $0 < x < \pi$, $y(0) = 0$, $y'(\pi) = 0$.

4. $y'' + 9y = 0$; $0 < x < \pi$, $y(0) = 0$, $y'(\pi) = -6$.

5. $y'' - y = 1 - 2x$; $0 < x < 1$, $y(0) = 0$, $y(1) = 1 + e$.

6. $y'' + y = 0$; $0 < x < 2\pi$, $y(0) = 0$, $y(2\pi) = 1$.

7. $y'' + y = 0$; $0 < x < 2\pi$, $y(0) = 1$, $y(2\pi) = 1$.

8. $y'' - 2y' + y = 0$; $-1 < x < 1$, $y(-1) = 0$, $y(1) = 2$.

In Problems 9 through 14 find the values of λ (eigenvalues) for which the given problem has a nontrivial solution. Also determine the corresponding nontrivial solutions (eigenfunctions).

9. $y'' + \lambda y = 0$; $0 < x < \pi$, $y(0) = 0$, $y'(\pi) = 0$.

10. $y'' + \lambda y = 0$; $0 < x < \pi$, $y'(0) = 0$, $y(\pi) = 0$.

11. $y'' + \lambda y = 0$; $0 < x < 2\pi$, $y(0) = y(2\pi)$, $y'(0) = y'(2\pi)$.

12. $y'' + \lambda y = 0$; $0 < x < \pi/2$, $y'(0) = 0$, $y'(\pi/2) = 0$.

13. $y'' + \lambda y = 0$; $0 < x < \pi$, $y(0) - y'(0) = 0$, $y(\pi) = 0$.

14. $y'' - 2y' + \lambda y = 0$; $0 < x < \pi$, $y(0) = 0$, $y(\pi) = 0$.

In Problems 15 through 18 solve the heat flow problem (1)–(3) with $\beta = 3$, $L = \pi$, and the given initial function $f(x)$.

15. $f(x) = \sin x - 6 \sin 4x$.

16. $f(x) = \sin 3x + 5 \sin 7x - 2 \sin 13x$.

17. $f(x) = \sin x - 7 \sin 3x + \sin 5x$.

18. $f(x) = \sin 4x + 3 \sin 6x - \sin 10x$.

In Problems 19 through 22 solve the vibrating string problem (29)–(32) with $\alpha = 3$, $L = \pi$ and the given initial functions $f(x)$ and $g(x)$.

19. $f(x) = 3 \sin 2x + 12 \sin 13x$, $g(x) \equiv 0$.

20. $f(x) \equiv 0$, $g(x) = -2 \sin 3x + 9 \sin 7x - \sin 10x$.

21. $f(x) = 6 \sin 2x + 2 \sin 6x$, $g(x) = 11 \sin 9x - 14 \sin 15x$.

22. $f(x) = \sin x - \sin 2x + \sin 3x$, $g(x) = 6 \sin 3x - 7 \sin 5x$.

23. Find the formal solution to the heat flow problem (1)–(3) with $\beta = 2$ and $L = 1$ if

$$f(x) = \sum_{n=1}^{\infty} \frac{1}{n^2} \sin n\pi x.$$

24. Find the formal solution to the vibrating string problem (29)–(32) with $\alpha = 4$, $L = \pi$, and

$$f(x) = \sum_{n=1}^{\infty} \frac{1}{n^2} \sin nx, \qquad g(x) = \sum_{n=1}^{\infty} \frac{(-1)^{n+1}}{n} \sin nx.$$

25. By considering the behavior of the solutions of the equation

$$T'(t) - \beta K T(t) = 0, \qquad t > 0,$$

give an argument that is based on physical grounds to rule out the case where $K > 0$ in equation (8).

26. Verify that the solutions $u_n(x, t)$ given in equation (20) satisfy equation (1) and the boundary conditions in (2) by substituting $u_n(x, t)$ directly into the equations involved.

27. When the temperature in the wire reaches a steady state, that is, when u depends only upon x, then $u(x)$ satisfies Laplace's equation $\partial^2 u/\partial x^2 = 0$.

    (a) Find the steady-state solution when the ends of the wire are kept at a constant temperature of 50°C, that is, when $u(0) = u(L) = 50$.
    (b) Find the steady-state solution when one end of the wire is kept at 10°C, while the other is kept at 40°C, that is, when $u(0) = 10$ and $u(L) = 40$.

11.3 Fourier Series

While solving the heat flow and vibrating string problems in the previous section, we encountered the problem of expressing a function in a trigonometric series (cf. equations (23) and (45) in Section 11.2). In the next two sections we will study the theory of Fourier series which deals with trigonometric series expansions for periodic functions.

In Section 7.2 we defined a **piecewise continuous** function on $[a, b]$ as a function $f(x)$ that is continuous at every point in $[a, b]$ except possibly for a finite number of points at which $f(x)$ has a *jump discontinuity*. Such functions are necessarily integrable over any finite interval on which they are piecewise continuous. In Section 7.6 we defined a function $f(x)$ as **periodic of period** T if $f(x + T) = f(x)$ for all x in the domain of f. The smallest positive value of T is called the **fundamental period.** The trigonometric functions $\sin x$ and $\cos x$ are examples of periodic functions with fundamental period 2π and $\tan x$ is periodic with fundamental period π. A constant function is a periodic function with arbitrary period T.

There are two symmetry properties of functions that will be useful in the study of Fourier series. A function $f(x)$ that satisfies $f(-x) = f(x)$ for all x in the domain of f has a graph that is symmetric with respect to the y-axis (see Figure 11.3(a)). We say that such a function is an **even** function. A function $f(x)$ that satisfies $f(-x) = -f(x)$ for all x in the domain of f has a graph that is symmetric with respect to the origin (see Figure 11.3(b)). It is said to be an **odd** function. The functions $1, x^2, x^4, \ldots$ are examples of even functions, while the functions $x, x^3, x^5, \ldots$ are odd. The trigonometric functions $\sin x$ and $\tan x$ are odd functions and $\cos x$ is an even function.

► *Example 1*   Determine whether the given function is even, odd, or neither.

$$\textbf{(a) } f(x) = \sqrt{1 + x^2}. \qquad \textbf{(b) } g(x) = x^{1/3} - \sin x. \qquad \textbf{(c) } h(x) = e^x.$$

Solution   **(a)** Since $f(-x) = \sqrt{1 + (-x)^2} = \sqrt{1 + x^2} = f(x)$, then $f(x)$ is an even function.

(b) Since $g(-x) = (-x)^{1/3} - \sin(-x) = -x^{1/3} + \sin x = -(x^{1/3} - \sin x) = -g(x)$, then $g(x)$ is an odd function.

(c) Here $h(-x) = e^{-x}$. Since $e^{-x} = e^x$ only when $x = 0$ and e^{-x} is never equal to $-e^x$, then $h(x)$ is neither an even nor an odd function. ◄

Knowing that a function is even or odd can be useful in evaluating definite integrals.

PROPERTIES OF SYMMETRIC FUNCTIONS

Theorem 1.   If $f(x)$ is an even piecewise continuous function on $[-a, a]$, then

$$\textbf{(1)} \qquad \int_{-a}^{a} f(x)\, dx = 2 \int_{0}^{a} f(x)\, dx.$$

If $f(x)$ is an odd piecewise continuous function on $[-a, a]$, then

$$\textbf{(2)} \qquad \int_{-a}^{a} f(x)\, dx = 0.$$

Proof   If $f(x)$ is an even function, then $f(-x) = f(x)$. Hence,

$$\int_{-a}^{a} f(x)\, dx = \int_{-a}^{0} f(x)\, dx + \int_{0}^{a} f(x)\, dx$$

$$= -\int_{a}^{0} f(u)\, du + \int_{0}^{a} f(x)\, dx = 2 \int_{0}^{a} f(x)\, dx,$$

where we used the change of variables $u = -x$. This is illustrated in Figure 11.3(a).

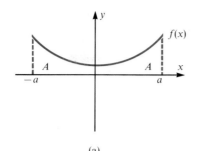
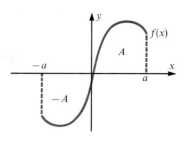

(a)   (b)

Figure 11.3 (a) Even function $\int_{-a}^{a} f = A + A = 2\int_{0}^{a} f$
(b) Odd function $\int_{-a}^{a} f = A - A = 0$

Formula (2) can be proved by a similar argument and is illustrated in Figure 11.3(b).

■ ■ ■

▶ **Example 2**   Evaluate the following integrals when m and n are positive integers:

$$\textbf{(a)}\ \int_{-T}^{T} \sin\frac{m\pi x}{T}\cos\frac{n\pi x}{T}\,dx. \qquad \textbf{(b)}\ \int_{-T}^{T} \sin\frac{m\pi x}{T}\sin\frac{n\pi x}{T}\,dx.$$

Solution   **(a)** Since $\sin\dfrac{m\pi(-x)}{T}\cos\dfrac{n\pi(-x)}{T} = -\sin\dfrac{m\pi x}{T}\cos\dfrac{n\pi x}{T}$, the integrand in part (a) is an odd function. Thus, by Theorem 1

(3) $$\int_{-T}^{T} \sin\frac{m\pi x}{T}\cos\frac{n\pi x}{T}\,dx = 0.$$

(b) Using the fact that the integrand is even (check this!) and the trigonometric identity

$$2\sin A \sin B = \cos(A - B) - \cos(A + B),$$

we find

$$\int_{-T}^{T} \sin\frac{m\pi x}{T}\sin\frac{n\pi x}{T}\,dx = 2\int_{0}^{T} \sin\frac{m\pi x}{T}\sin\frac{n\pi x}{T}\,dx$$

$$= \int_{0}^{T}\left\{\cos\frac{(m-n)\pi x}{T} - \cos\frac{(m+n)\pi x}{T}\right\}dx$$

$$= \frac{T}{\pi}\left[\frac{\sin\dfrac{(m-n)\pi x}{T}}{m-n} - \frac{\sin\dfrac{(m+n)\pi x}{T}}{m+n}\right]_{0}^{T} = 0,$$

provided $m \neq n$. When $m = n$, the integral in (b) becomes

$$\int_{-T}^{T} \left(\sin \frac{n\pi x}{T}\right)^2 dx = 2 \int_{0}^{T} \left(\sin \frac{n\pi x}{T}\right)^2 dx = \int_{0}^{T} \left\{1 - \cos \frac{2n\pi x}{T}\right\} dx$$

$$= \left[x - \frac{T}{2n\pi} \sin \frac{2n\pi x}{T}\right]_{0}^{T} = T.$$

Hence

(4) $$\int_{-T}^{T} \sin \frac{m\pi x}{T} \sin \frac{n\pi x}{T} dx = \begin{cases} 0, & m \neq n, \\ T, & m = n. \end{cases} \blacktriangleleft$$

We leave it as an exercise for the reader to verify that

(5) $$\int_{-T}^{T} \cos \frac{m\pi x}{T} \cos \frac{n\pi x}{T} dx = \begin{cases} 0, & m \neq n, \\ T, & m = n, \end{cases}$$

(see Problem 8). Equations (3)–(5) express an **orthogonality condition** satisfied by the set of trigonometric functions $\{\cos x, \sin x, \cos 2x, \sin 2x, \ldots\}$ where $T = \pi$. We will say more about this later in the section.

It is easy to verify that if each of the functions $f_1, \ldots, f_n$ is periodic of period T, then so is any linear combination

$$c_1 f_1(x) + \cdots + c_n f_n(x).$$

For example, the sum $7 + 3 \cos \pi x - 8 \sin \pi x + 4 \cos 2\pi x - 6 \sin 2\pi x$ has period 2 since each term has period 2. Furthermore, if the infinite series

$$\frac{a_0}{2} + \sum_{n=1}^{\infty} \left(a_n \cos \frac{n\pi x}{T} + b_n \sin \frac{n\pi x}{T}\right)$$

converges for all x, then the function to which it converges will be periodic of period $2T$.

Just as we can associate a Taylor series with a function that has derivatives of all orders at a fixed point, we can identify a particular trigonometric series with a piecewise continuous function. To illustrate this, let's assume that $f(x)$ has the series expansion[†]

(6) $$f(x) = \frac{a_0}{2} + \sum_{n=1}^{\infty} \left\{a_n \cos \frac{n\pi x}{T} + b_n \sin \frac{n\pi x}{T}\right\},$$

where the a_n's and b_n's are constants. (Necessarily, f has period $2T$.)

_____

[†] The choice of a constant $a_0/2$ instead of just a_0 will make the formulas easier to remember.

To determine the coefficients $a_0, a_1, b_1, a_2, b_2, \ldots$, we proceed as follows. Let's integrate $f(x)$ from $-T$ to T, assuming we can integrate term-by-term:

$$\int_{-T}^{T} f(x)\, dx = \int_{-T}^{T} \frac{a_0}{2}\, dx + \sum_{n=1}^{\infty} a_n \int_{-T}^{T} \cos \frac{n\pi x}{T}\, dx + \sum_{n=1}^{\infty} b_n \int_{-T}^{T} \sin \frac{n\pi x}{T}\, dx.$$

Since $\sin(n\pi x/T)$ is an odd function, $\int_{-T}^{T} \sin(n\pi x/T)\, dx = 0$. Moreover, for $n = 1, 2, \ldots$, it is easy to check that $\int_{-T}^{T} \cos(n\pi x/T)\, dx = 0$. Hence

$$\int_{-T}^{T} f(x)\, dx = \int_{-T}^{T} \frac{a_0}{2}\, dx = a_0 T,$$

and so

$$a_0 = \frac{1}{T} \int_{-T}^{T} f(x)\, dx.$$

(Notice that $a_0/2$ is the average value of f over one period $2T$.) Next, to find the coefficient a_m when $m \geq 1$, we multiply (6) by $\cos(m\pi x/T)$ and integrate:

(7)
$$\int_{-T}^{T} f(x) \cos \frac{m\pi x}{T}\, dx = \frac{a_0}{2} \int_{-T}^{T} \cos \frac{m\pi x}{T}\, dx + \sum_{n=1}^{\infty} a_n \int_{-T}^{T} \cos \frac{n\pi x}{T} \cos \frac{m\pi x}{T}\, dx$$

$$+ \sum_{n=1}^{\infty} b_n \int_{-T}^{T} \sin \frac{n\pi x}{T} \cos \frac{m\pi x}{T}\, dx.$$

We have already observed that

$$\int_{-T}^{T} \cos \frac{m\pi x}{T}\, dx = 0, \qquad m \geq 1,$$

and, by formula (3),

$$\int_{-T}^{T} \sin \frac{n\pi x}{T} \cos \frac{m\pi x}{T}\, dx = 0.$$

Using the formulas in (5), we also find that

$$\int_{-T}^{T} \cos \frac{n\pi x}{T} \cos \frac{m\pi x}{T}\, dx = \begin{cases} 0, & n \neq m, \\ T, & n = m. \end{cases}$$

Hence, in (7) we see that only one term survives and

$$\int_{-T}^{T} f(x) \cos \frac{m\pi x}{T}\, dx = a_m T.$$

Thus

(8) $\qquad a_m = \dfrac{1}{T} \displaystyle\int_{-T}^{T} f(x) \cos \dfrac{m\pi x}{T}\, dx.$

Similarly, multiplying (6) by $\sin(m\pi x/T)$ and integrating yields

$$\int_{-T}^{T} f(x) \sin \frac{m\pi x}{T}\, dx = b_m T,$$

so that

(9) $\qquad b_m = \dfrac{1}{T} \displaystyle\int_{-T}^{T} f(x) \sin \dfrac{m\pi x}{T}\, dx.$

Motivated by the above computations, we now make the following definition.

FOURIER SERIES

Definition 1. Let f be a piecewise continuous function on the interval $[-T, T]$. The **Fourier series** of f is the trigonometric series

(10) $\qquad f(x) \sim \dfrac{a_0}{2} + \displaystyle\sum_{n=1}^{\infty} \left\{ a_n \cos \dfrac{n\pi x}{T} + b_n \sin \dfrac{n\pi x}{T} \right\},$

where the a_n's and b_n's are given by the formulas[†]

(11) $\qquad a_n = \dfrac{1}{T} \displaystyle\int_{-T}^{T} f(x) \cos \dfrac{n\pi x}{T}\, dx, \qquad n = 0, 1, 2, \ldots,$

(12) $\qquad b_n = \dfrac{1}{T} \displaystyle\int_{-T}^{T} f(x) \sin \dfrac{n\pi x}{T}\, dx, \qquad n = 1, 2, 3, \ldots.$

Formulas (11) and (12) are called the **Euler formulas.** We use the symbol $\sim$ to remind us that this series is associated with $f(x)$, but may not converge to $f(x)$. We will return to the question of convergence later in the section. First let's consider a few examples of Fourier series.

[†] Notice that $f(x)$ need not be defined for every x in $[-T, T]$; we only need that the integrals in (11) and (12) exist.

▶ **Example 3** Compute the Fourier series for

$$f(x) = \begin{cases} 0, & -\pi < x < 0, \\ x, & 0 < x < \pi. \end{cases}$$

Solution Here $T = \pi$. Using formulas (11) and (12), we have

$$a_n = \frac{1}{\pi} \int_{-\pi}^{\pi} f(x) \cos nx \, dx = \frac{1}{\pi} \int_0^{\pi} x \cos nx \, dx$$

$$= \frac{1}{\pi n^2} \int_0^{\pi n} u \cos u \, du = \frac{1}{\pi n^2} [\cos u + u \sin u] \Big|_0^{\pi n}$$

$$= \frac{1}{\pi n^2} (\cos n\pi - 1) = \frac{1}{\pi n^2} [(-1)^n - 1], \qquad n = 1, 2, 3, \ldots,$$

$$a_0 = \frac{1}{\pi} \int_{-\pi}^{\pi} f(x) \, dx = \frac{1}{\pi} \int_0^{\pi} x \, dx = \frac{x^2}{2\pi} \Big|_0^{\pi} = \frac{\pi}{2},$$

$$b_n = \frac{1}{\pi} \int_{-\pi}^{\pi} f(x) \sin nx \, dx = \frac{1}{\pi} \int_0^{\pi} x \sin nx \, dx$$

$$= \frac{1}{\pi n^2} \int_0^{\pi n} u \sin u \, du = \frac{1}{\pi n^2} [\sin u - u \cos u] \Big|_0^{\pi n}$$

$$= \frac{-\cos n\pi}{n} = \frac{(-1)^{n+1}}{n}, \qquad n = 1, 2, 3, \ldots.$$

Therefore,

(13)
$$f(x) \sim \frac{\pi}{4} + \sum_{n=1}^{\infty} \left\{ \frac{1}{\pi n^2} [(-1)^n - 1] \cos nx + \frac{(-1)^{n+1}}{n} \sin nx \right\}$$

$$= \frac{\pi}{4} - \frac{2}{\pi} \left\{ \cos x + \frac{1}{9} \cos 3x + \frac{1}{25} \cos 5x + \cdots \right\}$$

$$+ \left\{ \sin x - \frac{1}{2} \sin 2x + \frac{1}{3} \sin 3x + \cdots \right\}. \quad ◀$$

▶ **Example 4** Compute the Fourier series for

$$f(x) = \begin{cases} -1, & -\pi < x < 0, \\ 1, & 0 < x < \pi. \end{cases}$$

Solution   Again, $T = \pi$. Notice that f is an odd function. Since the product of an odd function and an even function is odd (see Problem 7), $f(x) \cos nx$ is also an odd function. Thus

$$a_n = \frac{1}{\pi} \int_{-\pi}^{\pi} f(x) \cos nx \, dx = 0, \qquad n = 0, 1, 2, \ldots.$$

Furthermore, $f(x) \sin nx$ is the product of two odd functions and therefore is an even function, so

$$b_n = \frac{1}{\pi} \int_{-\pi}^{\pi} f(x) \sin nx \, dx = \frac{2}{\pi} \int_{0}^{\pi} \sin nx \, dx$$

$$= \frac{2}{\pi} \left[\frac{-\cos nx}{n} \right]_{0}^{\pi} = \frac{2}{\pi} \left[\frac{1}{n} - \frac{(-1)^n}{n} \right], \qquad n = 1, 2, 3, \ldots,$$

$$= \begin{cases} 0, & n \text{ even,} \\ \dfrac{4}{\pi n}, & n \text{ odd.} \end{cases}$$

Thus

(14) $\qquad f(x) \sim \dfrac{2}{\pi} \displaystyle\sum_{n=1}^{\infty} \dfrac{[1 - (-1)^n]}{n} \sin nx = \dfrac{4}{\pi} \left[\sin x + \dfrac{1}{3} \sin 3x + \dfrac{1}{5} \sin 5x + \cdots \right].$ ◀

In Figure 11.4 we have sketched the graph of f along with the graphs of the first two partial sums $(4/\pi) \sin x$ and $(4/\pi)[\sin x + (1/3) \sin 3x]$ of the Fourier expansion in (14).

In Example 4 the odd function f has a Fourier series consisting only of sine functions. It is easy to show that, in general, if f is any odd function, then its Fourier series consists only of sine terms.

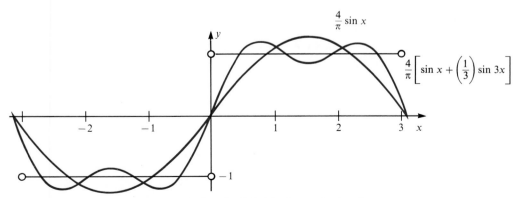

Figure 11.4 Graph of $f(x)$ in Example 4 and the first two partial sums of its Fourier series

▶ **Example 5** Compute the Fourier series for $f(x) = |x|$, $-1 < x < 1$.

Solution Here $T = 1$. Since f is an even function, $f(x) \sin n\pi x$ is an odd function. Therefore,

$$b_n = \int_{-1}^{1} f(x) \sin n\pi x \, dx = 0, \qquad n = 1, 2, 3, \ldots.$$

Since $f(x) \cos n\pi x$ is an even function, we have

$$a_0 = \int_{-1}^{1} f(x) \, dx = 2 \int_{0}^{1} x \, dx = x^2 \Big|_0^1 = 1,$$

$$a_n = \int_{-1}^{1} f(x) \cos n\pi x \, dx = 2 \int_{0}^{1} x \cos n\pi x \, dx$$

$$= \frac{2}{\pi^2 n^2} \int_{0}^{\pi n} u \cos u \, du = \frac{2}{\pi^2 n^2} [\cos u + u \sin u] \Big|_0^{\pi n} = \frac{2}{\pi^2 n^2} (\cos n\pi - 1)$$

$$= \frac{2}{\pi^2 n^2} [(-1)^n - 1], \qquad n = 1, 2, 3, \ldots.$$

Therefore,

(15) $$f(x) \sim \frac{1}{2} + \sum_{n=1}^{\infty} \frac{2}{\pi^2 n^2} [(-1)^n - 1] \cos n\pi x$$

$$= \frac{1}{2} - \frac{4}{\pi^2} \left\{ \cos x + \frac{1}{9} \cos 3x + \frac{1}{25} \cos 5x + \cdots \right\}. \quad ◀$$

Notice that the even function f of Example 5 has a Fourier series consisting only of cosine functions and the constant function $1 = \cos 0\pi x$. In general, if f is an even function, then its Fourier series consists only of cosine functions (including the constant function).

ORTHOGONAL EXPANSIONS

Fourier series are examples of orthogonal expansions.[†] A set of functions $\{f_n(x)\}_{n=1}^{\infty}$ is said to be an **orthogonal system** or just **orthogonal** with respect to the nonnegative weight function $w(x)$ on the interval $[a, b]$ if

(16) $$\int_a^b f_m(x) f_n(x) w(x) \, dx = 0, \quad \text{whenever} \quad m \neq n.$$

As we have seen, the set of trigonometric functions

(17) $\{1, \cos x, \sin x, \cos 2x, \sin 2x, \ldots\}$

---

† Orthogonality is also discussed in Section 8.9 on pages 477–478.

is orthogonal on $[-\pi, \pi]$ with respect to the weight function $w(x) \equiv 1$. If we define the **norm** of f as

$$
(18) \qquad \|f\| := \left[\int_a^b f^2(x) w(x) \, dx \right]^{1/2},
$$

then we say that a set of functions $\{f_n(x)\}_{n=1}^{\infty}$ (or $\{f_n(x)\}_{n=1}^{N}$) is an **orthonormal system with respect to** $w(x)$ if (16) holds and, for each n, $\|f_n\| = 1$. Equivalently, we say the set is an orthonormal system if

$$
(19) \qquad \int_a^b f_m(x) f_n(x) w(x) \, dx = \begin{cases} 0, & m \neq n, \\ 1, & m = n. \end{cases}
$$

We can always obtain an orthonormal system from an orthogonal system just by dividing each function by its norm. In particular, since

$$
\int_{-\pi}^{\pi} \cos^2 nx \, dx = \int_{-\pi}^{\pi} \sin^2 nx \, dx = \pi, \qquad n = 1, 2, 3, \dots,
$$

and

$$
\int_{-\pi}^{\pi} 1 \, dx = 2\pi,
$$

then the orthogonal system (17) gives rise on $[-\pi, \pi]$ to the orthonormal system

$$
\{(2\pi)^{-1/2}, \, \pi^{-1/2} \cos x, \, \pi^{-1/2} \sin x, \, \pi^{-1/2} \cos 2x, \, \pi^{-1/2} \sin 2x, \dots \}.
$$

If $\{f_n(x)\}_{n=1}^{\infty}$ is an orthogonal system with respect to $w(x)$ on $[a, b]$, we might ask if we can expand a function $f(x)$ in terms of these functions; that is, can we express f in the form

$$
(20) \qquad f(x) = c_1 f_1(x) + c_2 f_2(x) + \cdots
$$

for a suitable choice of constants $c_1, c_2, \dots$? Such an expansion is called an **orthogonal expansion,** or **generalized Fourier series.**

To determine the constants in (20), we can proceed as we did in deriving Euler's formulas for the coefficients of a Fourier series; this time using the orthogonality of the system. Multiply (20) by $f_m(x) w(x)$ and integrate to obtain

$$
(21) \qquad \int_a^b f(x) f_m(x) w(x) \, dx = c_1 \int_a^b f_1(x) f_m(x) w(x) \, dx + c_2 \int_a^b f_2(x) f_m(x) w(x) \, dx + \cdots
$$

$$
= \sum_{n=1}^{\infty} c_n \int_a^b f_n(x) f_m(x) w(x) \, dx.
$$

(Here we have again assumed that we can integrate term by term.) Since the system is orthogonal with respect to $w(x)$, every integral on the right-hand side of (21) is zero except when $n = m$. Solving for c_m gives

(22) $$c_m = \frac{\int_a^b f(x) f_m(x) w(x)\, dx}{\int_a^b f_m^2(x) w(x)\, dx} = \frac{\int_a^b f(x) f_m(x) w(x)\, dx}{\|f_m\|^2}, \qquad n = 1, 2, 3, \ldots.$$

The derivation of formula (22) was only *formal* since the question of the convergence of the expansion in (20) was not answered. If the series $\sum_{n=1}^{\infty} c_n f_n(x)$ converges *uniformly* to $f(x)$ on $[a, b]$, then each step can be justified and indeed, the coefficients are given by formula (22).

CONVERGENCE OF FOURIER SERIES

Let us now turn to the question of the convergence of a Fourier series. In Example 5 it is possible to use a comparison or limit comparison test to show that the series is absolutely dominated by a *p*-series of the form $\sum_{n=1}^{\infty} 1/n^2$ which converges. However, this is much harder to do in Example 4 since the terms go to zero like $1/n$. Matters can be even worse since there exist Fourier series that *diverge*. Moreover, not every convergent trigonometric series is a Fourier series. For example, although it is not obvious, the series

$$\sum_{n=1}^{\infty} \frac{\sin nx}{\ln(n + 1)}$$

converges for all x, but is not a Fourier series. We state two theorems that deal with the convergence of a Fourier series and two dealing with the properties of termwise differentiation and integration. For proofs of these results see *Partial Differential Equations of Mathematical Physics*, by Tyn Myint-U, Elsevier North Holland, Inc., New York, 1980, Chapter 5; *Advanced Calculus with Applications*, by N. J. DeLillo, Macmillan, New York, 1982, Chapter 9, or an advanced text on the theory of Fourier series.

Before proceeding we will need the following notation: Let

(23) $$f(x^+) := \lim_{h \to 0^+} f(x + h) \quad \text{and} \quad f(x^-) := \lim_{h \to 0^+} f(x - h).$$

POINTWISE CONVERGENCE OF FOURIER SERIES

Theorem 2. If $f(x)$ and $f'(x)$ are piecewise continuous on $[-T, T]$, then for any x in $(-T, T)$

(24) $$\frac{a_0}{2} + \sum_{n=1}^{\infty} \left\{ a_n \cos \frac{n\pi x}{T} + b_n \sin \frac{n\pi x}{T} \right\} = \tfrac{1}{2}[f(x^+) + f(x^-)],$$

where the a_n's and b_n's are given by the Euler formulas (11) and (12). For $x = \pm T$, the series converges to $\tfrac{1}{2}[f(-T^+) + f(T^-)]$.

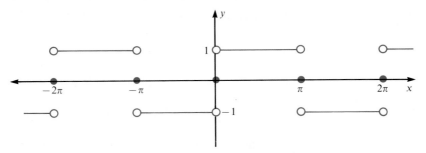

Figure 11.5 The limit function of the Fourier
series for $f(x) = \begin{cases} -1, & -\pi < x < 0, \\ 1, & 0 < x < \pi \end{cases}$

In other words, when f and f' are piecewise continuous, the Fourier series converges to $f(x)$ whenever f is continuous at x and converges to the average of the left- and right-hand limits at points where f is discontinuous.

Observe that the left-hand side of (24) is periodic of period $2T$. This means that if we extend $f(x)$ from the interval $(-T, T)$ to the entire real line using $2T$-periodicity,[†] then equation (24) holds for all x for the $2T$ periodic extension of $f(x)$.

▶ *Example 6*   To which function does the Fourier series for

$$f(x) = \begin{cases} -1, & -\pi < x < 0, \\ 1, & 0 < x < \pi, \end{cases}$$

converge?

Solution   In Example 4 we found that the Fourier series for $f(x)$ is given by (14), and in Figure 11.4 we sketched the graphs of two of its partial sums. Now $f(x)$ and $f'(x)$ are piecewise continuous in $[-\pi, \pi]$. Moreover, f is continuous except at $x = 0$. Thus by Theorem 2, the Fourier series of f in (14) converges to the 2π periodic function $g(x)$ where $g(x) = f(x) = -1$ for $-\pi < x < 0$, $g(x) = f(x) = 1$ for $0 < x < \pi$, $g(0) = \frac{1}{2}[f(0^+) + f(0^-)] = 0$, and at $\pm\pi$ we have $g(\pm\pi) = [f(-\pi^+) + f(\pi^-)]/2 = (-1 + 1)/2 = 0$. The graph of $g(x)$ is given in Figure 11.5. ◀

When f is a *smooth* function on $(-\infty, \infty)$ and is $2T$-periodic, its Fourier series not only converges at each point—it converges *uniformly on* $(-\infty, \infty)$. This means that for any prescribed tolerance $\varepsilon > 0$, the graph of the partial sum

$$s_N(x) := \frac{a_0}{2} + \sum_{n=1}^{N} \left\{ a_n \cos \frac{n\pi x}{T} + b_n \sin \frac{n\pi x}{T} \right\},$$

[†] From formula (24) we see that it doesn't matter how we define $f(x)$ at $-T$ and T since only the left- and right-hand limits are involved.

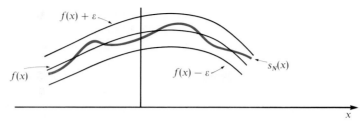

Figure 11.6 An ε-corridor about f

will, for all N large, lie in an ε-corridor about the graph of f on $(-\infty, \infty)$ (see Figure 11.6).

UNIFORM CONVERGENCE OF FOURIER SERIES

Theorem 3. Let $f(x)$ be a continuous function on $(-\infty, \infty)$ and periodic of period $2T$. If $f'(x)$ is piecewise continuous on $[-T, T]$, then the Fourier series for $f(x)$ converges uniformly to $f(x)$ on $[-T, T]$ and hence on any interval. That is, for each ε > 0, there exists an integer N_0 (that depends on ε) such that

$$\left| f(x) - \left\{ \frac{a_0}{2} + \sum_{n=1}^{N} \left\{ a_n\cos\frac{n\pi x}{T} + b_n\sin\frac{n\pi x}{T} \right\} \right\} \right| < \varepsilon,$$

for all $N \geq N_0$, and all $x \in (-\infty, \infty)$.

In Example 5 we obtained the Fourier series expansion given in (15) for $f(x) = |x|$, $-1 < x < 1$. Since $g(x)$, the periodic extension of $f(x)$ (see Figure 11.7), is continuous on $(-\infty, \infty)$ and

$$f'(x) = \begin{cases} -1, & -1 < x < 0, \\ 1, & 0 < x < 1, \end{cases}$$

is piecewise continuous on $[-1, 1]$, the Fourier series expansion (15) converges uniformly to $|x|$ on $[-1, 1]$.

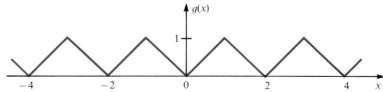

Figure 11.7 Periodic extension of $f(x) = |x|$, $-1 < x < 1$

The term-by-term differentiation of a Fourier series is not always permissible. For example, the Fourier series for $f(x) = x$, $-\pi < x < \pi$ (see Problem 9) is

(25) $$f(x) \sim 2 \sum_{n=1}^{\infty} (-1)^{n+1} \frac{\sin nx}{n},$$

which converges for all x, whereas its derived series

(26) $$2 \sum_{n=1}^{\infty} (-1)^{n+1} \cos nx$$

diverges for every x. The following theorem gives sufficient conditions for using termwise differentiation.

DIFFERENTIATION OF FOURIER SERIES

Theorem 4.   Let $f(x)$ be continuous on $(-\infty, \infty)$ and $2T$ periodic. Let $f'(x)$ and $f''(x)$ be piecewise continuous on $[-T, T]$. Then, the Fourier series of $f'(x)$ can be obtained from the Fourier series for $f(x)$ by termwise differentiation. In particular, if

$$f(x) = \frac{a_0}{2} + \sum_{n=1}^{\infty} \left\{ a_n \cos \frac{n\pi x}{T} + b_n \sin \frac{n\pi x}{T} \right\},$$

then

$$f'(x) \sim \sum_{n=1}^{\infty} \frac{\pi n}{T} \left\{ -a_n \sin \frac{n\pi x}{T} + b_n \cos \frac{n\pi x}{T} \right\}.$$

Termwise integration of a Fourier series is permissible under much weaker conditions.

INTEGRATION OF FOURIER SERIES

Theorem 5.   Let $f(x)$ be piecewise continuous on $[-T, T]$ with Fourier series

(27) $$f(x) \sim \frac{a_0}{2} + \sum_{n=1}^{\infty} \left\{ a_n \cos \frac{n\pi x}{T} + b_n \sin \frac{n\pi x}{T} \right\}.$$

Then, for any x in $[-T, T]$, we have

$$\int_{-T}^{x} f(t)\, dt = \int_{-T}^{x} \frac{a_0}{2}\, dt + \sum_{n=1}^{\infty} \int_{-T}^{x} \left\{ a_n \cos \frac{n\pi t}{T} + b_n \sin \frac{n\pi t}{T} \right\} dt.$$

EXERCISES 11.3

In Problems 1 through 6 determine whether the given function is even, odd, or neither.

1. $f(x) = x^3 + \sin 2x.$

2. $f(x) = \sin^2 x.$

3. $f(x) = (1 - x^2)^{-1/2}.$

4. $f(x) = \sin(x + 1).$

5. $f(x) = e^{-x} \cos 3x.$

6. $f(x) = x^{1/5} \cos x^2.$

7. Prove the following properties:

(a) If f and g are even functions, then so is the product fg.

(b) If f and g are odd functions, then fg is an even function.

(c) If f is an even function and g is an odd function, then fg is an odd function.

8. Verify formula (5).

In Problems 9 through 16 compute the Fourier series for the given function f on the specified interval.

9. $f(x) = x, \ -\pi < x < \pi.$

10. $f(x) = |x|, \ -\pi < x < \pi.$

11. $f(x) = \begin{cases} 1, & -2 < x < 0, \\ x, & 0 < x < 2. \end{cases}$

12. $f(x) = \begin{cases} 0, & -\pi < x < 0, \\ x^2, & 0 < x < \pi. \end{cases}$

13. $f(x) = x^2, \ -1 < x < 1.$

14. $f(x) = \begin{cases} x, & 0 < x < \pi, \\ x + \pi, & -\pi < x < 0. \end{cases}$

15. $f(x) = e^x, \ -\pi < x < \pi.$

16. $f(x) = \begin{cases} 0, & -\pi < x < -\pi/2, \\ -1, & -\pi/2 < x < 0, \\ 1, & 0 < x < \pi/2, \\ 0, & \pi/2 < x < \pi. \end{cases}$

In Problems 17 through 24 determine the function to which the Fourier series for f(x), given in the indicated problem, converges.

17. Problem 9.

18. Problem 10.

19. Problem 11.

20. Problem 12.

21. Problem 13.

22. Problem 14.

23. Problem 15.

24. Problem 16.

25. Find the functions represented by the series obtained by the termwise integration of the given series from $-\pi$ to x:

(a) $2 \sum_{n=1}^{\infty} \frac{(-1)^{n+1}}{n} \sin nx = x, \quad -\pi < x < \pi.$

(b) $-\frac{4}{\pi} \sum_{n=0}^{\infty} \frac{\sin(2n+1)x}{(2n+1)} \sim f(x) = \begin{cases} -1, & -\pi < x < 0, \\ 1, & 0 < x < \pi. \end{cases}$

26. (a) Show that the function $f(x) = x^2, \ -\pi < x < \pi$ has the Fourier series

$$f(x) \sim \frac{\pi^2}{3} + 4 \sum_{n=1}^{\infty} \frac{(-1)^n}{n^2} \cos nx.$$

(b) Use the result of part (a) and Theorem 2 to show that

$$\sum_{n=1}^{\infty} \frac{(-1)^{n+1}}{n^2} = \frac{\pi^2}{12}.$$

(c) Use the result of part (a) and Theorem 2 to show that

$$\sum_{n=1}^{\infty} \frac{1}{n^2} = \frac{\pi^2}{6}.$$

27. In Section 8.9 it was shown that the Legendre polynomials $P_n(x)$ are orthogonal on the interval $[-1, 1]$ with respect to the weight function $w(x) \equiv 1$. Using the fact that the first three Legendre polynomials are:

$$P_0(x) \equiv 1, \qquad P_1(x) = x, \qquad P_2(x) = (3/2)x^2 - (1/2),$$

find the first three coefficients in the expansion

$$f(x) = a_0 P_0(x) + a_1 P_1(x) + a_2 P_2(x) + \cdots,$$

where $f(x)$ is the function

$$f(x) := \begin{cases} -1, & -1 < x < 0, \\ 1, & 0 < x < 1. \end{cases}$$

28. As in Problem 27, find the first three coefficients in the expansion

$$f(x) = a_0 P_0(x) + a_1 P_1(x) + a_2 P_2(x) + \cdots,$$

when $f(x) = |x|$, $-1 < x < 1$.

29. The Hermite polynomials $H_n(x)$ are orthogonal on the interval $(-\infty, \infty)$ with respect to the weight function $W(x) = e^{-x^2}$. Verify this fact for the first three Hermite polynomials:

$$H_0(x) \equiv 1, \qquad H_1(x) = 2x, \qquad H_2(x) = 4x^2 - 2.$$

30. The Chebyshev (Tchebichef) polynomials $T_n(x)$ are orthogonal on the interval $[-1, 1]$ with respect to the weight function $w(x) = (1 - x^2)^{-1/2}$. Verify this fact for the first three Chebyshev polynomials:

$$T_0(x) \equiv 1, \qquad T_1(x) = x, \qquad T_2(x) = 2x^2 - 1.$$

31. Let $\{f_n(x)\}$ be an orthogonal set of functions on the interval $[a, b]$ with respect to the weight function $w(x)$. Show that they satisfy the **Pythagorean Property**

$$\|f_m + f_n\|^2 = \|f_m\|^2 + \|f_n\|^2, \quad \text{if} \quad m \neq n.$$

32. The norm of a function $\|f\|$ is like the **length** of a vector in R^n. In particular, show that the norm defined in (18) satisfies the following properties associated with length (assume f and g are continuous and $w(x) > 0$ on $[a, b]$);

   (a) $\|f\| \geq 0$, and $\|f\| = 0$ if and only if $f \equiv 0$.

   (b) $\|cf\| = |c| \|f\|$, where c is any real number.

   (c) $\|f + g\| \leq \|f\| + \|g\|$.

33. The integral in the orthogonality condition (16) is like the **dot product** of two vectors in R^n. In particular, show that

(28) $$\langle f, g \rangle := \int_a^b f(x)g(x)w(x)\,dx,$$

where $w(x)$ is a positive weight function, satisfies the following properties associated with the dot product (assume f, g, and h are continuous on $[a, b]$):

   (a) $\langle f + g, h \rangle = \langle f, h \rangle + \langle g, h \rangle$.

   (b) $\langle cf, h \rangle = c \langle f, h \rangle$, where c is any real number.

   (c) $\langle f, g \rangle = \langle g, f \rangle$.

34. Complex Form of the Fourier Series.

   (a) Using the Euler formula $e^{i\theta} = \cos\theta + i\sin\theta$, $i = \sqrt{-1}$, prove that

$$\cos nx = \frac{e^{inx} + e^{-inx}}{2} \quad \text{and} \quad \sin nx = \frac{e^{inx} - e^{-inx}}{2i}.$$

   (b) Show that the Fourier series

$$f(x) \sim \frac{a_0}{2} + \sum_{n=1}^{\infty} \{a_n \cos nx + b_n \sin nx\}$$

$$= c_0 + \sum_{n=1}^{\infty} \{c_n e^{inx} + c_{-n}e^{-inx}\},$$

   where

$$c_0 = \frac{a_0}{2},$$

$$c_n = \frac{a_n - ib_n}{2},$$

$$c_{-n} = \frac{a_n + ib_n}{2}.$$

   (c) Finally, use the results of part (b) to show that

$$f(x) \sim \sum_{n=-\infty}^{\infty} c_n e^{inx}, \quad -\pi < x < \pi,$$

where

$$c_n = \frac{1}{2\pi} \int_{-\pi}^{\pi} f(x)e^{-inx}\, dx.$$

35. The Nth partial sum of the Fourier series gives the best mean square approximation of f by a trigonometric polynomial. To prove this, proceed as follows: Let

$$f(x) \sim \frac{a_0}{2} + \sum_{n=1}^{\infty} \{a_n\cos nx + b_n\sin nx\},$$

and let

$$F(x) = \frac{\alpha_0}{2} + \sum_{n=1}^{N} \{\alpha_n\cos nx + \beta_n\sin nx\}.$$

Define

$$E := \int_{-\pi}^{\pi} [f(x) - F(x)]^2\, dx,$$

which is the *total square error*. We can write

$$E = \int_{-\pi}^{\pi} f^2(x)\, dx - 2 \int_{-\pi}^{\pi} f(x)F(x)\, dx + \int_{-\pi}^{\pi} F^2(x)\, dx.$$

(a) Show that

$$\int_{-\pi}^{\pi} F^2(x)\, dx = \pi\left(\frac{\alpha_0^2}{2} + \alpha_1^2 + \cdots + \alpha_N^2 + \beta_1^2 + \cdots + \beta_N^2\right)$$

and

$$\int_{-\pi}^{\pi} f(x)F(x)\, dx = \pi\left(\frac{\alpha_0 a_0}{2} + \alpha_1 a_1 + \cdots + \alpha_N a_N + \beta_1 b_1 + \cdots + \beta_N b_N\right).$$

(b) If we let E^* be the error when we choose $\alpha_n = a_n$ and $\beta_n = b_n$, then show that

$$E^* = \int_{-\pi}^{\pi} f^2(x)\, dx - \pi\left(\frac{a_0^2}{2} + a_1^2 + \cdots + a_N^2 + b_1^2 + \cdots + b_N^2\right).$$

(c) Using the results of parts (a) and (b), show that $E - E^* \geq 0$, that is, $E \geq E^*$, by proving that

$$E - E^* = \pi\left\{\frac{(\alpha_0 - a_0)^2}{2} + (\alpha_1 - a_1)^2 + \cdots \right.$$

$$\left. + (\alpha_N - a_N)^2 + (\beta_1 - b_1)^2 + \cdots + (\beta_N - b_N)^2\right\}.$$

Hence the Nth partial sum of the Fourier series gives the least squares error since $E \geq E^*$.

36. Bessel's Inequality. Use the fact that E^*, defined in part (b) of Problem 35, is nonnegative to prove **Bessel's inequality**

$$(29) \qquad \frac{a_0^2}{2} + \sum_{n=1}^{\infty} \{a_n^2 + b_n^2\} \leq \frac{1}{\pi} \int_{-\pi}^{\pi} f^2(x)\,dx.$$

If f is continuous on $[-\pi, \pi]$ and $f(-\pi) = f(\pi)$, then we have equality in (29). This result is called **Parseval's identity.**

37. Gibbs' Phenomenon. The American mathematician Josiah Willard Gibbs (1839–1903) observed that near points of discontinuity of f the partial sums of the Fourier series for f may overshoot by approximately 9% of the jump. This is illustrated in Figure 11.8 for the function

$$f(x) = \begin{cases} -1, & -\pi < x < 0, \\ 1, & 0 < x < \pi, \end{cases}$$

whose Fourier series has the partial sums

$$f_{2n-1}(x) = \frac{4}{\pi}\left[\sin x + \frac{1}{3}\sin 3x + \cdots + \frac{\sin(2n-1)x}{(2n-1)} \right].$$

To verify this for $f(x)$:

(a) Show that

$$\pi \sin x f'_{2n-1}(x) = 4\sin x[\cos x + \cos 3x + \cdots + \cos(2n-1)x]$$
$$= 2\sin 2nx.$$

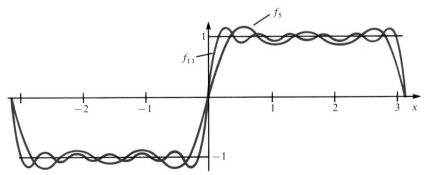

Figure 11.8 Gibbs' phenomenon

(b) Use the result of part (a) to determine that the maximum occurs at $x = \pi/(2n)$ and has the value

$$f_{2n-1}\left(\frac{\pi}{2n}\right) = \frac{4}{\pi}\left[\sin\frac{\pi}{2n} + \frac{1}{3}\sin\frac{3\pi}{2n} + \cdots\right.$$

$$\left. + \frac{1}{2n-1}\sin\frac{(2n-1)\pi}{2n}\right].$$

(c) Show that if one approximates

$$\int_0^\pi \frac{\sin x}{x}\,dx,$$

using the partition

$$x_k = (2k-1)\frac{\pi}{2n}, \qquad k = 1, 2, \ldots, n,$$

$$\Delta x_k = \frac{\pi}{n},$$

and choosing the midpoint of each interval as the place to evaluate the integrand, then

$$\int_0^\pi \frac{\sin x}{x}\,dx \approx \frac{\sin(\pi/2n)}{\pi/2n}\frac{\pi}{n} + \cdots + \frac{\sin[(2n-1)\pi/2n]}{(2n-1)\pi/2n}\frac{\pi}{n}$$

$$= \frac{\pi}{2}f_{2n-1}\left(\frac{\pi}{2n}\right).$$

(d) Use the result of part (c) to show that the overshoot satisfies

$$\lim_{n\to\infty} f_{2n-1}\left(\frac{\pi}{2n}\right) = \frac{2}{\pi}\int_0^\pi \frac{\sin x}{x}\,dx.$$

(e) Using the result of part (d) and a table of values for the **sine integral function**

$$Si(z) := \int_0^z \frac{\sin x}{x}\,dx,$$

show that $\lim_{n\to\infty} f_{2n-1}(\pi/(2n)) \approx 1.18$. Thus, the approximations overshoot the true value of $f(0^+) = 1$ by 0.18 or 9% of the jump from $f(0^-)$ to $f(0^+)$.

11.4 Fourier Cosine and Sine Series

A typical problem encountered in using separation of variables to solve a partial differential equation is the problem of representing a function defined on some finite interval by a trigonometric series consisting of only sine functions or only cosine functions. For example, in Section 11.2, equation (23), we needed to express the initial values $u(x, 0) = f(x)$, $0 < x < L$, of the solution to the initial-boundary value problem associated with the problem of heat flow as a trigonometric series of the form

$$(1) \qquad \sum_{n=1}^{\infty} c_n \sin\left(\frac{n\pi x}{L}\right).$$

Recalling that the Fourier series for an odd function defined on $[-L, L]$ consists entirely of sine terms, we might try to extend the function $f(x)$, $0 < x < L$, to the interval $(-L, L)$ in such a way that the extended function is odd. This is accomplished by defining the function

$$(2) \qquad f_o(x) := \begin{cases} f(x), & 0 < x < L, \\ -f(-x), & -L < x < 0, \end{cases}$$

and extending $f_o(x)$ to all x using $2L$-periodicity. Since $f_o(x)$ is an odd function, it has a Fourier series consisting entirely of sine terms. Moreover, $f_o(x)$ is an extension of $f(x)$, since $f_o(x) = f(x)$ on $(0, L)$. This extension is called the **odd $2L$-periodic extension** of $f(x)$. The resulting Fourier series expansion is called a half-range expansion for $f(x)$, since it represents the function $f(x)$ on $(0, L)$, which is half of the interval $(-L, L)$ where it represents $f_o(x)$.

In a similar fashion, we can define the **even $2L$-periodic extension** of $f(x)$ as the function

$$(3) \qquad f_e(x) := \begin{cases} f(x), & 0 < x < L, \\ f(-x), & -L < x < 0, \end{cases}$$

with $f_e(x + 2L) = f_e(x)$.

To illustrate the various extensions, let's consider the function $f(x) = x$, $0 < x < \pi$. If we extend $f(x)$ to the interval $(-\pi, \pi)$ using π periodicity, then the extension $\tilde{f}$ is given by

$$\tilde{f}(x) = \begin{cases} x, & 0 < x < \pi, \\ x + \pi, & -\pi < x < 0, \end{cases}$$

with $\tilde{f}(x + 2\pi) = \tilde{f}(x)$. In Problem 14 in Exercises 11.3 the reader computed the Fourier series for $\tilde{f}(x)$ and found

$$(4) \qquad \tilde{f}(x) \sim \frac{\pi}{2} - \sum_{n=1}^{\infty} \frac{1}{n} \sin 2nx,$$

which consists of both odd functions (the sine terms) and even functions (the constant term) since the π periodic extension $\tilde{f}(x)$ is neither an even nor an odd function. The odd 2π-periodic extension of $f(x)$ is just $f_o(x) = x$, $-\pi < x < \pi$, which has the Fourier series expansion

(5) $$f_o(x) \sim 2 \sum_{n=1}^{\infty} \frac{(-1)^{n+1}}{n} \sin nx,$$

(see Problem 9 in Exercises 11.3). Since $f_o(x) = f(x)$ on the interval $(0, \pi)$, the expansion in (5) is a half-range expansion for $f(x)$. The even 2π periodic extension of $f(x)$ is the function $f_e(x) = |x|$, $-\pi < x < \pi$, which has the Fourier series expansion

(6) $$f_e(x) = \frac{\pi}{2} - \frac{4}{\pi} \sum_{n=0}^{\infty} \frac{1}{(2n+1)^2} \cos(2n+1)x$$

(see Problem 10 in Exercises 11.3).

The preceding three extensions, the π periodic function $\tilde{f}(x)$, the odd 2π-periodic function $f_o(x)$, and the even 2π-periodic function $f_e(x)$, are natural extensions of $f(x)$. There are many other ways of extending $f(x)$. For example, the function

$$g(x) = \begin{cases} x, & 0 < x < \pi, \\ 0, & -\pi < x < 0, \end{cases} \qquad g(x + 2\pi) = g(x),$$

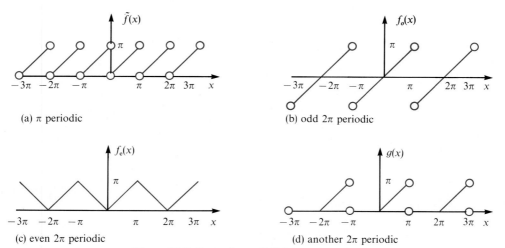

(a) π periodic

(b) odd 2π periodic

(c) even 2π periodic

(d) another 2π periodic

Figure 11.9 Extensions of $f(x) = x$, $0 < x < \pi$

which we studied in Example 3 of Section 11.3 is also an extension of $f(x)$. However, its Fourier series contains both sine and cosine terms and hence is not as useful as previous extensions. The graphs of these extensions of $f(x)$ are given in Figure 11.9.

The Fourier series expansions for $f_o(x)$ and $f_e(x)$ given in (5) and (6) represent $f(x)$ on the interval $(0, \pi)$ (actually, they equal $f(x)$ on $(0, \pi)$). This motivates the following definitions.

FOURIER COSINE AND SINE SERIES

Definition 2. Let $f(x)$ be piecewise continuous on the interval $[0, T]$. The **Fourier cosine series** of $f(x)$ on $[0, T]$ is

(7) $$\frac{a_0}{2} + \sum_{n=1}^{\infty} a_n \cos \frac{n\pi x}{T},$$

where

(8) $$a_n = \frac{2}{T} \int_0^T f(x) \cos \frac{n\pi x}{T} \, dx.$$

The **Fourier sine series** of $f(x)$ on $[0, T]$ is

(9) $$\sum_{n=1}^{\infty} b_n \sin \frac{n\pi x}{T},$$

where

(10) $$b_n = \frac{2}{T} \int_0^T f(x) \sin \frac{n\pi x}{T} \, dx.$$

The trigonometric series in (7) is just the Fourier series for $f_e(x)$, the even $2T$-periodic extension of $f(x)$ and (9) is the Fourier series for $f_o(x)$, the odd $2T$-periodic extension of $f(x)$. These are called **half-range expansions** for $f(x)$.

▶ *Example 1*   Compute the Fourier sine series for

$$f(x) = \begin{cases} x, & 0 < x \le \pi/2, \\ \pi - x, & \pi/2 \le x < \pi. \end{cases}$$

Solution Using formula (10) with $T = \pi$, we find

(11) $$b_n = \frac{2}{\pi} \int_0^\pi f(x) \sin nx \, dx = \frac{2}{\pi} \int_0^{\pi/2} x \sin nx \, dx + \frac{2}{\pi} \int_{\pi/2}^\pi (\pi - x) \sin nx \, dx$$

$$= \frac{2}{\pi n^2} \int_0^{\pi n/2} u \sin u \, du + 2 \int_{\pi/2}^\pi \sin nx \, dx - \frac{2}{\pi n^2} \int_{\pi n/2}^{\pi n} u \sin u \, du$$

$$= \frac{2}{\pi n^2} [\sin u - u \cos u]_0^{\pi n/2} - \frac{2}{n} \left[\cos \pi n - \cos \frac{n\pi}{2} \right]$$

$$- \frac{2}{\pi n^2} [\sin u - u \cos u]_{\pi n/2}^{\pi n}$$

$$= \frac{4}{\pi n^2} \sin \frac{n\pi}{2} = \begin{cases} 0, & n \text{ even}, \\ \dfrac{4(-1)^{(n-1)/2}}{\pi n^2}, & n \text{ odd}. \end{cases}$$

So, on letting $n = 2k + 1$, the Fourier sine series for $f(x)$ is

(12) $$\frac{4}{\pi} \sum_{k=0}^\infty \frac{(-1)^k}{(2k+1)^2} \sin(2k+1)x = \frac{4}{\pi} \left\{ \sin x - \frac{1}{9} \sin 3x + \frac{1}{25} \sin 5x + \cdots \right\}. \blacktriangleleft$$

Since, in Example 1, the function $f(x)$ is continuous and $f'(x)$ is piecewise continuous on $(0, \pi)$, it follows from Theorem 2 on pointwise convergence of Fourier series that

(13) $$f(x) = \frac{4}{\pi} \left\{ \sin x - \frac{1}{9} \sin 3x + \frac{1}{25} \sin 5x - \frac{1}{49} \sin 7x + \cdots \right\},$$

for all x in $(0, \pi)$.

Let's return to the problem of heat flow in one dimension.

▶ *Example 2* Find the solution to the heat flow problem

(14) $$\frac{\partial u}{\partial t} = 2 \frac{\partial^2 u}{\partial x^2}; \qquad 0 < x < \pi, \qquad t > 0,$$

(15) $$u(0, t) = u(\pi, t) = 0, \qquad t > 0,$$

(16) $$u(x, 0) = \begin{cases} x, & 0 < x \le \pi/2, \\ \pi - x, & \pi/2 \le x < \pi. \end{cases}$$

Solution Comparing equation (14) with equation (1) in Section 11.2, we see that $\beta = 2$ and $L = \pi$. Hence we need only represent $u(x, 0) = f(x)$ in a Fourier sine series (cf. equation

(23) on page 607) of the form

$$\sum_{n=1}^{\infty} c_n \sin nx.$$

In Example 1 we obtained such an expansion and showed that

(17) $$c_n = \frac{4}{\pi n^2} \sin \frac{n\pi}{2} = \begin{cases} 0, & n \text{ even} \\ \dfrac{4(-1)^{(n-1)/2}}{\pi n^2}, & n \text{ odd.} \end{cases}$$

Hence, from equation (21) on page 607, the solution to the heat flow problem (14)–(16) is

(18) $$u(x, t) = \sum_{n=1}^{\infty} c_n e^{-2n^2 t} \sin nx$$

$$= \frac{4}{\pi} \sum_{k=0}^{\infty} \frac{(-1)^k}{(2k+1)^2} e^{-2(2k+1)^2 t} \sin(2k+1)x$$

$$= \frac{4}{\pi} \left\{ e^{-2t}\sin x - \frac{1}{9} e^{-18t}\sin 3x + \frac{1}{25} e^{-50t}\sin 5x + \cdots \right\}. \blacktriangleleft$$

EXERCISES 11.4

In Problems 1 through 4 determine (a) the π-periodic extension $\tilde{f}$, (b) the odd 2π-periodic extension f_o, and (c) the even 2π-periodic extension f_e for the given function f and sketch their graphs.

1. $f(x) = x^2,$ $0 < x < \pi.$

2. $f(x) = \sin 2x,$ $0 < x < \pi.$

3. $f(x) = \begin{cases} 0, & 0 < x < \pi/2, \\ 1, & \pi/2 < x < \pi. \end{cases}$

4. $f(x) = \pi - x,$ $0 < x < \pi.$

In Problems 5 through 10 compute the Fourier sine series for the given function.

5. $f(x) = -1,$ $0 < x < 1.$

6. $f(x) = \cos x,$ $0 < x < \pi.$

7. $f(x) = x^2,$ $0 < x < \pi.$

8. $f(x) = \pi - x,$ $0 < x < \pi.$

9. $f(x) = x - x^2,$ $0 < x < 1.$

10. $f(x) = e^x,$ $0 < x < 1.$

In Problems 11 through 16 compute the Fourier cosine series for the given function.

11. $f(x) = \pi - x,$ $0 < x < \pi.$

12. $f(x) = 1 + x,$ $0 < x < \pi.$

13. $f(x) = e^x,$ $0 < x < 1.$

14. $f(x) = e^{-x},$ $0 < x < 1.$

15. $f(x) = \sin x,$ $0 < x < \pi.$

16. $f(x) = x - x^2,$ $0 < x < 1.$

In Problems 17 and 18 find the solution to the heat flow problem

$$\frac{\partial u}{\partial t} = 5\frac{\partial^2 u}{\partial x^2}; \qquad 0 < x < \pi, \qquad t > 0,$$

$$u(0, t) = u(\pi, t) = 0, \qquad t > 0,$$

$$u(x, 0) = f(x), \qquad 0 < x < \pi,$$

where $f(x)$ is given.

17. $f(x) = 1 - \cos 2x.$

18. $f(x) = x(\pi - x).$

11.5 The Heat Equation

In Section 11.1 we developed a model for heat flow in an insulated wire whose ends are kept at the constant temperature 0°C. In particular, we found that the temperature $u(x, t)$ in the wire is governed by the initial-boundary value problem

(1) $$\frac{\partial u}{\partial t} = \beta\frac{\partial^2 u}{\partial x^2}; \qquad 0 < x < L, \qquad t > 0,$$

(2) $$u(0, t) = u(L, t) = 0, \qquad t > 0,$$

(3) $$u(x, 0) = f(x), \qquad 0 < x < L,$$

(see equations (8)–(10) in Section 11.1). Here equation (2) specifies that the temperature at the ends of the wire is zero, whereas equation (3) specifies the initial temperature distribution.

In Section 11.2 we also derived a formal solution to (1)–(3) using separation of variables. There we found the solution to (1)–(3) to have the form

(4) $$u(x, t) = \sum_{n=1}^{\infty} c_n e^{-\beta(n\pi/L)^2 t}\sin\frac{n\pi x}{L},$$

where the c_n's are the coefficients in the Fourier sine series for $f(x)$:

(5) $$f(x) = \sum_{n=1}^{\infty} c_n\sin\frac{n\pi x}{L}.$$

In other words, solving (1)–(3) reduces to computing the Fourier sine series for the initial value function $f(x)$.

In this section we will discuss heat flow problems where the ends of the wire are insulated or kept at a constant, but nonzero, temperature. (The latter involves nonhomogeneous boundary conditions.) We will also discuss the problem in which a heat source is adding heat to the wire. (This results in a nonhomogeneous partial differential equation.) The problem of heat flow in a rectangular plate will also be discussed and leads to the topic of double Fourier series. We will conclude this section with a discussion of the existence and uniqueness of solutions to the heat flow problem.

In the model of heat flow in a wire, let's replace the assumption that the ends of the wire are kept at a constant temperature zero and instead assume that the ends of the wire are insulated, that is, no heat flows out (or in) at the ends of the wire. It follows from the principle of heat conduction (see Section 11.1) that the temperature gradient must be zero at these end points, that is,

$$\text{(6)} \qquad \frac{\partial u}{\partial x}(0, t) = \frac{\partial u}{\partial x}(L, t) = 0, \qquad t > 0.$$

In the next example we obtain the formal solution to the heat flow problem with these boundary conditions.

▶ *Example 1*   Find a formal solution to the heat flow problem governed by the initial-boundary value problem

$$\text{(7)} \qquad \frac{\partial u}{\partial t} = \beta \frac{\partial^2 u}{\partial x^2}; \qquad 0 < x < L, \qquad t > 0,$$

$$\text{(8)} \qquad \frac{\partial u}{\partial x}(0, t) = \frac{\partial u}{\partial x}(L, t) = 0, \qquad t > 0,$$

$$\text{(9)} \qquad u(x, 0) = f(x), \qquad 0 < x < L.$$

Solution   Using the method of separation of variables, we first assume

$$u(x, t) = X(x)T(t).$$

Substituting into equation (7) and separating variables as was done in Section 11.2 (cf. equations (8) on page 604) yield the two equations

$$\text{(10)} \qquad X''(x) - KX(x) = 0,$$

$$\text{(11)} \qquad T'(t) - \beta K T(t) = 0,$$

where K is some constant. The boundary conditions in (8) become

$$\text{(12)} \qquad X'(0)T(t) = 0 \quad \text{and} \quad X'(L)T(t) = 0.$$

In order for the equations in (12) to hold for all $t > 0$, either $T(t) \equiv 0$, which implies that $u(x, t) \equiv 0$, or

$$\text{(13)} \qquad X'(0) = X'(L) = 0.$$

Combining the boundary conditions in (13) with equation (10) gives the boundary value problem

(14) $X''(x) - KX(x) = 0;$ $X'(0) = X'(L) = 0,$

where K can be any constant.

To solve for the nontrivial solutions to (14), we begin with the auxiliary equation $r^2 - K = 0$. When $K > 0$, arguments similar to those used in Section 11.2 show that there are no nontrivial solutions to (14).

When $K = 0$, the auxiliary equation has the repeated root 0 and a general solution to the differential equation is

$$X(x) = A + Bx.$$

The boundary conditions in (14) reduce to $B = 0$ with A arbitrary. Thus, for $K = 0$, the nontrivial solutions to (14) are of the form

(15) $X(x) = c_0,$

where c_0 is an arbitrary nonzero constant.

When $K < 0$, the auxiliary equation has the roots $r = \pm i\sqrt{-K}$. Thus, a general solution to equation (14) is

(16) $X(x) = C_1 \cos \sqrt{-K}\, x + C_2 \sin \sqrt{-K}\, x.$

The boundary conditions in (14) lead to the system

(17)
$$\sqrt{-K}\, C_2 = 0,$$
$$-\sqrt{-K}\, C_1 \sin \sqrt{-K}\, L + \sqrt{-K}\, C_2 \cos \sqrt{-K}\, L = 0.$$

Hence $C_2 = 0$ and the system reduces to solving $C_1 \sin \sqrt{-K}\, L = 0$. Since $\sin \sqrt{-K}\, L = 0$ only when $\sqrt{-K}\, L = n\pi$, where n is an integer, we obtain a nontrivial solution only when $\sqrt{-K} = n\pi/L$ or $K = -(n\pi/L)^2$, $n = 1, 2, 3, \ldots$. Furthermore, the nontrivial solutions (eigenfunctions) X_n corresponding to the eigenvalue $K = -(n\pi/L)^2$ are given by

(18) $X_n(x) = c_n \cos \dfrac{n\pi x}{L},$

where the c_n's are arbitrary nonzero constants. In fact, formula (18) also holds for $n = 0$, since $K = 0$ has the eigenfunctions $X_0(x) = c_0$.

Having determined that $K = -(n\pi/L)^2$, $n = 0, 1, 2, \ldots$, let's consider equation (11) for such K:

(19) $T'(t) + \beta(n\pi/L)^2 T(t) = 0.$

For $n = 0, 1, 2, \ldots$, the general solution to (19) is

(20) $$T_n(t) = b_n e^{-\beta(n\pi/L)^2 t},$$

where the b_n's are arbitrary constants. Combining this with equation (18), we obtain the functions

(21)
$$u_n(x, t) = X_n(x)T_n(t) = \left[c_n \cos \frac{n\pi x}{L} \right] \left[b_n e^{-\beta(n\pi/L)^2 t} \right],$$

$$u_n(x, t) = a_n e^{-\beta(n\pi/L)^2 t} \cos \frac{n\pi x}{L},$$

where $a_n = b_n c_n$ is an arbitrary constant.

If we take an infinite series of these functions, we obtain

(22) $$u(x, t) = \sum_{n=0}^{\infty} a_n e^{-\beta(n\pi/L)^2 t} \cos \frac{n\pi x}{L},$$

which will be a solution to (7)–(8) provided the series has the proper convergence behavior.

Assuming a solution to (7)–(8) is given by the series in (22) and substituting into the initial condition (9), we get

(23) $$u(x, 0) = \sum_{n=0}^{\infty} a_n \cos \frac{n\pi x}{L} = f(x), \qquad 0 < x < L.$$

This means that if we choose the a_n's as the coefficients in the Fourier cosine series for f,

(24) $$f(x) = \sum_{n=0}^{\infty} a_n \cos \frac{n\pi x}{L},$$

then $u(x, t)$ given in (22) will be a **formal solution** to the heat flow problem (7)–(9). Again, if this expansion converges to a continuous function with continuous second partial derivatives, then the formal solution is an actual solution. ◀

When the temperature at the ends of the wire are kept at $0°C$ or when the ends are insulated, the boundary conditions are said to be **homogeneous.** But, when the temperature at the ends of the wire are kept at temperatures different from zero, that is,

(25) $$u(0, t) = U_1 \quad \text{and} \quad u(L, t) = U_2, \qquad t > 0,$$

then the boundary conditions are called **nonhomogeneous.**

From our experience with vibration problems in Chapter 5 we expect that the solution to the heat flow problem with nonhomogeneous boundary conditions will consist of a

steady-state solution $v(x)$ plus a **transient solution** $w(x, t)$. That is,

(26) $u(x, t) = v(x) + w(x, t),$

where $w(x, t)$ and its partial derivatives tend to zero as $t \to \infty$.

▶ *Example 2*   Find a formal solution to the heat flow problem governed by the initial-boundary value problem

(27) $$\frac{\partial u}{\partial t} = \beta \frac{\partial^2 u}{\partial x^2}; \qquad 0 < x < L, \qquad t > 0,$$

(28) $u(0, t) = U_1, \qquad u(L, t) = U_2, \qquad t > 0,$

(29) $u(x, 0) = f(x), \qquad 0 < x < L.$

Solution   Let's assume the solution $u(x, t)$ consists of a steady-state solution $v(x)$ and a transient solution $w(x, t)$, that is,

(30) $u(x, t) = v(x) + w(x, t).$

Substituting for $u(x, t)$ in equations (27)–(29) leads to

(31) $$\frac{\partial w}{\partial t} = \beta v''(x) + \beta \frac{\partial^2 w}{\partial x^2}; \qquad 0 < x < L, \qquad t > 0,$$

(32) $v(0) + w(0, t) = U_1, \qquad v(L) + w(L, t) = U_2, \qquad t > 0,$

(33) $v(x) + w(x, 0) = f(x), \qquad 0 < x < L.$

If we allow $t \to \infty$ in (31)–(32), assuming $w(x, t)$ is a transient solution, we obtain the steady-state boundary value problem

(34) $v''(x) = 0, \qquad 0 < x < L,$

(35) $v(0) = U_1, \qquad v(L) = U_2.$

Solving (34) for v, we obtain $v(x) = Ax + B$ and choosing A and B so that the boundary conditions in (35) are satisfied yields

(36) $$v(x) = U_1 + \frac{(U_2 - U_1)x}{L},$$

as the steady-state solution.

With this choice for $v(x)$, the initial-boundary value problem (31)–(33) becomes the following initial-boundary value problem for $w(x, t)$:

(37) $$\frac{\partial w}{\partial t} = \beta \frac{\partial^2 w}{\partial x^2}, \qquad 0 < x < L, \qquad t > 0,$$

(38) $$w(0, t) = w(L, t) = 0, \qquad t > 0,$$

(39) $$w(x, 0) = f(x) - U_1 - \frac{(U_2 - U_1)x}{L}, \qquad 0 < x < L.$$

In Section 11.2 we found the formal solution to (37)–(39) to be given by equation (4). Hence,

(40) $$w(x, t) = \sum_{n=1}^{\infty} c_n e^{-\beta(n\pi/L)^2 t} \sin \frac{n\pi x}{L},$$

where

(41) $$f(x) - U_1 - \frac{(U_2 - U_1)x}{L} = \sum_{n=1}^{\infty} c_n \sin \frac{n\pi x}{L}.$$

Therefore, the formal solution to (27)–(29) is

(42) $$u(x, t) = U_1 + \frac{(U_2 - U_1)x}{L} + \sum_{n=1}^{\infty} c_n e^{-\beta(n\pi/L)^2 t} \sin \frac{n\pi x}{L},$$

where the c_n's are given by the Fourier sine series in (41). ◀

In the next example we consider the heat flow problem when a heat source P is present but is independent of time.

▶ **Example 3** Find a formal solution to the heat flow problem governed by the initial-boundary value problem

(43) $$\frac{\partial u}{\partial t} = \beta \frac{\partial^2 u}{\partial x^2} + P(x); \qquad 0 < x < L, \qquad t > 0,$$

(44) $$u(0, t) = U_1, \qquad u(L, t) = U_2, \qquad t > 0,$$

(45) $$u(x, 0) = f(x), \qquad 0 < x < L.$$

Solution We begin by assuming that the solution consists of a steady-state solution $v(x)$ and a transient solution $w(x, t)$, namely,

(46) $$u(x, t) = v(x) + w(x, t),$$

where $w(x, t)$ and its partial derivatives tend to zero as $t \to \infty$. Substituting for $u(x, t)$ in (43)–(45) yields

(47) $$\frac{\partial w}{\partial t} = \beta v''(x) + \beta \frac{\partial^2 w}{\partial x^2} + P(x), \qquad 0 < x < L, \qquad t > 0,$$

(48) $\qquad v(0) + w(0, t) = U_1, \qquad v(L) + w(L, t) = U_2, \qquad t > 0,$

(49) $\qquad v(x) + w(x, 0) = f(x), \qquad 0 < x < L.$

Letting $t \to \infty$ in (47)–(48), we obtain the steady-state boundary value problem

(50) $\qquad v''(x) = -\dfrac{1}{\beta} P(x), \qquad 0 < x < L,$

(51) $\qquad v(0) = U_1, \qquad v(L) = U_2.$

The solution to the boundary value problem (50)–(51) can be obtained by direct integration of equation (50) using the boundary conditions to determine the constants of integration. The reader can verify that the solution to (50)–(51) is given by the formula

(52) $\qquad v(x) = \left[U_2 - U_1 + \displaystyle\int_0^L \left(\int_0^z \frac{1}{\beta} P(s)\, ds \right) dz \right] \frac{x}{L} + U_1 - \displaystyle\int_0^x \left(\int_0^z \frac{1}{\beta} P(s)\, ds \right) dz.$

With this choice for $v(x)$, we find that the initial-boundary value problem (47)–(49) reduces to the following initial-boundary value problem for $w(x, t)$:

(53) $$\frac{\partial w}{\partial t} = \beta \frac{\partial^2 w}{\partial x^2}, \qquad 0 < x < L, \qquad t > 0,$$

(54) $\qquad w(0, t) = w(L, t) = 0, \qquad t > 0,$

(55) $\qquad w(x, 0) = f(x) - v(x), \qquad 0 < x < L,$

where $v(x)$ is given by formula (52). As before, the solution to the initial-boundary value problem (53)–(55) is

(56) $\qquad w(x, t) = \displaystyle\sum_{n=1}^{\infty} c_n e^{-\beta(n\pi/L)^2 t} \sin \frac{n\pi x}{L},$

where the c_n's are determined by the Fourier sine series

(57) $\qquad f(x) - v(x) = \displaystyle\sum_{n=1}^{\infty} c_n \sin \frac{n\pi x}{L}.$

The formal solution to (43)–(45) is given by

$$u(x, t) = v(x) + w(x, t)$$

where $v(x)$ is given in (52) and $w(x, t)$ is given in (56) and (57). ◄

    The method of separation of variables is also applicable to problems in higher dimensions. For example, consider the problem of heat flow in a rectangular plate with sides $x = 0$, $x = L$, $y = 0$, and $y = W$. Assuming the two sides $y = 0$, $y = W$ are kept at a constant temperature of $0°C$ and the two sides $x = 0$, $x = L$ are perfectly insulated, then heat flow is governed by the initial-boundary value problem in Example 4.

► **Example 4**   Find a formal solution $u(x, y, t)$ to the initial-boundary value problem

(58)
$$\frac{\partial u}{\partial t} = \beta \left\{ \frac{\partial^2 u}{\partial x^2} + \frac{\partial^2 u}{\partial y^2} \right\}; \qquad 0 < x < L, \qquad 0 < y < W, \qquad t > 0,$$

(59)
$$\frac{\partial u}{\partial x}(0, y, t) = \frac{\partial u}{\partial x}(L, y, t) = 0, \qquad 0 < y < W, \qquad t > 0,$$

(60)
$$u(x, 0, t) = u(x, W, t) = 0, \qquad 0 < x < L, \qquad t > 0,$$

(61)
$$u(x, y, 0) = f(x, y), \qquad 0 < x < L, \qquad 0 < y < W.$$

Solution   If we assume a solution of the form $u(x, y, t) = V(x, y)T(t)$, then equation (58) separates into the two equations

(62)
$$T'(t) - \beta K T(t) = 0,$$

(63)
$$\frac{\partial^2 V}{\partial x^2}(x, y) + \frac{\partial^2 V}{\partial y^2}(x, y) - KV(x, y) = 0,$$

where K can be any constant. To solve equation (63), we again use separation of variables. Here we assume $V(x, y) = X(x)Y(y)$. This allows us to separate equation (63) into the two equations

(64)
$$X''(x) - JX(x) = 0,$$

(65)
$$Y''(y) + (J - K)Y(y) = 0,$$

where J can be any constant.
    To solve for $X(x)$, we observe that the boundary conditions in (59), in terms of the separated variables, become

$$X'(0)Y(y)T(t) = X'(L)Y(y)T(t) = 0, \qquad 0 < y < W, \qquad t > 0.$$

Hence, in order to get a nontrivial solution we must have

(66) $X'(0) = X'(L) = 0.$

The boundary value problem for X given in equations (64) and (66) was solved in Example 1 (cf. equations (14) and (18)). Here $J = -(m\pi/L)^2$, $m = 0, 1, 2, \ldots,$ and

(67) $X_m(x) = c_m \cos \dfrac{m\pi x}{L},$

where the c_m's are arbitrary.

To solve for $Y(y)$, we first observe that the boundary conditions in (60) become

(68) $Y(0) = Y(W) = 0.$

Next, substituting $J = -(m\pi/L)^2$ into equation (65) yields

$$Y''(y) - (K + (m\pi/L)^2)Y(y) = 0,$$

which we can rewrite as

(69) $Y''(y) - EY(y) = 0,$

where $E = K + (m\pi/L)^2$. The boundary value problem for Y consisting of (68)–(69) has also been solved before. In Section 11.2 (cf. equations (11) and (17)) we showed that $E = -(n\pi/W)^2$, $n = 1, 2, 3, \ldots,$ and the nontrivial solutions are given by

(70) $Y_n(y) = a_n \sin \dfrac{n\pi y}{W},$

where the a_n's are arbitrary.

Since $K = E - (m\pi/L)^2$, we have

$$K = -(n\pi/W)^2 - (m\pi/L)^2, \qquad m = 0, 1, 2, \ldots, \qquad n = 1, 2, 3, \ldots.$$

Substituting K into equation (62), we can solve for $T(t)$ and obtain

(71) $T_{mn}(t) = b_{mn}e^{-(m^2/L^2 + n^2/W^2)\beta\pi^2 t}.$

Substituting in for X, Y, and T, we get

$$u_{mn}(x, y, t) = \left(c_m \cos \frac{m\pi x}{L}\right)\left(a_n \sin \frac{n\pi y}{W}\right)(b_{mn}e^{-(m^2/L^2 + n^2/W^2)\beta\pi^2 t}),$$

(72) $u_{mn}(x, y, t) = a_{mn}e^{-(m^2/L^2 + n^2/W^2)\beta\pi^2 t}\cos \dfrac{m\pi x}{L} \sin \dfrac{n\pi y}{W},$

where $a_{mn} := a_n b_{mn} c_m$, $m = 0, 1, 2, \ldots, n = 1, 2, 3, \ldots,$ are arbitrary constants.

If we now take a doubly infinite series of such functions, then we obtain the formal series

$$(73) \qquad u(x, y, t) = \sum_{m=0}^{\infty} \sum_{n=1}^{\infty} a_{mn} e^{-(m^2/L^2 + n^2/W^2)\beta\pi^2 t} \cos \frac{m\pi x}{L} \sin \frac{n\pi y}{W}.$$

We are now ready to apply the initial conditions (61). Setting $t = 0$, we obtain

$$(74) \qquad u(x, y, 0) = f(x, y) = \sum_{m=0}^{\infty} \sum_{n=1}^{\infty} a_{mn} \cos \frac{m\pi x}{L} \sin \frac{n\pi y}{W}.$$

This is a **double Fourier Series.**[†] In fact, it is a double Fourier series for a function $f(x, y)$ that is an even function in the variable x and an odd function in the variable y. The formulas for the coefficients a_{mn} are

$$(75) \qquad a_{0n} = \frac{2}{LW} \int_0^L \int_0^W f(x, y) \sin \frac{n\pi y}{W} \, dx \, dy, \qquad n = 1, 2, 3, \ldots,$$

and, for $m \geq 1$, $n \geq 1$,

$$(76) \qquad a_{mn} = \frac{4}{LW} \int_0^L \int_0^W f(x, y) \cos \frac{m\pi x}{L} \sin \frac{n\pi y}{W} \, dx \, dy.$$

The solution to the initial-boundary value problem (58)–(62) is given by equation (73) where the coefficients are given by equations (75) and (76). ◄

EXISTENCE AND UNIQUENESS OF SOLUTIONS

In the examples that we have studied in this section and in Section 11.2, we were able to obtain formal solutions in the sense that we could express the solution in terms of a series expansion consisting of exponentials, sines, and cosines. To prove that these series converge to actual solutions requires results on the convergence of Fourier series and results from real analysis on uniform convergence. We will not go into these details here, but refer the reader to the text by Tyn Myint-U, *Partial Differential Equations of Mathematical Physics*, Elsevier North Holland, Inc., New York, 1980, Section 6.5 for a proof of the existence of a solution to the heat flow problem discussed in Sections 11.1 and 11.2. (A proof of uniqueness is also given there.)

As might be expected, using Fourier series and the method of separation of variables one can also obtain "solutions" when the initial data is discontinuous since the formal solutions only require the existence of a convergent Fourier series. This allows one to study

---

[†] For a discussion of double Fourier series see *Partial Differential Equations of Mathematical Physics*, by Tyn Myint-U, Elsevier North Holland, Inc., New York, 1980, Section 5.14.

idealized problems in which the initial conditions do not agree with the boundary conditions or the initial conditions involve a jump discontinuity. For example, we may assume that initially one half of the wire is at one temperature, whereas the other half is at a different temperature, that is,

$$f(x) = \begin{cases} U_1, & 0 < x < L/2, \\ U_2, & L/2 < x < L. \end{cases}$$

The formal solution that we obtained will make sense for $0 < x < L$, $t > 0$, but we must take care in interpreting the results near the points of discontinuity $x = 0$, $L/2$, and L.

The question of the uniqueness of the solution to the heat flow problem can be answered in various ways. One is tempted to argue that the method of separation of variables yields *formulas* for the solutions and therefore a unique solution. However, this does *not* exclude the possibility of solutions existing that cannot be obtained by the method of separation of variables.

An argument using the physical principles discussed in Section 11.1 can be given which states that the maximum temperature of the wire over all time $t \geq 0$, must occur either at one of the ends or in the initial temperature distribution. These results are called **maximum principles** and exist for the heat equation and Laplace's equation. One such result, which we will not prove, is the following:[†]

MAXIMUM PRINCIPLE FOR THE HEAT EQUATION

Theorem 6. Let $u(x, t)$ be a continuously differentiable function that satisfies the heat equation

$$(77) \qquad \frac{\partial u}{\partial t} = \beta \frac{\partial^2 u}{\partial x^2}; \qquad 0 < x < L, \qquad t > 0,$$

and the boundary conditions

$$(78) \qquad u(0, t) = u(L, t) = 0, \qquad t > 0.$$

Then, $u(x, t)$ attains its maximum value at $t = 0$ for some x in $[0, L]$, that is,

$$(79) \qquad \max_{\substack{t \geq 0 \\ 0 \leq x \leq L}} u(x, t) = \max_{0 \leq x \leq L} u(x, 0).$$

We can use the maximum principle to show that the heat flow problem has a unique solution.

[†] For a discussion of maximum principles and their applications see *Maximum Principles in Differential Equations*, by M. H. Protter and H. F. Weinberger, Prentice Hall, Inc., Englewood Cliffs, New Jersey, 1967.

UNIQUENESS OF SOLUTION

Theorem 7. The initial-boundary value problem

(80)
$$\frac{\partial u}{\partial t} = \beta \frac{\partial^2 u}{\partial x^2}; \qquad 0 < x < L, \qquad t > 0,$$

(81) $u(0, t) = u(L, t) = 0, \qquad t \geq 0,$

(82) $u(x, 0) = f(x), \qquad 0 \leq x \leq L,$

has at most one continuously differentiable solution.

Proof Assume $u(x, t)$ and $v(x, t)$ are continuously differentiable functions that satisfy the initial-boundary value problem (80)–(82). Let $w = u - v$. Now w is a continuously differentiable solution to the boundary value problem (77)–(78). By the maximum principle, w must attain its maximum at $t = 0$, and since

$$w(x, 0) = u(x, 0) - v(x, 0) = f(x) - f(x) = 0,$$

we have $w(x, t) \leq 0$. Hence, $u(x, t) \leq v(x, t)$ for all $0 \leq x \leq L$, $t \geq 0$. A similar argument using $\hat{w} = v - u$ yields $v(x, t) \leq u(x, t)$. Therefore, we have $u(x, t) = v(x, t)$, for all $0 \leq x \leq L$, $t \geq 0$. Thus, there is at most one continuously differentiable solution to the problem (80)–(82). ∎

EXERCISES 11.5

In Problems 1 through 10 find a formal solution to the given initial-boundary value problem.

1. $\dfrac{\partial u}{\partial t} = 5 \dfrac{\partial^2 u}{\partial x^2}, \qquad 0 < x < 1, \qquad t > 0,$

$u(0, t) = u(1, t) = 0, \qquad t > 0,$

$u(x, 0) = (1 - x)x^2, \qquad 0 < x < 1.$

2. $\dfrac{\partial u}{\partial t} = \dfrac{\partial^2 u}{\partial x^2}; \qquad 0 < x < \pi, \qquad t > 0,$

$u(0, t) = u(\pi, t) = 0, \qquad t > 0,$

$u(x, 0) = x^2, \qquad 0 < x < \pi.$

3. $\dfrac{\partial u}{\partial t} = 3 \dfrac{\partial^2 u}{\partial x^2}; \qquad 0 < x < \pi, \qquad t > 0,$

$\dfrac{\partial u}{\partial x}(0, t) = \dfrac{\partial u}{\partial x}(\pi, t) = 0, \qquad t > 0,$

$u(x, 0) = x, \qquad 0 < x < \pi.$

4. $\dfrac{\partial u}{\partial t} = 2 \dfrac{\partial^2 u}{\partial x^2}; \qquad 0 < x < 1, \qquad t > 0,$

$\dfrac{\partial u}{\partial x}(0, t) = \dfrac{\partial u}{\partial x}(1, t) = 0, \qquad t > 0,$

$u(x, 0) = x(1 - x), \qquad 0 < x < 1.$

5. $\dfrac{\partial u}{\partial t} = \dfrac{\partial^2 u}{\partial x^2}; \qquad 0 < x < \pi, \qquad t > 0,$

$\dfrac{\partial u}{\partial x}(0, t) = \dfrac{\partial u}{\partial x}(\pi, t) = 0, \qquad t > 0,$

$u(x, 0) = e^x, \qquad 0 < x < \pi.$

6. $\dfrac{\partial u}{\partial t} = 7 \dfrac{\partial^2 u}{\partial x^2}, \qquad 0 < x < \pi, \qquad t > 0,$

$\dfrac{\partial u}{\partial x}(0, t) = \dfrac{\partial u}{\partial x}(\pi, t) = 0, \qquad t > 0,$

$u(x, 0) = 1 - \sin x, \qquad 0 < x < \pi.$

7. $\dfrac{\partial u}{\partial t} = 2\dfrac{\partial^2 u}{\partial x^2};$ $0 < x < \pi,$ $t > 0,$

   $u(0, t) = 5,$ $u(\pi, t) = 10,$ $t > 0,$

   $u(x, 0) = \sin 3x - \sin 5x,$ $0 < x < \pi.$

8. $\dfrac{\partial u}{\partial t} = \dfrac{\partial^2 u}{\partial x^2};$ $0 < x < \pi,$ $t > 0,$

   $u(0, t) = 0,$ $u(\pi, t) = 3\pi,$ $t > 0,$

   $u(x, 0) = 0,$ $0 < x < \pi.$

9. $\dfrac{\partial u}{\partial t} = \dfrac{\partial^2 u}{\partial x^2} + e^{-x};$ $0 < x < \pi,$ $t > 0,$

   $u(0, t) = u(\pi, t) = 0,$ $t > 0,$

   $u(x, 0) = \sin 2x,$ $0 < x < \pi.$

10. $\dfrac{\partial u}{\partial t} = 3\dfrac{\partial^2 u}{\partial x^2} + x;$ $0 < x < \pi,$ $t > 0,$

   $u(0, t) = u(\pi, t) = 0,$ $t > 0,$

   $u(x, 0) = \sin x,$ $0 < x < \pi.$

11. Find a formal solution to the initial-boundary value problem

$$\frac{\partial u}{\partial t} = 4\frac{\partial^2 u}{\partial x^2}; \quad 0 < x < \pi, \quad t > 0,$$

$$\frac{\partial u}{\partial x}(0, t) = 0, \quad u(\pi, t) = 0, \quad t > 0,$$

$$u(x, 0) = f(x), \quad 0 < x < \pi.$$

12. Find a formal solution to the initial-boundary value problem

$$\frac{\partial u}{\partial t} = \frac{\partial^2 u}{\partial x^2}; \quad 0 < x < \pi, \quad t > 0,$$

$$u(0, t) = 0, \quad u(\pi, t) + \frac{\partial u}{\partial x}(\pi, t) = 0, \quad t > 0,$$

$$u(x, 0) = f(x), \quad 0 < x < \pi.$$

13. Find a formal solution to the initial-boundary value problem

$$\frac{\partial u}{\partial t} = 2\frac{\partial^2 u}{\partial x^2} + 4x; \quad 0 < x < \pi, \quad t > 0,$$

$$u(0, t) = u(\pi, t) = 0, \quad t > 0,$$

$$u(x, 0) = \sin x, \quad 0 < x < \pi.$$

14. Find a formal solution to the initial-boundary value problem

$$\frac{\partial u}{\partial t} = 3\frac{\partial^2 u}{\partial x^2} + 5; \quad 0 < x < \pi, \quad t > 0,$$

$$u(0, t) = u(\pi, t) = 1, \quad t > 0,$$

$$u(x, 0) = 1, \quad 0 < x < \pi.$$

In Problems 15 through 18 find a formal solution to the initial-boundary value problem

$$\frac{\partial u}{\partial t} = \frac{\partial^2 u}{\partial x^2} + \frac{\partial^2 u}{\partial y^2}; \quad 0 < x < \pi, \quad 0 < y < \pi, \quad t > 0,$$

$$\frac{\partial u}{\partial x}(0, y, t) = \frac{\partial u}{\partial x}(\pi, y, t) = 0, \quad 0 < y < \pi, \quad t > 0,$$

$$u(x, 0, t) = u(x, \pi, t) = 0, \quad 0 < x < \pi, \quad t > 0,$$

$$u(x, y, 0) = f(x, y), \quad 0 < x < \pi, \quad 0 < y < \pi,$$

for the given function $f(x, y)$.

15. $f(x, y) = \cos 6x \sin 4y - 3 \cos x \sin 11y.$

16. $f(x, y) = \cos x \sin y + 4 \cos 2x \sin y - 3 \cos 3x \sin 4y.$

17. $f(x, y) = y.$

18. $f(x, y) = x \sin y.$

11.6 The Wave Equation

In Section 11.2 we presented a model for the motion of a vibrating string. If $u(x, t)$ represents the displacement (deflection) of the string and the ends of the string are held fixed, then the motion of the string is governed by the initial-boundary value problem

$$(1) \qquad \frac{\partial^2 u}{\partial t^2} = \alpha^2 \frac{\partial^2 u}{\partial x^2}; \qquad 0 < x < L, \qquad t > 0,$$

$$(2) \qquad u(0, t) = u(L, t) = 0, \qquad t > 0,$$

$$(3) \qquad u(x, 0) = f(x), \qquad 0 < x < L,$$

$$(4) \qquad \frac{\partial u}{\partial t}(x, 0) = g(x), \qquad 0 < x < L.$$

Equation (1) is called the **wave equation.**

The constant α^2 appearing in (1) is strictly positive and depends on the linear density and tension of the string. The boundary conditions in (2) reflect the fact that the string is held fixed at the two end points $x = 0$ and $x = L$.

Equations (3) and (4) specify, respectively, the initial displacement and the initial velocity of each point on the string. For the initial and boundary conditions to be consistent, we assume $f(0) = f(L) = 0$ and $g(0) = g(L) = 0$.

Using the method of separation of variables, we found in Section 11.2 that a formal solution to (1)–(4) is given by (cf. equations (52)–(54) on page 610.)

$$(5) \qquad u(x, t) = \sum_{n=1}^{\infty} \left[a_n \cos \frac{n\pi\alpha}{L} t + b_n \sin \frac{n\pi\alpha}{L} t \right] \sin \frac{n\pi x}{L},$$

where the a_n's and b_n's are determined from the Fourier sine series

$$(6) \qquad f(x) = \sum_{n=1}^{\infty} a_n \sin \frac{n\pi x}{L},$$

$$(7) \qquad g(x) = \sum_{n=1}^{\infty} b_n \left(\frac{n\pi\alpha}{L}\right) \sin \frac{n\pi x}{L}.$$

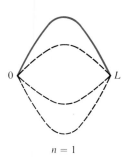 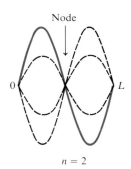 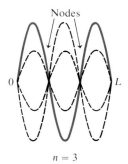

$n = 1$ $n = 2$ $n = 3$

Figure 11.10 Standing waves

Each term in expansion (5) can be viewed as a **standing wave.** For example, the first term,

$$\left(a_1 \cos \frac{\pi\alpha}{L} t + b_1 \sin \frac{\pi\alpha}{L} t\right) \sin \frac{\pi x}{L},$$

consists of a sine wave $\sin(\pi x/L)$ multiplied by a time varying amplitude. The second term is also a sine wave $\sin(2\pi x/L)$ with a time varying amplitude. In the latter case there is a *node* in the middle at $x = L/2$ which never moves. For the nth term, we have a sine wave $\sin(n\pi x/L)$ with a time varying amplitude and the sine wave has $(n-1)$ nodes. This is illustrated in Figure 11.10. Thus the solution in (5) can be interpreted as the superposition of infinitely many standing waves.

The method of separation of variables can also be used to solve problems with non-homogeneous boundary conditions and nonhomogeneous equations where the forcing term is time independent, just as was done for the heat equation with nonhomogeneous boundary conditions and with a heat source independent of time. In the next example, we will consider a problem with a time dependent forcing term.

▶ **Example 1**   Find a formal solution to the initial-boundary value problem

(8) $$\frac{\partial^2 u}{\partial t^2} = \alpha^2 \frac{\partial^2 u}{\partial x^2} + h(x, t); \qquad 0 < x < L, \qquad t > 0.$$

(9) $u(0, t) = u(L, t) = 0, \qquad t > 0,$

(10) $u(x, 0) = f(x), \qquad 0 < x < L,$

(11) $\dfrac{\partial u}{\partial t}(x, 0) = g(x), \qquad 0 < x < L.$

Solution   The boundary conditions in (9) certainly require that the solution be zero for $x = 0$ and $x = L$. Motivated by the fact that the solution to the corresponding homogeneous system (1)–(4) consists of a superposition of standing waves, let's try to find a solution to (8)–(11) of the form

(12) $$u(x, t) = \sum_{n=1}^{\infty} u_n(t) \sin \frac{n\pi x}{L},$$

where the $u_n(t)$'s are functions of t to be determined.

For each fixed t, we can compute a Fourier sine series for $h(x, t)$. If we assume the series is convergent to $h(x, t)$, then

(13) $$h(x, t) = \sum_{n=1}^{\infty} h_n(t) \sin \frac{n\pi x}{L},$$

where the coefficient $h_n(t)$ is given by (recall equation (10) on page 635)

(14) $$h_n(t) = \frac{2}{L} \int_0^L h(x, t) \sin \frac{n\pi x}{L} dx, \qquad n = 1, 2, \ldots.$$

If the series in (13) has the proper convergence properties, then we can substitute (12) and (13) into equation (8) and obtain

(15) $$\sum_{n=1}^{\infty} \left[u_n''(t) + \left(\frac{n\pi\alpha}{L} \right)^2 u_n(t) \right] \sin \frac{n\pi x}{L} = \sum_{n=1}^{\infty} h_n(t) \sin \frac{n\pi x}{L}.$$

Equating the coefficients in each series (why?), we have

(16) $$u_n''(t) + \left(\frac{n\pi\alpha}{L} \right)^2 u_n(t) = h_n(t).$$

This is a nonhomogeneous, constant coefficient equation which can be solved using variation of parameters. The reader should verify that

(17) $$u_n(t) = a_n \cos \frac{n\pi\alpha}{L} t + b_n \sin \frac{n\pi\alpha}{L} t + \frac{L}{n\pi\alpha} \int_0^t h_n(s) \sin \left[\frac{n\pi\alpha}{L} (t - s) \right] ds$$

(cf. Problem 24 in Exercises 4.9). Hence,

$$u(x, t) = \sum_{n=1}^{\infty} u_n(t) \sin \frac{n\pi x}{L},$$

where $u_n(t)$ is given in equation (17). Since[†]

$$u_n(0) = a_n \quad \text{and} \quad u_n'(0) = b_n \left(\frac{n\pi\alpha}{L} \right),$$

[†] To compute $u_n'(0)$, we use the fact that $\dfrac{d}{dt} \int_0^t G(s, t) ds = G(t, t) + \int_0^t \dfrac{\partial G}{\partial t} (s, t) ds.$

substituting into the initial conditions (10)–(11) yields

(18) $$u(x, 0) = f(x) = \sum_{n=1}^{\infty} a_n \sin \frac{n\pi x}{L},$$

(19) $$\frac{\partial u}{\partial t}(x, 0) = g(x) = \sum_{n=1}^{\infty} b_n \left(\frac{n\pi\alpha}{L} \right) \sin \frac{n\pi x}{L}.$$

If we choose the a_n's and b_n's so that equations (18) and (19) are satisfied, then a formal solution to (8)–(11) is given by

(20) $$u(x, t) = \sum_{n=1}^{\infty} \left\{ a_n \cos \frac{n\pi\alpha}{L} t + b_n \sin \frac{n\pi\alpha}{L} t \right.$$

$$\left. + \frac{L}{n\pi\alpha} \int_0^t h_n(s) \sin \left[\frac{n\pi\alpha}{L} (t - s) \right] ds \right\} \sin \frac{n\pi x}{L}. \blacktriangleleft$$

The method of separation of variables can also be used to solve initial-boundary value problems for the wave equation in higher dimensions. For example, a vibrating rectangular membrane of length L and width W (see Figure 11.11) is governed by the following initial-boundary value problem for $u(x, y, t)$:

(21) $$\frac{\partial^2 u}{\partial t^2} = \alpha^2 \left(\frac{\partial^2 u}{\partial x^2} + \frac{\partial^2 u}{\partial y^2} \right); \qquad 0 < x < L, \qquad 0 < y < W, \qquad t > 0,$$

(22) $$u(0, y, t) = u(L, y, t) = 0, \qquad 0 < y < W, \qquad t > 0,$$

(23) $$u(x, 0, t) = u(x, W, t) = 0, \qquad 0 < x < L, \qquad t > 0,$$

(24) $$u(x, y, 0) = f(x, y), \qquad 0 < x < L, \qquad 0 < y < W,$$

(25) $$\frac{\partial u}{\partial t}(x, y, 0) = g(x, y), \qquad 0 < x < L, \qquad 0 < y < W.$$

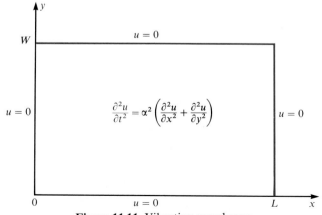

Figure 11.11 Vibrating membrane

Using an argument similar to the one given for the problem of heat flow in a rectangular plate (Example 4 in Section 11.5), we find that the initial-boundary value problem (21)–(25) has a formal solution

$$
(26) \qquad u(x, y, t) = \sum_{m=1}^{\infty} \sum_{n=1}^{\infty} \left\{ a_{mn} \cos \left(\sqrt{\frac{m^2}{L^2} + \frac{n^2}{W^2}}\ \alpha \pi t \right) \right.
$$

$$
\left. + b_{mn} \sin \left(\sqrt{\frac{m^2}{L^2} + \frac{n^2}{W^2}}\ \alpha \pi t \right) \right\} \sin \frac{m \pi x}{L} \sin \frac{n \pi y}{W},
$$

where the constants a_{mn} and b_{mn} are determined from the double Fourier series

$$
(27) \qquad f(x, y) = \sum_{m=1}^{\infty} \sum_{n=1}^{\infty} a_{mn} \sin \frac{m \pi x}{L} \sin \frac{n \pi y}{W},
$$

$$
(28) \qquad g(x, y) = \sum_{m=1}^{\infty} \sum_{n=1}^{\infty} \alpha \pi \sqrt{\frac{m^2}{L^2} + \frac{n^2}{W^2}}\ b_{mn} \sin \frac{m \pi x}{L} \sin \frac{n \pi y}{W}.
$$

In particular,

$$
(29) \qquad a_{mn} = \frac{4}{LW} \int_0^L \int_0^W f(x, y) \sin \frac{m \pi x}{L} \sin \frac{n \pi y}{W}\, dx\, dy,
$$

$$
(30) \qquad b_{mn} = \frac{4}{LW \pi \alpha \sqrt{\dfrac{m^2}{L^2} + \dfrac{n^2}{W^2}}} \int_0^L \int_0^W g(x, y) \sin \frac{m \pi x}{L} \sin \frac{n \pi y}{W}\, dx\, dy.
$$

We leave the derivation of this solution as an exercise (see Problem 19).

We mentioned earlier that the solution to the vibrating string problem (1)–(4) consisted of a superposition of standing waves. There are also **traveling waves** associated with the wave equation. Traveling waves arise naturally out of d'Alembert's solution to the wave equation for an "infinite" string.

▶ *Example 2*   Find a solution to the initial value problem

$$
(31) \qquad \frac{\partial^2 u}{\partial t^2} = \alpha^2 \frac{\partial^2 u}{\partial x^2}; \qquad -\infty < x < \infty, \qquad t > 0,
$$

$$
(32) \qquad u(x, 0) = f(x), \qquad -\infty < x < \infty,
$$

$$
(33) \qquad \frac{\partial u}{\partial t}(x, 0) = g(x), \qquad -\infty < x < \infty.
$$

Solution   To solve equation (31), we use the change of variables

(34) $\psi = x + \alpha t, \qquad \eta = x - \alpha t.$

If u has continuous second partial derivatives, then $\partial u/\partial x = \partial u/\partial \psi + \partial u/\partial \eta$ and $\partial u/\partial t = \alpha(\partial u/\partial \psi - \partial u/\partial \eta)$, from which we obtain

$$\frac{\partial^2 u}{\partial x^2} = \frac{\partial^2 u}{\partial \psi^2} + 2\frac{\partial^2 u}{\partial \psi \partial \eta} + \frac{\partial^2 u}{\partial \eta^2},$$

$$\frac{\partial^2 u}{\partial t^2} = \alpha^2 \left\{ \frac{\partial^2 u}{\partial \psi^2} - 2\frac{\partial^2 u}{\partial \psi \partial \eta} + \frac{\partial^2 u}{\partial \eta^2} \right\}.$$

Substituting these into equation (31) and simplifying, yields

(35) $\dfrac{\partial^2 u}{\partial \psi \partial \eta} = 0.$

We can solve equation (35) directly by first integrating with respect to ψ to obtain

$$\frac{\partial u}{\partial \eta} = b(\eta),$$

where $b(\eta)$ is an arbitrary function of η, and then integrating with respect to η to find

(36) $u(\psi, \eta) = A(\psi) + B(\eta),$

where $A(\psi)$ and $B(\eta)$ are arbitrary functions. Substituting the original variables x and t gives

(37) $u(x, t) = A(x + \alpha t) + B(x - \alpha t).$

It is easy to check by direct substitution that $u(x, t)$, defined by formula (37), is a solution to the wave equation (31) provided A and B are twice differentiable functions.
    In order for the initial conditions (32)–(33) to be satisfied, we need

(38) $u(x, 0) = A(x) + B(x) = f(x),$

(39) $\dfrac{\partial u}{\partial t}(x, 0) = \alpha A'(x) - \alpha B'(x) = g(x).$

Integrating equation (39) from x_0 to x, x_0 arbitrary, and dividing by α gives

(40) $A(x) - B(x) = \dfrac{1}{\alpha} \displaystyle\int_{x_0}^{x} g(s)\,ds + C,$

where C is also arbitrary. Solving the system (38) and (40), we obtain

(41) $A(x) = \dfrac{1}{2} f(x) + \dfrac{1}{2\alpha} \displaystyle\int_{x_0}^{x} g(s)\, ds + \dfrac{C}{2},$

(42) $B(x) = \dfrac{1}{2} f(x) - \dfrac{1}{2\alpha} \displaystyle\int_{x_0}^{x} g(s)\, ds - \dfrac{C}{2}.$

Using these functions in formula (37) gives

$$u(x, t) = \frac{1}{2}\left[f(x + \alpha t) + f(x - \alpha t) \right] + \frac{1}{2\alpha}\left[\int_{x_0}^{x+\alpha t} g(s)\, ds - \int_{x_0}^{x-\alpha t} g(s)\, ds \right],$$

which simplifies to

(43) $u(x, t) = \dfrac{1}{2}\left[f(x + \alpha t) + f(x - \alpha t) \right] + \dfrac{1}{2\alpha} \displaystyle\int_{x-\alpha t}^{x+\alpha t} g(s)\, ds.$

Formula (43) is called **d'Alembert's solution** to the initial value problem (31)–(33). ◀

In the next example we apply d'Alembert's formula to solve an initial value problem.

▶ **Example 3**   Find the solution to the initial value problem

(44) $\dfrac{\partial^2 u}{\partial t^2} = 4\,\dfrac{\partial^2 u}{\partial x^2};$ $-\infty < x < \infty,$ $t > 0,$

(45) $u(x, 0) = \sin x,$ $-\infty < x < \infty,$

(46) $\dfrac{\partial u}{\partial t}(x, 0) = 1,$ $-\infty < x < \infty.$

Solution   Substituting in formula (43) the values $\alpha = 2$, $f(x) = \sin x$, and $g(x) = 1$, we obtain the solution

(47) $u(x, t) = \frac{1}{2}\left[\sin(x + 2t) + \sin(x - 2t) \right] + \frac{1}{4} \displaystyle\int_{x-2t}^{x+2t} ds$

          $= \sin x \cos 2t + t.$ ◀

We now use d'Alembert's formula to show that the solution to the "infinite" string problem consists of traveling waves.

$h(x + a)$ $h(x)$

$x_0 - a$ $x_1 - a$ x_0 x_1

Figure 11.12 Graphs of $h(x)$ and $h(x + a)$

Let $h(x)$ be a function defined on $(-\infty, \infty)$. The function $h(x + a)$, where $a > 0$, is a translation of the function $h(x)$ in the sense that its "shape" is the same as $h(x)$, but the coordinate system has been shifted to the left by an amount a. This is illustrated in Figure 11.12 for a function $h(x)$ whose graph consists of a triangular "bump." If we let $t \geq 0$ be a parameter (say time), then the functions $h(x + \alpha t)$ represent a family of functions, with the same shape, but shifted further and further to the left as $t \to \infty$. We say that $h(x + \alpha t)$ is a **traveling wave** moving to the left with speed α. In a similar fashion $h(x - \alpha t)$ is a traveling wave moving to the right with speed α.

If we refer back to equation (37), we find that the solution to equation (31) consists of traveling waves $A(x + \alpha t)$ moving to the left with speed α and $B(x - \alpha t)$ moving to the right at the same speed.

In the special case when the initial velocity $g(x) \equiv 0$, we have

(48) $$u(x, t) = \tfrac{1}{2}[f(x + \alpha t) + f(x - \alpha t)].$$

Hence $u(x, t)$ is the sum of the traveling waves

$$\tfrac{1}{2}f(x + \alpha t) \quad \text{and} \quad \tfrac{1}{2}f(x - \alpha t).$$

These waves are initially superimposed, since

$$u(x, 0) = \tfrac{1}{2}f(x) + \tfrac{1}{2}f(x) = f(x).$$

As t increases, the two waves move away from each other with speed 2α. This is illustrated in Figure 11.13 for a square wave.

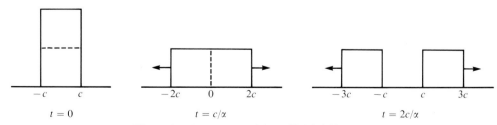

$-c$ c $-2c$ 0 $2c$ $-3c$ $-c$ c $3c$

$t = 0$ $t = c/\alpha$ $t = 2c/\alpha$

Figure 11.13 Decomposition of initial displacement into traveling waves

EXISTENCE AND UNIQUENESS OF SOLUTIONS

In Example 1, the method of separation of variables was used to derive a formal solution to the given initial-boundary value problem. To show that these series converge to an actual solution requires results from real analysis just as was the case for the formal solutions to the heat equation in Section 11.5. In Examples 2 and 3, the validity of d'Alembert's solution can be established by direct substitution into the initial value problem, assuming sufficient differentiability of the initial functions. We leave it as an exercise for the reader to show that if f has a continuous second derivative and g has a continuous first derivative, then d'Alembert's solution is a true solution (see Problem 12).

The question of the uniqueness of the solution to the initial-boundary value problem (1)–(4) can be answered using an **energy argument.**

UNIQUENESS OF THE SOLUTION TO THE VIBRATING STRING PROBLEM

Theorem 8.   The initial-boundary value problem

$$(49) \qquad \frac{\partial^2 u}{\partial t^2} = \alpha^2 \frac{\partial^2 u}{\partial x^2}; \qquad 0 < x < L, \qquad t > 0,$$

$$(50) \qquad u(0, t) = u(L, t) = 0, \qquad t \geq 0,$$

$$(51) \qquad u(x, 0) = f(x), \qquad 0 \leq x \leq L,$$

$$(52) \qquad \frac{\partial u}{\partial t}(x, 0) = g(x), \qquad 0 \leq x \leq L,$$

has at most one twice continuously differentiable solution.

Proof   Assume that both $u(x, t)$ and $v(x, t)$ are twice continuously differentiable solutions to (49)–(52), and let $w(x, t) := u(x, t) - v(x, t)$. It is easy to check that $w(x, t)$ satisfies the initial boundary value problem (49)–(52) with zero initial data; that is, for $0 \leq x \leq L$,

$$(53) \qquad w(x, 0) = 0 \quad \text{and} \quad \frac{\partial w}{\partial t}(x, 0) = 0.$$

We will now show that $w(x, t) \equiv 0$ for $0 \leq x \leq L$, $t \geq 0$.

If $w(x, t)$ is the displacement of the vibrating string at location x for time t, then with the appropriate units, the total energy $E(t)$ of the vibrating string at time t is defined by the integral

$$(54) \qquad E(t) := \frac{1}{2} \int_0^L \left[\alpha^2 \left(\frac{\partial w}{\partial x} \right)^2 + \left(\frac{\partial w}{\partial t} \right)^2 \right] dx.$$

We now consider the derivative of $E(t)$:

(55)
$$\frac{dE}{dt} = \frac{d}{dt}\left\{\frac{1}{2}\int_0^L\left[\alpha^2\left(\frac{\partial w}{\partial x}\right)^2 + \left(\frac{\partial w}{\partial t}\right)^2\right]dx\right\}.$$

Since w has continuous second partial derivatives (because u and v do), we can interchange the order of integration and differentiation in (55):

(56)
$$\frac{dE}{dt} = \int_0^L\left[\alpha^2\frac{\partial w}{\partial x}\frac{\partial^2 w}{\partial t\,\partial x} + \frac{\partial w}{\partial t}\frac{\partial^2 w}{\partial t^2}\right]dx.$$

Again the continuity of the second partials of w guarantee that the mixed partials are equal; that is,

$$\frac{\partial^2 w}{\partial t\,\partial x} = \frac{\partial^2 w}{\partial x\,\partial t}.$$

Combining this fact with integration by parts, we obtain

(57)
$$\int_0^L \alpha^2\frac{\partial w}{\partial x}\frac{\partial^2 w}{\partial t\,\partial x}\,dx = \int_0^L \alpha^2\frac{\partial w}{\partial x}\frac{\partial^2 w}{\partial x\,\partial t}\,dx$$

$$= \alpha^2\frac{\partial w}{\partial x}(L,t)\frac{\partial w}{\partial t}(L,t) - \alpha^2\frac{\partial w}{\partial x}(0,t)\frac{\partial w}{\partial t}(0,t)$$

$$- \int_0^L \alpha^2\frac{\partial^2 w}{\partial x^2}\frac{\partial w}{\partial t}\,dx.$$

The boundary conditions $w(0,t) = w(L,t) = 0$, $t \geq 0$, imply that $(\partial w/\partial t)(0,t) = (\partial w/\partial t)(L,t) = 0$, $t \geq 0$. This reduces equation (57) to

$$\int_0^L \alpha^2\frac{\partial w}{\partial x}\frac{\partial^2 w}{\partial t\,\partial x}\,dx = -\int_0^L \alpha^2\frac{\partial w}{\partial t}\frac{\partial^2 w}{\partial x^2}\,dx.$$

Substituting this in for the first integrand in (56), we find

(58)
$$\frac{dE}{dt} = \int_0^L \frac{\partial w}{\partial t}\left[\frac{\partial^2 w}{\partial t^2} - \alpha^2\frac{\partial^2 w}{\partial x^2}\right]dx.$$

Since w satisfies equation (49), the integrand in (58) is zero for all x. Thus $dE/dt = 0$, and so $E(t) = C$, where C is a constant. This means that the total energy is conserved within the vibrating string.

The first boundary condition in (53) states that $w(x,0) = 0$ for $0 \leq x \leq L$. Hence $(\partial w/\partial x)(x,0) = 0$ for $0 < x < L$. Combining this with the second boundary condition in (53), we find that, when $t = 0$, the integrand in (54) is zero for $0 < x < L$. Therefore $E(0) = 0$.

Since $E(t) = C$, we must have $C = 0$, and so

(59) $$E(t) = \frac{1}{2} \int_0^L \left[\alpha^2 \left(\frac{\partial w}{\partial x} \right)^2 + \left(\frac{\partial w}{\partial t} \right)^2 \right] dx \equiv 0.$$

That is, the total energy of the system is zero.

Since the integrand in (59) is nonnegative and continuous and the integral is zero, then the integrand must be zero for $0 \le x \le L$. Moreover, the integrand is the sum of two squares and so each term must be zero. Hence

$$\frac{\partial w}{\partial x}(x, t) = 0 \quad \text{and} \quad \frac{\partial w}{\partial t}(x, t) = 0,$$

for all $0 \le x \le L$, $t \ge 0$. Thus $w(x, t) = K$, where K is a constant. Physically, this says that there is no motion in the string.

Finally, since w is constant and w is zero when $t = 0$, then $w(x, t) \equiv 0$. Consequently, $u(x, t) = v(x, t)$ and the initial-boundary value problem has at most one solution. ∎

EXERCISES 11.6

In Problems 1 through 4 find a formal solution to the vibrating string problem governed by the given initial-boundary value problem.

1. $\dfrac{\partial^2 u}{\partial t^2} = \dfrac{\partial^2 u}{\partial x^2}$; $\quad 0 < x < 1, \quad t > 0,$

$u(0, t) = u(1, t) = 0, \quad t > 0,$

$u(x, 0) = x(1 - x), \quad 0 < x < 1,$

$\dfrac{\partial u}{\partial t}(x, 0) = \sin 7\pi x, \quad 0 < x < 1.$

2. $\dfrac{\partial^2 u}{\partial t^2} = 16 \dfrac{\partial^2 u}{\partial x^2}$; $\quad 0 < x < \pi, \quad t > 0,$

$u(0, t) = u(\pi, t) = 0, \quad t > 0,$

$u(x, 0) = \sin^2 x, \quad 0 < x < \pi,$

$\dfrac{\partial u}{\partial t}(x, 0) = 1 - \cos x, \quad 0 < x < \pi.$

3. $\dfrac{\partial^2 u}{\partial t^2} = 4 \dfrac{\partial^2 u}{\partial x^2}$; $\quad 0 < x < \pi, \quad t > 0,$

$u(0, t) = u(\pi, t) = 0, \quad t > 0,$

$u(x, 0) = x^2(\pi - x), \quad 0 < x < \pi,$

$\dfrac{\partial u}{\partial t}(x, 0) = 0, \quad 0 < x < \pi.$

4. $\dfrac{\partial^2 u}{\partial t^2} = 9 \dfrac{\partial^2 u}{\partial x^2}$; $\quad 0 < x < \pi, \quad t > 0,$

$u(0, t) = u(\pi, t) = 0, \quad t > 0,$

$u(x, 0) = \sin 4x + 7 \sin 5x, \quad 0 < x < \pi,$

$\dfrac{\partial u}{\partial t}(x, 0) = \begin{cases} x & 0 < x < \pi/2, \\ \pi - x, & \pi/2 < x < \pi. \end{cases}$

5. The Plucked String. A vibrating string is governed by the initial-boundary value problem (1)–(4). If the string is lifted to a height h_0 at $x = a$ and released, then the initial conditions are

$$f(x) = \begin{cases} h_0 x/a, & 0 < x \le a, \\ h_0(L - x)/(L - a), & a < x < L, \end{cases}$$

and $g(x) \equiv 0$. Find a formal solution.

6. **The Struck String.** A vibrating string is governed by the initial-boundary value problem (1)–(4). If the string is struck at $x = a$, then the initial conditions may be expressed by $f(x) \equiv 0$ and

$$g(x) = \begin{cases} v_0 x/a, & 0 < x \le a, \\ v_0(L - x)/(L - a), & a < x < L, \end{cases}$$

where v_0 is a constant. Find a formal solution.

In Problems 7 and 8 find a formal solution to the vibrating string problem governed by the given nonhomogeneous initial-boundary value problem.

7. $\dfrac{\partial^2 u}{\partial t^2} = \dfrac{\partial^2 u}{\partial x^2} + tx; \qquad 0 < x < \pi, \qquad t > 0,$

$u(0, t) = u(\pi, t) = 0, \qquad t > 0,$

$u(x, 0) = \sin x, \qquad 0 < x < \pi,$

$\dfrac{\partial u}{\partial t}(x, 0) = 5 \sin 2x - 3 \sin 5x, \qquad 0 < x < \pi.$

8. $\dfrac{\partial^2 u}{\partial t^2} = \dfrac{\partial^2 u}{\partial x^2} + x \sin t; \qquad 0 < x < \pi, \qquad t > 0,$

$u(0, t) = u(\pi, t) = 0, \qquad t > 0,$

$u(x, 0) = 0, \qquad 0 < x < \pi,$

$\dfrac{\partial u}{\partial t}(x, 0) = 0, \qquad 0 < x < \pi.$

9. If one end of the string is held fixed while the other is free, then the motion of the string is governed by the initial-boundary value problem

$$\frac{\partial^2 u}{\partial t^2} = \alpha^2 \frac{\partial^2 u}{\partial x^2}; \qquad 0 < x < L, \qquad t > 0,$$

$$u(0, t) = 0 \quad \text{and} \quad \frac{\partial u}{\partial x}(L, t) = 0, \qquad t > 0,$$

$$u(x, 0) = f(x), \qquad 0 < x < L,$$

$$\frac{\partial u}{\partial t}(x, 0) = g(x), \qquad 0 < x < L.$$

Derive a formula for a formal solution.

10. Derive a formula for the solution to the following initial-boundary value problem involving nonhomogenous boundary conditions

$$\frac{\partial^2 u}{\partial t^2} = \alpha^2 \frac{\partial u}{\partial x^2}; \qquad 0 < x < L, \qquad t > 0,$$

$$u(0, t) = U_1, \qquad u(L, t) = U_2, \qquad t > 0,$$

$$u(x, 0) = f(x), \qquad 0 < x < L,$$

$$\frac{\partial u}{\partial t}(x, 0) = g(x), \qquad 0 < x < L,$$

where U_1 and U_2 are constants.

11. The Telegraph Problem.† Use the method of separation of variables to derive a formal solution to the telegraph problem

$$\frac{\partial^2 u}{\partial t^2} + \frac{\partial u}{\partial t} + u = \alpha^2 \frac{\partial^2 u}{\partial x^2}; \qquad 0 < x < L, \qquad t > 0,$$

$$u(0, t) = u(L, t) = 0, \qquad t > 0,$$

$$u(x, 0) = f(x), \qquad 0 < x < L,$$

$$\frac{\partial u}{\partial t}(x, 0) = 0, \qquad 0 < x < L.$$

12. Verify d'Alembert's solution (43) to the initial value problem (31)–(33) when $f(x)$ has a continuous second derivative and $g(x)$ has a continuous first derivative, by substituting it directly into the equations.

In Problems 13 through 18 find the solution to the initial value problem

$$\frac{\partial^2 u}{\partial t^2} = \alpha^2 \frac{\partial^2 u}{\partial x^2}; \qquad -\infty < x < \infty, \qquad t > 0,$$

$$u(x, 0) = f(x), \qquad -\infty < x < \infty,$$

$$\frac{\partial u}{\partial t}(x, 0) = g(x), \qquad -\infty < x < \infty,$$

for the given functions $f(x)$ and $g(x)$.

13. $f(x) = 0$, $\quad g(x) = \cos x$.

14. $f(x) = x^2$, $\quad g(x) = 0$.

15. $f(x) = x$, $\quad g(x) = x$.

16. $f(x) = \sin 3x$, $\quad g(x) = 1$.

17. $f(x) = e^{-x^2}$, $\quad g(x) = \sin x$.

18. $f(x) = \cos 2x$, $\quad g(x) = 1 - x$.

19. Derive the formal solution given in equations (26), (29), and (30) to the vibrating membrane problem governed by the initial-boundary value problem (21)–(25).

11.7 Laplace's Equation

In Section 11.1 we showed how Laplace's equation,

$$\frac{\partial^2 u}{\partial x^2} + \frac{\partial^2 u}{\partial y^2} = 0,$$

---

† For a discussion of the telegraph problem see *Methods of Mathematical Physics*, by R. Courant and D. Hibert, Volume II, Wiley-Interscience, New York, 1962.

arises in the study of steady-state or time-independent solutions to the heat equation. Since these solutions do not depend upon time, initial conditions are irrelevant and only boundary conditions are specified for solutions to Laplace's equation. There are two basic types of boundary conditions that are usually associated with Laplace's equation: **Dirichlet boundary conditions,** where the solution $u(x, y)$ to Laplace's equation in a domain D is required to satisfy

$$u(x, y) = f(x, y), \qquad \text{on } \partial D,$$

where $f(x, y)$ is a specified function defined on the boundary ∂D of D; and **Neumann boundary conditions,** where the directional derivative $\partial u/\partial n$ along the outward normal to the boundary is required to satisfy

$$\frac{\partial u}{\partial n}(x, y) = g(x, y), \qquad \text{on } \partial D,$$

where $g(x, y)$ is a specified function defined on ∂D. We say that the boundary conditions are **mixed** if the solution is required to satisfy $u(x, y) = f(x, y)$ on part of the boundary and $(\partial u/\partial n)(x, y) = g(x, y)$ on the remaining portion of the boundary.

In this section we will use the method of separation of variables to find solutions to Laplace's equation with various boundary conditions for rectangular, circular, and cylindrical domains. We will also discuss the existence and uniqueness of such solutions.

▶ *Example 1* Find a solution to the following mixed boundary value problem for a rectangle (see Figure 11.14):

(1) $\qquad \dfrac{\partial^2 u}{\partial x^2} + \dfrac{\partial^2 u}{\partial y^2} = 0; \qquad 0 < x < a, \qquad 0 < y < b,$

(2) $\qquad \dfrac{\partial u}{\partial x}(0, y) = \dfrac{\partial u}{\partial x}(a, y) = 0, \qquad 0 \le y \le b,$

(3) $\qquad u(x, b) = 0, \qquad 0 \le x \le a,$

(4) $\qquad u(x, 0) = f(x), \qquad 0 \le x \le a.$

Solution Separating variables, we first let $u(x, y) = X(x)Y(y)$. Substituting into equation (1), we have

$$X''(x)Y(y) + X(x)Y''(y) = 0,$$

which separates into

$$\frac{X''(x)}{X(x)} = -\frac{Y''(y)}{Y(y)} = K,$$

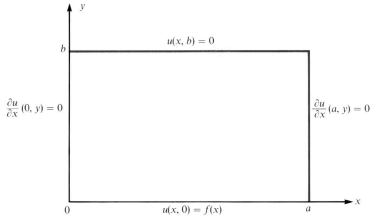

$u(x, b) = 0$

b

$\dfrac{\partial u}{\partial x}(0, y) = 0$

$\dfrac{\partial u}{\partial x}(a, y) = 0$

0

$u(x, 0) = f(x)$

a

x

y

Figure 11.14 Mixed boundary value problem

where K is some constant. This leads to the two ordinary differential equations

(5) $X''(x) - KX(x) = 0,$

(6) $Y''(y) + KY(y) = 0.$

From the boundary condition (2) we observe that

(7) $X'(0) = X'(a) = 0.$

We have encountered the eigenvalue problem in (5) and (7) before (see Example 1 in Section 11.5). The eigenvalues are $K = K_n = -(n\pi/a)^2$, $n = 0, 1, 2, \ldots$ with corresponding solutions

(8) $X_n(x) = a_n\cos\left(\dfrac{n\pi x}{a}\right),$

where the a_n's are arbitrary constants.

Setting $K = K_n = -(n\pi/a)^2$ in equation (6) and solving for Y gives

$$Y_0(y) = A_0 + B_0 y,$$

$$Y_n(y) = A_n\cosh\left(\dfrac{n\pi y}{a}\right) + B_n\sinh\left(\dfrac{n\pi y}{a}\right), \qquad n = 1, 2, \ldots,$$

which (just as for trigonometric functions) can be written in the form

$$Y_0(y) = A_0 + B_0 y,$$

(9)

$$Y_n(y) = C_n\sinh\left(\dfrac{n\pi}{a}(y + D_n)\right), \qquad n = 1, 2, \ldots,$$

where C_n and D_n are arbitrary constants (see Problem 18).

Now the boundary condition $u(x, b) = 0$ in (3) will be satisfied if $Y(b) = 0$. Setting $y = b$ in (9), we want $A_0 + B_0 b = 0$ and

$$C_n \sinh\left(\frac{n\pi}{a}(b + D_n)\right) = 0, \qquad n = 1, 2, \ldots .$$

This is true if we take $A_0 = -bB_0$ and $D_n = -b$. Combining the results in (8) and (9), we find that there are solutions to (1)–(3) of the form

$$u_0(x, y) = X_0(x)Y_0(y) = a_0 B_0(y - b) = E_0(y - b),$$

(10)
$$u_n(x, y) = X_n(x)Y_n(y) = a_n \cos\left(\frac{n\pi x}{a}\right) C_n \sinh\left[\frac{n\pi}{a}(y - b)\right]$$

$$= E_n \cos\left(\frac{n\pi x}{a}\right) \sinh\left[\frac{n\pi}{a}(y - b)\right], \qquad n = 1, 2, \ldots ,$$

where the E_n's are constants. In fact, by the superposition principle,

(11)
$$u(x, y) = E_0(y - b) + \sum_{n=1}^{\infty} E_n \cos\left(\frac{n\pi x}{a}\right) \sinh\left[\frac{n\pi}{a}(y - b)\right],$$

is a formal solution to (1)–(3).

Applying the remaining nonhomogeneous boundary condition in (4), we have

(12)
$$u(x, 0) = f(x) = -E_0 b + \sum_{n=1}^{\infty} E_n \sinh\left(-\frac{n\pi b}{a}\right) \cos\left(\frac{n\pi x}{a}\right).$$

This is a Fourier cosine series for $f(x)$ and hence the coefficients are given by the formulas

(13)
$$E_0 = \frac{1}{(-ba)} \int_0^a f(x)\, dx,$$

$$E_n = \frac{2}{a \sinh\left(-\dfrac{n\pi b}{a}\right)} \int_0^a f(x) \cos\left(\frac{n\pi x}{a}\right) dx, \qquad n = 1, 2, \ldots .$$

Thus a formal solution is given by (11) with the constants E_n given by (13). ◀

In Example 1 the boundary conditions were homogeneous on three sides of the rectangle and nonhomogeneous on the fourth side, $\{(x, y): y = 0, 0 \leq x \leq a\}$. It is important to note that the method used in Example 1 can also be used to solve problems for which the boundary conditions are nonhomogeneous on all sides. This is accomplished by solving four separate boundary value problems in which three sides have homogeneous boundary conditions and only one side is nonhomogeneous. The solution is then obtained by a superposition of these four solutions (see Problem 5).

For problems involving circular domains it is usually more convenient to use polar coordinates. In rectangular coordinates the Laplacian has the form

$$\Delta u = \frac{\partial^2 u}{\partial x^2} + \frac{\partial^2 u}{\partial y^2}.$$

In polar coordinates (r, θ), we let

$$x = r \cos \theta, \qquad y = r \sin \theta,$$

so that

$$r = \sqrt{x^2 + y^2}, \qquad \tan \theta = y/x.$$

With patience and a little care in applying the chain rule, one can show that the Laplacian in polar coordinates is

(14) $$\Delta u = \frac{\partial^2 u}{\partial r^2} + \frac{1}{r} \frac{\partial u}{\partial r} + \frac{1}{r^2} \frac{\partial^2 u}{\partial \theta^2},$$

(see Problem 6). In the next example we obtain a solution to the **Dirichlet problem** in a disk of radius a.

▶ **Example 2** Find a solution to the following boundary value problem depicted in Figure 11.15.

(15) $$\frac{\partial^2 u}{\partial r^2} + \frac{1}{r} \frac{\partial u}{\partial r} + \frac{1}{r^2} \frac{\partial^2 u}{\partial \theta^2} = 0; \qquad 0 \le r < a, \qquad -\pi \le \theta \le \pi,$$

(16) $$u(a, \theta) = f(\theta), \qquad -\pi \le \theta \le \pi.$$

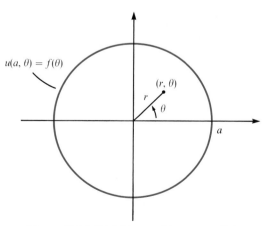

Figure 11.15 Dirichlet problem on a disk

Solution   To use the method of separation of variables, we first set

$$u(r, \theta) = R(r)T(\theta),$$

where $0 \leq r < a$ and $-\pi \leq \theta \leq \pi$. Substituting into (15) and separating variables give

$$\frac{r^2 R''(r) + rR'(r)}{R(r)} = -\frac{T''(\theta)}{T(\theta)} = \lambda,$$

where λ is any constant. This leads to the two ordinary differential equations

(17) $r^2 R''(r) + rR'(r) - \lambda R(r) = 0,$

(18) $T''(\theta) + \lambda T(\theta) = 0.$

In order for $u(r, \theta)$ to be continuous in the disk $0 \leq r < a$, we need $T(\theta)$ to be 2π-periodic; in particular, we require

(19) $T(-\pi) = T(\pi)$ and $T'(-\pi) = T'(\pi).$

Therefore, we seek nontrivial solutions to the eigenvalue problem (18) and (19). When $\lambda < 0$, it is easy to see that there are no nontrivial solutions.

When $\lambda = 0$, we find $T(\theta) = A\theta + B$ is the solution to (18). Substituting into the periodic boundary conditions in (19), we have

$$-A\pi + B = A\pi + B \quad \text{and} \quad A = A.$$

Thus B is arbitrary and A is zero. Hence $T_0(\theta) = B$ is a solution corresponding to $\lambda = 0$.

When $\lambda > 0$, the solution to (18) is

$$T(\theta) = A \cos \sqrt{\lambda}\, \theta + B \sin \sqrt{\lambda}\, \theta.$$

Here the boundary conditions in (19) imply that

$$A \cos \sqrt{\lambda}(-\pi) + B \sin \sqrt{\lambda}(-\pi) = A \cos \sqrt{\lambda}\, \pi + B \sin \sqrt{\lambda}\, \pi,$$

and

$$-\sqrt{\lambda}\, A \sin \sqrt{\lambda}(-\pi) + \sqrt{\lambda}B \cos \sqrt{\lambda}(-\pi) = -\sqrt{\lambda}\, A \sin \sqrt{\lambda}\, \pi + \sqrt{\lambda}\, B \cos \sqrt{\lambda}\, \pi,$$

which simplify to

$$B \sin \sqrt{\lambda}\, \pi = 0 \quad \text{and} \quad A \sin \sqrt{\lambda}\, \pi = 0.$$

Hence we choose $\sqrt{\lambda} = n$, $n = 1, 2, \ldots$, and obtain the nontrivial solutions

(20) $T_n(\theta) = A_n \cos n\theta + B_n \sin n\theta.$

Now for $\lambda = n^2$, $n = 0, 1, 2, \ldots$, equation (17) is the Cauchy-Euler equation (see Section 4.10)

(21) $\qquad r^2 R''(r) + r R'(r) - n^2 R(r) = 0.$

When $n = 0$, equation (21) has the general solution

(22) $\qquad R_0(r) = C + D \ln r.$

Since $\ln r \to -\infty$, as $r \to 0^+$ this solution is unbounded near $r = 0$ when $D \neq 0$. Therefore, we must choose $D = 0$ if $u(r, \theta)$ is to be continuous at $r = 0$. We now have $R_0(r) = C$ and so $u_0(r, \theta) = R_0(r)T(\theta) = CB$ which, for convenience, we write in the form

(23) $\qquad u_0(r, \theta) = \dfrac{A_0}{2},$

where A_0 is an arbitrary constant.

When $\lambda = n^2$, $n = 1, 2, \ldots$, the reader should verify that equation (21) has the general solution

$$R_n(r) = C_n r^n + D_n r^{-n}.$$

Since $r^{-n} \to \infty$ as $r \to 0^+$, we must set $D_n = 0$ in order for $u(r, \theta)$ to be continuous at $r = 0$. Thus

(24) $\qquad R_n(r) = C_n r^n.$

Now for each $n = 1, 2, \ldots$, we have the solutions

(25) $\qquad u_n(r, \theta) = R_n(r)T_n(\theta) = C_n r^n (A_n \cos n\theta + B_n \sin n\theta),$

and by the superposition principle, an infinite series of the solutions in (23) and (25) gives a formal solution to (15) of the form

$$u(r, \theta) = \frac{A_0}{2} + \sum_{n=1}^{\infty} C_n r^n (A_n \cos n\theta + B_n \sin n\theta).$$

It is more convenient to write this series in the equivalent form

(26) $\qquad u(r, \theta) = \dfrac{a_0}{2} + \sum_{n=1}^{\infty} \left(\dfrac{r}{a}\right)^n (a_n \cos n\theta + b_n \sin n\theta),$

where the a_n's and b_n's are constants.

Substituting u given in (26) into the boundary condition (16), we get

(27) $$f(\theta) = \frac{a_0}{2} + \sum_{n=1}^{\infty} (a_n \cos n\theta + b_n \sin n\theta).$$

Hence if $f(\theta)$ is 2π-periodic with the Fourier series given by (27), then the constants a_n and b_n can be determined from the formulas

(28) $$a_n = \frac{1}{\pi} \int_{-\pi}^{\pi} f(\theta) \cos n\theta \, d\theta, \qquad n = 0, 1, \ldots,$$

(29) $$b_n = \frac{1}{\pi} \int_{-\pi}^{\pi} f(\theta) \sin n\theta \, d\theta, \qquad n = 1, 2, \ldots.$$

If a_n and b_n are defined by formulas (28) and (29), then $u(r, \theta)$ given in (26) is a formal solution to the Dirichlet problem (15)–(16). ◀

The procedure in Example 2 can also be used to study the **Neumann problem** in a disk:

(30) $$\Delta u = 0, \qquad 0 \le r < a, \qquad -\pi \le \theta \le \pi,$$

(31) $$\frac{\partial u}{\partial r}(a, \theta) = f(\theta), \qquad -\pi \le \theta \le \pi.$$

For this problem there is not a unique solution since if u is a solution, then so is $u +$ constant. Moreover f must satisfy the **consistency condition**

(32) $$\int_{-\pi}^{\pi} f(\theta) \, d\theta = 0.$$

We leave the solution of the Neumann problem and the derivation of the consistency condition for the exercises.

The technique used in Example 2 also applies to annular domains, $\{(r, \theta): 0 < a < r < b\}$, and to exterior domains, $\{(r, \theta): a < r\}$. We leave these applications as exercises.

Laplace's equation in cylindrical coordinates arises in the study of steady-state temperature distributions in a solid cylinder and in determining the electric potential inside a cylinder. In the cylindrical coordinates

$$x = r \cos \theta, \qquad y = r \sin \theta, \qquad z = z,$$

Laplace's equation becomes

(33) $$\Delta u = \frac{\partial^2 u}{\partial r^2} + \frac{1}{r} \frac{\partial u}{\partial r} + \frac{1}{r^2} \frac{\partial^2 u}{\partial \theta^2} + \frac{\partial^2 u}{\partial z^2} = 0.$$

The Dirichlet problem for the cylinder $\{(r, \theta, z): 0 \leq r \leq a, 0 \leq z \leq b\}$ has the boundary conditions

(34) $u(a, \theta, z) = f(\theta, z),$ $-\pi \leq \theta \leq \pi,$ $0 \leq z \leq b,$

(35) $u(r, \theta, 0) = g(r, \theta),$ $0 \leq r \leq a,$ $-\pi \leq \theta \leq \pi,$

(36) $u(r, \theta, b) = h(r, \theta),$ $0 \leq r \leq a,$ $-\pi \leq \theta \leq \pi.$

To solve the Dirichlet boundary value problem (33)–(36), we first solve the three boundary value problems corresponding to: (i) $g \equiv 0$ and $h \equiv 0$; (ii) $f \equiv 0$ and $h \equiv 0$; and (iii) $f \equiv 0$ and $g \equiv 0$. Then by the superposition principle, the solution to (33)–(36) will be the sum of these three solutions. This is the same method that was discussed in dealing with Dirichlet problems on rectangular domains. (See the remarks following Example 1.) In the next example we solve the Dirichlet problem when $g \equiv 0$ and $h \equiv 0$.

▶ **Example 3**   The base $(z = 0)$ and the top $(z = b)$ of a charge-free cylinder are grounded and therefore are at zero potential. The potential on the lateral surface $(r = a)$ of the cylinder is given by $u(a, \theta, z) = f(\theta, z)$, where $f(\theta, 0) = f(\theta, b) = 0$. Inside the cylinder the potential $u(r, \theta, z)$ satisfies Laplace's equation. Determine the potential u inside the cylinder by finding a solution to the Dirichlet boundary value problem

(37) $$\frac{\partial^2 u}{\partial r^2} + \frac{1}{r}\frac{\partial u}{\partial r} + \frac{1}{r^2}\frac{\partial^2 u}{\partial \theta^2} + \frac{\partial^2 u}{\partial z^2} = 0, \quad 0 \leq r < a, \quad -\pi \leq \theta \leq \pi, \quad 0 < z < b,$$

(38) $$u(a, \theta, z) = f(\theta, z), \quad -\pi \leq \theta \leq \pi, \quad 0 \leq z \leq b,$$

(39) $$u(r, \theta, 0) = u(r, \theta, b) = 0, \quad 0 \leq r < a, \quad -\pi \leq \theta \leq \pi.$$

Solution   Using the method of separation of variables, we first assume

$$u(r, \theta, z) = R(r)T(\theta)Z(z).$$

Substituting into equation (37) and separating out the Z's, we find

(40) $$\frac{R''(r) + (1/r)R'(r)}{R(r)} + \frac{1}{r^2}\frac{T''(\theta)}{T(\theta)} = -\frac{Z''(z)}{Z(z)} = \lambda,$$

where λ can be any constant. Separating further the R's and T's gives

(41) $$\frac{r^2 R''(r) + rR'(r)}{R(r)} - r^2\lambda = -\frac{T''(\theta)}{T(\theta)} = \mu,$$

where μ can also be any constant. From (40) and (41) we obtain the three ordinary differential equations

(42) $\qquad r^2 R''(r) + rR'(r) - (r^2\lambda + \mu)R(r) = 0,$

(43) $\qquad\qquad\qquad\quad T''(\theta) + \mu T(\theta) = 0,$

(44) $\qquad\qquad\qquad\quad Z''(z) + \lambda Z(z) = 0.$

In order for u to be continuous in the cylinder, $T(\theta)$ must be 2π-periodic. Thus let's begin with the eigenvalue problem

(45) $\qquad T''(\theta) + \mu T(\theta) = 0, \qquad -\pi < \theta < \pi,$

(46) $\qquad T(-\pi) = T(\pi) \quad \text{and} \quad T'(-\pi) = T'(\pi).$

In Example 2 we showed that this problem has nontrivial solutions for $\mu = n^2$, $n = 0, 1, 2, \ldots$, that are given by

(47) $\qquad T_n(\theta) = A_n\cos n\theta + B_n\sin n\theta,$

where the A_n's and B_n's are arbitrary constants.

The boundary conditions in (39) imply that $Z(0) = Z(b) = 0$. Therefore, Z must satisfy the eigenvalue problem

(48) $\qquad Z''(z) + \lambda Z(z) = 0, \qquad 0 < z < b,$

(49) $\qquad\qquad\quad Z(0) = Z(b) = 0.$

We have seen this eigenvalue problem several times before. Nontrivial solutions exist for $\lambda = (m\pi/b)^2$, $m = 1, 2, 3, \ldots$ and are given by

(50) $\qquad Z_m(z) = C_m\sin\left(\dfrac{m\pi z}{b}\right),$

where the C_m's are arbitrary constants.

Substituting for μ and λ in equation (42) gives

(51) $\qquad r^2 R''(r) + rR'(r) - \left(r^2\left(\dfrac{m\pi}{b}\right)^2 + n^2\right)R(r) = 0, \qquad 0 \le r < a.$

The reader should verify that the change of variables $s = (m\pi r/b)$ transforms (51) into the **modified Bessel's equation of order n**[†]

(52) $\qquad s^2 R''(s) + sR'(s) - (s^2 + n^2)R(s) = 0, \qquad 0 \le s < \dfrac{m\pi a}{b}.$

[†] The modified Bessel's equation of order n arises in many applications and has been studied extensively. We refer the reader to the text *Special Functions*, by E. D. Raineville, Macmillan Publishing Co., Inc., New York, 1960 for details about its solution.

The modified Bessel's equation of order n has two linearly independent solutions:

$$I_n(s) = \sum_{k=0}^{\infty} \frac{(s/2)^{2k+n}}{k!\,\Gamma(k+n+1)},$$

the **modified Bessel function of the first kind** which remains bounded near zero, and

$$K_n(s) = \lim_{v \to n} \frac{\pi}{2} \frac{I_{-v}(s) - I_v(s)}{\sin v\pi},$$

the **modified Bessel function of the second kind** which becomes unbounded as $s \to 0$. (Recall that Γ is the gamma function discussed in Section 7.6 of the text.) Since u must remain bounded near $s = 0$ we take $I_n(s)$ as the solution to (52) and hence

$$(53) \qquad R_{mn}(r) = D_{mn}I_n\left(\frac{m\pi r}{b}\right), \qquad n = 0, 1, \ldots, \qquad m = 1, 2, \ldots,$$

as the solution to (51) where the D_{mn}'s are arbitrary constants.

If we multiply the functions in (47), (50), and (53), and then sum over m and n, we obtain the following series solution to (37) and (39):

$$(54) \qquad u(r, \theta, z) = \sum_{m=1}^{\infty} a_{m0}I_0\left(\frac{m\pi r}{b}\right)\sin\left(\frac{m\pi z}{b}\right)$$

$$+ \sum_{n=1}^{\infty}\sum_{m=1}^{\infty} (a_{mn}\cos n\theta + b_{mn}\sin n\theta)I_n\left(\frac{m\pi r}{b}\right)\sin\left(\frac{m\pi z}{b}\right),$$

where the a_{mn}'s and b_{mn}'s are arbitrary constants.

The constants in (54) can be obtained by imposing boundary condition (38). Setting $r = a$ and rearranging terms, we have

$$(55) \qquad f(\theta, z) = \sum_{m=1}^{\infty} a_{m0}I_0\left(\frac{m\pi a}{b}\right)\sin\left(\frac{m\pi z}{b}\right)$$

$$+ \sum_{n=1}^{\infty}\left[\sum_{m=1}^{\infty} a_{mn}I_n\left(\frac{m\pi a}{b}\right)\sin\left(\frac{m\pi z}{b}\right)\right]\cos n\theta$$

$$+ \sum_{n=1}^{\infty}\left[\sum_{m=1}^{\infty} b_{mn}I_n\left(\frac{m\pi a}{b}\right)\sin\left(\frac{m\pi z}{b}\right)\right]\sin n\theta.$$

If we let

$$(56) \qquad \frac{\alpha_0(z)}{2} := \sum_{m=1}^{\infty} a_{m0}I_0\left(\frac{m\pi a}{b}\right)\sin\left(\frac{m\pi z}{b}\right),$$

$$(57) \qquad \alpha_n(z) := \sum_{m=1}^{\infty} a_{mn}I_n\left(\frac{m\pi a}{b}\right)\sin\left(\frac{m\pi z}{b}\right), \qquad n = 1, 2, \ldots,$$

$$(58) \qquad \beta_n(z) := \sum_{m=1}^{\infty} b_{mn}I_n\left(\frac{m\pi a}{b}\right)\sin\left(\frac{m\pi z}{b}\right), \qquad n = 1, 2, \ldots,$$

Fourier series and the method of separation of variables are used to solve boundary value problems and initial-boundary value problems for the three classical equations:

Heat equation
$$\frac{\partial u}{\partial t} = \beta \frac{\partial^2 u}{\partial x^2}.$$

Wave equation
$$\frac{\partial^2 u}{\partial t^2} = \alpha^2 \frac{\partial^2 u}{\partial x^2}.$$

Laplace's equation
$$\frac{\partial^2 u}{\partial x^2} + \frac{\partial^2 u}{\partial y^2} = 0.$$

Projects for Chapter 11

A. STEADY-STATE TEMPERATURE DISTRIBUTION IN A CIRCULAR CYLINDER

When the temperature inside a circular cylinder reaches a steady state, the temperature u satisfies Laplace's equation $\Delta u = 0$. If the temperature on the lateral surface $(r = a)$ is kept at zero, the temperature on the top $(z = b)$ is kept at zero, and the temperature on the bottom $(z = 0)$ is given by $u(r, \theta, 0) = f(r, \theta)$, then the steady-state temperature satisfies the boundary value problem

$$\frac{\partial^2 u}{\partial r^2} + \frac{1}{r}\frac{\partial u}{\partial r} + \frac{1}{r^2}\frac{\partial^2 u}{\partial \theta^2} + \frac{\partial^2 u}{\partial z^2} = 0, \quad 0 \le r < a, \quad -\pi \le \theta \le \pi, \quad 0 < z < b,$$

$$u(a, \theta, z) = 0, \quad -\pi \le \theta \le \pi, \quad 0 \le z \le b,$$

$$u(r, \theta, b) = 0, \quad 0 \le r < a, \quad -\pi \le \theta \le \pi,$$

$$u(r, \theta, 0) = f(r, \theta), \quad 0 \le r < a, \quad -\pi \le \theta \le \pi,$$

where $f(a, \theta) = 0$ for $-\pi \le \theta \le \pi$. To find a solution to this boundary value problem, proceed as follows.

(a) Let $u(r, \theta, z) = R(r)T(\theta)Z(z)$. Show that R, T, and Z must satisfy the three ordinary differential equations

$$r^2 R'' + rR' - (r^2\lambda + \mu)R = 0,$$
$$T'' + \mu T = 0,$$
$$Z'' + \lambda Z = 0.$$

(b) Show that $T(\theta)$ has the form

$$T(\theta) = A \cos n\theta + B \sin n\theta$$

for $\mu = n^2$, $n = 0, 1, 2, \ldots$.

      (c) Show that $Z(z)$ has the form

$$Z(z) = C \sinh \beta(b - z)$$

for $\lambda = -\beta^2$, where $\beta > 0$.

      (d) Show that $R(r)$ has the form, for each n,

$$R_n(r) = DJ_n(\beta r),$$

where J_n is the Bessel function of the first kind.

      (e) Show that the boundary conditions require $R(a) = 0$ and so

$$J_n(\beta a) = 0.$$

Hence, for each n, if $0 < \alpha_{n1} < \alpha_{n2} < \cdots < \alpha_{nm} < \cdots$ are the zeros of J_n, then

$$\beta_{nm} = \alpha_{nm}/a.$$

Moreover,

$$R_n(r) = DJ_n(\alpha_{nm}r/a).$$

      (f) Use the preceding results to show that $u(r, \theta, z)$ has the form

$$u(r, \theta, z) = \sum_{n=0}^{\infty} \sum_{m=1}^{\infty} J_n\left(\frac{\alpha_{nm}r}{a}\right)(a_{nm} \cos n\theta + b_{nm} \sin n\theta) \sinh\left(\frac{\alpha_{nm}(b - z)}{a}\right),$$

where a_{nm} and b_{nm} are constants.

      (g) Use the final boundary condition and a double orthogonal expansion involving Bessel functions and trigonometric functions to derive the formulas

$$a_{0m} = \frac{1}{\pi a^2 \sinh(\alpha_{0m}/a)[J_1(\alpha_{0m})]^2} \int_0^a \int_0^{2\pi} f(r, \theta)J_0\left(\frac{\alpha_{0m}r}{a}\right)r\, dr\, d\theta,$$

for $m = 1, 2, 3, \ldots$ and for $n, m = 1, 2, 3, \ldots$,

$$a_{nm} = \frac{2}{\pi a^2 \sinh(\alpha_{nm}/a)[J_{n+1}(\alpha_{nm})]^2} \int_0^a \int_0^{2\pi} f(r, \theta)J_n\left(\frac{\alpha_{nm}r}{a}\right)\cos(n\theta)r\, dr\, d\theta,$$

$$b_{nm} = \frac{2}{\pi a^2 \sinh(\alpha_{nm}/a)[J_{n+1}(\alpha_{nm})]^2} \int_0^a \int_0^{2\pi} f(r, \theta)J_n\left(\frac{\alpha_{nm}r}{a}\right)\sin(n\theta)r\, dr\, d\theta.$$

B. A LAPLACE TRANSFORM SOLUTION OF THE WAVE EQUATION

Laplace transforms can be used to solve certain partial differential equations. To illustrate this technique, consider the initial-boundary value problem

(1)
$$\frac{\partial^2 u}{\partial t^2} = \alpha^2 \frac{\partial^2 u}{\partial x^2}; \qquad 0 < x < \infty, \qquad t > 0,$$

(2)
$$u(0, t) = h(t), \qquad t > 0,$$

(3)
$$u(x, 0) = 0, \qquad 0 < x < \infty,$$

(4)
$$\frac{\partial u}{\partial t}(x, 0) = 0, \qquad 0 < x < \infty,$$

(5)
$$\lim_{x \to \infty} u(x, t) = 0, \qquad t \ge 0.$$

This problem arises in studying a semi-infinite string that is initially horizontal and at rest and where one end is being moved vertically. Let $u(x, t)$ be the solution to (1)–(5). For each x, let

$$U(x, s) := \mathscr{L}\{u(x, t)\}(x, s) = \int_0^\infty e^{-st} u(x, t) \, dt.$$

(a) Using the fact that

$$\mathscr{L}\left\{\frac{\partial^2 u}{\partial x^2}\right\} = \frac{\partial^2}{\partial x^2} \mathscr{L}\{u\},$$

show that $U(x, s)$ satisfies the equation

(6)
$$s^2 U(x, s) = \alpha^2 \frac{\partial^2 U}{\partial x^2}, \qquad 0 < x < \infty.$$

(b) Show that the general solution to (6) is

$$U(x, s) = A(s) e^{-sx/\alpha} + B(s) e^{sx/\alpha},$$

where $A(s)$ and $B(s)$ are arbitrary functions of s.

(c) Since $u(x, t) \to 0$ as $x \to \infty$ for all $0 \le t < \infty$, we have $U(x, s) \to 0$ as $x \to \infty$. Use this fact to show that the $B(s)$ in part (b) must be zero.

(d) Using equation (2), show that

$$A(s) = F(s) = \mathscr{L}\{f\}(s),$$

where $A(s)$ is given in part (b).

(e) Use the results of parts (b), (c), and (d) to obtain a formal solution to (1)–(5).

Appendix
A. Newton's Method

To solve an equation $g(x) = 0$, we must find the point or points where the graph of $y = g(x)$ meets the x-axis. One procedure for approximating a solution is **Newton's method.**

To motivate Newton's method geometrically, let $\tilde{x}$ be a root of $g(x) = 0$ and let x_1 be our guess at the value of $\tilde{x}$. If $g(x_1) = 0$, we are done. If $g(x_1) \neq 0$, then we are off by some amount that we call dy (see Figure A.1 on page A-2). Then

$$\frac{dy}{dx} = g'(x_1),$$

and so

(1) $$dx = \frac{dy}{g'(x_1)}.$$

Now $dx = x_1 - x_2$ or $x_2 = x_1 - dx$, where x_2 is at the point where the tangent line through $(x_1, g(x_1))$ intersects the x-axis (Figure A.1). Using equation (1) and the fact that $dy = g(x_1)$, we obtain

$$x_2 = x_1 - \frac{dy}{g'(x_1)} = x_1 - \frac{g(x_1)}{g'(x_1)},$$

which we use as the next approximation to the root $\tilde{x}$.

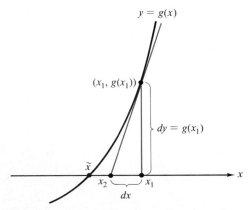

Figure A.1 Tangent line approximation of root

Repeating this process with x_2 in place of x_1, we obtain the next approximation x_3 to the root $\tilde{x}$. In general, we find the next approximation x_{n+1} by the formula

$$(2) \qquad x_{n+1} = x_n - \frac{g(x_n)}{g'(x_n)}, \qquad n = 1, 2, \dots .$$

The process is illustrated in Figure A.2.

If the initial guess x_1 is sufficiently close to a root $\tilde{x}$, then the sequence of iterations $\{x_n\}_{n=1}^{\infty}$ usually converges to the root $\tilde{x}$. However, if we make a bad guess for x_1, then the process may lead away from $\tilde{x}$.

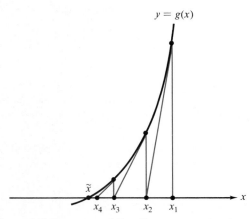

Figure A.2 Sequence of iterations converging to root

▶ *Example 1*   Find a root to four decimal places of the equation

(3) $x^3 + 2x - 4 = 0.$

Solution   Setting $g(x) = x^3 + 2x - 4$, we find that $g'(x) = 3x^2 + 2$ is positive for all x. Hence, g is increasing and has at most one zero. Furthermore, since $g(1) = -1$ and $g(2) = 8$, this zero must lie between 1 and 2. Thus we begin the procedure with the initial guess $x_1 = 1.5$. For $g(x) = x^3 + 2x - 4$, equation (2) becomes

(4) $x_{n+1} = x_n - \dfrac{x_n^3 + 2x_n - 4}{3x_n^2 + 2}, \qquad n = 1, 2, \dots.$

With $x_1 = 1.5$, equation (4) gives

$$x_2 = 1.5 - \frac{(1.5)^3 + 2(1.5) - 4}{3(1.5)^2 + 2} = 1.5 - \frac{2.375}{8.75} \approx 1.22857.$$

Using x_2 to compute x_3 and so on, we find

$$x_3 = 1.18085,$$
$$x_4 = 1.17951,$$
$$x_5 = 1.17951,$$

where we have rounded off the computations to five decimal places. Since x_4 and x_5 agree to four decimal places and we are uncertain of the fifth decimal place because of roundoff, we surmise that the root $\tilde{x}$ of (3) agrees with 1.1795 to four decimal places. Indeed,

$$g(1.1795) = -0.00005 \dots \quad \text{and} \quad g(1.1796) = 0.00056 \dots,$$

and so $1.1795 < \tilde{x} < 1.1796$. Consequently, $\tilde{x} = 1.1795 \dots$. ◀

Observe that Newton's method transforms the problem of finding a root to the equation $g(x) = 0$ into the problem of finding a fixed point for the function $h(x) = x - g(x)/g'(x)$; that is, finding a number x such that $x = h(x)$.

There are several theorems that give conditions that guarantee that the sequence of iterations $\{x_n\}_{n=1}^{\infty}$ defined by (2) will converge to a zero of $g(x)$. We mention one such result.

CONVERGENCE OF NEWTON'S METHOD

Theorem 1. Suppose that a zero $\tilde{x}$ of $g(x)$ lies in the interval (a, b), and that in this interval

$$g'(x) > 0 \quad \text{and} \quad g''(x) > 0.$$

If we select x_1 so that $\tilde{x} < x_1 < b$, then the sequence of iterations defined by (2) will decrease to $\tilde{x}$.

We do not give a proof of this theorem, but refer the reader to an introductory numerical analysis text such as *Numerical Analysis*, Third Edition, by R. Burden and J. Faires, Prindle, Weber, and Schmidt, Boston, 1985.

B. Simpson's Rule

A useful procedure for approximating the value of a definite integral is **Simpson's rule.**
    Let the interval $[a, b]$ be divided into $2n$ equal parts and let $x_0, x_1, \ldots, x_{2n}$ be the points of the partition, that is,

$$x_k := a + kh, \qquad k = 0, 1, \ldots, 2n,$$

where $h := (b - a)/(2n)$. If

$$y_k := f(x_k), \qquad k = 0, 1, \ldots, 2n,$$

then the Simpson's rule approximation I_S for the value of the definite integral

$$\int_a^b f(x)\, dx$$

is given by

(1)
$$I_S = \frac{h}{3} \left[y_0 + 4y_1 + 2y_2 + 4y_3 + \cdots + 2y_{2n-2} + 4y_{2n-1} + y_{2n} \right]$$

$$= \frac{h}{3} \sum_{k=1}^{n} (y_{2k-2} + 4y_{2k-2} + y_{2k}).$$

If

$$E := \int_a^b f(x)\, dx - I_S$$

is the error that results from using Simpson's rule to approximate the value of the definite integral, then

(2) $$|E| \leq \frac{(b-a)}{180} h^4 M,$$

where $M := \max|f^{(4)}(x)|$ for all x in $[a, b]$.

▶ **Example 1** Use Simpson's rule with $n = 4$ to approximate the value of the definite integral

(3) $$\int_0^1 \frac{1}{1 + x^2} \, dx.$$

Solution Here $h = \frac{1}{8}$, $x_k = k/8$, $k = 0, 1, \ldots, 8$, and

$$y_k = (1 + x_k^2)^{-1} = \frac{1}{1 + \dfrac{k^2}{64}} = \frac{64}{64 + k^2}.$$

By Simpson's rule (1), we find

$$I_S = \frac{\left(\frac{1}{8}\right)}{3} \left[1 + 4\left(\frac{64}{64+1}\right) + 2\left(\frac{64}{64+4}\right) + 4\left(\frac{64}{64+9}\right) \right.$$

$$+ 2\left(\frac{64}{64+16}\right) + 4\left(\frac{64}{64+25}\right) + 2\left(\frac{64}{64+36}\right)$$

$$\left. + 4\left(\frac{64}{64+49}\right) + \left(\frac{64}{64+64}\right) \right] = 0.76456.$$

Hence, the value of the definite integral is (3) is approximately $I_S = 0.76456$. ◀

For a more detailed discussion of Simpson's rule, we refer the reader to a numerical analysis book such as *Numerical Analysis*, Third Edition, by R. Burden and J. Faires, Prindle, Weber, and Schmidt, Boston, 1985.

C. Cramer's Rule

When a system of n linear equations in n unknowns has a unique solution, determinants can be used to obtain a formula for the unknowns. This procedure is called **Cramer's rule.** When n is small, these formulas provide a simple procedure for solving the system.

Suppose that, for a system of n linear equations in n unknowns,

(1)
$$
\begin{aligned}
a_{11}x_1 + a_{12}x_2 + \cdots + a_{1n}x_n &= b_1, \\
a_{21}x_1 + a_{22}x_2 + \cdots + a_{2n}x_n &= b_2, \\
\vdots \qquad \vdots \qquad\qquad \vdots \qquad \vdots & \\
a_{n1}x_1 + a_{n2}x_2 + \cdots + a_{nn}x_n &= b_n,
\end{aligned}
$$

the coefficient matrix

(2)
$$
\mathbf{A} := \begin{bmatrix}
a_{11} & a_{12} & \cdots & a_{1n} \\
a_{21} & a_{22} & \cdots & a_{2n} \\
\vdots & \vdots & & \vdots \\
a_{n1} & a_{n2} & \cdots & a_{nn}
\end{bmatrix}
$$

has a nonzero determinant. Then Cramer's rule gives the solutions

(3)
$$
x_i = \frac{\det \mathbf{A}_i}{\det \mathbf{A}}, \qquad i = 1, 2, \ldots, n,
$$

where $\mathbf{A}_i$ is the matrix obtained from $\mathbf{A}$ by replacing the ith column of $\mathbf{A}$ by the column vector

$$\begin{bmatrix} b_1 \\ b_2 \\ \vdots \\ b_n \end{bmatrix}$$

consisting of the constants on the right-hand side of system (1). Again, we assume det $\mathbf{A} \neq 0$.

▶ *Example 1*   Use Cramer's rule to solve the system

$$x_1 + 2x_2 - x_3 = 0,$$
$$2x_1 + x_2 + x_3 = 9,$$
$$x_1 - x_2 - 2x_3 = 1.$$

Solution   We first compute the determinant of the coefficient matrix:

$$\Delta = \det \begin{bmatrix} 1 & 2 & -1 \\ 2 & 1 & 1 \\ 1 & -1 & -2 \end{bmatrix} = 12.$$

Using formula (3), we find

$$x_1 = \frac{1}{12} \det \begin{bmatrix} 0 & 2 & -1 \\ 9 & 1 & 1 \\ 1 & -1 & -2 \end{bmatrix} = \frac{48}{12} = 4,$$

$$x_2 = \frac{1}{12} \det \begin{bmatrix} 1 & 0 & -1 \\ 2 & 9 & 1 \\ 1 & 1 & -2 \end{bmatrix} = \frac{-12}{12} = -1,$$

$$x_3 = \frac{1}{12} \det \begin{bmatrix} 1 & 2 & 0 \\ 2 & 1 & 9 \\ 1 & -1 & 1 \end{bmatrix} = \frac{24}{12} = 2. \ \blacktriangleleft$$

For a more detailed discussion of Cramer's rule, we refer the reader to an introductory linear algebra text such as *Elementary Linear Algebra* by A. Wayne Roberts, Benjamin/Cummings Publishing Co., Menlo Park, California, 1982.

Answers to Odd-Numbered Problems

CHAPTER 1

Exercises 1.1, page 5

1. ODE, 2nd order, ind. var. t, dep. var. x, linear.
3. ODE, 4th order, ind. var. x, dep. var. y, linear.
5. ODE, 1st order, ind. var. x, dep. var. y, nonlinear.
7. ODE, 2nd order, ind. var. x, dep. var. y, linear.
9. ODE, 1st order, ind. var. t, dep. var. y, nonlinear.
11. PDE, 2nd order, ind. var. t, r, dep. var. N.
13. ODE, 2nd order, ind. var. x, dep. var. y, nonlinear.

Exercises 1.2, page 14

3. Yes.   5. No.   7. Yes.   9. No.   11. Yes.
13. Yes.   19. The left-hand side is always ≥ 3.
21. (a) ± 1.   (b) $1 \pm \sqrt{6}$.   23. Yes.   25. Yes.
27. No.

Exercises 1.3, page 23

1.

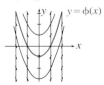

Figure B.1

3.

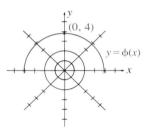

Figure B.2

5.

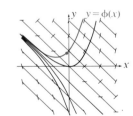

Figure B.3

7.

x_n	0.1	0.2	0.3	0.4	0.5
y_n	4.000	3.998	3.992	3.985	3.975

(rounded to three decimal places).

9.

x_n	0.1	0.2	0.3	0.4	0.5
y_n	1.100	1.220	1.362	1.528	1.721

(rounded to three decimal places).

11.

x_n	y_n
1.1	0.1
1.2	0.209
1.3	0.32463
1.4	0.44409
1.5	0.56437

13.

n	$\phi(1)$
1	1
2	1.06185
4	1.13920
8	1.19157

15.

x_n	y_n
1.1	−0.9
1.2	−0.81654
1.3	−0.74572
1.4	−0.68480
1.5	−0.63176
1.6	−0.58511
1.7	−0.54371
1.8	−0.50669
1.9	−0.47335
2.0	−0.44314

17. 1.46635.   **21.** $T(1) \approx 82.694,\ T(2) \approx 76.446$.

CHAPTER 2

Exercises 2.2, page 37

1. Yes.   **3.** Yes.   **5.** No.
7. $y = (x^3 - 3x + C)^{1/3}$.   **9.** $y = Ce^{x^3}$.
11. $y = \tan(x^3 + C)$.   **13.** $4v^2 = 1 + Cx^{-8/3}$.
15. $y = 1/(C - e^{\cos x})$.
17. $y = \sqrt{4 - x^3/3}$.   **19.** $y = -3e^{-1-\cos x}$.
21. $y = \sin^2 x + 2\sin x$.
23. $y = \tan[\pi/3 - \ln(\cos x)]$.   **25.** $y = 4e^{x^3/3} - 1$.
27. (a) $y(x) = \int_0^x e^{t^2}\, dt$.

(b) $y(x) = \left(1 + 3\int_0^x e^{t^2}\, dt\right)^{1/3}$.

(c) $y(x) = \tan\left(\int_0^x \sqrt{1 + \sin t}\, dt + \pi/4\right)$.

(d) $y(0.5) \approx 1.381$.
29. (d) $\partial f/\partial y$ is not continuous at $(0, 0)$.
33. 281 kg.   **35.** (a) 82.2 min.   (b) 31.8 min.
(c) Never attains desired temperature.

Exercises 2.3, page 48

1. Exact.   **3.** Neither.   **5.** Exact.
7. $y = (C - 3x)/(x^2 - 1)$.   **9.** Not exact.
11. $\sin x \cos y + x^2 - y^2 = C$.

13. $r = (C - e^\theta)\sec\theta$.
15. $y = [C + e^t(t - 1)]/(1 + e^t)$.
17. $x^2 + xy^2 - \sin(x + y) - e^y = C$.
19. $y = (e - x)/(e^x - 1)$.   **21.** $y = -2/(te^t + 2)$.
23. $\sin x - x \cos x = \ln y + 1/y + \pi - 1$ (equation is separable, not exact).
25. (a) $x\cos(xy) + g(y)$;   (b) $xe^{xy} - x^4 + g(y)$, where g is a function of y only.
27. (c) $y = x^2/(C - x)$.   (d) Yes, $y \equiv 0$.
33. (a) $x^2 + 4y^2 = c$.
  (b) $2y^2 \ln y - y^2 + 2x^2 = c$.
  (c) $2x^2 + y^2 = c$.

Exercises 2.4, page 56

1. Linear.   **3.** Linear.
5. Exact, linear with x as dep. var.   **7.** Linear.
9. $y = e^{3x}/2 + Ce^x$.   **11.** $y = x^3e^{-4x}/3 + Ce^{-4x}$.
13. $r = \sin\theta + C\cos\theta$.   **15.** $x = y^3 + Cy^{-2}$.
17. $y = x^3/6 - 2x^2/5 + x + Cx^{-3}$.
19. $y = xe^x - x$.   **21.** $y = 1 - x\cot x + \csc x$.
23. $y = x^{-1}/2 - 2x^{-3}$.   **25.** $x = e^{4y}/2 + Ce^{2y}$.
27. (a) $y = e^{-x^2}\int_2^x e^{t^2}\, dt + e^{4-x^2}$.

(b) $y = \left(\int_0^x \sqrt{1 + \sin^2 t}\, dt\right)\Big/\sqrt{1 + \sin^2 x}$.

(c) $y(2.5) \approx 0.297$.
29. (a) $y = x - 1 + Ce^{-x}$.
  (b) $y = x - 1 + 2e^{-x}$.
  (c) $y = x/3 - 1/9 + Ce^{-3x}$.
  (d) $y = \begin{cases} x - 1 + 2e^{-x}, & 0 \le x \le 2, \\ x/3 - 1/9 + (4e^6/9 + 2e^4)e^{-3x}, & 2 < x. \end{cases}$
  (e)

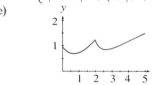

Figure B.4

31. (a) $y = x$ is only solution in a neighborhood of $x = 0$.
  (b) $y = -3x + Cx^2$ satisfies $y(0) = 0$ for any C.

35. $x(t) = \dfrac{1}{2} - \dfrac{2\cos(\pi t/12)}{4 + (\pi/12)^2} - \dfrac{(\pi/12)\sin(\pi t/12)}{4 + (\pi/12)^2}$
$+ \left(\dfrac{19}{2} + \dfrac{2}{4 + (\pi/12)^2}\right)e^{-2t}$.

Exercises 2.5, page 64

1. Integrating factor depending on x alone.
3. Integrating factor depending on y alone.
5. Integrating factor depending on y alone.
7. $\mu = x^{-2}$; $y^2/2 - y/x + 3x = C$, or $x \equiv 0$.
9. Exact; $x^2y^3 + x - \ln|y| = C$.
11. $\mu = x^{-2}$ (also linear); $y = x^4/3 - x \ln|x| + Cx$.
13. $\mu = xy$; $x^2y^3 - 2x^3y^2 = C$.

15. $\mu(z) = \exp\left(\int H(z)\,dz \right)$; $z = xy$.

17. $\mu = x^2y^{-2}$; $x^2 + y^2 = Cy$.

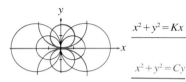

$x^2 + y^2 = Kx$

$x^2 + y^2 = Cy$

Figure B.5

Exercises 2.6, page 74

1. $y' = G(ax + by)$.   3. Linear coefficients.
5. Bernoulli.   7. Linear coefficients.
9. $x^3 + 3xy^2 = C$.
11. $y = x/(\ln|x| + C)$ or $y \equiv 0$.
13. $\sqrt{1 + y^2/x^2} = \ln|x| + C$.
15. $(x^2 - 4y^2)^3 x^2 = C$.   17. $y = (x + C)^2/4 - x$.
19. $y = -x - 2 + \tan(x + C)$.
21. $y^{-2} = Ce^{-2x} - e^{2x}/2$ or $y \equiv 0$.
23. $y = 5x^2/(x^5 + C)$ or $y \equiv 0$.
25. $y^{-2} = 2x^2\ln|x| + Cx^2$ or $y \equiv 0$.
27. $y = x^2/(C - x)$ or $y \equiv 0$.
29. $(y + 2)^2 + 2(x + 1)(y + 2) - 3(x + 1)^2 = C$.
31. $(x + 6/5)^2 + (x + 6/5)(y + 8/5) - (y + 8/5)^2 = C$.
33. $y = 4x + (3 + Ce^{4x})/(1 - Ce^{4x})$.
35. $\ln[(y + 3)^2 + 3(x - 1)^2]$
$\quad + (2/\sqrt{3})\arctan[(y + 3)/\sqrt{3}(x - 1)] = C$.
37. $y^{-2} = -e^{2x}/2 + Ce^{-2x}$ or $y \equiv 0$.
39. $\ln[(y + 1)^2 + (x - 1)^2]$
$\quad + 2 \arctan[(y + 1)/(x - 1)] = C$.
41. $(x - y + 2)^2 = Ce^{2x} + 1$.
45. $(y - 4x)^2(y + x)^3 = C$.

Review Problems, page 78

1. $e^x + ye^{-y} = C$.   3. $x^2y - x^3 + y^{-2} = C$.
5. $y + x \sin(xy) = C$.   7. $y = (7 \ln|x| + C)^{-1/7}$.
9. $(x^2 + 4y^2)^3 x^2 = C$.   11. $\tan(x - y) + x = C$.

13. $y = -(x^2/2)\cos(2x) + (x/4)\sin(2x) + Cx$.
15. $y = 2x + 3 - (x + C)^2/4$.
17. $y = 2/(1 + Ce^{2x})$ or $y \equiv 0$.
19. $y^2 = x^2 + Cx^3$ or $x \equiv 0$.
21. $xy - x^2 - x + y^2/2 - 4y = C$.
23. $y^2 + 2xy - x^2 = C$.
25. $x^2y^{-2} - 2xy^{-1} - 4xy^{-2} = C$ or $y \equiv 0$.
27. $[(y - 4)^2 - 3(x - 3)^2]\{[\sqrt{3}(x - 3) + (y - 4)]/$
$\quad [\sqrt{3}(x - 3) - (y - 4)]\}^{1/\sqrt{3}} = C$.
29. $x^4y^3 - 3x^3y^2 + x^4y^2 = C$.
31. $y = -x^3/2 + 7x/2$.   33. $y = -x - 2 + 3e^{-x}$.
35. $y = -2x\sqrt{2x^2 - 1}$.
37. $\ln[(y - 2)^2 + 2(x - 1)^2]$
$$+ \sqrt{2} \arctan\left[\frac{y - 2}{\sqrt{2}(x - 1)}\right] = \ln 2.$$
39. $y = \sqrt{(19x^4 - 1)/2}$.

CHAPTER 3

Exercises 3.2, page 95

1. $50 - 45e^{-2t/25}$ kg, 5.07 min.
3. $(0.4)(100 - t) - (39 \times 10^{-8})(100 - t)^4$ L; 19.96 min.
5. 0.0097%; 73.24 hr.
7. $(0.2)(1 - e^{-3t/125})$ g/cm^3; 28.88 sec.
9. 4804; 27,000.   11. 5769; 6000.
13. 1527; 1527.   15. 1 hr; 2 hr.   17. 11.7%.
19. 31,606 yr.

Exercises 3.3, page 104

1. $82.9°$F; $90.5°$F; 1:09 P.M.   3. $60.5°$F; $65.9°$F; $89.5°$F; $84.1°$F.   5. 30.2 min.   7. $148.6°$F.
9. 20.7 min.   11. 22.6 min.
13. $T - M = C(T + M) \exp[2 \arctan(T/M) - 4M^3kt]$; for T near M, $M^4 - T^4 \approx 4M^3(M - T)$, and so $dT/dt \approx k_1(M - T)$, where $k_1 = 4M^3k$.

Exercises 3.4, page 112

1. $(0.981)t + (0.0981)e^{-10t} - 0.0981$ m; 1019 sec.
3. 18.6 sec.
5. $4.91t + 22.55 - 22.55e^{-2t}$ m; 97.3 sec.
7. 241 sec.
9. $95.65t + 956.5e^{-t/10} - 956.5$ m; 13.2 sec.
11. $e^{kv}(kv - mg)^{mg} = e^{v_0k}(kv_0 - mg)^{mg} e^{-k^2x/m}$.
13. 16.48 sec; 1535 m.   15. $(\omega_0 - T/k)e^{-kt/I} + T/k$.
17. 1164 sec.

19. $2636e^{-t/20} + 131.8t - 2636$ m; 1.768 sec.
21. $5e^{-2t}/2 + 6t - 5/2$; 6 m/sec.   **23.** Sailboat B.

Exercises 3.5, page 125

3.

h	"e"
1	3
0.1	2.720551414
0.01	2.718304482
0.001	2.718282082
0.0001	2.718281824

7.

x_n	y_n
1.1	0.10450
1.2	0.21668
1.3	0.33382
1.4	0.45300
1.5	0.57135

9.

x_n	y_n
0.2	0.61784
0.4	1.23864
0.6	1.73653
0.8	1.98111
1.0	1.99705
1.2	1.88461
1.4	1.72447
1.6	1.56184
1.8	1.41732
2.0	1.29779

11. $\phi(1) \approx y(1; 2^{-3}) = 1.25494$.
13. $\phi(1) \approx y(1; 2^{-3}) = 0.71698$.
15. $\phi(1) \approx y(1; 2^{-4}) = 0.71647$.

17.

x_n	$y_n\,(h = 0.2)$	$y_n\,(h = 0.1)$	$y_n\,(h = 0.025)$
0.1		-1	0.06250
0.2	-3	1	0.00391
0.3		-1	0.00024
0.4	9	1	0.00002
0.5		-1	0.00000
0.6	-27	1	0.00000
0.7		-1	0.00000
0.8	81	1	0.00000
0.9		-1	0.00000
1.0	-243	1	0.00000

We conclude that step size can dramatically affect convergence.

19.

x_n	y_n		
	$r = 1.5$	$r = 2$	$r = 3$
0.25	1.58286	1.53125	1.39063
0.5	2.35144	2.04960	1.55347
0.75	3.26750	2.44003	1.62885
1.0	4.25316	2.68675	1.66999
1.25	5.21675	2.82920	1.69406
1.5	6.08340	2.90804	1.70858
1.75	6.81163	2.95080	1.71748
2.0	7.39215	2.97377	1.72298
2.25	7.83709	2.98604	1.72640
2.5	8.16851	2.99257	1.72852
2.75	8.41036	2.99605	1.72985
3.0	8.58432	2.99790	1.73067
3.25	8.70817	2.99889	1.73119
3.5	8.79571	2.99941	1.73151
3.75	8.85729	2.99969	1.73171
4.0	8.90044	2.99983	1.73184
4.25	8.93062	2.99991	1.73192
4.5	8.95168	2.99995	1.73197
4.75	8.96637	2.99997	1.73200
5.0	8.97660	2.99999	1.73202

21.

Time	T_n		
	$K = 0.2$	$K = 0.4$	$K = 0.6$
Midnight	65.0000	65.0000	65.0000
4 A.M.	69.1639	68.5644	68.1299
8 A.M.	71.4836	72.6669	73.6678
Noon	72.9089	75.1605	76.9783
4 P.M.	72.0714	73.5977	74.7854
8 P.M.	69.8095	69.5425	69.2832
Midnight	68.3852	67.0500	65.9740

Exercises 3.6, page 137

1. $y_{n+1} = y_n + h \cos(x_n + y_n)$
$$- \frac{h^2}{2} \sin(x_n + y_n)[1 + \cos(x_n + y_n)].$$

3. $y_{n+1} = y_n + h(x_n - y_n) + \frac{h^2}{2}(1 - x_n + y_n)$
$$- \frac{h^3}{6}(1 - x_n + y_n) + \frac{h^4}{24}(1 - x_n + y_n).$$

5. Order 2: $\phi(1) \approx 1.3725$; order 4: $\phi(1) \approx 1.3679$.
7. -11.7679.
9. $h = 0.5$: $\phi(1) \approx 0.75085$; $h = 0.25$: $\phi(1) \approx 0.75007$.
11. 1.36789.   **13.** 0.70139 with $h = 0.25$.

15.

x_n	y_n
0.5	0.21462
1.0	0.13890
1.5	-0.02668
2.0	-0.81879
2.5	-1.69491
3.0	-2.99510

19. $v(3) \approx 0.24193$ with $h = 0.0625$.
21. $z(1) \approx 2.87080$ with $h = 0.0625$.

CHAPTER 4

Exercises 4.2, page 161

1. Linear, homogeneous, variable coefficients.
3. Nonlinear.
5. Linear, nonhomogeneous, variable coefficients.
7. Linear, nonhomogeneous, constant coefficients.
9. (a) $3x^2 - 8x + 2$.   (b) 0.
    (c) $(r^2 - 4r + 3)e^{rx}$.
13. (a) $e^{2x}\cos x - 3e^{2x}\sin x$.
    (b) $-4e^{2x}\cos x + 3e^{2x}\sin x$.
15. Unique solution on $(0, \infty)$.
17. Unique solution on $(0, 3)$.
19. Does not apply; equation is nonlinear.
21. Unique solution on $(-\infty, 1)$.
23. $D^2 - 3D + 2$.
25. $D^2 + x$.   **27.** (a) 2.   (b) $x \sin x + \cos x$.
31. $-2; 1; 5$.
33. (a) $3x^2 - x^3$.   (b) $6x + 3x^2 - 2x^3$.
    (c) $3x^2 + 2x^3$.   (d) $6x + 3x^2 - 2x^3$.
    (e) $D^2 + D - 2$.   (f) $6x + 3x^2 - 2x^3$.
35. (a) $(D + 4)(D - 1)$.   (b) $(D + 3)(D - 2)$.
    (c) $(2D - 1)(D + 5)$.   (d) $(D + \sqrt{2})(D - \sqrt{2})$.

Exercises 4.3, page 173

1. Lin. indep.; $-7e^{-x}$.   **3.** Lin. indep.; $-e^{4x}$.
5. Lin. dep.; 0.
7. (b) $y = c_1 e^{2x} + c_2 e^{3x}$.   (c) $y = e^{2x} - 2e^{3x}$.
9. (b) $y = c_1 e^x \cos 2x + c_2 e^x \sin 2x$.
    (c) $y = 2e^x \cos 2x - e^x \sin 2x$.
11. (b) $y = c_1 x^2 + c_2 x^{-1}$.   (c) $y = -3x^2 + x^{-1}$.
13. (c) $\phi(x) = (1)e^x + (-1)(e^x - e^{-6x})$,
    $\phi(x) = (-3)e^x + (1)(3e^x + e^{-6x})$.
15. The function in (b) cannot be a Wronskian of solutions.
17. (a) True.   (b) False.   **19.** $W = Cxe^{-x}$.

Exercises 4.4, page 178

1. $y = e^{2x}$.   **3.** $y = x^{-3}$.   **5.** $y = x + 1$.
7. $xw'' + 2xw' + (x + 1)w = 0$.
9. (a) $y = x \int x^{-2} e^{x^2/2}\, dx$.
    (b) $y = \sum_{n=0}^{\infty} \frac{x^{2n}}{n!2^n(2n-1)} = -1 + \frac{x^2}{2} + \frac{x^4}{24} + \cdots$.
13. (a) $y = (1 - 2x^2) \int (1 - 2x^2)^{-2} e^{x^2}\, dx$.
    (b) $y = (3x - 2x^3) \int (3x - 2x^3)^{-2} e^{x^2}\, dx$.
15. (a) $y = x \int x^{-2}(1 - x^2)^{-1}\, dx$.
    (b) $y = (3x^2 - 1) \int (3x^2 - 1)^{-2}(1 - x^2)^{-1}\, dx$.
    (c) $y = (5x^3 - 3x) \int (5x^3 - 3x)^{-2}(1 - x^2)^{-1}\, dx$.
17. (b) $g(2) \approx 10.7983$.

Exercises 4.5, page 185

1. $c_1 e^x + c_2 e^{-2x}$.   **3.** $c_1 e^{4x} + c_2 x e^{4x}$.
5. $c_1 e^{(-1-\sqrt{5})x/2} + c_2 e^{(-1+\sqrt{5})x/2}$.   **7.** $ce^{-10x/7}$.
9. $c_1 e^{x/2} + c_2 e^{-2x/3}$.   **11.** $c_1 e^{-5x/2} + c_2 x e^{-5x/2}$.
13. $3 - e^{-x}$.   **15.** $e^{-x} - 2xe^{-x}$.
17. $(\sqrt{3}/2)[e^{(1+\sqrt{3})x} - e^{(1-\sqrt{3})x}]$.
19. $(2 - x)e^{2x-2}$.   **21.** $c_1 e^{-x} + c_2 e^x + c_3 e^{6x}$.
23. $c_1 e^{2x} + c_2 e^{-2x} + c_3 x e^{-2x}$.
25. (b) $c_1 x^{-3} + c_2 x^2$.   (c) $c_1 x^{-2} + c_2 x^{-2}\ln x$.
29. $b = 2000\sqrt{3}$, multiply by the factor $\sqrt{2}$.

Exercises 4.6, page 192

1. $c_1 \cos x + c_2 \sin x$.   **3.** $c_1 e^{3x}\cos x + c_2 e^{3x}\sin x$.
5. $c_1 e^{-2x}\cos \sqrt{2}x + c_2 e^{-2x}\sin \sqrt{2}x$.
7. $c_1 e^{-x/2}\cos(\sqrt{5}x/2) + c_2 e^{-x/2}\sin(\sqrt{5}x/2)$.
9. $c_1 e^{-2x}\cos 2x + c_2 e^{-2x}\sin 2x$.
11. $c_1 e^{-5x} + c_2 x e^{-5x}$.
13. $c_1 e^{-x}\cos 2x + c_2 e^{-x}\sin 2x$.
15. $c_1 e^{(3+\sqrt{53})x/2} + c_2 e^{(3-\sqrt{53})x/2}$.
17. $c_1 e^{x/2}\cos(3\sqrt{3}x/2) + c_2 e^{x/2}\sin(3\sqrt{3}x/2)$.
19. $c_1 e^{-2x/3}\cos(\sqrt{23}x/3) + c_2 e^{-2x/3}\sin(\sqrt{23}x/3)$.
21. $2e^{-x}\cos x + 3e^{-x}\sin x$.
23. $(\sqrt{2}/4)[e^{(2+\sqrt{2})x} - e^{(2-\sqrt{2})x}]$.   **25.** $e^x - 3xe^x$.
27. $e^x \sin x - e^x \cos x$.
29. (a) $c_1 e^{-x} + c_2 e^x \cos \sqrt{2}x + c_3 e^x \sin \sqrt{2}x$.
    (b) $c_1 e^{2x} + c_2 e^{-2x}\cos 3x + c_3 e^{-2x}\sin 3x$.

33. (a) $x(t) = 30e^{-3t}\cos 4t + 20e^{-3t}\sin 4t$ cm.
 (b) $2/\pi$.
 (c) Decreases the frequency of oscillation, introduces the factor e^{-3t}, causing the solution to decay to zero.
35. $b \geq 2\sqrt{Ik}$

Exercises 4.7, page 198

1. $c_1 + c_2 e^{-x} + x$. **3.** $c_1 e^{2x} + c_2 e^{-x} + x - 1$.
5. $e^{-x}(c_1\cos\sqrt{3}x + c_2\sin\sqrt{3}x) + \sin 2x$.
7. $e^{t/2}[c_1\cos(\sqrt{3}t/2) + c_2\sin(\sqrt{3}t/2)] + \cos t$.
9. $c_1 e^{\sqrt{2}x} + c_2 e^{-\sqrt{2}x} + \tan x$.
11. (a) $5\cos x$. **(b)** $\cos x - e^{2x}$.
 (c) $4\cos x + 6e^{2x}$.
13. (a) $(1 + \tan x)/2$. **(b)** $1 - x/2$.
 (c) $\tan x - 3x/2 + 2$. **(d)** $-(x + \tan x)/8$.
15. (a) $v = e^x/2 + c_1 e^{-x}$.
 (b) $y = -e^x/2 + c_1 e^{-x} + c_2 e^{2x}$.

Exercises 4.8, page 208

1. $y_p \equiv -10$. **3.** e^{2x}. **5.** $3x^2 - 2x + 4$.
7. $\sin 2x$. **9.** $xe^x/2 + 3e^x/4$.
11. $-(x\sin x + \cos x)/2$. **13.** $4x^2 e^x$.
15. $x^2/9 + 4x/27 + 2/27 + e^x/4$.
17. $c_1 e^x + c_2 e^{-x} + 11x - 1$.
19. $c_1 e^x + c_2 e^{-2x} - x^2/2 + x/2 - 7/4$.
21. $c_1 e^x + c_2 e^{2x} + e^x(\cos x - \sin x)/2$.
23. $e^{-x}(c_1\cos x + c_2\sin x) + (xe^{-x}\sin x)/2$.
25. $c_1 e^{2x} + c_2 x e^{2x} + x^3 e^{2x}/6$.
27. $e^{-2x}(c_1\cos x + c_2\sin x) + e^{-x}/2 - (1/65)\sin 2x$
$+ (8/65)\cos 2x$.
29. $e^{-x/2}[c_1\cos(\sqrt{3}x/2) + c_2\sin(\sqrt{3}x/2)] + \sin x$
$+ e^x(-x^2/3 + 2x/3 - 4/9)$.
31. $e^x - 1$. **33.** $e^{-x} + \sin x - \cos x$.
35. $(3/20)\sin 2x - (1/20)\cos 2x - (3/10)\cos x$
$- (1/10)\sin x$.
37. $e^{-4x}/60 + 1/12 - e^x/10 - e^{2x}/6 + 7e^{3x}/6$.
39. $-(1/2)\sin x - e^{2x}/3 + 3e^x/4 + 7e^{-x}/12$.
41. $(Ax^2 + Bx)\sin x + (Cx^2 + Dx)\cos x + E10^x$.
43. $e^x(A\cos x + B\sin x) + Cx^2 + Dx + E$.
45. $e^{2x}(Ax^4 + Bx^3 + Cx^2)$.
47. $Axe^x + B + C\sin x + D\cos x$.
49. $(1/5)\cos x + (2/5)\sin x$.
51. (a) $-e^{-x}\sin 2x - 2e^{-x}\cos 2x + 2$.
 (b) $e^{-x}(c_1\sin 2x + c_2\cos 2x)$.
 (c) $y = \begin{cases} -e^{-x}\sin 2x - 2e^{-x}\cos 2x + 2, & 0 \leq x \leq 3\pi/2, \\ (-1 - e^{3\pi/2})e^{-x}\sin 2x + (-2 - e^{3\pi/2})e^{-x}\cos 2x, & x \geq 3\pi/2. \end{cases}$

55. (a) $x(t) = A\sin\beta t + B\cos\beta t + x_h$, where
$$A = \frac{k - m\beta^2}{(k - m\beta^2)^2 + b^2\beta^2},$$
$$B = \frac{-b\beta}{(k - m\beta^2)^2 + b^2\beta^2} \quad \text{and}$$
$$x_h = e^{-bt/2m}\left[c_1\cos\left(\frac{\sqrt{4mk - b^2}}{2m}t\right)\right.$$
$$\left. + c_2\sin\left(\frac{\sqrt{4mk - b^2}}{2m}t\right)\right].$$
 (b) In each case, $x_h \to 0$ as $t \to \infty$. So as $t \to \infty$, $x(t)$ approaches the function $x_p(t) = A\sin\beta t + B\cos\beta t$.

Exercises 4.9, page 215

1. $c_1\cos 2x + c_2\sin 2x$
$- (1/4)(\cos 2x)\ln|\sec 2x + \tan 2x|$.
3. $c_1 e^{2x} + c_2 e^{-x} + e^{3x}/4$.
5. $c_1 e^x + c_2 x e^x + x e^x \ln|x|$.
7. $c_1\cos 4x + c_2\sin 4x + (x/4)\sin 4x$
$+ (1/16)(\cos 4x)\ln|\cos 4x|$.
9. $c_1\cos 2x + c_2\sin 2x$
$+ [(\cos 2x)\ln|\csc 2x + \cot 2x| - 1]/4$.
11. $c_1\cos x + c_2\sin x + e^{3x}/10 - 1$
$- (\cos x)\ln|\sec x + \tan x|$.
13. $c_1\cos 2x + c_2\sin 2x + (1/24)\sec^2 2x - 1/8$
$+ (1/8)(\sin 2x)\ln|\sec 2x + \tan 2x|$.
15. $c_1\cos x + c_2\sin x - x^2 + 3 + 3x\sin x$
$+ 3(\cos x)\ln|\cos x|$.
17. $c_1\cos 2x + c_2\sin 2x - e^x/5$
$- (1/2)(\cos 2x)\ln|\sec 2x + \tan 2x|$.
19. $c_1 e^x + c_2(x + 1) - x^2$.
21. $c_1(5x - 1) + c_2 e^{-5x} - x^2 e^{-5x}/10$.
23. $c_1 x^{-1/2}\cos x + c_2 x^{-1/2}\sin x + x^{1/2}$.
25. $y = e^{1-x} - e^{x-1} + \frac{e^x}{2}\int_1^x \frac{e^{-t}}{t}dt - \frac{e^{-x}}{2}\int_1^x \frac{e^t}{t}dt$,
$y(2) \approx -1.93$.

Exercises 4.10, page 220

1. $c_1 x + c_2 x^{-7}$. **3.** $c_1 x^2 + c_2 x^2 \ln x$.
5. $c_1 x\cos(2\ln x) + c_2 x\sin(2\ln x)$.
7. $c_1 x^2\cos(\sqrt{2}\ln x) + c_2 x^2\sin(\sqrt{2}\ln x)$.

9. $c_1 x + c_2 x^{-3} + x^3/12$.

11. $c_1 x^3 + c_2 x^{-2} - (1/5)x^{-2} \ln x + 1$

13. $x^{-1}[c_1 \cos(2 \ln x) + c_2\sin(2 \ln x)] + x^2/13$.

15. $c_1\cos(\ln x) + c_2\sin(\ln x) - (1/4)(\ln x)^2\cos(\ln x)$
$$+ (1/4)(\ln x)\sin(\ln x).$$

17. $x - 3x^4$.

19. $-6x + 2x^3 + 3(\ln x)^2 + 8 \ln x + 10$.

21. No.   **23.** $c_1 x^{-2} + c_2(-x)^{-1/2}$.

25. $c_1 x + c_2 x \ln x + c_3 x^3$.

27. $c_1 x^{-1} + c_2 x^{-1}\ln x + c_3 x^4$.

31. $c_1 x + c_2 x \ln x$.

Exercises 4.11, page 226

1. $2x^2 + c_1\ln x + c_2$.

3. $x^5/5 + 2c_1 x^3/3 + c_1^2 x + c_2$ or $y \equiv c$.

5. $\ln|\sec(x + c_1)| + c_2$.

7. $\pm(1/3)(2x + c_1)^{3/2} + c_2$.

9. $x = c_1 + c_2 y + y^3/6$ or $y \equiv c$.

11. $y = c_1\tan(c_2 - c_1 x/2)$ or
$$y = c_1(c_2 e^{c_1 x} - 1)/(c_2 e^{c_1 x} + 1)$$ or
$$y = 2(x + c)^{-1}.$$

13. $x^4/4 - 3x^5/10 + x^6/18 + c_1 + c_2 x^3$.

15. $y - \ln|e^y + c_1| = c_1 x + c_2$ for $c_1 \neq 0$ or
$$y = -\ln(c - x)$$ for $x < c$ or $y \equiv c$.

17. $x = c_2 - c_1 y + (1 + c_1^2)\ln|y + c_1|$ or $y \equiv c$.

19. $(a/2)(e^{x/a} + e^{-x/a}) = a \cosh(x/a)$.

Review Problems, page 229

1. $c_1 e^{-9x} + c_2 e^x$.

3. $c_1 e^{x/2}\cos(3x/2) + c_2 e^{x/2}\sin(3x/2)$.

5. $c_1 e^{5x/3} + c_2 x e^{5x/3}$.

7. $c_1 e^{-x/3}\cos(x/6) + c_2 e^{-x/3}\sin(x/6)$.

9. $c_1 e^{7x/4} + c_2 x e^{7x/4}$.

11. $x^{1/2}\{c_1\cos[(\sqrt{19}/2)\ln x] + c_2\sin[(\sqrt{19}/2)\ln x]\}$.

13. $x = c_1 + c_2 y - y^3/6$ or $y \equiv c$.

15. $c_1 e^{-2x} + c_2 e^{-x} + c_3 e^{-x/3}$.

17. $e^{-x}[c_1 + c_2\cos \sqrt{2}x + c_3\sin \sqrt{2}x]$.

19. $c_1 e^{-3x} + c_2 e^{x/2} + c_3 x e^{x/2}$.

21. $c_1 e^{3x/2}\cos (\sqrt{19}x/2) + c_2 e^{3x/2}\sin (\sqrt{19}x/2) - e^x/5$
$$+ x^2 + 6x/7 + 4/49.$$

23. $c_1\cos 4x + c_2\sin 4x$
$$- (1/16)(\cos 4x)\ln|\sec 4x + \tan 4x|.$$

25. $c_1 e^{3x/2} + c_2 x e^{3x/2} + e^{3x}/9 + e^{5x}/49$.

27. $c_1 x + c_2 x^{-2} - 2x^{-2}\ln x + x \ln x$.

29. $e^{x/2}\cos x - 6e^{x/2}\sin x$.

31. $2e^x\cos 3x - (7/3)e^x\sin 3x - \sin 3x$.

33. $-e^{-x} - 3e^{5x} + e^{8x}$.

35. $\cos x + 2 \sin x + x \sin x + (\cos x)\ln|\cos x|$.

37. $c_1 e^{-x} + c_2(x - 1)$.

39. $c_1 x + c_2\left[\dfrac{x}{2} \ln\left(\dfrac{1 + x}{1 - x}\right) - 1\right]$.

CHAPTER 5

Exercises 5.1, page 243

1. $x(t) = (1/4)\cos 8t - (1/16)\sin 8t =$
$$(\sqrt{17}/16)\sin(8t + \phi), \quad \text{where}$$
$$\phi = \pi - \arctan 4 \approx 1.816; \sqrt{17}/16; \pi/4; 4/\pi.$$

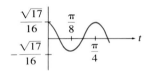

Figure B.6

3. $x(t) = (1/4)\sin 4t - (1/2)\cos 4t =$
$$(\sqrt{5}/4)\sin(4t + \phi), \quad \text{where} \quad \phi = -\arctan 2 \approx$$
$$-1.107; \text{ down at } 0.823 \text{ ft/sec.}$$

5. $x(t) = (1/10)\cos(7\sqrt{10}t/5)$
$$- (1/(14\sqrt{10}))\sin(7\sqrt{10}t/5)$$
$$\approx (0.103)\sin(4.427t + 1.793); 1.369 \text{ sec.}$$

7. $x(t) = (1/2)\cos 4t - (1/8)\sin 4t$
$$= (\sqrt{17}/8)\sin(4t + \phi),$$
$$\text{where} \quad \phi = \pi - \arctan 4 \approx 1.816; 0.331 \text{ sec.}$$

Exercises 5.2, page 251

1. $b = 6$: $x(t) = e^{-3t}\cos \sqrt{7}t + (3/\sqrt{7})e^{-3t}\sin \sqrt{7}t =$
$$(4/\sqrt{7})e^{-3t}\sin(\sqrt{7}t + \phi), \quad \text{where}$$
$$\phi = \arctan \sqrt{7}/3 \approx 0.723.$$

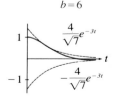

Figure B.7

$b = 8$: $x(t) = (1 + 4t)e^{-4t}$.

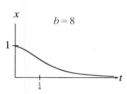

Figure B.8

$b = 10$: $x(t) = (4/3)e^{-2t} - (1/3)e^{-8t}$.

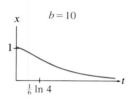

Figure B.9

3. $k = 20$: $x(t) = [(1 + \sqrt{5})/2]e^{(-5+\sqrt{5})t}$
$\qquad + [(1 - \sqrt{5})/2]e^{(-5-\sqrt{5})t}$.

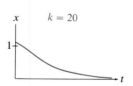

Figure B.10

$k = 25$: $x(t) = (1 + 5t)e^{-5t}$.

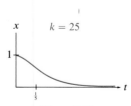

Figure B.11

$k = 30$: $x(t) = e^{-5t}\cos\sqrt{5}t + \sqrt{5}e^{-5t}\sin\sqrt{5}t = \sqrt{6}e^{-5t}\sin(\sqrt{5}t + \phi)$, where
$\phi = \arctan(1/\sqrt{5}) \approx 0.421$.

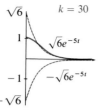

Figure B.12

5. $x(t) = -(1/6)e^{-2t}\cos(2\sqrt{31}t)$
$\qquad - [5/(12\sqrt{31})]e^{-2t}\sin(2\sqrt{31}t)$
$\qquad = [\sqrt{149}/(12\sqrt{31})]e^{-2t}\sin(2\sqrt{31}t + \phi)$,
where $\phi = \pi + \arctan(2\sqrt{31}/5) \approx 4.290$;
$[\sqrt{149}/(12\sqrt{31})]e^{-2t}$; $\pi/\sqrt{31}$; $\sqrt{31}/\pi$.
7. 0.242 m. 9. 0.080 sec.
11. Relative extrema at $t = [\pi/3 + n\pi - \arctan(\sqrt{3}/2)]/(2\sqrt{3})$ for $n = 0, 1, 2, \ldots$; but touches curves $\pm\sqrt{7/12}e^{-2t}$ at $t = [\pi/2 + m\pi - \arctan(\sqrt{3}/2)]/(2\sqrt{3})$ for $m = 0, 1, 2, \ldots$.

Exercises 5.3, page 257

1. $x_p(t) = (0.08)\cos 2t + (0.06)\sin 2t$
$\qquad = (0.1)\sin(2t + \theta)$,
where $\theta = \arctan(4/3) \approx 0.927$.
3. $x(t) = -(120/901)e^{-t/2}\cos(\sqrt{255}t/2)$
$\qquad - [8/(53\sqrt{255})]e^{-t/2}\sin(\sqrt{255}t/2)$
$\qquad + (4/\sqrt{901})\sin(2t + \theta)$, where
$\theta = \arctan 30 \approx 1.537$; $\sqrt{63.5}/(2\pi) \approx 1.268$.
5. $M(\gamma) = 1/\sqrt{(1 - 4\gamma^2)^2 + 4\gamma^2}$.

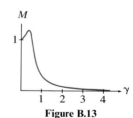

Figure B.13

7. $x(t) = \cos 3t + (1/3)t \sin 3t$.

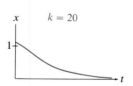

Figure B.14

9. (a) $x(t) = -[F_0/(k - m\gamma^2)]\cos(\sqrt{k/m}t)$
$\qquad + [F_0/(k - m\gamma^2)]\cos \gamma t$
$\qquad = (F_0/[m(\omega^2 - \gamma^2)])(\cos \gamma t - \cos \omega t)$.
(c) $x(t) = \sin 8t \sin t$.

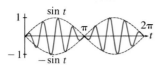

Figure B.15

Exercises 5.4, page 264

1. $I(t) = (19/\sqrt{21})[e^{(-25 - 5\sqrt{21})t/2} - e^{(-25 + 5\sqrt{21})t/2}]$.
3. $I_p(t) = (4/51)\cos 20t - (1/51)\sin 20t$; resonance frequency is $5/\pi$.
5. $M(\gamma) = 1/\sqrt{(100 - 4\gamma^2)^2 + 100\gamma^2}$.

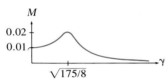

Figure B.16

7. $L = 35$ henrys, $R = 10$ ohms, $C = 1/15$ farads, and $E(t) = 50 \cos 10t$ volts.

Exercises 5.5, page 273

1. $c_1(2)^n + c_2(4)^n$.
3. $c_1[-(3/2) + (\sqrt{13}/2)]^n + c_2[-(3/2) - (\sqrt{13}/2)]^n$.
5. $c_1 11^{n/2}\cos n\theta + c_2 11^{n/2}\sin n\theta$, where
$\quad \theta = \arctan(\sqrt{2}/3)$.
7. $c_1(-5)^n + c_2 n(-5)^n$.
9. $c_1 2^n\cos(n\theta) + c_2 2^n\sin(n\theta)$, where $\theta = \arctan\sqrt{15}$.
11. $c_1\cos(n\pi/2) + c_2\sin(n\pi/2) + (1/2)n^2 - n$.
13. $c_1 + c_2(-1)^n - (1/2)\cos(3n)$
$\qquad + (1/2)[\sin 6/(1 - \cos 6)]\sin(3n)$.
15. $c_1(-1)^n + c_2(-5)^n + (1/21)2^n$.
17. $c_1 2^n + c_2 n2^n + (1/8)n^2 2^n$.
19. $c_1(-1)^n + c_2 2^n + c_3(-2)^n$.
21. $c_1 + c_2 2^{n/2}\cos(n\pi/4) + c_3 2^{n/2}\sin(n\pi/4)$.
23. $5^{n/2}\cos n\theta$, where $\theta = \pi - \arctan 2$.
25. $(n/6)3^n - (1/4)3^n + 1/4$.
27. $1 + (7/3)n - (1/2)n^2 + (1/6)n^3$.
31. Unstable for $h \geq 1$.

Exercises 5.6, page 280

1. i	t_i	$y(t_i)$
1	0.250	0.96924
2	0.500	0.88251
3	0.750	0.75486
4	1.000	0.60656

3. i	t_i	$y(t_i)$
1	1.250	0.80761
2	1.500	0.71351
3	1.750	0.69724
4	2.000	0.74357

5. $y(8) \approx 24.01540$.
7. $y(1) \approx x_1(1, 2^{-2}) = 2.76925$.
9. $t_{n+1} = t_n + h, \quad n = 0, 1, 2, \ldots$;
$$x_{n+1,i} = x_{n,i} + \frac{h}{2}\,[f_i(t_n, x_{n,1}, \ldots, x_{n,m})$$
$$+ f_i(t_n + h, x_{n,1} + hf_1(t_n, x_{n,1}, \ldots, x_{n,m}),$$
$$\ldots, x_{n,m} + hf_m(t_n, x_{n,1}, \ldots, x_{n,m}))],$$
$$i = 1, 2, \ldots, m.$$

11. i	t_i	$x_1(t_i) \approx H(t_i)$
1	0.5	0.09573
2	1.0	0.37389
3	1.5	0.81045
4	2.0	1.37361
5	2.5	2.03111
6	3.0	2.75497
7	3.5	3.52322
8	4.0	4.31970
9	4.5	5.13307
10	5.0	5.95554

13. Yes, yes.

CHAPTER 6

Exercises 6.2, page 296

1. $(-\infty, 0)$.   **3.** $(3\pi/2, 5\pi/2)$.   **5.** $(0, \infty)$.
7. Lin. indep.; $48e^{7x}$.   **9.** Lin. dep.; 0.
11. Lin. indep.; $(3/2)x^{-5/2}$.   **13.** Lin. indep.; $12x^4$
15. $c_1 e^{3x} + c_2 e^{-x} + c_3 e^{-4x}$.   **17.** $c_1 x + c_2 x^2 + c_3 x^3$.
19. (a) $c_1 e^x + c_2 e^{-x}\cos 2x + c_3 e^{-x}\sin 2x + x^2$.
(b) $-e^x + e^{-x}\sin 2x + x^2$.
21. (a) $c_1 x + c_2 x \ln x + c_3 x(\ln x)^2 + \ln x$.
(b) $3x - x \ln x + x(\ln x)^2 + \ln x$.
23. (a) $2 \sin x - x$.   **(b)** $4x - 6 \sin x$.
29. (b) Let $f_1(x) = |x - 1|$ and $f_2(x) = x - 1$.

Exercises 6.3, page 304

1. $c_1 e^x + c_2 e^{-x} + c_3 e^{3x}$.
3. $c_1 e^{-x} + c_2 e^{-2x/3} + c_3 e^{x/2}$.
5. $c_1 e^{-x} + c_2 e^{(-1+\sqrt{7})x} + c_3 e^{(-1-\sqrt{7})x}$.
7. $c_1 e^{-x} + c_2 e^x\cos x + c_3 e^x\sin x$.
9. $c_1 e^{3x} + c_2 xe^{3x} + c_3 x^2 e^{3x}$.
11. $c_1 e^x + c_2 e^{-3x} + c_3 xe^{-3x}$.

13. $c_1\cos\sqrt{2}x + c_2x\cos\sqrt{2}x + c_3\sin\sqrt{2}x$
$$+ c_4x\sin\sqrt{2}x.$$

15. $c_1e^x + c_2xe^x + c_3e^{-3x} + (c_4 + c_5x)e^{-x}\cos 2x$
$$+ (c_6 + c_7x)e^{-x}\sin 2x.$$

17. $(c_1 + c_2x + c_3x^2)e^x + c_4e^{2x} + c_5e^{-x/2}\cos(\sqrt{3}x/2)$
$$+ c_6e^{-x/2}\sin(\sqrt{3}x/2) + (c_7 + c_8x + c_9x^2)e^{-3x}\cos x$$
$$+ (c_{10} + c_{11}x + c_{12}x^2)e^{-3x}\sin x.$$

19. $e^{-x} - e^{-2x} + e^{-4x}.$ **21.** $e^{2x} - \sqrt{2}e^x\sin\sqrt{2}x.$

25. $c_1e^{1.120x} + c_2e^{0.296x} + c_3e^{-0.520x} + c_4e^{-2.896x}.$

27. (a) $\{x, x^{-1}, x^2\}.$ **(b)** $\{x, x^2, x^{-1}, x^{-2}\}.$
   (c) $\{x, x^2\cos(3\ln x), \ x^2\sin(3\ln x)\}.$

29. (b) $x(t) = c_1\cos t + c_2\sin t + c_3\cos\sqrt{6}t$
$$+ c_4\sin\sqrt{6}t.$$
   (c) $y(t) = 2c_1\cos t + 2c_2\sin t - (c_3/2)\cos\sqrt{6}t$
$$- (c_4/2)\sin\sqrt{6}t.$$
   (d) $x(t) = (3/5)\cos t + (2/5)\cos\sqrt{6}t.$
$$y(t) = (6/5)\cos t - (1/5)\cos\sqrt{6}t.$$

Exercises 6.4, page 312

1. $D^3.$ **3.** $D - 5.$ **5.** $(D - 2)(D - 1).$
7. $[(D + 1)^2 + 4]^3.$ **9.** $D^4(D - 1)^3(D^2 + 16)^2.$
11. $c_3\cos 2x + c_4\sin 2x + c_5.$
13. $c_3xe^{3x} + c_4x^2 + c_5x + c_6.$ **15.** $c_3x^2 + c_4x + c_5.$
17. $c_3xe^{-x}\cos x + c_4xe^{-x}\sin x + c_5x^2 + c_6x + c_7.$
19. $c_2x + c_3x^2 + c_6x^2e^x.$
21. $c_1xe^x + c_2 + c_3x + c_4x^2.$ **23.** $c_1x^2e^{-2x}.$
25. $c_1e^x + c_2e^{3x} + c_3e^{-2x} - (1/6)xe^x + (1/6)x^2$
$$+ (5/18)x + 37/108.$$
27. $c_1e^x + c_2e^{-2x} + c_3xe^{-2x} - (1/6)x^2e^{-2x}.$
29. $c_1e^{2x} + c_2e^{-3x}\cos 2x + c_3e^{-3x}\sin 2x$
$$+ (5/116)xe^{-3x}\cos 2x - (1/58)xe^{-3x}\sin 2x$$
$$- (1/26)x - 1/676.$$
31. $-2e^{3x} + e^{-2x} + x^2 - 1.$ **33.** $x^2e^{-2x} - x^2 + 3.$
39. $x(t) = (2/5)\cos t + (4/5)\sin t - (2/5)\cos\sqrt{6}t$
$$+ (\sqrt{6}/5)\sin\sqrt{6}t - \sin 2t;$$
$$y(t) = (4/5)\cos t + (8/5)\sin t + (1/5)\cos\sqrt{6}t$$
$$- (\sqrt{6}/10)\sin\sqrt{6}t - (1/2)\sin 2t.$$

Exercises 6.5, page 318

1. $(1/2)x^2 + 2x.$ **3.** $e^{2x}/16.$
5. $\ln(\sec x) - (\sin x)\ln(\sec x + \tan x).$
7. $c_1x + c_2x^2 + c_3x^3 - (1/24)x^{-1}.$
9. $-(1/2)e^x\int e^{-x}g(x)\,dx + (1/6)e^{-x}\int e^xg(x)\,dx$
$$+ (1/3)e^{2x}\int e^{-2x}g(x)\,dx.$$
11. $c_1x + c_2x^{-1} + c_3x^3 - x\sin x - 3\cos x$
$$+ 3x^{-1}\sin x.$$

Review Problems, page 321

1. (a) $(0, \infty).$ **(b)** $(-4, -1), (-1, 1), (1, \infty).$
5. (a) $e^{-5x}(c_1 + c_2x) + e^{2x}(c_3 + c_4x + c_5x^2)$
$$+ (\cos x)(c_6 + c_7x) + (\sin x)(c_8 + c_9x).$$
   (b) $c_1 + c_2x + c_3x^2 + c_4x^3 + e^x(c_5 + c_6x)$
$$+ (e^{-x}\cos\sqrt{3}x)(c_7 + c_8x)$$
$$+ (e^{-x}\sin\sqrt{3}x)(c_9 + c_{10}x).$$
7. (a) $D^3.$ **(b)** $D^2(D - 3).$
   (c) $[D^2 + 4]^2.$ **(d)** $[(D + 2)^2 + 9]^3.$
   (e) $D^3(D + 1)^2(D^2 + 4)(D^2 + 9).$
9. $c_1x + c_2x^5 + c_3x^{-1} - (1/21)x^{-2}.$

CHAPTER 7

Exercises 7.2, page 335

1. $\dfrac{1}{s^2}, \quad s > 0.$ **3.** $\dfrac{1}{s - 6}, \quad s > 6.$

5. $\dfrac{s}{s^2 + 4}, \quad s > 0.$ **7.** $\dfrac{2}{(s + 1)^2 + 4}, \quad s > -1.$

9. $e^{-2s}\left(\dfrac{2s + 1}{s^2}\right), \quad s > 0.$

11. $\dfrac{1 - e^{6-3s}}{s - 2} + \dfrac{e^{-3s}}{s}, \quad s > 2.$

13. $\dfrac{5}{s} - \dfrac{1}{s - 2} + \dfrac{12}{s^3}, \quad s > 2.$

15. $\dfrac{2}{s^3} - \dfrac{3}{s^2} - \dfrac{6}{(s + 1)^2 + 9}, \quad s > 0.$

17. $\dfrac{6}{(s - 3)^2 + 36} - \dfrac{6}{s^4} + \dfrac{1}{s - 1}, \quad s > 3.$

19. $\dfrac{s + 2}{(s + 2)^2 + 3} - \dfrac{2}{(s + 2)^3}, \quad s > -2.$

21. Piecewise continuous.
23. Piecewise continuous.
25. Continuous (hence piecewise continuous).
27. Neither.   **29.** All but functions (c), (e), and (h).

Exercises 7.3, page 341

1. $\dfrac{6}{s^3} - \dfrac{1}{s - 2}.$ **3.** $\dfrac{s + 1}{(s + 1)^2 + 9} + \dfrac{1}{s - 6} - \dfrac{1}{s}.$

5. $\dfrac{2}{(s + 2)^2 + 4} + \dfrac{2}{(s - 3)^3}.$

7. $\dfrac{24}{s^5} - \dfrac{24}{s^4} + \dfrac{12}{s^3} - \dfrac{4}{s^2} + \dfrac{1}{s}.$ **9.** $\dfrac{(s - 2)^2 - 25}{[(s - 2)^2 + 25]^2}.$

11. $\dfrac{b}{s^2 - b^2}$.   **13.** $\dfrac{1}{2s} - \dfrac{s}{2(s^2 + 4)}$.

15. $\dfrac{3s}{4(s^2 + 1)} + \dfrac{s}{4(s^2 + 9)}$.

17. $\dfrac{s}{2(s^2 + 9)} - \dfrac{s}{2(s^2 + 49)}$.

19. $\dfrac{n + m}{2[s^2 + (n + m)^2]} + \dfrac{m - n}{2[s^2 + (m - n)^2]}$.

21. $\dfrac{s - a}{(s - a)^2 + b^2}$.   **23.** $\dfrac{s^2 + 2}{s(s^2 + 4)}$.

25. (a) $\dfrac{s^2 - b^2}{(s^2 + b^2)^2}$.   (b) $\dfrac{2s^3 - 6sb^2}{(s^2 + b^2)^3}$.

29. $\dfrac{1}{s^2 + 6s + 10}$.

Exercises 7.4, page 353

1. $\sin 2t$.   **3.** $e^{-t}\cos 3t$.   **5.** $(3/16)e^{-5t/2}t^2$.
7. $2e^{-2t}\cos 3t + 4e^{-2t}\sin 3t$.
9. $(1/2)e^{-t/4}\cos(\sqrt{47}t/4) - (5/2\sqrt{47})e^{-t/4}\sin(\sqrt{47}t/4)$.

11. $\dfrac{2}{s + 1} - \dfrac{3}{s - 2}$.   **13.** $\dfrac{1}{(s + 1)^2} - \dfrac{2}{s}$.

15. $-\dfrac{3}{s + 1} + \dfrac{(s - 1) + 2}{(s - 1)^2 + 4}$.

17. $-\dfrac{5}{6s} + \dfrac{11}{10(s - 2)} - \dfrac{4}{15(s + 3)}$.

19. $\dfrac{1}{17}\left[\dfrac{1}{(s - 3)} - \dfrac{s + 1}{(s + 1)^2 + 1} - \dfrac{4}{(s + 1)^2 + 1}\right]$.

21. $3e^t - 2e^{-3t}$.   **23.** $-e^{-3t} + 2te^{-3t} + 6e^{-t}$.
25. $8e^{2t} - e^{-t}\cos 2t + 3e^{-t}\sin 2t$.
27. $-2/3 + 5e^{-t}/6 + 4e^{2t}/15 - 13e^{-3t}/30$.
29. $-7e^{-t}/4 - 3te^{-t}/2 + 7e^{t}/4$.
31. $F_1(s) = F_2(s) = F_3(s) = 1/s^2$,
$\mathcal{L}^{-1}\{1/s^2\}(t) = f_3(t) = t$.
33. $e^{5t}/t - e^{-2t}/t$.   **35.** $2(\cos t - \cos 3t)/t$.

39. $\dfrac{A}{s} + \dfrac{B}{s - 1} + \dfrac{C}{s + 2}$,   where

$A = \dfrac{2s + 1}{(s - 1)(s + 2)}\Big|_{s=0} = \dfrac{-1}{2}$,

$B = \dfrac{2s + 1}{s(s + 2)}\Big|_{s=1} = 1$,

$C = \dfrac{2s + 1}{s(s - 1)}\Big|_{s=-2} = \dfrac{-1}{2}$.

41. $2e^{-t} - 4e^{3t} + 5e^{2t}$.

Exercises 7.5, page 362

1. $e^{2t} - 3e^{-t}$.   **3.** $-e^{-3t} + 3te^{-3t}$.
5. $t^2 + \cos t - \sin t$.   **7.** $2e^{3t} + e^{2t}\sin t$.
9. $3te^t - e^{-6t}$.   **11.** $2 - t + e^{2-t} + 2e^{t-2}$.

13. $t + \pi \cos t + \sin t$.   **15.** $\dfrac{-s^2 + s - 1}{(s^2 + 1)(s - 1)(s - 2)}$.

17. $\dfrac{-s^3 - s^2 + 2}{s^3(s^2 + 6)}$.   **19.** $\dfrac{2s^3 - 17s^2 + 28s - 12}{(s - 1)^3(s - 5)}$.

21. $\dfrac{s^3 + s^2 + 2s}{(s^2 + 1)(s - 1)^2}$.

23. $\dfrac{s^3 + 2s^2 + s + 2se^{-3s} + e^{-3s}}{s^2(s - 1)(s + 1)}$.

25. $2e^t - \cos t - \sin t$.   **27.** $2 + e^t - 3e^{-2t} + e^{-3t}$.
29. $(3a - b)e^t/2 + (b - a)e^{3t}/2$.
31. $(3a - b + 6)e^{2t} + 6te^{2t} + 3t^2e^{2t}$
$\qquad\qquad\qquad + (b - 2a - 6)e^{3t}$.
35. $t^2/2$.   **37.** $2 - t$.   **39.** $e(t) = -a \cos \sqrt{k/I}t$.
41. $e(t) =$
$\qquad (-2aI/\sqrt{4Ik - \mu^2})e^{-\mu t/2I}\sin(\sqrt{4Ik - \mu^2}t/2I)$.

Exercises 7.6, page 374

1. $(e^{-s} - e^{-4s})/s$.   **3.** $2e^{-s}/s^3$.   **5.** $e^{-s}(s + 1)/s^2$.
7. $e^{3-3s}/(s - 1)$.   **9.** $(t - 3)u(t - 3)$.
11. $\frac{1}{2}[\sin 2(t - 1)]u(t - 1)$.
13. $e^{-2(t - 3)}[\cos(t - 3) - 2 \sin(t - 3)]u(t - 3)$.
15. $(7e^{6-2t} - 6e^{3-t})u(t - 3)$.
17. $\sin t + \sin 2t + \cos 2t$
$\qquad\qquad + [(1/2)\sin 2t - \sin t]u(t - 2\pi)$.

19. $\dfrac{1 - 2se^{-2s} - e^{-2s}}{s^2(1 - e^{-2s})}$.

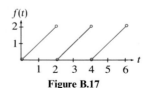

Figure B.17

21. $\dfrac{1}{1 - e^{-2s}}\left[\dfrac{1 - e^{-s-1}}{s + 1} + \dfrac{e^{-s} - e^{-2s}}{s}\right]$.

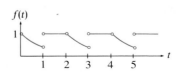

Figure B.18

23. $\dfrac{1}{s(1 + e^{-as})}$.   25. $\dfrac{1}{(s^2 + 1)(1 - e^{-\pi s})}$.

27. $\sin t + [1 - \cos(t - 3)]u(t - 3)$.

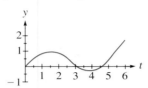

Figure B.19

29. $t + [4 - t + \sin(t - 2) - 2\cos(t - 2)]u(t - 2)$.

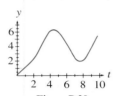

Figure B.20

31. $e^{-t}\cos t + 2e^{-t}\sin t$
$\qquad + (1/2)[1 - e^{2\pi - t}(\cos t + \sin t)]u(t - 2\pi)$
$\qquad - (1/2)[1 - e^{4\pi - t}(\cos t + \sin t)]u(t - 4\pi)$.

33. $e^{-t} + e^{-2t}$
$\qquad + (1/2)[e^{-3t} + 2e^{-2(t+1)} - e^{-(t+4)}]u(t - 2)$.

35. $e^{-t} + e^{t} + \dfrac{1}{2}\sum\limits_{n=1}^{4} (-1)^{n+1}[e^{n-t} + e^{t-n} - 2]u(t - n)$.

41. $\dfrac{e^{t-n}}{6} - \dfrac{e^{-t}}{2}\left[\dfrac{e^{n+1} - 1 - e^{n+2} + e^{2}}{e - 1}\right]$
$\qquad + \dfrac{e^{-2t}}{3}\left[\dfrac{e^{2n+2} - 1 - e^{2n+3} + e^{3}}{e^{2} - 1}\right]$,

for $n < t < n + 1$.

43. $\sum\limits_{n=1}^{\infty} \dfrac{1}{s^n} = \dfrac{1}{s - 1}$.

45. $\sum\limits_{n=1}^{\infty} \dfrac{(-1)^{n+1}}{2ns^{2n}} = \dfrac{1}{2}\ln(1 + 1/s^2)$.

47. (a) $\sqrt{\pi/s}$.   (b) $105\sqrt{\pi}/(16s^{9/2})$.

55. $e^{t} - e^{-t} + (1/2)[e^{t-1} + e^{1-t} - 2]u(t - 1)$
$\qquad - (1/2)[e^{t-4} + e^{4-t} - 2]u(t - 4)$.

Exercises 7.7, page 385

1. $\int_0^t g(v)\sin(t - v)\,dv + \sin t$.

3. $\int_0^t g(v)e^{2v - 2t}\sin(t - v)\,dv + e^{-2t}\cos t + 3e^{-2t}\sin t$.

5. $e^{-t} - e^{-2t}$.   7. $(1/16)\sin 2t - (t/8)\cos 2t$.

9. $t - \sin t$.   11. $(2/3)e^{-2t} + (1/3)e^{t}$.

13. $(s^2 + 1)^{-1}(s - 1)^{-1}$.   15. $2 - 2\cos t$.

17. $\cos t + \sin t - 1$.   19. 3.

21. $e^{-t/2}\cos(\sqrt{3}t/2) - (1/\sqrt{3})e^{-t/2}\sin(\sqrt{3}t/2)$.

23. $(s^2 + 9)^{-1}$; $(1/3)\sin 3t$.

25. $(s - 3)^{-1}(s + 2)^{-1}$; $(1/5)e^{3t} - (1/5)e^{-2t}$.

27. $[(s + 1)^2 + 4]^{-1}$; $(1/2)e^{-t}\sin 2t$.   29. $t^2/2$.

Exercises 7.8, page 392

1. 1.   3. -1.   5. 1.   7. $3e^{-s}$.   9. e^{-s}.

11. $e^{3 - 3s}$.   13. $-(\sin t)u(t - \pi)$.

15. $e^{t} + e^{-3t} + (1/4)(e^{t-1} - e^{3-3t})u(t - 1)$
$\qquad - (1/4)(e^{t-2} - e^{6-3t})u(t - 2)$.

17. $(4/3)e^{2t} - (1/2)e^{t} - (5/6)e^{-t}$
$\qquad + (e^{2t-2} - e^{1-t})u(t - 1)$.

19. $e^{-t} - e^{-5t} + (e/4)(e^{1-t} - e^{5-5t})u(t - 1)$.

21. $\sin t + (\sin t)u(t - 2\pi)$.

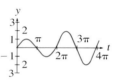

Figure B.21

23. $\sin t + (\sin t)u(t - \pi) + (\sin t)u(t - 2\pi)$.

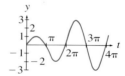

Figure B.22

25. $(1/2)e^{-2t}\sin 2t$.   27. $(1/2)e^{3t}\sin 2t$.

29. The mass remains stopped at $x(t) \equiv 0$, $t > \pi/2$.

35. $\dfrac{L}{6EI}[3\lambda x^2 - x^3 + (x - \lambda)^3 u(x - \lambda)]$.

Review Problems, page 397

1. $\dfrac{3}{s} + e^{-2s}\left[\dfrac{1}{s} - \dfrac{1}{s^2}\right]$.   3. $\dfrac{2}{(s + 9)^3}$.

5. $\dfrac{1}{s - 2} - \dfrac{6}{s^4} + \dfrac{2}{s^3} - \dfrac{5}{s^2 + 25}$.   7. $\dfrac{s^2 - 36}{(s^2 + 36)^2}$.

9. $2e^{-4s}\left[\dfrac{1}{s^3} + \dfrac{4}{s^2} + \dfrac{8}{s}\right]$.   11. $(7/2)t^2 e^{-3t}$.

13. $2e^{t} + 2e^{-2t}\cos 3t + e^{-2t}\sin 3t$.

15. $e^{-2t} + e^{-t} - 2te^{-t}$.

17. $[2e^{t-2} + 2e^{4-2t}]u(t - 2)$.   19. $e^{2t} - e^{5t}$.

21. $-(3/2) + t + t^2/2 + (3/2)e^{-t}\cos t$.

23. $(2/\sqrt{7})e^{-3t/2}\sin(\sqrt{7}t/2) + \{(1/4)$
$\quad -(3/(4\sqrt{7}))e^{-3(t-1)/2}\sin(\sqrt{7}(t-1)/2)$
$\quad -(1/4)e^{-3(t-1)/2}\cos(\sqrt{7}(t-1)/2)\}u(t-1)$.

25. $c[t + te^{-2t} + e^{-2t} - 1]$.

27. $(9/10)e^{-3t} + (1/10)\cos t - (3/10)\sin t$.

29. $(s^2 - 5s + 6)^{-1}$; $e^{3t} - e^{2t}$.

CHAPTER 8

Exercises 8.2, page 413

1. $(-\infty, \infty)$. 3. $(-4, 0)$. 5. $(-3, -1)$.

7. $\displaystyle\sum_{n=0}^{\infty}\left[\frac{1}{n+1} + 2^{-n-1}\right]x^n$.

9. $x + x^2 + (1/3)x^3 + \cdots$.

11. $x - (2/3)x^3 + (2/15)x^5 + \cdots$.

13. (c) $1 - (1/2)x + (1/4)x^2 - (1/24)x^3 + \cdots$.

15. $\displaystyle\sum_{n=1}^{\infty}(-1)^n nx^{n-1}$. 17. $\displaystyle\sum_{n=1}^{\infty}a_n nx^{n-1}$.

19. $\ln(x+1) = \displaystyle\sum_{n=0}^{\infty}\frac{(-1)^n}{n+1}x^{n+1}$.

21. $\displaystyle\sum_{k=0}^{\infty}(k+1)a_{k+1}x^k$. 23. $\displaystyle\sum_{k=1}^{\infty}a_{k-1}x^k$.

25. $\displaystyle\sum_{k=3}^{\infty}(k-1)(k-2)a_{k-1}x^k$.

27. $\displaystyle\sum_{n=0}^{\infty}\frac{(-1)^{n+1}(x-\pi)^{2n}}{(2n)!}$. 29. $\displaystyle\sum_{n=1}^{\infty}\frac{(-1)^{n+1}}{n}x^n$.

31. $6(x-1) + 3(x-1)^2 + (x-1)^3$.

33. (a) $\displaystyle\sum_{n=0}^{\infty}(-1)^n(x-1)^n$.

(b) $\displaystyle\sum_{n=1}^{\infty}\frac{(-1)^{n-1}}{n}(x-1)^n$.

35. $1 + x + x^2 + \cdots$.

37. $x + x^2 + (1/2)x^3 + \cdots$.

39. $x - (1/6)x^3 + (1/120)x^5 + \cdots$.

41. $1 - (\sin 1)x^2/2 + (\cos 1)(\sin 1)x^4/24 + \cdots$.

45. $t + (1/2)t^2 - (1/6)t^3 + \cdots$.

Exercises 8.3, page 425

1. 0. 3. $\pm\sqrt{2}$. 5. -1.

7. $x = n\pi$, n an integer.

9. $x \leq 0$ and $x = n\pi$, $n = 1, 2, 3, \ldots$.

11. $y = a_0(1 - 2x + (3/2)x^2 - x^3/3 + \cdots)$.

13. $a_0(1 + x^4/12 + \cdots) + a_1(x + x^5/20 + \cdots)$.

15. $a_0(1 - x^2/2 - x^3/6 + \cdots)$
$\quad + a_1(x + x^2/2 - x^3/6 + \cdots)$.

17. $a_0(1 - x^2/2 + \cdots) + a_1(x - x^3/6 + \cdots)$.

19. $a_0\displaystyle\sum_{n=0}^{\infty}\frac{1}{n!}x^{2n}$.

21. $a_0(1 - 2x^2 + x^4/3)$
$\quad + a_1\left(x + \displaystyle\sum_{k=1}^{\infty}\frac{(-3)(-1)\cdots(2k-5)}{(2k+1)!}x^{2k+1}\right)$.

23. $a_{3k+2} = 0$, $k = 0, 1, \ldots$.
$a_0\left(1 + \displaystyle\sum_{k=1}^{\infty}\frac{1\cdot4\cdots(3k-5)(3k-2)}{(3k)!}x^{3k}\right)$
$\quad + a_1\left(x + \displaystyle\sum_{k=1}^{\infty}\frac{2\cdot5\cdots(3k-4)(3k-1)}{(3k+1)!}x^{3k+1}\right)$.

25. $2 + x^2 - (5/12)x^4 + (11/72)x^6 + \cdots$.

27. $1 - 2x + x^2 - (1/6)x^3 + \cdots$.

29. $x + (1/2)x^2 + (1/2)x^3 + (1/3)x^4 + \cdots$.

31. $-1 - (1/2)x^2 - (1/3)x^3 - (1/8)x^4 + \cdots$.

35. (a) $1 - (1/6)x^3 + (1/180)x^6 - (1/12,960)x^9 + \cdots$.
Power series solution has only one zero, which is near 2.

(b) $y(10) \approx -1.99$. Numerical approximation has zeros near 2.00, 3.85, 5.30, 6.60, 7.80, 8.85, and 9.90.

(c) $y(-10) \approx 3.70 \times 10^8$. No zeros in $[-10, 0]$.

(d) The numerical solution because the solutions of $y'' + ky = 0$ oscillate when $k > 0$ and do not when $k < 0$.

Exercises 8.4, page 432

1. Infinite. 3. $\sqrt{2}$. 5. $\pi/2$.

7. $a_0[1 - 2(x+1) + 3(x+1)^2$
$\quad - (10/3)(x+1)^3 + \cdots]$.

9. $a_0[1 + (x-1)^2 + \cdots]$
$\quad + a_1[(x-1) + (1/3)(x-1)^3 + \cdots]$.

11. $a_0[1 + (1/2)(x+1)^2 + (2/3)(x+1)^3 + \cdots]$
$\quad + a_1[(x+1) + 2(x+1)^2 + (7/3)(x+1)^3 + \cdots]$.

13. $1 - (1/2)x^2 + (1/6)x^4 - (31/720)x^5 + \cdots$.

15. $-x + (1/3)x^3 + (1/12)x^4 + (1/24)x^5 + \cdots$.

17. $1 - (1/6)(x-\pi)^3 + (1/120)(x-\pi)^5$
$\quad + (1/180)(x-\pi)^6 + \cdots$.

19. $-1 + x + x^2 + (1/2)x^3 + \cdots$.

21. $a_0[1 + (1/2)x^2 + (1/8)x^4 + (1/48)x^6 + \cdots]$
$\quad + [(1/2)x^2 + (1/12)x^4 + (11/720)x^6 + \cdots]$.

23. $a_0[1 - (1/2)x^2 + \cdots] + a_1[x - (1/3)x^3 + \cdots]$
$\quad + [(1/2)x^2 + (1/3)x^3 + \cdots]$.

25. $a_0[1 - x^2] + a_1[x - (1/6)x^3 + \cdots]$
$\quad + [(1/2)x^2 + \cdots]$.

27. $a_0[1 - (1/2)x^2 - (1/6)x^3 + \cdots]$
$\quad + a_1[x + (1/2)x^2 + \cdots] + [(1/6)x^3 + \cdots]$.

29. (a) $a_0 \left[1 + \sum\limits_{k=1}^{\infty} (-1)^k \dfrac{n(n-2)(n-4) \cdots (n-2k+2)(n+1)(n+3) \cdots (n+2k-1)}{(2k)!} x^{2k} \right.$

$\left. + a_1 \left[x + \sum\limits_{k=1}^{\infty} (-1)^k \dfrac{(n-1)(n-3) \cdots (n-2k+1)(n+2)(n+4) \cdots (n+2k)}{(2k+1)!} x^{2k+1} \right] \right.$

(c) $P_0(x) = 1$, $P_1(x) = x$, $P_2(x) = (1/2)(3x^2 - 1)$.

Exercises 8.5, page 436

1. $c_1 x^{-5/2} + c_2 x^{-3}$.

3. $c_1 x^{-(1+\sqrt{13})/2} + c_2 x^{-(1-\sqrt{13})/2}$.

5. $c_1 x^3 \cos(2 \ln x) + c_2 x^3 \sin(2 \ln x)$.

7. $c_1 x^{-2} + c_2 x^{1/2}$.

9. $c_1 x + c_2 x^{-1} \cos(3 \ln x) + c_3 x^{-1} \sin(3 \ln x)$.

11. $c_1 x^{-2} + c_2 x^{-2} \ln x + c_3 x^{-2} (\ln x)^2$.

13. $c_1 x + c_2 x^2 + (4/15) x^{-1/2}$.   15. $2x^4 + x^{-3}$.

17. $(31/17)x + (3/17)x^{-2} \cos(5 \ln x)$

$\qquad - (76/85)x^{-2} \sin(5 \ln x)$.

Exercises 8.6, page 449

1. 0 is regular.   3. ± 2 are regular.

5. 1 is regular, -1 is irregular.

7. 2 is regular, -1 is irregular.

9. 0 and 1 are regular.

11. $r^2 + 3r + 2 = 0$; $r_1 = -1$, $r_2 = -2$.

13. $r^2 - 5r/9 - 4/3 = 0$; $r_1 = (5 + \sqrt{457})/18$,

$\quad r_2 = (5 - \sqrt{457})/18$.

15. $r^2 - 5r/4 - 3/4 = 0$; $r_1 = (5 + \sqrt{73})/8$,

$\quad r_2 = (5 - \sqrt{73})/8$.

17. $r^2 - 1 = 0$; $r_1 = 1$, $r_2 = -1$.

19. $a_0 [1 - (1/3)x - (1/15)x^2 - (1/35)x^3 + \cdots]$.

21. $a_0 [1 - (1/4)x^2 + (1/64)x^4 - (1/2304)x^6 + \cdots]$.

23. $a_0 [x - (1/3)x^2 + (1/12)x^3 - (1/60)x^4 + \cdots]$.

25. $a_0 \sum\limits_{n=0}^{\infty} \dfrac{(-1)^n x^{n+(3/2)}}{2^{n-1}(n+2)!}$.

27. $a_0 \sum\limits_{n=0}^{\infty} \dfrac{x^{2n+2}}{2^{2n}(n+1)! n!}$.

29. $a_0 \left[x^{1/3} + \sum\limits_{n=1}^{\infty} \dfrac{2^{n-2}(3n+4)x^{n+(1/3)}}{3^n n!} \right]$.

31. $a_0 \sum\limits_{n=0}^{\infty} \dfrac{x^n}{n!} = a_0 e^x$.

33. $a_0 [1 + (4/5)x + (1/5)x^2]$.

35. $a_0 [x^{5/6} - (1/11)x^{11/6} + (1/374)x^{17/6}$

$\qquad - (1/25,806)x^{23/6} + \cdots]$.

37. $a_0 [x + (1/20)x^2 + (1/1960)x^3$

$\qquad + (1/529,200)x^4 + \cdots]$.

39. The expansion $\sum\limits_{n=0}^{\infty} n! x^n$ diverges for $x \neq 0$.

41. The transformed equation is $z \, d^2y/dz^2 +$
$3 \, dy/dz - y = 0$. Also $zp(z) = 3$ and $z^2 q(z) = -z$
are analytic at $z = 0$; hence $z = 0$ is a regular
singular point.

$$y_1(x) = a_0 [1 + (1/3)x^{-1} + (1/24)x^{-2}$$
$$+ (1/360)x^{-3} + \cdots].$$

45. $a_0 [x^{-3} - (1/2)x^{-1} - (1/8)x - (1/144)x^3 + \cdots]$

$\qquad + a_3 [1 + (1/10)x^2 + (1/280)x^4$

$\qquad + (1/15,120)x^6 + \cdots]$.

Exercises 8.7, page 460

1. $c_1 [1 - (1/3)x - (1/15)x^2 + \cdots] + c_2 (x^{-1/2} - x^{1/2})$.

3. $c_1 y_1(x) + c_2 y_2(x)$, where

$\quad y_1(x) = 1 - (1/4)x^2 + (1/64)x^4 + \cdots$ and

$\quad y_2(x) = y_1(x) \ln x + (1/4)x^2 - (3/128)x^4$

$\qquad + (11/13,824)x^6 + \cdots$.

5. $c_1 [x - (1/3)x^2 + (1/12)x^3 + \cdots] + c_2 [x^{-1} - 1]$.

7. $c_1 y_1(x) + c_2 y_2(x)$, where

$\quad y_1(x) = x^{3/2} - (1/6)x^{5/2} + (1/48)x^{7/2} + \cdots$ and

$\quad y_2(x) = x^{-1/2} - (1/2)x^{1/2}$.

9. $c_1 y_1 + c_2 y_2$, where $y_1(x) = x^2 + (1/8)x^4 +$

$\quad (1/192)x^6 + \cdots$ and $y_2(x) = y_1(x) \ln x + 2$

$\quad - (3/32)x^4 - (7/1728)x^6 + \cdots$.

11. $c_1 y_1(x) + c_2 y_2(x)$, where

$\quad y_1(x) = x^{1/3} + (7/6)x^{4/3} + (5/9)x^{7/3} + \cdots$ and

$\quad y_2(x) = 1 + 2x + (6/5)x^2 + \cdots$.

13. $c_1 y_1(x) + c_2 y_2(x)$, where

$\quad y_1(x) = 1 + x + (1/2)x^2 + \cdots$ and

$\quad y_2(x) = y_1(x) \ln x - [x + (3/4)x^2$

$\qquad + (11/36)x^3 + \cdots]$.

15. $c_1 y_1(x) + c_2 y_2(x)$, where

$\quad y_1(x) = 1 + (4/5)x + (1/5)x^2$ and

$\quad y_2(x) = x^{-4} + 4x^{-3} + 5x^{-2}$.

17. $c_1 y_1(x) + c_2 y_2(x) + c_3 y_3(x)$, where

$\quad y_1(x) = x^{5/6} - (1/11)x^{11/6} + (1/374)x^{17/6} + \cdots$,

$\quad y_2(x) = 1 - x + (1/14)x^2 + \cdots$, and

$\quad y_3(x) = y_2(x) \ln x + 7x - (117/196)x^2$

$\qquad + (4997/298116)x^3 + \cdots$.

19. $c_1 y_1(x) + c_2 y_2(x) + c_3 y_3(x)$, where

$\quad y_1(x) = x + (1/20)x^2 + (1/1960)x^3 + \cdots$,

$\quad y_2(x) = x^{2/3} + (3/26)x^{5/3} + (9/4940)x^{8/3} + \cdots$,

$\quad$ and $y_3(x) = x^{-1/2} + 2x^{1/2} + (2/5)x^{3/2} + \cdots$.

21. $c_1 y_1(x) + c_2 y_2(x)$, where
$y_1(x) = 1 + 2x + 2x^2$ and
$y_2(x) = -(1/6)x^{-1} - (1/24)x^{-2}$
$\qquad - (1/120)x^{-3} + \cdots$.

23. For $n = 0$, $c_1 + c_2[\ln x + x + (1/4)x^2$
$+ (1/18)x^3 + \cdots]$ and for $n = 1$,
$c_1(1-x) + c_2[(1-x)\ln x + 3x - (1/4)x^2$
$\qquad - (1/36)x^3 + \cdots]$.

Exercises 8.8, page 467

1. $y_1(x) = \sum_{n=0}^{\infty} \dfrac{4^n x^n}{(n!)^2}$ and

$y_2(x) = y_1(x)\ln x$
$\qquad - \sum_{n=1}^{\infty} \dfrac{2^{2n+1}}{(n!)^2}\left[1 + \dfrac{1}{2} + \dfrac{1}{3} + \cdots + \dfrac{1}{n}\right]x^n$.

3. $y_1(x) = \sum_{n=0}^{\infty} \dfrac{(-1)^n x^{n+1}}{n!}$ and

$y_2(x) = y_1(x)\ln x$
$\qquad - \sum_{n=1}^{\infty} \dfrac{(-1)^n}{n!}\left[1 + \dfrac{1}{2} + \dfrac{1}{3} + \cdots + \dfrac{1}{n}\right]x^{n+1}$.

5. $y_1(x) = x^{-1} + 3$ and
$y_2(x) = y_1(x)\ln x - \left[9 + \sum_{n=2}^{\infty} \dfrac{(-3)^n x^{n-1}}{n(n-1)n!}\right]$.

7. $y_1(x) = \sum_{n=0}^{\infty} \dfrac{3^n x^n}{(n!)^2}$ and

$y_2(x) = y_1(x)\ln x$
$\qquad - \sum_{n=1}^{\infty} \dfrac{2 \cdot 3^n}{(n!)^2}\left[1 + \dfrac{1}{2} + \dfrac{1}{3} + \cdots + \dfrac{1}{n}\right]x^n$.

9. (c) $a_0[x^{-3} - (1/2)x^{-1} - (1/8)x - (1/144)x^3 + \cdots]$
$\qquad + a_3[1 + (1/10)x^2 + (1/280)x^4 + \cdots]$.

11. $y_1(x) = 1 + (2/3)x + (1/3)x^2$ and

$y_2(x) = \sum_{n=4}^{\infty} (n-3)x^n$.

13. $y_1(x) = 2 + x$ and
$y_2(x) = y_1(x)\ln x + x^{-1} - 3 - 4x$
$\qquad + \sum_{n=3}^{\infty} \dfrac{2(-1)^n x^{n-1}}{n!(n-1)(n-2)}$.

15. $y_1(x) = x^2$ and

$y_2(x) = y_1(x)\ln x - 1 + 2x + 2\sum_{n=3}^{\infty} \dfrac{(-x)^n}{n!(n-2)}$.

17. $y_1(x) = x^{1/2} + \sum_{n=1}^{\infty} \dfrac{(4n^2 - 8n + 7) \cdots 39 \cdot 19 \cdot 7 \cdot 3}{[(2n+2)(2n-1) \cdots 5 \cdot 3]^2 2^n n!}x^{n+1/2}$,

$y_2(x) = 1 + \sum_{n=1}^{\infty} a_n(0)x^n$,

$y_3(x) = y_2(x)\ln x + \sum_{n=1}^{\infty} a_n(0)\left\{\left[\dfrac{2n-3}{n^2-3n+3} + \dfrac{2n-5}{(n-1)^2-3(n-1)+3} + \cdots + \dfrac{1}{1} + \dfrac{-1}{1}\right]\right.$
$\qquad \left. - 2\left[\dfrac{1}{n} + \dfrac{1}{n-1} + \cdots + \dfrac{1}{1}\right] - 2\left[\dfrac{1}{2n-1} + \dfrac{1}{2n-3} + \cdots + \dfrac{1}{3} + \dfrac{1}{1}\right]\right\}x^n$, where

$a_n(0) = \dfrac{(n^2 - 3n + 3) \cdots 7 \cdot 3 \cdot 1 \cdot 1}{[(2n-1)(2n-3) \cdots 3 \cdot 1](n!)^2}$.

19. $y_1(x) = \sum_{n=0}^{\infty} \dfrac{x^n}{(n!)^3}$,

$y_2(x) = y_1(x)\ln x - 3\sum_{n=1}^{\infty} \dfrac{1}{(n!)^3}\left[1 + \dfrac{1}{2} + \dfrac{1}{3} + \cdots + \dfrac{1}{n}\right]x^n$,

$y_3(x) = y_1(x)(\ln x)^2 - 6(\ln x)\sum_{n=1}^{\infty} \dfrac{1}{(n!)^3}\left[1 + \dfrac{1}{2} + \dfrac{1}{3} + \cdots + \dfrac{1}{n}\right]x^n$
$\qquad + \sum_{n=1}^{\infty} \dfrac{3}{(n!)^3}\left[1 + \dfrac{1}{2} + \dfrac{1}{3} + \cdots + \dfrac{1}{n}\right]\left[1 + \dfrac{1}{2^2} + \dfrac{1}{3^2} + \cdots + \dfrac{1}{n^2}\right]x^n$.

21. $a_{2n+1} \equiv 0$ and $a_{2n} = \dfrac{(2n+2+r)(2+r)r}{[(2n+2+r)(2n+r) \cdots (2+r)]^2}$.

Exercises 8.9, page 479

1. $c_1 F\left(1, 2; \dfrac{1}{2}; x\right) + c_2 x^{1/2} F\left(\dfrac{3}{2}, \dfrac{5}{2}; \dfrac{3}{2}; x\right).$

3. $c_1 F\left(3, 5; \dfrac{1}{3}; x\right) + c_2 x^{2/3} F\left(\dfrac{11}{3}, \dfrac{17}{3}; \dfrac{5}{3}; x\right).$

5. $F(\alpha, \beta; \beta; x) = \displaystyle\sum_{n=0}^{\infty} (\alpha)_n x^n/n! = (1 - x)^{-\alpha}.$

7. $F\left(\dfrac{1}{2}, 1; \dfrac{3}{2}; x^2\right) = \displaystyle\sum_{n=0}^{\infty} (1/2)_n x^{2n}/(3/2)_n$

$\qquad = \displaystyle\sum_{n=0}^{\infty} x^{2n}/(2n + 1)$

$\qquad = \dfrac{1}{2} x^{-1} \ln\left(\dfrac{1 + x}{1 - x}\right).$

9. $(1 - x)^{-1}, \quad (1 - x)^{-1}\ln x.$

13. $c_1 J_{1/2}(x) + c_2 J_{-1/2}(x).$

15. $c_1 J_1(x) + c_2 Y_1(x).$ 17. $c_1 J_{4/3}(x) + c_2 J_{-4/3}(x).$

19. $J_1(x)\ln x - x^{-1} + (3/64)x^3 - (7/2304)x^5 + \cdots.$

21. $x^{3/2} J_{3/2}(x).$

27. $J_0(x)\ln x + \displaystyle\sum_{n=1}^{\infty} \dfrac{(-1)^{n+1}}{2^{2n}(n!)^2}\left[1 + \dfrac{1}{2} + \cdots + \dfrac{1}{n}\right]x^{2n}.$

29. $1, \quad x, \quad (3x^2 - 1)/2, \quad (5x^3 - 3x)/2,$
$(35x^4 - 30x^2 + 3)/8.$

37. $1, \quad 2x, \quad 4x^2 - 2, \quad 8x^3 - 12x.$

39. $1, \quad 1 - x, \quad (2 - 4x + x^2)/2,$
$(6 - 18x + 9x^2 - x^3)/6.$

Review Problems, page 485

1. **(a)** $1 - x + (3/2)x^2 - (5/3)x^3 + \cdots.$
(b) $-1 + x - (1/6)x^3 + (1/6)x^4 + \cdots.$

3. **(a)** $a_0[1 + x^2 + \cdots] + a_1[x + (1/3)x^3 + \cdots].$
(b) $a_0[1 + (1/2)x^2 - (1/6)x^3 + \cdots] +$
$\qquad a_1[x - (1/2)x^2 + (1/2)x^3 + \cdots].$

5. $a_0[1 + (1/2)(x - 2)^2 - (1/24)(x - 2)^4 + \cdots]$
$\qquad\qquad\qquad\qquad\qquad + a_1(x - 2).$

7. **(a)** $a_0[x^3 + x^4 + (1/4)x^5 + (1/36)x^6 + \cdots].$
(b) $a_0[x - (1/4)x^2 + (1/20)x^3 - (1/120)x^4 + \cdots].$

9. **(a)** $c_1 y_1(x) + c_2 y_2(x)$, where
$y_1(x) = x + x^2 + (1/2)x^3 + \cdots = xe^x$ and
$y_2(x) = y_1(x)\ln x - x^2 - (3/4)x^3$
$\qquad -(11/36)x^4 + \cdots.$
(b) $c_1 y_1(x) + c_2 y_2(x)$, where
$y_1(x) = 1 + 2x + x^2 + \cdots$ and $y_2(x) =$
$y_1(x)\ln x - [4x + 3x^2 + (22/27)x^3 + \cdots].$
(c) $c_1 y_1(x) + c_2 y_2(x)$, where
$y_1(x) = 1 - (1/6)x + (1/96)x^2 + \cdots$ and
$y_2(x) = y_1(x)\ln x - 8x^{-2} - 4x^{-1}$
$\qquad + (29/36) + \cdots.$

(d) $c_1 y_1(x) + c_2 y_2(x)$, where
$y_1(x) = x^2 - (1/4)x^3 + (1/40)x^4 + \cdots$ and
$y_2(x) = x^{-1} + (1/2) + (1/4)x + \cdots$

CHAPTER 9

Exercises 9.2, page 498

1. $x = (3/2)c_1 e^{2t} - c_2 e^{-3t}; \quad y = c_1 e^{2t} + c_2 e^{-3t}.$

3. $x = -(1/2)c_1 e^{3t} + (1/2)c_2 e^{-t}; \quad y = c_1 e^{3t} + c_2 e^{-t}.$

5. $x = -5; \quad y = 1.$

7. $x = c_1 + c_2 e^{-t} + (1/2)e^t + (5/3)t;$
$y = c_1 - 2c_2 e^{-t} + (5/3)t.$

9. $x = c_1 e^t + (1/4)\cos t - (1/4)\sin t;$
$y = -3c_1 e^t - (3/4)\cos t - (1/4)\sin t.$

11. $x = c_1 e^{2t} + c_2 e^{-2t} + 1;$
$y = -2c_1 e^{2t} + 2c_2 e^{-2t} + 2t + c_3.$

13. $x = -c_1 \sin t + c_2 \cos t + 2t - 1;$
$y = c_1 \cos t + c_2 \sin t + t^2 - 2.$

15. $x = -(2/3)c_1 e^{2t} + c_2 e^{7t} + t + 1;$
$y = c_1 e^{2t} + c_2 e^{7t} - 5t - 2.$

17. $x = \sin t - \cos t; \quad y = \sin t.$

19. $x = (1/2)e^t\{(c_1 - c_2)\cos t + (c_1 + c_2)\sin t\}$
$\qquad + c_3 e^{2t}; \quad y = e^t(c_1 \cos t + c_2 \sin t);$
$z = (3/2)e^t\{(c_1 - c_2)\cos t + (c_1 + c_2)\sin t\}$
$\qquad + c_3 e^{2t}.$

21. Infinitely many solutions satisfying
$x + y = e^t + e^{-2t}.$

23. $x_1' = x_2, \quad x_2' = x_1^2 + \cos(t - x_1); \quad x_1(0) = 1,$
$x_2(0) = 0.$

25. $x_1' = x_2, \quad x_2' = x_3, \quad x_3' = x_4,$
$x_4' = x_4 - 7x_1 + \cos t; \quad x_1(0) = x_2(0) = 1,$
$x_3(0) = 0, \quad x_4(0) = 2.$

27. $10I_1' + 30I_2' + 40I_2 = 20, \quad 10I_1' + 10I_3 = 20,$
$I_1 = I_2 + I_3; \quad I_1(0) = I_2(0) = I_3(0) = 0;$
$I_1 = -(1/4)e^{-2t} - (9/4)e^{-2t/3} + 5/2,$
$I_2 = (1/4)e^{-2t} - (3/4)e^{-2t/3} + 1/2,$
$I_3 = -(1/2)e^{-2t} - (3/2)e^{-2t/3} + 2.$

29. $(1/2)I_1' + 2q_3 = \cos 3t$ (where $I_3 = q_3'$),
$(1/2)I_1' + I_2 = 0, \quad I_1 = I_2 + I_3;$
$I_1(0) = I_2(0) = I_3(0) = 0;$
$I_1 = -(36/61)e^{-t}\cos \sqrt{3}t$
$\qquad - (42\sqrt{3}/61)e^{-t}\sin \sqrt{3}t + (36/61)\cos 3t$
$\qquad + (30/61)\sin 3t,$
$I_2 = (45/61)e^{-t}\cos \sqrt{3}t - (39\sqrt{3}/61)e^{-t}\sin \sqrt{3}t$
$\qquad - (45/61)\cos 3t + (54/61)\sin 3t,$
$I_3 = -(81/61)e^{-t}\cos \sqrt{3}t$
$\qquad - (3\sqrt{3}/61)e^{-t}\sin \sqrt{3}t + (81/61)\cos 3t$
$\qquad - (24/61)\sin 3t.$

Exercises 9.3, page 501

1. $x = e^{3t} - 2e^{2t}$; $y = -2e^{3t} + 2e^{2t}$.
3. $x = 2e^{-2t} - 3$; $y = 2e^{-2t}$.
5. $x = -(7/10)e^t\cos 2t + (2/5)e^t\sin 2t + (7/10)\cos t$
$\quad - (1/10)\sin t$;
$\quad y = -(11/10)e^t\cos 2t - (3/10)e^t\sin 2t$
$\quad\quad + (11/10)\cos t + (7/10)\sin t$.

7. $x = -(150/17)e^{5t/2}\cos(\sqrt{15}t/2)$
$\quad - (334\sqrt{15}/85)e^{5t/2}\sin(\sqrt{15}t/2) - (3/17)e^{-3t}$;
$\quad y = (46/17)e^{5t/2}\cos(\sqrt{15}t/2)$
$\quad\quad - (146\sqrt{15}/85)e^{5t/2}\sin(\sqrt{15}t/2)$
$\quad\quad + (22/17)e^{-3t}$.

9. $x = 4e^{-2t} - e^{-t} - \cos t$; $y = 5e^{-2t} - e^{-t}$.
11. $x = e^{-t} + e^{t/2}\sin(\sqrt{3}t/2) + 2t + 2$;
$\quad y = e^{-t} + (\sqrt{3}/2)e^{t/2}\cos(\sqrt{3}t/2)$
$\quad\quad - (1/2)e^{t/2}\sin(\sqrt{3}t/2) - t^2$.

13. $x = -7e^{-t} + e^t$; $y = 2e^{-t}$; $z = -13e^{-t} + e^t$.
15. $2I_1 + (0.1)I_3' + (0.2)I_1' = 6$, $(0.1)I_3' - I_2 = 0$,
$\quad I_1 = I_2 + I_3$; $I_1(0) = I_2(0) = I_3(0) = 0$;
$\quad I_1 = -e^{-20t} - 2e^{-5t} + 3$,
$\quad I_2 = -2e^{-20t} + 2e^{-5t}$,
$\quad I_3 = e^{-20t} - 4e^{-5t} + 3$.

Exercises 9.4, page 509

1. $x_1 = (2/5)\cos t - (2/5)\cos\sqrt{6}t$;
$\quad x_2 = (4/5)\cos t + (1/5)\cos\sqrt{6}t$.
3. The normal frequency, $(1/2\pi)\sqrt{(2+\sqrt{2})(k/m)}$,
has the mode $x_1(t) = x_3(t) = -(1/\sqrt{2})x_2(t)$; the
normal frequency $(1/2\pi)\sqrt{(2-\sqrt{2})(k/m)}$ has the
mode $x_1(t) = x_3(t) = (1/\sqrt{2})x_2(t)$; and the normal
frequency $(1/2\pi)\sqrt{2k/m}$ has the mode
$x_1(t) = -x_3(t), x_2(t) \equiv 0$.
5. $x_1 = -e^{-t} - te^{-t} - \cos t$;
$\quad x_2 = e^{-t} + te^{-t} - \cos t$.
7. $(1/2\pi)\sqrt{g/l}$; $(1/2\pi)\sqrt{(g/l)+(2k/m)}$.
9. $x = -100e^{-t/10} + 150$;
$\quad y = -50e^{-t/10} - 10te^{-t/10} + 150$.
11. $100/3 \approx 33°F$. 13. $90.4°F$.

Exercises 9.5, page 519

1.
i	t_i	$x(t_i)$	$y(t_i)$
1	0.250	−0.59733	1.15365
2	0.500	−1.58112	0.48705
3	0.750	−3.41862	−0.19129
4	1.000	−7.01992	−1.13136

3.
i	t_i	$x(t_i)$	$y(t_i)$
1	0.250	0.98661	0.75492
2	0.500	0.91749	1.04259
3	0.750	0.79823	1.38147
4	1.000	0.63303	1.77948

5.
i	t_i	$y(t_i)$
1	0.25	0.75755
2	0.50	0.55876
3	0.75	0.44552
4	1.00	0.46272

7.
i	t_i	$y(t_i)$
1	0.25	−0.72103
2	0.50	−0.39038
3	0.75	−0.01072
4	1.00	0.42498

9. $x(1) \approx 127.773$; $y(1) \approx -423.476$.
11. $x(1; 2^{-2}) = y(1; 2^{-2}) = 0.36789$.
13. $y(1) \approx x_1(1; 2^{-3}) = 1.25958$.
15. $x(1) \approx 0.80300$; $y(1) \approx 0.59598$; $z(1) \approx 0.82316$

17.
x_i	$y(x_i)$
0.1	0.00647
0.2	0.02524
0.3	0.05530
0.4	0.09573
0.5	0.14560
0.6	0.20407
0.7	0.27032
0.8	0.34363
0.9	0.42333
1.0	0.50882
1.1	0.59958
1.2	0.69515
1.3	0.79515
1.4	0.89926
1.5	1.00722
1.6	1.11886
1.7	1.23402
1.8	1.35263
1.9	1.47465
2.0	1.60009

19.

		Part (a)		Part (b)		Part (c)	
i	t_i	$x(t_i)$	$y(t_i)$	$x(t_i)$	$y(t_i)$	$x(t_i)$	$y(t_i)$
1	0.5	1.95247	2.25065	1.48118	2.42311	0.91390	2.79704
2	1.0	3.34588	1.83601	2.66294	1.45358	1.63657	1.13415
3	1.5	4.53662	3.36527	5.19629	2.40348	4.49334	1.07811
4	2.0	2.47788	4.32906	3.10706	4.64923	5.96115	5.47788
5	2.5	1.96093	2.71900	1.92574	3.32426	1.51830	5.93110
6	3.0	2.86412	1.96166	2.34143	2.05910	0.95601	2.18079
7	3.5	4.28449	2.77457	3.90106	2.18977	2.06006	0.98131
8	4.0	3.00965	4.11886	3.83241	3.89043	5.62642	1.38072
9	4.5	2.18643	3.14344	2.32171	3.79362	5.10594	5.10462
10	5.0	2.63187	2.25824	2.21926	2.49307	1.74187	5.02491

Exercises 9.6, page 530

1. $x = y^3, \quad y > 0.$

Figure B.23

19. $y = cx^{2/3}.$

Figure B.26

3. $(1/\sqrt{2}, 1/\sqrt{2}), \quad (-1/\sqrt{2}, -1/\sqrt{2}).$ **5.** $(0, 0).$
7. $(1, 1)$ and line $y = 2.$ **9.** $e^x + ye^{-y} = c.$
11. $y = x/(\ln|x| + c).$ **13.** $e^x + xy - y^2 = c.$
15. $y^2 - x^2 = c.$

21. $v^2 - x^2 = c.$

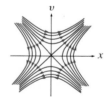

Figure B.27

Figure B.24

23. $3v^2 + 3x^2 + x^6 = c.$

17. $(x - 1)^2 + (y - 1)^2 = c.$

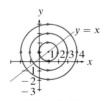

Figure B.25

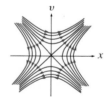

Figure B.28

25. Critical points are the line $I = 0$; integral curves are $I = -S + (b/a)\ln S + c$; an epidemic occurs because $I'(t) > 0$ if $I > 0$ and $S > b/a$.

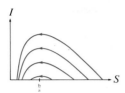

Figure B.29

27. Critical point is $(0, 0)$; integral curves are $2v^2 + 2x^2 + x^4 = c$; motion is periodic about equilibrium position.

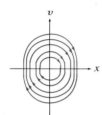

Figure B.30

Review Problems, page 533

1. $x = c_1 e^{\sqrt{3}t} + c_2 e^{-\sqrt{3}t}$;
$y = \sqrt{3}c_1 e^{\sqrt{3}t} - \sqrt{3}c_2 e^{-\sqrt{3}t}$.
3. $x = c_1 e^{-t/5} + t - 4$; $y = (3/2)c_1 e^{-t/5} + t - 6$.
5. $x(t) = y(t) \equiv 0$.   **7.** $x = e^t$; $y \equiv 0$.
9. $x = (1/3)e^t + (2/3)e^{-t/2}\cos(\sqrt{3}t/2)$;
$y = (1/3)e^t - (1/3)e^{-t/2}\cos(\sqrt{3}t/2)$
$\quad + (1/\sqrt{3})e^{-t/2}\sin(\sqrt{3}t/2)$.
11. $x_1' = x_2$, $x_2' = x_3$,
$x_3' = 2e^{-t} - tx_3 - 3x_2 - 2x_1$; $x_1(0) = 2$,
$x_2(0) = 3$, $x_3(0) = 2$.
13. Critical point $(0, 0)$; integral curves $x = cy^2$.

Figure B.31

15. Critical point $(0, 0)$; integral curves $y^2 - 4x^2 = c$.

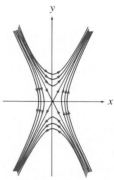

Figure B.32

17. Critical points $y \equiv 0$; integral curves $y = c \cos x$.

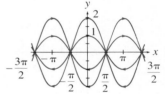

Figure B.33

19. A runaway arms race.

CHAPTER 10

Exercises 10.2, page 546

1. (a) $\begin{bmatrix} 2 & 3 \\ 1 & 5 \end{bmatrix}$. **(b)** $\begin{bmatrix} 1 & 1 \\ 5 & 2 \end{bmatrix}$. **(c)** $\begin{bmatrix} 7 & 3 \\ 7 & 18 \end{bmatrix}$.

3. (a) $\begin{bmatrix} 18 & 10 \\ 4 & 4 \end{bmatrix}$. **(b)** $\begin{bmatrix} 8 & 12 \\ 3 & 5 \end{bmatrix}$. **(c)** $\begin{bmatrix} 16 & 0 \\ 0 & 16 \end{bmatrix}$.

5. (a) $\begin{bmatrix} -1 & -2 \\ -1 & -3 \end{bmatrix}$. **(b)** $\begin{bmatrix} -5 & -1 \\ -8 & -1 \end{bmatrix}$.

(c) $\begin{bmatrix} -6 & -3 \\ -9 & -4 \end{bmatrix}$.

7. (a) 21. **(b)** 21. **(c)** 6. **(d)** 6.

9. $\begin{bmatrix} 4/9 & -1/9 \\ 1/9 & 2/9 \end{bmatrix}$. **11.** Doesn't exist.

13. $\begin{bmatrix} 1 & 0 & 1 \\ -2 & 1 & -2 \\ 1 & 1 & 0 \end{bmatrix}$.

15. $\begin{bmatrix} (4/3)e^{-t} & -(1/3)e^{-t} \\ -(1/3)e^{-4t} & (1/3)e^{-4t} \end{bmatrix}.$

17. $\begin{bmatrix} e^{-t} & (1/2)e^{-t} & -(1/2)e^{-t} \\ (1/3)e^{t} & -(1/2)e^{t} & (1/6)e^{t} \\ -(1/3)e^{-2t} & 0 & (1/3)e^{-2t} \end{bmatrix}.$

19. 11.   **21.** $-12.$ **23.** 25.   **25.** 2, 3.

27. 0, 1, 1.   **29.** $\begin{bmatrix} 3e^{3t} \\ 6e^{3t} \\ -3e^{3t} \end{bmatrix}.$ **31.** $\begin{bmatrix} 5e^{5t} & 6e^{2t} \\ -10e^{5t} & -2e^{2t} \end{bmatrix}.$

37. (a) $\begin{bmatrix} (1/2)t^2 + c_1 & e^t + c_2 \\ t + c_3 & e^t + c_4 \end{bmatrix}.$

(b) $\begin{bmatrix} \sin 1 & -1 + \cos 1 \\ 1 - \cos 1 & \sin 1 \end{bmatrix}.$

(c) $\begin{bmatrix} (1 + e^t)\cos t + (e^t - t)\sin t & (e^t - t)\cos t - (e^t + 1)\sin t \\ (e^t - 1)\sin t + e^t\cos t & (e^t - 1)\cos t - e^t\sin t \end{bmatrix}.$

23. $\frac{3}{2}\begin{bmatrix} te^t \\ te^t \end{bmatrix} - \frac{1}{4}\begin{bmatrix} e^t \\ 3e^t \end{bmatrix} + \begin{bmatrix} t \\ 2t \end{bmatrix} - \begin{bmatrix} 0 \\ 1 \end{bmatrix}$
$+ c_1\begin{bmatrix} e^t \\ e^t \end{bmatrix} + c_2\begin{bmatrix} e^{-t} \\ 3e^{-t} \end{bmatrix}.$

27. $\mathbf{X}^{-1}(t) = \begin{bmatrix} 0 & (1/4)e^t & -(1/4)e^t \\ -(1/5)e^{2t} & (4/5)e^{2t} & -(2/5)e^{2t} \\ (1/5)e^{-3t} & (9/20)e^{-3t} & (3/20)e^{-3t} \end{bmatrix};$
$\begin{bmatrix} -(3/2)e^{-t} + (3/5)e^{-2t} - (1/10)e^{3t} \\ (1/4)e^{-t} - (1/5)e^{-2t} - (1/20)e^{3t} \\ (5/4)e^{-t} - (1/5)e^{-2t} - (1/20)e^{3t} \end{bmatrix}.$

Exercises 10.3, page 555

1. $\begin{bmatrix} x'(t) \\ y'(t) \end{bmatrix} = \begin{bmatrix} 3 & -1 \\ -1 & 2 \end{bmatrix}\begin{bmatrix} x(t) \\ y(t) \end{bmatrix} + \begin{bmatrix} t^2 \\ e^t \end{bmatrix}.$

3. $\begin{bmatrix} dx/dt \\ dy/dt \\ dz/dt \end{bmatrix} = \begin{bmatrix} 1 & 1 & 1 \\ 2 & -1 & 3 \\ 1 & 0 & 5 \end{bmatrix}\begin{bmatrix} x \\ y \\ z \end{bmatrix}.$

5. $\begin{bmatrix} x_1'(t) \\ x_2'(t) \end{bmatrix} = \begin{bmatrix} 0 & 1 \\ 10 & 3 \end{bmatrix}\begin{bmatrix} x_1(t) \\ x_2(t) \end{bmatrix} + \begin{bmatrix} 0 \\ \sin t \end{bmatrix}.$

7. $\begin{bmatrix} x_1'(t) \\ x_2'(t) \\ x_3'(t) \\ x_4'(t) \end{bmatrix} = \begin{bmatrix} 0 & 1 & 0 & 0 \\ 0 & 0 & 1 & 0 \\ 0 & 0 & 0 & 1 \\ -1 & 0 & 0 & 0 \end{bmatrix}\begin{bmatrix} x_1(t) \\ x_2(t) \\ x_3(t) \\ x_4(t) \end{bmatrix} + \begin{bmatrix} 0 \\ 0 \\ 0 \\ t^2 \end{bmatrix}.$

9. $x_1'(t) = 2x_1(t) + x_2(t) + te^t;$
$x_2'(t) = -x_1(t) + 3x_2(t) + e^t.$

11. $x_1'(t) = x_1(t) + x_3(t) + e^t;$
$x_2'(t) = -x_1(t) + 2x_2(t) + 5x_3(t) + t;$
$x_3'(t) = 5x_2(t) + x_3(t).$

13. LI.   **15.** LI.   **17.** LI.

19. Yes; $\begin{bmatrix} 3e^{-t} & e^{4t} \\ 2e^{-t} & -e^{4t} \end{bmatrix}; \quad c_1\begin{bmatrix} 3e^{-t} \\ 2e^{-t} \end{bmatrix} + c_2\begin{bmatrix} e^{4t} \\ -e^{4t} \end{bmatrix}.$

21. Yes; $\begin{bmatrix} e^{-t} & e^t & e^{3t} \\ 2e^{-t} & 0 & -e^{3t} \\ e^{-t} & e^t & 2e^{3t} \end{bmatrix}; \quad c_1\begin{bmatrix} e^{-t} \\ 2e^{-t} \\ e^{-t} \end{bmatrix}$
$+ c_2\begin{bmatrix} e^t \\ 0 \\ e^t \end{bmatrix} + c_3\begin{bmatrix} e^{3t} \\ -e^{3t} \\ 2e^{3t} \end{bmatrix}.$

Exercises 10.4, page 567

1. Eigenvalues are $r_1 = 0$ and $r_2 = -5$ with associated eigenvectors $\mathbf{u}_1 = \begin{bmatrix} s \\ 2s \end{bmatrix}$ and $\mathbf{u}_2 = \begin{bmatrix} 2s \\ -s \end{bmatrix}.$

3. Eigenvalues are $r_1 = 2$ and $r_2 = 3$ with associated eigenvectors $\mathbf{u}_1 = s\begin{bmatrix} 1 \\ -1 \end{bmatrix}$ and $\mathbf{u}_2 = s\begin{bmatrix} 1 \\ -2 \end{bmatrix}.$

5. Eigenvalues are $r_1 = 1$, $r_2 = 2$, and $r_3 = -2$ with associated eigenvectors $\mathbf{u}_1 = s\begin{bmatrix} 1 \\ 0 \\ 0 \end{bmatrix},$
$\mathbf{u}_2 = s\begin{bmatrix} 0 \\ 1 \\ 1 \end{bmatrix},$ and $\mathbf{u}_3 = s\begin{bmatrix} 0 \\ -1 \\ 1 \end{bmatrix},$

7. Eigenvalues are $r_1 = 1$, $r_2 = 2$, and $r_3 = 5$ with associated eigenvectors $\mathbf{u}_1 = s\begin{bmatrix} 2 \\ -3 \\ 2 \end{bmatrix},$
$\mathbf{u}_2 = s\begin{bmatrix} 0 \\ -1 \\ 1 \end{bmatrix},$ and $\mathbf{u}_3 = s\begin{bmatrix} 0 \\ 1 \\ 2 \end{bmatrix}.$

9. $c_1 e^{7t} \begin{bmatrix} 1 \\ 2 \end{bmatrix} + c_2 e^{-5t} \begin{bmatrix} 1 \\ -2 \end{bmatrix}$.

11. $c_1 e^{-t} \begin{bmatrix} -2 \\ 1 \\ 1 \end{bmatrix} + c_2 e^{-3t} \begin{bmatrix} 0 \\ -1 \\ 1 \end{bmatrix} + c_3 e^{5t} \begin{bmatrix} 1 \\ 1 \\ 1 \end{bmatrix}$.

13. $c_1 e^{-t} \begin{bmatrix} -1 \\ 0 \\ 1 \end{bmatrix} + c_2 e^{-2t} \begin{bmatrix} 1 \\ -1 \\ 3 \end{bmatrix} + c_3 e^{3t} \begin{bmatrix} 1 \\ 4 \\ 3 \end{bmatrix}$.

15. $\begin{bmatrix} e^t & 4e^{4t} \\ -e^t & -e^{4t} \end{bmatrix}$. **17.** $\begin{bmatrix} e^t & e^{2t} & e^{4t} \\ e^t & 2e^{2t} & 4e^{4t} \\ e^t & 4e^{2t} & 16e^{4t} \end{bmatrix}$.

19. $\begin{bmatrix} -e^t & -2e^{2t} & -e^{3t} \\ e^t & e^{2t} & e^{3t} \\ 2e^t & 4e^{2t} & 4e^{3t} \end{bmatrix}$. **21.** $\begin{bmatrix} 2e^{3t} - 12e^{4t} \\ 2e^{3t} - 8e^{4t} \end{bmatrix}$.

23. $\begin{bmatrix} -3e^{-t} + e^{5t} \\ -2e^{-t} - e^{5t} \\ e^{-t} + e^{5t} \end{bmatrix}$.

25. (b) $\mathbf{x}_1(t) = e^{-t} \begin{bmatrix} 1 \\ 2 \end{bmatrix}$.

(c) $\mathbf{x}_2(t) = te^{-t} \begin{bmatrix} 1 \\ 2 \end{bmatrix} + e^{-t} \begin{bmatrix} 1 \\ 1 \end{bmatrix}$.

27. (b) $\mathbf{x}_1(t) = e^{2t} \begin{bmatrix} 1 \\ 0 \\ 0 \end{bmatrix}$.

(c) $\mathbf{x}_2(t) = te^{2t} \begin{bmatrix} 1 \\ 0 \\ 0 \end{bmatrix} + e^{2t} \begin{bmatrix} 0 \\ 1 \\ 0 \end{bmatrix}$.

(d) $\mathbf{x}_3(t) = \dfrac{t^2}{2} e^{2t} \begin{bmatrix} 1 \\ 0 \\ 0 \end{bmatrix} + te^{2t} \begin{bmatrix} 0 \\ 1 \\ 0 \end{bmatrix} + e^{2t} \begin{bmatrix} 0 \\ -6/5 \\ 1/5 \end{bmatrix}$.

29. (b) $\mathbf{x}_1(t) = e^t \begin{bmatrix} -1 \\ 1 \\ 0 \end{bmatrix}$; $\mathbf{x}_2(t) = e^t \begin{bmatrix} -1 \\ 0 \\ 1 \end{bmatrix}$.

(c) $\mathbf{x}_3(t) = te^t \begin{bmatrix} 1 \\ 1 \\ -2 \end{bmatrix} + e^t \begin{bmatrix} 1 \\ 0 \\ 0 \end{bmatrix}$.

33. $c_1 \begin{bmatrix} 3t^2 \\ t^2 \end{bmatrix} + c_2 \begin{bmatrix} t^4 \\ t^4 \end{bmatrix}$.

35. $x_1(t) = (25/2)(e^{-3t/25} + e^{-t/25})$,
$x_2(t) = (25/4)(e^{-t/25} - e^{-3t/25})$.

37. (a) $r_1 = 2.39091$, $r_2 = -2.94338$, $r_3 = 3.55247$.

(b) $\mathbf{u}_1 = \begin{bmatrix} 1 \\ -2.64178 \\ -9.31625 \end{bmatrix}$; $\mathbf{u}_2 = \begin{bmatrix} 1 \\ -1.16825 \\ 0.43862 \end{bmatrix}$;

$\mathbf{u}_3 = \begin{bmatrix} 1 \\ 0.81004 \\ -0.12236 \end{bmatrix}$.

(c) $c_1 e^{r_1 t}\mathbf{u}_1 + c_2 e^{r_2 t}\mathbf{u}_2 + c_3 e^{r_3 t}\mathbf{u}_3$, where the r_i's and the $\mathbf{u}_i$'s are given in parts (a) and (b).

Exercises 10.5, page 575

1. $c_1 \begin{bmatrix} -5\cos t \\ 2\cos t - \sin t \end{bmatrix} + c_2 \begin{bmatrix} -5\sin t \\ 2\sin t + \cos t \end{bmatrix}$.

3. $c_1 e^t \cos t \begin{bmatrix} -1 \\ 1 \\ 0 \end{bmatrix} - c_1 e^t \sin t \begin{bmatrix} -2 \\ 0 \\ 1 \end{bmatrix} + c_2 e^t \sin t \begin{bmatrix} -1 \\ 1 \\ 0 \end{bmatrix}$
$+ c_2 e^t \cos t \begin{bmatrix} -2 \\ 0 \\ 1 \end{bmatrix} + c_3 e^t \begin{bmatrix} 1 \\ 0 \\ 0 \end{bmatrix}$.

5. $\begin{bmatrix} \cos 2t & \sin 2t \\ \sin 2t - \cos 2t & -\sin 2t - \cos 2t \end{bmatrix}$.

7. $\begin{bmatrix} 1 & \cos t & \sin t \\ 0 & -\cos t & -\sin t \\ 0 & -\sin t & \cos t \end{bmatrix}$. **9.** $\begin{bmatrix} e^{-2t}(\sin t - \cos t) \\ -2e^{-2t}\sin t \end{bmatrix}$.

13. $c_1 \begin{bmatrix} t^{-1} \\ 0 \\ -2t^{-1} \end{bmatrix} + c_2 \begin{bmatrix} t^{-1}\cos(\ln t) \\ t^{-1}\sin(\ln t) \\ -t^{-1}\cos(\ln t) \end{bmatrix}$
$+ c_3 \begin{bmatrix} t^{-1}\sin(\ln t) \\ -t^{-1}\cos(\ln t) \\ -t^{-1}\sin(\ln t) \end{bmatrix}$.

15. $\dfrac{\sqrt{9 - \sqrt{17}}}{2\sqrt{2}\pi} \approx 0.249$; $\dfrac{\sqrt{9 + \sqrt{17}}}{2\sqrt{2}\pi} \approx 0.408$.

Exercises 10.6, page 581

1. $c_1 e^{7t} \begin{bmatrix} 1 \\ 1 \end{bmatrix} + c_2 e^{2t} \begin{bmatrix} 1 \\ -4 \end{bmatrix} + \begin{bmatrix} 2 \\ -1 \end{bmatrix}$.

3. $c_1 e^{-3t} \begin{bmatrix} 1 \\ 1 \\ -1 \end{bmatrix} + c_2 e^{3t} \begin{bmatrix} 1 \\ 0 \\ 1 \end{bmatrix} + c_3 e^{3t} \begin{bmatrix} -1 \\ 1 \\ 0 \end{bmatrix} + e^t \begin{bmatrix} 1 \\ 0 \\ -1 \end{bmatrix}$.

5. $c_1 e^{4t} \begin{bmatrix} 2 \\ 3 \end{bmatrix} + c_2 e^{-t} \begin{bmatrix} 1 \\ -1 \end{bmatrix} + \begin{bmatrix} 1 \\ -1 \end{bmatrix}$.

7. $c_1 e^t \begin{bmatrix} 1 \\ -1 \end{bmatrix} + c_2 e^{-t} \begin{bmatrix} 1 \\ -3 \end{bmatrix} + \begin{bmatrix} 5te^t - (3/2)e^t \\ -5te^t + (9/2)e^t \end{bmatrix}$.

9. $c_1 \begin{bmatrix} 1 \\ 2 \end{bmatrix} + c_2 e^{-5t} \begin{bmatrix} -2 \\ 1 \end{bmatrix} + \begin{bmatrix} \ln|t| + (8/5)t - 8/25 \\ 2\ln|t| + (16/5)t + 4/25 \end{bmatrix}$.

11. $c_1 e^{2t} \begin{bmatrix} 1 \\ 1 \\ 1 \end{bmatrix} + c_2 e^{-t} \begin{bmatrix} -1 \\ 0 \\ 1 \end{bmatrix} + c_3 e^{-t} \begin{bmatrix} -1 \\ 1 \\ 0 \end{bmatrix} + e^t \begin{bmatrix} 1 \\ -1 \\ -1 \end{bmatrix}$.

13. $\begin{bmatrix} 4te^t + 5e^t \\ 2te^t + 4e^t \end{bmatrix}$. **15. (a)** $\left\{ \begin{bmatrix} e^t \\ e^t \end{bmatrix}, \begin{bmatrix} e^{2t} \\ 2e^{2t} \end{bmatrix} \right\}$.

(c) $te^t \begin{bmatrix} 2 \\ 2 \end{bmatrix} + e^t \begin{bmatrix} 0 \\ 1 \end{bmatrix}$.

(d) $c_1 e^t \begin{bmatrix} 1 \\ 1 \end{bmatrix} + c_2 e^{2t} \begin{bmatrix} 1 \\ 2 \end{bmatrix} + te^t \begin{bmatrix} 2 \\ 2 \end{bmatrix} + e^t \begin{bmatrix} 0 \\ 1 \end{bmatrix}$.

17. $c_1 e^{2t} \begin{bmatrix} 1 \\ 1 \\ 1 \end{bmatrix} + c_2 e^{-t} \begin{bmatrix} -1 \\ 0 \\ 1 \end{bmatrix} + c_3 e^{-t} \begin{bmatrix} -1 \\ 1 \\ 0 \end{bmatrix}$

$+ te^{-t} \begin{bmatrix} 1 \\ 0 \\ -1 \end{bmatrix} + e^{-t} \begin{bmatrix} 1 \\ 0 \\ 0 \end{bmatrix} + \begin{bmatrix} 0 \\ 0 \\ 1 \end{bmatrix}$.

19. $c_1 t \begin{bmatrix} 1 \\ 1 \end{bmatrix} + c_2 t^{-1} \begin{bmatrix} 1 \\ 3 \end{bmatrix}$

$+ \begin{bmatrix} -(3/4)t^{-1} - (1/2)t^{-1}\ln t + 1 \\ -(3/4)t^{-1} - (3/2)t^{-1}\ln t + 2 \end{bmatrix}$.

Exercises 10.7, page 591

1. (a) $r = 2; \quad k = 2.$ **(b)** $e^{2t} \begin{bmatrix} 1-t & -t \\ t & 1+t \end{bmatrix}$.

3. (a) $r = -1; \quad k = 3.$

(b) $e^{-t} \begin{bmatrix} 1 + 3t - (3/2)t^2 & t & -t + (1/2)t^2 \\ -3t & 1 & t \\ 9t - (9/2)t^2 & 3t & 1 - 3t + (3/2)t^2 \end{bmatrix}$.

5. (a) $r = -2; \quad k = 2.$ **(b)** $e^{-2t} \begin{bmatrix} 1 & 0 & 0 \\ 4t & 1 & 0 \\ t & 0 & 1 \end{bmatrix}$.

7. $\begin{bmatrix} (1/2)e^{3t} + (1/2)e^{-t} & (1/4)e^{3t} - (1/4)e^{-t} \\ e^{3t} - e^{-t} & (1/2)e^{3t} + (1/2)e^{-t} \end{bmatrix}$.

9. $\dfrac{1}{2} \begin{bmatrix} e^t + \cos t - \sin t & 2\sin t & e^t - \cos t - \sin t \\ e^t - \sin t - \cos t & 2\cos t & e^t + \sin t - \cos t \\ e^t - \cos t + \sin t & -2\sin t & e^t + \cos t + \sin t \end{bmatrix}$.

11. $\dfrac{1}{25} \begin{bmatrix} -4 + 29e^{5t} - 20te^{5t} & 20 - 20e^{5t} & -8 + 8e^{5t} - 40te^{5t} \\ -5 + 5e^{5t} & 25 & -10 + 10e^{5t} \\ 2 - 2e^{5t} + 10te^{5t} & -10 + 10e^{5t} & 4 + 21e^{5t} + 20te^{5t} \end{bmatrix}$.

13. $c_1 e^{-t} \begin{bmatrix} 1 \\ -1 \\ 1 \end{bmatrix} + c_2 e^{-t} \begin{bmatrix} -t \\ -1+t \\ 2-t \end{bmatrix} + c_3 e^{-2t} \begin{bmatrix} 1 \\ -2 \\ 4 \end{bmatrix}$.

15. $c_1 e^t \begin{bmatrix} -4 \\ 1 \\ 0 \end{bmatrix} + c_2 e^t \begin{bmatrix} 3-4t \\ t \\ 2 \end{bmatrix} + c_3 e^t \begin{bmatrix} 1 - 2t + 4t^2 \\ -t - t^2 \\ -4t \end{bmatrix}$.

17. $\begin{bmatrix} e^{-2t} \\ 4te^{-2t} + e^{-2t} \\ te^{-2t} - e^{-2t} \end{bmatrix}$.

19. $e^{-t} \begin{bmatrix} 3t \\ 3 \\ 9t \end{bmatrix} + e^{\mathbf{A}t} \begin{bmatrix} 2 - e^t(t^2 - 2t + 2) \\ 1 + e^t(t - 1) \\ 6 - 3e^t(t^2 - 2t + 2) \end{bmatrix}$, where $e^{\mathbf{A}t}$

is the matrix in the answer to Problem 3.

Review Problems, page 596

1. $c_1 e^{3t} \begin{bmatrix} 1 \\ 1 \end{bmatrix} + c_2 e^{4t} \begin{bmatrix} 3 \\ 2 \end{bmatrix}$.

3. $c_1 e^{-t} \begin{bmatrix} 1 \\ -1 \\ 0 \\ 0 \end{bmatrix} + c_2 e^{-t} \begin{bmatrix} 0 \\ 0 \\ 1 \\ -1 \end{bmatrix} + c_3 e^{3t} \begin{bmatrix} 1 \\ 1 \\ 0 \\ 0 \end{bmatrix} + c_4 e^{3t} \begin{bmatrix} 0 \\ 0 \\ 1 \\ 1 \end{bmatrix}$.

5. $\begin{bmatrix} e^{2t} & e^{3t} \\ -e^{2t} & -2e^{3t} \end{bmatrix}$.

7. $c_1 e^{-t} \begin{bmatrix} 1 \\ -2 \end{bmatrix} + c_2 e^{3t} \begin{bmatrix} 1 \\ 2 \end{bmatrix} + \begin{bmatrix} -1/3 \\ -14/3 \end{bmatrix}$.

9. $c_1 e^{-t} \begin{bmatrix} 1 \\ 0 \\ 3 \end{bmatrix} + c_2 e^{-t} \begin{bmatrix} t \\ 1 \\ 3t \end{bmatrix}$

$+ c_3 e^{-t} \begin{bmatrix} -t + (1/2)t^2 \\ t \\ 1 - 3t + (3/2)t^2 \end{bmatrix} + \begin{bmatrix} 2+t \\ 7-3t \\ 10 \end{bmatrix}$.

11. $\begin{bmatrix} 3e^t - 2e^{2t} \\ 3e^t - 4e^{2t} \end{bmatrix}$.

13. $c_1 t^{-1} \begin{bmatrix} -3 \\ 1 \\ 0 \end{bmatrix} + c_2 t^{-1} \begin{bmatrix} -1 \\ 0 \\ 1 \end{bmatrix} + c_3 t^4 \begin{bmatrix} 1 \\ 1 \\ 1 \end{bmatrix}$.

15.
$$\begin{bmatrix} (1/2)e^t + (2/3)e^{5t} - (1/6)e^{-t} & -e^t + (2/3)e^{5t} + (1/3)e^{-t} & -(1/2)e^t + (2/3)e^{5t} - (1/6)e^{-t} \\ (1/3)e^{5t} - (1/3)e^{-t} & (1/3)e^{5t} + (2/3)e^{-t} & (1/3)e^{5t} - (1/3)e^{-t} \\ -(1/2)e^t + (1/2)e^{-t} & e^t - e^{-t} & (1/2)e^t + (1/2)e^{-t} \end{bmatrix}.$$

CHAPTER 11

Exercises 11.2, page 612

1. $y = [4/(e - e^{-1})](e^{-x} - e^x)$.　**3.** $y \equiv 0$.

5. $y = e^x + 2x - 1$.

7. $y = \cos x + c \sin x$; c arbitrary.

9. $\lambda_n = (2n - 1)^2/4$ and $y_n = c_n\sin[(2n - 1)x/2]$, where $n = 1, 2, 3, \ldots$ and the c_n's are arbitrary.

11. $\lambda_n = n^2$, $n = 0, 1, 2, \ldots$; $y_0 = a_0$ and $y_n = a_n\cos nx + b_n\sin nx$, $n = 1, 2, 3, \ldots$, where a_0, a_n, and b_n are arbitrary.

13. The eigenvalues are the roots of $\tan(\sqrt{\lambda_n}\pi) + \sqrt{\lambda_n} = 0$, where $\lambda_n > 0$. For n large, $\lambda_n \approx (2n - 1)^2/4$, n a positive integer. The eigenfunctions are $y_n = c_n[\sin(\sqrt{\lambda_n}x) + \sqrt{\lambda_n}\,\cos(\sqrt{\lambda_n}x)]$, where the c_n's are arbitrary.

15. $u(x, t) = e^{-3t}\sin x - 6e^{-48t}\sin 4x$.

17. $u(x, t) = e^{-3t}\sin x - 7e^{-27t}\sin 3x + e^{-75t}\sin 5x$.

19. $u(x, t) = 3 \cos 6t \sin 2x + 12 \cos 39t \sin 13x$.

21. $u(x, t) = 6 \cos 6t \sin 2x + 2 \cos 18t \sin 6x + (11/27)\sin 27t \sin 9x - (14/45)\sin 45t \sin 15x$.

23. $u(x, t) = \sum\limits_{n=1}^{\infty} n^{-2}e^{-2\pi^2 n^2 t}\sin n\pi x$.

25. If $K > 0$, then $T(t)$ becomes unbounded as $t \to \infty$, and so the temperature $u(x, t) = X(x)T(t)$ becomes unbounded at each position x. Since the temperature must remain bounded for all time, $K \not> 0$.

27. (a) $u(x) \equiv 50$.　**(b)** $u(x) = 30x/L + 10$.

Exercises 11.3, page 627

1. Odd　**3.** Even.　**5.** Neither.

9. $f(x) \sim \sum\limits_{n=1}^{\infty} \dfrac{2(-1)^{n+1}}{n} \sin nx$.

11. $f(x) \sim 1 + \sum\limits_{n=1}^{\infty} \left[\dfrac{2}{\pi^2 n^2}(-1 + (-1)^n)\cos \dfrac{n\pi x}{2} \right.$
$\left. + \dfrac{1}{\pi n}((-1)^{n+1} - 1)\sin \dfrac{n\pi x}{2} \right]$.

13. $f(x) \sim \tfrac{1}{3} + \sum\limits_{n=1}^{\infty} \dfrac{4(-1)^n}{n^2\pi^2} \cos n\pi x$.

15. $f(x) \sim [(\sinh \pi)/\pi]\left(1 + \sum\limits_{n=1}^{\infty} \left[\dfrac{(-1)^n}{1 + n^2} \cos nx \right.\right.$
$\left.\left. + \dfrac{(-1)^{n+1}n}{1 + n^2} \sin nx \right] \right)$.

17. The 2π periodic function $g(x)$, where
$$g(x) = \begin{cases} x, & -\pi < x < \pi, \\ 0, & x = \pm\pi. \end{cases}$$

19. The 4 periodic function $g(x)$, where
$$g(x) = \begin{cases} 1, & -2 < x < 0, \\ x, & 0 < x < 2, \\ 1/2, & x = 0, \\ 3/2, & x = \pm 2. \end{cases}$$

21. The 2 periodic function $g(x)$, where
$$g(x) = x^2, \qquad -1 \leq x \leq 1.$$

23. The 2π periodic function $g(x)$, where
$$g(x) = \begin{cases} e^x, & -\pi < x < \pi, \\ (e^\pi + e^{-\pi})/2, & x = \pm\pi. \end{cases}$$

25. (a) $F(x) = (x^2 - \pi^2)/2$.　**(b)** $F(x) = |x| - \pi$.

27. $a_0 = 0$; $a_1 = 3/2$; $a_2 = 0$.

Exercises 11.4, page 637

1. (a) The π periodic function $\tilde{f}(x)$, where
$$\tilde{f}(x) = x^2, \qquad 0 < x < \pi.$$

(b) The 2π periodic function $f_o(x)$, where
$$f_o(x) = \begin{cases} x^2, & 0 < x < \pi, \\ -x^2, & -\pi < x < 0. \end{cases}$$

(c) The 2π periodic function $f_e(x)$, where
$$f_e(x) = \begin{cases} x^2, & 0 < x < \pi, \\ x^2, & -\pi < x < 0. \end{cases}$$

3. (a) The π periodic function $\tilde{f}(x)$, where
$$\tilde{f}(x) = \begin{cases} 0, & 0 < x < \pi/2, \\ 1, & \pi/2 < x < \pi. \end{cases}$$

(b) The 2π periodic function $f_o(x)$, where
$$f_o(x) = \begin{cases} -1, & -\pi < x < -\pi/2, \\ 0, & -\pi/2 < x < 0, \\ 0, & 0 < x < \pi/2, \\ 1, & \pi/2 < x < \pi. \end{cases}$$

(c) The 2π periodic function $f_e(x)$, where

$$f_e(x) = \begin{cases} 1, & -\pi < x < -\pi/2, \\ 0, & -\pi/2 < x < 0, \\ 0, & 0 < x < \pi/2, \\ 1, & \pi/2 < x < \pi. \end{cases}$$

5. $f(x) \sim -\dfrac{4}{\pi} \displaystyle\sum_{k=1}^{\infty} \dfrac{1}{2k-1} \sin(2k-1)\pi x.$

7. $f(x) \sim \displaystyle\sum_{n=1}^{\infty} \left[\dfrac{2\pi(-1)^{n+1}}{n} + \dfrac{4}{\pi n^3}((-1)^n - 1) \right] \sin nx.$

9. $f(x) \sim \displaystyle\sum_{k=0}^{\infty} \dfrac{8}{(2k+1)^3 \pi^3} \sin(2k+1)\pi x.$

11. $f(x) \sim \dfrac{\pi}{2} + \dfrac{4}{\pi} \displaystyle\sum_{k=1}^{\infty} \dfrac{1}{(2k-1)^2} \cos(2k-1)x.$

13. $f(x) \sim e - 1 + 2 \displaystyle\sum_{n=1}^{\infty} \dfrac{(-1)^n e - 1}{1 + \pi^2 n^2} \cos n\pi x.$

15. $f(x) \sim \dfrac{2}{\pi} + \dfrac{2}{\pi} \displaystyle\sum_{k=1}^{\infty} \left(\dfrac{1}{2k+1} + \dfrac{1}{2k-1} \right) \cos 2kx.$

17. $u(x, t) = \dfrac{2}{\pi} \displaystyle\sum_{k=1}^{\infty} \left[\dfrac{2}{2k-1} - \dfrac{1}{2k+1} - \dfrac{1}{2k-3} \right]$
$\times e^{-5(2k-1)^2 t} \sin(2k-1)x.$

Exercises 11.5, page 649

1. $u(x, t) = \displaystyle\sum_{n=1}^{\infty} \dfrac{8(-1)^{n+1} - 4}{\pi^3 n^3} e^{-5\pi^2 n^2 t} \sin n\pi x.$

3. $u(x, t) = \dfrac{\pi}{2} - \displaystyle\sum_{k=0}^{\infty} \dfrac{4}{\pi(2k+1)^2}$
$\times e^{-3(2k+1)^2 t} \cos(2k+1)x.$

5. $u(x, t) = \dfrac{2(e^\pi - 1)}{\pi} + \displaystyle\sum_{n=1}^{\infty} \dfrac{2e^\pi(-1)^n - 2}{\pi(1 + n^2)} e^{-n^2 t} \cos nx.$

7. $u(x, t) = 5 + \dfrac{5}{\pi} x - \dfrac{30}{\pi} e^{-2t} \sin x + \dfrac{5}{\pi} e^{-8t} \sin 2x$
$+ \left(1 - \dfrac{10}{\pi} \right) e^{-18t} \sin 3x$
$+ \dfrac{5}{2\pi} e^{-32t} \sin 4x - \left(1 + \dfrac{6}{\pi} \right) e^{-50t} \sin 5x$
$+ \displaystyle\sum_{n=6}^{\infty} \dfrac{10}{\pi n} [2(-1)^n - 1] e^{-2n^2 t} \sin nx.$

9. $u(x, t) = \dfrac{e^{-\pi} - 1}{\pi} x - e^{-x+1} + \displaystyle\sum_{n=1}^{\infty} c_n e^{-n^2 t} \sin nx,$

where

$$c_n = \begin{cases} \dfrac{2e^{-\pi} - 2}{\pi n}(-1)^n + \dfrac{2n}{\pi(1 + n^2)}((-1)^{n+1} e^{-\pi} + 1) \\ \quad + \dfrac{2}{\pi n}[(-1)^n - 1], \quad n \neq 2, \\ \dfrac{e^{-\pi} - 1}{\pi} + \dfrac{4}{5\pi}(1 - e^{-\pi}) + 1, \quad n = 2. \end{cases}$$

11. $u(x, t) = \displaystyle\sum_{n=0}^{\infty} a_n e^{-4(n+1/2)^2 t} \cos(n + 1/2)x,$ where
$f(x) = \displaystyle\sum_{n=0}^{\infty} a_n \cos(n + 1/2)x.$

13. $u(x, t) = \dfrac{\pi^2}{3} x - \dfrac{1}{3} x^3 - 3e^{-2t} \sin x$
$+ \displaystyle\sum_{n=2}^{\infty} \dfrac{4(-1)^n}{n^3} e^{-2n^2 t} \sin nx.$

15. $u(x, y, t) = e^{-52t} \cos 6x \sin 4y$
$- 3e^{-122t} \cos x \sin 11y.$

17. $u(x, y, t) = 2 \displaystyle\sum_{n=1}^{\infty} \dfrac{(-1)^{n+1}}{n} e^{-n^2 t} \sin ny.$

Exercises 11.6, page 661

1. $u(x, t) = \dfrac{1}{7\pi} \sin 7\pi t \sin 7\pi x +$
$\displaystyle\sum_{k=0}^{\infty} \dfrac{8}{((2k+1)\pi)^3} \cos(2k+1)\pi t \sin(2k+1)\pi x.$

3. $u(x, t) = \displaystyle\sum_{n=1}^{\infty} \dfrac{4}{n^2} [2(-1)^{n+1} - 1] \cos 2nt \sin nx.$

5. $u(x, t) = \dfrac{2h_o L^2}{\pi^2 a(L - a)} \displaystyle\sum_{n=1}^{\infty} \dfrac{1}{n^2} \sin \dfrac{n\pi a}{L} \sin \dfrac{n\pi x}{L}$
$\times \cos \dfrac{n\pi at}{L}.$

7. $u(x, t) = \cos t \sin x + \dfrac{5}{2} \sin 2t \sin 2x$
$- \dfrac{3}{5} \sin 5t \sin 5x$
$+ 2 \displaystyle\sum_{n=1}^{\infty} \dfrac{(-1)^{n+1}}{n^3} \left[t - \dfrac{\sin nt}{n} \right] \sin nx.$

9. $u(x, t) = \displaystyle\sum_{n=0}^{\infty} \left(a_n \cos \dfrac{(2n+1)\pi at}{2L} + \right.$
$\left. b_n \sin \dfrac{(2n+1)\pi at}{2L} \right) \sin \dfrac{(2n+1)\pi x}{2L},$ where
$f(x) = \displaystyle\sum_{n=0}^{\infty} a_n \sin \dfrac{(2n+1)\pi x}{2L}$ and

$$g(x) = \sum_{n=0}^{\infty} b_n \frac{(2n+1)\pi\alpha}{2L} \sin \frac{(2n+1)\pi x}{2L}.$$

11. $u(x, t) = \sum_{n=1}^{\infty} a_n T_n(t) \sin \frac{n\pi x}{L}$, where

$$a_n = \frac{2}{L} \int_0^L f(x) \sin \frac{n\pi x}{L} \, dx,$$

and

$$T_n(t) = e^{-t/2} \left(\cos \beta_n t + \frac{1}{2\beta_n} \sin \beta_n t \right),$$

where

$$\beta_n = \frac{1}{2L} \sqrt{3L^2 + 4\alpha^2 \pi^2 n^2}.$$

13. $u(x, t) = \dfrac{1}{2\alpha} [\sin(x + \alpha t) - \sin(x - \alpha t)]$

$$= \frac{1}{\alpha} \sin \alpha t \cos x.$$

15. $u(x, t) = x + tx.$

17. $u(x, t) = \dfrac{1}{2} \Bigg[e^{-(x+\alpha t)^2} + e^{-(x-\alpha t)^2}$

$$+ \frac{\cos(x - \alpha t) - \cos(x + \alpha t)}{\alpha} \Bigg].$$

Exercises 11.7, page 675

1. $u(x, y) = \dfrac{4 \cos 6x \sinh(6(y-1))}{\sinh(-6)}$

$$+ \frac{\cos 7x \sinh(7(y-1))}{\sinh(-7)}.$$

3. $u(x, y) = \sum_{n=1}^{\infty} A_n \sin nx \sinh(ny - n\pi)$, where

$$A_n = \frac{2}{\pi \sinh(-n\pi)} \int_0^{\pi} f(x) \sin nx \, dx.$$

5. $u(x, y) = \dfrac{\cos x \sinh(y-1)}{\sinh(-1)} - \dfrac{\cos 3x \sinh(3y-3)}{\sinh(-3)}$

$$+ \frac{\cos 2x \sinh 2y}{\sinh(2)}.$$

7. $u(r, \theta) = \dfrac{\pi}{2} - \sum_{k=0}^{\infty} \dfrac{r^{2k+1}}{(2k+1)^2 \pi 2^{2k-1}} \cos(2k+1)\theta.$

9. $u(r, \theta) = \dfrac{a_0}{2} + \sum_{n=1}^{\infty} \left(\dfrac{r}{a} \right)^n (a_n \cos n\theta + b_n \sin n\theta),$

where a_0 is arbitrary, and for $n = 1, 2, 3, \dots$

$$a_n = \frac{a}{\pi n} \int_{-\pi}^{\pi} f(\theta) \cos n\theta \, d\theta,$$

$$b_n = \frac{a}{n\pi} \int_{-\pi}^{\pi} f(\theta) \sin n\theta \, d\theta.$$

11. $u(r, \theta) = \left(\dfrac{1}{3} r - \dfrac{4}{3} r^{-1} \right) \cos \theta$

$$+ \left(\frac{2}{3} r - \frac{2}{3} r^{-1} \right) \sin \theta$$

$$+ \left(-\frac{1}{255} r^4 + \frac{256}{255} r^{-4} \right) \sin 4\theta.$$

13. $u(r, \theta) = \dfrac{a_0}{2} + \sum_{n=1}^{\infty} r^{-n}(a_n \cos n\theta + b_n \sin n\theta),$

where

$$a_n = \frac{1}{\pi} \int_{-\pi}^{\pi} f(\theta) \cos n\theta \, d\theta, \qquad n = 0, 1, 2, \dots,$$

and

$$b_n = \frac{1}{\pi} \int_{-\pi}^{\pi} f(\theta) \sin n\theta \, d\theta, \qquad n = 1, 2, 3, \dots.$$

15. $u(r, \theta) = r^3 \sin 3\theta.$

17. $u(r, \theta) = a_0 + b_0 \ln r + \sum_{n=1}^{\infty} [(a_n r^n + b_n r^{-n}) \cos n\theta$

$$+ (c_n r^n + d_n r^{-n}) \sin n\theta], \text{ where}$$

$$a_0 = \frac{1}{2\pi} \int_{-\pi}^{\pi} f(\theta) \, d\theta,$$

$$b_0 = \frac{3}{2\pi} \int_{-\pi}^{\pi} g(\theta) \, d\theta,$$

and for $n = 1, 2, 3, \dots$

$$a_n + b_n = \frac{1}{\pi} \int_{-\pi}^{\pi} f(\theta) \cos n\theta \, d\theta,$$

$$n3^{n-1} a_n - n3^{-n-1} b_n = \frac{1}{\pi} \int_{-\pi}^{\pi} g(\theta) \cos n\theta \, d\theta,$$

and

$$c_n + d_n = \frac{1}{\pi} \int_{-\pi}^{\pi} f(\theta) \sin n\theta \, d\theta,$$

$$n3^{n-1} c_n - n3^{-n-1} d_n = \frac{1}{\pi} \int_{-\pi}^{\pi} g(\theta) \sin n\theta \, d\theta.$$

21. $u(r, \theta, z) = [I_0(r)/I_0(\pi)] \sin z.$

Index

TABLE 4.1 UNDETERMINED COEFFICIENTS FOR $L[y](x) = g(x)$

Type	$g(x)$	$y_p(x)$
(I)	$p_n(x) = a_n x^n + \cdots + a_1 x + a_0$	$x^s P_n(x) = x^s\{A_n x^n + \cdots + A_1 x + A_0\}$
(II)	$ae^{\alpha x}$	$x^s A e^{\alpha x}$
(III)	$a \cos \beta x + b \sin \beta x$	$x^s\{A \cos \beta x + B \sin \beta x\}$
(IV)	$p_n(x)e^{\alpha x}$	$x^s P_n(x)e^{\alpha x}$
(V)	$p_n(x) \cos \beta x + q_m(x) \sin \beta x$	$x^s\{P_N(x) \cos \beta x + Q_N(x) \sin \beta x\}$
	where $q_m(x) = b_m x^m + \cdots + b_1 x + b_0$	where $Q_N(x) = B_N x^N + \cdots + B_1 x + B_0$
		and $N = \max(n, m)$
(VI)	$ae^{\alpha x} \cos \beta x + be^{\alpha x} \sin \beta x$	$x^s\{Ae^{\alpha x} \cos \beta x + Be^{\alpha x} \sin \beta x\}$
(VII)	$p_n(x)e^{\alpha x} \cos \beta x + q_m(x)e^{\alpha x} \sin \beta x$	$x^s e^{\alpha x}\{P_N(x) \cos \beta x + Q_N(x) \sin \beta x\}$
		where $N = \max(n, m)$

The nonnegative integer s is chosen to be the smallest integer so that no term in the particular solution $y_p(x)$ is a solution to the corresponding homogeneous equation $L[y](x) = 0$.

LINEAR FIRST ORDER EQUATIONS

A general solution to the first order linear equation $dy/dx + P(x)y = Q(x)$ is

$$y(x) = [\mu(x)]^{-1}\left(\int \mu(x)Q(x)\,dx + C\right), \quad \text{where} \quad \mu(x) = \exp\left(\int P(x)\,dx\right).$$

REDUCTION OF ORDER FORMULA

Given a nontrivial solution $f(x)$ to $y'' + py' + qy = 0$, a second linearly independent solution is

$$y(x) = f(x)\int \frac{e^{-\int p(x)\,dx}}{[f(x)]^2}\,dx.$$

VARIATION OF PARAMETERS FORMULA

If y_1 and y_2 are two linearly independent solutions to $y'' + py' + qy = 0$, then a particular solution to $y'' + py' + qy = g$ is $y = v_1 y_1 + v_2 y_2$, where

$$v_1(x) = \int \frac{-g(x)y_2(x)}{W[y_1, y_2](x)}\,dx, \qquad v_2(x) = \int \frac{g(x)y_1(x)}{W[y_1, y_2](x)}\,dx,$$

and $\quad W[y_1, y_2](x) = y_1(x)y_2'(x) - y_1'(x)y_2(x)$.